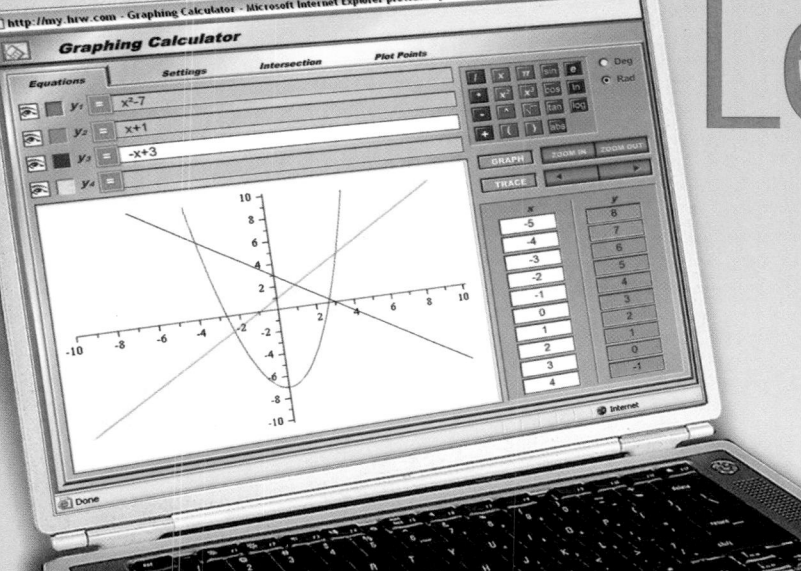

HOLT CALIFORNIA
Algebra 1

Edward B. Burger

David J. Chard

Earlene J. Hall

Paul A. Kennedy

Steven J. Leinwand

Freddie L. Renfro

Tom W. Roby

Dale G. Seymour

Bert K. Waits

HOLT, RINEHART AND WINSTON

A Harcourt Education Company

Orlando • **Austin** • New York • San Diego • London

Cover photo: Golden Gate Bridge, San Francisco,
California; © George Steinmetz/Corbis

Cover photo: windsurfing, San Simeon,
California; © DY Riess MD/Alamy

Cover photo: Joshua tree at sunset,
California; © Frank Krahmer/zefa/Corbis

Cover photo: skyscrapers, Los Angeles,
California; © Toyohiro Yamada/Getty Images

Cover photo: Garapata Beach, Big Sur,
California; © David Muench/Corbis

ISBN 978-0-03-092339-5

ISBN 0-03-092339-5

4 5 048 10 09 08

California Algebra 1
Contents in Brief

Student Handbook

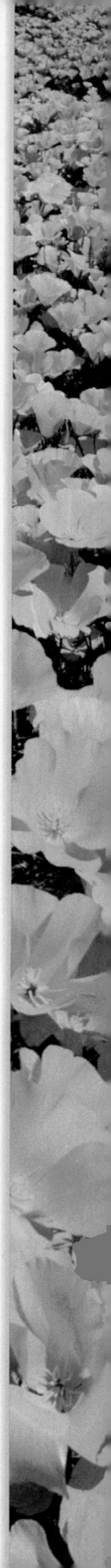

AUTHORS

Edward B. Burger, Ph.D. is Professor of Mathematics and Chair at Williams College and is the author of numerous articles, books, and videos. He has won several of the most prestigious writing and teaching awards offered by the Mathematical Association of America. Dr. Burger has made numerous television and radio appearances, and has given innumerable mathematical performances around the world.

Steven J. Leinwand spent 22 years as the Mathematics Supervisor with the Connecticut Department of Education. He is currently a Principal Research Analyst at the American Institutes for Research.

David J. Chard, Ph.D., is an Associate Dean of Curriculum and Academic Programs at the University of Oregon. He is the President of the Division for Research at the Council for Exceptional Children, is a member of the International Academy for Research on Learning Disabilities, and is the Principal Investigator on two major research projects for the U.S. Department of Education.

Freddie L. Renfro, MA, has 35 years of experience in Texas education as a classroom teacher and director/coordinator of Mathematics PreK-12 for school districts in the Houston area. She has served as a reviewer and team trainer for Texas Math Institutes and has presented at numerous math workshops.

CONSULTING AUTHORS

Lee Haines is an International Baccalaureate Coordinator and Math Academic Coach for San Bernardino City Schools. In 2004, he was awarded the Region 10 California League of Middle Schools Educator of the Year Award.

Robin Scarcella, Ph.D., is the director of the Academic English and English as a Second Language Program at the University of California at Irvine. She has written numerous articles and books about ESL teaching and secondary language acquisition.

Paul A. Kennedy, Ph.D. is a professor in the Department of Mathematics at Colorado State University. Dr. Kennedy is a leader in mathematics education. His research focuses on developing algebraic thinking by using multiple representations and technology. He is the author of numerous publications.

Earlene J. Hall, Ed.D., is the middle school mathematics supervisor for Detroit Public Schools and an adjunct professor at Wayne State University in Detroit, Michigan, where she teaches graduate courses in the College of Education.

Tom W. Roby, Ph.D., is Associate Professor of Mathematics and Director of the Quantitative Learning Center at the University of Connecticut. He founded and co-directed the ACCLAIM professional development program. He also chaired the advisory board of the California Mathematics Project, and reviewed content for the California Standards Tests.

Dale G. Seymour is a retired mathematics teacher, author, speaker and publisher. Dale founded Creative Publications in 1968, and went on to found two other mathematics publishing companies. Creating mathematical sculptures is one of his many hobbies.

Bert K. Waits, Ph.D., is a Professor Emeritus of Mathematics at The Ohio State University and co-founder of T^3 (Teachers Teaching with Technology), a national professional development program.

CALIFORNIA ADVISORS

Charlie Bialowas is the Mathematics Curriculum Specialist for the Anaheim Union High School District. He also serves as a mathematics student teacher supervisor for California State University, Fullerton, and was the Math Chairperson at Oxford Academy in Cypress.

Wendy Taub-Hoglund is a Teacher Expert Secondary Math with Los Angeles Unified School District. She has received numerous awards for excellence in teaching, and has coauthored math review books for test preparation.

CALIFORNIA TEACHER ADVISORY PANEL

Kay Barrie
Math Department Chair
Rio Vista MS
Fresno, CA

Youshi Berry
Math Teacher
Emerson MS
Pomona, CA

Charlie Bialowas
Math Curriculum
    Specialist
Anaheim Union HS
    District
Anaheim, CA

Lorrie Wineberg Buehler
Principal
Baldy View Elementary
    School
Upland, CA

Mary Chiaverini
Math Teacher
Plaza Vista MS
Irvine, CA

Dennis Deets
Assistant Principal
AB Miller HS
Fontana, CA

Pauline Embree
Math Department Chair
Rancho San Joaquin MS
Irvine, CA

Sandi Enochs
Math Lead Teacher
Desert Hot Springs HS
Desert Hot Springs, CA

Tricia Gough
Math Department Chair
Emerson MS
Pomona, CA

Lee Haines
IB Coordinator/Math
    Coach
San Bernardino City
    Schools
San Bernardino, CA

Shannon Kelly
Math Teacher
Centennial HS
Corona, CA

Lisa Kernaghan
Math Teacher/
    Administrator
Oak Creek Intermediate
    School
Oakhurst, CA

Mary Ann Kremenliev
Math Teacher
Foothill MS
Walnut Creek, CA

Carole Kuck
Math Department Chair
Jean Farb MS
San Diego, CA

David V. Mattoon
Math Teacher
Potter Junior HS
Fallbrook, CA

Lynette McClintock
Math/Science Teacher
Thompson MS
Murrieta, CA

Nancy Nazarian-Carroll
Math Teacher
Curtiss MS
Carson, CA

John (Jack) P. Nunes
Math Teacher and
    Department Leader
Fern Bacon MS
Sacramento, CA

Suzanne O'Rourke
Math Teacher
Antioch MS
Antioch, CA

Jong Sun Park
Math Teacher
Holmes International MS
Northridge, CA

Barbara Parr
Math Teacher
Emerson MS
Bakersfield, CA

Donna Phair
Math Department Chair
William Hopkins Junior
    HS
Fremont, CA

Donald R. Price
Math Teacher
Alvarado Intermediate
    School
Irvine, CA

Jennifer Randel
Math/Science Teacher,
    Grade Level Chair
Thompson MS
Murrieta, CA

Wendy Taub-Hoglund
Teacher Expert Secondary
    Math
Los Angeles USD
Los Angeles, CA

Matthew Ting
Math Coach
Peary MS
Gardena, CA

CALIFORNIA REVIEWERS

Youshi Berry
Math Teacher
Emerson MS
Pomona, CA

Charlie Bialowas
Mathematics Curriculum
  Specialist
Anaheim Union HS District
Anaheim, CA

Lorrie Wineberg Buehler
Principal
Baldy View Elementary School
Upland, CA

Mary Chiaverini
Math Department Head
Plaza Vista MS
Irvine, CA

Michael Davoudian
Math Coach
Luther Burbank MS
Burbank, CA

DeAnn DeBey
Math Teacher
Irvine Unified School District
Irvine, CA

Pauline Embree
Math Department Chair
Rancho San Joaquin MS
Irvine, CA

Tricia Gough
Math Department Chair
Emerson MS
Pomona, CA

Lee Haines
IB Coordinator/Math Coach
San Bernardino City Schools
San Bernardino, CA

Lisa Kernaghan
Math Teacher/Administrator
Oak Creek Intermediate School
Oakhurst, CA

David Mattoon
Math Teacher
Potter Junior HS
Fallbrook, CA

Michael Nagaran
Mathematics Coach
Los Angeles Unified School
  District
Los Angeles, CA

Nancy Nazarian-Carroll
Math Teacher
Curtiss MS
Carson, CA

John (Jack) P. Nunes
Math Teacher and
  Department Leader
Fern Bacon MS
Sacramento, CA

Jong Sun Park
Math Teacher
Holmes International MS
Northridge, CA

Raylene Paustain
Teacher on Special Assignment
Clovis Unified School District
Clovis, CA

Donna Phair
Math Department Chair
William Hopkins Junior HS
Fremont, CA

Donald R. Price
Math Teacher
Alvarado Intermediate School
Rowland Heights, CA

Golden T. Quinn
Math Teacher
Audubon MS
Los Angeles, CA

Wendy Taub-Hoglund
Teacher Expert Secondary Math
Los Angeles USD
Los Angeles, CA

CALIFORNIA FIELD TEST PARTICIPANTS

Carmencita Ancora
Dana MS
San Diego, CA

Henry Ashe
Vail Ranch MS
Temecula, CA

Susan Battistv
High Tech MS
San Diego, CA

Donna Campbell
Mesa Intermediate
  School
Palmdale, CA

Todd Cardosa
Encina HS
Sacramento, CA

Lou Catti
Creekside MS
Patterson, CA

Marcie Charlesworth
Excelsior Elementary
  School
Roseville, CA

Peggy Clarke
Temecula MS
Temecula, CA

Sheryl Cleveland
Golden Valley HS
Bakersfield, CA

Joyanna Deutsch
Forty-Niners Academy
East Palo Alto, CA

Andrea Farrow
Margarita MS
Temecula, CA

Ryan Gallagher
High Tech MS
San Diego, CA

Laura Grant
McKinleyville MS
McKinleyville, CA

Sally Haggerty
Martin Luther King MS
Oceanside, CA

V J Hirsch
Lincoln HS
Los Angeles, CA

Mollie Holmgren
Monument MS
Rio Dell, CA

Rayetta Lawson
Kastner Intermediate
  School
Fresno, CA

Tami Llewellyn
Ruth Musser MS
Alta Loma, CA

Lisa Madigan
Helms MS
San Pablo, CA

Eric Manabe
Aptos HS
Aptos, CA

David McKinley
Fort Miller MS
Fresno, CA

Viola Okoro
Franklin HS
Elk Grove, CA

William Olmeda
Lincoln HS
Los Angeles, CA

Breeze Patten
Bella Vista MS
Murrieta, CA

Jeff Perkins
Casa Roble HS
Orangevale, CA

Laurie Pines
Homestead HS
Cupertino, CA

Julie Prater
James L. Day MS
Temecula, CA

Wallace Rayford
Frisbie MS
Rialto, CA

Carey Resch
Leroy F. Greene MS
Sacramento, CA

Katherine Ringer
Heritage Intermediate
  School
Fontana, CA

Wendy Salcedo
Jordan MS
Burbank, CA

Chris Schmidt
Thurgood Marshall MS
San Diego, CA

Mary Ann Sheridan
McKinleyville MS
McKinleyville, CA

Byron Wright
Vail Ranch MS
Temecula, CA

Seunghwan Yom
Abraham Lincoln HS
Los Angeles, CA

Using Your Book to Master the Standards

Holt California Algebra 1 provides many opportunities for you to master the California Mathematics Content Standards for Algebra 1.

Countdown to Mastery

Countdown to Mastery **provides practice with the standards every day.**

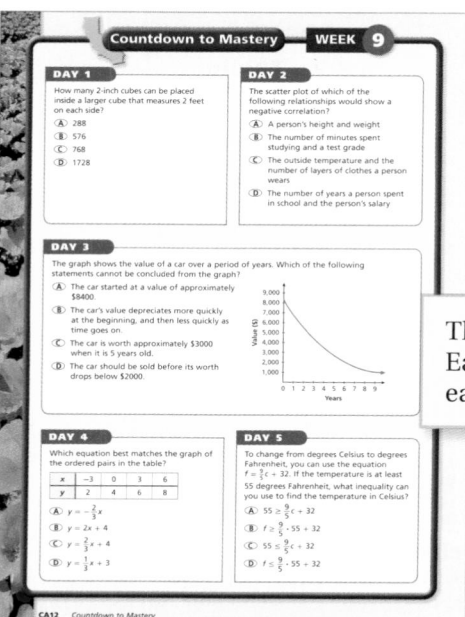

Step 1

✔ **Complete one item each day before you start the lesson.**

There are 24 pages of standards practice. Each page has five questions, one for each day of the week.

California Standards

The California Standards taught in each lesson are listed at the start of the lesson.

Step 2

✔ **Preview the standards before you start the lesson.**

Complete standards are shown. The words in bold tell you which part of the standard is the focus of the lesson.

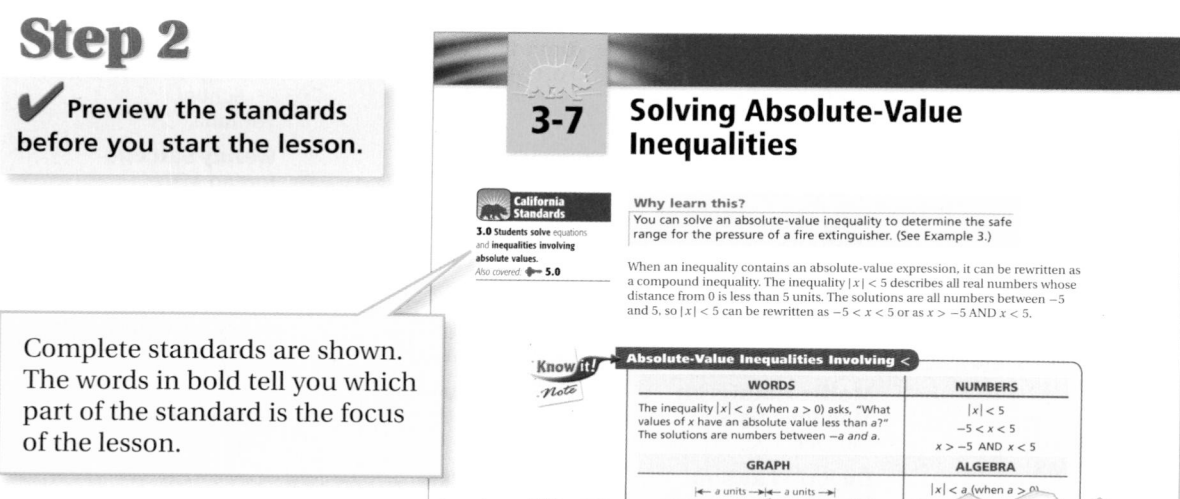

3-7 Solving Absolute-Value Inequalities

California Standards
3.0 Students solve equations and **inequalities involving absolute values.**
Also covered: ◆ **5.0**

Why learn this?
You can solve an absolute-value inequality to determine the safe range for the pressure of a fire extinguisher. (See Example 3.)

When an inequality contains an absolute-value expression, it can be rewritten as a compound inequality. The inequality $|x| < 5$ describes all real numbers whose distance from 0 is less than 5 units. The solutions are all numbers between -5 and 5, so $|x| < 5$ can be rewritten as $-5 < x < 5$ or as $x > -5$ AND $x < 5$.

Know it!
Note

Absolute-Value Inequalities Involving <	
WORDS	**NUMBERS**
The inequality $|x| < a$ (when $a > 0$) asks, "What values of x have an absolute value less than a?" The solutions are numbers between $-a$ and a.	$|x| < 5$ $-5 < x < 5$ $x > -5$ AND $x < 5$
GRAPH	**ALGEBRA**
⟵ a units ⟶⟵ a units ⟶	$|x| < a$ (when $a > 0$)

SPIRAL STANDARDS REVIEW

Use the Spiral Standards Review for constant review of standards taught in previous lessons.

Step 3

✔ Keep your skills fresh by practicing the standards daily.

2.	$\|2x - 6\| \le 2$		?
3.	$2x - 6 \ge -2$ AND $2x - 6 \le 2$		Definition of absolute value
4.	$2x \ge 4$ AND $2x \le 8$		?
5.	$x \ge 2$ AND $x \le 4$		?

 **SPIRAL STANDARDS REVIEW**
7AF1.4, ← 5.0

Solve each proportion. Check your answer. *(Lesson 2-5)*

61. $\dfrac{x+1}{4} = \dfrac{5}{8}$ **62.** $\dfrac{2}{15} = \dfrac{6}{y-5}$ **63.** $\dfrac{12}{m+2} = \dfrac{8}{3}$ **64.** $\dfrac{7+g}{10} = \dfrac{6}{8}$

Describe the solutions of each inequality in words. *(Lesson 3-1)*

65. $16 > 8m$ **66.** $c + 4 < 11$ **67.** $-4 \le x + 2$ **68.** $0 \ge x + 7$

If you need help with a problem, go to the lesson referenced at the end of the problem.

Solve each compound inequality and graph the solutions. *(Lesson 3-6)*

69. $-3 < x - 3 < 1$ **70.** $-3 \le 2x + 1 \le 9$

71. $x - 2 < -1$ OR $x - 2 > 2$ **72.** $x + 4 \le 3$ OR $x + 4 \ge 6$

3-7 Solving Absolute-Value Inequalities **183**

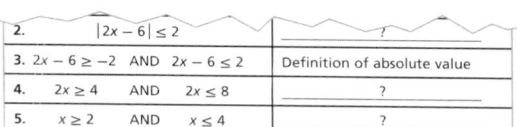

MASTERING THE STANDARDS

Use Mastering the Standards for review of standards taught in the current and previous chapters.

Step 4

✔ After finishing each chapter, review your knowledge of the standards.

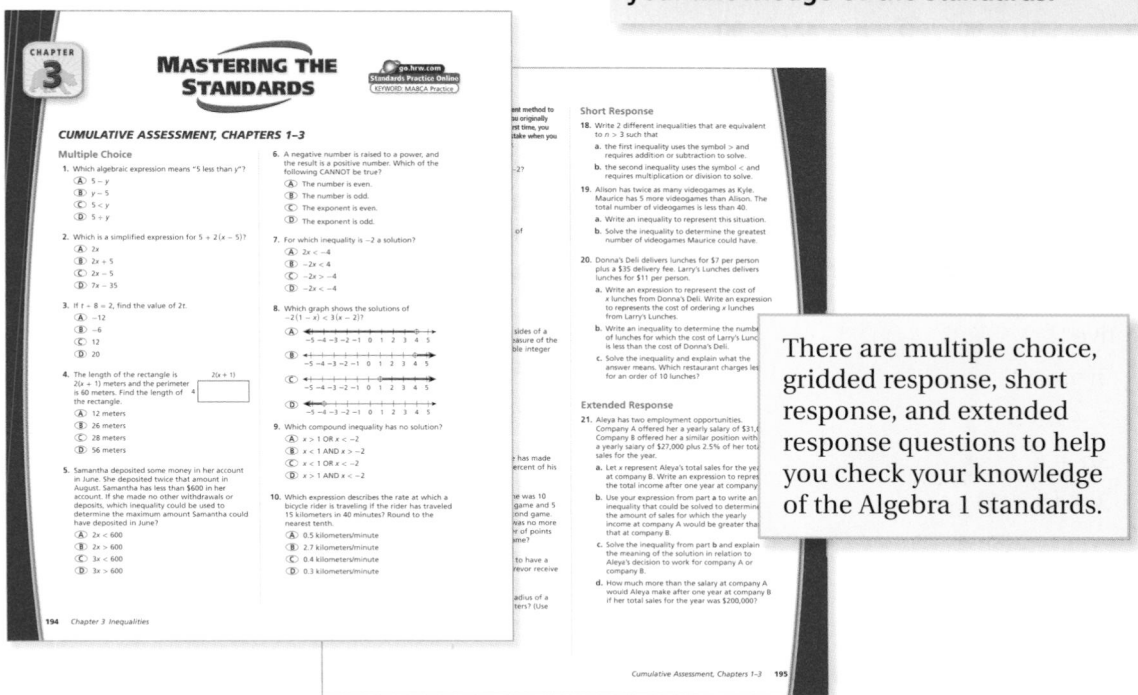

There are multiple choice, gridded response, short response, and extended response questions to help you check your knowledge of the Algebra 1 standards.

COUNTDOWN TO MASTERY

DAY 1

Which expression always represents an odd number?

(A) $n^2 + 1$

(B) $2n + 1$

(C) n^2

(D) $n + 1$

DAY 2

Cell phone bills are based on a flat monthly fee and the number of minutes used. In the equation $c = 0.07m + 29.99$, what does the variable m represent?

(A) The number of months billed

(B) The total amount of the bill

(C) The number of minutes used

(D) The phone number

DAY 3

Look at the table. Which equation best describes the relationship between the number of students and the number of tables in the cafeteria?

Students (n)	Tables (t)
720	18
600	15
960	24

(A) $n = 40t$

(C) $t = 40n$

(B) $n = 35t + 90$

(D) $n = 45t - 90$

DAY 4

Which expression represents the verbal phrase "the sum of three times a number and five"?

(A) $3(n + 5)$

(B) $3 + n \cdot 5$

(C) $3n + 5$

(D) $3 + (n + 5)$

DAY 5

Sara has $140. What computation will give the number of days she can skate at a skatepark if it costs $30 for a five day pass plus $3 a day for rental of a helmet?

(A) Divide 140 by 5

(B) Divide 140 by 9

(C) Divide 140 by 5 and subtract 15

(D) Divide 140 by 30 and subtract 3

CA4   *Countdown to Mastery*

DAY 1

Katie has a part-time job for 2 hours after school and 4 hours on Saturdays. If she spends 1 hour each night doing homework, what are Katie's earnings on Thursday? What other information is needed in order to solve this problem?

(A) The number of days Katie works per week

(B) The number of hours Katie does homework per week

(C) The average number of hours Katie works per week

(D) The amount of money Katie earns per hour

DAY 2

If $x = 5$, then $2(3x - 4) - 8x + 3 =$

(A) -42

(B) -29

(C) -21

(D) -15

DAY 3

Based on the table, which inequality represents the relationship between x and y?

x	2	3	5	6
y	−3	−8	−10	−9

(A) $x > -y$

(B) $2x < -y$

(C) $x < -y$

(D) $2x > -y$

DAY 4

If you get 18 questions wrong on a test that has 72 questions, what percent of the questions did you get right?

(A) 75%

(B) 72%

(C) 54%

(D) 25%

DAY 5

The Earth's mass is approximately 5,900,000,000,000,000,000,000,000 kilograms. What is this number in scientific notation?

(A) 5.9×10^{-24}

(B) 59×10^{23}

(C) 5.9×10^{24}

(D) 0.59×10^{25}

Countdown to Mastery

WEEK 3

DAY 1

Which expression is equivalent to 2^3?

Ⓐ $2 \cdot 3$

Ⓑ $3 + 3$

Ⓒ $2 + 2 + 2$

Ⓓ $2 \cdot 2 \cdot 2$

DAY 2

Which number is not a solution of $-7y + 19 < 75$?

Ⓐ 13

Ⓑ 0

Ⓒ −2

Ⓓ −8

DAY 3

Lydia received a gift card for $25.00 worth of smoothies from the Smoothie Spot. If the cost of each smoothie is $3.25, which table best describes *b*, the balance remaining on the gift card after she buys *n* smoothies?

Ⓐ

n	*b*
1	$21.75
3	$15.25
4	$12.00
7	$2.25

Ⓑ

n	*b*
2	$18.50
4	$12.00
6	$6.50
8	$0

Ⓒ

n	*b*
1	$21.75
2	$18.50
5	$15.25
7	$12.00

Ⓓ

n	*b*
2	$18.50
3	$15.25
5	$7.75
6	$4.50

DAY 4

The band is trying to raise money to take a field trip to the Rock and Roll Hall of Fame. They decide to sell sweatshirts. The equation for the amount of money *a* that they will make for selling *t* sweatshirts is $a = 22t - 350$. In order to make at least $2100, how many sweatshirts do the band members need to sell?

Ⓐ 112

Ⓑ 111

Ⓒ 80

Ⓓ 79

DAY 5

What is the solution to the equation $8x - 10 = 54$?

Ⓐ 5.5

Ⓑ 6.75

Ⓒ 8

Ⓓ 12

DAY 1

Which number equals $(5)^{-3}$?

A -15

B $-\dfrac{1}{125}$

C $\dfrac{1}{125}$

D $\dfrac{1}{15}$

DAY 2

What is the value of $3x^2 - 5x + 2$ when $x = -4$?

A -66

B -26

C 30

D 70

DAY 3

Which graph matches the values from the table?

x	−3	−1	2	4
y	6	2	−4	−8

A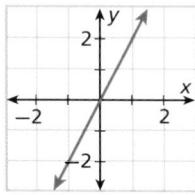

C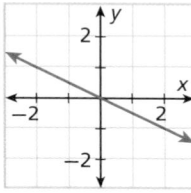

B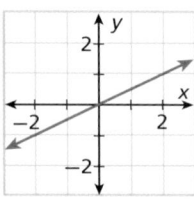

D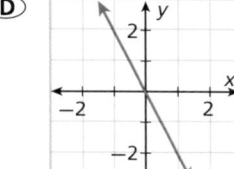

DAY 4

What is $\dfrac{11}{12} + \dfrac{4}{15}$?

A $\dfrac{5}{9}$

B $\dfrac{21}{20}$

C $\dfrac{71}{60}$

D $\dfrac{55}{16}$

DAY 5

Which of the following is equivalent to $4(x + 5) - 2(x + 5) = 14$?

A $4x + 5 - 2x + 5 = 14$

B $4x + 5 - 2x - 5 = 14$

C $4x + 20 - 2x + 10 = 14$

D $4x + 20 - 2x - 10 = 14$

Countdown to Mastery WEEK 5

DAY 1

The table shows all of the possible outcomes when flipping a coin twice.

First flip	Second flip
H	H
H	T
T	H
T	T

Which of the following statements must be true?

(A) The probability that two flips will have at least one tail is $\frac{1}{2}$.

(B) The probability that two flips will have the same outcome is $\frac{1}{2}$.

(C) The probability of getting exactly two heads is higher than the probability of getting exactly two tails.

(D) The probability of getting exactly one head and one tail is higher than the probability of getting at least one head.

DAY 2

Which of the following is equivalent to $(4^6)^3$?

(A) 4^2

(B) 4^3

(C) 4^9

(D) 4^{18}

DAY 3

The square root of 200 is between

(A) 11 and 12

(B) 12 and 13

(C) 13 and 14

(D) 14 and 15

DAY 4

A piano regularly sells for \$950. It is marked up 45%. How much does the piano sell for now?

(A) \$427.50

(B) \$522.50

(C) \$1377.50

(D) \$1472.50

DAY 5

If $|x| = 5$, what is the value of x?

(A) -5 or 0

(B) -5 or 5

(C) 0 or 5

(D) -10 or 10

Countdown to Mastery WEEK 6

DAY 1

Which equation represents the data in the table?

x	3	1	−2	6
y	2	4	7	−1

Ⓐ $y = -x + 5$

Ⓑ $y = 2x - 1$

Ⓒ $y = x + 3$

Ⓓ $y = -3x + 11$

DAY 2

A fair number cube is rolled. What is the probability that the number cube will land showing a number that is greater than 3?

Ⓐ 0.17

Ⓑ 0.33

Ⓒ 0.5

Ⓓ 0.67

DAY 3

Ryan's first 5 test scores in Algebra were 80, 87, 84, 92, and 87. What was his mean score?

Ⓐ 85

Ⓑ 86

Ⓒ 87

Ⓓ 92

DAY 4

Jonathan tosses a fair coin 30 times, and it lands showing heads 18 times. Using Jonathan's results, what is the difference between the experimental probability of tossing heads and the theoretical probability of tossing heads?

Ⓐ 0.1

Ⓑ 0.5

Ⓒ 0.6

Ⓓ 1.1

DAY 5

This year the average cost of tuition and fees for a public four-year college is $20,528. In three years the estimated average cost will be $27,914. What is the percent increase of the cost to the nearest percent?

Ⓐ 74%

Ⓑ 36%

Ⓒ 26%

Ⓓ 14%

Countdown to Mastery — WEEK 7

DAY 1

Daniel's recipe for 24 cookies calls for $2\frac{1}{2}$ cups of flour. How much flour will Daniel need to make 60 cookies?

(A) 1 cup

(B) $6\frac{1}{4}$ cups

(C) $6\frac{1}{2}$ cups

(D) $7\frac{1}{2}$ cups

DAY 2

What is the value of $2x^2 + 3x - 5$ when $x = -2$?

(A) -7

(B) -3

(C) 5

(D) 9

DAY 3

Which graph shows a line where each value of y is three more than half of x?

(A)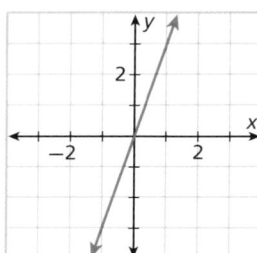

(C)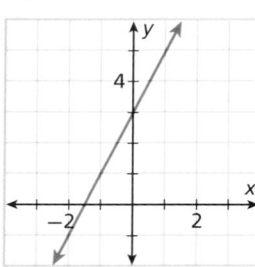

(B)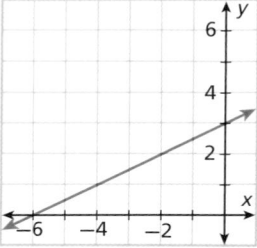

(D)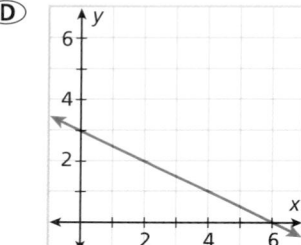

DAY 4

Solve for x.

$$2(x + 4) < 3x - 4$$

(A) $x < 12$

(B) $x > \dfrac{12}{5}$

(C) $x > 12$

(D) $x < \dfrac{12}{5}$

DAY 5

Solve for x.

$$3(5x - 8) = 2(2x - 1)$$

(A) $x = \dfrac{7}{11}$

(B) $x = 2$

(C) $x = 1\frac{1}{2}$

(D) $x = 3$

Countdown to Mastery   WEEK 8

DAY 1

A swimming pool charges an annual $75 membership fee, and it costs $1.50 each time a member brings a guest. Which equation shows the yearly cost y in terms of the number of guests g?

(A) $y = 75g + 1.5$

(B) $y = -1.5g + 75$

(C) $y = 1.5g + 75$

(D) $y = 1.5g + 75g$

DAY 2

On a certain standardized test, the equation $s = 9q + 218$ is used to determine a student's score. In this equation, s is the score and q is the number of questions answered correctly. If the maximum score on the test is 650, how many questions are on the test?

(A) 96 questions

(B) 72 questions

(C) 48 questions

(D) 24 questions

DAY 3

In the election for class treasurer, 220 ballots were tallied. How many more people voted for Pauley than for Sue?

(A) 10

(B) 22

(C) 29

(D) 37

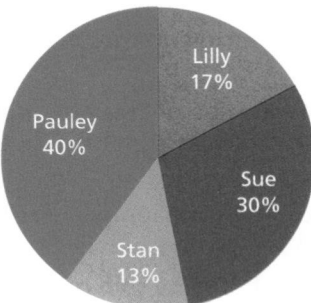

Election Results

Lilly 17%

Pauley 40%

Sue 30%

Stan 13%

DAY 4

Jaclyn has two hats. The first hat contains 26 slips of paper on which the letters of the alphabet are written, one letter per slip. The second hat contains 10 slips numbered 0 through 9. If Jaclyn draws 1 slip of paper from each hat, what is the probability that she will draw a letter that is a vowel and a number less than 2?

(A) 0.038

(B) 0.046

(C) 0.058

(D) 0.392

DAY 5

The surface area of cube A is 96 square meters. The surface area of cube B is half the surface area of cube A. What is the area of one face of cube B in square meters?

(A) 3.6

(B) 8

(C) 16

(D) 32

DAY 1

How many 2-inch cubes can be placed inside a larger cube that measures 2 feet on each side?

(A) 288

(B) 576

(C) 768

(D) 1728

DAY 2

The scatter plot of which of the following relationships would show a negative correlation?

(A) A person's height and weight

(B) The number of minutes spent studying and a test grade

(C) The outside temperature and the number of layers of clothes a person wears

(D) The number of years a person spent in school and the person's salary

DAY 3

The graph shows the value of a car over a period of years. Which of the following statements cannot be concluded from the graph?

(A) The car started at a value of approximately $8400.

(B) The car's value depreciates more quickly at the beginning, and then less quickly as time goes on.

(C) The car is worth approximately $3000 when it is 5 years old.

(D) The car should be sold before its worth drops below $2000.

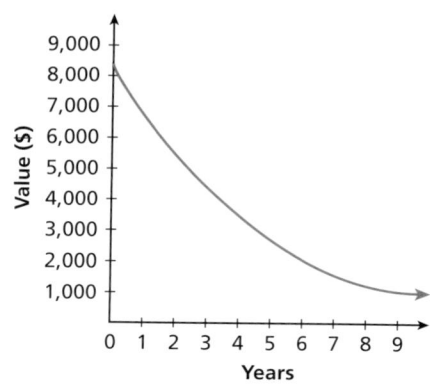

DAY 4

Which equation best matches the graph of the ordered pairs in the table?

x	−3	0	3	6
y	2	4	6	8

(A) $y = -\frac{2}{3}x$

(B) $y = 2x + 4$

(C) $y = \frac{2}{3}x + 4$

(D) $y = \frac{1}{3}x + 3$

DAY 5

To change from degrees Celsius to degrees Fahrenheit, you can use the equation $f = \frac{9}{5}c + 32$. If the temperature is at least 55 degrees Fahrenheit, what inequality can you use to find the temperature in Celsius?

(A) $55 \geq \frac{9}{5}c + 32$

(B) $f \geq \frac{9}{5} \cdot 55 + 32$

(C) $55 \leq \frac{9}{5}c + 32$

(D) $f \leq \frac{9}{5} \cdot 55 + 32$

DAY 1

What is the surface area of the figure represented by this net?

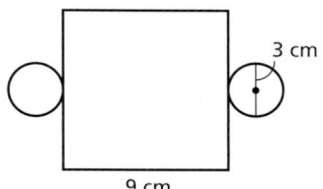

3 cm

9 cm

- (A) 84.82 square centimeters
- (B) 94.25 square centimeters
- (C) 98.91 square centimeters
- (D) 226.19 square centimeters

DAY 2

What is the area of the shaded region in the figure shown?

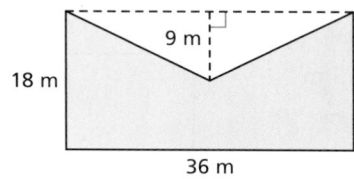

9 m

18 m

36 m

- (A) 270 square meters
- (B) 486 square meters
- (C) 648 square meters
- (D) 810 square meters

DAY 3

What is the equation of the graph of the line shown?

- (A) $y = 2x$
- (B) $y = -2x$
- (C) $y = \frac{1}{2}x$
- (D) $y = -\frac{1}{2}x$

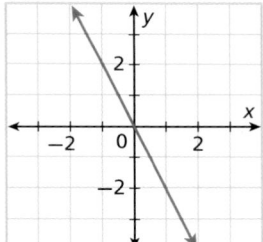

DAY 4

Three thousand rotations in 60 seconds is the same rate as which of the following?

- (A) 5 rotations per second
- (B) 50 rotations per minute
- (C) 500 rotations per second
- (D) 3000 rotations per minute

DAY 5

On a certain day, the exchange rate was 60 U.S. dollars for 50 euro. At this rate about how many U.S. dollars were 70 euro worth that day?

- (A) $20
- (B) $43
- (C) $58
- (D) $84

DAY 1

The actual length (ℓ) of the base of a building is 57 meters (m). Use the scale drawing of the base to find the actual width (w).

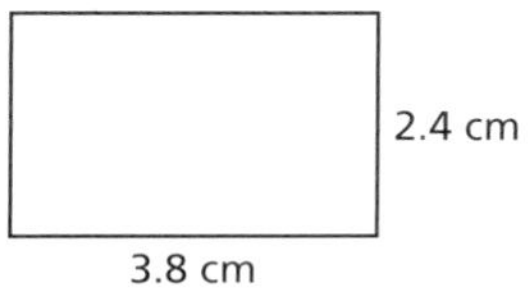

(A) 28.5 m

(B) 36 m

(C) 38 m

(D) 90.25 m

2.4 cm

3.8 cm

DAY 2

In the diagram, triangle QRM is congruent to triangle PSM.

Which side is the same length as $\overline{QR}$?

(A) $\overline{PS}$

(B) $\overline{SM}$

(C) $\overline{PM}$

(D) $\overline{PQ}$

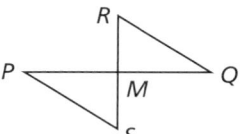

DAY 3

The scatter plot shows the relationship between the size of a diamond in Carats and its retail price. Based on these data, what is the approximate retail price of a 0.30 Carat diamond?

(A) $400

(B) $600

(C) $800

(D) $1000

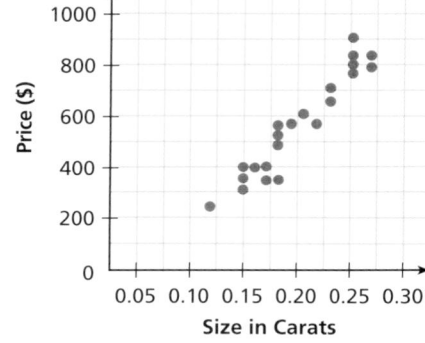

DAY 4

How many miles of fencing are needed to enclose a rectangular farm with a length of 12 miles and a diagonal length of 15 miles?

(A) 42 miles

(B) 48 miles

(C) 54 miles

(D) 60 miles

DAY 5

The points $(-2, 3)$, $(1, -2)$, $(2, 4)$, and $(5, -1)$ are the vertices of a polygon. What type of polygon is formed by these points?

(A) Kite

(B) Parallelogram

(C) Pentagon

(D) Trapezoid

DAY 1

The volume *V* of a cylinder may be found by using the formula $V = \pi r^2 h$, where *r* is the radius and *h* is the height. What is the radius of a cylinder with a volume of 54π cubic meters and a height of 6 meters?

Ⓐ 3 meters

Ⓑ 9 meters

Ⓒ 9.4 meters

Ⓓ 18 meters

DAY 2

What is the domain of the function shown in the table?

x	1	3	5	8
f(x)	2	−2	0	2

Ⓐ {1, 3, 5, 8}

Ⓑ {4}

Ⓒ {−2, 0, 2}

Ⓓ {7}

DAY 3

Which of the following could be the graph of $y = x^3 + 1$?

Ⓐ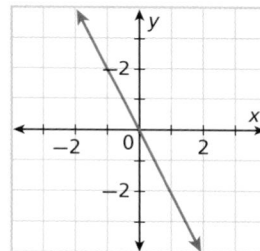

Ⓒ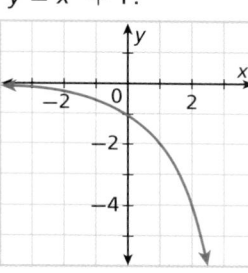

Ⓑ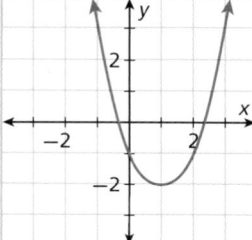

Ⓓ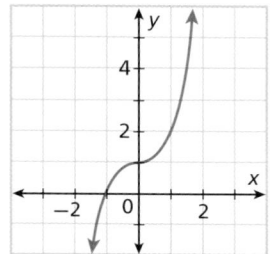

DAY 4

What is the solution for this equation?
$6(x - 9) = -12x + 36$

Ⓐ $x = 5$

Ⓑ $x = 2.5$

Ⓒ $x = -1$

Ⓓ $x = -5$

DAY 5

What is the solution set for this equation?
$$|5x - 2| = 7$$

Ⓐ {−1, −1.8}

Ⓑ {−1, 1.8}

Ⓒ {1, −1.8}

Ⓓ {1, 1.8}

Countdown to Mastery WEEK 13

DAY 1

Which of the following points lies on the line $2x + 3y = 6$?

Ⓐ (0, 2)

Ⓑ (0, 3)

Ⓒ (1, 2)

Ⓓ (3, 1)

DAY 2

A taxi company charges a $2.50 fee per ride plus an additional $2.10 per mile traveled. If the taxi fee increases to $2.75, what characteristic of a graph of this relationship would change?

Ⓐ The slope

Ⓑ The x-intercept

Ⓒ The y-intercept

Ⓓ There would be no changes.

DAY 3

What is the equation of the line shown in the graph?

Ⓐ $y = x - 3$

Ⓑ $y = 2x$

Ⓒ $y = \frac{1}{3}x$

Ⓓ $y = 3x$

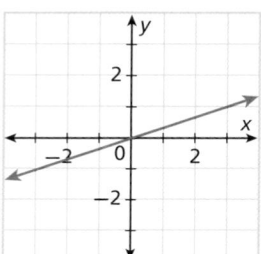

DAY 4

Paul's swimming coach recorded the following data during Paul's swim meet.

Time (s)	Distance (yd)
21.2	25
42.4	50
63.6	75

If Paul continues to swim at the rate shown in the table, how many yards will he swim in 127.2 seconds?

Ⓐ 100

Ⓑ 125

Ⓒ 150

Ⓓ 175

DAY 5

Jessika runs at a speed of 6 miles per hour. She runs for 25 minutes in a straight line at this rate. Approximately what distance does Jessika run?

Ⓐ $1\frac{1}{4}$ miles

Ⓑ 2 miles

Ⓒ $2\frac{1}{2}$ miles

Ⓓ 4 miles

DAY 1

What is the equation of a line that has a slope of $-\frac{3}{2}$ and passes through the point $(-4, 2)$?

(A) $y = -\frac{3}{2}x - 4$

(B) $y = -\frac{3}{2}x - 20$

(C) $y = -\frac{3}{2}x - 8$

(D) $y = -\frac{3}{2}x + 4$

DAY 2

What is the slope of a line parallel to the line whose equation is $3x - 4y = -8$?

(A) $m = 3$

(B) $m = 2$

(C) $m = \frac{3}{4}$

(D) $m = -3$

DAY 3

Using the line of best fit shown on the scatter plot, which of the following best approximates the amount of monthly rainfall in month 9?

(A) 10 inches

(B) 11 inches

(C) 12 inches

(D) 13 inches

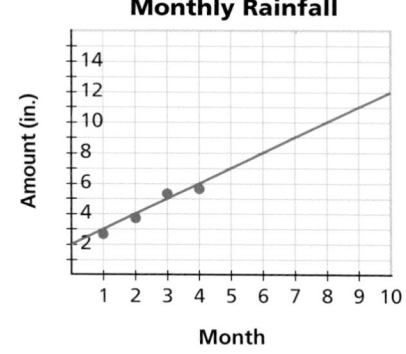

Monthly Rainfall

DAY 4

Which relation is a function?

(A) $\{(11, -2), (12, -1), (13, 0), (21, 8)\}$

(B) $\{(1, -2), (2, -1), (3, 0), (1, 4)\}$

(C) $\{(1, -2), (1, -1), (1, 0), (1, 1)\}$

(D) $\{(11, -2), (10, -1), (10, 9), (11, 9)\}$

DAY 5

The wholesale cost of a TV at Terry's Video is $1250. The company makes a 40% profit on the sale of this TV. How much did Terry's Video sell the TV for?

(A) $1300

(B) $1650

(C) $1750

(D) $2000

Countdown to Mastery WEEK 15

DAY 1

Pam used the following process to find the y-intercept of the line described by the equation $2x - y = 11$.

Step 1 Subtract $2x$ from both sides. $-y = -2x + 11$
Step 2 Divide each side by -1. $y = 2x - 11$
Step 3 The y-intercept of $y = mx + b$ is b. y-intercept is -11

According to Pam's method, which expression gives the y-intercept of the line described by the equation $ax + by = c$?

Ⓐ $-\frac{a}{b}$ Ⓑ $\frac{b}{a}$ Ⓒ $-\frac{b}{c}$ Ⓓ $\frac{c}{b}$

DAY 2

Which number serves as a counterexample to the statement below?

A prime number plus one is not prime.

Ⓐ 2
Ⓑ 3
Ⓒ 11
Ⓓ 17

DAY 3

The sum of the angle measures of a triangle is 180°. Two angles of a triangle measure 35° and 65°. What can you conclude is the measure of the third angle of the triangle?

Ⓐ 80°
Ⓑ 90°
Ⓒ 100°
Ⓓ It cannot be determined.

DAY 4

What are the x- and y-intercepts of the graph of $y = \frac{2}{5}x - 2$?

Ⓐ x-intercept: -2; y-intercept: 5
Ⓑ x-intercept: $\frac{2}{5}$; y-intercept: -2
Ⓒ x-intercept: 0; y-intercept: -2
Ⓓ x-intercept: 5; y-intercept: -2

DAY 5

A system of equations is set up to determine how many pounds of hazelnut coffee and how many pounds of Colombian coffee were mixed together to make a blend. The total mixture was 20 pounds of coffee. Which of the following is not a possible solution to the system?

Ⓐ (7, 13)
Ⓑ (32, –12)
Ⓒ (11, 9)
Ⓓ (1, 19)

Countdown to Mastery — WEEK 16

DAY 1

The equations $|x| = 3$ and $x = |3|$ have the same solution.

- (A) This statement is sometimes true.
- (B) This statement is always true.
- (C) This statement is never true.
- (D) This statement is true for positive numbers only.

DAY 2

Which equation represents a line parallel to the one shown?

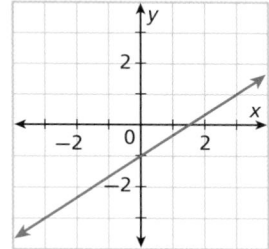

- (A) $y = \dfrac{3}{2}x + 1$
- (B) $y = \dfrac{2}{3}x + 1$
- (C) $y = -\dfrac{3}{2}x - 1$
- (D) $y = -\dfrac{2}{3}x$

DAY 3

When Miles began heating a frozen substance, its temperature was $-3°F$. Miles recorded the temperature of the substance every 20 minutes. If the temperature continued to rise at about the same rate, which is the best estimate of the temperature after 2 hours of heating?

- (A) 6°F
- (B) 10°F
- (C) 15°F
- (D) 18°F

DAY 4

Simplify.
$$\left(7x^2 + 3x - 1\right) + \left(x^2 - 4x + 5\right)$$

- (A) $8x^2 - x + 4$
- (B) $8x^2 - x - 6$
- (C) $8x^2 + 7x + 4$
- (D) $8x^2 + x - 6$

DAY 5

What is the solution to the system of equations graphed below?

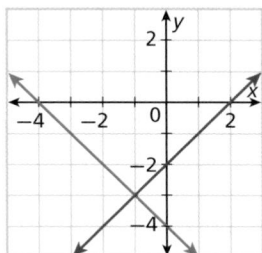

- (A) $(-1, 3)$
- (B) $(-1, -3)$
- (C) $(-3, -1)$
- (D) $(3, -1)$

DAY 1

A store manager increases the wholesale cost of an item by 35%. Which statement best represents the functional relationship between the wholesale cost of the item and the markup on the item?

- (A) The markup is dependent on the wholesale cost.
- (B) The wholesale cost is dependent on the markup.
- (C) The markup and the wholesale cost are independent of each other.
- (D) The relationship cannot be determined.

DAY 2

In one high school 40 of the school's 1100 students work on the school paper. About what percent of the students work on the paper?

- (A) 3.6%
- (B) 10.3%
- (C) 27.5%
- (D) 36.4%

DAY 3

The scatter plot shows the percent of households that own a car versus the household income. Based on these data, what is a reasonable estimate for the percent of households that own a car if the household income is $50,000?

- (A) 50%
- (B) 65%
- (C) 77%
- (D) 85%

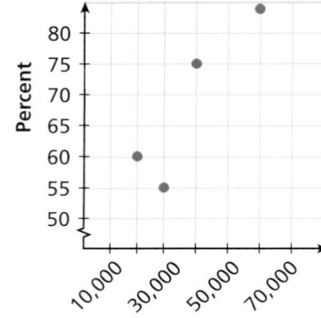

Income ($)

DAY 4

Greg has two similar rectangular boxes. The dimensions of box 1 are half those of box 2. How many times greater is the volume of box 2 than the volume of box 1?

- (A) 3
- (B) 8
- (C) 9
- (D) 27

DAY 5

Which of the following is the prime factored form of the lowest common denominator of $\frac{15}{28} - \frac{5}{12}$?

- (A) 3×5
- (B) $2 \times 2 \times 3 \times 7$
- (C) $3 \times 4 \times 7$
- (D) $3 \times 4 \times 4 \times 7$

DAY 1

What is the range of the function
$f(x) = 2x^2 + 1$ if the domain is $\{-2, 0, 3\}$?

Ⓐ $\{1, 9, 19\}$

Ⓑ $\{0, 8, 18\}$

Ⓒ $\{-9, 1, 19\}$

Ⓓ $\{-2, 0, 3\}$

DAY 2

What is the equation of the line with a slope of $\frac{5}{4}$ and a y-intercept of -2?

Ⓐ $5x + 4y = 2$

Ⓑ $y - 2 = \frac{5}{4}x$

Ⓒ $y = -\frac{5}{4}x + 2$

Ⓓ $5x - 4y = 8$

DAY 3

The graph shows the relationship between a person's height and weight. Which of the following statements would be an invalid conclusion for these data?

Ⓐ The graph shows data for 20 people.

Ⓑ A person who is tall is likely to have a higher weight.

Ⓒ The tallest person in this study weighed the most.

Ⓓ A person who has a lower weight has a fast metabolism.

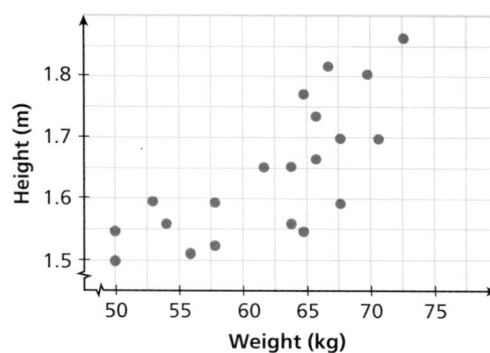

DAY 4

In the figure shown, all the corners form right angles. What is the area of the figure in square centimeters?

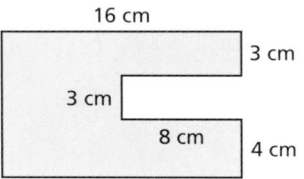

16 cm

3 cm

3 cm

8 cm

4 cm

Ⓐ 104 square centimeters

Ⓑ 112 square centimeters

Ⓒ 120 square centimeters

Ⓓ 136 square centimeters

DAY 5

A circle with a 6-inch diameter is cut out of a rectangular piece of cloth. Find the area of the remaining piece of cloth. ($A = \pi r^2$ and $\pi \approx 3.14$)

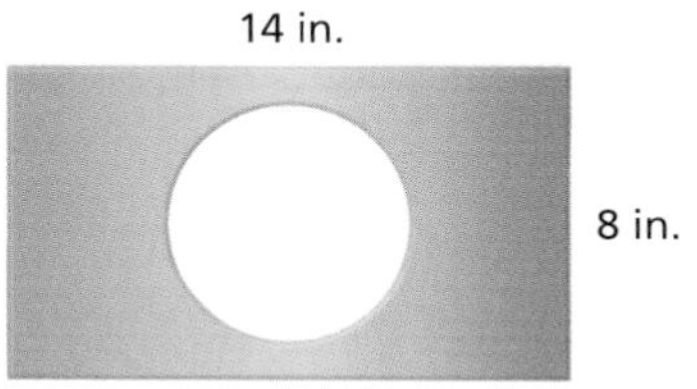

14 in.

8 in.

Ⓐ 15.7 square inches

Ⓑ 74.32 square inches

Ⓒ 83.7 square inches

Ⓓ 93.16 square inches

DAY 1

Kristin rode her bicycle 56 miles in 4 hours. What was Kristin's speed in feet per second to the nearest tenth?

(A) 6.8

(B) 20.5

(C) 23.3

(D) 123.0

DAY 2

What is the *y*-intercept of the line with a slope of $-\frac{1}{3}$ that passes through the point $(-6, 4)$?

(A) 6

(B) 2

(C) −2

(D) −6

DAY 3

The graph of rectangle *JKLM* is shown. What is the area in square units of rectangle *JKLM*?

(A) 6

(B) 8

(C) 10

(D) 12

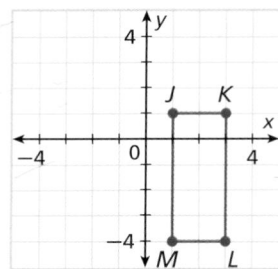

DAY 4

Miguel earns a 15% commission on his sales in addition to a salary of $500 a week. His weekly earnings can be modeled by the equation $p = 0.15s + 500$. What restrictions on the values of *p* and *s* best fit this situation?

(A) $p \geq 0$, *s* can be any value.

(B) $s \geq 0$, *p* can be any value.

(C) $s \geq 500$, $p \geq 0$

(D) $s \geq 0$, $p \geq 500$

DAY 5

Which is the greatest common factor of the terms in $4x^3 + 2x^2 - 6x$?

(A) *x*

(B) $x + 2$

(C) $2x$

(D) $2x^3$

DAY 1

How many times does the graph of $y = x^2 - 3$ intersect the x-axis?

- (A) none
- (B) one
- (C) two
- (D) three

DAY 2

What is the slope of a line parallel to the line shown?

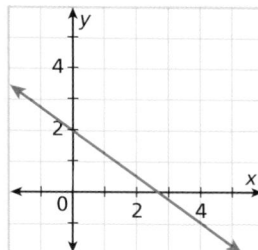

- (A) $-\dfrac{4}{3}$
- (B) $-\dfrac{3}{4}$
- (C) $\dfrac{3}{4}$
- (D) $\dfrac{4}{3}$

DAY 3

The graph shows the proposed balanced in Ashley's bank account. What is the average amount Ashley saves each week?

- (A) $2
- (B) $10
- (C) $15
- (D) $20

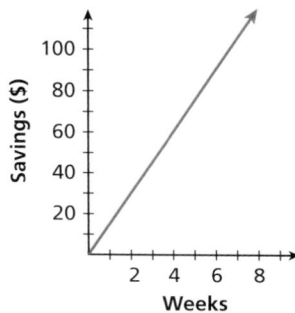

DAY 4

A map has the scale 1 inch:10 miles. On the map the area of a national park is about 12.5 square inches. Approximately how many acres are in the park? (1 square mile = 640 acres)

- (A) 800
- (B) 8000
- (C) 80,000
- (D) 800,000

DAY 5

Which is a factor of $4x^2 - 121$?

- (A) $2x + 11$
- (B) $(2x + 11)^2$
- (C) $2(x - 11)$
- (D) $4(x - 11)$

Countdown to Mastery WEEK 21

DAY 1

Simplify the expression.

$$(2a^2b^3c^5)(4ab^2c^4)$$

(A) $6a^3b^5c^9$
(B) $8a^2b^5c^9$
(C) $8a^3b^5c^9$
(D) $8a^2b^6c^{20}$

DAY 2

Simplify the expression.

$$\frac{a^7b^5c^3}{a^2b^3c^2}$$

(A) $a^5b^2c^{-1}$
(B) a^5b^2c
(C) $a^9b^8c^5$
(D) $a^{14}b^{15}c^6$

DAY 3

Peter's solution to find the value of x is shown.

Which property of real numbers did Peter use for Step 1?

(A) Multiplication Property of Equality
(B) Division Property of Equality
(C) Distributive Property of Equality
(D) Zero Product Property of Multiplication

Given:	$ax^2 + bx = 0$
Step 1:	$x^2 + \frac{b}{a}x = 0$
Step 2:	$x\left(x + \frac{b}{a}\right) = 0$
Step 3:	$x = 0$ or $x + \frac{b}{a} = 0$
Step 4:	$x = 0$ or $x = -\frac{b}{a}$

DAY 4

What are the solutions for the equation $y = (2x - 1)(x + 5)$?

(A) $\frac{1}{2}$ and -5
(B) -1 and 5
(C) 1 and -5
(D) $-\frac{1}{2}$ and 5

DAY 5

What quantity should be added to both sides of this equation to complete the square?

$$x^2 + 14x = 15$$

(A) 7
(B) 28
(C) 49
(D) 196

DAY 1

The graph of the equation $y = x^2 + 6x + 8$ is shown. For what values of x is $y = 0$?

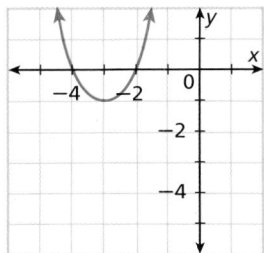

(A) 2 and 4

(B) −2 and −4

(C) −2 and 4

(D) 2 and −4

DAY 2

What is the range of the function shown?

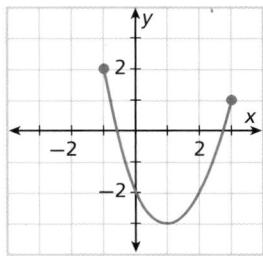

(A) $-2 < y < 3$

(B) $-3 < y \le 6$

(C) $-3 \le y \le 6$

(D) $-2 \le y \le 3$

DAY 3

The graph shows the height of a baseball from the time it is thrown until the time it hits the ground. What value is **not** shown on the graph?

(A) The amount of time that the ball was in the air

(B) The height at which the ball started

(C) The maximum height that the ball reached

(D) The speed at which the ball was thrown

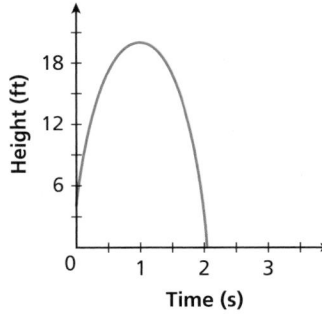

DAY 4

What are the solution(s) of the quadratic equation $x^2 - 10x - 24 = 0$?

(A) $x = -4, 6$

(B) $x = 2, -12$

(C) $x = -2, 12$

(D) $x = 4, -6$

DAY 5

What is the solution to the system of equations?

$$\begin{cases} 3x - 4y = 19 \\ y = 2x - 11 \end{cases}$$

(A) $(5, -1)$

(B) $(-5, -21)$

(C) $(5, 1)$

(D) $(-5, -8.5)$

Countdown to Mastery WEEK 23

DAY 1

Which of the following is the graph of $y = -x^2$?

Ⓐ

Ⓒ

Ⓑ

Ⓓ

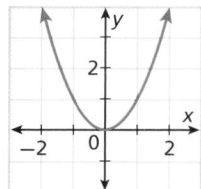

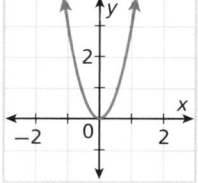

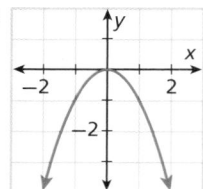

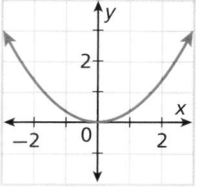

DAY 2

What is the value of x in the triangle shown?

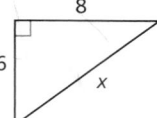

Ⓐ 5

Ⓑ 7

Ⓒ 10

Ⓓ 14

DAY 3

The graph shows the height of water coming out of a fountain over time. How many seconds pass before the water reaches the ground?

Ⓐ 0

Ⓑ 2

Ⓒ 4

Ⓓ 18

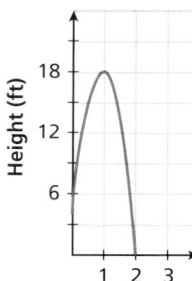

DAY 4

What is one solution to the equation $2x^2 + 7x + 3 = 0$?

Ⓐ $x = 3$

Ⓑ $x = \frac{1}{2}$

Ⓒ $x = -\frac{1}{2}$

Ⓓ $x = -1$

DAY 5

What is the solution to the system of equations?

$$\begin{cases} 4x + 2y = -8 \\ x - 2y = 13 \end{cases}$$

Ⓐ (25, 6)

Ⓑ (1, 6)

Ⓒ (−1, −6)

Ⓓ (1, −6)

DAY 1

What is the surface area of the figure represented by this net?

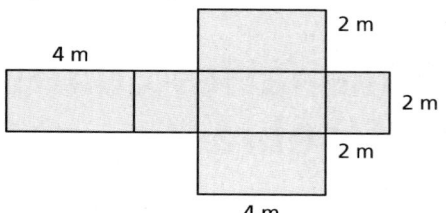

- **A** 32 square meters
- **B** 36 square meters
- **C** 40 square meters
- **D** 44 square meters

DAY 2

The graph of the equation $y = \frac{2}{3}x + 2$ is shown. For what value of x is $y = 0$?

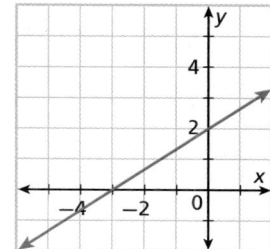

- **A** $x = -3$
- **B** $x = -2$
- **C** $x = 2$
- **D** $x = 3$

DAY 3

What values would you use for a, b, and c in the Quadratic Formula to solve $2x^2 = 5x + 140$?

- **A** $a = 2$; $b = 5$; $c = 140$
- **B** $a = 2$; $b = -5$; $c = -140$
- **C** $a = 5$; $b = -2$; $c = 140$
- **D** $a = 5$; $b = 2$; $c = 140$

DAY 4

Simplify $\dfrac{x^2 + 7x}{x^2 - 49}$ to lowest terms.

- **A** $-\dfrac{x}{7}$
- **B** $-\dfrac{1}{7}$
- **C** $\dfrac{x}{x - 7}$
- **D** $\dfrac{x}{x + 7}$

DAY 5

Which fraction equals the product

$$\left(\frac{3t + 4}{5t}\right)\left(\frac{10t}{t + 4}\right)?$$

- **A** $\dfrac{3t + 4}{t + 2}$
- **B** $\dfrac{6t + 8}{t + 4}$
- **C** $\dfrac{6}{1}$
- **D** $\dfrac{8}{1}$

California
the golden state

California Mathematics Content Standards for Algebra 1

Symbolic reasoning and calculations with symbols are central in algebra. Through the study of algebra, a student develops an understanding of the symbolic language of mathematics and the sciences. In addition, algebraic skills and concepts are developed and used in a wide variety of problem-solving situations.

1.0 Students identify and use the arithmetic properties of subsets of integers and rational, irrational, and real numbers, including closure properties for the four basic arithmetic operations where applicable:

1.1 Students use properties of numbers to demonstrate whether assertions are true or false.

2.0 Students understand and use such operations as taking the opposite, finding the reciprocal, taking a root, and raising to a fractional power. They understand and use the rules of exponents.

3.0 Students solve equations and inequalities involving absolute values.

4.0 Students simplify expressions before solving linear equations and inequalities in one variable, such as $3(2x - 5) + 4(x - 2) = 12$.

5.0 Students solve multistep problems, including word problems, involving linear equations and linear inequalities in one variable and provide justification for each step.

6.0 Students graph a linear equation and compute the x- and y-intercepts (e.g., graph $2x + 6y = 4$). They are also able to sketch the region defined by linear inequalities (e.g., they sketch the region defined by $2x + 6y < 4$).

7.0 Students verify that a point lies on a line, given an equation of the line. Students are able to derive linear equations by using the point-slope formula.

8.0 Students understand the concepts of parallel lines and perpendicular lines and how those slopes are related. Students are able to find the equation of a line perpendicular to a given line that passes through a given point.

9.0 Students solve a system of two linear equations in two variables algebraically and are able to interpret the answer graphically. Students are able to solve a system of two linear inequalities in two variables and to sketch the solution sets.

10.0 Students add, subtract, multiply, and divide monomials and polynomials. Students solve multistep problems, including word problems, by using these techniques.

Continued

11.0 Students apply basic factoring techniques to second- and simple third-degree polynomials. These techniques include finding a common factor for all terms in a polynomial, recognizing the difference of two squares, and recognizing perfect squares of binomials.

12.0 Students simplify fractions with polynomials in the numerator and denominator by factoring both and reducing them to the lowest terms.

13.0 Students add, subtract, multiply, and divide rational expressions and functions. Students solve both computationally and conceptually challenging problems by using these techniques.

14.0 Students solve a quadratic equation by factoring or completing the square.

15.0 Students apply algebraic techniques to solve rate problems, work problems, and percent mixture problems.

16.0 Students understand the concepts of a relation and a function, determine whether a given relation defines a function, and give pertinent information about given relations and functions.

Bay Bridge

California Mathematics Content Standards for Algebra 1

17.0 Students determine the domain of independent variables and the range of dependent variables defined by a graph, a set of ordered pairs, or a symbolic expression.

18.0 Students determine whether a relation defined by a graph, a set of ordered pairs, or a symbolic expression is a function and justify the conclusion.

19.0 Students know the quadratic formula and are familiar with its proof by completing the square.

20.0 Students use the quadratic formula to find the roots of a second-degree polynomial and to solve quadratic equations.

21.0 Students graph quadratic functions and know that their roots are the x-intercepts.

22.0 Students use the quadratic formula or factoring techniques or both to determine whether the graph of a quadratic function will intersect the x-axis in zero, one, or two points.

23.0 Students apply quadratic equations to physical problems, such as the motion of an object under the force of gravity.

Continued

California
the golden state

24.0 **Students use and know simple aspects of a logical argument:**

24.1 Students explain the difference between inductive and deductive reasoning and identify and provide examples of each.

24.2 Students identify the hypothesis and conclusion in logical deduction.

24.3 Students use counterexamples to show that an assertion is false and recognize that a single counterexample is sufficient to refute an assertion.

San Diego Beach

25.0 Students use properties of the number system to judge the validity of results, to justify each step of a procedure, and to prove or disprove statements:

25.1 Students use properties of numbers to construct simple, valid arguments (direct and indirect) for, or formulate counterexamples to, claimed assertions.

25.2 Students judge the validity of an argument according to whether the properties of the real number system and the order of operations have been applied correctly at each step.

25.3 Given a specific algebraic statement involving linear, quadratic, or absolute value expressions or equations or inequalities, students determine whether the statement is true sometimes, always, or never.

Balboa Park, San Diego

Los Angeles skyline

Mesquite Flat Dunes, Death Valley

Yosemite National Park

Golden Gate Bridge

Borrego, California

Mono Lake

Foundations of Algebra

go.hrw.com
Online Resources
KEYWORD: MA8CA TOC

Table of Contents

Tools for Success

Reading and Writing Math

Reading Math 34
Writing Math 6, 7, 32, 33
Vocabulary 3, 4, 9, 17, 23, 29, 35, 45, 51

Study Skills

Know-It Notes 15, 20, 21, 34, 43, 44
Graphic Organizers 8, 17, 22, 28, 35, 45, 50
Homework Help Online 9, 17, 23, 29, 35, 45, 51

MASTERING THE STANDARDS

Countdown to Mastery Weeks 1, 2
Spiral Standards Review 11, 19, 25, 31, 37, 47, 53
Ready to Go On? 41, 57
Mastering the Standards 66

CHAPTER

2

Equations

Tools for Success

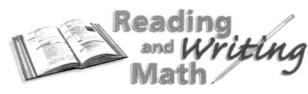

Reading Math 104
Writing Math 72, 94
Vocabulary 69, 70, 75, 95, 105, 111

Study Strategy 71
Know-It Notes 73, 103, 114, 115
Graphic Organizers 75, 82, 87, 95, 104, 111, 116
Homework Help Online 75, 82, 88, 95, 105, 111, 116

MASTERING THE STANDARDS

Countdown to Mastery Weeks 3, 4, 5
Spiral Standards Review 77, 84, 90, 98, 107, 113, 119
Ready to Go On? 101, 121
Mastering the Standards 130

Inequalities

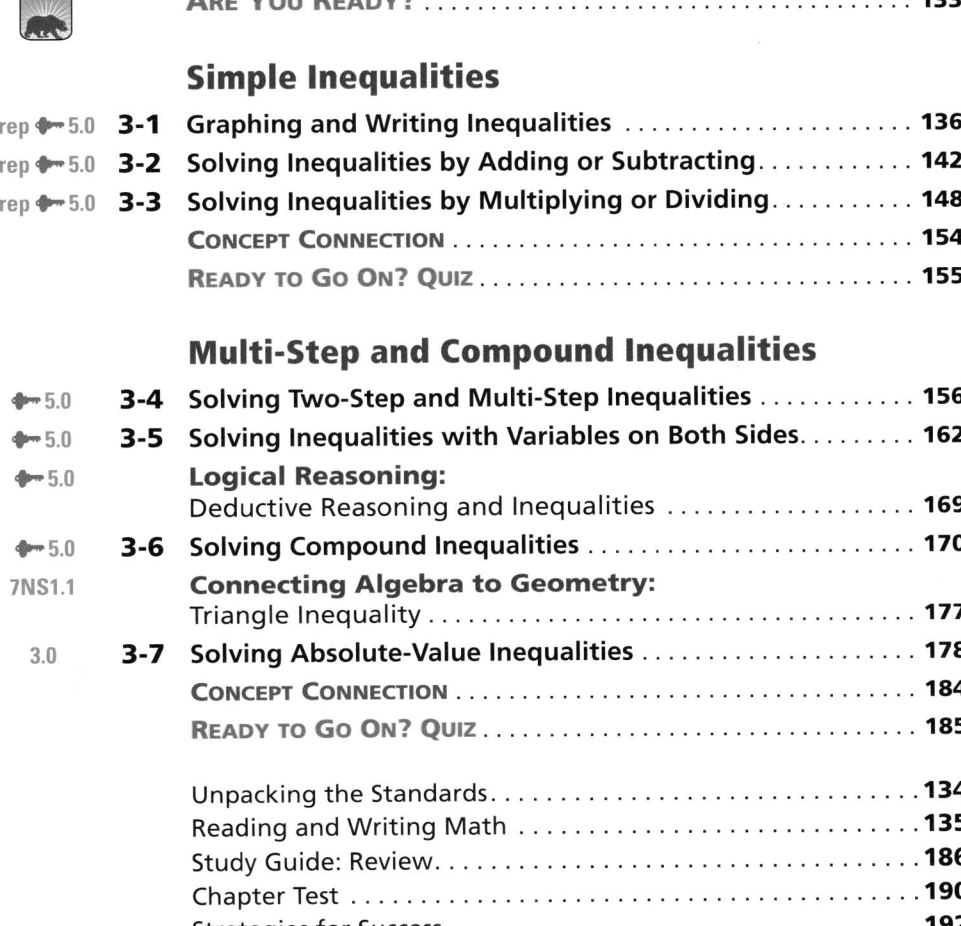

go.hrw.com
Online Resources
KEYWORD: MA8CA TOC

Tools for Success

Reading and Writing Math

Reading Math 138, 170
Vocabulary 133, 134, 139, 174, 186

Study Skills

Study Strategy 135
Know-It Notes 137, 142, 148, 149, 170, 178, 179
Graphic Organizers 138, 145, 150, 158, 165, 173, 181
Homework Help Online 139, 145, 151, 159, 165, 174, 181

MASTERING THE STANDARDS

Countdown to Mastery Weeks 5, 6, 7
Spiral Standards Review 141, 147, 153, 161, 168, 176, 183
Ready to Go On? 155, 185
Mastering the Standards 194

Functions

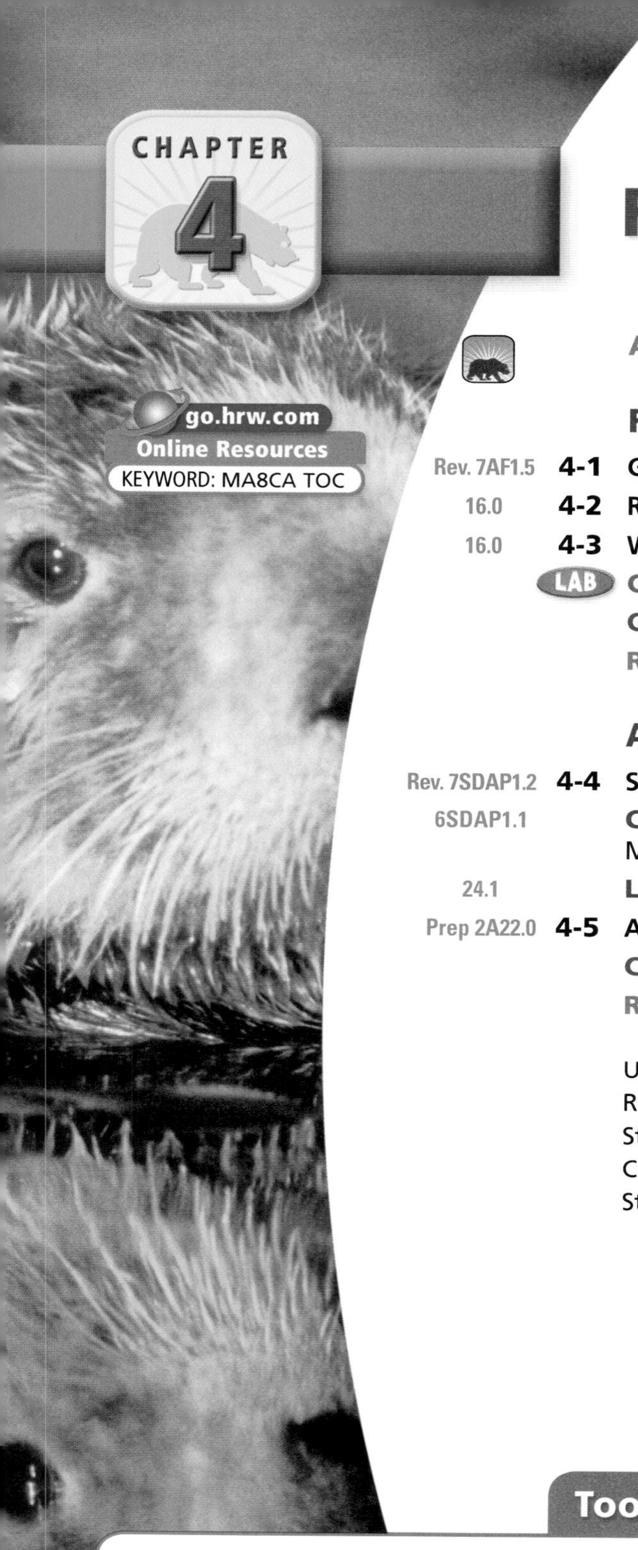

Tools for Success

Reading Math 217, 234

Writing Math 207

Vocabulary 197, 198, 203, 209, 218, 228, 237

Know-It Notes 214, 225, 235

Graphic Organizers 202, 208, 217, 227, 236

Homework Help Online 203, 209, 218, 228, 237

Countdown to Mastery Weeks 7, 8, 9

Spiral Standards Review 205, 212, 220, 231, 239

Ready to Go On? 223, 241

Mastering the Standards 250

Linear Functions

go.hrw.com
Online Resources
KEYWORD: MA8CA TOC

Tools for Success

Reading Math 273
Writing Math 290
Vocabulary 253, 254, 260, 266, 276, 285, 308

Study Strategy 255
Know-It Notes 258, 272, 291, 298, 304, 306
Graphic Organizers 259, 265, 276, 285, 293, 300, 307
Homework Help Online 260, 266, 276, 285, 294, 301, 308

Countdown to Mastery Weeks 9, 10, 11, 12
Spiral Standards Review 262, 268, 279, 287, 296, 303, 310
Ready to Go On? 213, 289
Mastering the Standards 322

go.hrw.com
Online Resources
KEYWORD: MA8CA TOC

Systems of Equations and Inequalities

Tools for Success

Reading and Writing Math

Writing Math 331
Vocabulary 325, 326, 332, 353, 368, 374

Study Skills

Know-It Notes 336, 343, 346, 351, 365
Graphic Organizers 331, 339, 347, 353, 359, 367, 373
Homework Help Online 332, 340, 347, 353, 359, 368, 374

MASTERING THE STANDARDS

Countdown to Mastery Weeks 12, 13, 14
Spiral Standards Review 334, 342, 349, 355, 361, 370, 376
Ready to Go On? 363, 379
Mastering the Standards 388

Exponents and Polynomials

go.hrw.com
Online Resources
KEYWORD: MA8CA TOC

Tools for Success

Reading and Writing Math

Reading Math 394, 401, 402
Writing Math 400, 416, 439
Vocabulary 391, 392, 403, 425, 433, 459

Study Skills

Know-It Notes 394, 400, 401, 408, 410, 411, 415, 417, 418, 423
Graphic Organizers 396, 402, 411, 419, 424, 432, 440, 450, 459
Homework Help Online 397, 403, 412, 419, 425, 433, 441, 451, 459

MASTERING THE STANDARDS

Countdown to Mastery Weeks 14, 15, 16, 17
Spiral Standards Review 399, 405, 414, 421, 427, 435, 443, 453, 461
Ready to Go On? 429, 463
Mastering the Standards 472

CHAPTER

8

Factoring Polynomials

go.hrw.com
Online Resources
KEYWORD: MA8CA TOC

Tools for Success

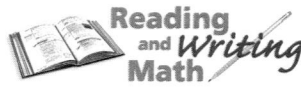
Reading and Writing Math

Reading Math 517
Writing Math 487
Vocabulary 475, 476, 481

Study Skills

Know-It Notes 497, 514, 516, 524
Graphic Organizers 480, 490, 499, 508, 517, 524
Homework Help Online 481, 491, 500, 509, 518, 525

MASTERING THE STANDARDS

Countdown to Mastery Weeks 17, 18, 19
Spiral Standards Review 483, 493, 503, 511, 520, 527
Ready to Go On? 513, 529
Mastering the Standards 538

Quadratic Functions and Equations

ARE YOU READY? 541

go.hrw.com
Online Resources
KEYWORD: MA8CA TOC

Quadratic Functions

17.0	**9-1**	Quadratic Equations and Functions	**544**
24.1	**LAB**	Explore the Axis of Symmetry	**552**
21.0	**9-2**	Characteristics of Quadratic Functions	**553**
21.0	**9-3**	Graphing Quadratic Functions	**560**
		CONCEPT CONNECTION	**566**
		READY TO GO ON? QUIZ	**567**

Solving Quadratic Equations

21.0	**9-4**	Solving Quadratic Equations by Graphing	**568**
	LAB	Explore Roots, Zeros, and *x*-intercepts	**574**
14.0	**9-5**	Solving Quadratic Equations by Factoring	**576**
2.0	**9-6**	Solving Quadratic Equations by Using Square Roots	**582**
7MG3.2		**Connecting Algebra to Geometry:** The Distance Formula	**588**
Prep 14.0	**LAB**	Model Completing the Square	**590**
14.0	**9-7**	Completing the Square	**591**
19.0	**9-8**	The Quadratic Formula	**598**
22.0	**9-9**	The Discriminant	**605**
		CONCEPT CONNECTION	**610**
		READY TO GO ON? QUIZ	**611**

Unpacking the Standards	**542**
Reading and Writing Math	**543**
Study Guide: Review	**612**
Chapter Test	**616**
Strategies for Success	**618**

Tools for Success

Reading Math 582

Writing Math 592

Vocabulary 541, 542, 548, 557, 571, 594, 607

Study Strategy 543

Know-It Notes 546, 554, 555, 568, 576, 582, 591, 592, 598, 601, 605

Graphic Organizers 547, 557, 563, 570, 579, 585, 594, 601, 607

Homework Help Online 548, 557, 563, 571, 579, 585, 594, 602, 607

Countdown to Mastery Weeks 19, 20, 21, 22

Spiral Standards Review 551, 559, 565, 573, 581, 587, 597, 604, 609

Ready to Go On? 567, 611

Mastering the Standards 620

CHAPTER 10

Rational Functions and Equations

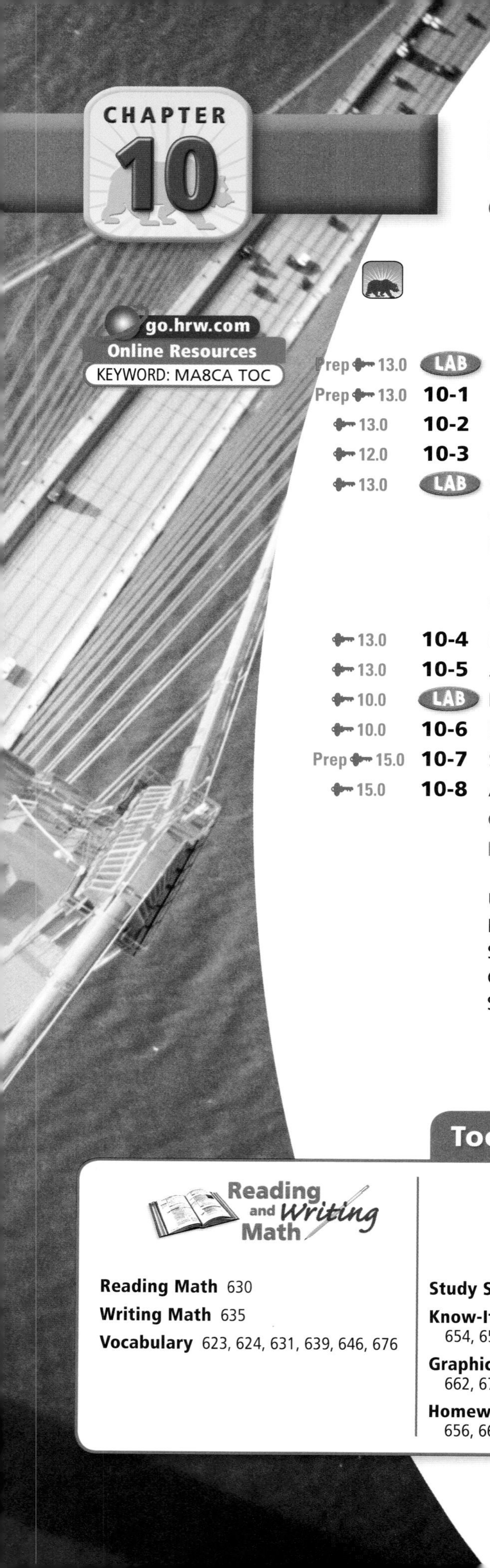

go.hrw.com
Online Resources
KEYWORD: MA8CA TOC

Tools for Success

Reading and Writing Math

Reading Math 630
Writing Math 635
Vocabulary 623, 624, 631, 639, 646, 676

Study Skills

Study Strategy 625
Know-It Notes 627, 629, 635, 638, 652, 654, 659, 667
Graphic Organizers 630, 638, 645, 655, 662, 671, 676, 681
Homework Help Online 631, 639, 646, 656, 663, 671, 676, 681

MASTERING THE STANDARDS

Countdown to Mastery Weeks 22, 23, 24
Spiral Standards Review 633, 641, 648, 658, 665, 673, 678, 683
Ready to Go On? 651, 685
Mastering the Standards 694

Preview of Algebra II
Exponential and Radical Functions

go.hrw.com
Online Resources
KEYWORD: MA8CA TOC

Tools for Success

Reading Math 748

Vocabulary 697, 698, 703, 708, 713, 726, 735, 742, 751

Study Strategy 699

Know-It Notes 700, 705, 706, 722, 733, 738, 741, 747, 748, 749, 757

Graphic Organizers 702, 708, 713, 718, 726, 734, 741, 750, 758

Homework Help Online 703, 708, 713, 719, 726, 735, 742, 751, 759

Spiral Standards Review 704, 710, 715, 721, 729, 737, 744, 754, 761

Ready to Go On? 731, 763

Mastering the Standards 772

Focus on Problem Solving

The Problem-Solving Plan

To be a good problem solver you need a good problem-solving plan. Using a problem-solving plan along with a problem-solving strategy helps you organize your work and correctly solve the problem. The plan used in this book is outlined below.

UNDERSTAND the Problem

- **What are you asked to find?**

  Make sure you understand exactly what the problem is asking. Restate the problem in your own words.

- **What information is given in the problem?**

  List every piece of information the problem gives you.

- **Is all the information relevant?**

  Sometimes problems have extra information that is not needed to solve the problem. Try to determine what is and is not needed. This helps you stay organized when you are making a plan.

- **Were you given enough information to solve the problem?**

  Sometimes there simply is not enough information to solve the problem. List what else you need to know to solve the problem.

Make a PLAN

- **What problem-solving strategy or strategies can you use to help you solve the problem?**

  Think about strategies you have used in the past to solve problems. Would any of them be helpful in solving this problem?

- **Create a step-by-step plan of how you will solve the problem.**

  Write out your plan in words to help you get a clearer idea of how to solve the problem mathematically.

SOLVE

- **Use your plan to solve the problem.**

  Translate your plan from words to math. Show each step in your solution and write your answer in a complete sentence.

LOOK BACK

- **Did you completely answer the question that was asked?**

  Be sure you answered the question that asked and that your answer is complete.

- **Is your answer reasonable?**

  Your answer should make sense.

- **Could you have used a different strategy to solve the problem?**

  Solving the problem again with a different strategy is a good way to check your answer.

- **Did you learn anything that could help you solve similar problems in the future?**

  You may want to take notes about this kind of problem and the strategy you used to solve it.

Using the Problem Solving Plan

During a skating competition, Jules skated around the track 35 times. One lap is 0.9 mile. If Jules finished in 1 hour 30 minutes, what was his average speed?

UNDERSTAND the Problem

You are asked to find Jules's average speed for 35 laps. You know the distance of each lap and the amount of time it took him to finish the competition.

Make a PLAN

Solve a simpler problem by using easier numbers to do the computations.

SOLVE

Find the total distance skated.

$$35(0.9)$$ *There were 35 laps that measured 0.9 mile.*

$$35(1 - 0.1)$$ *Write 0.9 as 1 − 0.1*

$$35(1) - 3.5(0.1)$$ *Use the Distributive Property.*

$$35 - 3.5$$

$$31.5$$

Use the distance formula to find the average speed.

$$d = rt$$

$$31.5 = r \times 1.5$$ *1 hour 30 minutes = 1.5 hours*

$$\frac{31.5}{1.5} = r$$ *Solve for r.*

$$\frac{315}{15} = r$$ *Multiply the numerator and denominator by 10 to eliminate the decimals.*

$$\frac{1}{15}(315) = r$$

$$\frac{1}{15}(300 + 15) = r$$ *Write 315 as 300 + 15.*

$$\frac{1}{15}(300) + \frac{1}{15}(15) = r$$ *Use the Distributive Property.*

$$20 + 1 = r$$

$$21 = r$$

Jules skated at an average speed of 21 miles per hour.

LOOK BACK

Each lap is a little less than 1 mile, so 35 laps is less than 35 miles. Round this distance to 30 miles and use $d = rt$ to find the rate when the time is 1.5 hours: $30 \text{ mi} = (1.5 \text{ h})r \rightarrow r = 20 \text{ mi/h}$. This is close to 21 mi/h.

Using Your Book for Success

Holt California Algebra 1 has many features designed to help you learn and study math. Becoming familiar with these features will prepare you for greater success.

Learn

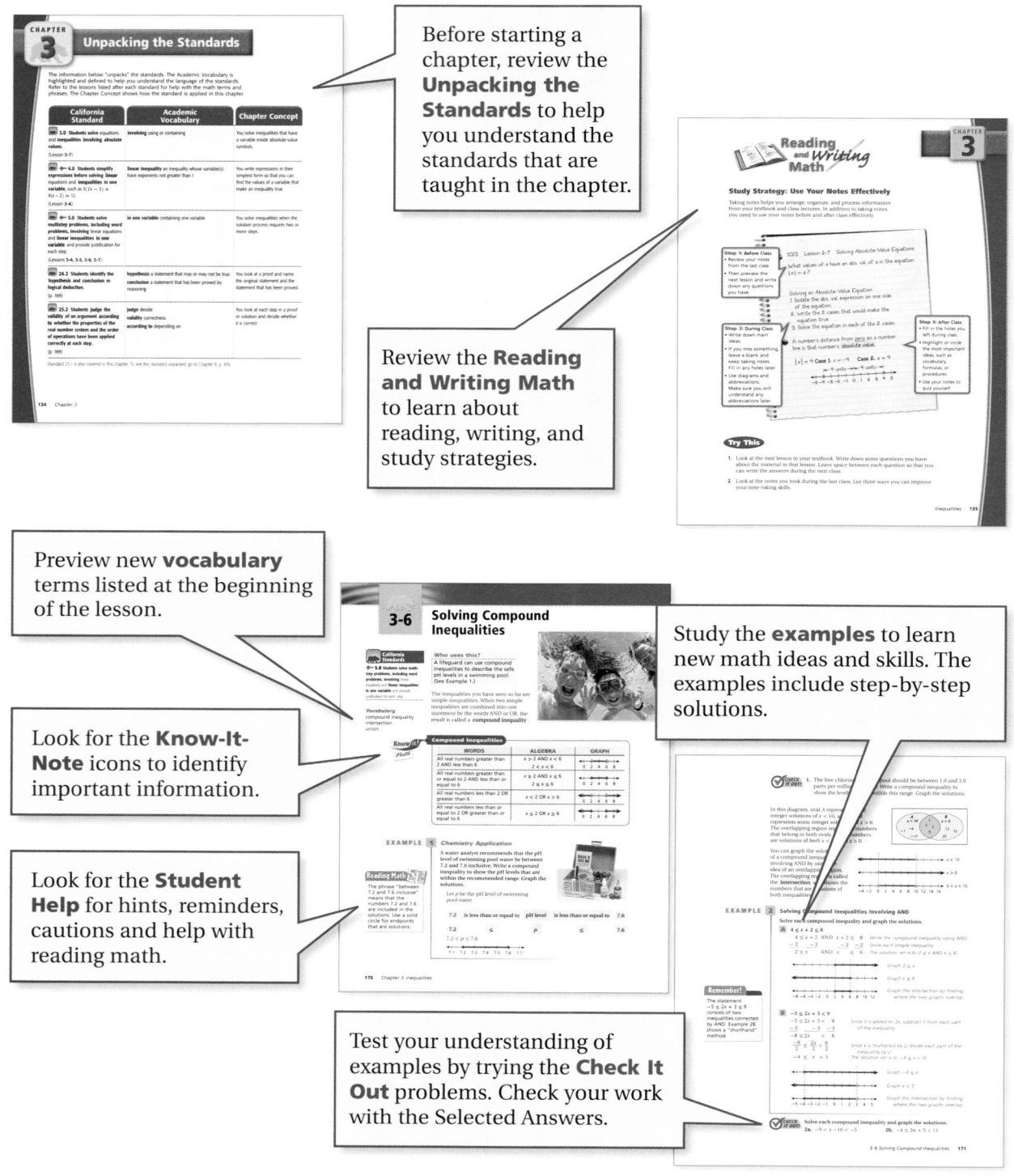

Before starting a chapter, review the **Unpacking the Standards** to help you understand the standards that are taught in the chapter.

Review the **Reading and Writing Math** to learn about reading, writing, and study strategies.

Preview new **vocabulary** terms listed at the beginning of the lesson.

Look for the **Know-It-Note** icons to identify important information.

Look for the **Student Help** for hints, reminders, cautions and help with reading math.

Study the **examples** to learn new math ideas and skills. The examples include step-by-step solutions.

Test your understanding of examples by trying the **Check It Out** problems. Check your work with the Selected Answers.

Practice

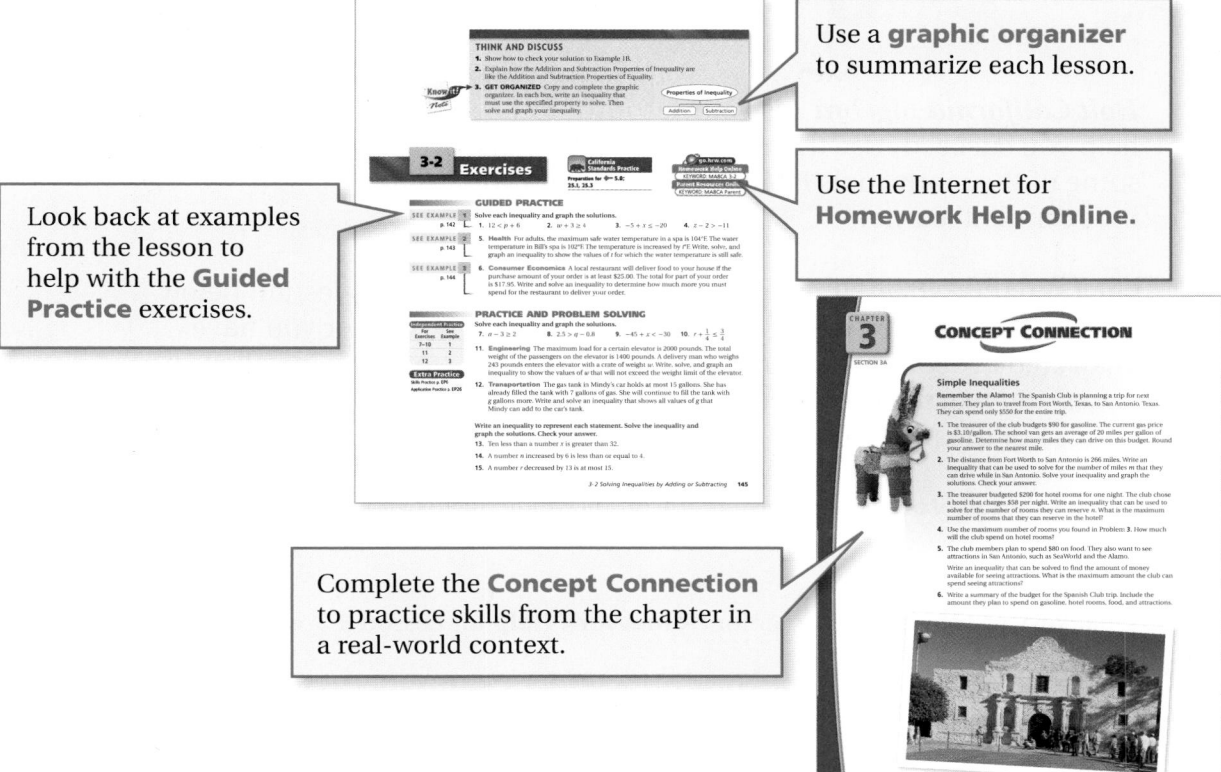

Look back at examples from the lesson to help with the **Guided Practice** exercises.

Use a **graphic organizer** to summarize each lesson.

Use the Internet for **Homework Help Online.**

Complete the **Concept Connection** to practice skills from the chapter in a real-world context.

Review

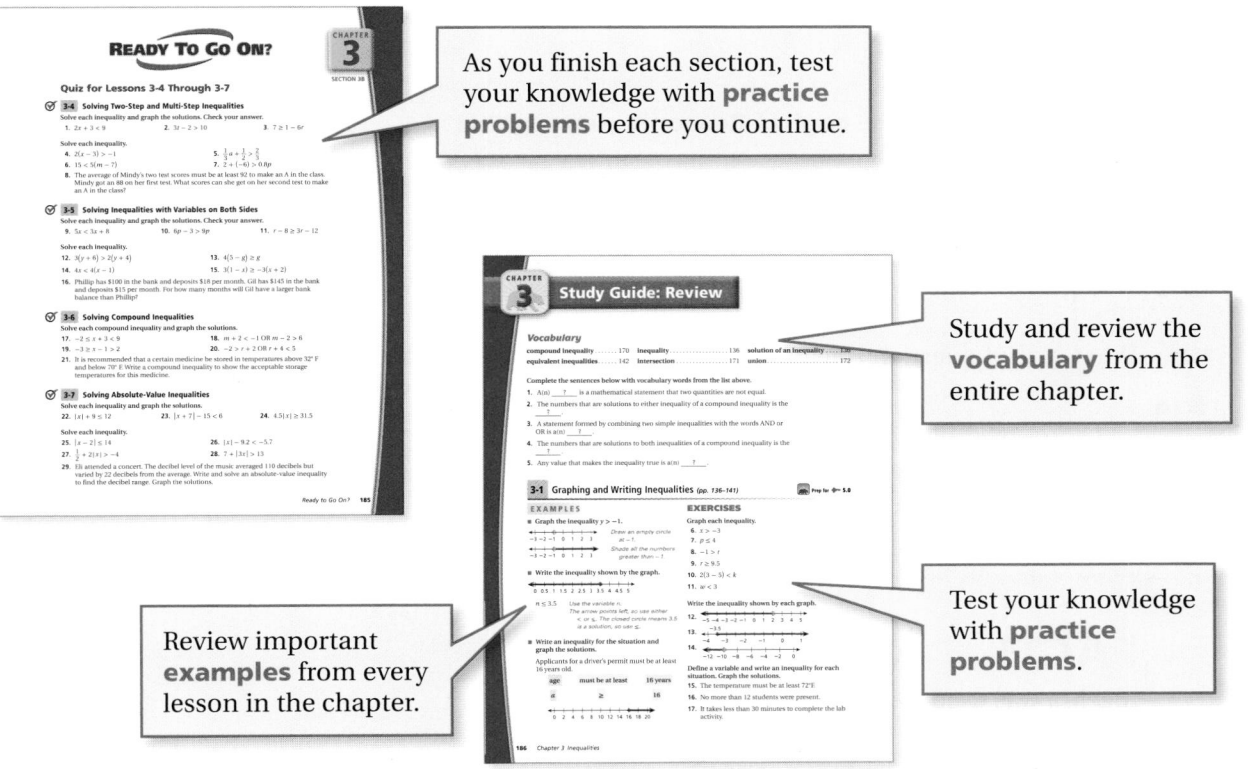

As you finish each section, test your knowledge with **practice problems** before you continue.

Study and review the **vocabulary** from the entire chapter.

Review important **examples** from every lesson in the chapter.

Test your knowledge with **practice problems.**

Scavenger Hunt

Holt California Algebra 1 is your resource to help you succeed. Use this scavenger hunt to discover some of the many tools Holt provides to help you be an independent learner.

On a separate sheet of paper, write the answers to each question below. Within each answer, one letter will be in a yellow box. After you have answered every question, identify the letters that would be in yellow boxes and rearrange them to reveal the answer to the question at the bottom of the page.

1. What is the last **Vocabulary** term in the Study Guide: Review for Chapter 2?

▪▪▪▪ ▪▪▪▪ ▪▪▪▪

2. What keyword should you enter for **Homework Help** for Lesson 6-3?

▪▪▪▪▪▪▪▪▪

3. In Lesson 7-3, what is **Example 1** teaching you to find?

▪▪▪▪▪▪▪▪ ▪▪ ▪▪▪▪▪▪

4. In Chapter 4, what is the last academic vocabulary word listed in **Unpacking the Standards**?

▪▪▪▪▪▪▪

5. What is the topic of the **Logical Reasoning** on page 311?

▪▪▪▪▪▪▪▪▪ ▪▪▪▪▪▪▪▪▪▪▪

6. To what school subject is **Exercise 35** in Lesson 3-6 linked?

▪▪▪▪▪▪▪▪▪

7. What type of question is featured in Chapter 9 **Strategies for Success**?

▪▪▪▪▪▪▪▪▪ ▪▪▪▪▪▪▪▪

8. The Chapter 7 **Reading and Writing Math** is about what strategy?

▪▪▪▪▪ ▪▪▪ ▪▪▪▪▪▪▪▪▪
▪▪▪ ▪▪▪▪▪▪▪

FACT!

Algebra was used to build what ancient structures?

▪▪▪▪▪▪▪▪▪

Math Builders

The Math Builders on the following pages present important standards using a step-by-step, layered approach.

Function Builder ← 6.0, ← 7.0

Overlays that show multiple representations of a linear function and how to go from one representation to another

Use with Lessons 5-1, 5-5, and 5-6.

System Builder ← 6.0, ← 9.0

Overlays that show the steps involved to solve a system of equations or inequalities by graphing

Use with Lessons 6-1 and 6-7.

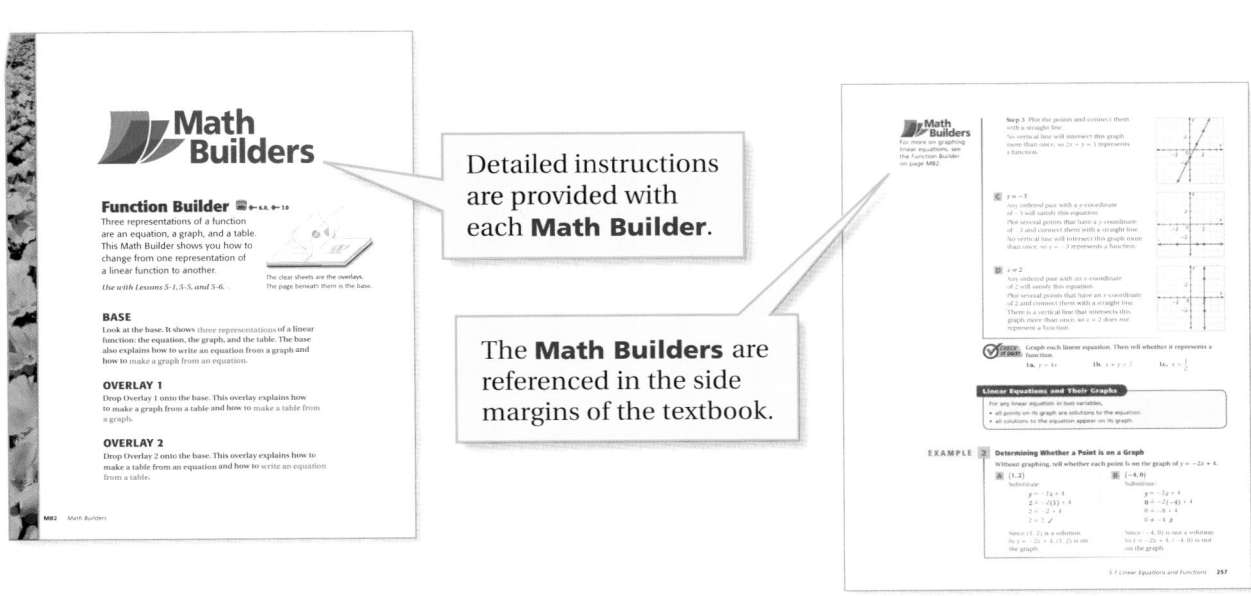

Detailed instructions are provided with each **Math Builder**.

The **Math Builders** are referenced in the side margins of the textbook.

Math Builders

Function Builder 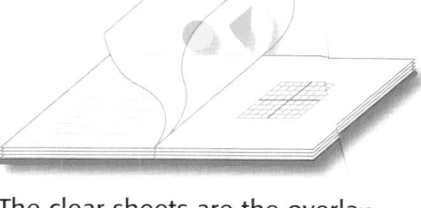 6.0, 7.0

Three representations of a function are an equation, a graph, and a table. This Math Builder shows you how to change from one representation of a linear function to another.

Use with Lessons 5-1, 5-5, and 5-6.

The clear sheets are the overlays. The page beneath them is the base.

BASE

Look at the base. It shows three representations of a linear function: the equation, the graph, and the table. The base also explains how to write an equation from a graph and how to make a graph from an equation.

OVERLAY 1

Drop Overlay 1 onto the base. This overlay explains how to make a graph from a table and how to make a table from a graph.

OVERLAY 2

Drop Overlay 2 onto the base. This overlay explains how to make a table from an equation and how to write an equation from a table.

To write an equation from a graph, use the slope and *y*-intercept.

$$2x + 4y = 8$$
$$y = -\frac{1}{2}x + 2$$

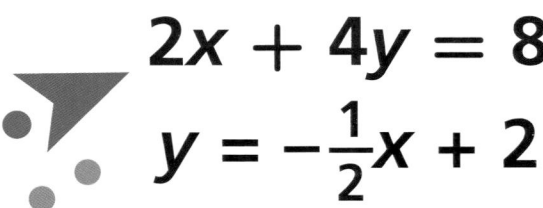

Equation

To make a graph from an equation, use the intercepts or the slope and *y*-intercept.

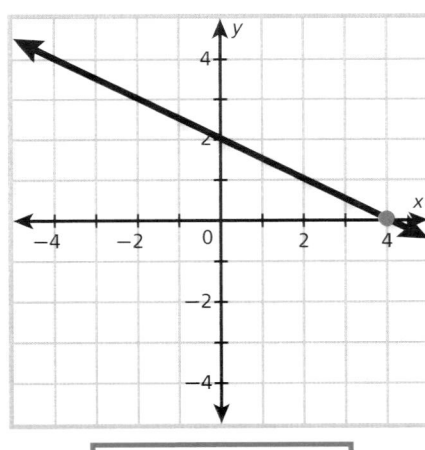

Graph

x	y
−1	2.5
0	2
1	1.5
2	1
3	0.5
4	0

Table

Math Builders

System Builder  6.0, 9.0

To solve a system of equations or inequalities in two variables, you find ordered pairs that are solutions of all equations or inequalities in the system. This Math Builder shows how to solve systems by graphing.

Use with Lessons 6-1 and 6-7.

The clear sheets are the overlays. The page beneath them is the base.

BASE

Look at the base. It shows a system of equations, a system of inequalities, and the graphs of one equation or inequality in each system.

OVERLAY 1

Drop Overlay 1 onto the base. This overlay shows the graphs of the next equation or inequality in each system.

OVERLAY 2

Drop Overlay 2 onto the base. This overlay shows the solutions of each system.

System of Equations $\begin{cases} y = \dfrac{1}{2}x - 2 \\ y = -2x + 3 \end{cases}$

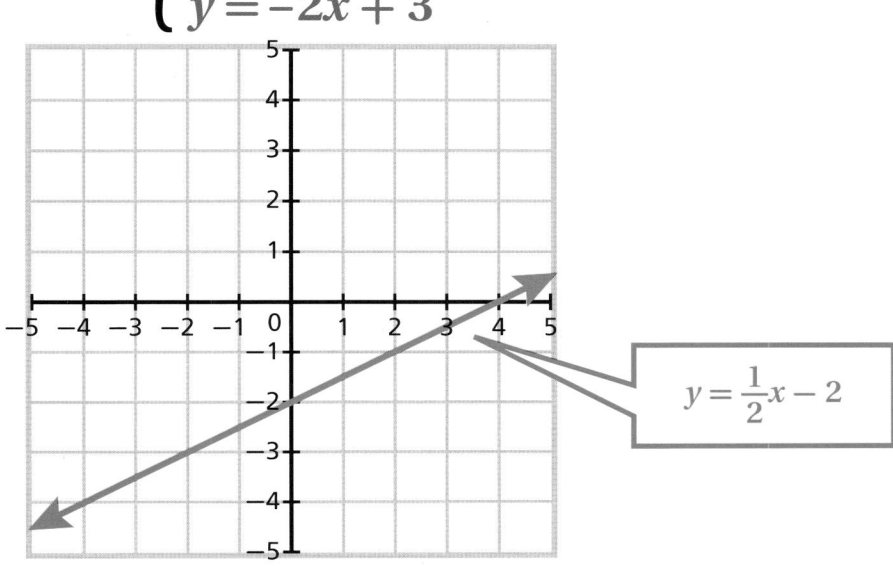

$y = \dfrac{1}{2}x - 2$

System of Inequalities $\begin{cases} y \geq \dfrac{1}{2}x - 2 \\ y < -2x + 3 \end{cases}$

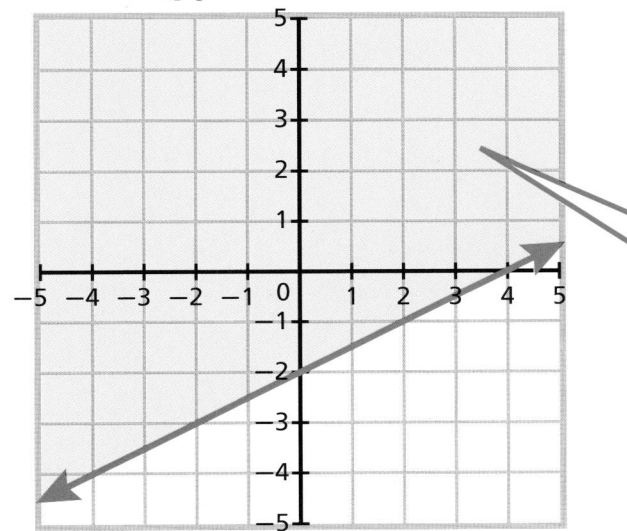

$y \geq \dfrac{1}{2}x - 2$

Since the inequality symbol is $\geq$, use a solid line and shade above the line.

CHAPTER 1

Foundations of Algebra

go.hrw.com
Chapter Project Online
KEYWORD: MA8CA ChProj

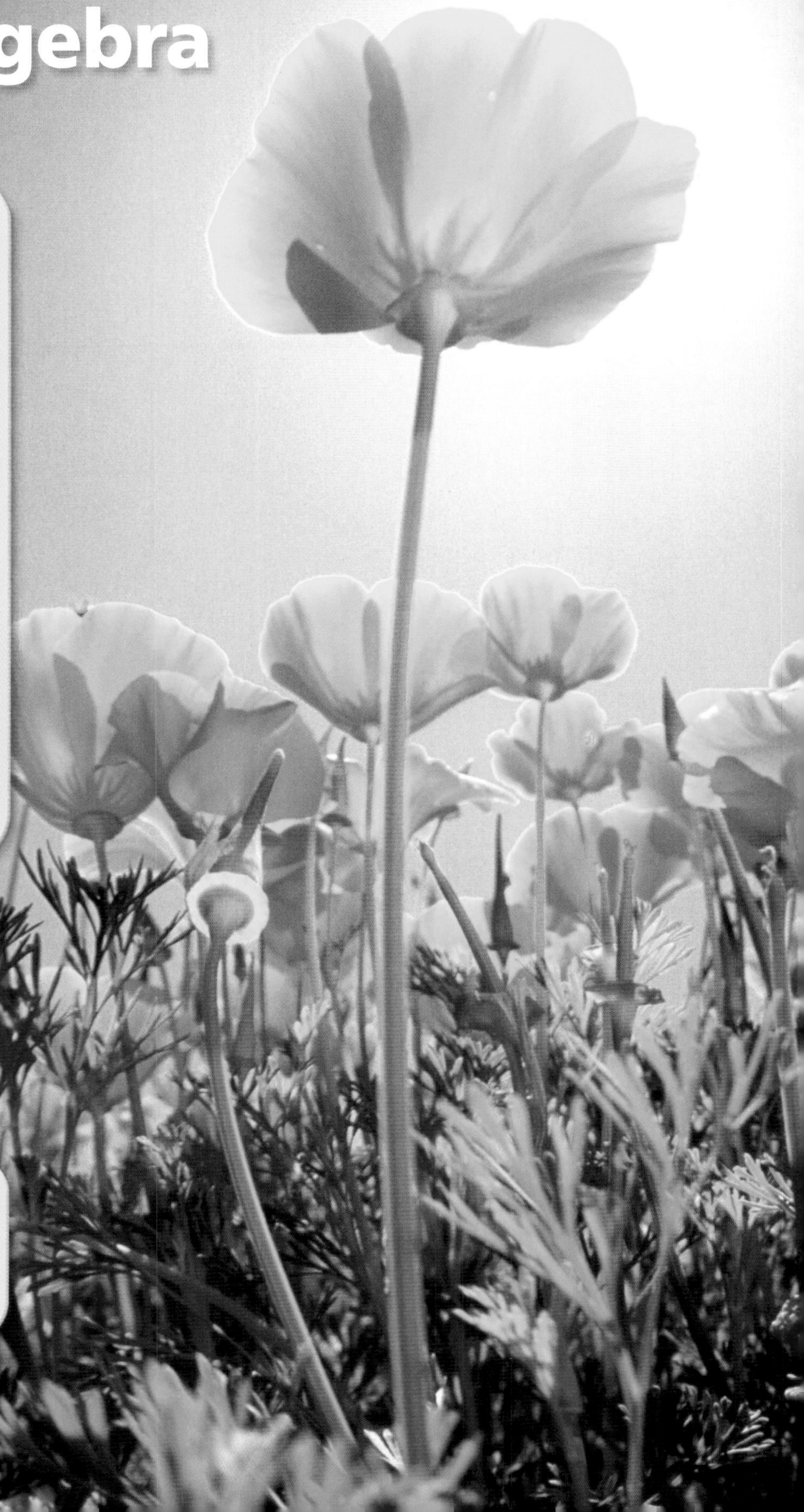

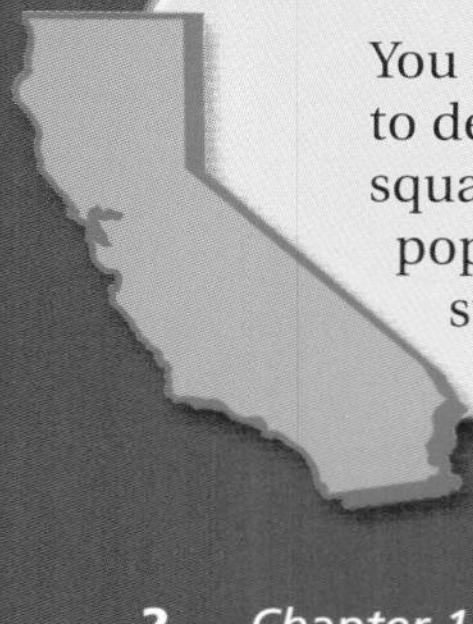

You can use square roots to determine the size of a square garden of California poppies. The poppy is the state flower of California.

ARE YOU READY?

✓ Vocabulary

Match each term on the left with a definition on the right.

1. difference
2. factor
3. perimeter
4. area

A. the distance around a figure

B. a number that is multiplied by another number to form a product

C. a result of division

D. the number of square units a figure covers

E. a result of subtraction

✓ Whole Number Operations

Add, subtract, multiply, or divide.

5. $23 + 6$
6. $156 \div 12$
7. 18×96
8. $85 - 62$

✓ Add and Subtract Decimals

Add or subtract.

9. $2.18 + 6.9$
10. $0.32 - 0.18$
11. $29.34 + 0.27$
12. $4 - 1.82$

✓ Multiply Decimals

Multiply.

13. 0.7×0.6
14. 2.5×0.1
15. 1.5×1.5
16. 3.04×0.12

✓ Divide Decimals

Divide.

17. $6.15 \div 3$
18. $8.64 \div 2$
19. $7.2 \div 0.4$
20. $92.7 \div 0.3$

✓ Multiply and Divide Fractions

Multiply or divide. Give your answer in simplest form.

21. $\frac{3}{5} \times \frac{1}{2}$
22. $\frac{2}{3} \div \frac{1}{6}$
23. $\frac{7}{8} \times \frac{4}{7}$
24. $4 \div \frac{2}{3}$

✓ Add and Subtract Fractions

Add or subtract. Give your answer in simplest form.

25. $\frac{2}{5} + \frac{2}{5}$
26. $\frac{3}{8} - \frac{1}{8}$
27. $\frac{1}{2} + \frac{1}{4}$
28. $\frac{2}{3} - \frac{4}{9}$

Unpacking the Standards

The information below "unpacks" the standards. The Academic Vocabulary is highlighted and defined to help you understand the language of the standards. Refer to the lessons listed after each standard for help with the math terms and phrases. The Chapter Concept shows how the standard is applied in this chapter.

California Standard	Academic Vocabulary	Chapter Concept
1.0 Students identify and use the arithmetic properties of subsets of integers and rational, irrational, and real numbers, including closure properties for the four basic arithmetic operations where applicable. (Lesson **1-6**)	**identify** know or be able to name **subset** a part of a set or group **property** a feature or characteristic that describes an object or a rule or law that the object satisfies	You learn properties of sets of numbers so that you can identify each set. You also use properties to simplify expressions.
1.1 Students use properties of numbers to demonstrate whether assertions are true or false. (Lesson **1-7**)	**demonstrate** show **assertion** statement that is made without proof	You use properties to decide whether statements about numbers are true or false.
2.0 Students understand and use such operations as taking the opposite, finding the reciprocal, taking a root, and raising to a fractional power. They understand and use the rules of exponents. (Lessons **1-2, 1-3, 1-5**)	**reciprocals** numbers that have a product of 1 ***Example:*** $3 \cdot \dfrac{1}{3} = \dfrac{3}{1} \cdot \dfrac{1}{3} = \dfrac{3}{3} = 1$ So 3 and $\dfrac{1}{3}$ are reciprocals.	You perform operations on numbers and find their roots.
24.3 Students use counterexamples to show that an assertion is false and recognize that a single counterexample is sufficient to refute an assertion. (Lesson **1-6**)	**recognize** know or understand **sufficient** enough **refute** show that a statement is not true	You find an example to show that a statement about numbers is false.
25.1 Students use properties of numbers to construct simple, valid arguments (direct and indirect) for, or formulate counterexamples to, claimed assertions. (Lessons **1-6, 1-7**)	**construct** make or prepare **valid** true and correct **formulate** make or prepare	You use properties to prove whether a statement about numbers is true or false.

Standard 25.2 is also covered in this chapter. To see this standard unpacked go to Chapter 3, p. 134.

 Reading and Writing Math

Reading Strategy: Use Your Book for Success

Understanding how your textbook is organized will help you locate and use helpful information.

Pay attention to the **margin notes.** Know-It Note icons point out key information. Writing Math notes, Helpful Hints, and Caution notes help you understand concepts and avoid common mistakes.

 Know it! Note

Writing Math
These expressions mean "2 times y":
$2y$ $2(y)$

Helpful Hint
You can write the reciprocal of a number by switch

Caution!
In the expression -5^2, 5 is the base because the nega

The **Glossary** is found in the back of your textbook. Use it as a resource when you need the definition of an unfamiliar word or property.

The **Index** is located at the end of your textbook. Use it to locate the page where a particular concept is taught.

The **Skills Bank** is found in the back of your textbook. These pages review concepts from previous math courses, including geometry skills.

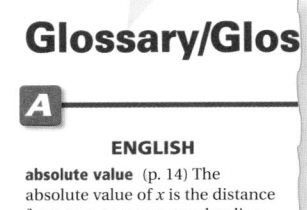 **Glossary/Glos**

A

ENGLISH
absolute value (p. 14) The absolute value of x is the distance from zero to x on a number line,

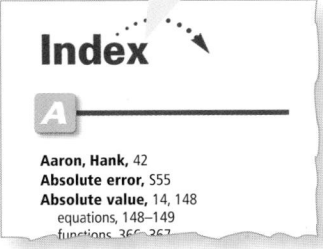 **Index**

A

Aaron, Hank, 42
Absolute error, S55
Absolute value, 14, 148
  equations, 148–149
  functions, 366–367

 **Skills Bank**

Using Multiplicati

EXAMPLE 1 Solve each
    4 =

Try This

Use your textbook for the following problems.

1. Use the index to find the page where each word is defined: *algebraic expression, like terms, real numbers.*

2. Use the glossary to find the definition of each word: *additive inverse, constant, perfect square, reciprocal.*

3. Where can you review the concepts of area and perimeter?

1-1 Variables and Expressions

California Standards

Preparation for ⟵ 4.0
Students simplify expressions before solving linear equations and inequalities **in one variable,** such as $3(2x - 5) + 4(x - 2) = 12$.

Vocabulary
variable
constant
numerical expression
algebraic expression
evaluate
replacement set

Why learn this?
Variables and expressions can be used to determine how many plastic drink bottles must be recycled to make enough carpet for a house.

A home that is "green built" uses many recycled products, including carpet made from recycled plastic drink bottles. You can determine how many square feet of carpet can be made from a certain number of plastic drink bottles by using *variables*, *constants*, and *expressions*.

Container City, in East London, UK, is a development of buildings made from recycled sea containers.

A **variable** is a letter or symbol used to represent a value that can change.

A **constant** is a value that does not change.

A **numerical expression** contains only constants and/or operations.

An **algebraic expression** contains variables, constants, and/or operations.

You will need to translate between algebraic expressions and words to be successful in math. The diagram below shows some of the ways to write mathematical operations with words.

| Plus, sum, increased by | Minus, difference, less than | Times, product, equal groups of | Divided by, quotient |

EXAMPLE 1 **Translating from Algebra to Words**

Give two ways to write each algebraic expression in words.

Writing Math

These expressions all mean "2 times y":
$2y$ $2(y)$
$2 \cdot y$ $(2)(y)$
$2 \times y$ $(2)y$

A $x + 3$
the sum of x and 3
x increased by 3

B $m - 7$
the difference of m and 7
7 less than m

C $2 \cdot y$
2 times y
the product of 2 and y

D $k \div 5$
k divided by 5
the quotient of k and 5

 **Give two ways to write each algebraic expression in words.**

     1a. $4 - n$ **1b.** $\dfrac{t}{5}$ **1c.** $9 + q$ **1d.** $3(h)$

To translate words into algebraic expressions, read the problem to determine what actions are taking place.

Add	Subtract	Multiply	Divide
↑	↑	↑	↑
Put together, combine	Find how much more or less	Put together equal groups	Separate into equal groups

EXAMPLE 2 | **Translating from Words to Algebra**

A Eve reads 25 pages per hour. Write an expression for the number of pages she reads in h hours.

h represents the number of hours that Eve reads.

$25 \cdot h$ or $25h$ *Think: h groups of 25 pages.*

B Sam is 2 years younger than Sue. Sue is y years old. Write an expression for Sam's age.

y represents Sue's age.

$y - 2$ *Think: "younger than" means "less than."*

C William runs a mile in 12 minutes. Write an expression for the number of miles that William runs in m minutes.

m represents the total time William runs.

$\dfrac{m}{12}$ *Think: How many groups of 12 are in m?*

 **2.** Miriam is 5 cm taller than Jan. Jan is m cm tall. Write an expression for Miriam's height in centimeters.

To **evaluate** an expression is to find its value. To evaluate an algebraic expression, substitute numbers for the variables in the expression and then simplify the expression. A **replacement set** is a set of numbers that can be substituted for a variable.

EXAMPLE 3 | **Evaluating Algebraic Expressions**

Evaluate each expression for the replacement set {2, 4, 5.7}

A $x + 8$

Substitute each value in the replacement set for x and simplify.

$x + 8$	$x + 8$	$x + 8$
$2 + 8$	$4 + 8$	$5.7 + 8$
10	12	13.7

B $\dfrac{x}{2}$

Substitute each value in the replacement set for x and simplify.

$\dfrac{x}{2}$	$\dfrac{x}{2}$	$\dfrac{x}{2}$
$\dfrac{2}{2}$	$\dfrac{4}{2}$	$\dfrac{5.7}{2}$
1	2	2.85

Writing Math

One way to indicate a set is to use braces, {}. The items in a set are called elements.

 Evaluate each expression for the replacement set {2, 3, 9}.

3a. $\dfrac{2}{3}n$ **3b.** $15 - n$ **3c.** $n + 0.15$

EXAMPLE 4 *Recycling Application*

Approximately fourteen 20-ounce plastic drink bottles must be recycled to produce 1 square foot of carpet.

a. **Write an expression for the number of bottles needed to make *c* square feet of carpet.**

The expression $14c$ models the number of bottles needed to make c square feet of carpet.

b. **Find the number of bottles needed to make 40, 120, and 224 square feet of carpet.**

Evaluate $14c$ for the replacement set {40, 120, 224}.

c	14c
40	$14(40) = 560$
120	$14(120) = 1680$
224	$14(224) = 3136$

To make 40 ft² of carpet, 560 bottles are needed.
To make 120 ft² of carpet, 1680 bottles are needed.
To make 224 ft² of carpet, 3136 bottles are needed.

 **4.** To make one sweater, sixty-three 20-ounce plastic drink bottles must be recycled.

a. Write an expression for the number of bottles needed to make *s* sweaters.

b. Find the number of bottles needed to make 12, 25, and 50 sweaters.

THINK AND DISCUSS

1. Write two ways to suggest each of the following, using words or phrases: addition, subtraction, multiplication, division.

2. Explain the difference between a numerical expression and an algebraic expression.

 **3. GET ORGANIZED** Copy and complete the graphic organizer. Next to each operation, write a word phrase in the left box and its corresponding algebraic expression in the right box.

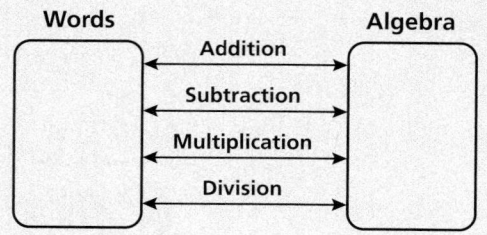

California Standards Practice

Preparation for 🔑 4.0

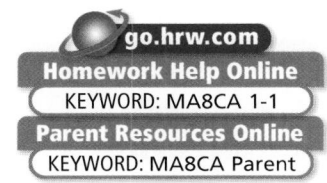

go.hrw.com
Homework Help Online
KEYWORD: MA8CA 1-1
Parent Resources Online
KEYWORD: MA8CA Parent

GUIDED PRACTICE

1. **Vocabulary** A(n) ___?___ is a value that can change. (*algebraic expression, constant,* or *variable*)

SEE EXAMPLE 1
p. 6

Give two ways to write each algebraic expression in words.

2. $n - 5$
3. $\dfrac{f}{3}$
4. $c + 15$
5. $9 - y$

6. $\dfrac{x}{12}$
7. $t + 12$
8. $8x$
9. $x - 3$

SEE EXAMPLE 2
p. 7

10. George drives at 45 mi/h. Write an expression for the number of miles George travels in h hours.

11. The length of a rectangle is 4 units greater than its width w. Write an expression for the length of the rectangle.

SEE EXAMPLE 3
p. 7

Evaluate each expression for the replacement set {3, 4, 9}.

12. $a - 2$
13. $4a$
14. $6 \div a$
15. $2a$

SEE EXAMPLE 4
p. 8

16. Brianna practices the piano 30 minutes each day.
   a. Write an expression for the number of hours she practices in d days.
   b. Find the number of hours Brianna practices in 2, 4, and 10 days.

PRACTICE AND PROBLEM SOLVING

Independent Practice

For Exercises	See Example
17–24	1
25–26	2
27–30	3
31	4

Extra Practice

Skills Practice p. EP2

Application Practice p. EP24

Give two ways to write each algebraic expression in words.

17. $5p$
18. $4 - y$
19. $3 + x$
20. $3y$

21. $-3s$
22. $r \div 5$
23. $14 - t$
24. $x + 0.5$

25. Friday's temperature was 20° warmer than Monday's temperature t. Write an expression for Friday's temperature.

26. Ann sleeps 8 hours per night. Write an expression for the number of hours Ann sleeps in n nights.

Evaluate each expression for the replacement set {2, 8, 13}.

27. $r - 1$
28. $6 + r$
29. $r \div 2$
30. $15r$

31. Jim is paid for overtime when he works more than 40 hours per week.
   a. Write an expression for the number of hours he works overtime when he works h hours.
   b. Find the number of hours Jim works overtime when he works 40, 44, 48, and 52 hours.

 32. **Write About It** Write a paragraph that explains to another student how to evaluate an expression.

Write an algebraic expression for each verbal expression. Then write a real-world situation that could be modeled by the expression.

33. the product of 2 and x
34. b less than 17
35. 10 more than y

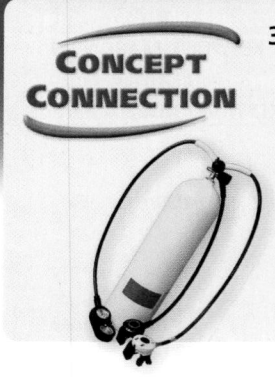

CONCEPT CONNECTION

36. This problem will prepare you for the Concept Connection on page 40.

The air around you puts pressure on your body equal to 14.7 pounds per square inch (psi). When you are underwater, the water exerts additional pressure on your body. For each foot you are below the surface of the water, the pressure increases by 0.445 psi.

a. What does 14.7 represent in the expression $14.7 + 0.445d$?

b. What does d represent in the expression?

c. What is the total pressure exerted on a person's body when $d = 8$ ft?

37. Geometry The length of a rectangle is 9 inches. Write an expression for the area of the rectangle if the width is w inches. Find the area of the rectangle if the replacement set for the width is 1, 8, 9, and 11 inches.

38. Geometry The perimeter of any rectangle is the sum of the lengths of its sides. The area of any rectangle is the length ℓ times the width w.

a. Write an expression for the perimeter of a rectangle.

b. Find the perimeter of the rectangle shown.

c. Write an expression for the area of a rectangle.

d. Find the area of the rectangle shown.

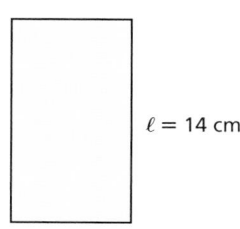

$\ell = 14$ cm

$w = 8$ cm

Complete each table. Evaluate the expression for each value of x.

39.

x	x + 12
1	
2	
3	
4	

40.

x	10x
1	
5	
10	
15	

41.

x	x ÷ 2
12	
20	
26	
30	

Astronomy

A crater on Canada's Devon Island is geologically similar to the surface of Mars. However, the temperature on Devon Island is about 37°F in summer, and the average summer temperature on Mars is −85°F.

42. Astronomy An object's weight on Mars can be found by multiplying 0.38 by the object's weight on Earth.

a. An object weighs p pounds on Earth. Write an expression for its weight on Mars.

b. Dana weighs 120 pounds, and her bicycle weighs 44 pounds. How much would Dana and her bicycle together weigh on Mars?

43. Meteorology Use the bar graph to write an expression for the average annual precipitation in New York, New York.

a. The average annual precipitation in New York is m inches more than the average annual precipitation in Houston, Texas.

b. The average annual precipitation in New York is s inches less than the average annual precipitation in Miami, Florida.

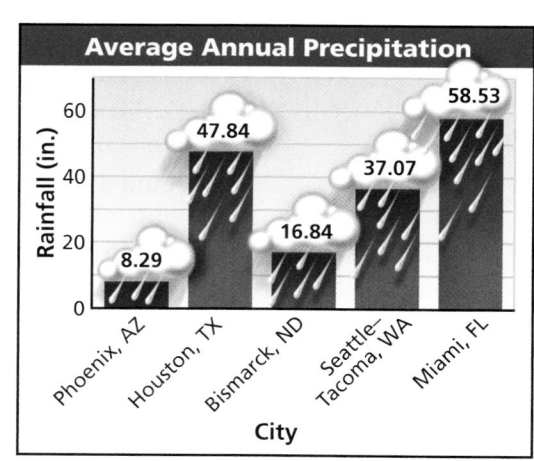

Average Annual Precipitation

Rainfall (in.)

8.29 — Phoenix, AZ
47.84 — Houston, TX
16.84 — Bismarck, ND
37.07 — Seattle-Tacoma, WA
58.53 — Miami, FL

City

44. Critical Thinking Compare algebraic expressions and numerical expressions. Give examples of each.

Write an algebraic expression for each verbal expression. Then evaluate the algebraic expression for the given values of *x*.

	Verbal	Algebraic	x = 12	x = 14
	x reduced by 5	x − 5	12 − 5 = 7	14 − 5 = 9
45.	7 more than x	▒	▒	▒
46.	The quotient of x and 2	▒	▒	▒
47.	The sum of x and 3	▒	▒	▒

Multiple Choice For Exercises 48–50, choose the best answer.

48. Claire has had her driver's license for 3 years. Bill has had his license for *b* fewer years than Claire. Which expression can be used to show the number of years Bill has had his driver's license?

Ⓐ $3 + b$ Ⓑ $b + 3$ Ⓒ $3 - b$ Ⓓ $b < 3$

49. Which expression represents *x*?

Ⓐ $12 - 5$ Ⓒ $7 - x$
Ⓑ $x + 5$ Ⓓ $12 - 7$

50. Which situation is best modeled by the expression $25 - x$?

Ⓐ George places *x* more video games on a shelf with 25 games.
Ⓑ Sarah has driven *x* miles of a 25-mile trip.
Ⓒ Amelia paid 25 dollars of an *x* dollar lunch that she shared with Ariel.
Ⓓ Jorge has 25 boxes full of *x* baseball cards each.

CHALLENGE AND EXTEND

Evaluate each expression for the given values of the variables.

51. $2ab; a = 6, b = 3$ **52.** $2x + y; x = 4, y = 5$ **53.** $3x \div 6y; x = 6, y = 3$

54. Multi-Step An Internet service provider charges $9.95/month for the first 20 hours and $0.50 for each additional hour. Write an expression representing the charges for *h* hours of use in one month when *h* is more than 20 hours. What is the charge for 35 hours?

 SPIRAL STANDARDS REVIEW  6MG2.2

The sum of the angle measures in a triangle is 180°. Find the measure of the third angle given the other two angle measures. *(Previous course)*

55. 45° and 90° **56.** 120° and 20° **57.** 30° and 60°

Write an equivalent fraction for each percent. *(Previous course)*

58. 25% **59.** 50% **60.** 75% **61.** 100%

Find a possible pattern and use it to give the next three numbers. *(Previous course)*

62. 4, 12, 20, 28, … **63.** 3, 9, 27, 81, 243, … **64.** 2, 3, 5, 8, 12, …

1-1
Technology LAB

Use Technology to Evaluate Expressions

You can use a graphing calculator to quickly evaluate expressions for many values of the variable.

Use with Lesson 1-1

go.hrw.com
Lab Resources Online
KEYWORD: MA8CA Lab1

Activity 1

Evaluate $2x + 7$ for $x = 25, 125, 225, 325,$ and 425.

1 Press **Y=** and enter **2X+7** for **Y1**.

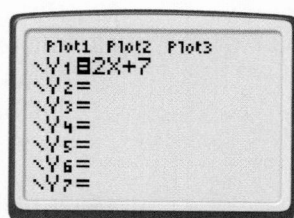

2 Determine a pattern for values of x.

The x-values start with 25 and increase by 100.

3 Press **2nd** **WINDOW** (TBLSET) to view the *Table Setup* window.

Enter **25** as the starting value in **TblStart=**.

Enter **100** as the amount by which x changes in △**Tbl=**.

4 Press **2nd** **GRAPH** (TABLE) to create a table of values.

The first column shows values of x starting with 25 and increasing by 100.

The second column shows values of the expression $2x + 7$ when x is equal to the value in the first column.

You can use the arrow keys to view the table when x is greater than 625.

The answers are 57, 257, 457, 657, and 857.

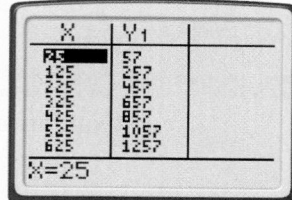

Try This

1. Use the table feature of a graphing calculator to evaluate $5x - 7$ for $x = 4, 6, 8, 10,$ and 12.

   a. What value did you enter in **TblStart=**?

   b. What value did you enter in △**Tbl=**?

2. Use the table feature of a graphing calculator to evaluate $3x + 4$ for $x = -5, -1, 3, 7,$ and 11.

   a. What value did you enter in **TblStart=**?

   b. What value did you enter in △**Tbl=**?

You can also use a spreadsheet program to evaluate expressions.

Activity 2

Evaluate $2x + 7$ for $x = 3, 5, 7, 9$, and 11.

1 In the first column, enter the values 3, 5, 7, 9, and 11.

	A	B	C	D	E	F	G
	126		f_x				
1	3						
2	5						
3	7						
4	9						
5	11						
6							

2 Enter the expression in cell B1.

To do this, type the following:
=2*A1+7

	A	B	C	D	E	F	G
	SUM	✗ ✓ f_x =2*A1+7					
1	3	=2*A1+7					
2	5						
3	7						
4	9						
5	11						
6							

3 Press Enter.

The value of $2x + 7$ when $x = 3$ appears in cell B1.

	A	B	C	D	E	F	G
	B1	f_x =2*A1+7					
1	3	13					
2	5						
3	7						
4	9						
5	11						
6							

4 Copy the formula into cells B2, B3, B4, and B5.

Use the mouse to click on the lower right corner of cell B1. Hold down the mouse button and drag the cursor through cell B5.

	A	B	C	D	E	F	G
	B1	f_x =2*A1+7					
1	3	13					
2	5	17					
3	7	21					
4	9	25					
5	11	29					
6							

For each row in column B, the number that is substituted for x is the value in the same row of column A.

	A	B	C	D	E	F	G
	B2	f_x =2(A2)+7					
1	3	13					
2	5	17					
3	7	21					
4	9	25					
5	11	29					
6							

You can continue the table by entering more values in column A and copying the formula from B1 into more cells in column B.

Try This

3. Use a spreadsheet program to evaluate $-2x + 9$ for $x = -5, -2, 1, 4$, and 7.

  a. What values did you enter in column A?

  b. What did you type in cell B1?

4. Use a spreadsheet program to evaluate $7x - 10$ for $x = 2, 7, 12, 17$, and 22.

  a. What values did you enter in column A?

  b. What did you type in cell B1?

5. What is an advantage to using technology to evaluate expressions?

1-2 Adding and Subtracting Real Numbers

Vocabulary
real numbers
absolute value
opposites
additive inverse

Why learn this?

The total length of a penguin's dive can be determined by adding real numbers. (See Example 4.)

The set of all numbers that can be represented on a number line are called **real numbers**. You can use a number line to model addition and subtraction of real numbers.

Addition
To model addition of a positive number, move right. To model addition of a negative number, move left.

Subtraction
To model subtraction of a positive number, move left.
To model subtraction of a negative number, move right.

EXAMPLE 1 **Adding and Subtracting Numbers on a Number Line**

Add or subtract using a number line.

A $-3 + 6$

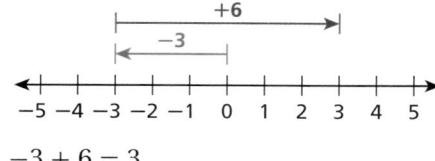

Start at 0. Move left to -3.
To add 6, move right 6 units.

$-3 + 6 = 3$

B $-2 - (-9)$

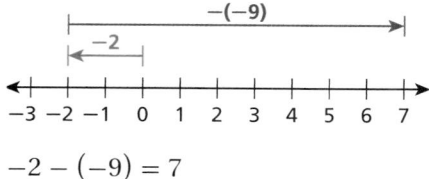

Start at 0. Move left to -2.
To subtract -9, move right 9 units.

$-2 - (-9) = 7$

 **Add or subtract using a number line.**

1a. $-3 + 7$ **1b.** $-3 - 7$ **1c.** $-5 - (-6.5)$

The **absolute value** of a number is its distance from zero on a number line. The absolute value of 5 is written as $|5|$.

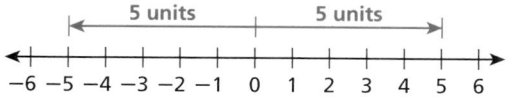

$|5| = 5$

$|-5| = 5$

Adding Real Numbers

WORDS	NUMBERS	
Adding Numbers with the Same Sign Add the absolute values and use the sign of the numbers.	$3 + 6$ 9	$-2 + (-9)$ -11
Adding Numbers with Different Signs Subtract the absolute values and use the sign of the number with the greater absolute value.	$-8 + 12$ 4	$3 + (-15)$ -12

EXAMPLE 2 **Adding Real Numbers**

Add.

A $-3 + (-16)$
$(3 + 16 = 19)$ *Same signs: add the absolute values.*
-19 *Both numbers are negative, so the sum is negative.*

B $-13 + 7$
$(13 - 7 = 6)$ *Different signs: subtract the absolute values.*
-6 *Use the sign of the number with the greater absolute value.*

C $6.2 + (-4.9)$
$(6.2 - 4.9 = 1.3)$ *Different signs: subtract the absolute values.*
1.3 *Use the sign of the number with the greater absolute value.*

 **Add.**
2a. $-5 + (-7)$ **2b.** $-13.5 + (-22.3)$ **2c.** $52 + (-68)$

Two numbers are **opposites** if their sum is 0. A number and its opposite are **additive inverses** and are the same distance from zero. They have the same absolute value.

Inverse Property of Addition

WORDS	NUMBERS	ALGEBRA
The sum of a real number and its opposite is 0.	$6 + (-6) = (-6) + 6 = 0$	For any real number a, $a + (-a) = (-a) + a = 0$

To subtract signed numbers, you can use additive inverses. Subtracting a number is the same as adding the opposite of the number.

Subtracting Real Numbers

WORDS	NUMBERS	ALGEBRA
To subtract a number, add its opposite. Then follow the rules for adding signed numbers.	$3 - 8 = 3 + (-8)$ $= -5$	$a - b = a + (-b)$

EXAMPLE 3 **Subtracting Real Numbers**

Subtract.

A 7 − 10

$7 - 10 = 7 + (-10)$ *To subtract 10, add −10.*
$(10 - 7 = 3)$ *Different signs: subtract absolute values.*
−3   *Use the sign of the number with the greater absolute value.*

B −3 − (−12)

$-3 - (-12) = -3 + 12$ *To subtract −12, add 12.*
$(12 - 3 = 9)$ *Different signs: subtract absolute values.*
9   *Use the sign of the number with the greater absolute value.*

C −11 − 22

$-11 - 22 = -11 + (-22)$ *To subtract 22, add −22.*
$(22 + 11 = 33)$ *Same signs: add absolute values.*
−33   *Both numbers are negative, so the sum is negative.*

D 22.5 − (−4)

$22.5 - (-4) = 22.5 + 4$ *To subtract −4, add 4.*
$(22.5 + 4 = 26.5)$ *Same signs: add absolute values.*
26.5   *Both numbers are positive, so the sum is positive.*

 Subtract.

3a. $13 - 21$ **3b.** $\frac{1}{2} - \left(-3\frac{1}{2}\right)$ **3c.** $-14 - (-12)$

> **Helpful Hint**
>
> On many scientific and graphing calculators, there is one button to express the opposite of a number and a different button to express subtraction.

EXAMPLE 4 *Biology Application*

An emperor penguin stands on an iceberg that extends 10 feet above the water. Then the penguin dives to an elevation of −67 feet to catch a fish. What is the total length of the penguin's dive?

Find the difference in the elevations.

elevation of iceberg	minus	elevation of fish
10	−	−67

$10 - (-67)$
$10 - (-67) = 10 + 67$ *To subtract −67, add 67.*
$\qquad = 77$ *Same signs: add absolute values.*

The total length of the penguin's dive is 77 feet.

 **4. What if...?** The tallest known iceberg in the North Atlantic rose 550 feet above the ocean's surface. How many feet would it be from the top of the tallest iceberg to the wreckage of the *Titanic*, which is at an elevation of −12,468 feet?

THINK AND DISCUSS

1. The difference of -7 and -5 is -2. Explain why the difference is greater than -7.

2. GET ORGANIZED Copy and complete the graphic organizer. For each pair of points, tell whether the sum and the difference of the first point and the second point are positive or negative.

Points	Sum	Difference
A, B		
B, A		
C, B		
D, A		

1-2 Exercises

California Standards Practice
🔑 2.0, 25.2

go.hrw.com
Homework Help Online
KEYWORD: MA8CA 1-2
Parent Resources Online
KEYWORD: MA8CA Parent

GUIDED PRACTICE

1. Vocabulary The sum of a number and its ____?____ is always zero. (*opposite* or *absolute value*)

SEE EXAMPLE 1 p. 14

Add or subtract using a number line.

2. $-4 + 7$ **3.** $-3.5 - 5$ **4.** $5.6 - 9.2$ **5.** $3 - \left(-6\frac{1}{4}\right)$

SEE EXAMPLE 2 p. 15

Add.

6. $91 + (-11)$ **7.** $4\frac{3}{4} + \left(-3\frac{3}{4}\right)$ **8.** $15.6 + (-17.9)$

SEE EXAMPLE 3 p. 16

Subtract.

9. $23 - 36$ **10.** $4.3 - 8.4$ **11.** $1\frac{1}{5} - 2\frac{4}{5}$

SEE EXAMPLE 4 p. 16

12. Economics The Dow Jones Industrial Average (DJIA) reports the average prices of stocks for 30 companies. Use the table to determine the total decrease in the DJIA for the two days.

DJIA 1987	
Friday, Oct. 16	-108.35
Monday, Oct. 19	-507.99

PRACTICE AND PROBLEM SOLVING

Independent Practice	
For Exercises	See Example
13–16	1
17–19	2
20–22	3
23	4

Extra Practice
Skills Practice p. EP2
Application Practice p. EP24

Add or subtract using a number line.

13. $-2 + 6$ **14.** $6 + (-2)$ **15.** $\frac{1}{4} - 12$ **16.** $-\frac{2}{5} + 6$

Add.

17. $-18 + (-12)$ **18.** $-2.3 + 3.5$ **19.** $-15 + 29$

Subtract.

20. $12 - 22$ **21.** $-\frac{3}{4} - \left(-\frac{1}{4}\right)$ **22.** $38 - 24.6$

23. Meteorology A meteorologist reported that the day's high temperature was $17°F$ and the low temperature was $-6°F$. What was the difference between the day's high and low temperatures?

Evaluate the expression $n + (-5)$ for each value of n.

24. $n = 312$ **25.** $n = 5.75$ **26.** $n = -\dfrac{7}{12}$ **27.** $n = -7\dfrac{2}{5}$

Add or subtract.

28. $-8 - 3$ **29.** $-9 + (-3)$ **30.** $16 - (-16)$ **31.** $100 - 63$

32. $5.2 - 2.5$ **33.** $-4.7 - (-4.7)$ **34.** $\dfrac{2}{5} - \dfrac{7}{8}$ **35.** $\dfrac{2}{5} - \dfrac{3}{10}$

36. Business A restaurant manager lost $415 in business during the month of January. Business picked up in February, and he ended that month with a profit of $1580.

     a. What was the manager's profit after January and February?

     b. What if...? The restaurant lost $245 in business during the month of March. What was the manager's profit after January, February, and March?

Compare. Write $<$, $>$, or $=$.

37. $-4 - (-6)$ ▨ $-7 - 3$ **38.** $|-51|$ ▨ $|0|$ **39.** $3 - (-3)$ ▨ $0 - (-3)$

40. $-3 - 8$ ▨ $-22 + 11$ **41.** $|-10 + 5|$ ▨ $|-15|$ **42.** $9 + (-8)$ ▨ $-12 + 13$

43. Travel Death Valley National Park is located in California. Use the table to determine the difference in elevation between the highest and lowest locations.

Death Valley National Park	
Location	**Elevation (ft)**
Badwater	−282
Emigrant Pass	5,318
Furnace Creek Airport	−210
Telescope Creek	11,049

 Reasoning Tell whether each statement is sometimes, always, or never true. Explain.

44. The difference of two negative numbers is positive.

45. The sum of two negative numbers is negative.

46. The difference of a negative number and a positive number is negative.

47. ///**ERROR ANALYSIS**/// Which is incorrect? Explain the error.

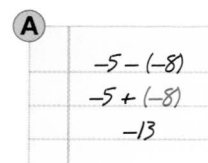

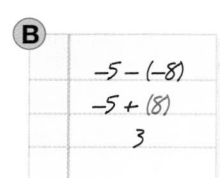

CONCEPT CONNECTION

48. This problem will prepare you for the Concept Connection on page 40.

     a. A plane flies at a height of 1800 feet directly over a 150-foot-tall building. How far above the building is the plane? Draw a diagram to explain your answer.

     b. The same plane then flies directly over a diver who is 80 feet below the surface of the water. How far is the plane above the diver? Draw a diagram to explain your answer.

     c. Subtract the diver's altitude of −80 feet from the plane's altitude of 1800 feet. Explain why this distance is greater than 1800 feet.

49. Write About It Explain why addition and subtraction are called inverse operations. Use the following examples in your explanation:

$$8 + (-2) = 8 - 2 \qquad 8 - (-2) = 8 + 2$$

Multiple Choice For Exercises 50–52, choose the best answer.

50. A rectangle has a length of 23.8 cm and a width of 14.5 cm. What is its perimeter?

    Ⓐ 9.3 cm   Ⓑ 38.3 cm   Ⓒ 62.1 cm   Ⓓ 76.6 cm

51. At midnight, the temperature was $-12°F$. By noon, the temperature had risen $25°F$. During the afternoon, it fell $10°F$ and fell another $3°F$ by midnight. What was the temperature at midnight?

    Ⓐ 0°F   Ⓑ 3°F   Ⓒ 12°F   Ⓓ 24°F

52. The table shows the amounts Mr. Espinosa spent on lunch each day one week. What is the total amount Mr. Espinosa spent for lunch this week?

Day	Monday	Tuesday	Wednesday	Thursday	Friday
Amount ($)	5.40	4.16	7.07	5.40	9.52

    Ⓐ $21.83   Ⓑ $22.03   Ⓒ $31.55   Ⓓ $36.95

CHALLENGE AND EXTEND

Simplify each expression.

53. $-1\frac{1}{5} + (-7.8)$ **54.** $-\frac{1}{5} + 2.1$ **55.** $9.75 + \left(-7\frac{3}{4}\right)$ **56.** $-2\frac{3}{10} + 8.5$

For each pattern shown below, describe a possible rule for finding the next term. Then use your rule to write the next 3 terms.

57. $14, 10, 6, 2, \ldots$ **58.** $-2, -\frac{8}{5}, -\frac{6}{5}, -\frac{4}{5}, \ldots$

59. Geography Sam visited two volcanoes, Cotapaxi and Sangay, and two caves, Sistema Huautla and Sistema Cheve. Cotapaxi, in Ecuador, has an elevation of 19,347 ft. Sangay, also in Ecuador, has an elevation of 17,159 ft. The main entrance of Sistema Huautla, in Mexico, has an elevation of 5051 ft. The main entrance of Sistema Cheve, also in Mexico, has an elevation of 9085 ft. What is the average elevation of these places?

 SPIRAL STANDARDS REVIEW   ⬥— 7AF4.1, 7MG2.1

Give the area of the figure described. *(Previous course)*

60. rectangle; $\ell = 12$ cm, $w = 5$ cm   **61.** triangle; $b = 8$ in., $h = 11$ in.

Find the length of the third side of the triangle. *(Previous course)*

62. perimeter = 12 cm   **63.** perimeter = 30 cm   **64.** perimeter = 56 cm

Evaluate each expression for $x = 8$, $y = 4$, and $z = 2$. *(Lesson 1-1)*

65. $x + y$ **66.** $\frac{x}{z}$ **67.** $x - y$ **68.** $\frac{y}{z}$

1-3 Multiplying and Dividing Real Numbers

California Standards

⟸ **2.0** Students understand and use such operations as taking the opposite, **finding the reciprocal,** taking a root, and raising to a fractional power. They understand and use the rules of exponents.

Vocabulary
reciprocal
multiplicative inverse

Who uses this?

Hot-air balloon pilots can determine how far away from liftoff they will land by using multiplication. (See Example 4.)

When you multiply or divide two numbers, the signs of the numbers determine whether the result is positive or negative.

Numbers	Product/Quotient
Both positive	Positive
One negative	Negative
Both negative	Positive

Multiplying and Dividing Real Numbers

WORDS	NUMBERS
Multiplying and Dividing Numbers with the Same Sign	
If two numbers have the same sign, their product or quotient is positive.	$4 \cdot 5 = 20$ $\quad$ $-15 \div (-3) = 5$
Multiplying and Dividing Numbers with Different Signs	
If two numbers have different signs, their product or quotient is negative.	$6(-3) = -18$ $\quad$ $-18 \div 2 = -9$ $(-7)2 = -14$ $\quad$ $10 \div (-5) = -2$

EXAMPLE **1** **Multiplying and Dividing Signed Numbers**

Find the value of each expression.

A $-12 \cdot 5$
-60
  The product of two numbers with different signs is negative.

B $8\left(-\dfrac{5}{4}\right)$

$\left(\dfrac{8}{1}\right)\left(-\dfrac{5}{4}\right)$ *Multiply.*

$= -\dfrac{40}{4} = -10$ *The quotient of two numbers with different signs is negative.*

Find the value of each expression.

1a. $35 \div (-5)$ $\qquad$ **1b.** $-11(-4)$ $\qquad$ **1c.** $-6(7)$

Two numbers are **reciprocals** if their product is 1. A number and its reciprocal are called **multiplicative inverses** .

Inverse Property of Multiplication

WORDS	NUMBERS	ALGEBRA
The product of a nonzero real number and its reciprocal is 1.	$4 \cdot \dfrac{1}{4} = \dfrac{1}{4} \cdot 4 = 1$ $-3 \cdot \left(-\dfrac{1}{3}\right) = -\dfrac{1}{3} \cdot (-3) = 1$	For any real number a ($a \neq 0$), $a \cdot \dfrac{1}{a} = \dfrac{1}{a} \cdot a = 1$

To divide by a number, you can multiply by its multiplicative inverse.

EXAMPLE 2 **Dividing with Fractions**

Divide.

A $-\dfrac{4}{5} \div \left(-\dfrac{8}{15}\right)$

$$-\dfrac{4}{5} \div \left(-\dfrac{8}{15}\right) = -\dfrac{4}{5}\left(-\dfrac{15}{8}\right)$$

To divide by $-\dfrac{8}{15}$, multiply by $-\dfrac{15}{8}$.

$$= \dfrac{(-4)(-15)}{5(8)}$$

Multiply the numerators and multiply the denominators.

$$= \dfrac{60}{40} = \dfrac{3}{2}$$

$-\dfrac{4}{5}$ and $-\dfrac{8}{15}$ have the same sign, so the quotient is positive.

Helpful Hint

You can write the reciprocal of a number by switching the numerator and denominator. A number written without a denominator has a denominator of 1.

B $-4 \div 9\dfrac{1}{4}$

$$-4 \div 9\dfrac{1}{4} = -\dfrac{4}{1} \div \dfrac{37}{4}$$

Write 4 as a fraction with a denominator of 1. Write $9\dfrac{1}{4}$ as an improper fraction.

$$= -\dfrac{4}{1} \cdot \dfrac{4}{37}$$

To divide by $\dfrac{37}{4}$, multiply by $\dfrac{4}{37}$.

$$= -\dfrac{4(4)}{1(37)} = -\dfrac{16}{37}$$

-4 and $9\dfrac{1}{4}$ have different signs, so the quotient is negative.

 **CHECK IT OUT!** Divide.

2a. $-\dfrac{3}{4} \div (-9)$ **2b.** $\dfrac{3}{10} \div \left(-\dfrac{6}{5}\right)$ **2c.** $-\dfrac{5}{6} \div 1\dfrac{2}{3}$

The number 0 has special properties for multiplication and division.

Properties of Zero

WORDS	NUMBERS	ALGEBRA
Multiplication by Zero The product of any number and 0 is 0.	$\dfrac{1}{3} \cdot 0 = 0$ $0(-17) = 0$	$a \cdot 0 = 0$ $0 \cdot a = 0$
Zero Divided by a Number The quotient of 0 and any nonzero number is 0.	$\dfrac{0}{6} = 0$ $0 \div \dfrac{2}{3} = 0$	$\dfrac{0}{a} = 0$ $(a \neq 0)$
Division by Zero Division by 0 is undefined.	$12 \div 0$ ✗ $\dfrac{-5}{0}$ ✗	$a \div 0$ ✗ $\dfrac{a}{0}$ ✗

 **EXAMPLE 3** **Multiplying and Dividing with Zero**

Multiply or divide if possible.

A $0 \div 16.568$ *Zero is divided by a nonzero number.*
0   *The quotient of zero and any nonzero number is 0.*

B $63\frac{7}{8} \div 0$ *A number is divided by zero.*
              Division by zero is undefined.
undefined

C $1 \cdot 0$ *A number is multiplied by zero.*
0   *The product of any number and 0 is 0.*

CHECK IT OUT! **Multiply or divide.**

3a. $0 \div \left(-8\frac{1}{6}\right)$ **3b.** $2.04 \div 0$ **3c.** $(-12{,}350)(0)$

 **EXAMPLE 4** *Recreation Application*

A hot-air balloon is taken for a 2.5-hour trip. The wind speed (and the speed of the balloon) is 4.75 mi/h. The balloon travels in a straight line parallel to the ground. How many miles away from the liftoff site will the balloon land?

Find the distance traveled at a rate of 4.75 mi/h for 2.5 hours. To find distance, multiply rate by time.

rate	times	time
4.75	•	2.5

$4.75 \cdot 2.5$
11.875

The hot-air balloon will land 11.875 miles from the liftoff site.

CHECK IT OUT! **4. What if...?** On another hot-air balloon trip, the wind speed is 5.25 mi/h. The trip is planned for 1.5 hours. The balloon travels in a straight line parallel to the ground. How many miles away from the liftoff site will the balloon land?

THINK AND DISCUSS

1. Explain how to use mental math to find the missing value: $\frac{4}{5} \cdot ? = 1$.

2. GET ORGANIZED Copy and complete the graphic organizer. In each blank, write "pos" or "neg" to indicate positive or negative.

Multiplying and Dividing Numbers	
Multiplication	**Division**
pos × ___ = pos	pos ÷ ___ = pos
pos × ___ = neg	pos ÷ ___ = neg
neg × ___ = neg	neg ÷ ___ = neg
neg × ___ = pos	neg ÷ ___ = pos

1-3

Exercises

California
Standards Practice
🔑 2.0

go.hrw.com
Homework Help Online
KEYWORD: MA8CA 1-3
Parent Resources Online
KEYWORD: MA8CA Parent

GUIDED PRACTICE

1. **Vocabulary** How do you find the *reciprocal* of $\frac{1}{2}$?

SEE EXAMPLE **1**
p. 20

Find the value of each expression.

2. $-72 \div (-9)$ 3. $11(-11)$ 4. $-7.2 \div 3.6$

SEE EXAMPLE **2**
p. 21

Divide.

5. $5 \div \frac{5}{7}$ 6. $\frac{4}{5} \div \left(-\frac{7}{5}\right)$ 7. $-\frac{2}{3} \div \left(-\frac{1}{3}\right)$ 8. $-\frac{16}{25} \div \left(-\frac{4}{5}\right)$

SEE EXAMPLE **3**
p. 22

Multiply or divide if possible.

9. $3.8 \div 0$ 10. $0(-27)$ 11. $0 \div \frac{2}{3}$ 12. $\frac{7}{8} \div 0$

SEE EXAMPLE **4**
p. 22

13. **Entertainment** It is estimated that 7 million people saw off-Broadway shows in 2002. Assume that the average price of a ticket was $30. How much money was spent on tickets for off-Broadway shows in 2002?

PRACTICE AND PROBLEM SOLVING

Independent Practice	
For Exercises	See Example
14–16	1
17–20	2
21–24	3
25	4

Extra Practice
Skills Practice p. EP2
Application Practice p. EP24

Find the value of each expression.

14. $-30 \div (-6)$ 15. $8(-4)$ 16. $-25(-12)$

Divide.

17. $-\frac{3}{20} \div \left(-\frac{1}{6}\right)$ 18. $\frac{3}{14} \div \frac{15}{28}$ 19. $-4\frac{1}{2} \div 1\frac{1}{2}$ 20. $2\frac{3}{4} \div \left(-1\frac{1}{2}\right)$

Multiply or divide if possible.

21. $0 \cdot 15$ 22. $-0.25 \div 0$ 23. $0 \div 1$ 24. $\frac{0}{1} \div 3$

25. **Weather** A cold front changes the temperature by $-3°F$ each day. If the temperature started at $0°F$, what will the temperature be after 5 days?

Multiply or divide.

26. $21 \div (-3)$ 27. $-100 \div 25$ 28. $-6 \div (-14)$ 29. $-6.2(10)$

30. $\frac{1}{2} \div \frac{1}{2}$ 31. $-3.75(-5)$ 32. $-12\frac{1}{2}(-3)$ 33. $17\left(\frac{1}{17}\right)$

34. **Critical Thinking** What positive number is the same as its reciprocal?

Evaluate each expression for $a = 4$, $b = -3$, and $c = -\frac{1}{2}$.

35. ab 36. $a \div c$ 37. bc 38. $c \div a$

Let p represent a positive number, n represent a negative number, and z represent zero. Tell whether each expression is positive, negative, zero, or undefined.

39. pn 40. pnz 41. $\frac{n}{p}$ 42. $-pz$

43. $-\frac{p}{n}$ 44. $-(pn)$ 45. $\frac{pn}{z}$ 46. $\frac{z}{n}$

Evaluate the expression $y \div \frac{3}{4}$ for each value of y.

47. $y = \frac{3}{4}$ **48.** $y = -\frac{9}{16}$ **49.** $y = \frac{3}{8}$ **50.** $y = -2\frac{1}{4}$

Evaluate the expression $\frac{1}{2} \div m$ for each value of m.

51. $m = -\frac{5}{2}$ **52.** $m = \frac{7}{8}$ **53.** $m = \frac{4}{9}$ **54.** $m = -5$

55. Education Benjamin must have 120 credit hours of instruction to receive his college degree. Benjamin wants to graduate in 8 semesters without attending summer sessions. How many credit hours must Benjamin take on average each semester to graduate in 8 semesters?

56. Diving An underwater exploration team is swimming at a depth of −20 feet. Then they dive to an underwater cave that is at 7 times this depth. What is the depth of the underwater cave?

Multiply or divide. Then compare using <, >, or =.

57. $10\left(-\frac{1}{2}\right) \;\blacksquare\; 20 \div 4$ **58.** $16 \div (-2) \;\blacksquare\; -2(-4)$ **59.** $-2\frac{2}{3} \div 3 \;\blacksquare\; 5(-2.4)$

60. $20 \div 4 \;\blacksquare\; \frac{3}{4} \div \left(-\frac{1}{2}\right)$ **61.** $2.1(-3.4) \;\blacksquare\; 2.1(-3.4)$ **62.** $0\left(-\frac{3}{5}\right) \;\blacksquare\; \frac{1}{2} \div \frac{1}{2}$

63. Critical Thinking There is a relationship between the number of negative factors and the sign of the product.
   a. What is the sign of the product of an even number of negative factors?
   b. What is the sign of the product of an odd number of negative factors?
   c. Explain why the number of negative factors affects the sign of the product.
   d. Does the number of positive factors affect the sign of the product? Explain.

Write each division expression as a multiplication expression.

64. $12 \div (-3)$ **65.** $75 \div 15$ **66.** $\frac{80}{-8}$ **67.** $\frac{-121}{11}$

Determine whether each statement is sometimes, always, or never true.

68. The quotient of two negative numbers is negative.

69. The quotient of two numbers with the same sign has that sign.

70. The product of two numbers with different signs is positive.

71. Reasoning The product of two factors is positive. One of the factors is negative. Show that the second factor must be negative.

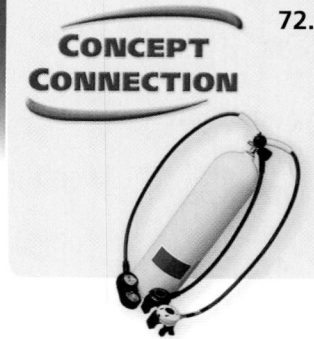

CONCEPT CONNECTION

72. This problem will prepare you for the Concept Connection on page 40.
   a. You swam 20 feet in 5 seconds. Use the formula $r = \frac{d}{t}$ to determine how fast you were swimming.
   b. A diver descended at a rate of 15 feet per minute. Make a table to show the diver's depth after 1, 2, and 5 minutes.
   c. Show two ways to find how far the diver descended in 5 minutes. Remember that multiplication is repeated addition.

Multiple Choice For Exercises 73 and 74, choose the best answer.

73. In which situation below would you multiply 5 • 35 to find the final balance?

   Ⓐ Marc had $35 in his bank account, and for 5 weeks, he withdrew $5 a week.

   Ⓑ Marc opened a new bank account, and for the first 5 months, he deposited $35 a month.

   Ⓒ Marc opened a bank account with $35. For 5 weeks, he deposited $5 a week.

   Ⓓ Marc withdrew $35 a month from his bank account for 5 months.

74. Robyn is buying carpet for her bedroom floor, which is a 15-foot-by-12-foot rectangle. If carpeting costs $1.25 per square foot, how much will it cost Robyn to carpet her bedroom?

   Ⓐ $68   Ⓑ $144   Ⓒ $180   Ⓓ $225

75. **Short Response** In music notation, a half note is played $\frac{1}{2}$ the length of a whole note. A quarter note is played $\frac{1}{4}$ the length of a whole note. In a piece of music, the clarinets play 8 half notes. In the same length of time, the flutes play x quarter notes. Determine how many quarter notes the flutes play. Explain your method.

CHALLENGE AND EXTEND

Find the value of each expression.

76. $(-2)(-2)(-2)$ **77.** $\frac{5}{7} \cdot \frac{5}{7}$ **78.** $5\left(-\frac{4}{5}\right)\left(-\frac{3}{4}\right)$

79. $\left|-\frac{1}{4}\right| \cdot |20|$ **80.** $5 \cdot 4 \cdot 3 \cdot 2 \cdot 1$ **81.** $\left|-\frac{2}{5}\right| \cdot \left|\frac{5}{2}\right|$

82. $\frac{1}{2} \cdot \frac{2}{3} \cdot \frac{3}{4} \cdot \frac{4}{5}$ **83.** $\left(-\frac{3}{4}\right)\left(-\frac{3}{4}\right)\left(-\frac{3}{4}\right)$ **84.** $\left(2^3\right)^2$

For each pattern shown below, describe a possible rule for finding the next term. Then use your rule to write the next 3 terms.

85. $-1, 2, -4, 8, \ldots$ **86.** $\frac{1}{63}, -\frac{1}{21}, \frac{1}{7}, -\frac{3}{7}, \ldots$

87. $-5, 10, -15, 20, -25, \ldots$ **88.** $0.5, 0.25, 0.125, 0.0625, \ldots$

89. A cleaning service charges $49.00 to clean a one-bedroom apartment. If the work takes longer than 2 hours, the service charges $18.00 for each additional hour. What would be the total cost for a job that took 4 hours to complete?

Each regular polygon has a side length of 2.1 cm. Find the perimeter.
(Previous course)

90. 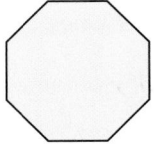   **91.** 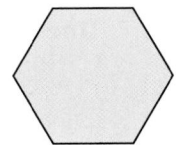   **92.** 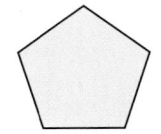   **93.**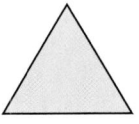

94. A prepaid phone card has a credit of 200 minutes. Write an expression for the number of minutes left on the card after t minutes have been used. *(Lesson 1-1)*

Add or subtract. *(Lesson 1-2)*

95. $12 - 18$ **96.** $-6 + 14$ **97.** $3 - (-5)$ **98.** $11 + (-8)$

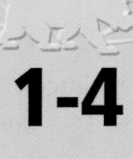

1-4 Powers and Exponents

California Standards

Preparation for 🗝 2.0
Students understand and use such operations as taking the opposite, finding the reciprocal, **taking a root, and raising to a fractional power. They understand and use the rules of exponents.**

Vocabulary
power
base
exponent

Who uses this?
Biologists use exponents to model the growth patterns of living organisms.

When bacteria divide, their number increases exponentially. This means that the number of bacteria is multiplied by the same factor each time the bacteria divide. Instead of writing repeated multiplication to express a product, you can write it as a *power*.

A **power** is an expression written with an *exponent* and a *base* or the value of such an expression. 3^2 is an example of a power.

The **base**, 3, is the number that is used as a factor.

3²

The **exponent**, 2, tells how many times the base, 3, is used as a factor.

When a number is raised to the second power, we usually say it is "squared." The area of a *square* is $s \cdot s = s^2$, where s is the side length.

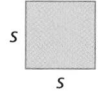

When a number is raised to the third power, we usually say it is "cubed." The volume of a *cube* is $s \cdot s \cdot s = s^3$, where s is the side length.

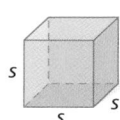

EXAMPLE 1 **Writing Powers for Geometric Models**

Write the power represented by each geometric model.

A

There are 3 rows of 3 dots. 3 × 3
The factor 3 is used 2 times.

3^2

B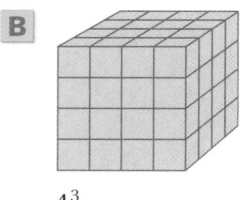

The figure is 4 cubes long, 4 cubes wide, and 4 cubes tall. 4 × 4 × 4
The factor 4 is used 3 times.

4^3

CHECK IT OUT! Write the power represented by each geometric model.

1a.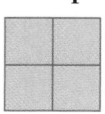

1b.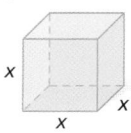

There are no easy geometric models for numbers raised to exponents greater than 3, but you can still write them using repeated multiplication or with a base and exponent.

Reading Exponents			
Words	Multiplication	Power	Value
3 to the first power	3	3^1	3
3 to the second power, or 3 squared	$3 \cdot 3$	3^2	9
3 to the third power, or 3 cubed	$3 \cdot 3 \cdot 3$	3^3	27
3 to the fourth power	$3 \cdot 3 \cdot 3 \cdot 3$	3^4	81
3 to the fifth power	$3 \cdot 3 \cdot 3 \cdot 3 \cdot 3$	3^5	243

EXAMPLE 2 **Evaluating Powers**

Simplify each expression.

A $(-2)^3$
$(-2)(-2)(-2)$ *Use −2 as a factor 3 times.*
-8

In the expression -5^2, 5 is the base because the negative sign is not in parentheses.
In the expression $(-2)^3$, −2 is the base because of the parentheses.

B -5^2
$-1 \cdot 5 \cdot 5$ *Think of a negative sign in front of a power as*
$-1 \cdot 25$ *multiplying by −1. Find the product of −1*
-25 *and two 5's.*

C $\left(\dfrac{2}{3}\right)^2$

$\dfrac{2}{3} \cdot \dfrac{2}{3}$ *Use $\frac{2}{3}$ as a factor 2 times.*

$\dfrac{2}{3} \cdot \dfrac{2}{3} = \dfrac{4}{9}$

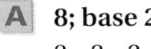 Simplify each expression.

2a. $(-5)^3$ **2b.** -6^2 **2c.** $\left(\dfrac{3}{4}\right)^3$

EXAMPLE 3 **Writing Powers**

Write each number as a power of the given base.

A 8; base 2
$2 \cdot 2 \cdot 2$ *The product of three 2's is 8.*
2^3

B −125; base −5
$(-5)(-5)(-5)$ *The product of three −5's is −125.*
$(-5)^3$

 Write each number as a power of the given base.
3a. 64; base 8   **3b.** −27; base −3

EXAMPLE 4 **Problem-Solving Application**

A certain bacterium divides into 2 bacteria every hour. There is 1 bacterium on a slide. If each bacterium on the slide divides each hour, how many bacteria will be on the slide after 6 hours?

1 Understand the Problem

The **answer** will be the number of bacteria on the slide after 6 hours.
List the **important information:**
- There is 1 bacterium on a slide that divides into 2 bacteria.
- Each bacterium then divides into 2 more bacteria.

2 Make a Plan

Draw a diagram to show the number of bacteria after each hour.

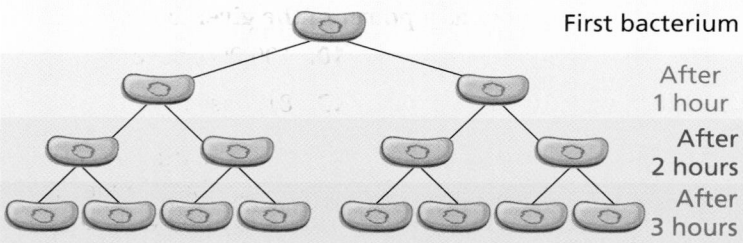

First bacterium
After 1 hour
After 2 hours
After 3 hours

3 Solve

Notice that after each hour, the number of bacteria is a power of 2.

After 1 hour:　　$1 \cdot 2 = 2$ or 2^1 bacteria on the slide
After 2 hours:　　$2 \cdot 2 = 4$ or 2^2 bacteria on the slide
After 3 hours:　　$4 \cdot 2 = 8$　or 2^3 bacteria on the slide

So, after the 6th hour, there will be 2^6 bacteria.

$2^6 = 2 \cdot 2 \cdot 2 \cdot 2 \cdot 2 \cdot 2 = 64$　　　*Multiply six 2's.*

After 6 hours, there will be 64 bacteria on the slide.

4 Look Back

The numbers become too large for a diagram quickly, but a diagram helps you recognize a pattern. Then you can write the numbers as powers of 2.

 **4. What if...?** How many bacteria will be on the slide after 8 hours?

THINK AND DISCUSS

1. Express 8^3 in words two ways.

2. GET ORGANIZED Copy and complete the graphic organizer. In each box, give an example and tell whether the expression is positive or negative.

	Even Exponent	Odd Exponent
Positive Base		
Negative Base		

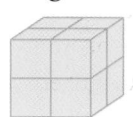
California Standards Practice
Preparation for ✦ 2.0; 24.1

GUIDED PRACTICE

1. Vocabulary What does the *exponent* in the expression 5^6 tell you?

SEE EXAMPLE **1**
p. 26

Write the power represented by each geometric model.

2. (dot array)

3. (cube)

4. (square labeled 9 and 9)

SEE EXAMPLE **2**
p. 27

Simplify each expression.

5. 7^2 **6.** $(-2)^4$ **7.** $(-2)^5$ **8.** $-\left(\dfrac{1}{2}\right)^4$

SEE EXAMPLE **3**
p. 27

Write each number as a power of the given base.

9. 81; base 9   **10.** 100,000; base 10   **11.** -64; base -4

12. 10; base 10   **13.** 81; base 3   **14.** 36; base -6

SEE EXAMPLE **4**
p. 28

15. Technology Jan wants to predict the number of hits she will get on her Web page. Her Web page received 3 hits during the first week it was posted. If the number of hits triples every week, how many hits will the Web page receive during the 5th week?

PRACTICE AND PROBLEM SOLVING

Independent Practice

For Exercises	See Example
16–18	1
19–22	2
23–28	3
29	4

Extra Practice
Skills Practice p. EP2
Application Practice p. EP24

Write the power represented by each geometric model.

16. (square labeled 5 and 5)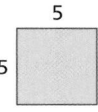

17. (cube labeled 3, 3, 3)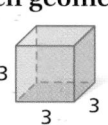

18. (large cube)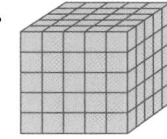

Simplify each expression.

19. 3^3 **20.** $(-4)^2$ **21.** -4^2 **22.** $\left(-\dfrac{3}{5}\right)^2$

Write each number as a power of the given base.

23. 49; base 7   **24.** 1000; base 10   **25.** -8; base -2

26. 1,000,000; base 10   **27.** 64; base 4   **28.** 343; base 7

29. Biology Protozoa are single-celled organisms. *Paramecium aurelia* is one type of protozoan. The number of *Paramecium aurelia* protozoa doubles every 1.25 days. There was one protozoan on a slide 5 days ago. How many protozoa are on the slide now?

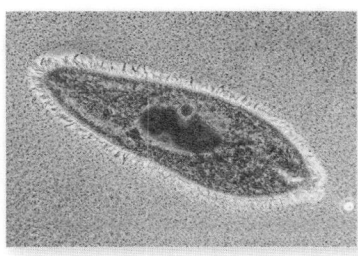

 30. Write About It A classmate says that any number raised to an even power is positive. Explain whether your classmate is correct.

Compare. Write <, >, or =.

31. 3^2 ▢ 3^3 **32.** 5^2 ▢ 2^5 **33.** 4^2 ▢ 2^4 **34.** 1^9 ▢ 1^4

35. -2^3 ▢ $(-2)^3$ **36.** -3^2 ▢ $(-3)^2$ **37.** 10^2 ▢ 2^6 **38.** 2^2 ▢ 4^1

Write each expression as repeated multiplication. Then simplify the expression.

39. 2^3 **40.** 1^7 **41.** $(-4)^3$ **42.** -4^3

43. $(-1)^3$ **44.** $(-1)^4$ **45.** $\left(\dfrac{1}{3}\right)^3$ **46.** -2.2^2

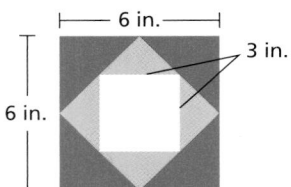
6 in.
3 in.
6 in.

47. Geometry The diagram shows an ornamental tile design.
 a. What is the area of the whole tile?
 b. What is the area of the white square?
 c. What is the total area of the two shaded regions?

Write each expression using a base and an exponent.

48. $3 \cdot 3 \cdot 3 \cdot 3$ **49.** $6 \cdot 6$ **50.** $8 \cdot 8 \cdot 8 \cdot 8 \cdot 8$

51. $(-1)(-1)(-1)(-1)$ **52.** $(-7)(-7)(-7)$ **53.** $\left(\dfrac{1}{9}\right)\left(\dfrac{1}{9}\right)\left(\dfrac{1}{9}\right)$

54. Art A painting is made of 3 concentric squares. The side length of the largest square is 24 cm. What is the area of the painting?

55. Estimation A box is shaped like a cube with edges 22.7 centimeters long. What is the approximate volume of the box?

Write the exponent that makes each equation true.

56. $2^{\blacksquare} = 4$ **57.** $4^{\blacksquare} = 16$ **58.** $(-2)^{\blacksquare} = 16$ **59.** $5^{\blacksquare} = 625$

60. $-2^{\blacksquare} = -8$ **61.** $10^{\blacksquare} = 100$ **62.** $5^{\blacksquare} = 125$ **63.** $3^{\blacksquare} = 81$

64. Entertainment Mark and Becky play a coin toss game. Both start with one point. Every time the coin comes up heads, Mark doubles his score. Every time the coin comes up tails, Becky triples her score. The results of their game so far are shown in the table.
 a. What is Mark's score?
 b. What is Becky's score?
 c. **What if...?** If they toss the coin 50 more times, who do you think will win? Why?

Coin Toss Results	
Heads	**Tails**
✓	✓
✓	✓
✓	✓
✓	
✓	

65. Critical Thinking The number of zeros in powers of 10 follow a pattern.
 a. Evaluate each of the following: 10^2, 10^3, 10^4.
 b. Use your answers to part *a* to make a prediction about the relationship between the exponent of a power of 10 and the number of zeros in the answer.

CONCEPT CONNECTION

66. This problem will prepare you for the Concept Connection on page 40.

The formula $p = \dfrac{F}{A}$ shows that pressure *p* is the amount of force *F* exerted over an area *A* in square units.

 a. A bag of flour sits on a block and exerts a force of 50 pounds over an area of 100 in². What is the pressure exerted on the block by the bag of flour?
 b. Water pressure exerts 64 pounds on each square foot of a diver's body. What force is exerted on each square *inch* of the diver's body? (*Hint:* Determine how many square inches are in one square foot.)

Multiple Choice For Exercises 67–70, choose the best answer.

67. Which of the following is equal to 9^2?

    (A) $9 \cdot 2$ (B) 27 (C) 3^4 (D) -9^2

68. Which power represents the same value as the product $(-16)(-16)(-16)(-16)$?

    (A) $(-16)4$ (B) $(-16)^4$ (C) -16^4 (D) $-(16 \cdot 4)$

69. A number raised to the third power is negative. What is true about the number?

    (A) The number is positive.   (C) The number is even.

    (B) The number is negative.   (D) The number is odd.

70. The table shows the results of raising -1 to consecutive whole numbers. If the pattern in the table continues, what is the value of -1 raised to the 100th power?

$(-1)^n$	$(-1)^1$	$(-1)^2$	$(-1)^3$	$(-1)^4$	$(-1)^5$	$(-1)^6$
Value	-1	1	-1	1	-1	1

    (A) -1^{100} (B) -1 (C) 1 (D) 0

CHALLENGE AND EXTEND

Simplify each expression.

71. $(2^2)(2^2)(2^2)$ **72.** $(2^3)(2^3)(2^3)$ **73.** $(-4^2)(-4^2)(-4^2)(-4^2)$

74. Design The diagram shows the layout of a pool and the surrounding path. The path is 2.5 feet wide.

    a. What is the total area of the pool and path?

    b. What is the area of the pool?

    c. What is the area of the path?

    d. One bag of pebbles covers 10 square feet. How many bags of pebbles are needed to cover the path?

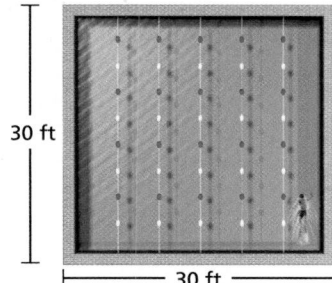

30 ft

30 ft

75. Exponents and powers have special properties.

    a. Write both 4^2 and 4^3 as a product of 4's.

    b. Write the product of the two expressions from part **a.** Write this product as a power of 4.

    c. Write About It Add the exponents in the expressions 4^2 and 4^3. Describe any relationship you see between your answer to part **b** and the sum of the exponents.

SPIRAL STANDARDS REVIEW   6NS2.2, ⬥ 6NS2.3, 6SDAP1.1, ⬥ 7NS1.2

Find the mean of each data set by dividing the sum of the data by the number of items in the data set. *(Previous course)*

76. 7, 7, 8, 8   **77.** 1, 3, 5, 7, 9   **78.** 10, 9, 9, 12, 12

Give two ways to write each algebraic expression in words. *(Lesson 1-1)*

79. $5 - x$ **80.** $6n$ **81.** $c \div d$ **82.** $a + b$

Multiply or divide if possible. *(Lesson 1-3)*

83. $\dfrac{4}{5} \div \dfrac{8}{25}$ **84.** $0 \div \dfrac{6}{7}$ **85.** $-20(-14)$ **86.** $\dfrac{1}{2}\left(-\dfrac{4}{5}\right)$

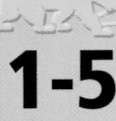

1-5 Roots and Irrational Numbers

California Standards

🔑 **2.0 Students understand and use such operations as** taking the opposite, finding the reciprocal, **taking a root**, and raising to a fractional power. They understand and use the rules of exponents.

Vocabulary
square root
principal square root
perfect square
cube root
natural numbers
whole numbers
integers
rational numbers
terminating decimal
repeating decimal
irrational numbers

Why learn this?

Square roots can be used to find the side length of a square garden when you know its area. (See Example 3.)

A number that is multiplied by itself to form a product is a **square root** of that product. The radical symbol $\sqrt{}$ is used to represent square roots. For nonnegative numbers, the operations of squaring and finding a square root are inverse operations. In other words, for $x \geq 0$, $\sqrt{x} \cdot \sqrt{x} = x$.

Positive real numbers have two square roots. The **principal square root** of a number is the positive square root and is represented by $\sqrt{}$. A negative square root is represented by $-\sqrt{}$. The symbol $\pm\sqrt{}$ is used to represent both square roots.

$$4 \cdot 4 = 4^2 = 16 \longrightarrow \sqrt{16} = 4 \longleftarrow \text{Positive square root of 16}$$

$$(-4)(-4) = (-4)^2 = 16 \longrightarrow -\sqrt{16} = -4 \longleftarrow \text{Negative square root of 16}$$

A **perfect square** is a number whose positive square root is a whole number. Some examples of perfect squares are shown in the table.

0	1	4	9	16	25	36	49	64	81	100
0^2	1^2	2^2	3^2	4^2	5^2	6^2	7^2	8^2	9^2	10^2

A number that is raised to the third power to form a product is a **cube root** of that product. The symbol $\sqrt[3]{}$ indicates a cube root. Since $2^3 = 8$, $\sqrt[3]{8} = 2$. Similarly, the symbol $\sqrt[4]{}$ indicates a fourth root: $2^4 = 16$, so $\sqrt[4]{16} = 2$.

EXAMPLE 1 **Finding Roots**

Find each root.

A $\sqrt{49}$
$\sqrt{49} = \sqrt{7^2}$ *Think: What number squared equals 49?*
$= 7$

B $-\sqrt{36}$
$-\sqrt{36} = -\sqrt{6^2}$ *Think: What number squared equals 36?*
$= -6$

C $\sqrt[3]{-125}$
$\sqrt[3]{-125} = \sqrt[3]{(-5^3)}$ *Think: What number cubed equals −125?*
$= -5$ $(-5)(-5)(-5) = 25(-5) = -125$

Writing Math

The small number to the left of the root is the *index*. In a square root, the index is understood to be 2. In other words, $\sqrt{}$ is the same as $\sqrt[2]{}$.

 **Find each root.**

1a. $\sqrt{4}$ **1b.** $-\sqrt{25}$ **1c.** $\sqrt[4]{81}$

EXAMPLE 2 **Finding Roots of Fractions**

Find $\sqrt{\dfrac{1}{4}}$.

$\dfrac{1}{2} \cdot \dfrac{1}{2} = \dfrac{1}{4}$ *Think: What number squared equals $\dfrac{1}{4}$?*

$\sqrt{\dfrac{1}{4}} = \dfrac{1}{2}$

 **Find each root.**

2a. $\sqrt{\dfrac{4}{9}}$ **2b.** $\sqrt[3]{\dfrac{1}{8}}$ **2c.** $-\sqrt{\dfrac{4}{49}}$

Square roots of numbers that are not perfect squares, such as 15, are not whole numbers. A calculator can approximate the value of $\sqrt{15}$ as 3.872983346... Without a calculator, you can use the square roots of perfect squares to help estimate the square roots of other numbers.

EXAMPLE 3 *Gardening Application*

Nancy wants to plant a square garden of wildflowers. She has enough wildflower seeds to cover 19 ft². Estimate to the nearest tenth the side length of a square with an area of 19 ft².

Since the area of the square is 19 ft², then each side of the square is $\sqrt{19}$ ft. 19 is not a perfect square, so find the two consecutive perfect squares that 19 is between: 16 and 25. $\sqrt{19}$ is between $\sqrt{16}$ and $\sqrt{25}$, or 4 and 5. Refine the estimate.

4.3:	$4.3^2 = 18.49$	too low	*$\sqrt{19}$ is greater than 4.3.*
4.4:	$4.4^2 = 19.36$	too high	*$\sqrt{19}$ is less than 4.4.*
4.35:	$4.35^2 = 18.9225$	too low	*$\sqrt{19}$ is greater than 4.35.*

Since 4.35 is too low and 4.4 is too high, $\sqrt{19}$ is between 4.35 and 4.4. Rounded to the nearest tenth, $\sqrt{19} \approx 4.4$.

The side length of the plot is $\sqrt{19} \approx 4.4$ ft.

> **Writing Math**
> The symbol $\approx$ means "is approximately equal to."

 **3. What if...?** Nancy decides to buy more wildflower seeds and now has enough to cover 26 ft². Estimate to the nearest tenth the side length of a square with an area of 26 ft².

Real numbers can be classified according to their characteristics.

Natural numbers are the counting numbers: 1, 2, 3, ...

Whole numbers are the natural numbers and zero: 0, 1, 2, 3, ...

Integers are the whole numbers and their opposites: $-3, -2, -1, 0, 1, 2, 3, ...$

Rational numbers are numbers that can be expressed in the form $\dfrac{a}{b}$, where a and b are both integers and $b \neq 0$. When expressed as a decimal, a rational number is either a *terminating decimal* or a *repeating decimal*.

> **Writing Math**
> To show that one or more digits repeat continuously, write a bar over those digits.
> $1.333333333... = 1.\overline{3}$
> $2.14141414... = 2.\overline{14}$

- A **terminating decimal** has a finite number of digits after the decimal point (for example, 1.25, 2.75, and 4.0).

- A **repeating decimal** has a block of one or more digits after the decimal point that repeat continuously (where all digits are not zeros).

Irrational numbers are all numbers that are not rational. They cannot be expressed in the form $\frac{a}{b}$ where a and b are both integers and $b \neq 0$. They are neither terminating decimals nor repeating decimals. For example:

0.10100100010000100000...   *After the decimal point, this number contains 1 followed by one 0, and then 1 followed by two 0's, and then 1 followed by three 0's, and so on.*

This decimal neither terminates nor repeats, so it is an irrational number.

If a whole number is not a perfect square, then its square root is irrational. For example, 2 is not a perfect square, and $\sqrt{2}$ is irrational.

The real numbers are made up of all rational and irrational numbers.

Reading Math

Note the symbols for the sets of numbers.

$\mathbb{R}$: real numbers
$\mathbb{Q}$: rational numbers
$\mathbb{Z}$: integers
$\mathbb{W}$: whole numbers
$\mathbb{N}$: natural numbers

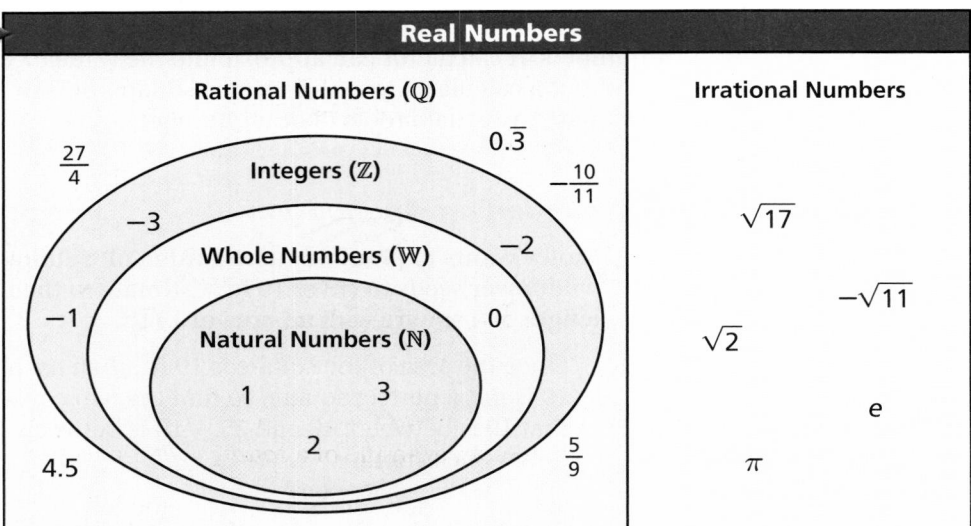

EXAMPLE 4   Classifying Real Numbers

Write all classifications that apply to each real number.

A $\frac{8}{9}$

  $\frac{8}{9}$ *is in the form* $\frac{a}{b}$*, where a and b are integers and b ≠ 0.*

  $8 \div 9 = 0.8888...$

  $= 0.\overline{8}$ $\frac{8}{9}$ *can be written as a repeating decimal.*

  rational, repeating decimal

B 18

  $18 = \frac{18}{1}$ *18 can be written in the form* $\frac{a}{b}$*.*

  $18 = 18.0$ *18 can be written as a terminating decimal.*

  rational, terminating decimal, integer, whole, natural

C $\sqrt{20}$

  irrational   *20 is not a perfect square, so $\sqrt{20}$ is irrational.*

 Write all classifications that apply to each real number.

4a. $7\frac{4}{9}$ **4b.** -12

4c. $\sqrt{10}$ **4d.** $\sqrt{100}$

THINK AND DISCUSS

1. Write $\frac{2}{3}$ and $\frac{3}{5}$ as decimals. Identify what number classifications the two numbers share and how their classifications are different.

2. **GET ORGANIZED** Copy the graphic organizer and use the flowchart to classify each of the given numbers. Write each number in the box with the most specific classification that applies. $4, \sqrt{25}, 0, \frac{1}{3}, -15, -2.25, \frac{1}{4}, \sqrt{21}, 2^4, (-1)^2$

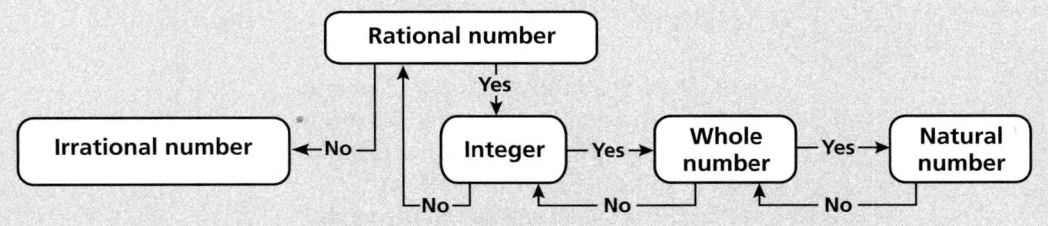

1-5 Exercises

California Standards Practice
🔑 2.0

go.hrw.com
Homework Help Online
KEYWORD: MA8CA 1-5
Parent Resources Online
KEYWORD: MA8CA Parent

GUIDED PRACTICE

1. **Vocabulary** Give an example of a *square root* that is not a *rational number*.

Find each root.

SEE EXAMPLE 1
p. 32

2. $\sqrt{64}$ 3. $-\sqrt{225}$ 4. $\sqrt[3]{-64}$ 5. $\sqrt[4]{625}$

6. $\sqrt{81}$ 7. $-\sqrt[3]{27}$ 8. $-\sqrt[3]{-27}$ 9. $-\sqrt{16}$

SEE EXAMPLE 2
p. 33

10. $\sqrt{\frac{1}{16}}$ 11. $\sqrt[3]{\frac{8}{27}}$ 12. $-\sqrt{\frac{1}{9}}$ 13. $\sqrt{\frac{9}{64}}$

14. $\sqrt{\frac{1}{36}}$ 15. $\sqrt[3]{\frac{1}{64}}$ 16. $-\sqrt{\frac{4}{81}}$ 17. $\sqrt[3]{-\frac{1}{125}}$

SEE EXAMPLE 3
p. 33

18. A contractor is told that a potential client's kitchen floor is in the shape of a square. The area of the floor is 45 ft². Estimate to the nearest tenth the side length of the floor.

SEE EXAMPLE 4
p. 34

Write all classifications that apply to each real number.

19. -27 20. $\frac{1}{6}$ 21. $\sqrt{33}$ 22. -6.8

PRACTICE AND PROBLEM SOLVING

Find each root.

23. $\sqrt{121}$ 24. $\sqrt[3]{-1000}$ 25. $-\sqrt{100}$ 26. $\sqrt[4]{256}$

27. $\sqrt{\frac{1}{25}}$ 28. $\sqrt[4]{\frac{1}{16}}$ 29. $\sqrt[3]{-\frac{1}{8}}$ 30. $-\sqrt{\frac{25}{36}}$

31. A new house will have a foundation in the shape of a square. The house will cover 222 square yards. Estimate to the nearest tenth the length of one side of the house.

Independent Practice	
For Exercises	**See Example**
23–26	1
27–30	2
31	3
32–35	4

Extra Practice

Skills Practice p. EP3

Application Practice p. EP24

Write all classifications that apply to each real number.

32. $\dfrac{5}{12}$ **33.** $\sqrt{49}$ **34.** -3 **35.** $\sqrt{18}$

36. Geometry The cube root of the volume of a cube gives the length of one side of the cube.

    a. Find the side length of the cube shown.

    b. Find the area of each face of the cube.

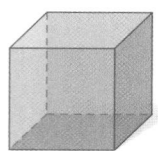

Volume = 343 cm³

Compare. Write <, >, or =.

37. $8 \;\rule{1em}{0.6em}\; \sqrt{63}$ **38.** $\sqrt{88} \;\rule{1em}{0.6em}\; 9$ **39.** $6 \;\rule{1em}{0.6em}\; \sqrt{40}$ **40.** $\sqrt{\dfrac{9}{25}} \;\rule{1em}{0.6em}\; 0.61$

Travel During a cross-country road trip, Madeline recorded the distance between several major cities and the time it took her to travel between those cities. Find Madeline's average speed for each leg of the trip and classify that number.

Madeline's Cross-Country Road Trip				
	Distance (mi)	**Time (h)**	**Speed (mi/h)**	**Classification**
41. Portland, ME, to Memphis, TN	1485	33		
42. Memphis, TN, to Denver, CO	1046	27		
43. Denver, CO, to Boise, ID	831	24		
44. Boise, ID, to Portland, OR	424	9		

Reasoning Determine whether each statement is *sometimes, always,* or *never* true. If it is sometimes true, give one example that makes the statement true and one example that makes it false. If it is always true, explain. If it is never true, rewrite the statement so that it is always true.

45. Mixed numbers are rational numbers.

46. The decimal form of an irrational number is a repeating decimal.

47. A terminating decimal is a rational number.

48. A negative number is irrational.

49. Critical Thinking A positive number has two square roots, one that is positive and one that is negative. Is the same thing true for the cube root of a positive number? What about the fourth root of a positive number? Explain.

CONCEPT CONNECTION

50. This problem will prepare you for the Concept Connection on page 40.

The equation $a^2 + b^2 = c^2$ relates the lengths of the sides of a right triangle. Sides a and b make the right angle of the triangle.

    a. What is the value of c^2 when $a = 5$ and $b = 12$? Determine the square root of c^2 to find the value of c.

    b. A diver is a horizontal distance of 50 feet from a boat and 120 feet beneath the surface of the water. What distance will the diver swim if he swims diagonally to the boat?

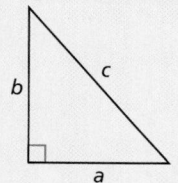

51. **Entertainment** In a board game, players place different-colored stones on a grid. Each player tries to make rows of 5 or more stones in their color while preventing their opponent(s) from doing the same. The square game board has 324 squares on it. How many squares are on each side of the board?

 52. **Write About It** Explain why you cannot take the square root of a negative number but you can take the cube root of a negative number.

Multiple Choice For Exercises 53–56, choose the best answer.

53. Which point on the number line is closest to $-\sqrt{11}$?

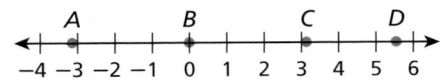

   Ⓐ A   Ⓑ B   Ⓒ C   Ⓓ D

54. What is the area of the figure at right?

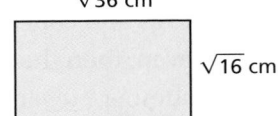

   Ⓐ 24 cm²   Ⓒ 104 cm²
   Ⓑ 52 cm²   Ⓓ 576 cm²

55. Which number is irrational?

   Ⓐ $-\sqrt{9}$ Ⓒ 4.0005
   Ⓑ $2.\overline{17}$ Ⓓ $\sqrt{40}$

56. The square root of 175 is between which two whole numbers?

   Ⓐ 11 and 12   Ⓑ 12 and 13   Ⓒ 13 and 14   Ⓓ 14 and 15

CHALLENGE AND EXTEND

Find each root.

57. $\sqrt{0.81}$ 58. $\sqrt{0.25}$ 59. $\sqrt[3]{-0.001}$ 60. $\sqrt{2.25}$

Evaluate each expression for $a = 9$ and $b = 7$.

61. $\sqrt{a + b}$ 62. $b\sqrt{a} - a$ 63. $\sqrt[4]{b + a} + ab$ 64. $\sqrt{ab + 1}$

 65. **Reasoning** The *Density Property of Real Numbers* states that between any two real numbers, there is another real number.

   a. Does the set of integers have this property? Explain.

   b. Use the Density Property to write a convincing argument that there are infinitely many real numbers between 0 and 1.

Add or subtract. *(Lesson 1-2)*

66. $-14 + (-16)$ 67. $-\frac{1}{4} - \left(-\frac{3}{4}\right)$ 68. $25 - 17.6$

Multiply or divide. *(Lesson 1-3)*

69. $\frac{1}{8} \div \left(-\frac{2}{3}\right)$ 70. $(-2.5)(-8)$ 71. $-\frac{21}{6}$

Simplify each expression. *(Lesson 1-4)*

72. -3^4 73. $\left(-\frac{2}{5}\right)^3$ 74. 14^2 75. 4^3

LOGICAL REASONING

Use with Lesson 1-5

Conditional Statements

A **conditional statement** is a statement that can be written in "if-then" form. The **hypothesis** is the part of the statement that follows *if*. The **conclusion** is the part of the statement that follows *then*.

24.2 Students identify the hypothesis and conclusion in logical deduction.

If *a* and *b* are real numbers, then *a* + *b* is a real number.

Hypothesis

Conclusion

Example 1

Identify the hypothesis and conclusion in each conditional statement.

1 If a number is even, then the number is divisible by 2.

Hypothesis: A number is even.   Conclusion: The number is divisible by 2.

2 If a triangle has an obtuse angle, then the triangle is not a right triangle.

Hypothesis: A triangle has an obtuse angle.   Conclusion: The triangle is not a right triangle.

3 If a shape is a rectangle, then the shape has four right angles.

Hypothesis: A shape is a rectangle.   Conclusion: The shape has four right angles.

4 If two angles are vertical angles, then the angles are congruent.

Hypothesis: Two angles are vertical angles.   Conclusion: The angles are congruent.

Try This

Identify the hypothesis and conclusion in each conditional statement.

1. If two lines are perpendicular, then the lines intersect.

2. If an angle is a right angle, then the angle measures 90°.

3. If two numbers are opposites, then the sum of the two numbers is zero.

4. If a number is a whole number, then the number is an integer.

Mathematical properties can often be written as conditional statements.

- Commutative Property of Addition: If *a* and *b* are real numbers, then $a + b = b + a$.

- Distributive Property: If *a*, *b*, and *c* are real numbers, then $a(b + c) = ab + ac$.

Try This

Write each mathematical property as a conditional statement.

5. Commutative Property of Multiplication

6. Associative Property of Addition

7. Associative Property of Multiplication

The **converse of a conditional statement** is formed by exchanging the hypothesis and the conclusion.

Conditional statement:

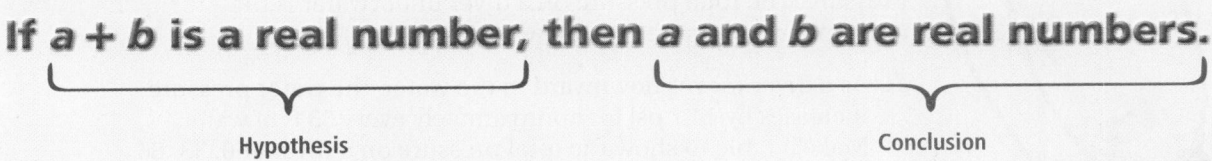

If *a* and *b* are real numbers, then *a* + *b* is a real number.

Hypothesis   Conclusion

Converse:

If *a* + *b* is a real number, then *a* and *b* are real numbers.

Hypothesis   Conclusion

A conditional statement may be true while its converse is false.

Example 2

Tell whether each conditional statement in Example 1 is true. Then find each statement's converse and tell whether the converse is true.

1 **If a number is even, then the number is divisible by 2.**

True; all even numbers are divisible by 2.
Converse: If a number is divisible by 2, then the number is even.
True; a number that is divisible by 2 is defined to be even.

2 **If a triangle has an obtuse angle, then the triangle is not a right triangle.**

True; if a triangle has an obtuse angle, then it cannot be a right triangle.
Converse: If a triangle is not a right triangle, then the triangle has an obtuse angle.
Not true; a triangle may have three acute angles.

3 **If a shape is a rectangle, then the shape has four right angles.**

True; all rectangles have four right angles.
Converse: If a shape has four right angles, then the shape is a rectangle.
True; a shape with four right angles is defined to be a rectangle.

4 **If two angles are vertical angles, then the angles are congruent.**

True; vertical angles are always congruent.
Converse: If two angles are congruent, then the angles are vertical angles.
Not true; two angles may be congruent without being vertical angles.

Try This

Tell whether each conditional statement is true. Then find each statement's converse and tell whether the converse is true.

8. If two lines are perpendicular, then the lines intersect.

9. If an angle is a right angle, then the angle measures 90°.

10. If two numbers are opposites, then the sum of the two numbers is zero.

11. If a number is a whole number, then the number is an integer.

CONCEPT CONNECTION

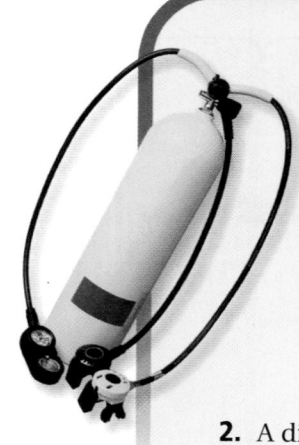

The Language of Algebra

Under Pressure Atmospheric pressure is 14.7 pounds per square inch (psi). Underwater, the water exerts additional pressure. The total pressure on a diver underwater is the atmospheric pressure plus the water pressure.

1. As a diver moves downward in the water, the water pressure increases by 14.7 psi for approximately every 33 ft of water. Make a table to show the total pressure on a diver at 0, 33, 66, and 99 ft below the surface of the water. At what depth would the total pressure equal 73.5 psi? Explain your method.

2. A diver is 40 ft below the surface of the water when a hot-air balloon flies directly over her. The hot-air balloon is 849 ft above the surface of the water. Draw a diagram and write an expression to find the distance between the diver and the balloon when the balloon is directly above her.

3. The diver swam 62.5 ft in 5 minutes. How fast was she swimming? What total distance will she have traveled after an additional 4 minutes if she maintains this same speed?

4. The total pressure on each square foot of the diver's body is given by the expression $2116.8 + 64.145d$, where d is the depth in feet. At a depth of 66 ft, what is the total pressure on each square foot of her body? What is the total pressure on each square *inch* of her body at this depth? How does your answer compare to your results for problem **1**?

5. The diver realizes that she has drifted horizontally about 30 ft from the boat she left. She is at a depth of 40 ft from the surface. What is the diver's diagonal distance from the boat?

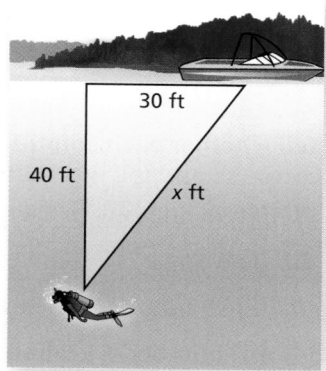

30 ft
40 ft
x ft

READY TO GO ON?

Quiz for Lessons 1-1 Through 1-5

1-1 Variables and Expressions

Give two ways to write each algebraic expression in words.

1. $4 + n$ **2.** $m - 9$ **3.** $\dfrac{g}{2}$ **4.** $4z$

5. Bob earns \$15 per hour. Write an expression for the amount of money he earns in h hours.

6. A soccer practice is 90 minutes long. Write an expression for the number of minutes left after m minutes have elapsed.

Evaluate each expression for the replacement set {2, 3, 6}.

7. $y \div 2$ **8.** $3y$ **9.** $3 + y$ **10.** $3 - y$

1-2 Adding and Subtracting Real Numbers

Add or subtract.

11. $81 + (-15)$ **12.** $27 - 32$ **13.** $2 - \left(-1\frac{1}{4}\right)$ **14.** $-7 + (-14)$

15. Brandon's bank statement shows a balance of $-\$45.00$. What will the balance be after Brandon deposits \$70.00?

1-3 Multiplying and Dividing Real Numbers

Find the value of each expression if possible.

16. $9(-9)$ **17.** $6 \div \dfrac{3}{5}$ **18.** $9.6 \div 0$ **19.** $-\dfrac{1}{2}\left(-\dfrac{1}{2}\right)$

20. Simon drove for $2\frac{1}{2}$ hours to get from his house to the beach. Simon averaged 55 miles per hour on the trip. What is the distance from Simon's house to the beach?

1-4 Powers and Exponents

Simplify each expression.

21. $(-3)^2$ **22.** -3^2 **23.** $\left(-\dfrac{2}{3}\right)^3$ **24.** $\left(-\dfrac{1}{2}\right)^5$

25. The number of bytes in a kilobyte is 2 to the 10th power. Express this number in two ways.

1-5 Roots and Irrational Numbers

Find each root.

26. $\sqrt{225}$ **27.** $-\sqrt{49}$ **28.** $\sqrt[3]{8}$ **29.** $\sqrt{\dfrac{16}{25}}$

30. Mindy is building a patio that is in the shape of a square. The patio will cover 56 square yards. Find the length of a side of the patio to the nearest tenth of a yard.

Write all classifications that apply to each real number.

31. $\dfrac{1}{11}$ **32.** $\sqrt{12}$ **33.** $\sqrt{900}$ **34.** -6

1-6 Properties of Real Numbers

California Standards

1.0 Students identify and use the arithmetic properties of subsets of integers and rational, irrational, and real numbers, including closure properties for the four basic arithmetic operations where applicable. **24.3** Students use counterexamples to show that an assertion is false and recognize that a single counterexample is sufficient to refute an assertion.
Also covered: **25.1**

Vocabulary
counterexample
closure

Who uses this?
Triathletes can use properties to calculate overall times mentally. (See Exercise 31.)

The Commutative and Associative Properties of Addition and Multiplication allow you to rearrange an expression.

Properties of Addition and Multiplication

WORDS	NUMBERS	ALGEBRA
Commutative Property You can add real numbers in any order. You can multiply real numbers in any order.	$2 + 7 = 7 + 2$ $3 \cdot 9 = 9 \cdot 3$	For real numbers a and b, $a + b = b + a$ $ab = ba$
Associative Property When you are only adding, changing the grouping will not change the sum. When you are only multiplying, changing the grouping will not change the product.	$(6 + 8) + 2 = 6 + (8 + 2)$ $(7 \cdot 4) \cdot 5 = 7 \cdot (4 \cdot 5)$	For real numbers a, b, and c, $(a + b) + c = a + (b + c)$ $(ab)c = a(bc)$

EXAMPLE 1 **Identifying Properties**

Name the property that is illustrated in each equation.

A $(4 + x) + y = 4 + (x + y)$

$(4 + x) + y = 4 + (x + y)$ *The grouping is different.*
Associative Property of Addition

B $-5 \cdot b = b \cdot (-5)$

$-5 \cdot b = b \cdot (-5)$ *The order is different.*
Commutative Property of Multiplication

C $2 + (6 + m) = 2 + (m + 6)$

$2 + (6 + m) = 2 + (m + 6)$ *The order is different.*
Commutative Property of Addition

Name the property that is illustrated in each equation.
1a. $n + (-7) = -7 + n$
1b. $1.5 + (g + 2.3) = (1.5 + g) + 2.3$
1c. $(xy)z = (yx)z$

Student to Student | **Commutative and Associative Properties**

I used to get the Commutative and Associative Properties mixed up.

To remember the Commutative Property, I think of people commuting back and forth to work. When people commute, they move. I can move numbers around without changing the value of the expression.

For the Associative Property, I think of associating with my friends. They're the group I hang out with. In math, it's about how numbers are grouped.

Lorna Anderson
Pearson High School

The Commutative and Associative Properties are true for addition and multiplication. They may not be true for other operations. A **counterexample** is an example that *disproves* a statement, or shows that it is false. One counterexample is enough to disprove a statement.

Caution! /////

One counterexample is enough to disprove a statement, but one example is not enough to prove a statement.

Counterexamples	
Statement	**Counterexample**
No month has fewer than 30 days.	February has fewer than 30 days, so the statement is false.
Every integer that is divisible by 2 is also divisible by 4.	The integer 18 is divisible by 2 but not by 4, so the statement is false.

EXAMPLE **2** **Finding Counterexamples to Statements About Properties**

 Reasoning

Find a counterexample to disprove the statement "The Associative Property is true for subtraction."

Find three real numbers, a, b, and c, such that $a - (b - c) \neq (a - b) - c$.

Try $a = 10$, $b = 7$, and $c = 2$.

$$a - (b - c) \qquad\qquad (a - b) - c$$
$$10 - (7 - 2) \qquad\qquad (10 - 7) - 2$$
$$10 - 5 = 5 \qquad\qquad 3 - 2 = 1$$

Since $10 - (7 - 2) \neq (10 - 7) - 2$, this is a counterexample. The statement is false.

 **2.** Find a counterexample to disprove the statement "The Commutative Property is true for division."

 **Distributive Property**

NUMBERS	ALGEBRA
$3(4 + 8) = 3(4) + 3(8)$ $3(12) = 12 + 24$ $36 = 36$	For real numbers a, b, and c, $a(b + c) = ab + ac$

The Distributive Property also works with subtraction because subtraction is the same as adding the opposite.

EXAMPLE 3 Using the Distributive Property with Mental Math

Write each product using the Distributive Property. Then simplify.

 **15(103)**

$$15(103) = 15(100 + 3)$$ *Rewrite 103 as 100 + 3.*
$$= 15(100) + 15(3)$$ *Use the Distributive Property.*
$$= 1500 + 45$$ *Multiply (mentally).*
$$= 1545$$ *Add (mentally).*

Helpful Hint

Break the greater factor into a sum or difference that contains a multiple of 10.

B 6(19)

$$6(19) = 6(20 - 1)$$ *Rewrite 19 as 20 − 1.*
$$= 6(20) - 6(1)$$ *Use the Distributive Property.*
$$= 120 - 6$$ *Multiply (mentally).*
$$= 114$$ *Subtract (mentally).*

 **Write each product using the Distributive Property. Then simplify.**
3a. $9(52)$ **3b.** $12(98)$ **3c.** $7(34)$

A set of numbers is said to be closed, or to have **closure** , under an operation if the result of the operation on any two numbers in the set is also in the set.

Closure Properties of the Real Numbers

WORDS	NUMBERS	ALGEBRA
The real numbers are closed under addition, subtraction, and multiplication.	$6.1 + \sqrt{2}$, $6.1 - \sqrt{2}$, and $6.1 \times \sqrt{2}$ are all real numbers.	For real numbers a and b, $a + b$, $a - b$, and ab are all real numbers.

EXAMPLE 4 Finding Counterexamples to Statements About Closure

Find a counterexample to show that each statement is false.

A The integers are closed under division.

Find two integers, a and b, such that the quotient, $\frac{a}{b}$, is not an integer.
Try $a = 1$ and $b = 3$.
$$\frac{a}{b} = \frac{1}{3}$$
Since $\frac{1}{3}$ is not an integer, this is a counterexample. The statement is false.

B The whole numbers are closed under subtraction.

Find two whole numbers, a and b, such that the difference, $a - b$, is not a whole number.
Try $a = 4$ and $b = 9$.
$$a - b = 4 - 9 = -5$$
Since -5 is not a whole number, this is a counterexample. The statement is false.

 **Find a counterexample to show that each statement is false.**
4a. The set of negative integers is closed under multiplication.
4b. The whole numbers are closed under the operation of taking a square root.

THINK AND DISCUSS

1. Tell which property is being described: When adding three numbers, you can add the first number to the sum of the second and third numbers. You can also add the third number to the sum of the first and second numbers. The result is the same.

2. **GET ORGANIZED** Copy and complete the graphic organizer below. In each box, give an example to illustrate the given property.

(Associative)   (Commutative)   (Distributive)
[   ]   [   ]   [   ]

1-6 Exercises

California Standards Practice
1.0, 24.3, 25.1

go.hrw.com
Homework Help Online
KEYWORD: MA8CA 1-6
Parent Resources Online
KEYWORD: MA8CA Parent

GUIDED PRACTICE

1. **Vocabulary** The ___?___ Property of Addition states the following:

$(a + b) + c = a + (b + c)$. (*Associative, Commutative, or Distributive*)

SEE EXAMPLE 1 p. 42

Name the property that is illustrated in each equation.

2. $16 + r = r + 16$

3. $4 + (x + 3y) = (4 + x) + 3y$

4. $(4 + 12) + 9 = (12 + 4) + 9$

5. $m \cdot (-20) = -20m$

SEE EXAMPLE 2 p. 43

6. Find a counterexample to disprove the statement "The Commutative Property is true for subtraction."

SEE EXAMPLE 3 p. 44

Write each product using the Distributive Property. Then simplify.

7. $14(1002)$

8. $16(19)$

9. $9(38)$

10. $8(57)$

11. $12(112)$

12. $7(109)$

SEE EXAMPLE 4 p. 44

Reasoning Find a counterexample to show that each statement is false.

13. The natural numbers are closed under division.

14. The set of negative integers is closed under the operation of taking the absolute value.

PRACTICE AND PROBLEM SOLVING

Name the property that is illustrated in each equation.

15. $(3 + s) + t = (s + 3) + t$

16. $(5.2 + p) + 2q = 5.2 + (p + 2q)$

17. $(5x)y = 5(xy)$

18. $-2(a + b) = -2(b + a)$

19. $-16a = a(-16)$

20. $-4.1 + 3x = 3x + (-4.1)$

21. Find a counterexample to disprove the statement "The Associative Property is true for division."

Independent Practice

For Exercises	See Example
15–20	1
21	2
22–27	3
28–29	4

Extra Practice

Skills Practice p. EP3

Application Practice p. EP24

Write each product using the Distributive Property. Then simplify.

22. $9(62)$ **23.** $8(29)$ **24.** $11(25)$

25. $6(53)$ **26.** $12(999)$ **27.** $3(149)$

Reasoning **Find a counterexample to show that each statement is false.**

28. The set of odd numbers is closed under addition.

29. The terminating decimals are closed under division.

30. Estimation Tavon bought 5 spiral notebooks. The notebooks cost $1.97 each.

    a. Estimate the total amount that Tavon spent on the notebooks.

    b. Show how to use the Distributive Property to calculate the exact amount that Tavon spent.

31. Sports In a triathlon, athletes race in swimming, biking, and running events. The athlete with the least total time to complete the events is the winner.

Times from Triathlon			
Athlete	**Swim (min:s)**	**Bike (min:s)**	**Run (min:s)**
Amy	18:51	45:17	34:13
Julie	17:13	40:27	23:32
Mardi	19:09	38:58	25:32

    a. Use mental math and the properties in this lesson to find the total time for each athlete. (*Hint:* 1 minute = 60 seconds)

    b. Use the total times for the athletes to determine the order in which they finished the triathlon.

Name the property that is illustrated in each equation.

32. $(3m + 5p) + 12r = 3m + (5p + 12r)$ **33.** $3(2r - 7) = 3(2r) - 3(7)$

34. $y - 2 = -2 + y$ **35.** $45x - 35 = 5(9x - 7)$

36. Gardening A gardener is planting several rows of cauliflower and several rows of strawberries. There will be 6 plants per row.

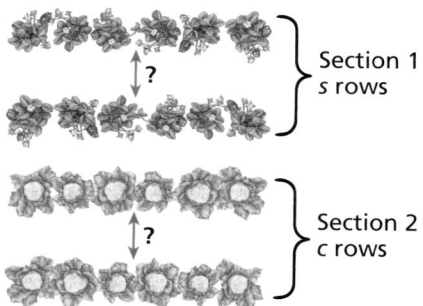

Section 1 — s rows

Section 2 — c rows

    a. There are s rows of strawberries and c rows of cauliflower. Write an expression that can be used to find the total number of plants.

    b. Write an equivalent expression using the Distributive Property.

    c. Find the total number of plants when there are 8 rows of strawberries and 9 rows of cauliflower.

CONCEPT CONNECTION

37. This problem will prepare you for the Concept Connection on page 56.

Jared is painting three rectangular walls in his apartment. The walls have widths of 12 feet, 14 feet, and 16 feet. The ceiling is 8 feet high.

    a. Find the total area of the walls by first calculating the area of each wall and then adding the areas together.

    b. Find the total area of the walls by first adding the widths of the walls and then multiplying this sum by the height.

    c. Use a property to explain why parts **a** and **b** give the same result.

38. Critical Thinking Explain why the integers are closed under addition. (*Hint: When written as a decimal, an integer has no digits to the right of the decimal point. What can you say about the sum of two such numbers?*)

39. Write About It Describe a real-world situation that can be represented by the Distributive Property. Translate your situation into an algebraic expression. Define each variable you use.

Multiple Choice For Exercises 40–42, choose the best answer.

40. Which equation is an example of the Distributive Property?

- Ⓐ $(25 + 18) + 33 = 25 + (18 + 33)$
- Ⓑ $33 + (25 \cdot 18) = (25 \cdot 18) + 33$
- Ⓒ $33 \cdot 25 + 33 \cdot 18 = 33 \cdot (25 + 18)$
- Ⓓ $3 + 25 \cdot 33 + 18 = 18 + 33 \cdot 25 + 3$

41. Which property is illustrated in the equation $(4 + x) + 15 = 4 + (x + 15)$?

- Ⓐ Associative Property
- Ⓑ Closure Property
- Ⓒ Commutative Property
- Ⓓ Distributive Property

42. Which pair of numbers can be used as a counterexample to disprove the statement "The integers are closed under division"?

- Ⓐ -2 and 2
- Ⓑ 3 and 3
- Ⓒ 5 and 7
- Ⓓ 6.5 and 8.2

CHALLENGE AND EXTEND

Explain whether each set is closed under the given operation.

43. $\{-1, 0, 1\}$; multiplication

44. $\{-1, 0, 1\}$; addition

45. $\{-2, 0, 2\}$; multiplication

46. $\{0, 3, 6, 9, 12, 15...\}$; multiplication

Consider a new operation on the real numbers, $\odot$, that is defined as follows: For real numbers a and b, $a \odot b = ab + 1$. For example, $4 \odot 7 = 4 \cdot 7 + 1 = 28 + 1 = 29$.

47. Find $-3 \odot 2$ and $5 \odot 12$.

48. Is the Commutative Property true for the operation $\odot$? Explain why or why not.

49. Are the real numbers closed under the operation $\odot$? Explain why or why not.

50. Find a counterexample to show that the Associative Property is not true for the operation $\odot$. (*Hint: Find three numbers, a, b, and c, for which $a \odot (b \odot c) \neq (a \odot b) \odot c$.*)

Evaluate each expression for the replacement set $\{3, 5, 6\}$. (*Lesson 1-1*)

51. $4 - r$ **52.** $2 \div r$ **53.** $9r$ **54.** $r + 8$

Write the power represented by each geometric model. (*Lesson 1-4*)

55. 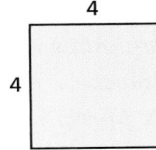   **56.** 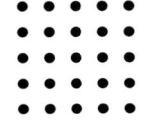   **57.**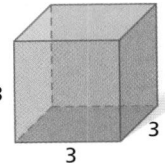

Find each root. (*Lesson 1-5*)

58. $\sqrt{400}$ **59.** $-\sqrt{81}$ **60.** $\sqrt[3]{8}$ **61.** $\sqrt[4]{\dfrac{16}{81}}$

1-7 Simplifying Expressions

 **California Standards**

1.1 Students use properties of numbers to demonstrate whether assertions are true or false.
25.1 Students use properties of numbers to construct simple, valid arguments (direct and indirect) for, or formulate counterexamples to, claimed assertions.

Vocabulary
order of operations
terms
like terms
coefficient

Who uses this?
Sports statisticians can simplify expressions to calculate data. (See Example 2.)

When an expression contains more than one operation, the **order of operations** tells you which operation to perform first.

Order of Operations	
First:	Perform operations inside grouping symbols.
Second:	Evaluate powers.
Third:	Perform multiplication and division from left to right.
Fourth:	Perform addition and subtraction from left to right.

Grouping symbols include parentheses $(\ )$, brackets $[\ ]$, and braces $\{\ \}$. If an expression contains more than one set of grouping symbols, begin with the innermost set. Follow the order of operations within that set of grouping symbols and then work outward.

EXAMPLE **1** **Simplifying Numerical Expressions**

Simplify each expression.

A $-4^2 + 24 \div 3 \cdot 2$

$-4^2 + 24 \div 3 \cdot 2$	*There are no grouping symbols.*
$-16 + 24 \div 3 \cdot 2$	*Evaluate powers. The exponent applies only to the 4.*
$-16 + 8 \cdot 2$	*Divide.*
$-16 + 16$	*Multiply.*
0	*Add.*

B $|10 - 5^2| \div 5$

$|10 - 5^2| \div 5$	*The absolute-value symbols are grouping symbols.*
$|10 - 25| \div 5$	*Evaluate the power.*
$|-15| \div 5$	*Subtract within the absolute-value symbols.*
$15 \div 5$	*Write the absolute value of −15.*
3	*Divide.*

Helpful Hint

Fraction bars, radical symbols, and absolute-value symbols can also be used as grouping symbols. Remember that a fraction bar indicates division.

C $3[2(3 + 4)] - 1$

$3[2(3 + 4)] - 1$	*There are two sets of grouping symbols.*
$3[2(7)] - 1$	*Add within the innermost parentheses.*
$3[14] - 1$	*Multiply within the brackets.*
$42 - 1$	*There are no powers. Multiply.*
41	*Subtract.*

 **Simplify each expression.**

1a. $8 \div \dfrac{1}{2} \cdot 3$ **1b.** $3\sqrt{50 - 1}$ **1c.** $\dfrac{(5 + 2)(-8)}{(-2)^3 - 3}$

EXAMPLE 2 | **Sports Application**

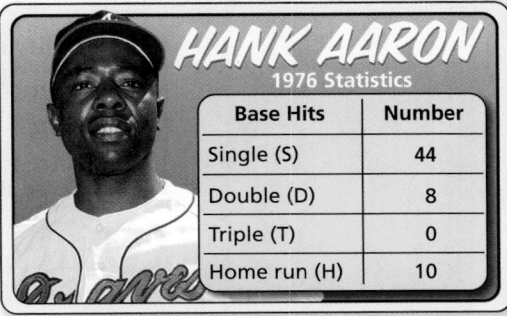

Hank Aaron's last season in the Major League was in 1976. A player's total number of bases can be found using the expression $S + 2D + 3T + 4H$. Use the table to find Hank Aaron's total bases for 1976.

$$S + 2D + 3T + 4H$$
$$44 + 2(8) + 3(0) + 4(10) \qquad \textit{First substitute values for each variable.}$$
$$44 + 16 + 0 + 40 \qquad \textit{Multiply.}$$
$$60 + 0 + 40 \qquad \textit{Add from left to right.}$$
$$100 \qquad \textit{Add.}$$

Hank Aaron's total number of bases for 1976 was 100.

CHECK IT OUT! 2. Another formula for a player's total number of bases is $\text{Hits} + D + 2T + 3H$. Use this expression to find Hank Aaron's total bases for 1959, when he had 223 hits, 46 doubles, 7 triples, and 39 home runs.

The **terms** of an expression are the parts that are added or subtracted. **Like terms** contain the same variables raised to the same powers. Constants are also like terms.

A **coefficient** is a number multiplied by a variable. Like terms may have different coefficients. A variable written without a coefficient has a coefficient of 1.

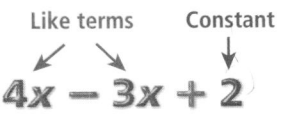

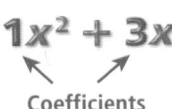

Like terms can be combined. To combine like terms, use the Distributive Property.

Distributive Property	Example
$ax - bx = (a - b)x$	$7x - 4x = (7 - 4)x$
	$= 3x$

Notice that you can combine like terms by adding or subtracting the coefficients. Keep the variables and exponents the same.

EXAMPLE 3 | **Combining Like Terms**

Simplify each expression by combining like terms.

A $12x + 30x$
$$12x + 30x \qquad \textit{12x and 30x are like terms.}$$
$$42x \qquad \textit{Add the coefficients.}$$

B $6.8y^2 - y^2 + 4y$
$$6.8y^2 - y^2 + 4y \qquad \textit{6.8y}^2 \textit{ and y}^2 \textit{ are like terms.}$$
$$6.8y^2 - 1y^2 + 4y \qquad \textit{A variable without a coefficient has a coefficient of 1.}$$
$$5.8y^2 + 4y \qquad \textit{Subtract the coefficients of the like terms.}$$

Caution!

Add or subtract only the coefficients.
$6.8y^2 - y^2 \neq 6.8$

Simplify each expression by combining like terms.

C $4n + 11n^2$

$4n + 11n^2$ *4n and 11n² are not like terms.*

$4n + 11n^2$ *Do not combine the terms.*

 CHECK IT OUT! Simplify each expression by combining like terms.

3a. $16p + 84p$ **3b.** $-20t - 8.5t$ **3c.** $3m^2 + m^3 - m^2$

EXAMPLE 4 Simplifying Algebraic Expressions

 Reasoning

Use properties and operations to show that the first expression simplifies to the second expression.

A $2(x + 6) + 3x, 5x + 12$

	Statements	Reasons
1.	$2(x + 6) + 3x$	
2.	$[2x + 2(6)] + 3x$	Distributive Property
3.	$(2x + 12) + 3x$	Multiply.
4.	$3x + (2x + 12)$	Commutative Property of Addition
5.	$(3x + 2x) + 12$	Associative Property of Addition
6.	$5x + 12$	Combine like terms.

B $4x + 2 - 3x + 4, x + 6$

	Statements	Reasons
1.	$4x + 2 - 3x + 4$	
2.	$4x - 3x + 2 + 4$	Commutative Property of Addition
3.	$(4x - 3x) + (2 + 4)$	Associative Property of Addition
4.	$x + 6$	Combine like terms.

 CHECK IT OUT! **4.** Use properties and operations to show that $6(x - 4) + 9$ simplifies to $6x - 15$.

THINK AND DISCUSS

1. Explain whether you always perform addition before subtraction when simplifying a numerical or algebraic expression.

2. Identify the coefficient for the term r^8. Then give a like term and an unlike term.

 **3.** **GET ORGANIZED** Copy and complete the graphic organizer. In each box, give an example of an expression that can be simplified using the given method. Then simplify your expressions.

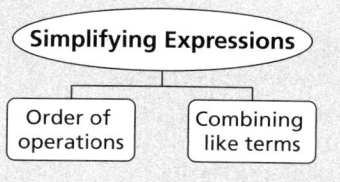

1-7
Exercises

California Standards Practice
1.1, 25.1, 25.2

go.hrw.com
Homework Help Online
KEYWORD: MA8CA 1-7
Parent Resources Online
KEYWORD: MA8CA Parent

GUIDED PRACTICE

1. **Vocabulary** Explain why the *order of operations* is necessary for simplifying numerical expressions.

SEE EXAMPLE 1
p. 48

Simplify each expression.

2. $5 - [12 \div (-2)]$

3. $30 - 5 \cdot 3$

4. $50 - 6 + 8$

5. $\dfrac{0 - 24}{6 \div 2}$

6. $\dfrac{2 + 3(6)}{2^2}$

7. $-44 \div \sqrt{12 \div 3}$

SEE EXAMPLE 2
p. 49

8. **Geometry** The surface area of a cylinder can be found using the expression $2\pi r(h + r)$. Find the surface area of the cylinder shown. Use 3.14 for π and give your final answer to the nearest tenth.

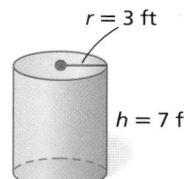
$r = 3$ ft
$h = 7$ ft

SEE EXAMPLE 3
p. 49

Simplify each expression by combining like terms.

9. $6x + 10x$

10. $35x - 15x$

11. $-3a + 9a$

12. $-8r - r$

13. $17x^2 + x + 3x^2$

14. $3.2x + 4.7x$

SEE EXAMPLE 4
p. 50

Reasoning Use properties and operations to show that the first expression simplifies to the second expression.

15. $5(x + 3) - 7x, \ 15 - 2x$

16. $9(a - 3) - 4, \ 9a - 31$

17. $6x - x - 3x^2 + 2x, \ 7x - 3x^2$

18. $12x + 8x + t - 7x, \ 13x + t$

PRACTICE AND PROBLEM SOLVING

Independent Practice

For Exercises	See Example
19–27	1
28	2
29–36	3
37–40	4

Extra Practice
Skills Practice p. EP3
Application Practice p. EP24

Simplify each expression.

19. $3 + 4(-5)$

20. $20 - 4 + 5 - 2$

21. $41 + 12 \div 2$

22. $3[(-9) + (-2)(-6)]$

23. $10^2 \div (10 - 20)$

24. $(6 + 2 \cdot 3) \div (9 - 7)^2$

25. $-4|2.5 - 6|$

26. $\dfrac{8 - 8}{2 - 1}$

27. $\sqrt{3^2 - 5} \div 8$

28. **Geometry** The perimeter of a rectangle can be found using the expression $2(\ell + w)$. Find the perimeter of the rectangle shown.

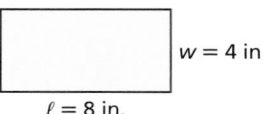
$w = 4$ in.
$\ell = 8$ in.

Simplify each expression by combining like terms.

29. $3x + 9x$

30. $14x^2 - 5x^2$

31. $-7x + 8x$

32. $3x^2 - 4$

33. $5x^2 - 2x + 3x^2$

34. $3x + 2 - 2x - 1$

35. $7y - 3 + 6y - 7$

36. $4a - 2a + 2$

Reasoning Use properties and operations to show that the first expression simplifies to the second expression.

37. $4(y + 6) + 9, \ 4y + 33$

38. $-7(x + 2) + 4x, \ -3x - 14$

39. $5x - 3x + 3x^2 + 9x, \ 11x + 3x^2$

40. $8x + 2x - 3y - 9x, \ x - 3y$

41. Simplify each expression.

    a. $50 + 10 \div 2$ **b.** $50 \cdot 10 - 2$ **c.** $50 \cdot 10 \div 2$

    d. $50 \div 10 \cdot 2$ **e.** $50 - 10 \cdot 2$ **f.** $50 + 10 \cdot 2$

Evaluate each expression for the given value of the variable.

42. $5 + 2x - 9$ for $x = 4$ **43.** $30 \div 2 - d$ for $d = 14$ **44.** $51 - 91 + g$ for $g = 20$

45. $2(3 + n)$ for $n = 4$ **46.** $4(b - 4)^2$ for $b = 5$ **47.** $12 + \left[20(5 - k)\right]$ for $k = 1$

Geometry Give an expression in simplified form for the perimeter of each figure.

48.
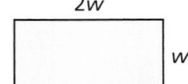
2w / w

49.

4p / 8 − p / 3p + 1

50.
2s + 3 / 2s + 3

51. Sports At the 2004 Summer Olympics, U.S. gymnast Paul Hamm received the scores shown in the table during the individual all-around competition.

2004 Summer Olympics Individual Scores for Paul Hamm						
Event	Floor	Pommel horse	Rings	Vault	Parallel bars	Horizontal bar
Score	9.725	9.700	9.587	9.137	9.837	9.837

    a. Write a numerical expression to show the average of Hamm's scores.

        (*Hint:* The average of a set of values is the sum of the values divided by the number of values in the set.)

    b. Simplify the expression to find Hamm's average score.

52. Critical Thinking Are parentheses required when translating the word phrase "the sum of 8 and the product of 3 and 2" into a numerical phrase? Explain.

53. Write About It Many everyday processes must be done in a certain order to be completed successfully. Describe a process that requires several steps and tell why the steps must be followed in a certain order.

54. /// ERROR ANALYSIS /// Which simplification is incorrect? Explain the error.

Ⓐ
$$24 + 6(x - 2)$$
$$24 + 6x - 2$$
$$22 + 6x$$

Ⓑ
$$24 + 6(x - 2)$$
$$24 + 6x - 12$$
$$6x + 12$$

CONCEPT CONNECTION

55. This problem will help prepare you for the Concept Connection on page 56.

    a. The diagram shows a pattern of shapes that can be folded to make a cylinder. How is the length ℓ of the rectangle related to the circumference of (distance around) each circle?

    b. An expression for the area of each circle is πr^2. Write an expression for the area of the rectangle.

    c. Use these expressions to write an expression for the total area of the figures. Leave the symbol π in your expression.

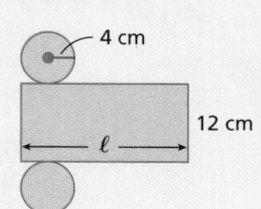

4 cm

12 cm

ℓ

Multiple Choice For Exercises 56–58, choose the best answer.

56. Ariel has 19 more CDs than her sister Tiffany has. Victor has 3 times as many CDs as Ariel has. Tiffany has x CDs. Which expression can be used to show how many CDs the three have in total?

    (A) $19 + 3x$ (B) $51 + 3x$ (C) $76 + 3x$ (D) $76 + 5x$

57. Which expression can be used to represent the perimeter of the rectangle?

    (A) $16k$ (C) $3k + 13$

    (B) $32k$ (D) $6k + 26$

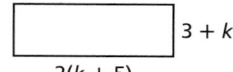
$3 + k$
$2(k + 5)$

58. The perimeter of the Norman window shown is approximated by the expression $2(3 + 8) + 3.14(3)$. Which is the closest approximation of the perimeter of the window?

    (A) 23.4 ft   (C) 31.4 ft

    (B) 28.4 ft   (D) 51.4 ft

59. Gridded Response Evaluate $\sqrt{\dfrac{54 - (-2)(5)}{20 - 4^2}}$.

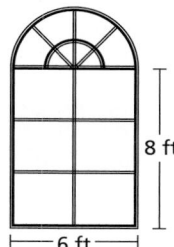
8 ft
6 ft

CHALLENGE AND EXTEND

Simplify each expression.

60. $\dfrac{3 + 9 \cdot 2}{2 - 3^2}$ **61.** $\left[(-6 \cdot 4) \div |-6 \cdot 4|\right]^2$ **62.** $\sqrt{\dfrac{8 + 10^2}{13 + (-10)}}$

63. $4[3(x + 9) + 2]$ **64.** $-[3(x - 2) + 5(x - 2)]$

65. $(2b + 5) - (8b + 6) + 3(b - 2)$ **66.** $\dfrac{1}{2}[(10 - g) + (-6 + 3g)]$

67. Use the numbers 2, 4, 5, and 8 to write an expression that has a value of 5. You may use any operations, and you must use each of the numbers at least once.

68. Use the numbers 2, 5, 6, and 9 to write an expression that has a value of 1. You may use any operations, and you must use each of the numbers at least once.

 69. Reasoning Fill in the missing reasons to show that $\dfrac{a + b}{c} = \dfrac{a}{c} + \dfrac{b}{c}$.

Statements	Reasons
1. $\dfrac{a + b}{c} = \dfrac{1}{c}(a + b)$	Definition of division
2. $= \dfrac{1}{c}(a) + \dfrac{1}{c}(b)$	a. _____?_____
3. $= \dfrac{a}{c} + \dfrac{b}{c}$	b. _____?_____

 SPIRAL STANDARDS REVIEW   🔑 7NS1.2, 🔑 2.0

Add or subtract. *(Lesson 1-2)*

70. $51 - (-49)$ **71.** $-5 + \left(-1\dfrac{1}{3}\right)$ **72.** $-3 + (-8)$ **73.** $2.9 - 5.3$

Evaluate each expression. *(Lesson 1-4)*

74. 2^6 **75.** 18^2 **76.** $-\left(\dfrac{1}{2}\right)^3$ **77.** $\left(-\dfrac{1}{2}\right)^2$

Find each root. *(Lesson 1-5)*

78. $\sqrt[3]{64}$ **79.** $\sqrt{324}$ **80.** $\sqrt{\dfrac{36}{49}}$ **81.** $-\sqrt{121}$

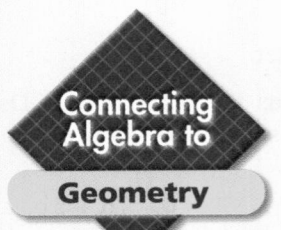

Perimeter

The distance around a geometric figure is called the *perimeter*. You can use what you have learned about combining like terms to simplify expressions for perimeter.

A closed figure with straight sides is called a *polygon*. To find the perimeter of a polygon, add the lengths of the sides.

California Standards

Reinforcement of 7MG2.0 **Students compute the perimeter,** area, and volume **of common geometric objects** and use the results to find measures of less common objects. **They know how perimeter,** area, and volume **are affected by changes of scale.**

Example 1

A Write an expression for the perimeter of the quadrilateral.

Add the lengths of the four sides.

$$P = (a + 3) + (2a - 8) + (3a - 3) + (a - 1)$$

Combine like terms to simplify.

$$P = (a + 2a + 3a + a) + (3 - 8 - 3 - 1)$$

$$= 7a - 9 \qquad \textit{This is a general expression for the perimeter.}$$

B Find the perimeter of this quadrilateral for $a = 5$.

Substitute 5 for a.

$$P = 7(5) - 9 \qquad \textit{Multiply; then subtract.}$$

$$= 35 - 9$$

$$= 26 \qquad \textit{This is the perimeter when } a = 5.$$

Try This

Write and simplify an expression for the perimeter of each figure.

1.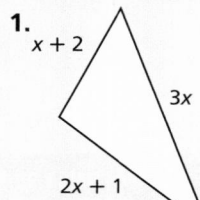

2.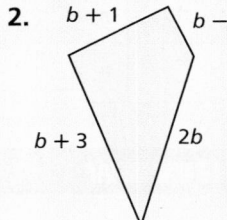

3.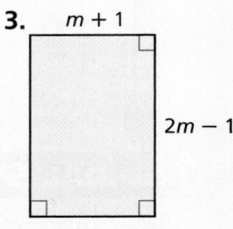

Find the perimeter of each figure for the given value of the variable.

4. $k = 3$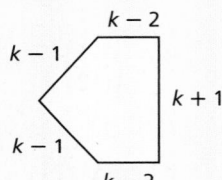

5. $n = 10$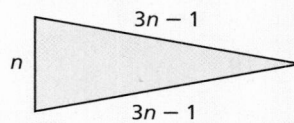

6. $y = 4$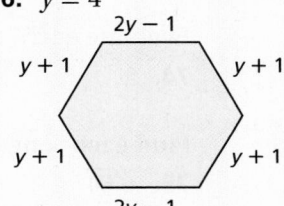

Combining like terms is one way to explore what happens to the perimeter
when you double the sides of a triangle or other polygon.

Example 2

What happens to the perimeter of this triangle when you double the length of each side?

Write an expression for the perimeter of the smaller triangle.
Combine like terms to simplify the expression.

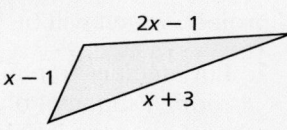

$(x - 1) + (2x - 1) + (x + 3)$

$(x + 2x + x) + (-1 - 1 + 3)$

$4x + 1$ *Perimeter of small triangle*

Double the length of each side of the triangle.

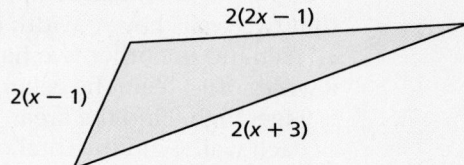

$2(x - 1) = 2x - 2$

$2(2x - 1) = 4x - 2$

$2(x + 3) = 2x + 6$

Find the perimeter of the larger triangle.
Combine like terms to simplify.

$(2x - 2) + (4x - 2) + (2x + 6)$ *Add the lengths of the sides.*

$(2x + 4x + 2x) + (-2 - 2 + 6)$ *Use the Associative Property and combine like terms.*

$8x + 2$ *Perimeter of large triangle*

Use the Distributive Property to show that the new perimeter is
twice the original perimeter.

$8x + 2 = 2(4x + 1)$

Try This

Each set of expressions represents the side lengths of a triangle. Use the Distributive Property to show that doubling the side lengths doubles the perimeter.

7. $2p + 1$	**8.** $c - 1$	**9.** $w + 5$	**10.** $h - 2$
$3p + 2$	$2c + 1$	$w + 5$	$3h$
$5p$	$3c - 1$	$3w - 1$	$2h + 3$

Solve each problem.

11. Use the triangles in Example 2. Find the side lengths and perimeters for $x = 5$.

12. The sides of a quadrilateral are $2x - 1$, $x + 3$, $3x + 1$, and $x - 1$. Double the length of each side. Then find an expression for the perimeter of the new figure.

13. What happens to the perimeter of this trapezoid when you triple the length of each side? Use the variables a, b, b, and c for the lengths of the sides. Explain your answer using the Distributive Property.

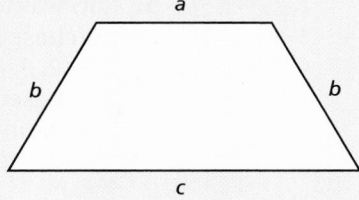

CONCEPT CONNECTION

The Tools of Algebra

Design Time Lori's family and Marie's family are redecorating a room in each other's home. They have three days for the decorating project, which will be filmed for a local TV show.

1. Lori decides to paint Marie's room a shade of blue. She measures the height and width of each wall in the rectangular room. She finds that two walls have a width of 12 feet and the other two have a width of 14 feet. The ceiling is 9 feet high. Find the area of each wall. Find the total area of all four walls plus the ceiling.

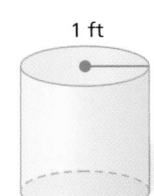

2. One gallon of paint covers 400 square feet. How many gallons are needed if Lori wants to apply 2 coats of paint to all the walls and the ceiling?

3. Lori decided to build a bedside table in the shape of a cylinder and cover it with yellow fabric on the top and the side. The fabric costs $2.50 per square yard. The table has a radius of 1 foot and a height of 2 feet. What is the cost to cover the table? Use 3.14 for π.

1 ft

2 ft

4. Lori will fill a vase with multicolored beads and place it on the bedside table. The vase is in the approximate shape of a cone. The height of the vase is 10 inches, and the radius of the vase at the top is 3 inches. Find the volume of the vase. Use 3.14 for π. (*Hint:* The formula for the volume of a cone is $V = \frac{1}{3}\pi r^2 h$, where r is the radius of the cone and h is the height of the cone.)

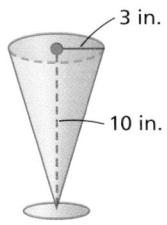

3 in.

10 in.

5. Lori wants to create a border around the room using stickers. She can purchase a package of 5 stickers for $6.00. Make a table to show the cost of 1, 2, 3, 4, and 5 packages of stickers. Make another table to show the cost based on the number of stickers (not the number of packages). How many stickers can Lori purchase if she has $32 left in her budget?

Quiz for Lessons 1-6 and 1-7

☑ 1-6 Properties of Real Numbers

Name the property that is illustrated in each equation.

1. $11 + (3 + 4) = (11 + 3) + 4$

2. $12 \cdot 26 = 26 \cdot 12$

3. $6 + 8 + 2 = 6 + 2 + 8$

4. $ar + 25 = 25 + ar$

5. $a(bc) + 2 = 2 + a(bc)$

6. $5 + (pq)t = 5 + p(qt)$

7. Find a counterexample to disprove the statement "The Associative Property is true for subtraction."

Write each product using the Distributive Property. Then simplify.

8. $4(29)$

9. $3(204)$

10. $5(37)$

11. $6(28)$

12. $7(85)$

13. $8(32)$

Find a counterexample to show that each statement is false.

14. The set of negative numbers is closed under division.

15. The real numbers are closed under the operation of taking a square root.

16. The set of negative numbers is closed under subtraction.

☑ 1-7 Simplifying Expressions

Simplify each expression.

17. $75 + 32 + 25$

18. $5 \cdot 18 \cdot 20$

19. $\frac{1}{4} \cdot 19 \cdot 8$

20. $2(3 + 5)^2$

21. $6 \div 2 + 2^2$

22. $2(3)(2 + 1)$

23. $4k + 15k$

24. $x^2 + 22x^2$

25. $-2g + 5g$

26. $5j + 12j$

27. $16c - 4c$

28. $17p^3 + 15p^3$

29. $2(5y + 2x) + 3(2y)$

30. $3x + 6y + 2x$

31. $12x^4 - 3x^2 + 5x^2$

Use properties and operations to show that the first expression simplifies to the second expression.

32. $3(x + 2) - 3x, 6$

33. $x - 6x^2 + 3x + 4x^2, 4x - 2x^2$

34. $-2(3x + 2y + 4x - 5y), -14x + 6y$

Vocabulary

Complete the sentences below with vocabulary words from the list above.

1. A(n) ___?___ is a value that does not change.

2. The ___?___ include the natural numbers and zero.

3. A(n) ___?___ is the numerical factor of a term that contains a variable.

4. A ___?___ is a part of an expression to be added or subtracted.

1-1 Variables and Expressions (pp. 6–11)

 **Prep for ← 4.0**

EXAMPLES

■ Barbara has saved d dollars for a $65 sweater. Write an expression for the amount of money she still needs to buy the sweater.

$65 - d$ *Think: d dollars less than the price of the sweater.*

■ Evaluate $b - 7$ for the replacement set $\{-1, 3, 15\}$.

$b - 7 = -1 - 7$ *Substitute the values for*
$\quad = -8$ *the variables.*
$b - 7 = 3 - 7$
$\quad = -4$
$b - 7 = 15 - 7$
$\quad = 8$

EXERCISES

5. Grapes cost $1.99 per pound. Write an expression for the cost of g pounds of grapes.

6. Today's temperature is 3 degrees warmer than yesterday's temperature t. Write an expression for today's temperature.

Evaluate each expression for the replacement set $\{-5, 0, 5\}$.

7. $p(1)$ **8.** $p \div 1$ **9.** $p + 1$

10. Each member of the art club will make the same number of posters to advertise their club. They will make 150 posters total. Write an expression for how many posters each member will make if there are m members. Find how many posters each member will make if there are 5, 6, and 10 members.

1-2 Adding and Subtracting Real Numbers (pp. 14–19)

 2.0

EXAMPLES

Add or subtract.

■ $-4 + (-9)$

$\quad -4 + (-9)$ *The signs are the same.*

$\quad 4 + 9 = 13$ *Add the absolute values and use*

$\quad -13$ *the sign of the numbers.*

■ $-8 - (-3)$

$\quad -8 - (-3)$

$\quad -8 + 3$ *To subtract −3, add 3.*

$\quad -5$

EXERCISES

Add or subtract.

11. $-2 + (-12)$ **12.** $-6 + 1.4$ **13.** $9\frac{1}{4} + \left(-4\frac{3}{4}\right)$

14. $\frac{1}{2} - \frac{3}{2}$ **15.** $-8 - 16$ **16.** $6.7 - (-7.6)$

17. $3\frac{1}{3} - \left(-1\frac{2}{3}\right)$

18. A trail starts at an elevation of 2278 feet. It descends 47 feet to a campsite. What is the elevation of the campsite?

1-3 Multiplying and Dividing Real Numbers (pp. 20–25)

 2.0

EXAMPLES

Multiply or divide.

■ $-12(9)$

$\quad -12(9) = -108$ *The signs are different.*

$\quad$ *The product is negative.*

■ $-\frac{5}{6} \div \left(-\frac{3}{4}\right)$

$\quad -\frac{5}{6} \div \left(-\frac{3}{4}\right) = -\frac{5}{6}\left(-\frac{4}{3}\right)$ *To divide by $-\frac{3}{4}$,*

$\quad\quad\quad\quad\quad\quad\quad\quad$ *multiply by $-\frac{4}{3}$.*

$\quad\quad = \frac{(-5)(-4)}{6(3)}$ *Multiply numerators and denominators.*

$\quad\quad = \frac{20}{18} = \frac{10}{9}$ *Simplify.*

EXERCISES

Multiply or divide if possible.

19. $-5(-18)$ **20.** $0 \cdot 10$ **21.** $-4(3.8)$

22. $-56 \div 7$ **23.** $0 \div 0.75$ **24.** $9 \div 0$

Divide.

25. $4 \div \frac{4}{9}$ **26.** $-\frac{1}{2} \div \frac{3}{4}$ **27.** $\frac{6}{7} \div \frac{2}{5}$

28. An exercise program recommends that a person walk at least 10,000 steps every day. At this rate, how many steps would the person walk in 1 year?

1-4 Powers and Exponents (pp. 26–31)

 Prep for 2.0

EXAMPLES

■ **Simplify** -3^4.

$\quad -3^4 = -1 \cdot 3 \cdot 3 \cdot 3 \cdot 3$ *Find the product of −1*

$\quad\quad = -81$ *and four 3's.*

EXERCISES

Write each expression as repeated multiplication. Then simplify the expression.

29. 4^3 **30.** $(-3)^3$ **31.** $(-3)^4$

32. -5^2 **33.** $\left(\frac{2}{3}\right)^3$ **34.** $\left(-\frac{4}{5}\right)^2$

■ Write −216 as a power of −6.
$$-216 = (-6)(-6)(-6)$$ *The product of three*
$$= (-6)^3$$ *−6's is −216.*

Write each number as a power of the given base.

35. 16; base 2 **36.** −1000; base −10

37. 64; base −8 **38.** 12; base 12

39. The interior of a safe is shaped like a cube with edges 9 inches long. What is the volume of the interior of the safe?

1-5 Roots and Irrational Numbers *(pp. 32–37)*

EXAMPLES

Find each root.

■ $-\sqrt{64}$

$$-\sqrt{64} = -\sqrt{8^2}$$
$$= -8$$

■ $\sqrt{\dfrac{16}{81}}$

$$\sqrt{\frac{16}{81}} = \sqrt{\left(\frac{4}{9}\right)^2}$$
$$= \frac{4}{9}$$

■ Classify −7. Write all classifications that apply.

$$-7 = \frac{-7}{1} = -7.0$$

rational

terminating decimal

integer

EXERCISES

Find each root.

40. $\sqrt{36}$ **41.** $\sqrt{196}$ **42.** $-\sqrt{169}$

43. $-\sqrt{144}$ **44.** $\sqrt{\dfrac{25}{36}}$ **45.** $\sqrt[3]{\dfrac{1}{27}}$

46. $\sqrt[3]{64}$ **47.** $\sqrt{\dfrac{81}{121}}$ **48.** $\sqrt[4]{81}$

Write all classifications that apply to each real number.

49. 21 **50.** 0 **51.** −13

52. 0.8 **53.** $\sqrt{3}$ **54.** $\dfrac{5}{6}$

55. $\sqrt{9}$ **56.** 1.61 **57.** −4.5

58. A tabletop is shaped like a square with an area of 13 square feet. Find the length of one side of the table to the nearest tenth of a foot.

59. Bobbie's new square rug covers an area of 17 square feet. Estimate the side length of the rug to the nearest tenth.

1-6 Properties of Real Numbers *(pp. 42–47)*

 1.0, 24.3, 25.1

EXAMPLES

Name the property that is illustrated in each equation.

■ $(x + 12x) + 4x = x + (12x + 4x)$
The grouping is different.
Associative Property of Addition

■ $x \cdot 7 = 7 \cdot x$
The order is different.
Commutative Property of Multiplication

EXERCISES

Name the property that is illustrated in each equation.

60. $(5 + 2) + 3 = 5 + (2 + 3)$

61. $w(xy) = (wx)y$

62. $(5x + 8) + 6 = (8 + 5x) + 6$

63. $7(3x + 1) = (3x + 1)7$

64. Find a counterexample to disprove the statement "The Commutative Property is true for division."

Write each product using the Distributive Property. Then simplify.

■ 5(25)

$$5(25) = 5(20 + 5) \qquad \textit{Rewrite 25 as 20 + 5.}$$
$$= 5(20) + 5(5) \qquad \textit{Use the Distributive Property.}$$
$$= 100 + 25 \qquad \textit{Mulitply.}$$
$$= 125 \qquad \textit{Add.}$$

Write each product using the Distributive Property. Then simplify.

65. $3(27)$ **66.** $6(12)$

67. $8(17)$ **68.** $7(22)$

69. Find a counterexample to disprove the statement "The irrational numbers are closed under multiplication."

1-7 Simplifying Expressions (pp. 48–53)

 1.1, 25.1

EXAMPLES

Simplify each expression.

■ $-6f^2 - 8f + 3f^2$

$-6f^2 + 3f^2 - 8f$	*Commutative Property*
$-3f^2 - 8f$	*Combine like terms.*

■ $3x - 4y$

$3x - 4y$	*There are no like terms. It cannot be simplified.*

■ $5x^2 - 3(x - 2) - x$

$5x^2 - 3x - 3(-2) - x$	*Distributive Property*
$5x^2 - 3x + 6 - x$	*Multiply.*
$5x^2 - 3x - x + 6$	*Commutative Property*
$5x^2 - 4x + 6$	*Combine like terms.*

■ Use properties and operations to show that $4(x + 2) + 5$ simplifies to $4x + 13$.

Statements	Reasons
1. 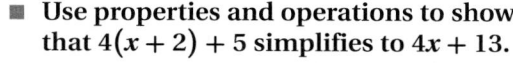 $4(x + 2) + 5$	
2. $[4x + 4(2)] + 5$	Distributive Property
3. $(4x + 8) + 5$	Multiply.
4. $4x + (8 + 5)$	Associative Property of Addition
5. $4x + 13$	Combine like terms.

EXERCISES

Simplify each expression.

70. $18 + 26 - 8 + 4$ **71.** $60 \cdot 27 \cdot \dfrac{1}{6}$

72. $2^2 + 12 \cdot 3 - 9$ **73.** $3 \cdot 5 - 14 + \sqrt{4}$

74. $\dfrac{1}{2} + 5 \cdot 4 + 15$ **75.** $\left[\dfrac{(6 \cdot 7)}{4 - 1}\right] 2 + 12$

76. The cost in dollars of magazine subscriptions at a particular company can be found by using the expression $\dfrac{1}{2}(m - 1) + 4$, where m equals the number of subscriptions. Use the expression to find the price of 5 subscriptions.

Simplify each expression.

77. $20x - 16x$ **78.** $2y^2 + 5y^2$

79. $6(x + 4) - 2x$ **80.** $-2(x^2 - 1) + 4x^2$

81. $-2y + 3y^2 - 3y + y$ **82.** $7y + 3y - a - 2y$

83. Rita bought a sandwich, 2 bottles of water, and an apple for lunch. The sandwich cost $4.99, the bottles of water cost $1.48 each, and the apple cost $0.89. How much did Rita spend on lunch?

Use properties and operations to show that the first expression simplifies to the second expression.

84. $2(x + 5) - 3, 2x + 7$

85. $(5 + y - 3) + 4y, 5y + 2$

CHAPTER TEST

Evaluate each expression for the replacement set {2, 3, 6}.

1. $6 - a$ **2.** $a(3)$ **3.** $6 \div a$ **4.** $\dfrac{a}{6}$ **5.** $a - 3$

6. Write two verbal expressions for $n - 5$.

7. Nate runs 8 miles each week. Write an expression for the number of miles he runs in n weeks. Find the number of miles Nate runs in 5 weeks.

Add or subtract.

8. $-5 + 8$ **9.** $-3 - 4$ **10.** $4 + (-7)$ **11.** $7 - (-2)$

The table shows the lowest temperatures recorded in four states.

12. What is the difference between the lowest temperatures in Hawaii and Alaska?

13. What is the difference between the lowest temperatures in Texas and Nebraska?

Lowest Temperatures in Four States	
Location	Temperature (°F)
Prospect Creek, Alaska	−80
Camp Clarke, Nebraska	−47
Mauna Kea, Hawaii	12
Seminole, Texas	−23

Multiply or divide if possible.

14. $(-3)(-6)$ **15.** $-\dfrac{1}{2} \div \dfrac{1}{4}$ **16.** $12 \div (-3)$ **17.** $0 \div (-4)$

Simplify each expression.

18. 5^4 **19.** $\left(-\dfrac{4}{5}\right)^3$ **20.** $\sqrt{25}$ **21.** $-\sqrt{36}$

Write all classifications that apply to each real number.

22. 30   **23.** $\sqrt{6}$ **24.** -12 **25.** $\dfrac{1}{2}$

Name the property that is illustrated in each equation.

26. $7 \cdot 13 = 13 \cdot 7$ **27.** $(1 + 32) + 6 = 1 + (32 + 6)$

28. $(qs)r = (sq)r$ **29.** $4 + (24 + 3) = 4 + (3 + 24)$

Simplify each expression.

30. $5\dfrac{1}{4} + 7 + 2\dfrac{3}{4}$ **31.** $-2(x + 5) + 4x$ **32.** $3x + 2x^2 - x$

33. $\dfrac{1}{2}y + \dfrac{3}{4}y$ **34.** $t^2 + 5t + 3t + 2t^2$ **35.** $5k - 4k + 6$

36. Find a counterexample to disprove the statement "The rational numbers are closed under the operation of taking the square root."

Use properties and operations to show that the first expression simplifies to the second expression.

37. $5(x + 4) - 10, \; 5x + 10$ **38.** $(x - 2 + 6x) + x, \; 8x - 2$

COLLEGE ENTRANCE EXAM PRACTICE

FOCUS ON SAT

The SAT is a 3-hour test that is often used to predict academic success at the college level. SAT scores are used to compare the math and verbal reasoning skills of students from all over the world.

You may want to time yourself as you take this practice test. It should take you about 8 minutes to complete.

In each section of SAT questions, the easier questions are at the beginning of the section and harder questions come later. Answer as many of the easy questions as you can first, and then move on to the more challenging questions.

---

1. The number 0 is NOT an example of which of the following?

(A) Real numbers

(B) Rational numbers

(C) Whole numbers

(D) Integers

(E) Natural numbers

---

2. A clothing store opens with 75 pairs of jeans on a sale table. By noon, 10 pairs have been sold. As of 2:00, another 8 pairs have been sold. A clerk then restocks with 12 pairs. Receipts show that 18 pairs of jeans were sold after 2:00. How many pairs of jeans are left at the end of the day?

(A) 51

(B) 27

(C) 123

(D) 36

(E) 23

---

3. If Jack is three times as old as his sister Judy, which of the following expressions represents Jack's age if Judy is j years old?

(A) $3j > j$

(B) $3j$

(C) $j + 3$

(D) $3 - j$

(E) $\frac{1}{3}j$

---

4. Which of the following is equal to -3^4?

(A) -64

(B) 12

(C) -12

(D) 81

(E) -81

---

5. What is the result after applying the following sequence of operations to a number n in the given order?

1. Subtract 2.   3. Add 7.
2. Divide by 3.   4. Multiply by -1.

(A) $\frac{n-2}{3} + 7(-1)$

(B) $\frac{(-n-2)+7}{3}$

(C) $-\left(-\frac{2}{3} + 7\right)n$

(D) $-\left(\frac{n-2}{3} + 7\right)$

(E) $n - \frac{2}{3} + 7(-1)$

---

6. Which property is illustrated by the equation $8(7) + 8(6) = 8(7 + 6)$?

(A) Distributive Property

(B) Associative Property of Multiplication

(C) Commutative Property of Addition

(D) Commutative Property of Multiplication

(E) Associative Property of Addition

STRATEGIES FOR SUCCESS

Multiple Choice: Eliminate Answer Choices

You can answer some problems without doing many calculations. Use logic to eliminate answer choices and save time.

EXAMPLE 1

Which number is the square of 123,765?

    (A) 15,317,775,225   (C) 15,317,775,230

    (B) 15,317,775,233   (D) 15,317,775,227

Your calculator will not help you on this question. Due to rounding, any of the answer choices are possible.

But you can use this fact to eliminate three of the answer choices:

The square of any number ending in 5 is also a number ending in 5.

The only answer choice that ends in 5 is A, 15,317,775,225.

EXAMPLE 2

What is a possible area of the wooden triangle shown?

    (A) 11 square feet   (C) 14 square feet

    (B) 20 square feet   (D) 24 square feet

The triangle is inside a rectangle with an area of $7 \times 4 = 28$ square feet.

If the triangle had the same base and height as the rectangle, its area would be half the area of the rectangle, 14 square feet.

However, the triangle fits inside the rectangle, so its area must be less than 14 square feet.

The only answer choice that is less than 14 square feet is A, 11 square feet.

Read each test item and answer the questions that follow.

Item A
The top speed of a three-toed sloth is 0.12 miles per hour. About how many feet can a sloth travel in an hour?

(A) 0.12 feet
(C) 2.27 feet
(B) 600 feet
(D) 7500 inches

1. Are there any answer choices you can eliminate immediately? If so, which choices and why?

2. Describe how you can use estimation to find the correct answer.

Item B
A city park is shaped like a triangle. The Liberty Street side of the park is 120 feet long, and the First Avenue side is 50 feet long.

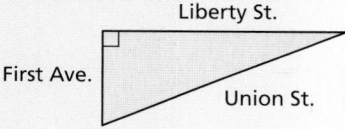

Liberty St.

First Ave.

Union St.

What is the approximate length of the side of the park that faces Union Street?

(A) 25 feet
(C) 65 feet
(B) 110 inches
(D) 130 feet

3. Can any of the answer choices be eliminated immediately? If so, which choices and why?

4. Are there any properties you can use to solve this problem? If so, what are they?

5. Describe how to find the correct answer without doing any calculations.

Item C
Approximately how long will the average 18-year-old have slept in his lifetime?

(A) 6 weeks
(C) 6 years
(B) 6 months
(D) 6 decades

6. Which answer choice can be eliminated immediately? Why?

7. Explain how to use mental math to solve this problem.

Item D
Sheila's paychecks for February and March were equal. If she worked every day during both months, for which month was her daily pay lower?

(A) February
(B) March
(C) Her daily pay did not change.
(D) Cannot be determined

8. What do you need to know to solve this problem?

9. Describe how you can find the correct answer.

Item E
Greg tripled the number of baseball cards he had last week. Which of these could be the number of cards Greg has now?

(A) 100
(C) 150
(B) 200
(D) 250

10. The number of cards that Greg has now must be divisible by what number? How can you tell if a number is divisible by this number?

11. Describe how to find the answer to this problem.

CUMULATIVE ASSESSMENT, CHAPTER 1

Multiple Choice

1. Eric is collecting gifts for a charity event. He needs 150 gifts. So far he has collected x gifts. Which expression represents how many gifts Eric still needs to collect?

(A) $150 + x$ (C) $x - 150$

(B) $150 - x$ (D) $150 \div x$

2. An online store sells birdhouses for $34.95 each. For each order, there is a one-time shipping and handling fee of $7.50. Which expression can be used to represent the cost of ordering x birdhouses?

(A) $x + 34.95 + 7.50$

(B) $(34.95 + 7.50)x$

(C) $7.50x + 34.95$

(D) $34.95x + 7.50$

3. The number of CDs in Olivia's collection can be found using the expression $6S + 8E + 10T + 15F$. Use the table to find the total number of CDs in Olivia's collection.

Stacks of CDs	Number
Stack of 6 (S)	4
Stack of 8 (E)	2
Stack of 10 (T)	3
Stack of 15 (F)	1

(A) 10   (C) 85

(B) 39   (D) 49

4. The equation $C = \frac{5}{9}(F - 32)$ relates the Celsius temperature C to the Fahrenheit temperature F. What is the Celsius temperature if the Fahrenheit temperature is -13 degrees?

(A) $-45°C$ (C) $-25°C$

(B) $-39.2°C$ (D) $-10.6°C$

5. Which equation is NOT true?

(A) $55 + 27 + 45 = 100 + 27$

(B) $5 \cdot 7 \cdot \frac{2}{5} = 2 \cdot 7$

(C) $14(126) = 14(100) + 14(26)$

(D) $31(152) = 30(150) + 1(2)$

6. The radius of a ball is 4 inches. What is the volume of the ball in cubic inches?

(A) 16π in³

(B) $\frac{64\pi}{3}$ in³

(C) $\frac{256\pi}{3}$ in³

(D) $\frac{4096\pi}{3}$ in³

7. Which of the following real numbers can be written as a terminating decimal?

(A) π

(B) $\frac{3}{2}$

(C) $\frac{4}{9}$

(D) $\frac{1}{3}$

8. At one time, a U.S. dollar had the same value as 11.32 Mexican pesos. To the nearest hundredth, how many Mexican pesos were equal to 16 U.S. dollars at that time?

(A) 1.41 pesos

(B) 4.68 pesos

(C) 27.32 pesos

(D) 181.12 pesos

Read each question carefully. Be sure you understand what the question is asking before looking at the answer choices or beginning your calculations.

9. Tickets to a festival cost $5.00 each, and lunch costs $8.50 per person. Renting a bus to transport everyone to and from the festival costs $47.00. Which expression gives the cost of x people going to the festival?

    Ⓐ $5.00 + 8.50 + 47.00$

    Ⓑ $5.00x + 8.50 + 47.00$

    Ⓒ $5.00 + 8.50x + 47.00$

    Ⓓ $5.00x + 8.50x + 47.00$

10. Tariq cut a rectangular piece of paper in half to make two triangles, as shown.

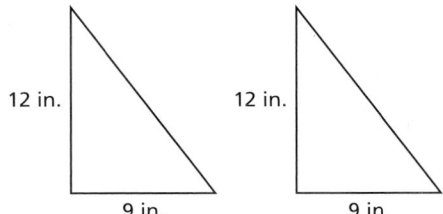

What was the area of the rectangle?

    Ⓐ 42 in.

    Ⓑ 54 in^2

    Ⓒ 72 in.

    Ⓓ 108 in^2

Gridded Response

11. A scientist prepares 4 beakers of an acid solution. Each beaker contains 70.9 milliliters of the solution. How many milliliters of acid solution did the scientist prepare in all?

12. At an accident scene, an insurance inspector finds a skid mark 60 feet long. The inspector can determine how fast the car was going in miles per hour when the driver applied the breaks by using the expression $\sqrt{21d}$, where d is the length of the skid mark in feet. To the nearest tenth, what was the speed of the car that left the skid mark?

13. What is the area in square meters of the robot sumo-wrestling ring shown below? Use 3.14 for π. Round to the nearest tenth.

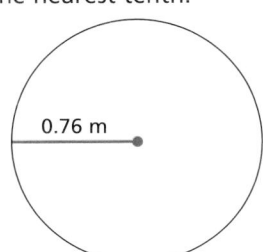

0.76 m

Short Response

14. Use the table to answer the questions below.

	Statements	Reasons
1.	$3(2 + z - 4) + 7z$	
2.	$3(2 - 4 + z) + 7z$	?
3.	$3(-2 + z) + 7z$	Combine like terms.
4.	$\big(3(-2) + 3(z)\big) + 7z$	Distributive Property
5.	$(-6 + 3z) + 7z$	Multiply.
6.	$-6 + (3z + 10z)$	Associative Property of Addition
7.	$-6 + 10z$	Combine like terms.
8.	$10z - 6$	Commutative Property of Addition

    a. What property was used to get from step 1 to step 2?

    b. Can $10z - 6$ be simplified any further?

    c. Would the expression be the same if step 4 was used before step 3? Explain.

15. As part of a challenge problem, a math teacher writes the following expression on the board:

$$-(-x).$$

    a. If x is 12, what is the value of the expression?

    b. If x is a negative number, is the value of the expression positive or negative? Explain how you found your answer.

    c. Simplify the expression.

Extended Response

16. Fatima enrolled in a traveler rewards program. She begins with 10,000 bonus points. For every trip she takes, she collects 3000 bonus points.

    a. Write an expression for the number of bonus points Fatima has after x trips.

    b. Make a table showing the number of bonus points Fatima has after 0, 1, 2, 3, 4, and 5 trips.

    c. When Fatima has collected 20,000 bonus points, she earns a free vacation. How many trips does Fatima need to take to earn a free vacation?

CHAPTER 2

Equations

go.hrw.com
Chapter Project Online
KEYWORD: MA8CA ChProj

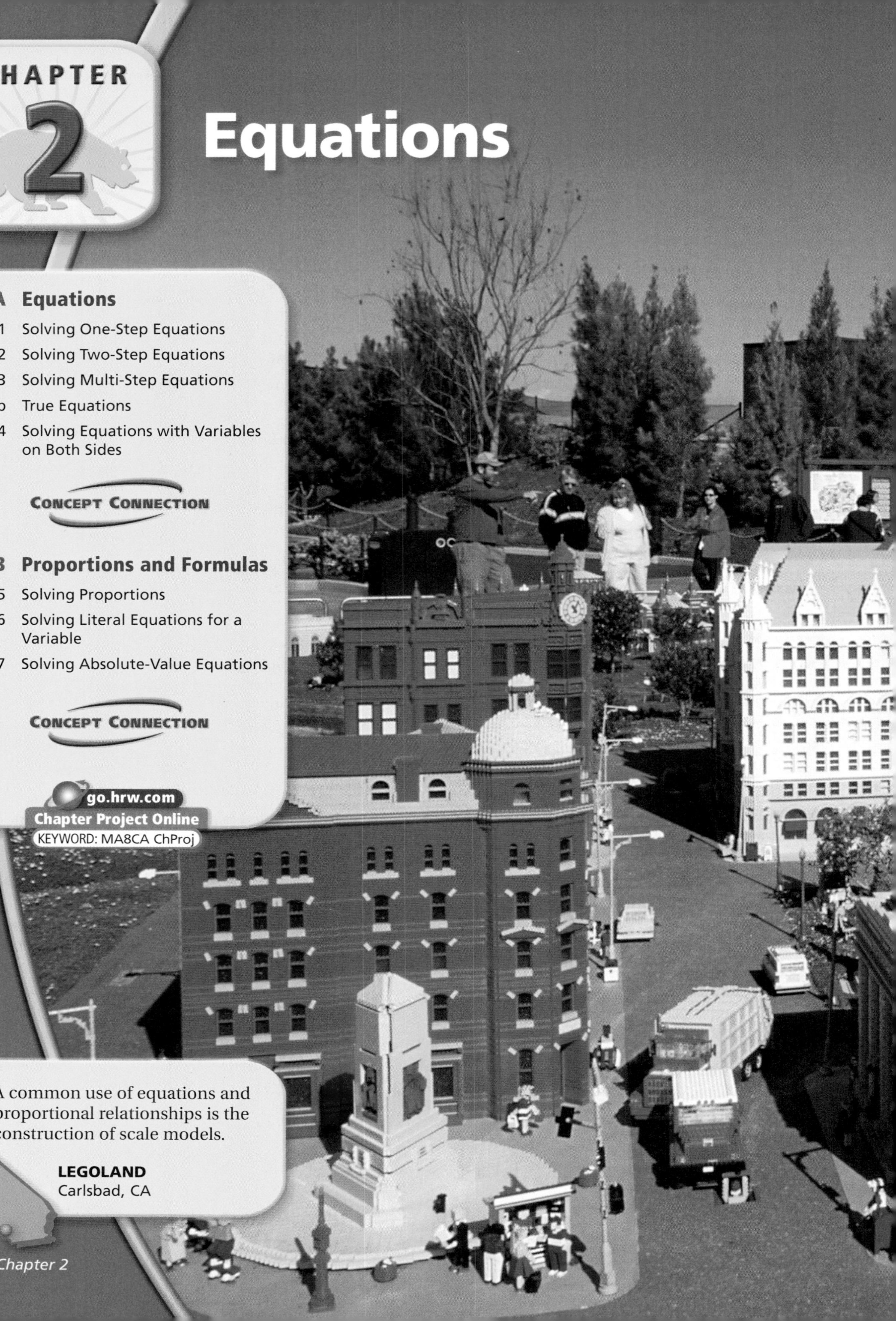

A common use of equations and proportional relationships is the construction of scale models.

LEGOLAND
Carlsbad, CA

ARE YOU READY?

✓ Vocabulary

Match each term on the left with a definition on the right.

1. constant

2. expression

3. order of operations

4. variable

A. a mathematical phrase that contains operations, numbers, and/or variables

B. a mathematical statement that two expressions are equivalent

C. a process for evaluating expressions

D. a symbol used to represent a quantity that can change

E. a value that does not change

✓ Order of Operations

Simplify each expression.

5. $(7 - 3) \div 2$

6. $4 \cdot 6 \div 3$

7. $12 - 3 + 1$

8. $2 \cdot 10 \div 5$

9. $125 \div 5^2$

10. $7 \cdot 6 + 5 \cdot 4$

✓ Add and Subtract Integers

Add or subtract.

11. $-15 + 19$

12. $-6 - (-18)$

13. $6 + (-8)$

14. $-12 + (-3)$

✓ Add and Subtract Fractions

Perform each indicated operation. Give your answer in the simplest form.

15. $\frac{1}{4} + \frac{2}{3}$

16. $1\frac{1}{2} - \frac{3}{4}$

17. $\frac{3}{8} + \frac{2}{3}$

18. $\frac{3}{2} - \frac{2}{3}$

✓ Evaluate Expressions

Evaluate each expression for the given value of the variable.

19. $2x + 3$ for $x = 7$

20. $3n - 5$ for $n = 7$

21. $13 - 4a$ for $a = 2$

22. $3y + 5$ for $y = 5$

✓ Connect Words and Algebra

23. Janie bought 4 apples and 6 bananas. Each apple cost $0.75, and each banana cost $0.60. Write an expression representing the total cost.

24. A rectangle has a width of 13 inches and a length of ℓ inches. Write an expression representing the area of the rectangle.

25. Write a phrase that could be modeled by the expression $n + 2n$.

CHAPTER 2

Unpacking the Standards

The information below "unpacks" the standards. The Academic Vocabulary is highlighted and defined to help you understand the language of the standards. Refer to the lessons listed after each standard for help with the math terms and phrases. The Chapter Concept shows how the standard is applied in this chapter.

California Standard	Academic Vocabulary	Chapter Concept
3.0 Students solve equations and inequalities **involving absolute values**. (Lesson 2-7)	**absolute value** a number's distance from 0 on a number line *Example:* $-2 \quad 0 \quad 2$ Both 2 and -2 are 2 units from 0. So $\lvert 2 \rvert = 2$ and $\lvert -2 \rvert = 2$.	You solve equations that have a variable inside absolute-value symbols.
4.0 Students simplify expressions before solving linear equations and inequalities **in one variable**, such as $3(2x - 5) + (4x - 2) = 12$. (Lessons 2-3, 2-4)	**simplify** (simplification) make things easier **linear equation** an equation whose variable(s) have exponents not greater than 1 **in one variable** containing one variable	You write expressions in their simplest form so that you can find the value of a variable that makes an equation true.
5.0 Students solve multistep problems, including word problems, involving linear equations and linear inequalities **in one variable** and provide **justification** for each step. (Lessons 2-3, 2-4, 2-7)	**multistep** more than one step **involving** needing the use of **justification** a correct reason	You solve equations when the solution process requires two or more steps.
15.0 Students apply algebraic techniques to solve rate problems, work problems, and percent mixture problems. (Lesson 2-5)	**algebraic** having to do with algebra **technique** a way of doing something	You use what you learn in algebra to solve real-world problems about rates.
25.3 Given a specific algebraic statement involving linear, quadratic, or absolute value expressions or **equations** or inequalities, **students determine whether the statement is true sometimes, always, or never.** (Lab 2-4)	**specific** single, exactly one **determine** tell or find out	You decide whether an equation is true for all values of the variable, for some values of the variable, or for no values of the variable.

Standards 2.0, 24.1, 24.2, 25.1, and 25.2 are also covered in this chapter. To see these standards unpacked go to Chapter 5, p. 254; Chapter 3, p. 134; and Chapter 1, p. 4.

California Standards

English-Language Arts Reading
8.1.3

Study Strategy: Use Your Own Words

Explaining a concept using your own words will help you better understand it. For example, learning to solve equations might seem difficult if the textbook doesn't use the same words that you would use.

As you work through each lesson:

- Identify the important ideas from the explanation in the book.
- Use your own words to explain the important ideas you identified.

What Arturo Reads

To evaluate an expression is to find its value.

To evaluate an algebraic expression, substitute numbers for the variables in the expression and then simplify the expression.

A replacement set is a set of numbers that can be substituted for a variable.

What Arturo Writes

Evaluate an expression— find the value.

Substitute a number for each variable (letter), and find the answer.

Replacement set—numbers that can be substituted for a letter.

Try This

Rewrite each paragraph in your own words.

1. Two numbers are opposites if their sum is 0. A number and its opposite are on opposite sides of zero on a number line, but are the same distance from zero.

2. The Commutative and Associative Properties of Addition and Multiplication allow you to rearrange an expression to simplify it.

3. The terms of an expression are the parts to be added or subtracted. Like terms are terms that contain the same variables raised to the same powers. Constants are also like terms.

Equations **71**

2-1 Solving One-Step Equations

California Standards

Preparation for ⬥ 5.0
Students solve multistep problems, including word problems, involving linear **equations** and linear inequalities **in one variable** and provide justification for each step.
Also covered: ⬥ **2.0**

Vocabulary
equation
solution of an equation
solution set

Why learn this?

You can use an equation to calculate your maximum heart rate. (See Example 4.)

An **equation** is a mathematical statement that two expressions are equal.

A **solution of an equation** is a value of the variable that makes the equation true. A **solution set** is the set of all solutions. Finding the solutions of an equation is also called *solving the equation*.

To find solutions, perform inverse operations until you have *isolated the variable*. A variable is isolated when it appears by itself on one side of an equation, and not at all on the other side.

Inverse Operations

Add x. ⟷ Subtract x.

Multiply by x. ⟷ Divide by x.

An equation is like a balanced scale. To keep the balance, you must perform the same inverse operation on both sides.

Addition and Subtraction Properties of Equality		
WORDS	**NUMBERS**	**ALGEBRA**
Addition Property of Equality You can add the same number to both sides of an equation, and the statement will still be true.	$3 = 3$ $3 + 2 = 3 + 2$	$a = b$ $a + c = b + c$
Subtraction Property of Equality You can subtract the same number from both sides of an equation, and the statement will still be true.	$7 = 7$ $7 - 5 = 7 - 5$	$a = b$ $a - c = b - c$

EXAMPLE **1** **Solving Equations by Using Addition or Subtraction**

Solve each equation.

A $x - 10 = 4$

$$\begin{array}{rcl} x - 10 &=& 4 \\ +10 & & +10 \\ \hline x &=& 14 \end{array}$$

Since 10 is subtracted from x, add 10 to both sides to undo the subtraction.

The solution set is {14}.

Check $x - 10 = 4$

$$\begin{array}{c|c} 14 - 10 & 4 \\ \hline 4 & 4 \checkmark \end{array}$$

To check your solution, substitute 14 for x in the original equation.

Writing Math

Solution sets are written in set notation using braces, { }. Solutions may be given in set notation, or they may be given in the form $x = 14$.

Solve each equation.

B $0.7 = r + 0.4$

$0.7 = r + 0.4$

$\underline{-0.4 \quad -0.4}$ *Since 0.4 is added to r, subtract 0.4 from both*
                                  sides to undo the addition.

$0.3 = r$ *The solution set is {0.3}.*

 **CHECK IT OUT!** Solve each equation. Check your answer.

1a. $n - 3.2 = 5.6$ **1b.** $-6 = k - 6$ **1c.** $6 + t = 14$

 **Know it! Note**

Multiplication and Division Properties of Equality

WORDS	NUMBERS	ALGEBRA
Multiplication Property of Equality You can multiply both sides of an equation by the same number, and the statement will still be true.	$6 = 6$ $6(3) = 6(3)$	$a = b$ $ac = bc$
Division Property of Equality You can divide both sides of an equation by the same nonzero number, and the statement will still be true.	$8 = 8$ $\dfrac{8}{4} = \dfrac{8}{4}$	$a = b$ $(c \neq 0),\ \dfrac{a}{c} = \dfrac{b}{c}$

EXAMPLE 2 **Solving Equations by Using Multiplication or Division**

Solve each equation.

A $13 = -2w$

$\dfrac{13}{-2} = \dfrac{-2w}{-2}$ *Since w is multiplied by −2, divide both*
                                       sides by −2 to undo the multiplication.

$w = -\dfrac{13}{2}$, or -6.5 *The solution set is {−6.5}.*

B $-4 = \dfrac{k}{-5}$

$(-5)(-4) = (-5)\left(\dfrac{k}{-5}\right)$ *Since k is divided by −5, multiply both sides*
                                                by −5 to undo the division.

$20 = k$ *The solution set is {20}.*

Check $-4 = \dfrac{k}{-5}$ *To check your solution, substitute 20 for k in*
                                                the original equation.

$\begin{array}{c|c} -4 & \dfrac{20}{-5} \\ \hline -4 & -4 \checkmark \end{array}$

 **CHECK IT OUT!** Solve each equation. Check your answer.

2a. $\dfrac{p}{5} = 10$ **2b.** $0.5y = -10$ **2c.** $\dfrac{c}{8} = 7$

When solving equations, you will sometimes find it easier to add an opposite to both sides instead of subtracting, or to multiply by a reciprocal instead of dividing. This is often true when an equation contains negative numbers or fractions.

EXAMPLE 3 **Solving Equations by Using Opposites or Reciprocals**

Solve each equation.

A $-8 + b = 2$

$$-8 + b = 2$$
$$\underline{+8 \qquad +8}$$
$$b = 10$$

Since -8 is added to b, add 8 to both sides.
The solution set is {10}.

B $\dfrac{5}{9}v = 35$

$$\left(\dfrac{9}{5}\right)\dfrac{5}{9}v = \left(\dfrac{9}{5}\right)35$$

The reciprocal of $\dfrac{5}{9}$ is $\dfrac{9}{5}$. Since v is multiplied by $\dfrac{5}{9}$, multiply both sides by $\dfrac{9}{5}$.

$$v = 63$$

The solution set is {63}.

 Solve each equation. Check your answer.

3a. $-2.3 + m = 7$ **3b.** $-\dfrac{3}{4} + z = \dfrac{5}{4}$ **3c.** $\dfrac{1}{6}w = 102$

EXAMPLE 4 **Fitness Application**

A person's maximum heart rate is the highest rate, in beats per minute, that the person's heart should reach. A person's age added to his or her maximum heart rate is 220. Write and solve an equation to find the maximum heart rate of a 15-year-old.

Age	added to	maximum heart rate	is	220.
a	$+$	r	$=$	220

$$a + r = 220$$

Write an equation to represent the relationship.

$$15 + r = 220$$

Substitute 15 for a. Since 15 is added to r, subtract 15 from both sides to undo the addition.

$$\underline{-15 \qquad -15}$$
$$r = 205$$

The maximum heart rate for a 15-year-old is 205 beats per minute.

 **4.** The distance in miles from the airport that a plane should begin descending divided by 3 equals the plane's height above the ground in thousands of feet. A plane is 10,000 feet above the ground. Write and solve an equation to find the distance from the airport at which this plane should begin descending.

Student to Student   *Zero As a Solution*

Ama Walker
Carson High School

I used to get confused when I got a solution of 0. But my teacher reminded me that 0 is a number just like any other number, so it can be a solution of an equation. Just check your answer and see if it works.

$$x + 6 = 6$$
$$\underline{-6 \quad -6}$$
$$x = 0$$

Check

$$x + 6 = 6$$

$0 + 6$	6
6	6 ✓

THINK AND DISCUSS

1. Describe how the Addition and Subtraction Properties of Equality are like a balanced scale.

2. By what number would you multiply both sides of the equation $\frac{b}{4} = 10$ to isolate the variable?

3. **GET ORGANIZED** Copy and complete the graphic organizer. In each box, write an example of an equation that can be solved by using the given property and solve it.

2-1 Exercises

California Standards Practice
Preparation for ◆ **5.0;**
◆ **2.0, 25.2**

go.hrw.com
Homework Help Online
KEYWORD: MA8CA 2-1
Parent Resources Online
KEYWORD: MA8CA Parent

GUIDED PRACTICE

1. **Vocabulary** Will the *solution of an equation* such as $x - 3 = 9$ be a variable or a number? Explain.

Solve each equation. Check your answer.

SEE EXAMPLE **1**
p. 72

2. $s - 5 = 3$
3. $17 = w - 4$
4. $k - 8 = -7$
5. $t + 5 = -25$
6. $b + \frac{2}{3} = 2$
7. $4.2 = m + 3.6$

SEE EXAMPLE **2**
p. 73

8. $\frac{k}{4} = 8$
9. $\frac{g}{1.9} = 10$
10. $-2 = \frac{w}{-7}$
11. $4x = 28$
12. $4m = 10$
13. $-9j = -45$

SEE EXAMPLE **3**
p. 74

14. $-10 + d = 7$
15. $20 = -12 + v$
16. $-4.6 + q = 5$
17. $\frac{1}{2}d = 7$
18. $-\frac{2}{3} + c = \frac{2}{3}$
19. $\frac{2}{3}s = -6$

SEE EXAMPLE **4**
p. 74

20. **Geology** In 1668, the Hope diamond was reduced from its original weight by about 45 carats, resulting in a diamond weighing about 67 carats. Write and solve an equation to find how many carats the original diamond weighed.

PRACTICE AND PROBLEM SOLVING

Independent Practice	
For Exercises	See Example
21–28	1
29–36	2
37–44	3
45	4

Extra Practice
Skills Practice p. EP4
Application Practice p. EP25

Solve each equation. Check your answer.

21. $1 = k - 8$
22. $m + 20 = 3$
23. $x - 7 = 10$
24. $v + 2300 = -800$
25. $b + \frac{1}{2} = \frac{1}{2}$
26. $q - 0.5 = 1.5$
27. $4\frac{2}{3} = r - \frac{1}{3}$
28. $2 = d + \frac{1}{4}$
29. $\frac{x}{2} = 12$
30. $11 = -2z$
31. $5t = -15$
32. $1.6 = \frac{d}{3}$
33. $-\frac{j}{6} = 6$
34. $-12 = -12u$
35. $-8.4 = -4n$
36. $\frac{h}{8.1} = -4$

Solve each equation. Check your answer.

37. $-12 + f = 3$ **38.** $-9 = -4 + g$ **39.** $\frac{4}{7}t = -2$ **40.** $-\frac{4}{5}g = -12$

41. $26 = -4 + y$ **42.** $\frac{5}{2}k = 5$ **43.** $-9 = \frac{3}{4}d$ **44.** $-5.2 + a = -8$

45. Nutrition An orange contains about 80 milligrams of vitamin C, which is 10 times as much as an apple contains. Write and solve an equation to find the amount of vitamin C in an apple.

California LINK

Oceanography

The ocean near Monterey reaches depths of more than 10,000 ft. Below 330 ft, there is little, if any, light. Many deep sea animals, such as jelly fish, make their own light (bioluminescence) to help them survive.

Write an equation to represent each relationship. Then solve the equation.

46. Ten less than a number is equal to 12.   **47.** Five times a number is 45.

48. The quotient of a number and 3 is -8.   **49.** Eight more than a number is 16.

50. ///**ERROR ANALYSIS**/// Below are two possible solutions to $x + 12.5 = 21.6$. Which is incorrect? Explain the error.

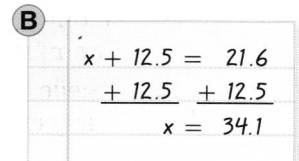

A

$$x + 12.5 = 21.6$$
$$\underline{\quad -12.5 \quad -12.5}$$
$$x = 9.1$$

B

$$x + 12.5 = 21.6$$
$$\underline{\quad +12.5 \quad +12.5}$$
$$x = 34.1$$

51. Oceanography The Atlantic Ocean's greatest depth (in feet) is 17,366 feet greater than its average depth. Use the information in the graph to write and solve an equation to find the average depth of the Atlantic Ocean.

52. Consumer Economics Dion's long-distance phone bill was $13.80. His long-distance calls cost $0.05 per minute. Write and solve an equation to find the number of minutes he was charged for.

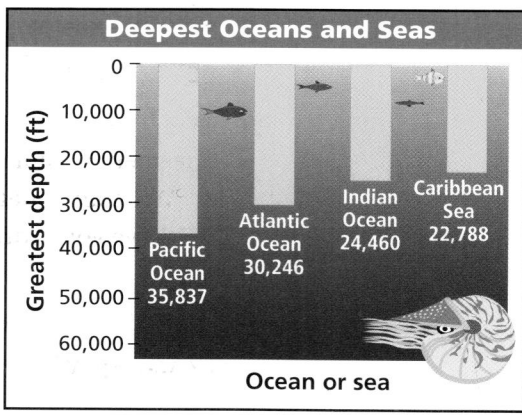

Deepest Oceans and Seas

Greatest depth (ft)

Pacific Ocean 35,837

Atlantic Ocean 30,246

Indian Ocean 24,460

Caribbean Sea 22,788

Ocean or sea

53. Write About It Describe a real-world situation that can be modeled by $x + 5 = 25$. Solve the equation and tell what the solution means in the context of your problem.

54. Critical Thinking Without solving, tell whether the solution of $-2 + z = 10$ is greater than 10 or less than 10. Explain.

CONCEPT CONNECTION

55. This problem will help prepare you for the Concept Connection on page 100.

Rates are often used to describe how quickly something is moving or changing.

a. A wildfire spreads at a rate of 1000 acres per day. How many acres will the fire cover in 2 days?

b. How many acres will the fire cover in 5 days?

c. Another wildfire spread for 7 days and covered a total of 780 square miles. How can you estimate the number of square miles the fire covered per day?

Geometry The angles in each pair are complementary. Write and solve an equation to find each value of *x*. (*Hint:* The measures of complementary angles add to 90°.)

56.
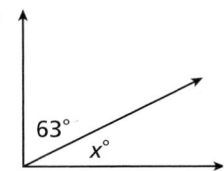
63°
x°

57.
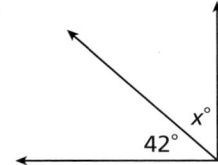
x°
42°

58.
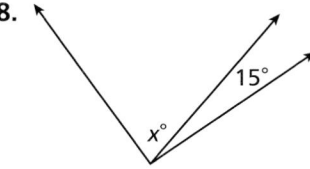
15°
x°

Multiple Choice For Exercises 59 and 60, choose the best answer.

59. Which situation is best represented by $x - 32 = 8$?

    Ⓐ Logan withdrew $32 from her bank account. After her withdrawal, her balance was $8. How much was originally in her account?

    Ⓑ Daniel has 32 baseball cards. Joseph has 8 fewer baseball cards than Daniel has. How many baseball cards does Joseph have?

    Ⓒ Room A contains 32 desks. Room B has 8 fewer desks. How many desks are in Room B?

    Ⓓ Janelle bought a bag of 32 craft sticks for a project. She used 8 craft sticks. How many craft sticks does she have left?

60. For which equation is $m = 10$ a solution?

    Ⓐ $5 = 2m$ Ⓒ $\dfrac{m}{2} = 5$

    Ⓑ $5m = 2$ Ⓓ $\dfrac{m}{10} = 2$

61. **Short Response** Luisa bought 6 cans of cat food that each cost the same amount. She spent a total of $4.80.

    a. Write an equation that can be used to determine the cost of one can of cat food.

    b. Solve your equation to find the cost of one can of cat food.

CHALLENGE AND EXTEND

Solve each equation. Check your answer.

62. $3\frac{1}{5} + b = \frac{4}{5}$ **63.** $x - \frac{7}{4} = \frac{2}{3}$ **64.** $\left(1\frac{1}{3}\right)x = 2\frac{2}{3}$ **65.** $\left(3\frac{1}{5}\right)b = \frac{4}{5}$

66. If $p - 4 = 2$, find the value of $5p - 20$.   **67.** If $2p = 4$, find the value of $6p + 10$.

68. If $3x = 15$, find the value of $12 - 4x$.   **69.** If $2 + n = -11$, find the value of $6n$.

Multiply or divide. *(Lesson 1-3)*

70. $-63 \div (-7)$ **71.** $\frac{3}{7} \div \left(-\frac{4}{7}\right)$ **72.** $(-12)(-6)$

Give the side length of a square with the given area. *(Lesson 1-5)*

73. 225 m^2 **74.** 36 ft^2 **75.** 100 cm^2

Write each product using the Distributive Property. Then simplify. *(Lesson 1-6)*

76. $11(104)$ **77.** $12(43)$ **78.** $3(46)$

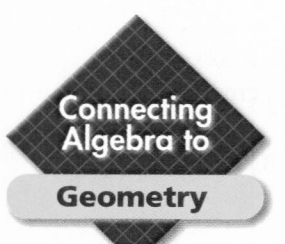

Area of Composite Figures

Review the area formulas for squares, rectangles, and triangles in the table below.

California Standards

Reinforcement of 7MG2.2 Estimate and **compute the area of more complex or irregular two-** and three-**dimensional figures by breaking the figure down into more basic geometric objects.**

Squares	Rectangles	Triangles
s	*ℓ*, *w*	*h*, *b*
$A = s^2$	$A = \ell w$	$A = \frac{1}{2}bh$

A *composite figure* is a figure that is composed of basic shapes. You can divide composite figures into combinations of squares, rectangles, and triangles to find their areas.

Example

Find the area of the figure shown.

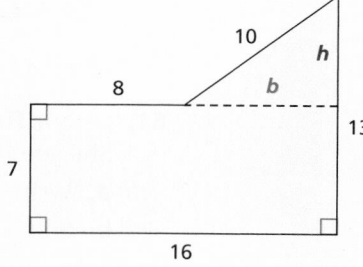

Divide the figure into a rectangle and a right triangle. Notice that you do not know the base or the height of the triangle. Use *b* and *h* to represent these lengths.

The bottom of the rectangle is 16 units long; the top of the rectangle is 8 units long plus the base of the triangle. Use this information to write and solve an equation.

$$\begin{aligned} b + 8 &= 16 \\ -8 \quad &-8 \\ \hline b \quad &= 8 \end{aligned}$$

The right side of the figure is 13 units long: 7 units from the rectangle plus the height of the triangle. Use this information to write and solve an equation.

$$\begin{aligned} h + 7 &= 13 \\ -7 \quad &-7 \\ \hline h \quad &= 6 \end{aligned}$$

The area of the figure is the sum of the areas of the rectangle and the triangle.

Area of rectangle
Area of triangle

$$A = \ell w + \frac{1}{2}bh$$
$$A = 16(7) + \frac{1}{2}(8)(6)$$
$$A = 112 + 24$$
$$A = 136 \text{ square units}$$

Try This

Find the area of each composite figure.

1.
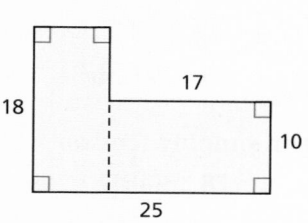

2.
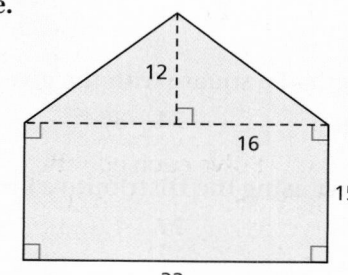

3.
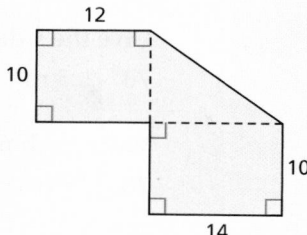

2-2 Solving Two-Step Equations

California Standards

Preparation for ◆━ **5.0**
Students solve multistep problems, including word problems, involving linear equations and linear inequalities in one variable and provide justification for each step.

Vocabulary
equivalent equations

Why learn this?

Equations containing two operations can model the cost of a music club membership. (See Example 3.)

Many equations contain more than one operation, such as $2x + 5 = 11$.

This equation contains multiplication and addition. Equations that contain two operations require two steps to solve. Identify the operations in the equation and the order in which they are applied to the variable. Then use inverse operations to undo them in reverse order one at a time.

$$2x + 5 = 11$$

Operations in the Equation	To Solve
❶ First *x* is **multiplied** by 2.	❶ **Subtract** 5 from both sides of the equation.
❷ Then 5 is **added**.	❷ Then **divide** both sides by 2.

$$
\begin{aligned}
2x + 5 &= 11 \\
-5 \quad & -5 \\
\hline
2x &= 6
\end{aligned}
$$ Subtract 5 from both sides of the equation.

$$\frac{2x}{2} = \frac{6}{2}$$ Divide both sides of the equation by 2.

$$x = 3$$ The solution set is {3}.

Each time you perform an inverse operation, you create an equation that is *equivalent* to the original equation. **Equivalent equations** have the same solutions, or the same solution set. In the example above, $2x + 5 = 11$, $2x = 6$, and $x = 3$ are all equivalent equations.

EXAMPLE 1 Solving Two-Step Equations

Solve $10 = 6 - 2x$.

$$
\begin{aligned}
10 &= 6 - 2x \\
-6 \quad & -6 \\
\hline
4 &= -2x
\end{aligned}
$$

First *x* is multiplied by −2. Then 6 is added.

Subtract 6 from both sides.

$4 = -2x$ is equivalent to $10 = 6 - 2x$.

$$\frac{4}{-2} = \frac{-2x}{-2}$$ Since *x* is multiplied by −2, divide both sides by −2 to undo the multiplication.

$$-2 = x$$ The solution set is {−2}.

Helpful Hint

Check your answer.

$10 = 6 - 2x$	
10	$6 - 2(-2)$
10	$6 - (-4)$
10	$6 + 4$
10	10 ✓

 **Solve each equation. Check your answer.**

1a. $-4 + 7x = 3$ **1b.** $1.5 = 1.2y - 5.7$ **1c.** $\frac{n}{7} + 2 = 2$

EXAMPLE 2 **Solving Two-Step Equations That Contain Fractions**

Solve each equation.

$\boxed{\text{A}}$ $\dfrac{q}{15} - \dfrac{1}{5} = \dfrac{3}{5}$

Method 1 Use fraction operations.

$$\dfrac{q}{15} - \dfrac{1}{5} = \dfrac{3}{5}$$
$$\underline{+\dfrac{1}{5} \quad +\dfrac{1}{5}}$$

Since $\frac{1}{5}$ is subtracted from $\frac{q}{15}$, add $\frac{1}{5}$ to both sides to undo the subtraction.

$$\dfrac{q}{15} = \dfrac{4}{5}$$

$$15\left(\dfrac{q}{15}\right) = 15\left(\dfrac{4}{5}\right)$$

Since q is divided by 15, multiply both sides by 15 to undo the division.

$$q = \dfrac{15 \cdot 4}{5}$$ *Simplify.*

$$q = \dfrac{60}{5}$$

$$q = 12$$ *The solution set is {12}.*

Method 2 Multiply by the least common denominator (LCD) to clear the fractions.

$$\dfrac{q}{15} - \dfrac{1}{5} = \dfrac{3}{5}$$

$$15\left(\dfrac{q}{15} - \dfrac{1}{5}\right) = 15\left(\dfrac{3}{5}\right)$$ *Multiply both sides by 15, the LCD of the fractions.*

$$15\left(\dfrac{q}{15}\right) - 15\left(\dfrac{1}{5}\right) = 15\left(\dfrac{3}{5}\right)$$ *Distribute 15 on the left side.*

$$q - 3 = 9$$
$$\underline{+3 \quad +3}$$ *Simplify. Since 3 is subtracted from q, add 3 to both sides to undo the subtraction.*
$$q = 12$$ *The solution set is {12}.*

Check

$$\dfrac{q}{15} - \dfrac{1}{5} = \dfrac{3}{5}$$

$$\begin{array}{c|c} \dfrac{12}{15} - \dfrac{1}{5} & \dfrac{3}{5} \\ \hline \dfrac{3}{5} & \dfrac{3}{5} \checkmark \end{array}$$

To check your solution, substitute 12 for q in the original equation.

$\boxed{\text{B}}$ $\dfrac{j}{4} + 2 = 9$

$$\dfrac{j}{4} + 2 = 9$$
$$\underline{-2 \quad -2}$$ *Since 2 is added to $\frac{j}{4}$, subtract 2 from both sides to undo the addition.*
$$\dfrac{j}{4} = 7$$

$$4\left(\dfrac{j}{4}\right) = 4(7)$$ *Since j is divided by 4, multiply both sides by 4 to undo the division.*

$$j = 28$$ *The solution set is {28}.*

> **Helpful Hint**
>
> You can multiply both sides of the equation by any common denominator of the fractions. Using the LCD is the most efficient.
> *To review fraction operations, including LCD, see Skills Bank pages SB8–SB9.*

 **Solve each equation. Check your answer.**

2a. $\dfrac{2x}{5} - \dfrac{1}{2} = 5$ **2b.** $\dfrac{3}{4}u + \dfrac{1}{2} = \dfrac{7}{8}$ **2c.** $\dfrac{1}{5}n - \dfrac{1}{3} = \dfrac{8}{3}$

EXAMPLE **3**

PROBLEM
SOLVING

Problem-Solving Application

Alex belongs to the Student Music Club and bought a discount card for $19.95. After one year, Alex has spent $63.40. Write and solve an equation to find how many CDs Alex bought during the year.

Student Music Club
Discount Card
CDs $3.95 each

 Understand the Problem

The **answer** will be the number of CDs that Alex bought during the year.

List the important information:

• Alex paid $19.95 for a student discount card.

• Alex paid $3.95 for each CD he purchased.

• After one year, Alex has spent $63.40.

 **Make a Plan**

Let *c* represent the number of CDs that Alex purchased. That means Alex has spent $3.95*c*. However, Alex must also add the amount he spent on the card. Write an equation to represent this situation.

total cost	=	cost of CDs	+	cost of discount card
63.40	=	3.95*c*	+	19.95

 Solve

$$63.40 = 3.95c + 19.95$$
$$\underline{-19.95 \qquad\qquad -19.95}$$
$$43.45 = 3.95c$$
$$\frac{43.45}{3.95} = \frac{3.95c}{3.95}$$
$$11 = c$$

Since 19.95 is added to 3.95c, subtract 19.95 from both sides to undo the addition.

Since c is multiplied by 3.95, divide both sides by 3.95 to undo the multiplication.

Alex bought 11 CDs during the year.

 **Look Back**

Check that the answer is reasonable. The cost per CD is about $4, so if Alex bought 11 CDs, this amount is about 11(4) = $44.

Add the cost of the discount card, which is about $20: 44 + 20 = 64. So the total cost was about $64, which is close to the amount given in the problem, $63.40.

CHECK IT OUT!

3a. Sara paid $15.95 to become a member at a gym. She then paid a monthly membership fee. Her total cost for 12 months was $735.95. How much was the monthly fee?

3b. Lynda has 12 records in her collection. She adds the same number of new records to her collection each month. After 7 months Lynda has 26 records. How many records does Lynda add each month?

THINK AND DISCUSS

1. Explain the steps you would follow to solve $2x + 1 = 7$. How is this procedure different from the one you would follow to solve $2x - 1 = 7$?

2. **GET ORGANIZED** Copy and complete the graphic organizer. In each box, write and solve a two-step equation. Use addition, subtraction, multiplication, and division.

Solving Two-Step Equations	

2-2 Exercises

California Standards Practice
Preparation for ⚷ 5.0

go.hrw.com
Homework Help Online
KEYWORD: MA8CA 2-2
Parent Resources Online
KEYWORD: MA8CA Parent

GUIDED PRACTICE

SEE EXAMPLE 1
p. 79

Solve each equation. Check your answer.

1. $4a + 3 = 11$
2. $8 = 3r - 1$
3. $\dfrac{x}{6} + 4 = 15$
4. $x + 0.3 = 3.3$
5. $15y + 31 = 61$
6. $9 - c = -13$

SEE EXAMPLE 2
p. 80

7. $\dfrac{1}{3}y + \dfrac{1}{4} = \dfrac{5}{12}$
8. $\dfrac{2}{7}j - \dfrac{1}{7} = \dfrac{3}{14}$
9. $\dfrac{x}{8} - \dfrac{1}{2} = 6$
10. $\dfrac{1}{2} + 12x = \dfrac{9}{2}$
11. $\dfrac{5}{6}x - \dfrac{1}{3} = \dfrac{5}{2}$
12. $3 - \dfrac{1}{2}r = 12$

SEE EXAMPLE 3
p. 81

13. **Transportation** Paul bought a student discount card for the bus. The card cost $7 and allows him to buy daily bus passes for $1.50. After one month, Paul spent $29.50. How many daily bus passes did Paul buy?

PRACTICE AND PROBLEM SOLVING

Independent Practice

For Exercises	See Example
14–19	1
20–25	2
26	3

Extra Practice
Skills Practice p. EP4
Application Practice p. EP25

Solve each equation. Check your answer.

14. $5 = 2g + 1$
15. $6h - 7 = 17$
16. $15 = \dfrac{a}{3} - 2$
17. $3x + 3 = 18$
18. $0.6g + 11 = 5$
19. $32 = 5 - 3t$
20. $2d + \dfrac{1}{5} = \dfrac{3}{5}$
21. $1 = 2x + \dfrac{1}{2}$
22. $\dfrac{z}{2} + 1 = \dfrac{3}{2}$
23. $\dfrac{2}{3} = \dfrac{4j}{6}$
24. $\dfrac{3}{4} = \dfrac{3}{8}x - \dfrac{3}{2}$
25. $\dfrac{1}{5} - \dfrac{x}{5} = -\dfrac{2}{5}$

26. **Consumer Economics** Jennifer is saving money to buy a bike. The bike costs $245. She has $125 saved, and each week she adds $15 to her savings. How many weeks will it take her to save enough money to buy the bike?

Write an equation to represent each relationship. Then solve.

27. Seven less than twice a number equals 19.

28. Eight decreased by 3 times a number equals 2.

29. 30 increased by 5 times a number equals 80.

30. 30 less than 4 times a number is equal to 14.

31. The sum of 64 and 3 times a number is −2.

32. 6 added to twice a number is equal to −8.

History

Martin Luther King Jr. entered college at age 15. During his life he earned 3 degrees and was awarded 20 honorary degrees.
Source: lib.lsu.edu

33. History In 1963, Dr. Martin Luther King Jr. began his famous "I have a dream" speech with the words "Five score years ago, a great American, in whose symbolic shadow we stand, signed the Emancipation Proclamation." The Proclamation was signed by President Abraham Lincoln in 1863.

  a. Using the dates given, write and solve an equation that can be used to find the number of years in a score.

  b. How many score would represent 60?

Solve each equation. Check your answer.

34. $3t + 44 = 50$

35. $3x - 6 = 18$

36. $15 = \dfrac{c}{3} - 2$

37. $2x + 6.5 = 15.5$

38. $3.9w - 17.9 = -2.3$

39. $20 = x - 3x$

40. $5x + 9 = 39$

41. $15 + 5.5m = 70$

42. $7j + 3 = 24$

43. $\dfrac{3}{4} + \dfrac{x}{2} = 3$

44. $50 = 3t - 4$

45. $14.5 = 5.5n - 2$

Biology Use the graph for Exercises 46 and 47.

46. The maximum height of an ostrich is 20 inches more than 4 times the maximum height of a kiwi. Write and solve an equation to find the maximum height of a kiwi.

47. Five times the maximum height of a kakapo minus 70 equals the maximum height of an emu. Write and solve an equation to find the maximum height of a kakapo.

48. Transportation A taxi company charges $1.10 plus $0.95 per mile. Karen's total fare was $12.50. How many miles did Karen travel?

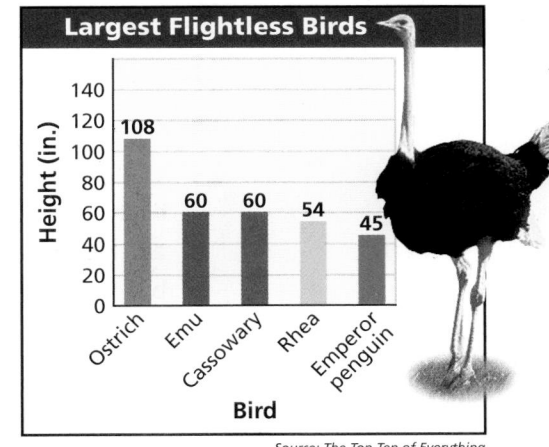

Source: The Top Ten of Everything

CONCEPT CONNECTION

49. This problem will help prepare you for the Concept Connection on page 100.

  a. The cost of fighting a particular forest fire is $225 per acre. Complete the table.

  b. Write an equation for the relationship between the cost c of fighting the fire and the number of acres n.

Cost of Fighting Fire	
Acres	**Cost ($)**
100	22,500
200	
500	
1000	
1500	
n	

50. Critical Thinking The equation $2 - m = 17$ has more than one solution method. Give at least two different "first steps" to solve this equation.

 51. Write About It Write a series of steps that you can use to solve any two-step equation.

Multiple Choice For Exercises 52 and 53, choose the best answer.

52. The equation $c = 48 + 0.06m$ represents the cost c of renting a car and driving m miles. Which statement best describes this cost?

Ⓐ The cost is a flat rate of $0.06 per mile.

Ⓑ The cost is $0.48 for the first mile and $0.06 for each additional mile.

Ⓒ The cost is a $48 fee plus $0.06 per mile.

Ⓓ The cost is a $6 fee plus $0.48 per mile.

53. Which equation is equivalent to $4m - 3 = 21$?

Ⓐ $4m + 3 = 24$ Ⓒ $4m = 18$

Ⓑ $4m - 3 = 18$ Ⓓ $4m = 24$

54. Gridded Response A telemarketer earns $150 a week plus $2 for each call that results in a sale. Her pay last week was $204. How many of her calls last week resulted in sales?

CHALLENGE AND EXTEND

Solve each equation. Check your answer.

55. $\dfrac{11}{2} + 3x = \dfrac{-5^2}{2}$

56. $\dfrac{15}{2^2}x - 15 = \dfrac{33}{2^2}$

57. $-5.2x + 1.69 = -8.71$

58. $\dfrac{1}{2}x - 12.75 = 21.25$

59. $169 = 37x - 4^2$

60. $8.49 = 4.6x - 5.31$

61. Business The formula $p = nc - e$ gives the profit p when a number of items n are each sold at a cost c and expenses e are subtracted.

   a. If $p = 2500$, $n = 2000$, and $e = 800$, what is the value of c?

   b. If $p = 2500$, $n = 1000$, and $e = 800$, what is the value of c?

   c. What if...? If n is divided in half while p and e remain the same, what is the effect on c?

 SPIRAL STANDARDS REVIEW   6AF1.1, 7NS1.4, 7NS1.5, 1.0

Write all classifications that apply to each real number. *(Lesson 1-5)*

62. $\sqrt{3}$ **63.** -58 **64.** $2\dfrac{1}{3}$ **65.** 0.17

Write each product using the Distributive Property. Then simplify. *(Lesson 1-6)*

66. $8(61)$ **67.** $9(28)$ **68.** $11(28)$ **69.** $13(21)$

70. $3(45)$ **71.** $7(19)$ **72.** $9(72)$ **73.** $8(33)$

Solve each equation. *(Lesson 2-1)*

74. $17 = k + 4$ **75.** $x - 18 = 3$ **76.** $a + 6 = -12$ **77.** $-7 = q - 7$

78. $12b = 60$ **79.** $7 = \dfrac{z}{4}$ **80.** $3a = 24$ **81.** $\dfrac{t}{6} = -7$

Solving Multi-Step Equations

California Standards

☞ **4.0** Students simplify expressions before solving linear equations and inequalities in one variable, such as $3(2x - 5) + 4(x - 2) = 12$.

☞ **5.0** Students solve multi-step problems, including word problems, involving linear equations and linear inequalities in one variable and provide justification for each step.

Why learn this?

Martial arts instructors can model enrollment costs with multi-step equations.

A martial arts school is offering a special where students can enroll for half price, after a $12.50 application fee.

Ten students enrolled and paid a total of $325. To find the regular price of enrollment, you can solve an equation.

Regular price of enrollment
↓

Number of students → $10\left(\dfrac{p}{2} + 12.50\right) = 325$ ← Total cost

↑
Application fee

Notice that this equation contains multiplication, division, and addition. An equation that contains multiple operations will require multiple steps to solve. You will create an equivalent equation at each step.

E X A M P L E **1** **Solving Multi-Step Equations**

Solve $\dfrac{4x + 1}{5} = 5$. Check your answer.

$5\left(\dfrac{4x + 1}{5}\right) = 5(5)$ *Since $4x + 1$ is divided by 5, multiply both sides by 5 to undo the division.*

$4x + 1 = 25$

$\underline{\quad -1 \quad\quad -1\quad}$ *Since 1 is added to $4x$, subtract 1 from both sides to undo the addition.*

$4x \quad = 24$

$\dfrac{4x}{4} = \dfrac{24}{4}$ *Since x is multiplied by 4, divide both sides by 4 to undo the multiplication.*

$x = 6$ *The solution set is {6}.*

Check $\dfrac{4x + 1}{5} = 5$ *To check your solution, substitute 6 for x in the original equation.*

$\dfrac{4(6) + 1}{5} \,\Big|\, 5$

$\dfrac{24 + 1}{5} \,\Big|\, 5$

$\dfrac{25}{5} \,\Big|\, 5$

$5 \,\Big|\, 5\ ✓$

CHECK IT OUT!

Solve each equation. Check your answer.

1a. $\dfrac{5m + 13}{2} = 1$ **1b.** $\dfrac{4 - 2z}{4} = -2$

You may have to combine like terms or use the Distributive Property before you begin solving.

EXAMPLE 2 **Simplifying Before Solving Equations**

Solve $6x + 3 - 8x = 13$.

$$6x + 3 - 8x = 13$$
$$6x - 8x + 3 = 13 \qquad \text{\textit{Use the Commutative Property of Addition.}}$$
$$-2x + 3 = 13 \qquad \text{\textit{Combine like terms.}}$$
$$\underline{\ -3 \quad -3} \qquad \text{\textit{Since 3 is added to $-2x$, subtract 3 from}}$$
$$-2x \quad = 10 \qquad \quad \text{\textit{both sides to undo the addition.}}$$
$$\frac{-2x}{-2} = \frac{10}{-2} \qquad \text{\textit{Since x is multiplied by -2, divide both sides}}$$
$$\qquad \qquad \quad \text{\textit{by -2 to undo the multiplication.}}$$
$$x = -5 \qquad \text{\textit{The solution set is \{-5\}.}}$$

 Solve each equation. Check your answer.
2a. $2a + 3 - 8a = 8$ **2b.** $-8 - 2d + 2 = 4$ **2c.** $4x - 8 + 2x = 40$

EXAMPLE 3 **Simplifying Using the Distributive Property**

Solve each equation.

A $9 = 6 - (x + 2)$

$$9 = 6 + (-1)(x + 2) \qquad \text{\textit{Write subtraction as addition of the}}$$
$$\qquad \qquad \qquad \qquad \quad \text{\textit{opposite.}}$$
$$9 = 6 + (-1)(x) + (-1)(2) \quad \text{\textit{Distribute -1.}}$$
$$9 = 6 - x - 2 \qquad \text{\textit{Simplify.}}$$
$$9 = 6 - 2 - x \qquad \text{\textit{Commutative Property of Addition}}$$
$$9 = \quad 4 - x \qquad \text{\textit{Combine like terms.}}$$
$$\underline{-4 \quad -4} \qquad \text{\textit{Since 4 is added to $-x$, subtract 4 from}}$$
$$5 = \quad -x \qquad \quad \text{\textit{both sides.}}$$
$$\frac{5}{-1} = \frac{-x}{-1} \qquad \text{\textit{Since x is multiplied by -1, divide both}}$$
$$\qquad \qquad \quad \text{\textit{sides by -1.}}$$
$$-5 = x$$

> **Helpful Hint**
>
> You can think of a negative sign as a coefficient of -1.
> $-(x + 2) = -1(x + 2)$
> $-x = -1x$

B $4(x + 1) + 2(x - 7) = 50$

$$4(x + 1) + 2(x - 7) = \quad 50$$
$$4(x) + 4(1) + 2(x) + 2(-7) = \quad 50 \qquad \text{\textit{Distribute 4 and 2.}}$$
$$4x + 4 + 2x - 14 = \quad 50 \qquad \text{\textit{Simplify.}}$$
$$4x + 2x + 4 - 14 = \quad 50 \qquad \text{\textit{Commutative Property of Addition}}$$
$$6x - 10 = \quad 50 \qquad \text{\textit{Combine like terms.}}$$
$$\underline{+10 \quad +10} \qquad \text{\textit{Since 10 is subtracted from 6x, add}}$$
$$6x \quad = \quad 60 \qquad \quad \text{\textit{10 to both sides.}}$$
$$\frac{6x}{6} = \frac{60}{6} \qquad \text{\textit{Since x is multiplied by 6, divide}}$$
$$\qquad \qquad \quad \text{\textit{both sides by 6.}}$$
$$x = \quad 10$$

 **Solve each equation. Check your answer.**
3a. $3(a + 1) - 4 = 5$ **3b.** $-4(2 - y) = 8$ **3c.** $d + 3(d - 4) = 20$

EXAMPLE 4 *Fitness Application*

A martial arts school is offering a special where a new student can enroll for half price, after paying a $12.50 application fee. Ten students enrolled, and the instructor collected a total of $325. Write and solve an equation to find the regular price of enrollment.

Let p represent the regular price of enrollment.

10 students each paid	(half the regular price	plus	$12.50)	for a total of	$325
10	$\left(\dfrac{p}{2}\right.$	+	$12.50\Big)$	=	325

$$10\left(\frac{p}{2} + 12.50\right) = 325$$

$$10\left(\frac{p}{2}\right) + 10(12.50) = 325 \qquad \text{\textit{Distribute 10.}}$$

$$5p + 125 = 325 \qquad \text{\textit{Simplify.}}$$

$$5p + 125 = 325$$

$$\underline{-125 \qquad -125} \qquad \text{\textit{Since 125 is added to 5p, subtract}}$$
$$5p \quad = \quad 200 \qquad \text{\textit{125 from both sides to undo the addition.}}$$

$$\frac{5p}{5} = \frac{200}{5} \qquad \text{\textit{Since p is multiplied by 5, divide both sides by 5 to undo the multiplication.}}$$
$$p = 40$$

The regular price of enrollment is $40.

CHECK IT OUT!

4a. At a local gym, there is a joining fee of $59.95 and a monthly membership fee. Sara and Martin both joined this gym. Their combined cost for 12 months was $1319.90. How much is the monthly fee?

4b. Lily and 4 of her friends want to enroll in a yoga class. After enrollment, the studio requires a $7 processing fee. The 5 girls pay a total of $125.75. How much does the class cost?

THINK AND DISCUSS

1. What would be your first step in solving the equation $3(z + 12) = 16$?

2. When an equation contains several operations, how do you know which operation to undo first?

3. GET ORGANIZED Copy and complete the graphic organizer. In each box, write and solve a multi-step equation. Use addition, subtraction, multiplication, and division at least one time each.

Solving Multi-Step Equations	

California
Standards Practice
◆ 4.0, ◆ 5.0, 25.2

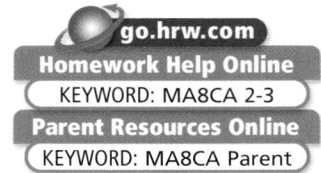

go.hrw.com
Homework Help Online
KEYWORD: MA8CA 2-3
Parent Resources Online
KEYWORD: MA8CA Parent

GUIDED PRACTICE

SEE EXAMPLE 1
p. 85

Solve each equation. Check your answer.

1. $\dfrac{d+3}{4} = 2$

2. $\dfrac{3x-2}{8} = 2$

3. $\dfrac{6a-1}{7} = 1$

4. $\dfrac{n+3}{4} = 12$

5. $\dfrac{2h-5}{2} = 0.5$

6. $\dfrac{10k+9}{4} = 5$

SEE EXAMPLE 2
p. 86

7. $9 - 2c + c = -13$

8. $15y + 21 + 10 = 61$

9. $8 = 3r - 5 + 4$

10. $42 = 4d - 6d + 6$

11. $2x + 0.3 - x = 3.3$

12. $2a + 3 + 2a = 11$

SEE EXAMPLE 3
p. 86

13. $3(x - 4) = 36$

14. $t(4 - 1) + 9 = 27$

15. $5(1 - 2w) + 8w = 15$

16. $17 = 4(a - 2) + 2a$

17. $\dfrac{1}{2}(m - 6) = 12$

18. $2\left(\dfrac{x}{4} - 1\right) = 8$

SEE EXAMPLE 4
p. 87

19. Kathryn organized her books onto 4 shelves. The top shelf holds 5 books, the second shelf holds 7, and the 2 bottom shelves hold the same number of books. Kathryn has a total of 24 books. How many books does each bottom shelf hold?

PRACTICE AND PROBLEM SOLVING

Independent Practice

For Exercises	See Example
20–22	1
23–28	2
29–34	3
35–36	4

Extra Practice
Skills Practice p. EP4
Application Practice p. EP25

Solve each equation. Check your answer.

20. $\dfrac{x-1}{2} = 5$

21. $6 = \dfrac{2w+3}{5}$

22. $\dfrac{-3+y}{4} = 25$

23. $5x - 2x + 3 = 24$

24. $11 = 2g + 6 - 5$

25. $2 + 0.5g + 9 = 61$

26. $4h - 7 + 2h = 7$

27. $34 = -5 - 6t + 3t$

28. $1.5v - 0.9v + 2.1 = 4.5$

29. $3(d + 5) = 23$

30. $8(x + 2) = 32$

31. $-12 = 5(k - 2)$

32. $15 = 3(k - 6)$

33. $5 = \dfrac{1}{2}(x - 6)$

34. $6(y - 4) = 0$

35. **Consumer Economics** Amanda and Casey's total restaurant bill, including tip, was $34. Amanda's portion of the bill was twice as much as Casey's, and they each left a tip of $2. How much did each person pay?

36. Marissa is buying a shirt for each of her brothers and each of her 2 sisters. Each shirt costs $7.50, and she spends a total of $30. How many brothers does Marissa have?

Solve each equation. Check your answer.

37. $5(w + 10) = 45$

38. $9(p - 2) = 54$

39. $\dfrac{1}{2} = \dfrac{1}{4}(y - 8)$

40. $2x + \dfrac{3}{4} + \dfrac{6}{4} = 16.75$

41. $2.3w - 3.2 + 4.1 = -6$

42. $19 = -4(h + 5) + h$

43. $3(2x - 4) + \dfrac{x}{2} = 1$

44. $2.5(4 - 2m) = 50$

45. $-4(d + 1) + 2(d - 2) = \dfrac{10}{3}$

Write an equation to represent each relationship. Then solve.

46. Three increased by a number, all multiplied by 6, equals 36.

47. Sixteen plus seven decreased by 4 times some number equals 3.

48. Three times the sum of a number and 4, minus the number, is equal to 18.

49. One-half of a number added to twice the difference of the number and 5 equals 0.

Geometry Write and solve an equation to find the value of x for each triangle. (*Hint:* The sum of the angle measures in any triangle is 180°.)

50.
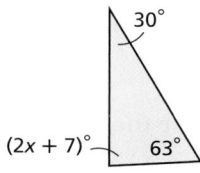
30°
$(2x + 7)°$ 63°

51.
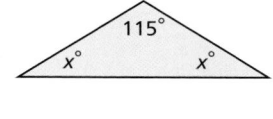
115°
$x°$ $x°$

52.
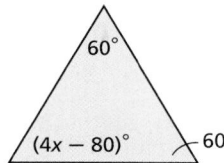
60°
$(4x - 80)°$ 60°

Solve each equation.

53. $x + 3 - 2x + 5 = 10$

54. $9x - 5 - 6x - 1.3 = 0$

55. $-5 = 7g + 5 - 6g$

56. $3(x - 2) - 5(2x + 1) = 3$

57. $5(2y - 7) + 8(y + 6) = 31$

58. $4x - 3(6 + x) - 1 = 2$

59. $17 - (4 - 6z) + 4 = 42$

60. $42r - 2(13 - 5r) + 7 = 85$

61. The sum of two consecutive whole numbers is 5. What are the two numbers? (*Hint:* Let n represent the first number. Then $n + 1$ is the next consecutive whole number.)

62. Stan's, Mark's, and Wayne's ages are consecutive whole numbers. Stan is the youngest, and Wayne is the oldest. The sum of their ages is 111. Find their ages.

63. The sum of two consecutive even whole numbers is 206. What are the two numbers? (*Hint:* Let n represent the first number. What expression can you use to represent the second number?)

64. **Multi-Step** Alexis and Martin helped the school set chairs in rows for an assembly. They put the same number of chairs in each row. Using the 92 chairs available, Alexis made 4 rows with 2 chairs left over while Martin made 5 rows with no chairs left over.

   a. Let c represent the number of chairs in each row. Write an equation that can be used to find c.

   b. Solve your equation from part **a.**

   c. Alexis and Martin are asked to remove 2 chairs from each row. Then how many of the 92 chairs were not used for the assembly?

65. **///ERROR ANALYSIS///** Below are two possible solutions to $3x + 5 - 4x = 19$. Which is incorrect? Explain the error.

A

$3x + 5 - 4x = 19$
$3x + 4x - 5 = 19$
$7x + 5 = 19$
$7x = 14$
$x = 2$

B

$3x + 5 - 4x = 19$
$3x - 4x + 5 = 19$
$-x + 5 = 19$
$-x = 14$
$x = -14$

CONCEPT CONNECTION

66. This problem will help prepare you for the Concept Connection on page 100.

   a. Suppose firefighters can extinguish a wildfire at a rate of 60 acres per day. Use this information to complete the table.

   b. Use the last row in the table to write an equation for acres A extinguished in terms of the number of days d.

Days	Acres
1	60
2	
3	180
4	
5	
d	

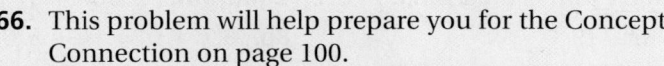

67. Critical Thinking The equation $3(2x - 5) + 4(x - 2) = 12$ requires several properties of multiplication and addition to solve. Name the properties.

68. Write About It Write a series of steps that you can use to solve any multi-step equation.

Multiple Choice For Exercises 69 and 70, choose the best answer.

69. Josh and Howard collect comic books. Josh has 12 more than Howard has, and together they want to triple their collection for a total of 66 comic books. Which equation can be used to find the number of comic books Howard owns?

ⓐ $3(2h - 12) = 66$ ⓒ $3h + 12 = 66$

ⓑ $2h + 6 = 66$ ⓓ $3(2h + 12) = 66$

70. What is the first incorrect step in the solution shown?

$$\frac{4g - 3}{7} = 3$$

Step 1: $4g - 3 = 21$

Step 2: $4g = 18$

Step 3: $g = 4.5$

ⓐ Step 1   ⓒ Step 3

ⓑ Step 2   ⓓ All steps are correct.

71. Gridded Response A band earns \$50 a show plus a bonus for every show they play. Last month they played 5 times for a total of \$300. How much is the bonus?

CHALLENGE AND EXTEND

Solve each equation. Check your answer.

72. $\frac{9}{2}x + 18 + 3x = \frac{11}{2}$ **73.** $12\left(\frac{1}{4}x - 1\right) = 12$

74. $(x + 6) - (2x + 7) - 3x = -9$ **75.** $(4x + 2) - (12x + 8) + 2(5x - 3) = 6 + 11$

76. $2(5 - y) - 5(y + 3) = -26$ **77.** $t(3 + 2) - 6(t - 5) - 22 = 6$

78. Given the equation $\dfrac{3x + 2(x + 6)}{2(5 + 4)} = 14$, answer the following questions.

    a. Find two equivalent equations.

    b. Reasoning Without solving the equation, predict what would happen to the solution if the numerator changed to $3x + 3(x + 6)$.

🐻 **SPIRAL STANDARDS REVIEW**   🔑 **7AF1.3,** 🔑 **7AF4.1, 1.0**

Name the property that is illustrated in each equation. *(Lesson 1-6)*

79. $-19 + n = n - 19$ **80.** $6(k + b) = (k + b)6$

Simplify each expression by combining like terms. *(Lesson 1-7)*

81. $5m + 3m$ **82.** $22c^2 - 14c$ **83.** $102v + 16v$

84. $51b - b$ **85.** $12c + x$ **86.** $\frac{1}{2}p + \frac{1}{2}$

Solve each equation. Check your answer. *(Lesson 2-2)*

87. $10w + 4 = 34$ **88.** $11 = 3d - 4$ **89.** $38 = -6d + 2$

True Equations

An equation such as $2x + 2 = 6$ is neither true nor false until a value is substituted for x. In Lessons 2-1 through 2-3, you have been solving equations like this one to find the value or values of x that make the equation true. These equations are considered "sometimes true"— they are true when x equals a solution and false when x equals any other value.

Use with Lesson 2-4

Equations may also be "always true" or "never true".

California Standards

25.3 Given a specific algebraic statement involving **linear**, quadratic, or absolute value expressions or **equations** or inequalities, **students determine whether the statement is true sometimes, always, or never.**

Activity

Determine whether each equation is sometimes, always, or never true.

$$3 + x = x + 3 \qquad 2x = x + 3 \qquad 3x + 2 = x + 2x$$

Use a spreadsheet to test several values of x in each equation.

1 Set up a column for x and a column for each equation. Under x, enter several values.

	A	B	C	D
1	x	3 + x = x + 3	2x = x + 3	3x+2=x+2x
2	-4	=3+A2=A2+3	=2*A2=A2+3	=3*A2+2=A2+2*A2
3	-3			

2 Enter the formulas as shown into row 2. These formulas will return TRUE if the equation is true for the value of x and FALSE if it is not.

3 Use the mouse to click on the lower right corner of cell B2. Hold down the mouse button and drag the cursor down to the last row in which you have entered an x-value. The equation $3 + x = x + 3$ appears to always be true. In fact, you know it is always true because it is an example of the Commutative Property of Addition.

	A	B	C	D
1	x	3 + x = x + 3	2x = x + 3	3x+2=x+2x
2	-4	TRUE	FALSE	FALSE
3	-3	TRUE	FALSE	FALSE
4	-2	TRUE	FALSE	FALSE
5	-1	TRUE	FALSE	FALSE
6	0	TRUE	FALSE	FALSE
7	1	TRUE	FALSE	FALSE
8	2	TRUE	FALSE	FALSE
9	3	TRUE	TRUE	FALSE
10	4	TRUE	FALSE	FALSE
11	5	TRUE	FALSE	FALSE

4 Repeat Step 3 for columns C and D. The equation $2x = x + 3$ is true only when $x = 3$. In other words, it is sometimes true. The equation $3x + 2 = x + 2x$ appears to never be true. If you simplify the right side of this equation, you get $3x + 2 = 3x$. You can see that this equation is never true because $3x + 2$ will always be greater than $3x$ for any value of x.

To test more values of x, enter more values of x into column A and copy the formulas as described above.

Try This

Determine whether each equation is sometimes, always, or never true.

1. $4a + 2 = 3a$

2. $-3z = 4z - 7z$

3. $5c + 8 = 5c + 8$

4. $6x = 2x - 8x$

5. $4x + 10 = 7x$

6. $6 + 2a = a + 5 + a$

7. $-4 + 3c + 6 = 2c + 2 + c$

8. $6g + 8 = -9 + 6g$

9. $3y + 4 = -2 + 5y$

2-4 Solving Equations with Variables on Both Sides

California Standards

← **4.0** Students simplify expressions before solving linear equations and inequalities **in one variable,** such as $3(2x - 5) + 4(x - 2) = 12$.

← **5.0** Students solve multi-step problems, including word problems, involving linear equations and linear inequalities in one variable and provide justification for each step.

Vocabulary
identity

Why learn this?
You can compare prices and find the best value.

Many phone companies offer low rates for long-distance calls without requiring customers to sign up for their services. To compare rates, solve an equation with variables on both sides.

To solve an equation like this, use inverse operations to "collect" variable terms on one side of the equation.

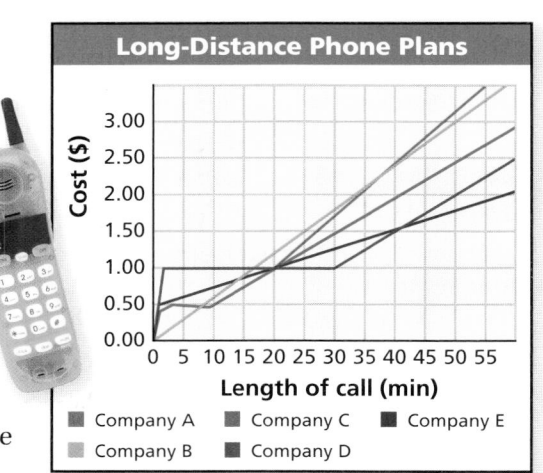

Long-Distance Phone Plans

Cost ($)
Length of call (min)

■ Company A   ■ Company C   ■ Company E
■ Company B   ■ Company D

EXAMPLE 1 Solving Equations with Variables on Both Sides

Solve each equation.

A $7k = 4k + 15$

$$
\begin{aligned}
7k &= 4k + 15 \\
\underline{-4k} & \underline{-4k} \\
3k &= 15 \\
\frac{3k}{3} &= \frac{15}{3} \\
k &= 5
\end{aligned}
$$

To collect the variable terms on one side, subtract 4k from both sides.

Since k is multiplied by 3, divide both sides by 3 to undo the multiplication.

> **Helpful Hint**
>
> Equations are often easier to solve when the variable has a positive coefficient. Keep this in mind when deciding on which side to "collect" variable terms.

B $5x - 2 = 3x + 4$

$$
\begin{aligned}
5x - 2 &= 3x + 4 \\
\underline{-3x} & \underline{-3x} \\
2x - 2 &= 4 \\
\underline{+2} & \underline{+2} \\
2x &= 6 \\
\frac{2x}{2} &= \frac{6}{2} \\
x &= 3
\end{aligned}
$$

To collect the variable terms on one side, subtract 3x from both sides.

Since 2 is subtracted from 2x, add 2 to both sides to undo the subtraction.

Since x is multiplied by 2, divide both sides by 2 to undo the multiplication.

Check

$$
\begin{array}{c|c}
5x - 2 &= 3x + 4 \\
\hline
5(3) - 2 & 3(3) + 4 \\
15 - 2 & 9 + 4 \\
13 & 13 \checkmark
\end{array}
$$

To check your solution, substitute 3 for x in the original equation.

 Solve each equation. Check your answer.

1a. $4b + 2 = 3b$

1b. $0.5 + 0.3y = 0.7y - 0.3$

To solve more complicated equations, you may need to first simplify by using the Distributive Property or combining like terms.

EXAMPLE 2 **Simplifying Each Side Before Solving Equations**

Solve each equation.

A $2(y + 6) = 3y$

$$2(y + 6) = 3y$$
$$2(y) + 2(6) = 3y$$
$$2y + 12 = 3y$$
$$\underline{-2y \qquad -2y}$$
$$12 = y$$

Distribute 2 to the expression in parentheses.

To collect the variable terms on one side, subtract 2y from both sides.

Check
$$2(y + 6) = 3y$$

$2(12 + 6)$	$3(12)$
$2(18)$	36
36	$36 \checkmark$

To check your solution, substitute 12 for y in the original equation.

B $2k - 5 = 3(1 - 2k)$

$$2k - 5 = 3(1 - 2k)$$
$$2k - 5 = 3(1) - 3(2k)$$
$$2k - 5 = 3 - 6k$$
$$\underline{+6k \qquad\qquad +6k}$$
$$8k - 5 = 3$$
$$\underline{\quad +5 \quad +5}$$
$$8k = 8$$
$$\frac{8k}{8} = \frac{8}{8}$$
$$k = 1$$

Distribute 3 to the expression in parentheses.

To collect the variable terms on one side, add 6k to both sides.

Since 5 is subtracted from 8k, add 5 to both sides.

Since k is multiplied by 8, divide both sides by 8.

C $3 - 5b + 2b = -2 - 2(1 - b)$

$$3 - 5b + 2b = -2 - 2(1 - b)$$
$$3 - 5b + 2b = -2 - 2(1) - 2(-b)$$
$$3 - 5b + 2b = -2 - 2 + 2b$$
$$3 - 3b = -4 + 2b$$
$$\underline{\quad +3b \qquad\quad +3b}$$
$$3 = -4 + 5b$$
$$\underline{+4 \qquad\quad +4}$$
$$7 = 5b$$
$$\frac{7}{5} = \frac{5b}{5}$$
$$1.4 = b$$

Distribute −2 to the expression in parentheses.

Combine like terms.

Add 3b to both sides.

Since −4 is added to 5b, add 4 to both sides.

Since b is multiplied by 5, divide both sides by 5.

Solve each equation. Check your answer.

2a. $\frac{1}{2}(b + 6) = \frac{3}{2}b - 1$

2b. $3x + 15 - 9 = 2(x + 2)$

An **identity** is an equation that is always true, no matter what value is substituted for the variable. The solution set of an identity is all real numbers. Some equations are always false. Their solution sets are empty. In other words, their solution sets contain no elements.

EXAMPLE **3** **Infinitely Many Solutions or No Solutions**

Solve each equation.

A $x + 4 - 6x = 6 - 5x - 2$

$x + 4 - 6x = 6 - 5x - 2$ *Identify like terms.*

$4 - 5x = 4 - 5x$ *Combine like terms on the left and the right.*

The statement $4 - 5x = 4 - 5x$ is true for all values of x. The equation $x + 4 - 6x = 6 - 5x - 2$ is an identity. All values of x will make the equation true. In other words, all real numbers are solutions.

B $-8x + 6 + 9x = -17 + x$

$-8x + 6 + 9x = -17 + x$ *Identify like terms.*

$x + 6 = -17 + x$ *Combine like terms.*

$\underline{- x - x}$ *Subtract x from both sides.*

$6 = -17$ ✗   *False statement; the solution set is ∅.*

Writing Math

The empty set can be written as ∅ or {}.

The equation $-8x + 6 + 9x = -17 + x$ is always false. There is no value of x that will make the equation true. There are no solutions.

**CHECK IT OUT!** Solve each equation.

3a. $4y + 7 - y = 10 + 3y$ **3b.** $2c + 7 + c = -14 + 3c + 21$

EXAMPLE **4** *Consumer Application*

The long-distance rates of two phone companies are shown in the table. How long is a call that costs the same amount no matter which company is used? What is the cost of that call?

Phone Company	Charges
Company A	36¢ plus 3¢ per minute
Company B	6¢ per minute

Let m represent minutes, and write expressions for each company's cost.

When is	36¢	plus	3¢ per minute	times number of minutes	the same as	6¢ per minute	times number of minutes	?
	36	+	3	(m)	=	6	(m)	

$36 + 3m = 6m$

$\underline{-3m -3m}$ *To collect the variable terms on one side,*

$36 = 3m$ *subtract 3m from both sides.*

$\dfrac{36}{3} = \dfrac{3m}{3}$ *Since m is multiplied by 3, divide both sides by 3 to undo the multiplication.*

$12 = m$

The charges will be the same for a 12-minute call using either phone service. To find the cost of this call, evaluate either expression for $m = 12$:

$36 + 3m = 36 + 3(12) = 36 + 36 = 72$ $6m = 6(12) = 72$

The cost of a 12-minute call through either company is 72¢.

**CHECK IT OUT!** **4.** Four times Greg's age, decreased by 3 is equal to 3 times Greg's age, increased by 7. How old is Greg?

THINK AND DISCUSS

1. Tell which of the following is an identity. Explain your answer.

   a. $4(a + 3) - 6 = 3(a + 3) - 6$ **b.** $8.3x - 9 + 0.7x = 2 + 9x - 11$

2. GET ORGANIZED Copy and complete the graphic organizer. In each box, write an example of an equation that has the indicated number of solutions.

> An equation with variables on both sides can have…
>
> | one solution: | many solutions: | no solution: |
> | --- | --- | --- |

2-4

Exercises

California Standards Practice

✦ 4.0 , ✦ 5.0, 25.3

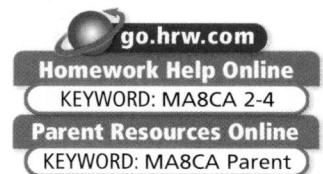
go.hrw.com
Homework Help Online
KEYWORD: MA8CA 2-4
Parent Resources Online
KEYWORD: MA8CA Parent

GUIDED PRACTICE

1. Vocabulary How can you recognize an *identity*?

SEE EXAMPLE **1**
p. 92

Solve each equation. Check your answer.

2. $2c - 5 = c + 4$ **3.** $8r + 4 = 10 + 2r$

4. $2x - 1 = x + 11$ **5.** $28 - 0.3y = 0.7y - 12$

SEE EXAMPLE **2**
p. 93

6. $-2(x + 3) = 4x - 3$ **7.** $3c - 4c + 1 = 5c + 2 + 3$

8. $1 + \frac{3}{5}(q - 4) = \frac{2}{5}(q + 1)$ **9.** $5 - (t + 3) = -1 + 2(t - 3)$

SEE EXAMPLE **3**
p. 94

10. $7x - 4 = -2x + 1 + 9x - 5$ **11.** $8x + 6 - 9x = 2 - x - 15$

12. $6y = 8 - 9 + 6y$ **13.** $6 - 2x - 1 = 4x + 8 - 6x - 3$

SEE EXAMPLE **4**
p. 94

14. Consumer Economics A house-painting company charges $376 plus $12 per hour. Another painting company charges $280 plus $15 per hour.

  a. How long is a job for which both companies will charge the same amount?

  b. What will that cost be?

PRACTICE AND PROBLEM SOLVING

Solve each equation. Check your answer.

15. $7a - 17 = 4a + 1$ **16.** $2b - 5 = 8b + 1$ **17.** $4x - 2 = 3x + 4$

18. $2x - 5 = 4x - 1$ **19.** $8x - 2 = 3x + 12.25$ **20.** $5x + 2 = 3x$

21. $3c - 5 = 2c + 5$ **22.** $-17 - 2x = 6 - x$ **23.** $3(t - 1) = 9 + t$

24. $5 - x - 2 = 3 + 4x + 5$ **25.** $2(x + 4) = 3(x - 2)$ **26.** $3m - 10 = 2(4m - 5)$

27. $5 - (n - 4) = 3(n + 2)$ **28.** $6(x + 7) - 20 = 6x$ **29.** $8(x + 1) = 4x - 8$

30. $x - 4 - 3x = -2x - 3 - 1$ **31.** $-2(x + 2) = -2x + 1$ **32.** $2(x + 4) - 5 = 2x + 3$

For Exercises	See Example
15–22	1
23–29	2
30–32	3
33	4

Independent Practice

Extra Practice

Skills Practice p. EP5

Application Practice p. EP25

33. **Multi-Step** Justin and Tyson are beginning an exercise program to train for football season. Justin weighs 150 lb and hopes to gain 2 lb per week. Tyson weighs 195 lb and hopes to lose 1 lb per week.

    a. If the plan works, in how many weeks will the boys weigh the same amount?

    b. What will that weight be?

Reasoning Tell whether each equation is sometimes, always, or never true.

34. $5(x + 3) - 2 = 5x + 13$

35. $2n + 1 = 2(n + 1) - 1$

36. $3(k - 1) - 3(2k + 2) = 24$

Solve each equation. Check your answer.

37. $2x - 2 = 4x + 6$ 38. $3x + 5 = 2x + 2$ 39. $4x + 3 = 5x - 4$

40. $-\dfrac{2}{5}p + 2 = \dfrac{1}{5}p + 11$ 41. $5x + 24 = 2x + 15$ 42. $5x - 10 = 14 - 3x$

43. $12 - 6x = 10 - 5x$ 44. $5x - 7 = -6x - 29$ 45. $1.8x + 2.8 = 2.5x + 2.1$

46. $2.6x + 18 = 2.4x + 22$ 47. $1 - 3x = 2x + 8$ 48. $\dfrac{1}{2}(8 - 6h) = h$

49. $\dfrac{1}{3}(x + 1) = \dfrac{2}{9}x + \dfrac{7}{9}$ 50. $9x - 8 + 4x = 7x + 16$ 51. $3(2x - 1) + 5 = 6(x + 1)$

52. **Travel** Rapid Rental Car company charges a $40 rental fee, $15 for gas, and $0.25 per mile driven. For the same car, Capital Cars charges $45 for rental and gas and $0.35 per mile.

    a. Find the number of miles for which the companies' charges will be the same. Then find that charge.

    b. The Barre family estimates that they will drive about 95 miles during their vacation to Hershey, Pennsylvania. Which company should they rent their car from? Explain.

    c. **What if...?** The Barres have extended their vacation and now estimate that they will drive about 120 miles. Should they still rent from the same company as in part **b**? Why or why not?

    d. Give a general rule for deciding which company to rent from.

 53. **Geometry** The triangles shown have the same perimeter. What is the value of x?

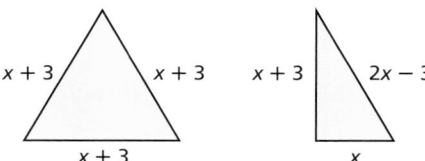

CONCEPT CONNECTION

54. This problem will prepare you for the Concept Connection on page 100.

    a. A fire currently covers 420 acres and continues to spread at a rate of 60 acres per day. How many total acres will be covered in the next 2 days?

    b. Write an expression for the total area covered by the fire in d days.

    c. The firefighters estimate that they can put out the fire at a rate of 80 acres per day. Write an expression for the total area that the firefighters can put out in d days.

    d. Set the expressions in parts **b** and **c** equal. Solve for d. What does d represent?

55. Critical Thinking Write an equation with variables on both sides that has no solution.

56. Biology The graph shows the maximum recorded speeds of the four fastest mammals.

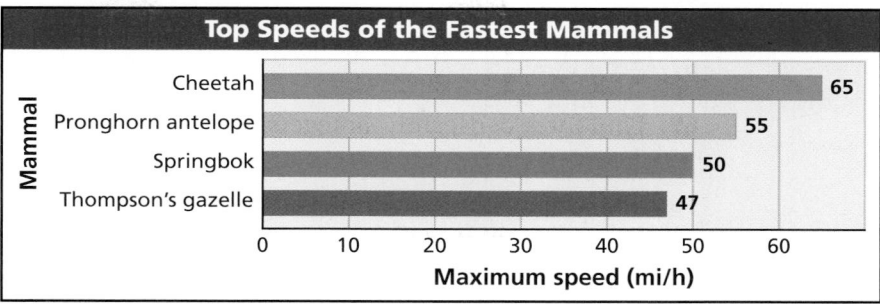

Top Speeds of the Fastest Mammals

Mammal	Maximum speed (mi/h)
Cheetah	65
Pronghorn antelope	55
Springbok	50
Thompson's gazelle	47

Source: The Top 10 of Everything

a. Write an expression for the distance in miles that a Thompson's gazelle can run at top speed in x hours.

b. Write an expression for the distance in miles that a cheetah can run at top speed in x hours.

c. A cheetah and a Thompson's gazelle are running at their top speeds. The cheetah is one mile behind the gazelle. Write an expression for the distance the cheetah must run to catch up with the gazelle.

d. Write and solve an equation that represents how long the cheetah will have to run at top speed to catch up with the gazelle.

e. A cheetah can maintain its top speed for only 300 yards. Will the cheetah be able to catch the gazelle? Explain. (*Hint:* 1 mile = 1760 yards)

57. Write About It Write a series of steps that you can use to solve any equation with variables on both sides.

Multiple Choice For Exercises 58–61, choose the best answer.

58. Lindsey's monthly magazine subscription costs \$1.25 per issue. Kenzie's monthly subscription costs \$1.50 per issue, but she received her first 2 issues free. Which equation can be used to find the number of months after which the girls will have paid the same amount?

Ⓐ $1.25m = 1.50m - 2$ Ⓒ $1.25m = 1.50(m - 2)$

Ⓑ $1.25m = 1.50m - 2m$ Ⓓ $1.25m = 3m - 1.50$

59. What is the numerical solution of the equation *7 times a number equals 3 less than 5 times that number*?

Ⓐ -1.5 Ⓑ 0.25 Ⓒ $\frac{2}{3}$ Ⓓ 4

60. Three packs of markers cost \$9.00 less than 5 packs of markers. Which equation best represents this situation?

Ⓐ $5x + 9 = 3x$ Ⓒ $3x - 9 = 5x$

Ⓑ $3x + 9 = 5x$ Ⓓ $9 - 3x = 5x$

61. Nicole has \$120. If she saves \$20 per week, in how many days will she have \$500?

Ⓐ 19 Ⓑ 25 Ⓒ 133 Ⓓ 175

62. Gridded Response Solve $-2(x - 1) + 5x = 2(2x - 1)$.

CHALLENGE AND EXTEND

Solve each equation.

63. $4x + 2[4 - 2(x + 2)] = 2x - 4$

64. $\dfrac{x + 5}{2} + \dfrac{x - 1}{2} = \dfrac{x - 1}{3}$

65. $\dfrac{2}{3}w - \dfrac{1}{4} = \dfrac{2}{3}\left(w - \dfrac{1}{4}\right)$

66. $-5 - 7 - 3f = -f - 2(f + 6)$

67. $\dfrac{2}{3}x + \dfrac{1}{2} = \dfrac{3}{5}x - \dfrac{5}{6}$

68. $x - \dfrac{1}{4} = \dfrac{x}{3} + 7\dfrac{3}{4}$

69. Find three consecutive integers such that twice the greatest integer is 2 less than 3 times the least integer.

70. Find three consecutive integers such that twice the least integer is 12 more than the greatest integer.

71. Rob had twice as much money as Sam. Then Sam gave Rob 1 quarter, 2 nickels, and 3 pennies. Rob then gave Sam 8 dimes. If they now have the same amount of money, how much money did Rob originally have? Check your answer.

SPIRAL STANDARDS REVIEW
6NS2.1, 6AF1.2, ☞ 7NS1.2, ☞ 7AF4.1

Write an expression for the perimeter of each figure. *(Lesson 1-1)*

72. square with side x cm

73. equilateral triangle with side y cm

Multiply or divide. *(Lesson 1-3)*

74. $6.1 \div 0$

75. $3(-21)$

76. $0 \div \dfrac{7}{8}$

77. $\dfrac{2}{5} \div \dfrac{1}{10}$

78. $5 \div (-5)$

79. $\dfrac{-16}{-8}$

80. $-1000 \div (-0.001)$

81. $500(-0.25)$

Solve each equation. *(Lesson 2-2)*

82. $4x - 44 = 8$

83. $2x - 6 = 24$

84. $-1 = \dfrac{x}{4} - 3$

85. $2x + 6 = 12$

Career Path

Beth Simmons
Biology major

go.hrw.com
Career Resources Online
KEYWORD: MA8CA Career

Q: What math classes did you take in high school?
A: Algebra 1 and 2, Geometry, and Precalculus

Q: What math classes have you taken in college?
A: Two calculus classes and a calculus-based physics class

Q: How do you use math?
A: I use math a lot in physics. Sometimes I would think a calculus topic was totally useless, and then we would use it in physics class! In biology, I use math to understand populations.

Q: What career options are you considering?
A: When I graduate, I could teach, or I could go to graduate school and do more research. I have a lot of options.

LOGICAL REASONING

Deductive Reasoning and Equations

Use with Lessons 2-1 through 2-4

Deductive reasoning is the process of using logic along with known facts, definitions, and properties to reach a conclusion. In mathematics, deductive reasoning can be used to prove whether given statements are true.

You may not realize it, but you use deductive reasoning every time you solve an equation. In fact, solving an equation can be thought of as a proof.

Example

California Standards

24.1 Students explain the difference between inductive and deductive reasoning and identify and **provide examples of each.** *Also covered:* 🔑 **5.0, 24.2, 25.1, 25.2**

Solve $3(x + 5) + 2(x + 3) = 26$. **Give a reason for each step in your solution process. Identify the conditional statement that is proved and its hypothesis and conclusion.**

One way to write down deductive reasoning is to use two columns—one for each step or statement and one for the facts, definitions, and/or properties that support each step.

Statements	Reasons
1. $3(x + 5) + 2(x + 3) = 26$	Given
2. $3x + 15 + 2x + 6 = 26$	Distributive Property
3. $(3x + 2x) + (15 + 6) = 26$	Commutative and Associative Properties of Addition
4. $5x + 21 = 26$	Combine like terms.
5. $5x = 5$	Subtraction Property of Equality (Subtract 21 from both sides.)
6. $x = 1$	Division Property of Equality (Divide both sides by 5.)

The above proves the conditional statement "If $3(x + 5) + 2(x + 3) = 26$, then $x = 1$."

Hypothesis: $3(x + 5) + 2(x + 3) = 26$ Conclusion: $x = 1$

Try This

Solve each equation. Give a reason for each step in your solution process. Identify the conditional statement that is proved and its hypothesis and conclusion.

1. $x - 2 = 4$

2. $x + 6 = 16$

3. $-5x = 25$

4. $\dfrac{x}{4} = 13$

5. $-2x + 5 = 9$

6. $6x - 5 = 2x - 21$

7. $6(x - 5) = 10$

8. $6x + 1 + x = 10 - 12$

9. What is the error in the solution below? Write a correct solution.

Statements	Reasons
1. $5x + 1 = 7$	Given
2. $5x = 8$	Addition Property of Equality (Add 1 to both sides.)
3. $x = \dfrac{8}{5}$	Division Property of Equality (Divide both sides by 5.)

CONCEPT CONNECTION

Equations and Formulas

All Fired Up A large forest fire in the western United States has been burning for 14 days, spreading to cover approximately 3850 acres. Firefighters have been doing their best to contain the fire, but hot temperatures and high winds have prompted them to request additional help.

1. Find the average number of acres the fire covered each day for the first 14 days.

2. When the fire began, officials estimated that, with no additional firefighting help, the fire would spread to cover 9075 acres before being contained. Write and solve an equation to find the total number of days it would take for the fire to cover 9075 acres.

3. Additional help arrives on day 15, and when the firefighters contain the fire, it has spread to cover a total of only 5775 acres. How many days did it take to contain the fire after the help arrived?

4. The total cost of fighting the fire was approximately $1,440,000. Write and solve an equation to find the approximate cost per day of fighting the fire.

READY TO GO ON?

Quiz for Lessons 2-1 Through 2-4

2-1 Solving One-Step Equations

Solve each equation.

1. $x - 32 = -18$
2. $1.1 = m - 0.9$
3. $j + 4 = -17$
4. $\frac{9}{8} = g + \frac{1}{2}$

5. $\frac{h}{3} = -12$
6. $-2.8 = \frac{w}{-3}$
7. $42 = 3c$
8. $-0.1b = 3.7$

9. When she first purchased it, Soledad's computer had 400 GB of hard drive space. After six months, there were only 313 GB available. Write and solve an equation to find the amount of hard drive space that Soledad used in the first six months.

2-2 Solving Two-Step Equations

Solve each equation.

10. $2k + 15 = 29$
11. $-6a - 12 = 24$
12. $7 + 3b = -11$
13. $1.6 = 0.4n - 2$

14. $2r + 20 = 200$
15. $21 = 3g - 6$
16. $\frac{3}{5}k + 5 = 7$
17. $2.5x + 4.5 = -8$

18. Christine's video store membership cost $5.00, and it costs $3.50 to rent a DVD. Christine spent $29.50 her first month. How many DVDs did she rent?

19. A fund-raiser raised $2400, which was $\frac{3}{5}$ of the goal. Write and solve an equation to find the amount of the goal.

2-3 Solving Multi-Step Equations

Solve each equation.

20. $4(x - 7) = 2$
21. $\frac{2}{3} - \frac{y}{4} = \frac{5}{12}$

22. $5n + 6 - 3n = -12$
23. $\frac{3}{4}(8 + 2y) = 3$

24. A taxicab company charges $2.10 plus $0.80 per mile. Carmen paid a fare of $11.70. Write and solve an equation to find the number of miles she traveled.

25. If $2(x + 3) = 24$, find the value of $x - 6$.

2-4 Solving Equations with Variables on Both Sides

Solve each equation.

26. $4x - 3 = 2x + 5$
27. $3(2x - 5) = 2(3x - 2)$
28. $2(2t - 3) = 6(t + 2)$
29. $7(x + 5) = -7(x + 5)$

30. On the first day of the year, Diego had $700 in his savings account and started spending $35 a week. His brother Juan had $450 and started saving $15 a week. After how many weeks will the brothers have the same amount? What will that amount be?

2-5 Solving Proportions

California Standards

15.0 Students apply algebraic techniques to solve rate problems, work problems, and percent mixture problems.

Why learn this?

Proportions are used to draw accurate maps. (See Example 5.)

A **ratio** is a comparison of two quantities. The ratio of a to b can be written $a{:}b$ or $\frac{a}{b}$, where $b \neq 0$.

A statement that two ratios are equal, such as $\frac{1}{12} = \frac{2}{24}$, is called a **proportion**.

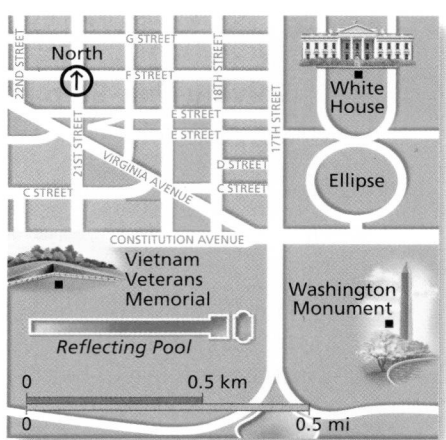

EXAMPLE 1   **Using Ratios**

Vocabulary

ratio   proportion
rate   unit rate
cross   percent
  products   scale
scale   scale
  drawing   model

The ratio of faculty members to students at a college is $1{:}15$. There are 675 students. How many faculty members are there?

$$\frac{\text{faculty}}{\text{students}} \longrightarrow \frac{1}{15}$$ *Write a ratio comparing faculty to students.*

$$\frac{1}{15} = \frac{x}{675}$$ *Write a proportion. Let x be the number of faculty members.*

$$675\left(\frac{x}{675}\right) = 675\left(\frac{1}{15}\right)$$ *Since x is divided by 675, multiply both sides by 675.*

$$x = 45$$ There are 45 faculty members.

 **1.** The ratio of red marbles to green marbles is $6{:}5$. There are 18 red marbles. How many green marbles are there?

A common application of proportions is *rates*. A **rate** is a ratio of two quantities with different units, such as $\frac{34\ \text{mi}}{2\ \text{gal}}$. Rates are usually written as *unit rates*. A **unit rate** is a rate with a second quantity of 1 unit, such as $\frac{17\ \text{mi}}{1\ \text{gal}}$ or 17 mi/gal. You can convert any rate to a unit rate.

EXAMPLE 2   **Finding Unit Rates**

Takeru Kobayashi of Japan ate 53.5 hot dogs in 12 minutes to win a contest. Find the unit rate. Round your answer to the nearest hundredth.

$$\frac{53.5}{12} = \frac{x}{1}$$ *Write a proportion to find an equivalent ratio with a second quantity of 1.*

$$4.46 \approx x$$ *Divide on the left side to find x.*

The unit rate is approximately 4.46 hot dogs per minute.

 Find each unit rate. Round to the nearest hundredth if necessary.

2a. Cory earns $52.50 in 7 hours.

2b. A machine seals 138 envelopes in 23 minutes.

In the proportion $\frac{a}{b} = \frac{c}{d}$, the products $a \cdot d$ and $b \cdot c$ are called **cross products**. You can solve a proportion for a missing value by using the Cross Products Property.

	Cross Products Property	
WORDS	**NUMBERS**	**ALGEBRA**
In a proportion, cross products are equal.	$\frac{2}{3} \diagdown\!\!\!\!\!\diagup \frac{4}{6}$ $2 \cdot 6 = 3 \cdot 4$	If $\frac{a}{b} \diagdown\!\!\!\!\!\diagup \frac{c}{d}$ and $b \neq 0$ and $d \neq 0$, then $ad = bc$.

EXAMPLE 3 **Solving Proportions**

Solve each proportion.

A $\dfrac{5}{9} = \dfrac{3}{w}$

$\dfrac{5}{9} \diagdown\!\!\!\!\!\diagup \dfrac{3}{w}$

$5(w) = 9(3)$ *Use cross products.*

$5w = 27$

$\dfrac{5w}{5} = \dfrac{27}{5}$ *Divide both sides by 5.*

$w = \dfrac{27}{5}$

B $\dfrac{8}{x + 10} = \dfrac{1}{12}$

$\dfrac{8}{x + 10} \diagdown\!\!\!\!\!\diagup \dfrac{1}{12}$

$8(12) = 1(x + 10)$ *Use cross products.*

$96 = x + 10$

$\dfrac{-10 \qquad -10}{86 = x}$ *Subtract 10 from both sides.*

 CHECK IT OUT! Solve each proportion. Check your answer.

3a. $\dfrac{-5}{2} = \dfrac{y}{8}$ **3b.** $\dfrac{g + 3}{5} = \dfrac{7}{4}$

Another common application of proportions is *percents*. A **percent** is a ratio that compares a number to 100. For example, $25\% = \frac{25}{100}$.

You can use the proportion $\frac{\text{part}}{\text{whole}} = \frac{\text{percent}}{100}$ to find unknown values.

EXAMPLE 4 **Percent Problems**

A Find 50% of 20.

Method 1 Use a proportion.

$\dfrac{\text{part}}{\text{whole}} = \dfrac{\text{percent}}{100}$ *Use the percent proportion.*

$\dfrac{x}{20} = \dfrac{50}{100}$ *Let x represent the part.*

$100x = 1000$ *Find the cross products. Since x is multiplied by 100, divide both sides by 100 to undo the multiplication.*

$\dfrac{100x}{100} = \dfrac{1000}{100}$

$x = 10$

50% of 20 is 10.

B **440 is what percent of 400?**

Method 2 Use an equation.

$440 = x \cdot 400$ *Write an equation. Let x represent the percent.*

$440 = 400x$

$\dfrac{440}{400} = \dfrac{400x}{400}$ *Since x is multiplied by 400, divide both sides by 400 to undo the multiplication.*

$1.1 = x$ *The answer is a decimal.*

$110\% = x$ *Write the decimal as a percent. This answer is reasonable; 440 is more than 100% of 400.*

440 is 110% of 400.

 **4a.** Find 20% of 60.   **4b.** 48 is 15% of what number?

Proportions are used to create *scale drawings* and *scale models*. A **scale** is a ratio between two sets of measurements, such as 1 in:5 mi. A **scale drawing** or **scale model** uses a scale to represent an object as smaller or larger than the actual object. A map is an example of a scale drawing.

EXAMPLE 5   **Scale Drawings and Scale Models**

On the map, the distance from Chicago to Evanston measures 0.625 in. What is the actual distance?

$\dfrac{\text{map}}{\text{actual}} \longrightarrow \dfrac{1 \text{ in.}}{18 \text{ mi}}$ *Write the scale as a fraction.*

$\dfrac{1}{18} \times \dfrac{0.625}{x}$ *Let x be the actual distance.*

$x \cdot 1 = 18(0.625)$ *Use cross products to solve.*

$x = 11.25$

The actual distance is 11.25 mi.

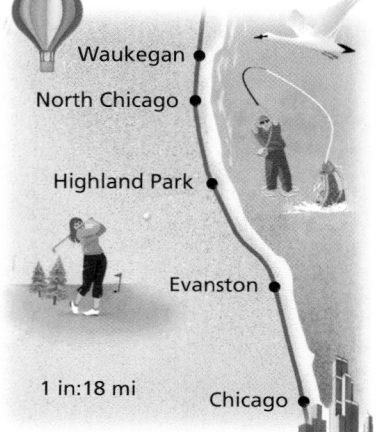

Waukegan
North Chicago
Highland Park
Evanston
1 in:18 mi
Chicago

Reading Math

A scale written without units, such as 32:1, means that 32 units of any measure correspond to 1 unit of that same measure.

 **5a.** The actual distance between North Chicago and Waukegan is 4 mi. What is this distance on the map above?

5b. A scale model of a human heart is 16 ft long. The scale is 32:1. How many inches long is the actual heart that the model represents?

THINK AND DISCUSS

1. Explain two ways to solve the proportion $\frac{t}{4} = \frac{3}{5}$.

Know it! Note **2. GET ORGANIZED** Copy and complete the graphic organizer. In each box, write an example of each use of ratios.

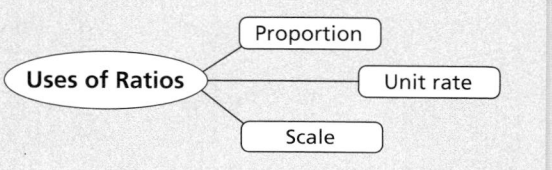

Uses of Ratios
Proportion
Unit rate
Scale

2-5 **Exercises**

California Standards Practice
5.0, 15.0, 25.1, 25.2

go.hrw.com
Homework Help Online
KEYWORD: MA8CA 2-5
Parent Resources Online
KEYWORD: MA8CA Parent

GUIDED PRACTICE

Vocabulary Apply the vocabulary from this lesson to answer each question.

1. What does it mean when two ratios form a *proportion*?

2. In your own words, write a definition of *percent*.

SEE EXAMPLE 1 p. 102

3. The ratio of the sale price of a jacket to the original price is $3:4$. The original price is $64. What is the sale price?

4. **Chemistry** The ratio of hydrogen atoms to oxygen atoms in water is $2:1$. If an amount of water contains 341 trillion atoms of oxygen, how many hydrogen atoms are there?

SEE EXAMPLE 2 p. 102

Find each unit rate.

5. A computer's fan rotates 2000 times in 40 seconds.

6. Twelve cows produce 224,988 pounds of milk.

SEE EXAMPLE 3 p. 103

Solve each proportion. Check your answer.

7. $\frac{3}{z} = \frac{1}{8}$ 8. $\frac{x}{3} = \frac{1}{5}$ 9. $\frac{b}{4} = \frac{3}{2}$

10. $\frac{f+3}{12} = \frac{7}{2}$ 11. $\frac{-1}{5} = \frac{3}{2d}$ 12. $\frac{3}{14} = \frac{s-2}{21}$

SEE EXAMPLE 4 p. 103

13. Find 75% of 40.   14. Find $12\frac{1}{2}$% of 168.

15. Find 115% of 57.   16. Find 70% of 8.

17. What percent of 40 is 25?   18. What percent of 225 is 180?

SEE EXAMPLE 5 p. 104

19. **Archaeology** Stonehenge II in Hunt, Texas, is a scale model of the ancient construction in Wiltshire, England. The scale of the model to the original is $3:5$. The Altar Stone of the original construction is 4.9 meters tall. Write and solve a proportion to find the height of the Texas model of the Altar Stone.

PRACTICE AND PROBLEM SOLVING

Independent Practice	
For Exercises	See Example
20–21	1
22–23	2
24–27	3
28–33	4
34	5

Extra Practice
Skills Practice p. EP5
Application Practice p. EP25

20. **Gardening** The ratio of the height of a bonsai ficus tree to the height of a full-size ficus tree is $1:9$. The bonsai ficus is 6 inches tall. What is the height of a full-size ficus?

21. **Manufacturing** At one factory, the ratio of defective light bulbs produced to total light bulbs produced is about $3:500$. How many light bulbs are expected to be defective when 12,000 are produced?

Find each unit rate.

22. Four gallons of gasoline weigh 25 pounds.

23. Fifteen ounces of gold cost $6,058.50.

Solve each proportion. Check your answer.

24. $\frac{v}{6} = \frac{1}{2}$ 25. $\frac{2}{5} = \frac{4}{y}$ 26. $\frac{2}{h} = \frac{-5}{6}$ 27. $\frac{3}{10} = \frac{b+7}{-20}$

Find each value. Round to the nearest tenth if necessary.

28. 60% of 80   **29.** 35% of 90   **30.** $\frac{1}{2}$% of 500   **31.** 210% of 30

32. What percent of 52 is 13?   **33.** What percent of 9 is 27?

34. Science The image shows a dust mite as seen under a microscope. The actual length of this dust mite is 0.3 millimeter. Use a ruler to measure the length of the dust mite in the image in millimeters. What is the scale of the drawing?

Solve each proportion.

35. $\dfrac{x-1}{3} = \dfrac{x+1}{5}$

36. $\dfrac{m}{3} = \dfrac{m+4}{7}$

37. $\dfrac{1}{x-3} = \dfrac{3}{x-5}$

38. $\dfrac{a}{2} = \dfrac{a-4}{30}$

39. $\dfrac{3}{2y} = \dfrac{16}{y+2}$

40. $\dfrac{n+3}{5} = \dfrac{n-1}{2}$

41. Multi-Step According to the 2000 U.S. Census, 138,053,563 Americans are male and 143,368,343 Americans are female. About what percent of the population is male? female? Round your answers to the nearest percent.

42. Write About It Give three examples of proportions. How do you know they are proportions? Then give three nonexamples of proportions. How do you know they are not proportions?

43. Entertainment The numbers of various types of movies rented over a period of time are indicated in the graph.

  a. What percent of the movies rented were comedies?

  b. What type of movie made up 25% of the rentals?

  c. What percent of the movies rented were in the "other" category?

  d. **What if...?** If 25 of the comedy rentals had instead been action rentals, what percent of the movies rented would have been comedies? Round your answer to the nearest tenth.

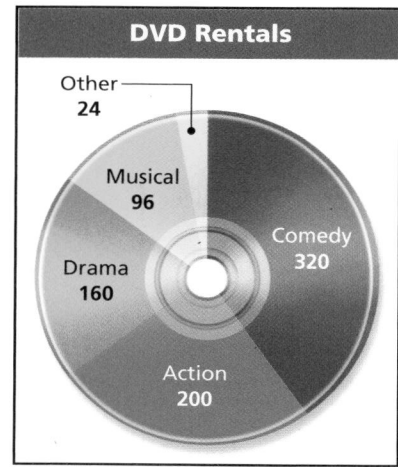

DVD Rentals

Other 24
Musical 96
Comedy 320
Drama 160
Action 200

CONCEPT CONNECTION

44. This problem will help prepare you for the Concept Connection on page 120.

Two notes are separated by an interval of a fourth if the ratio of the notes' frequencies is 4:3. The note D_4 has a frequency of 297 hertz (Hz).

  a. Write and solve a proportion that you can use to find the frequency of a note that has higher pitch (that is, a greater frequency) than the note D_4 and is separated from the note D_4 by an interval of a fourth.

  b. Find the frequency of a note with a higher pitch that is separated by an interval of a fourth from the note you found in part **a.**

45. ///ERROR ANALYSIS/// Below is a bonus question that appeared on an algebra test and a student's response.

> The ratio of junior varsity members to varsity members on the track team is 3:5. There are 24 members on the team. Write a proportion to find the number of junior varsity members.
>
> $\dfrac{3}{5} = \dfrac{x}{24}$

The student did not receive the bonus points. Why is this proportion incorrect?

Multiple Choice For Exercises 46 and 47, choose the best answer.

46. One day the U.S. dollar was worth approximately 100 Japanese yen. An exchange of 2500 yen was made that day. What was the value of the exchange in dollars?

Ⓐ $25   Ⓑ $2,400   Ⓒ $2,500   Ⓓ $270,000

47. Which proportion can be used to find 14% of 60?

Ⓐ $\dfrac{x}{100} = \dfrac{60}{14}$ Ⓑ $\dfrac{14}{100} = \dfrac{60}{x}$ Ⓒ $\dfrac{x}{100} = \dfrac{14}{60}$ Ⓓ $\dfrac{14}{100} = \dfrac{x}{60}$

48. Gridded Response Raul surveyed 35 students about their preferred lunch. Fourteen preferred chicken. Half of those students preferred chicken with barbecue sauce. What percent should Raul report as preferring chicken with barbecue sauce?

CHALLENGE AND EXTEND

49. Geometry Complementary angles are two angles whose measures add to 90°. The ratio of the measures of two complementary angles is 4:5. What are the measures of the angles?

50. Population The population density of Jackson, Mississippi, is 672.2 people per square kilometer. What is the population density in people per square meter? Show that your answer is reasonable. (*Hint:* There are 1000 meters in 1 kilometer. How many square meters are in 1 square kilometer?)

Find each value. Round to the nearest tenth if necessary.

51. What percent of 16 is 2.75?   **52.** 22 is 73.5% of what number?

53. Reasoning Without using cross products, show that $\dfrac{3}{x} = \dfrac{5}{x-1}$ is equivalent to $3(x-1) = 5x$.

Evaluate each expression. (*Lesson 1-4*)

54. 8^2 **55.** $(-3)^3$ **56.** $(-3)^2$ **57.** $-\left(\dfrac{1}{2}\right)^5$

Write the power represented by each geometric model. (*Lesson 1-4*)

58. 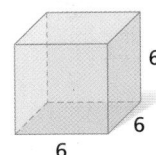   **59.** 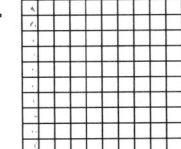   **60.**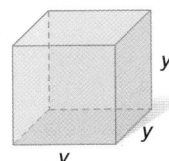

Solve each equation. Check your answer. (*Lesson 2-4*)

61. $2x - 12 = 5x + 3$ **62.** $3a - 4 = 6 - 7a$ **63.** $3x - 4 = 2x + 4$

LOGICAL REASONING

Use with Lesson 2-5

Proving Conditional Statements

In Lesson 2-5, you used the Cross Products Property:

If $\dfrac{a}{b} = \dfrac{c}{d}$ $(b \neq 0$ and $d \neq 0)$, then $ad = bc$.

Notice that the Cross Products Property is a conditional statement. You can use deductive reasoning to prove that it is true.

California Standards

25.1 Students use properties of numbers to construct simple, valid arguments (**direct** and indirect) **for**, or formulate counterexamples to, claimed assertions.

Also covered: **Ext. of ⚷ 5.0, 24.1, 24.2**

Example

Prove the Cross Products Property: If $\dfrac{a}{b} = \dfrac{c}{d}$ $(b \neq 0$ and $d \neq 0)$, then $ad = bc$.

Statements	Reasons
1. $\dfrac{a}{b} = \dfrac{c}{d}$ $(b \neq 0$ and $d \neq 0)$	Given
2. $\left(\dfrac{a}{b}\right)bd = \left(\dfrac{c}{d}\right)bd$	Multiplication Property of Equality (Multiply both sides by bd.)
3. $\dfrac{abd}{b} = \dfrac{cbd}{d}$	Multiply.
4. $ad = cb$	Simplify.
5. $ad = bc$	Commutative Property of Multiplication

Try This

1. Below is an incomplete proof of the following statement: If a and b are even, then $a + b$ is even. Fill in the blanks to complete the proof.

Statements	Reasons
1. a and b are ____?____ .	Given
2. a and b are each divisible by ▓. In other words, they can each be written as the product of ▓ and some other number: $a = 2m$ and $b = 2n$.	Definition of ____?____
3. $a + b = 2m + 2n$	Substitute ▓ for a and ▓ for b.
4. $a + b = 2\left(▓\right)$	____?____
5. Because $a + b$ is divisible by 2, ____?____ is even.	Definition of ____?____

2. Prove the following statement: If a and b are even, then ab is even.

2-6 Solving Literal Equations for a Variable

California Standards

Extension of ⬤➝ **5.0** Students solve multistep problems, including word problems, involving linear equations and linear inequalities in one variable and provide justification for each step.

Vocabulary
formula
literal equation

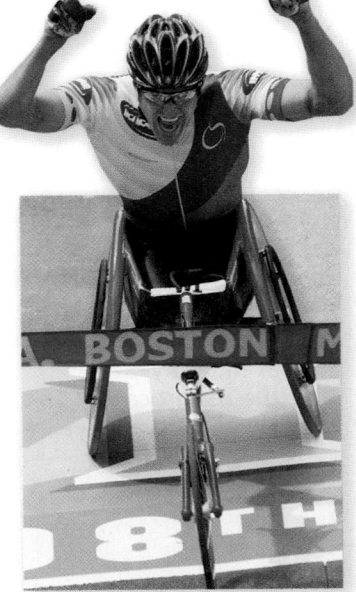

Who uses this?
Athletes can "rearrange" the distance formula to calculate their average speed.

Many wheelchair athletes compete in marathons, which cover about 26.2 miles. Using the time t it took to complete the race, the distance d, and the *formula* $d = rt$, racers can find their average speed r.

A **formula** is an equation that states a rule for a relationship among quantities.

In the formula $d = rt$, d is isolated. You can "rearrange" a formula to isolate any variable by using inverse operations. This is called *solving for a variable*.

Solving for a Variable
Step 1 Locate the variable you are asked to solve for in the equation.
Step 2 Identify the operations on this variable and the order in which they are applied.
Step 3 Use inverse operations to undo operations and isolate the variable.

EXAMPLE 1 **Sports Application**

In 2004, Ernst Van Dyk won the wheelchair race of the Boston Marathon with a time of about 1.3 hours. The race was about 26.2 miles. What was his average speed? Use the formula $d = rt$ and round your answer to the nearest tenth.

The question asks for speed, so first solve the formula $d = rt$ for r.

$d = \mathbf{r}t$ *Locate r in the equation.*

$\dfrac{d}{t} = \dfrac{rt}{t}$ *Since r is multiplied by t, divide both sides by t to undo the multiplication.*

$\dfrac{d}{t} = r$, or $r = \dfrac{d}{t}$

Now use this formula and the information given in the problem.

$r = \dfrac{d}{t} \approx \dfrac{26.2}{1.3}$

≈ 20.2

Van Dyk's average speed was about 20.2 miles per hour.

Helpful Hint

A nonzero number divided by itself equals 1. For $t \neq 0$, $\dfrac{t}{t} = 1$.

1. Solve the formula $d = rt$ for t. Find the time in hours that it would take Van Dyk to travel 26.2 miles if his average speed was 18 miles per hour. Round to the nearest hundredth.

EXAMPLE 2 Solving Formulas for a Variable

A The formula for a Fahrenheit temperature in terms of degrees Celsius is $F = \frac{9}{5}C + 32$. Solve for C.

$$F = \frac{9}{5}\mathbf{C} + 32 \qquad \text{Locate C in the equation.}$$

$$\underline{ -32 \qquad\qquad -32} \qquad \text{Since 32 is added to } \frac{9}{5}C, \text{ subtract 32 from both}$$
$$F - 32 = \frac{9}{5}C \qquad\qquad \text{sides to undo the addition.}$$

$$\left(\frac{5}{9}\right)(F - 32) = \left(\frac{5}{9}\right)\frac{9}{5}C \qquad \text{Since C is multiplied by } \frac{9}{5}, \text{ divide both}$$
$$\qquad\qquad\qquad\qquad \text{sides by } \frac{9}{5} \left(\text{multiply by } \frac{5}{9}\right) \text{ to undo the}$$
$$\frac{5}{9}(F - 32) = C \qquad\qquad \text{multiplication.}$$

Remember!

Dividing by a fraction is the same as multiplying by the reciprocal.

B The formula for a person's typing speed is $s = \frac{w - 10e}{m}$, where s is speed in words per minute, w is number of words typed, e is number of errors, and m is number of minutes typing. Solve for w.

$$s = \frac{\mathbf{w} - 10e}{m} \qquad \text{Locate w in the equation.}$$

$$m(s) = m\left(\frac{w - 10e}{m}\right) \qquad \text{Since } w - 10e \text{ is divided by m, multiply both}$$
$$\qquad\qquad\qquad\qquad \text{sides by m to undo the division.}$$

$$ms = w - 10e$$

$$\underline{+10e \qquad\qquad +10e} \qquad \text{Since 10e is subtracted from w, add 10e to}$$
$$ms + 10e = w \qquad\qquad \text{both sides to undo the subtraction.}$$

 **CHECK IT OUT!** **2.** The formula for an object's final velocity f is $f = i - gt$, where i is the object's initial velocity, g is acceleration due to gravity, and t is time. Solve for i.

A formula is a type of *literal equation*. A **literal equation** is an equation with two or more variables. To solve for one of the variables, use inverse operations.

EXAMPLE 3 Solving Literal Equations for a Variable

A Solve $m - n = 5$ for m.

$$\mathbf{m} - n = 5 \qquad \text{Locate m in the equation.}$$
$$\underline{+n \qquad +n} \qquad \text{Since n is subtracted from m, add n to both sides to}$$
$$m = 5 + n \qquad\qquad \text{undo the subtraction.}$$

B Solve $\frac{m}{k} = x$ for k.

$$\frac{m}{\mathbf{k}} = x \qquad \text{Locate k in the equation.}$$

$$k\left(\frac{m}{k}\right) = kx \qquad \text{Since k appears in the denominator, multiply both}$$
$$\qquad\qquad\qquad \text{sides by k.}$$

$$m = kx$$

$$\frac{m}{x} = \frac{kx}{x} \qquad \text{Since k is multiplied by x, divide both sides by x to}$$
$$\qquad\qquad\qquad \text{undo the multiplication.}$$

$$\frac{m}{x} = k$$

 **CHECK IT OUT!** **3a.** Solve $5 - b = 2t$ for t.   **3b.** Solve $D = \frac{m}{V}$ for V.

THINK AND DISCUSS

1. Describe a situation in which a formula could be used more easily if it were "rearranged." Include the formula in your description.

2. Explain how to solve $P = 2\ell + 2w$ for w.

3. **GET ORGANIZED** Copy and complete the graphic organizer. Write a formula that is used in each subject. Then solve the formula for each of its variables.

Common Formulas	
Subject	**Formula**
Geometry	
Physical science	
Earth science	

California Standards Practice
Extension of 🔑 5.0

go.hrw.com
Homework Help Online
KEYWORD: MA8CA 2-6
Parent Resources Online
KEYWORD: MA8CA Parent

GUIDED PRACTICE

SEE EXAMPLE **1**
p. 109

1. **Vocabulary** Explain why a *formula* is a type of *literal equation*.

2. **Construction** The formula $a = 46c$ gives the floor area a in square meters that can be wired using c circuits.

   a. Solve $a = 46c$ for c.

   b. If a room is 322 square meters, how many circuits are required to wire this room?

SEE EXAMPLE **2**
p. 110

3. The formula for the volume of a rectangular prism with length ℓ, width w, and height h is $V = \ell wh$. Solve this formula for w.

SEE EXAMPLE **3**
p. 110

4. Solve $st + 3t = 6$ for s.

5. Solve $m - 4n = 8$ for m.

6. Solve $\dfrac{f + 4}{g} = 6$ for f.

7. Solve $b + c = \dfrac{10}{a}$ for a.

PRACTICE AND PROBLEM SOLVING

Independent Practice

For Exercises	See Example
8	1
9	2
10–13	3

Extra Practice

Skills Practice p. EP5

Application Practice p. EP25

8. **Geometry** The formula $C = 2\pi r$ relates the circumference C of a circle to its radius r. (Recall that π is the constant ratio of circumference to diameter.)

   a. Solve $C = 2\pi r$ for r.

   b. If a circle's circumference is 15 inches, what is its radius? Leave the symbol π in your answer.

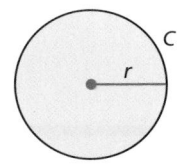

C is the distance around the circle.

r is the distance from the center of the circle to any point on the circle.

9. **Finance** The formula $A = P + I$ shows that the total amount of money A received from an investment equals the principal P (the original amount of money invested) plus the interest I. Solve this formula for I.

10. Solve $-2 = 4r + s$ for s.

11. Solve $xy - 5 = k$ for x.

12. Solve $\dfrac{m}{n} = p - 6$ for n.

13. Solve $\dfrac{x - 2}{y} = z$ for y.

Solve for the indicated variable.

14. $S = 180n - 360$ for n **15.** $\frac{x}{5} - g = a$ for x **16.** $A = \frac{1}{2}bh$ for b

17. $y = mx + b$ for x **18.** $a = 3n + 1$ for n **19.** $PV = nRT$ for T

20. $T + M = R$ for T **21.** $M = T - R$ for T **22.** $PV = nRT$ for R

23. $2a + 2b = c$ for b **24.** $5p + 9c = p$ for c **25.** $ax + r = 7$ for r

26. $3x + 7y = 2$ for y **27.** $4y + 3x = 5$ for x **28.** $y = 3x + 3b$ for b

29. Estimation The table shows the flying time and distance traveled for five flights on a certain airplane.

Flying Times		
Flight	Time (h)	Distance (mi)
A	2	1018
B	3	1485
C	4	2103
D	5	2516
E	6	2886

 a. Use the data in the table to write a rule that *estimates* the relationship between flying time t and distance traveled d.

 b. Use your rule from part **a** to estimate the time that it takes the airplane to fly 1300 miles.

 c. Solve your rule for d.

 d. Use your rule from part **c** to estimate the distance the airplane can fly in 8 hours.

30. Sports To find a baseball pitcher's earned run average (ERA), you can use the formula $Ei = 9r$, where E represents ERA, i represents number of innings pitched, and r represents number of earned runs allowed. Solve the equation for E. What is a pitcher's ERA if he allows 5 earned runs in 18 innings pitched?

31. Meteorology For altitudes up to 36,000 feet, the relationship between temperature and altitude can be described by the formula $t = -0.0035a + g$, where t is the temperature in degrees Fahrenheit, a is the altitude in feet, and g is the ground temperature in degrees Fahrenheit. Solve this formula for a.

32. Write About It In your own words, explain how to solve a literal equation for one of the variables.

33. Critical Thinking How is solving $a - ab = c$ for a different from the problems in this lesson? How might you solve this equation for a?

CONCEPT CONNECTION

34. This problem will help prepare you for the Concept Connection on page 120.

The formula $s = fw$ relates the speed of sound s in meters per second, the frequency of a note f in Hertz (Hz), and the wavelength of the note's sound wave w in meters.

 a. Solve the formula for f.

 b. The speed of sound is approximately 340 m/s. The note A_4 has a wavelength of approximately 0.773 m. Find the frequency of the note A_4 to the nearest whole number.

 c. As the wavelength of a note increases, what happens to the frequency? Explain.

Multiple Choice For Exercises 35–37, choose the best answer.

35. Which equation is the result of solving $9 + 3x = 2y$ for x?

   Ⓐ $\dfrac{9 + 3y}{2} = x$ Ⓑ $\dfrac{2}{3}y - 9 = x$ Ⓒ $x = \dfrac{2}{3}y - 3$ Ⓓ $x = 2y - 3$

36. Which of the following is a correct method for solving $2a - 5b = 10$ for b?

   Ⓐ Add $5b$ to both sides, then divide both sides by 2.
   Ⓑ Subtract $5b$ from both sides, then divide both sides by 2.
   Ⓒ Divide both sides by 5, then add $2a$ to both sides.
   Ⓓ Subtract $2a$ from both sides, then divide both sides by -5.

37. Anna wants to make a cardboard box with a length of 7 inches, a width of 5 inches, and a volume of 210 cubic inches. In the formula for the volume of a rectangular prism, which variable does Anna need to solve for in order to build the box?

   Ⓐ V Ⓑ ℓ Ⓒ w Ⓓ h

CHALLENGE AND EXTEND

Solve for the indicated variable.

38. $3.3x + r = 23.1$ for x 39. $\dfrac{2}{5}a - \dfrac{3}{4}b = c$ for a 40. $\dfrac{3}{5}x + 1.4y = \dfrac{2}{5}$ for y

41. $t = \dfrac{d}{500} + \dfrac{1}{2}$ for d 42. $s = \dfrac{1}{2}gt^2$ for g 43. $v^2 = u^2 + 2as$ for s

44. Solve $y = mx + 6$ for m. What can you say about y if $m = 0$?

45. **Entertainment** The formula $S = \dfrac{h \cdot w \cdot f \cdot t}{35{,}000}$ gives the approximate size in kilobytes (Kb) of a compressed video. The variables h and w represent the height and width of the frame measured in pixels, f is the number of frames per second (fps) the video plays, and t is the time the video plays in seconds. Estimate the time the movie trailer shown will play if it plays at 15 fps and has a size of 2370 Kb.

144 pixels

320 pixels

46. Jill spent $\frac{1}{4}$ of the money she made baby-sitting. She made $40 baby-sitting. How much did she spend? *(Previous course)*

47. In one class, $\frac{3}{5}$ of the students are boys. There are 30 students in the class. How many are girls? *(Previous course)*

Evaluate each expression for the given value of x. *(Lesson 1-7)*

48. $3 + 2 \cdot x + 4$ for $x = 3$ 49. $24 \div 4 - x$ for $x = 12$ 50. $43 - 62 + x$ for $x = 15$

Solve each equation. *(Lesson 2-1)*

51. $18 = -2 + w$ 52. $2 = -3 + c$ 53. $-8 + k = 4$ 54. $-15 + a = -27$

2-7 Solving Absolute-Value Equations

California Standards

3.0 Students solve equations and inequalities **involving absolute values.**

🔑 **5.0** Students solve **multistep problems, including word problems, involving linear equations** and linear inequalities **in one variable** and provide justification for each step.

Why learn this?

Engineers can solve absolute-value equations to calculate the length of the deck of a bridge. (See Example 3.)

Recall that the absolute value of a number is that number's distance from zero on a number line. For example, $|-5| = 5$ and $|5| = 5$.

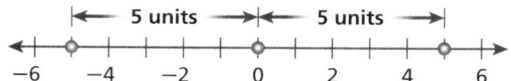

For any nonzero absolute value, there are exactly two numbers with that absolute value. For example, both 5 and -5 have an absolute value of 5.

To write this statement using algebra, you would write $|x| = 5$. This equation asks, "What values of x have an absolute value of 5?" The solutions are 5 and -5. Notice that this equation has two solutions.

Know it!
Note

Absolute-Value Equations

WORDS	NUMBERS
The equation $|x| = a$ asks, "What values of x have an absolute value of a?" The solutions are a and the opposite of a.	$|x| = 5$ $x = 5$ or $x = -5$

GRAPH	ALGEBRA
⟵a units⟶⟵a units⟶ $-a$ 0 a	$|x| = a$ $x = a$ or $x = -a$ $(a \geq 0)$

To solve absolute-value equations, perform inverse operations to isolate the absolute-value expression on one side of the equation. Then you must consider two cases.

EXAMPLE 1 **Solving Absolute-Value Equations**

Solve each equation.

A $|x| = 4$

$|x| = 4$ *Think: What numbers are 4 units from 0?*

⟵ 4 units ⟶⟵ 4 units ⟶
-5 -4 -3 -2 -1 0   1   2   3   4   5

Case 1	**Case 2**	*Rewrite the equation as two cases.*
$x = -4$	$x = 4$	

The solutions are -4 and 4. You can write the solution set as $\{-4, 4\}$.

Helpful Hint

Be sure to check both solutions when you solve an absolute-value equation.
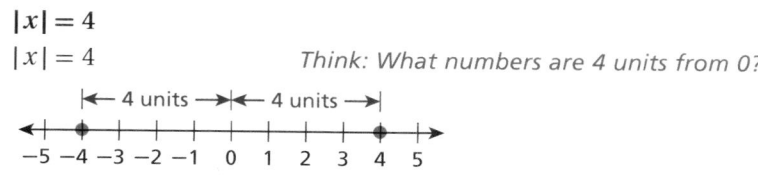

Solve each equation.

B $4|x + 2| = 24$

$$\frac{4|x + 2|}{4} = \frac{24}{4}$$

Since $|x + 2|$ is multiplied by 4, divide both sides by 4 to undo the multiplication.

$$|x + 2| = 6$$

Think: What numbers are 6 units from 0?

Case 1	Case 2
$x + 2 = -6$	$x + 2 = 6$
$\underline{-2 \quad -2}$	$\underline{-2 \quad -2}$
$x \quad\; = -8$	$x \quad\;\; = 4$

Rewrite the equation as two cases. Since 2 is added to x, subtract 2 from both sides of the equation.

The solution set is {−8, 4}.

 **CHECK IT OUT!** Solve each equation. Check your answer.

1a. $|x| - 3 = 4$ **1b.** $8 = |x - 2.5|$

The table summarizes the steps for solving absolute-value equations.

 **Know it! Note**

Solving an Absolute-Value Equation
1. Use inverse operations to isolate the absolute-value expression.
2. Rewrite the resulting equation as two cases that do not involve absolute values.
3. Solve the equation in each of the two cases.

Not all absolute-value equations have two solutions. If the absolute-value expression equals 0, there is one solution. If an equation states that an absolute value is negative, there are no solutions.

EXAMPLE 2 Special Cases of Absolute-Value Equations

Solve each equation.

A $|x + 3| + 4 = 4$

$$|x + 3| + 4 = 4$$

Since 4 is added to $|x + 3|$, subtract 4 from both sides to undo the addition.

$$\underline{ -4 \quad -4}$$

$$|x + 3| = 0$$

$$x + 3 = 0$$

There is only one case. Since 3 is added to x, subtract 3 from both sides to undo the addition.

$$\underline{ -3 \quad -3}$$

$$x = -3$$

The solution set is {−3}.

Remember!

Absolute value must be nonnegative because it represents a distance.

B $5 = |x + 2| + 8$

$$5 = |x + 2| + 8$$

Since 8 is added to $|x + 2|$, subtract 8 from both sides to undo the addition.

$$\underline{-8 -8}$$

$$-3 = |x + 2| \;\; ✗$$

Absolute value cannot be negative.

This equation has no solution. The solution set is the empty set, ∅.

 **CHECK IT OUT!** Solve each equation.

2a. $2 - |2x - 5| = 7$ **2b.** $-6 + |x - 4| = -6$

EXAMPLE **3** *Engineering Application*

Sydney Harbour Bridge in Australia is 1149 meters long. Because of changes in temperature, the bridge can expand or contract by as much as 420 millimeters. Write and solve an absolute-value equation to find the minimum and maximum lengths of the bridge.

First convert millimeters to meters.

420 mm = 0.4 2 0 m *Move the decimal point three places to the left.*

The length of the bridge can vary by 0.42 m, so find two numbers that are 0.42 units away from 1149 on a number line.

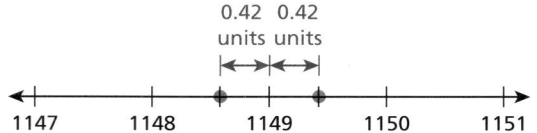

You can find these numbers by using the absolute-value equation $|x - 1149| = 0.42$. Solve the equation by rewriting it as two cases.

Case 1	**Case 2**	
$x - 1149 = \quad -0.42$	$x - 1149 = \quad 0.42$	*Since 1149 is subtracted*
$\underline{+1149 \quad +1149}$	$\underline{+1149 \quad +1149}$	*from x, add 1149 to both sides of each*
$x \quad = \quad 1148.58$	$x \quad = \quad 1149.42$	*equation.*

The minimum length of the bridge is 1148.58 m, and the maximum length is 1149.42 m.

3. Sydney Harbour Bridge is 134 meters tall. The height of the bridge can rise or fall by 180 millimeters because of changes in temperature. Write and solve an absolute-value equation to find the minimum and maximum heights of the bridge.

THINK AND DISCUSS

1. **Explain** the steps you would use to solve the equation $\frac{1}{5}|x - 3| = 2$.

2. **GET ORGANIZED** Copy and complete the graphic organizer. In each box, write an example of an absolute-value equation that has the indicated number of solutions, and then solve.

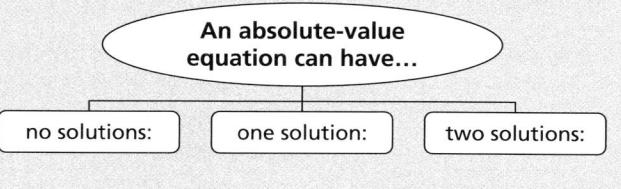

An absolute-value equation can have...

| no solutions: | one solution: | two solutions: |

Know it! Note

Exercises

California Standards Practice
3.0, ⚷ 5.0, 25.1, 25.3

go.hrw.com
Homework Help Online
KEYWORD: MA8CA 2-7
Parent Resources Online
KEYWORD: MA8CA Parent

GUIDED PRACTICE

SEE EXAMPLE 1
p. 114

Solve each equation.

1. $|x| = 6$

2. $9 = |x + 5|$

3. $|3x| + 2 = 8$

4. $2|x| = 18$

5. $\left|x + \frac{1}{2}\right| = 1$

6. $|x - 3| - 6 = 2$

SEE EXAMPLE 2
p. 115

7. $-8 = |x|$

8. $|x| = 0$

9. $|x + 4| = -7$

10. $7 = |3x + 9| + 7$

11. $|2.8 - x| + 1.5 = 1.5$

12. $5|x + 7| + 14 = 8$

SEE EXAMPLE 3
p. 116

13. Communication Barry's walkie-talkie has a range of 2 mi. Barry is traveling on a straight highway and is at mile marker 207. Write and solve an absolute-value equation to find the minimum and maximum mile marker from 207 that Barry's walkie-talkie will reach.

PRACTICE AND PROBLEM SOLVING

Extra Practice

Skills Practice p. EP5

Application Practice p. EP25

Solve each equation.

14. $|x| = \frac{1}{5}$

15. $|2x - 4| = 22$

16. $18 = 3|x - 1|$

17. $-2|x| = -4$

18. $3|x| - 12 = 18$

19. $|x - 42.04| = 23.24$

20. $\left|\frac{2}{3}x - \frac{2}{3}\right| = \frac{2}{3}$

21. $|3x + 1| = 13$

22. $|-2x + 3| = 5.8$

23. $|4x| + 9 = 9$

24. $8 = 7 - |x|$

25. $|x| + 6 = 12 - 6$

26. $|x - 3| + 14 = 5$

27. $0 = \left|\frac{2}{3} - x\right|$

28. $3 + |x - 1| = 3$

29. Space Shuttle The diameter of a valve for the space shuttle must be within 0.001 mm of 5 mm. Write and solve an absolute-value equation to find the boundary values for the acceptable diameters of the valve.

5 mm

30. The two numbers that are 5 units from 3 on the number line are represented by the equation $|n - 3| = 5$. What are these two numbers? Graph the solutions.

31. Write and solve an absolute-value equation that represents two numbers x that are 2 units from 7 on a number line. Graph the solutions.

32. Manufacturing A quality control inspector at a bolt factory examines random bolts that come off the assembly line. Any bolt whose diameter differs by more than 0.04 mm from 6.5 mm is sent back. Write and solve an absolute-value equation to find the maximum and minimum diameters of an acceptable bolt.

33. Construction A brick company guarantees to fill a contractor's order to within 5% accuracy. A contractor orders 1500 bricks. Write and solve an absolute-value equation to find the maximum and minimum number of bricks guaranteed.

34. Multi-Step A machine prints posters and then trims them to the correct size. The equation $|\ell - 65.1| = 0.2$ gives the maximum and minimum acceptable lengths for the posters in inches. Does a poster with a length of 64.8 inches fall within the acceptable range? Why or why not?

Write an absolute-value equation whose solutions are graphed on the number line.

35.
<-5 -4 -3 -2 -1 0 1 2 3 4 5>

36.
<-5 -4 -3 -2 -1 0 1 2 3 4 5>

37.
<-5 -4 -3 -2 -1 0 1 2 3 4 5>

38.
<-5 -4 -3 -2 -1 0 1 2 3 4 5>

 Reasoning Tell whether each statement is sometimes, always, or never true. Explain.

39. An absolute-value equation has two solutions.

40. The value of $|x + 4|$ is equal to the value of $|x| + 4$.

41. The absolute value of a number is nonnegative.

42. Temperature A thermostat is set so that the temperature in a laboratory freezer stays within 2.5°F of 2°F. Write and solve an absolute-value equation to find the maximum and minimum temperatures in the freezer.

43. Recreation To ensure safety, boaters must be aware of wind conditions while they are on the water. A particular anemometer gives a measurement of wind speed within a certain amount of the true wind speed, as shown in the table.

Measured Wind Speed (mi/h)	True Wind Speed (mi/h)
20	15–25
22	17–27
24	19–29
26	21–31
28	23–33
30	25–35

a. Use the table to write an absolute-value equation for the minimum and maximum possible true wind speeds t for the measured wind speed shown on the anemometer.

b. Solve your equation from part **a.** Check that the solution is correct by comparing it to the values given in the table when the measured wind speed is 24 mi/h.

c. Will your equation work for all of the values in the table? Explain.

d. Explain what your equation says about the instrument's measurements.

CONCEPT CONNECTION

44. This problem will help prepare you for the Concept Connection on page 120.

A violin can produce a range of notes. The center of the violin's frequency range is 1666 Hz.

a. Write an absolute-value expression that gives the distance on the number line of a violin note's frequency f from the value 1666.

b. The lowest and highest notes that a violin can produce have frequencies that differ by 1470 Hz from the frequency at the center of the range. Write an absolute-value equation for the frequencies of these notes.

c. Find the least and greatest frequencies that a violin can produce.

45. Write About It Do you agree with the following statement: "To solve an absolute-value equation, you need to solve two equations." Why or why not?

46. Critical Thinking Is there a value of a for which the equation $|x - a| = 1$ has exactly one solution? Explain.

Multiple Choice For Exercises 47–49, choose the best answer.

47. Which situation could be modeled by the equation $|x - 65| = 3$?

ⓐ Two numbers on the number line are 65 units away from 3.

ⓑ The length of a carpet is 3 inches less than 65 inches.

ⓒ The maximum and minimum weights of wrestlers on the team are within 3 kg of 65 kg.

ⓓ The members of an exercise club for seniors are all between 63 and 67 years old.

48. For which of the following is $n = -3$ a solution?

ⓐ $|n - 1| = 2$ ⓑ $|n + 2| = -1$ ⓒ $|n - 2| = 1$ ⓓ $|n + 1| = 2$

49. The minimum and maximum sound levels at a rock concert are 90 decibels and 95 decibels. Which equation models this situation?

ⓐ $|x - 90| = 5$ ⓑ $|x - 92.5| = 2.5$ ⓒ $|x - 92.5| = 5$ ⓓ $|x - 95| = 2.5$

CHALLENGE AND EXTEND

50. The perimeter of a rectangle is 100 inches. The length of the rectangle is $|2x - 4|$ inches, and the width is x inches. What are the possible values of x? Explain.

51. Reasoning Fill in the missing reasons to justify each step in solving the equation $3|2x + 1| = 21$.

Statements	Reasons
1. $3\|2x + 1\| = 21$	1. Given
2. $\|2x + 1\| = 7$	2. _____?_____
3. $2x + 1 = -7$ or $2x + 1 = 7$	3. Definition of absolute value
4. $2x = -8$ or $2x = 6$	4. _____?_____
5. $x = -4$ or $x = 3$	5. _____?_____

52. Solve $|x| = |x + 1|$. (*Hint:* Consider two cases: $x \geq 0$ and $x < 0$.)

SPIRAL STANDARDS REVIEW
6AF1.1, 6NS1.3

Solve each equation. Check your answer. *(Lesson 2-1)*

53. $5 = p - 4.5$ **54.** $-2 = y + 6\frac{1}{2}$ **55.** $-12 + q = 3$ **56.** $y - 4.3 = -5.7$

Solve each proportion. Check your answer. *(Lesson 2-5)*

57. $\dfrac{m}{8} = \dfrac{3}{4}$ **58.** $\dfrac{16}{y} = \dfrac{12}{18}$ **59.** $\dfrac{4}{5} = \dfrac{12}{x + 6}$ **60.** $\dfrac{-2}{3} = \dfrac{5}{2x}$

Solve for the indicated variable. *(Lesson 2-6)*

61. $m + 5n = 7$ for m **62.** $S = T + R$ for T **63.** $2y + 3x = 1$ for y

64. $\dfrac{3 + w}{z} = x$ for w **65.** $c + d = \dfrac{5}{e}$ for e **66.** $6M - N = S$ for N

CONCEPT CONNECTION

Proportions and Formulas

Make a Note of It Sounds are produced by vibrating objects, such as guitar strings. The number of vibrations per second is called the frequency, and the frequency determines the note that you hear. The table shows the approximate frequency for the notes in a scale, where 1 Hertz (Hz) = 1 vibration/second.

Musical Notes	
Note	**Frequency (Hz)**
C	264
D	297
E	330
F	352
G	396
A	440
B	495
C	528

1. Notes that sound pleasing when played at the same time have a special relationship. For example, two notes whose frequencies have a ratio of 5:4 are said to be separated by an interval of a third. Which note is separated by an interval of a third from the note F?

2. The speed of sound is approximately 340 m/s. The following formula relates the speed of sound *s*, the frequency *f*, and the wavelength *w*.

$$s = fw$$

Solve the formula for *w* to find the wavelength for the note G.

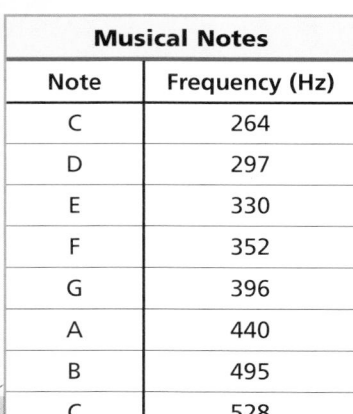

3. A piano can produce a wide range of notes. The center of the piano's frequency range is of 2106.75 Hz, while the frequencies at the extreme ends of the range differ from this value by 2079.25 Hz. Write and solve an absolute-value equation to find the minimum and maximum frequencies for notes on a piano.

READY TO GO ON?

Quiz for Lessons 2-5 Through 2-7

2-5 Solving Proportions

1. Last week, the ratio of laptops to desktops sold at a computer store was $2:3$. Eighteen desktop models were sold. How many laptop models were sold?

2. Anita read 150 pages in 5 hours. What is her reading rate in pages per minute?

Find the unit rate.

3. Twenty-six crackers contain 156 Calories.

4. A store developed 1024 photographs in 8 hours.

Solve each proportion.

5. $\dfrac{-18}{n} = \dfrac{9}{2}$

6. $\dfrac{d}{5} = \dfrac{2}{4}$

7. $\dfrac{4}{12} = \dfrac{r+2}{16}$

8. $\dfrac{-3}{7} = \dfrac{6}{x+6}$

Find each value. Round to the nearest tenth if necessary.

9. Find 40% of 25.

10. Find 130% of 9.

11. 35 is what percent of 70?

12. What percent of 400 is 640?

13. 16 is 80% of what number?

14. 200% of what number is 28?

15. A volunteer at the zoo is responsible for feeding the animals in 15 exhibits in the reptile house. This represents 20% of the total exhibits in the reptile house. How many exhibits are in the reptile house?

2-6 Solving Literal Equations for a Variable

16. Solve $5j + s = t - 2$ for t.

17. Solve $h + p = 3(k - 8)$ for k.

18. Solve $2x + 3y = 12$ for x.

19. Solve $\dfrac{x}{r} = v$ for x

20. The formula for the area of a triangle is $A = \dfrac{1}{2}bh$. Solve the formula for h. If the area of a triangle is 48 cm^2, and its base measures 12 cm, what is the height of a triangle?

2-7 Solving Absolute-Value Equations

Solve each equation.

21. $|r| = 7$

22. $|h + 4| = 11$

23. $|2x + 4| = 0$

24. $16 = 7|p + 3| + 30$

25. Collette is a contestant on a game show. She can win a car if she can guess the price of the car within $725. The price of the car is $16,785. Write and solve an absolute-value equation to find the values for the maximum and minimum price that Collette can guess to win the car.

Study Guide: Review

Vocabulary

Complete the sentences below with vocabulary words from the list above.

1. A formula is a type of a(n) ___?___.

2. A(n) ___?___ is used to compare two quantities.

2-1 Solving One-Step Equations *(pp. 72–77)*

EXAMPLES

Solve each equation. Check your answer.

■ $x - 12 = -8$

$$\underline{+ 12 \quad + 12}$$ *Add 12 to both sides.*

$x \qquad = \quad 4$

Check $x - 12 = -8$

$4 - 12$	-8
-8	-8 ✓

■ $-8x = 148$

$$\frac{-8x}{-8} = \frac{148}{-8}$$ *Divide both sides by –8.*

$x = -18.5$

Check $-8x = 148$

$-8\,(-18.5)$	148
148	148 ✓

EXERCISES

Solve each equation. Check your answer.

3. $b - 16 = 20$ **4.** $4 + x = 2$

5. $9 + a = -12$ **6.** $-7 + y = 11$

7. $z - \dfrac{1}{4} = \dfrac{7}{8}$ **8.** $w + \dfrac{2}{3} = 3$

9. $7.2 + t = 12.3$ **10.** $22.5 = x - 3$

11. $35 = 5x$ **12.** $-6s = 42$

13. $\dfrac{f}{15} = 8$ **14.** $3m = 45$

15. $4j = 28$ **16.** $\dfrac{n}{3} = 12$

17. $4k = 3.5$ **18.** $\dfrac{c}{5} = 2.5$

19. Robin needs 108 signatures for her petition. So far, she has 27. Write and solve an equation to determine how many more signatures she needs.

20. Mrs. Wilson gave some money to each of her 6 children. Each child received $35.50. How much money did Mrs. Wilson give to her 6 children in total?

2-2 Solving Two-Step Equations (pp. 79–84)

Prep for 5.0

EXAMPLES

Solve each equation.

- $\dfrac{z}{2.4} + 2 = 14$

$$\dfrac{z}{2.4} + 2 = 14$$

$$\underline{\quad -2 \quad -2\quad}$$ *Subtract 2 from both sides.*

$$\dfrac{z}{2.4} = 12$$

$$(2.4)\dfrac{z}{2.4} = (2.4)12$$ *Multiply both sides by 2.4.*

$$z = 28.8$$

- $5x - 6 = 79$

$$5x - 6 = 79$$

$$\underline{\quad +6 \quad +6\quad}$$ *Add 6 to both sides.*

$$5x = 85$$

$$\dfrac{5x}{5} = \dfrac{85}{5}$$ *Divide both sides by 5.*

$$x = 17$$

EXERCISES

Solve each equation. Check your answer.

21. $4t - 13 = 57$
22. $5 - 2y = 15$
23. $3z + 1 = 19$
24. $18 = 30 - 3h$
25. $\dfrac{k}{5} - 6 = 2$
26. $\dfrac{1}{6}f + \dfrac{3}{4} = \dfrac{1}{2}$
27. $6h - 7 = 25$
28. $17 = 29 - 4k$
29. $\dfrac{1}{4} + \dfrac{3}{4}t = 10$
30. $18 - 4a = 34$
31. $0.2x + 0.5 = 0.9$
32. $-0.6x + 1 = 0.4$

33. Thomas had the same score for 3 different quizzes. On one quiz he received 5 extra bonus points. His total score for the 3 quizzes was 281 points. What was his score on each quiz?

2-3 Solving Multi-Step Equations (pp. 85–90)

4.0, 5.0

EXAMPLE

Solve each equation.

- $\dfrac{3x}{5} - \dfrac{x}{4} + \dfrac{1}{2} = \dfrac{6}{5}$

$$20\left(\dfrac{3x}{5} - \dfrac{x}{4} + \dfrac{1}{2}\right) = 20\left(\dfrac{6}{5}\right)$$ *Multiply by the LCD.*

$$12x - 5x + 10 = 24$$ *Combine like terms.*

$$7x + 10 = 24$$

$$\underline{\quad -10 \quad -10\quad}$$ *Subtract 10 from both sides.*

$$7x = 14$$

$$\dfrac{7x}{7} = \dfrac{14}{7}$$ *Divide both sides by 7.*

$$x = 2$$

- $3(b + 1) = -9$

$$3(b) + 3(1) = -9$$ *Distribute 3.*

$$3b + 3 = -9$$

$$\underline{\quad -3 \quad -3\quad}$$ *Subtract 3 from both sides.*

$$3b = -12$$

$$\dfrac{3b}{3} = \dfrac{-12}{3}$$ *Divide both sides by 3.*

$$b = -4$$

EXERCISES

Solve each equation. Check your answer.

34. $a - 12 + 2a = 27$
35. $5y + 3 - 7y = 15$
36. $4 + 3a - 6 = 43$
37. $3(x + 2) = 24$
38. $h(5 - 2) + 8 = 17$
39. $8(z + 10) + z = 98$
40. $-6 = 2.5(w - 2)$
41. $0.3x - 1.1 - x = 0.3$

42. If $8n + 22 = 70$, find the value of $3n$.

43. If $0 = 6n - 36$, find the value of $n - 5$.

44. The sum of the measures of two angles is 180°. One angle measures $3a$, and the other angle measures $2a - 25$ Find a. Then find the measure of each angle.

45. A drama club sold 120 child tickets and 80 adult tickets to a play. A child ticket cost $3 less than an adult ticket. The club collected a total of $640 from ticket sales. What is the cost of an adult ticket? a child ticket?

2-4 Solving Equations with Variables on Both Sides (pp. 92–98)

(pp. 92–98)

EXAMPLE

Solve each equation.

■ $3y - 5 = 2y + 5$

$$3y - 5 = 2y + 5$$

$$\underline{-2y \qquad -2y}$$ *Subtract 2y from both sides.*

$$y - 5 = \qquad 5$$

$$\underline{+5 \qquad +5}$$ *Add 5 to both sides.*

$$y \quad = \qquad 10$$

■ $x + 7 = 12 + 3x - 7x$

$$x + 7 = 12 - 4x$$ *Combine like terms.*

$$\underline{+4x \qquad +4x}$$ *Add 4x to both sides.*

$$5x + 7 = 12$$

$$\underline{-7 \quad -7}$$ *Subtract 7 from both sides.*

$$5x \ = \ 5$$

$$\dfrac{5x}{5} = \dfrac{5}{5}$$ *Divide both sides by 5.*

$$x = 1$$

EXERCISES

Solve each equation. Check your answer.

46. $4x + 2 = 3x$

47. $-3r - 8 = -5r - 12$

48. $-a - 3 + 7 = 3a$

49. $-(x - 4) = 2x + 6$

50. $\dfrac{2}{3}n = 4n - \dfrac{10}{3}n - \dfrac{1}{2}$

51. $0.2(7 + 2t) = 0.4t + 1.4$

52. $0.5x - 1.7 = 0.3x - 1$

53. $-2c + 8 = 5c - 10$

54. $7x - 28 = 3x$

55. $9x - 3 = 6x + 15$

56. $\dfrac{3}{4}n + 1 = \dfrac{5}{4}n + 2$

57. $\dfrac{1}{3}x + \dfrac{2}{3} = \dfrac{5}{3}x$

58. One photo shop charges $0.36 per print. Another photo shop charges $2.52 plus $0.08 per print. Juan finds that the cost of developing his photos is the same at either shop. How many photos does Juan have to develop?

2-5 Solving Proportions (pp. 102–107)

(pp. 102–107)

EXAMPLES

■ Solve $\dfrac{3w - 7}{21} = \dfrac{3}{7}$.

$$\dfrac{3w - 7}{21} \times \dfrac{3}{7}$$

$$7(3w - 7) = 21(3)$$ *Use cross products.*

$$21w - 49 = \ 63$$

$$\underline{+49 \quad +49}$$ *Add 49 to both sides.*

$$21w \qquad = 112$$

$$\dfrac{21w}{21} = \dfrac{112}{21}$$ *Divide both sides by 21.*

$$w = \dfrac{16}{3}$$

EXERCISES

59. In the ninth grade there are 320 students and 20 teachers. What is the student-to-teacher ratio?

Solve each proportion. Check your answer.

60. $\dfrac{n}{8} = \dfrac{2}{10}$

61. $\dfrac{2}{9} = \dfrac{12}{x}$

62. Amelia Earhart made her 1932 solo flight across the Atlantic Ocean in a Lockheed Vega. One model of the plane is $\dfrac{1}{30}$ the size of the real airplane. The wingspan of the Lockheed was 41 feet. What is the wingspan of the model? Round your answer to the nearest hundredth.

- Earth has a surface area of approximately 197 million square miles. About 58 million square miles is land. Find the percent of Earth's surface area that is water.

197 million − 58 million = 139 million

$$\frac{\text{part}}{\text{whole}} = \frac{\text{percent}}{100}$$

$$\frac{139 \text{ million}}{197 \text{ million}} \diagdown \frac{n}{100}$$

$$197n = 13,900 \quad \textit{Use cross products.}$$

$$n = 70.56$$

About 71% of Earth's surface area is water.

63. Find 2.3% of 230.   **64.** Find 115% of 2700.

65. What percent of 18 is 12? Round your answer to the nearest tenth of a percent.

66. What percent of 14 is 56?

67. 90% of what number is 120? Round your answer to the nearest tenth.

68. 90 is 37.5% of what number?

69. A student answered 32 questions correctly and 8 incorrectly. What percent of the questions were answered correctly?

2-6 Solving Literal Equations for a Variable (pp. 109–113)    Ext. of 🔑 5.0

EXAMPLE

- Solve $A = P + Prt$ for r.

$$A = \quad P + Prt$$

$$\underline{-P \qquad -P} \qquad \textit{Subtract P from both sides.}$$

$$A - P = \qquad Prt$$

$$\frac{A - P}{Pt} = \frac{Prt}{Pt} \qquad \textit{Divide both sides by Pt.}$$

$$\frac{A - P}{Pt} = r$$

EXERCISES

Solve for the indicated variable.

70. $C = \frac{360}{n}$ for n **71.** $S = \frac{n}{2}(a + \ell)$ for a

72. $0.25x + y = 225$ for x

73. The formula $a = \frac{d}{g}$ gives the average gas mileage a of a vehicle that uses g gallons of gas to travel d miles. Use the formula to find how many gallons of gas a vehicle with an average gas mileage of 20.2 miles per gallon will use to travel 75 miles. Round your answer to the nearest tenth.

2-7 Solving Absolute-Value Equations (pp. 114–119)   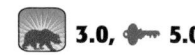 3.0, 🔑 5.0

EXAMPLE

- Solve $3|y + 4| = 30$.

$$\frac{3|y + 4|}{3} = \frac{30}{3} \qquad \textit{Divide both sides by 3.}$$

$$|y + 4| = 10$$

Case 1

$$y + 4 = \quad 10$$
$$\underline{-4 \qquad -4}$$
$$y \quad = 6$$

Case 2

$$y + 4 = -10$$
$$\underline{-4 \qquad -4}$$
$$y \quad = -14$$

EXERCISES

Solve each equation. Check your answer.

74. $|x + 6| = 21$ **75.** $7|y - 5| = 14$

76. $3|y| + 4 = 31$ **77.** $12 = |x - 5.4|$

78. $|g + 6| + 12 = 14$ **79.** $|x| = \frac{5}{7}$

80. Jason is driving his car at 55 mi/h. He needs to keep his car within 5 mi/h of his current speed. Write and solve an absolute-value equation to find Jason's maximum and minimum speeds.

Solve each equation.

1. $y - 7 = 2$

2. $x + 12 = 19$

3. $-5 + z = 8$

4. $9x = 72$

5. $\dfrac{m}{-8} = -2.5$

6. $\dfrac{7}{8}a = 42$

7. $15 = 3 - 4x$

8. $\dfrac{2a}{3} + \dfrac{1}{5} = \dfrac{7}{6}$

9. $8 - (b - 2) = 11$

10. $-2x + 4 = 5 - 3x$

11. $3(q - 2) + 2 = 5q - 7 - 2q$

12. $5z = -3(z + 7)$

13. $m - 2.7 = -1.5m + 1$

14. $x - 3.6 = 10.2 - 3.2$

15. $c + 13.5 = 20$

Solve for the indicated variable.

16. $r - 2s = 14$ for s

17. $V = \dfrac{1}{3}bh$ for b

18. $P = 2(\ell + w)$ for ℓ

19. $2x + a = 4$ for x

20. $4x + 6y = 12$ for x

21. $\dfrac{x}{r} = n$ for r

22. The ratio of red marbles to blue marbles in a bag is $4:7$. There are 16 red marbles. How many blue marbles are there?

Find each unit rate. Round to the nearest hundredth if necessary.

23. A store sells 3 videotapes for $4.99.

24. Twenty-five students use 120 sheets of paper.

Solve each proportion.

25. $\dfrac{5}{4} = \dfrac{x}{12}$

26. $\dfrac{8}{2z} = \dfrac{15}{60}$

27. $\dfrac{x + 10}{10} = \dfrac{18}{12}$

28. $\dfrac{x}{8} = \dfrac{1}{4}$

29. $\dfrac{5}{12} = \dfrac{-4}{f}$

30. $\dfrac{3}{10} = \dfrac{x + 1}{15}$

31. $\dfrac{c - 4}{5} = \dfrac{-c}{2}$

32. $\dfrac{3n}{2} = \dfrac{2}{3}$

33. $\dfrac{w}{6} = \dfrac{5}{2}$

34. The scale on a map is 1 inch : 500 miles. If two cities are 875 miles apart, how far apart are they on the map?

35. Order the following from least to greatest: 0.625, $\dfrac{1}{8}$, $\dfrac{1}{2}$, 1, 20%, 30%.

36. What is 23% of 46?

37. 37.5 is 60% of what number?

38. What percent of 175 is 35?

39. What is 29% of 32?

40. 84.41 is 23% of what number?

Solve each equation.

41. $|x - 14| = 21$

42. $13 = |y + 2| - 3$

43. $4|z| = 20$

44. $3|x| + 5 = 8$

45. $3|g + 1| + 5 = 7$

46. $|2v| = 6$

COLLEGE ENTRANCE EXAM PRACTICE

FOCUS ON ACT

The ACT Mathematics Test is one of four tests in the ACT. You have 60 minutes to answer 60 multiple-choice questions. The questions cover material typically taught through the end of eleventh grade. You will need to know some basic formulas.

There is no penalty for incorrect answers on the ACT. If you are unsure of the correct answer, eliminate as many answer choices as possible. Then make your best guess. Be sure you have marked an answer for every question before time runs out.

You may want to time yourself as you take this practice test. It should take you about 6 minutes to complete.

---

1. At a certain high school, the ratio of left-handed to right-handed basketball players is $1:4$. If there are a total of 20 players on the team, how many players are right-handed?

   (A) 1

   (B) 4

   (C) 5

   (D) 12

   (E) 16

2. If $y - 3 = \frac{2}{5}(x + 1)$, then $x = ?$

   (F) $\dfrac{5(y-3)-2}{2}$

   (G) $y - \dfrac{22}{5}$

   (H) $\dfrac{2(y-3)}{5} - 1$

   (J) $\dfrac{2(y+1)+15}{5}$

   (K) $\dfrac{5}{2}y - 4$

3. What is $\frac{1}{5}\%$ of 20?

   (A) 0.004

   (B) 0.04

   (C) 0.4

   (D) 4

   (E) 100

4. If $x - 3 = 4 - 2(x + 5)$, then $x = ?$

   (F) -3

   (G) -1

   (H) 1

   (J) $\dfrac{3}{2}$

   (K) $\dfrac{11}{3}$

5. If $\triangle ABC \sim \triangle DEF$, what is the length of $\overline{AC}$?

   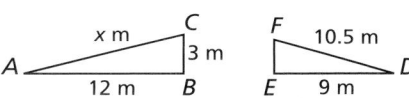

   (A) 2.6 meters

   (B) 3.5 meters

   (C) 7 meters

   (D) 14 meters

   (E) 15 meters

6. A movie theater makes 30% of its revenue from concession sales. If concession sales were $174,000, what was the total revenue?

   (F) $52,200

   (G) $121,800

   (H) $248,570

   (J) $580,000

   (K) $746,000

STRATEGIES FOR SUCCESS

Gridded Response: Fill in Answer Grids Correctly

When responding to a test item that requires you to place your answer in a grid, you must fill out the grid on your answer sheet correctly, or the item will be marked as incorrect.

EXAMPLE 1

Gridded Response: Simplify the expression $12^2 - 3(10 + 4)$.

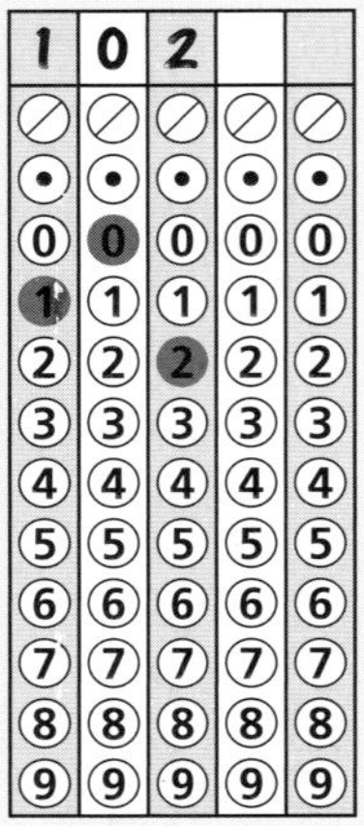

$$12^2 - 3(10 + 4)$$
$$12^2 - 3(14)$$
$$144 - 3(14)$$
$$144 - 42$$
$$102$$

The expression simplifies to 102.

- Write your answer in the answer boxes at the top of the grid.
- Put only one digit in each box. Do not leave a blank box in the middle of an answer.
- Shade the bubble for each digit in the same column as the digit in the answer box.

EXAMPLE 2

Gridded Response: Evaluate the expression $ba \div c$ for $a = -7$, $b = 2$, and $c = -6$.

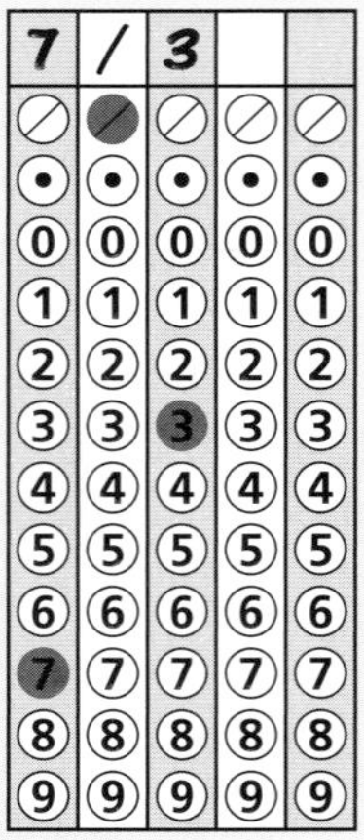

$$ba \div c$$
$$(2)(-7) \div (-6)$$
$$-14 \div (-6)$$
$$\frac{7}{3} = 2\frac{1}{3} = 2.\overline{3}$$

The expression simplifies to $\frac{7}{3}$, $2\frac{1}{3}$, or $2.\overline{3}$.

- Mixed numbers and repeating decimals cannot be gridded, so you must grid the answer as $\frac{7}{3}$.
- Write your answer in the answer boxes at the top of the grid.
- Put only one digit or symbol in each box. On some grids, the fraction bar and the decimal point have a designated box. Do not leave a blank box in the middle of an answer.
- Shade the bubble for each digit or symbol in the same column as the digit in the answer box.

Grid formats may vary from test to test. The grid in this book is used often, but it is not used on every test that has gridded response questions. Always examine the grid when taking a standardized test to be sure you know how to fill it in correctly.

Read each sample and then answer the questions that follow.

Sample A

A student correctly evaluated an expression and got $\frac{8}{15}$ as a result. Then the student filled in the grid as shown.

1. What error did the student make when filling out the grid?

2. Explain how to fill in the answer correctly.

Sample B

The square root of 6.25 is 2.5. This answer is displayed in the grid.

3. What error did the student make when filling in the grid?

4. Explain how to fill in the answer correctly.

Sample C

A student correctly simplified the expression $2\frac{1}{8} + 3\frac{5}{8} + \frac{7}{8}$. Then the student filled in the grid as shown.

5. What answer does the grid show?

6. Explain why you cannot fill in a mixed number.

7. Write the answer in two forms that could be entered in the grid correctly.

Sample D

A student added -10 and 25 and got an answer of 15. Then the student filled in the grid as shown.

8. What error does the grid show?

9. Another student got an answer of -15. Explain why the student knew this answer was wrong.

CUMULATIVE ASSESSMENT, CHAPTERS 1–2

Multiple Choice

1. What operation does ◊ represent if $x ◊ 2.2 = 4.5$ when $x = 9.9$?

   Ⓐ Addition

   Ⓑ Subtraction

   Ⓒ Multiplication

   Ⓓ Division

2. A couple earns $4819.25 a month. They pay 9.5% of their monthly income as the monthly payment on their car. To the nearest dollar, how much does the couple pay for their monthly car payment?

   Ⓐ $458   Ⓒ $4578

   Ⓑ $507   Ⓓ $4810

3. Naomi runs 8 miles each day. If she slows her pace by half, she runs this distance in 2 hours and 40 minutes. What is her normal pace?

   Ⓐ 6 miles per hour

   Ⓑ 8 miles per hour

   Ⓒ 4.75 miles per hour

   Ⓓ 6.75 miles per hour

4. A clock loses 5 minutes every day. How much time will it lose in 2 hours?

   Ⓐ 0.417 second   Ⓒ 240 seconds

   Ⓑ 25 seconds   Ⓓ 600 seconds

5. A statue is 8 feet tall. The display case for a model of the statue is 18 inches tall. Which scale allows for the tallest model of the statue that will fit in the display case?

   Ⓐ 1 inch:2 inches   Ⓒ 1 inch:5 inches

   Ⓑ 1 inch:7 inches   Ⓓ 1 inch:10 inches

6. What is the value of $-|6^2|$?

   Ⓐ −36   Ⓒ −8

   Ⓑ −12   Ⓓ −3

7. Mr. Phillips wants to install hardwood flooring in his den. The flooring costs $25.86 per square yard. The blueprint below shows his house. What other information do you need in order to find the total cost of the flooring?

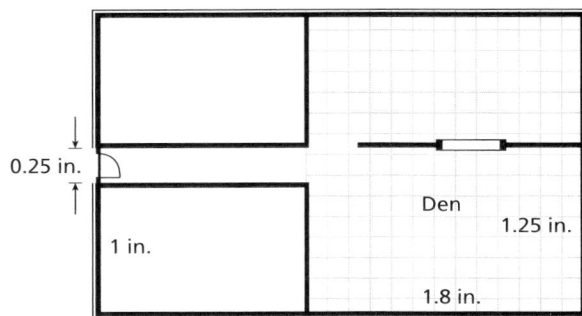

   Ⓐ The lengths and widths of the adjoining rooms in the blueprint

   Ⓑ The total area of the blueprint

   Ⓒ The scale of inches in the blueprint to yards in the house

   Ⓓ The width of the den

8. What value of n makes the equation below have no solution?

   $$2x + 2 = nx - 3$$

   Ⓐ −2

   Ⓑ 0

   Ⓒ 2

   Ⓓ 3

9. Which of the equations below represents the second step of the solution process?

   Step 1: $3(5x - 2) + 27 = -24$
   Step 2: ☐
   Step 3: $15x + 21 = -24$
   Step 4: $15x = -45$
   Step 5: $x = -3$

   Ⓐ $3(5x + 27) - 2 = -24$

   Ⓑ $3(5x + 25) = -24$

   Ⓒ $15x - 2 + 27 = -24$

   Ⓓ $15x - 6 + 27 = -24$

10. Cass drove 3 miles to school, and then she drove m miles to a friend's house. The total mileage for these two trips was 8 miles. Which equation CANNOT be used to determine the number of miles Cass drove?

Ⓐ $3 + m = 8$

Ⓑ $3 - m = 8$

Ⓒ $8 - 3 = m$

Ⓓ $8 - m = 3$

11. If $\dfrac{20}{x} = \dfrac{4}{x - 5}$, which of the following is a true statement?

Ⓐ $x(x - 5) = 80$

Ⓑ $20x = 4(x - 5)$

Ⓒ $20(x - 5) = 4x$

Ⓓ $24 = 2x - 5$

Gridded Response

12. Four times a number is two less than six times the same number minus ten. What is the number?

13. On August 1st, Melissa invested $6000 in a retirement account. A portion of her account record is shown below. Her balance can be found using the equation $B = 192m + 6000$, where B is the balance and m is the number of months after August. Find the missing balance, in dollars, in the table.

Date	Balance ($)
8/1	6000
9/1	6192
10/1	6384
1/1	

14. At 2:45 P.M. you are 112 miles from Dallas. You want to be in Dallas at 4:30 P.M. What is the average number of miles per hour you must travel to be on time?

15. A cyclist travels 45 miles in 4 hours. How many feet does she travel in one second?

16. A bike rental shop charges a one-time charge of $8 plus an hourly fee to rent a bike. Dan paid $24.50 to rent a bike for $5\frac{1}{2}$ hours. Find the bike shop's hourly fee in dollars.

Short Response

17. Alex buys 5 calendars to give as gifts. Each calendar has the same price. When the cashier rings up Alex's calendars, the total cost before tax is $58.75.

   a. Write and solve an equation to find the cost of each calendar.

   b. The total cost of Alex's calendars after tax is $63.45. Find the percent sales tax. Show your work and explain in words how you found your answer.

   c. Alex's friend Keisha buys some calendars for the same price. She uses her 15% discount card. The total cost before tax is $39.95. How many calendars did Keisha buy? Show your work and explain in words how you found your answer.

18. A student's solution for the absolute-value equation $6|x + 4| = 36$ was {2}. Explain why this answer is incorrect.

Extended Response

19. Korena is putting a decorative border around her rectangular flower garden. The total perimeter of the garden is 200 feet.

   a. Draw three different rectangles that could represent Korena's flower garden. Label the dimensions of your rectangles.

   b. Use the table to show the lengths and widths of five different rectangles that could represent Korena's flower garden. Do not use any of your rectangles from part **a.**

Possible Dimensions of Korena's Garden		
Length (ℓ)	**Width (w)**	**Perimeter (P)**

   c. The length of Korena's garden is 4 times its width. Explain how to use the perimeter formula $P = 2\ell + 2w$ to find the dimensions of Korena's garden.

   d. Find the dimensions of Korena's garden.

CHAPTER 3

Inequalities

3A Simple Inequalities

3-1 Graphing and Writing Inequalities

3-2 Solving Inequalities by Adding or Subtracting

3-3 Solving Inequalities by Multiplying or Dividing

CONCEPT CONNECTION

3B Multi-Step and Compound Inequalities

3-4 Solving Two-Step and Multi-Step Inequalities

3-5 Solving Inequalities with Variables on Both Sides

3-6 Solving Compound Inequalities

3-7 Solving Absolute-Value Inequalities

CONCEPT CONNECTION

go.hrw.com
Chapter Project Online
KEYWORD: MA8CA ChProj

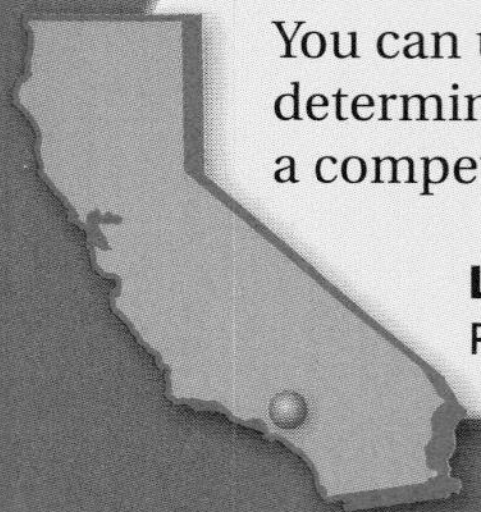

You can use inequalities to determine what is needed to win a competition at a county fair.

Los Angeles County Fair
Pomona, CA

132   Chapter 3

ARE YOU READY?

✓ Vocabulary

Match each term on the left with a definition on the right.

1. equation
2. evaluate
3. inverse operations
4. like terms
5. solution of an equation

A. mathematical phrase that contains operations, numbers, and/or variables

B. mathematical statement that two expressions are equivalent

C. value of a variable that makes a statement true

D. terms that contain the same variable raised to the same power

E. to find the value of an expression

F. operations that "undo" each other

✓ Evaluate Expressions

Evaluate each expression for $a = 2$ and $b = 6$.

6. $b - a$
7. ab
8. $b \div a$
9. $a + b$

✓ Compare and Order Real Numbers

Compare. Write $<$, $>$, or $=$.

10. $10 \ \blacksquare \ 21$
11. $5.27 \ \blacksquare \ 5.23$
12. $20\% \ \blacksquare \ 0.2$
13. $\frac{1}{3} \ \blacksquare \ \frac{2}{5}$

✓ Combine Like Terms

Simplify each expression by combining like terms.

14. $6x + x$
15. $-8a + 3a$
16. $9x^2 - 15x^2$
17. $2.1x + 4.3x$

✓ Distributive Property

Simplify each expression.

18. $2(x + 3)$
19. $(3 - d)5$
20. $4(r - 1)$
21. $3(4 + m)$

✓ Solve One-Step Equations

Solve.

22. $s - 3 = 8$
23. $-7x = 21$
24. $y + 11 = 2$
25. $\frac{h}{2} = 6$
26. $t + 2 = -2$
27. $6x = 42$
28. $r - 8 = -13$
29. $\frac{y}{3} = -12$

Unpacking the Standards

The information below "unpacks" the standards. The Academic Vocabulary is highlighted and defined to help you understand the language of the standards. Refer to the lessons listed after each standard for help with the math terms and phrases. The Chapter Concept shows how the standard is applied in this chapter.

California Standard	Academic Vocabulary	Chapter Concept
3.0 Students solve equations and **inequalities involving absolute values.** (Lesson **3-7**)	**involving** using or containing	You solve inequalities that have a variable inside absolute-value symbols.
4.0 Students simplify expressions before solving linear equations and **inequalities in one variable,** such as $3(2x - 5) + 4(x - 2) = 12$. (Lesson **3-4**)	**linear inequality** an inequality whose variable(s) have exponents not greater than 1	You write expressions in their simplest form so that you can find the values of a variable that make an inequality true.
5.0 Students solve multistep problems, including word problems, involving linear equations and **linear inequalities in one variable** and provide justification for each step. (Lessons **3-4, 3-5, 3-6, 3-7**)	**in one variable** containing one variable	You solve inequalities when the solution process requires two or more steps.
24.2 Students identify the hypothesis and conclusion in logical deduction. (p. 169)	**hypothesis** a statement that may or may not be true **conclusion** a statement that has been proved by reasoning	You look at a proof and name the original statement and the statement that has been proved.
25.2 Students judge the validity of an argument according to whether the properties of the real number system and the order of operations have been applied correctly at each step. (p. 169)	**judge** decide **validity** correctness **according to** depending on	You look at each step in a proof or solution and decide whether it is correct.

Standard 25.1 is also covered in this chapter. To see this standard unpacked, go to Chapter 8, p. 476.

Reading
and *Writing*
Math

Study Strategy: Use Your Notes Effectively

Taking notes helps you arrange, organize, and process information from your textbook and class lectures. In addition to taking notes, you need to use your notes before and after class effectively.

Step 1: Before Class
- Review your notes from the last class.
- Then preview the next lesson and write down any questions you have.

Step 2: During Class
- Write down main ideas.
- If you miss something, leave a blank and keep taking notes. Fill in any holes later.
- Use diagrams and abbreviations. Make sure you will understand any abbreviations later.

Step 3: After Class
- Fill in the holes you left during class.
- Highlight or circle the most important ideas, such as vocabulary, formulas, or procedures.
- Use your notes to quiz yourself.

10/3   Lesson 2-7   Solving Absolute-Value Equations

What values of x have an abs. val. of a in the equation $|x| = a$?

Solving an Absolute-Value Equation
1. Isolate the abs. val. expression on one side of the equation.
2. Write the 2 cases that would make the equation true.
3. Solve the equation in each of the 2 cases.

A number's distance from <u>zero</u> on a number line is that number's absolute value.

$|x| = 4$ **Case 1**: $x = -4$ **Case 2**: $x = 4$

$\longleftarrow$ 4 units $\longrightarrow$ $\longleftarrow$ 4 units $\longrightarrow$

-5 -4 -3 -2 -1 0 1 2 3 4 5

Try This

1. Look at the next lesson in your textbook. Write down some questions you have about the material in that lesson. Leave space between each question so that you can write the answers during the next class.

2. Look at the notes you took during the last class. List three ways you can improve your note-taking skills.

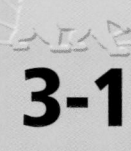

3-1 Graphing and Writing Inequalities

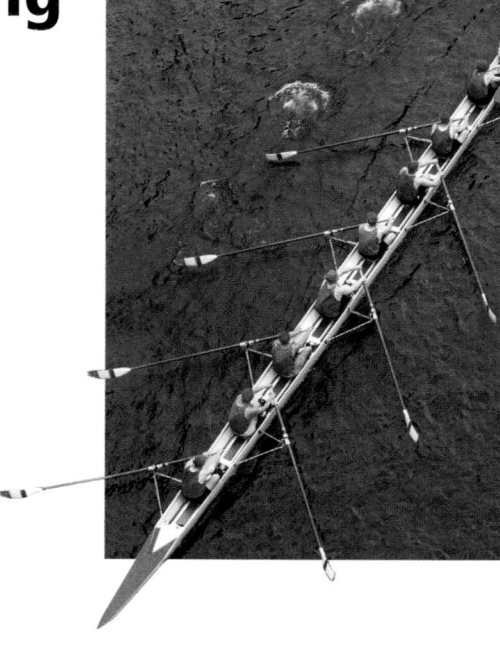

California Standards

Preparation for ⬦── 5.0
Students solve multistep problems, including word problems, involving linear equations and **linear inequalities in one variable** and provide justification for each step.

Vocabulary
inequality
solution of an inequality

Who uses this?
Members of a crew team can use inequalities to be sure they fall within a range of weights. (See Example 4.)

The athletes on a lightweight crew team must weigh 165 pounds or less. The acceptable weights for these athletes can be described using an *inequality*.

An **inequality** is a statement that two quantities are not equal. The quantities are compared by using one of the following signs:

$A < B$	$A > B$	$A \leq B$	$A \geq B$	$A \neq B$
A is less than *B*.	*A* is greater than *B*.	*A* is less than or equal to *B*.	*A* is greater than or equal to *B*.	*A* is not equal to *B*.

A **solution of an inequality** is any value that makes the inequality true. The set of all solutions of an inequality is its solution set.

EXAMPLE 1 **Identifying Solutions of Inequalities**

Describe the solutions of $3 + x < 9$ in words.

Test values of *x* that are positive, negative, and 0.

x	−2.75	0	5.99	6	6.01	6.1
3 + x	0.25	3	8.99	9	9.01	9.1
3 + x ≗ 9	0.25 ≗ 9	3 ≗ 9	8.99 ≗ 9	9 ≗ 9	9.01 ≗ 9	9.1 ≗ 9
Solution?	Yes	Yes	Yes	No	No	No

When the value of x is a number less than 6, the value of 3 + x is less than 9.
When the value of x is 6, the value of 3 + x is equal to 9.
When the value of x is a number greater than 6, the value of 3 + x is greater than 9.

The solutions of $3 + x < 9$ are numbers less than 6.

 **1.** Describe the solutions of $2p > 8$ in words.

An inequality like $3 + x < 9$ has too many solutions to list. One way to show all the solutions is to use a graph on a number line.

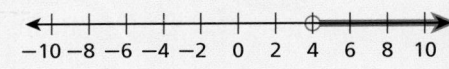

The solutions are shaded and an arrow shows that the solutions continue past those shown on the graph. To show that an endpoint is a solution, draw a solid circle at the number. To show that an endpoint is not a solution, draw an empty circle.

Graphing Inequalities

WORDS	ALGEBRA	GRAPH
All real numbers less than 5	$x < 5$	number line with empty circle at 5, shaded left, marks −4 to 6
All real numbers greater than −1	$x > -1$	number line with empty circle at −1, shaded right, marks −4 to 6
All real numbers less than or equal to $\frac{1}{2}$	$x \le \frac{1}{2}$	number line with solid circle at $\frac{1}{2}$, shaded left, marks −2 to 1
All real numbers greater than or equal to 0	$x \ge 0$	number line with solid circle at 0, shaded right, marks −4 to 6

EXAMPLE 2 Graphing Inequalities

Graph each inequality.

A $b < -1.5$

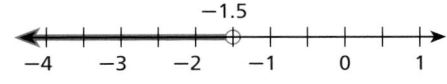

Draw an empty circle at −1.5.
Shade all the numbers less than −1.5 and draw an arrow pointing to the left.

B $r \ge 2$

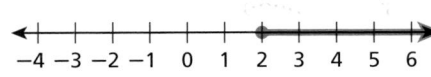

Draw a solid circle at 2.
Shade all the numbers greater than 2 and draw an arrow pointing to the right.

CHECK IT OUT! **Graph each inequality.**

2a. $c > 2.5$ **2b.** $2^2 - 4 \ge w$ **2c.** $m \le -3$

Student to Student   *Graphing Inequalities*

Victor Solomos
Palmer High School

To know which direction to shade a graph, I write inequalities with the variable on the left side of the inequality symbol. I know that the symbol has to point to the same number after I rewrite the inequality.

For example, I write $4 < y$ as $y > 4$.

Now the inequality symbol points in the direction that I should draw the shaded arrow on my graph.

3-1 Graphing and Writing Inequalities **137**

EXAMPLE **3** **Writing an Inequality from a Graph**

Write the inequality shown by each graph.

A

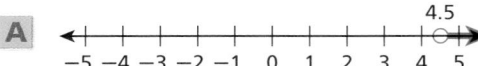

> *Use any variable. The arrow points to the right, so use either > or ≥.*
> *The empty circle at 4.5 means that 4.5 is not a solution, so use >.*

$h > 4.5$

B

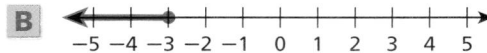

> *Use any variable. The arrow points to the left, so use either < or ≤.*
> *The solid circle at −3 means that −3 is a solution, so use ≤.*

$m \leq -3$

CHECK IT OUT! **3.** Write the inequality shown by the graph.

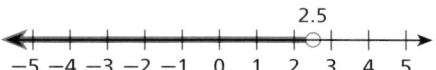

EXAMPLE **4** *Sports Application*

The members of a lightweight crew team can weigh no more than 165 pounds each. Define a variable and write an inequality for the acceptable weights of the team members. Graph the solutions.

Let w represent the weights that are allowed.

Athletes may weigh	no more than	165 pounds.
w	$\leq$	165

Reading Math

"No more than" or "at most" means "less than or equal to."(≤)

"At least" means "greater than or equal to." (≥)

$w \leq 165$

Stop the graph at 0 because a person's weight must be a positive number.

CHECK IT OUT! **4.** A store's employees earn at least $8.25 per hour. Define a variable and write an inequality for the amount the employees may earn per hour. Graph the solutions.

THINK AND DISCUSS

1. Compare the solutions of $x > 2$ and $x \geq 2$.

2. GET ORGANIZED Copy and complete the graphic organizer. Draw a graph in the first row and write the correct inequality in the second row.

Inequality	Graph
$x > 1$	
	(graph)

California Standards Practice
Preparation for ➤ 5.0

go.hrw.com
Homework Help Online
KEYWORD: MA8CA 3-1
Parent Resources Online
KEYWORD: MA8CA Parent

GUIDED PRACTICE

1. **Vocabulary** How is a *solution of an inequality* like a solution of an equation?

SEE EXAMPLE **1**
p. 136

Describe the solutions of each inequality in words.

2. $g - 5 \geq 6$ **3.** $-2 < h + 1$ **4.** $20 > 5t$ **5.** $5 - x \leq 2$

SEE EXAMPLE **2**
p. 137

Graph each inequality.

6. $x < -5$ **7.** $c \geq 3\frac{1}{2}$ **8.** $(4 - 2)^3 > m$ **9.** $p \geq \sqrt{17 + 8}$

SEE EXAMPLE **3**
p. 138

Write the inequality shown by each graph.

10.
```
←+++++●+++++++→
 -6 -5 -4 -3 -2 -1  0  1  2  3  4
```

11.
$-8\frac{1}{2}$
```
←○++++++++++++→
 -9 -8 -7 -6 -5 -4 -3 -2 -1  0  1
```

12.
5.5
```
←+++++++++○+→
 -4 -3 -2 -1  0  1  2  3  4  5  6
```

13.
-7
```
←++++++○++++++→
 -12 -10 -8  -6  -4  -2   0
```

14.
```
←++++++●+++→
 -4 -3 -2 -1  0  1  2  3  4  5  6
```

15.
```
←+++++++++●++→
 -2  0  2  4  6  8 10 12 14 16 18
```

SEE EXAMPLE **4**
p. 138

Define a variable and write an inequality for each situation. Graph the solutions.

16. There must be at least 20 club members present in order to hold a meeting.

17. A trainer advises an athlete to keep his heart rate under 140 beats per minute.

PRACTICE AND PROBLEM SOLVING

Independent Practice

For Exercises	See Example
18–21	1
22–25	2
26–31	3
32–33	4

Extra Practice

Skills Practice p. EP6

Application Practice p. EP26

Describe the solutions of each inequality in words.

18. $-2t > -8$ **19.** $0 > w - 2$ **20.** $3k > 9$ **21.** $\frac{1}{2}b \leq 6$

Graph each inequality.

22. $7 < x$ **23.** $t \leq -\frac{1}{2}$ **24.** $d > 4(5 - 8)$ **25.** $t \leq 3^2 - 2^2$

Write the inequality shown by each graph.

26.
```
←++++++++●++→
 -4 -3 -2 -1  0  1  2  3  4  5  6
```

27.
-11
```
←++++++○++++++→
 -16 -14 -12 -10  -8  -6  -4
```

28.
-3.5
```
←++○+++++++++→
 -6 -5 -4 -3 -2 -1  0  1  2  3  4
```

29.
-3.3
```
←++○++++++++++→
 -5 -4 -3 -2 -1  0  1  2  3  4  5
```

30.
```
←++++++++++⊕+→
 -5 -4 -3 -2 -1  0  1  2  3  4  5
```

31.
9
```
←++++●+++++++→
 -2  0  2  4  6  8 10 12 14 16 18
```

Define a variable and write an inequality for each situation. Graph the solutions.

32. The maximum speed allowed on Main Street is 25 miles per hour.

33. Applicants must have at least 5 years of experience.

Write each inequality in words.

34. $x > 7$ **35.** $h < -5$ **36.** $d \leq 23$ **37.** $r \geq -2$

Write each inequality with the variable on the left. Graph the solutions.

38. $19 < g$ **39.** $17 \geq p$ **40.** $10 < e$ **41.** $0 < f$

Define a variable and write an inequality for each situation. Graph the solutions.

42. The highest temperature ever recorded on Earth was 135.9°F at Al Aziziyah, Libya, on September 13, 1922.

43. Businesses with profits less than $10,000 per year will be shut down.

44. You must be at least 46 inches tall to ride the Indiana Jones Adventure ride at Disney's California Adventure Park.

45. Due to a medical condition, a hiker can hike only in areas with an elevation no more than 5000 feet above sea level.

Write a real-world situation that could be described by each inequality.

46. $x \geq 0$ **47.** $x < 10$ **48.** $x \leq 12$ **49.** $x > 8.5$

Match each inequality with its graph.

50. $x \geq 5$

A.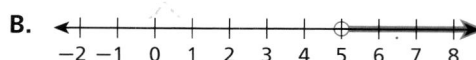

51. $x < 5$

B.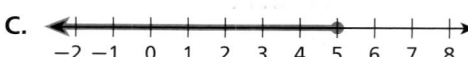

52. $x > 5$

C.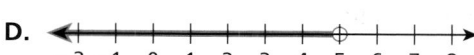

53. $x \leq 5$

D.

54. **/// ERROR ANALYSIS ///** Two students graphed the inequality $4 > b$. Which graph is incorrect? Explain the error.

Ⓐ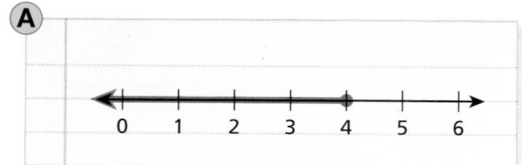

Ⓑ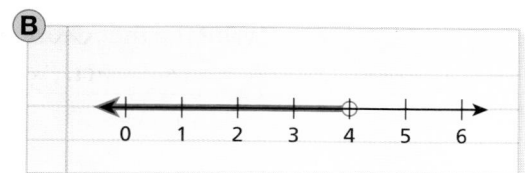

CONCEPT CONNECTION

55. This problem will prepare you for the Concept Connection on page 154.

 a. Mirna earned $125 baby-sitting during the spring break. She needs to save $90 for the German Club trip. She wants to spend the remainder of the money shopping. Write an inequality to show how much she can spend.

 b. Graph the inequality you wrote in part **a.**

 c. Mirna spends $15 on a bracelet. Write an inequality to show how much money she has left to spend.

56. Critical Thinking Graph all positive integer solutions of the inequality $x < 5$.

57. Write About It Explain how to write an inequality that is modeled by a graph. What characteristics do you look for in the graph?

58. Write About It You were told in the lesson that the phrase "no more than" means "less than or equal to" and the phrase "at least" means "greater than or equal to."

   a. What does the phrase "at most" mean?

   b. What does the phrase "no less than" mean?

Multiple Choice For Exercises 59–61, choose the best answer.

59. Which is NOT a solution of the inequality $5 - 2x \geq -3$?

   Ⓐ 0   Ⓑ 2   Ⓒ 4   Ⓓ 5

60. Which is NOT a solution of the inequality $3 - x < 2$?

   Ⓐ 1   Ⓑ 2   Ⓒ 3   Ⓓ 4

61. Which graph represents the solutions of $-2 \leq 1 - t$?

Ⓐ 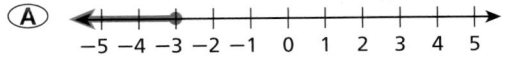   Ⓒ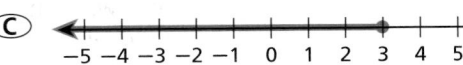

Ⓑ 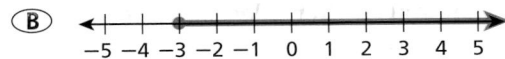   Ⓓ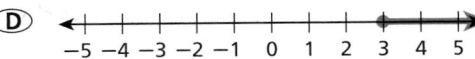

CHALLENGE AND EXTEND

Reasoning Describe the values for x and y that make each inequality true.

62. $x + y \leq |x + y|$ **63.** $x^2 < xy$ **64.** $x - y \geq y - x$

Complete each statement. Write $<$ or $>$.

65. If $a > b$, then b ▨ a.   **66.** If $x > y$ and $y > z$, then x ▨ z.

67. Name a value of x that makes the statement $0.35 < x < 1.27$ true.

68. Is $\frac{5}{6}$ a solution of $x < 1$? How many solutions of $x < 1$ are between 0 and 1?

69. Write About It Explain how to graph all the solutions of $x \neq 5$.

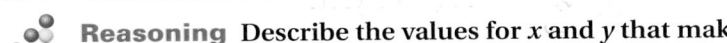

SPIRAL STANDARDS REVIEW   🔑 6NS2.3, 🔑 7AF1.3, 3.0, 🔑 4.0

Add or subtract. *(Lesson 1-2)*

70. $-7 + 5$ **71.** $6 - (-4)$ **72.** $8 - 13$ **73.** $12 + (-5)$

Simplify each expression. *(Lesson 1-7)*

74. $x + 3x$ **75.** $x + (x + 1) + (x + 2)$ **76.** $5 + (x + 3) + 5 + 2(x + 3)$

Solve each equation. Check your answer. *(Lesson 2-3)*

77. $2b - 6 = b + 3$ **78.** $-3(2 - x) = 5x + 2$ **79.** $2(y + 1) = 2y + 1$

80. Carrie is reading a book and wants to find the first page of a specific chapter. She is now on page 217. She knows that the chapter she is looking for starts within 40 pages of where she is now. Write and solve an absolute-value equation to find maximum and minimum page numbers where Carrie should look. *(Lesson 2-7)*

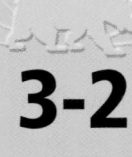

3-2 Solving Inequalities by Adding or Subtracting

California Standards

Preparation for ⬤━ 5.0
Students solve multistep problems, including word problems, involving linear equations and **linear inequalities in one variable** and provide justification for each step.

Who uses this?

You can use inequalities to determine how many more photos you can take. (See Example 2.)

Solving one-step inequalities is much like solving one-step equations. To solve an inequality, you need to isolate the variable using the properties of inequality and inverse operations. At each step, you will create an inequality that is equivalent to the original inequality. **Equivalent inequalities** have the same solution set.

Vocabulary
equivalent inequality

Properties of Inequality

Addition and Subtraction

WORDS	NUMBERS	ALGEBRA
Addition You can add the same number to both sides of an inequality, and the statement will still be true.	$3 < 8$ $3 + 2 < 8 + 2$ $5 < 10$	$a < b$ $a + c < b + c$
Subtraction You can subtract the same number from both sides of an inequality, and the statement will still be true.	$9 < 12$ $9 - 5 < 12 - 5$ $4 < 7$	$a < b$ $a - c < b - c$

These properties are also true for inequalities that use the symbols $>$, $\geq$, and $\leq$.

In Lesson 3-1, you saw that one way to show the solution set of an inequality is by using a graph. Another way is to use *set-builder notation*.

The set of all numbers x such that x has the given property

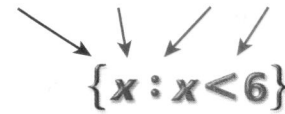

Read the above as "**the set of** all numbers x such that x is less than 6."

EXAMPLE 1 **Using Addition and Subtraction to Solve Inequalities**

Solve each inequality and graph the solutions.

A $x + 9 < 15$

$$\begin{array}{ll} x + 9 < 15 & \textit{Since 9 is added to x, subtract 9 from both sides} \\ \underline{-9 \quad -9} & \textit{to undo the addition.} \\ x \quad\ < 6 & \textit{The solution set is \{x:x < 6\}.} \end{array}$$

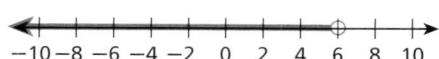

Solve each inequality and graph the solutions.

B $d - 3 > -6$

$$d - 3 > -6$$
$$\underline{+3 \quad +3}$$
$$d \quad\;\; > -3$$

Since 3 is subtracted from d, add 3 to both sides to undo the subtraction.

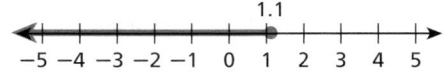

C $0.7 \geq n - 0.4$

$$0.7 \geq n - 0.4$$
$$\underline{+0.4 \qquad +0.4}$$
$$1.1 \geq n$$
$$n \leq 1.1$$

Since 0.4 is subtracted from n, add 0.4 to both sides to undo the subtraction.

 Solve each inequality and graph the solutions.

1a. $s + 1 \leq 10$ **1b.** $2\frac{1}{2} > -3 + t$ **1c.** $q - 3.5 < 7.5$

Since there can be an infinite number of solutions to an inequality, it is not possible to check all the solutions. You can check the endpoint and the direction of the inequality symbol.

Caution!

In Step 1, the endpoint should be a solution of the related equation, but it may or may not be a solution of the inequality.

The solutions of $x + 9 < 15$ are given by $x < 6$.	$x + 9 = 15$
Step 1 Check the endpoint.	$\begin{array}{c|c} 6 + 9 & 15 \end{array}$
Substitute 6 for x in the related equation $x + 9 = 15$. The endpoint should be a solution of the equation.	$\begin{array}{c|c} 15 & 15 ✓ \end{array}$
Step 2 Check the inequality symbol.	$x + 9 < 15$
Substitute a number less than 6 for x in the original inequality. The number you choose should be a solution of the inequality.	$\begin{array}{c|c} 4 + 9 & < 15 \\ 13 & < 15 ✓ \end{array}$

EXAMPLE 2

Problem Solving Application

The memory in Tenea's camera phone holds up to 20 pictures. Tenea has already taken 16 pictures. Write, solve, and graph an inequality to show how many more pictures Tenea could take.

1 Understand the Problem

The **answer** will be an inequality and a graph.

List the important information:
- Tenea can take up to, or *at most*, 20 pictures.
- Tenea has taken 16 pictures already.

2 Make a Plan

Write an inequality. Let p represent the remaining number of pictures Tenea can take.

Number taken	plus	number remaining	is at most	20 pictures.
16	+	p	$\leq$	20

 **Solve**

$$16 + p \leq 20$$ *Since 16 is added to p, subtract 16 from both sides to undo the addition.*
$$\underline{-16 \qquad -16}$$
$$p \leq 4$$

It is not reasonable for Tenea to take a negative or fractional number of pictures, so graph the nonnegative integers less than or equal to 4.

Tenea could take 0, 1, 2, 3, or 4 more pictures.

 Look Back

Check   Check the endpoint, 4.   Check a number less than 4.

$$16 + p = 20$$ $$16 + p \leq 20$$
$$\begin{array}{c|c} 16 + 4 & 20 \\ \hline 20 & 20 \checkmark \end{array}$$ $$\begin{array}{c|c} 16 + 2 & \leq 20 \\ \hline 18 & \leq 20 \checkmark \end{array}$$

Adding 0, 1, 2, 3, or 4 more pictures will not exceed 20.

 **2.** The Recommended Daily Allowance (RDA) of iron for a female in Sarah's age group (14–18 years) is 15 mg per day. Sarah has consumed 11 mg of iron today. Write and solve an inequality to show how many more milligrams of iron Sarah can consume without exceeding the RDA.

EXAMPLE  ***Sports Application***

Josh can bench press 220 pounds. He wants to bench press at least 250 pounds. Write and solve an inequality to determine how many more pounds Josh must lift to reach his goal. Check your answer.

Let p represent the number of additional pounds Josh must lift.

220 pounds	plus	additional pounds	is at least	250 pounds.
220	+	p	$\geq$	250

$$220 + p \geq 250$$ *Since 220 is added to p, subtract 220 from both*
$$\underline{-220 \qquad -220}$$ *sides to undo the addition.*
$$p \geq 30$$

Check   Check the endpoint, 30.   Check a number greater than 30.

$$220 + p = 250$$ $$220 + p \geq 250$$
$$\begin{array}{c|c} 220 + 30 & 250 \\ \hline 250 & 250 \checkmark \end{array}$$ $$\begin{array}{c|c} 220 + 40 & \geq 250 \\ \hline 260 & \geq 250 \checkmark \end{array}$$

Josh must lift at least 30 additional pounds to reach his goal.

 **3. What If...?** Josh has reached his goal of 250 pounds and now wants to try to break the school record of 282 pounds. Write and solve an inequality to determine how many more pounds Josh needs to break the school record. Check your answer.

THINK AND DISCUSS

1. Show how to check your solution to Example 1B.

2. Explain how the Addition and Subtraction Properties of Inequality are like the Addition and Subtraction Properties of Equality.

3. GET ORGANIZED Copy and complete the graphic organizer. In each box, write an inequality that must use the specified property to solve. Then solve and graph your inequality.

Properties of Inequality
- Addition
- Subtraction

California Standards Practice
Preparation for ✐ 5.0;
25.1, 25.3

go.hrw.com
Homework Help Online
KEYWORD: MA8CA 3-2
Parent Resources Online
KEYWORD: MA8CA Parent

GUIDED PRACTICE

SEE EXAMPLE **1**
p. 142

Solve each inequality and graph the solutions.

1. $12 < p + 6$ **2.** $w + 3 \geq 4$ **3.** $-5 + x \leq -20$ **4.** $z - 2 > -11$

SEE EXAMPLE **2**
p. 143

5. Health For adults, the maximum safe water temperature in a spa is 104°F. The water temperature in Bill's spa is 102°F. The temperature is increased by t°F. Write, solve, and graph an inequality to show the values of t for which the water temperature is still safe.

SEE EXAMPLE **3**
p. 144

6. Consumer Economics A local restaurant will deliver food to your house if the purchase amount of your order is at least $25.00. The total for part of your order is $17.95. Write and solve an inequality to determine how much more you must spend for the restaurant to deliver your order.

PRACTICE AND PROBLEM SOLVING

Independent Practice

For Exercises	See Example
7–10	1
11	2
12	3

Extra Practice
Skills Practice p. EP6
Application Practice p. EP26

Solve each inequality and graph the solutions.

7. $a - 3 \geq 2$ **8.** $2.5 > q - 0.8$ **9.** $-45 + x < -30$ **10.** $r + \dfrac{1}{4} \leq \dfrac{3}{4}$

11. Engineering The maximum load for a certain elevator is 2000 pounds. The total weight of the passengers on the elevator is 1400 pounds. A delivery man who weighs 243 pounds enters the elevator with a crate of weight w. Write, solve, and graph an inequality to show the values of w that will not exceed the weight limit of the elevator.

12. Transportation The gas tank in Mindy's car holds at most 15 gallons. She has already filled the tank with 7 gallons of gas. She will continue to fill the tank with g gallons more. Write and solve an inequality that shows all values of g that Mindy can add to the car's tank.

Write an inequality to represent each statement. Solve the inequality and graph the solutions. Check your answer.

13. Ten less than a number x is greater than 32.

14. A number n increased by 6 is less than or equal to 4.

15. A number r decreased by 13 is at most 15.

Solve each inequality and graph the solutions. Check your answer.

16. $x + 4 \leq 2$ **17.** $-12 + q > 39$ **18.** $x + \dfrac{3}{5} < 7$ **19.** $4.8 \geq p + 4$

20. $-12 \leq x - 12$ **21.** $4 < 206 + c$ **22.** $y - \dfrac{1}{3} > \dfrac{2}{3}$ **23.** $x + 1.4 \geq 1.4$

24. Use the inequality $s + 12 \geq 20$ to fill in the missing numbers.

     a. $s \geq$ ▨   **b.** $s +$ ▨ ≥ 30 **c.** $s - 8 \geq$ ▨

25. Health A particular type of contact lens can be worn up to 30 days in a row. Alex has been wearing these contact lenses for 21 days. Write, solve, and graph an inequality to show how many more days Alex could wear his contact lenses.

Solve each inequality and match the solution to the correct graph.

26. $1 \leq x - 2$

     A.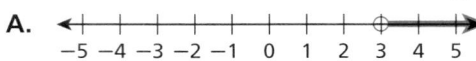

27. $8 > x - (-5)$

     B.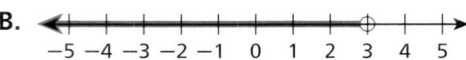

28. $x + 6 > 9$

     C.
```
←+—+—+—+—+—+—+—+—●—+—+→
 -5 -4 -3 -2 -1  0  1  2  3  4  5
```

29. $-4 \geq x - 7$

     D.
```
←+—+—+—+—+—+—+—●—+—+—+→
 -5 -4 -3 -2 -1  0  1  2  3  4  5
```

30. Estimation Is $x < 10$ a reasonable estimate for the solutions to the inequality $11.879 + x < 21.709$? Explain your answer.

31. Sports At the Seattle Mariners baseball team's home games, there are 45,611 seats in the four areas listed in the table. Suppose all the suite level and club level seats during a game are filled. Write and solve an inequality to determine how many people p could be sitting in the other types of seats.

Mariners Home Game Seating	
Type of Seat	**Number of Seats**
Main bowl	24,399
Upper bowl	16,022
Club level	4,254
Suite level	936

32. Critical Thinking Recall that in Chapter 2 a balance scale was used to model solving equations. Describe how a balance scale could model solving inequalities.

33. Critical Thinking Explain why $x + 4 \geq 6$ and $x - 4 \geq -2$ have the same solutions.

34. Write About It How do the solutions of $x + 2 \geq 3$ differ from the solutions of $x + 2 > 3$? How do the graphs of the solutions differ?

CONCEPT CONNECTION

35. This problem will prepare you for the Concept Connection on page 154.

     a. Daryl finds that the distance from Columbus, Ohio, to Washington, D.C, is 411 miles. What is the round-trip distance?

     b. Daryl can afford to drive a total of 1000 miles. Write an inequality to show the number of miles m he can drive while in Washington, D.C.

     c. Solve the inequality and graph the solutions on a number line.

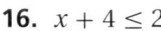

Health

Special-effects contact lenses are sometimes part of costumes for movies. All contact lenses should be worn under an eye doctor's supervision.

Multiple Choice For Exercises 36–39, choose the best answer.

36. Which is a reasonable solution of $4.7367 + p < 20.1784$?

Ⓐ 15 Ⓑ 16 Ⓒ 24 Ⓓ 25

37. Which statement can be modeled by $x + 3 \leq 12$?

Ⓐ Sam has 3 bottles of water. Together, Sam and Dave have at most 12 bottles of water.

Ⓑ Jennie sold 3 cookbooks. To earn a prize, Jennie must sell at least 12 cookbooks.

Ⓒ Peter has 3 baseball hats. Peter and his brothers have fewer than 12 baseball hats.

Ⓓ Kathy swam 3 laps in the pool this week. She must swim more than 12 laps.

38. Which represents the solutions of $p + 3 < 1$?

Ⓐ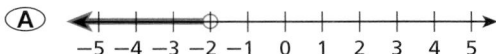

Ⓑ $\{p : p \leq -27\}$

Ⓒ
```
←——|——|——|——|——|——|——|——|——⊕——|——|——|——→
  −5 −4 −3 −2 −1  0  1  2  3  4  5
```

Ⓓ $\{p : p > 2\}$

39. Which inequality is NOT equivalent to $n + 12 \leq 26$?

Ⓐ $n \leq 14$ Ⓑ $n + 6 \leq 20$ Ⓒ $10 \geq n - 4$ Ⓓ $n - 12 \leq 14$

CHALLENGE AND EXTEND

Solve each inequality and graph the solutions. Check your answer.

40. $6\frac{9}{10} \geq 4\frac{4}{5} + x$ **41.** $r - 1\frac{2}{5} \leq 3\frac{7}{10}$ **42.** $6\frac{2}{3} + m > 7\frac{1}{6}$

 **Reasoning** Determine whether each statement is *sometimes, always,* or *never* true. Explain.

43. $a + b > a - b$

44. If $a > c$, then $a + b > c + b$.

45. If $a > b$ and $c > d$, then $a + c > b + d$.

 46. Reasoning If $x + b > c$ and $x > 0$ are equivalent, show that $b = c$.

Solve each equation for the indicated variable. *(Lesson 2-6)*

47. $2x + 3y = 9$ for y **48.** $P = 4s$ for s **49.** $2a + ab = c$ for a

50. $p + e = f$ for e **51.** $2s - k = 11$ for k **52.** $5m + n = 0$ for m

Solve each equation. Check your answer. *(Lesson 2-7)*

53. $|x| + 2 = 6$ **54.** $|z - 12| = 24$ **55.** $4|d| = 20$

56. $|-3r + 1| = 14$ **57.** $|6b + 2| - 4 = 22$ **58.** $0 = |3 - 2c|$

Write the inequality shown by each graph. *(Lesson 3-1)*

59.
```
←——|——|——|——|——●——|——|——|——|——|——|——→
  −4 −3 −2 −1  0  1  2  3  4  5  6
```

60.
```
←——|——|——|——|——|——|——|——|——⊕——|——|——→
  −4 −3 −2 −1  0  1  2  3  4  5  6
```

3-3 Solving Inequalities by Multiplying or Dividing

California Standards

Preparation for 🔑 **5.0**
Students solve multistep problems, including word problems, involving linear equations and **linear inequalities in one variable** and provide justification for each step.

Who uses this?
You can solve an inequality to determine how much you can buy with a certain amount of money. (See Example 3.)

Remember, solving inequalities is similar to solving equations. To solve an inequality that contains multiplication or division, undo the operation by dividing or multiplying both sides of the inequality by the same number.

The rules below show the properties of inequality for multiplying or dividing by a positive number. The rules for multiplying or dividing by a negative number appear later in this lesson.

"This is all I have, so I'll take 3 pencils, 3 notebooks, a binder, and 0.9 calculators."

Properties of Inequality

Multiplication and Division by Positive Numbers

WORDS	NUMBERS	ALGEBRA
Multiplication You can multiply both sides of an inequality by the same *positive* number, and the statement will still be true.	$7 < 12$ $7(3) < 12(3)$ $21 < 36$	If $a < b$ and $c > 0$, then $ac < bc$.
Division You can divide both sides of an inequality by the same *positive* number, and the statement will still be true.	$15 < 35$ $\dfrac{15}{5} < \dfrac{35}{5}$ $3 < 7$	If $a < b$ and $c > 0$, then $\dfrac{a}{c} < \dfrac{b}{c}$.

These properties are also true for inequalities that use the symbols $>$, $\geq$, and $\leq$.

EXAMPLE **1** **Multiplying or Dividing by a Positive Number**

Solve each inequality and graph the solutions.

A $3x > -27$

$3x > -27$ *Since x is multiplied by 3, divide both sides by 3 to*
$\dfrac{3x}{3} > \dfrac{-27}{3}$ *undo the multiplication.*

$x > -9$ *The solution set is {x : x > −9}.*

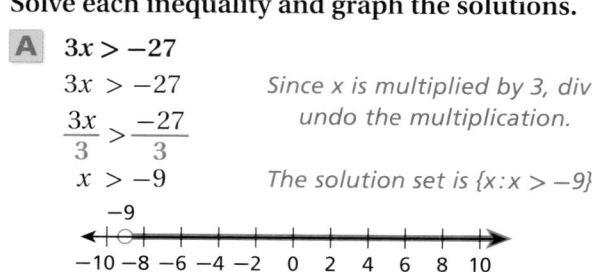

Solve each inequality and graph the solutions.

B $\frac{2}{3}r < 6$

$$\frac{2}{3}r < 6$$ *Since r is multiplied by $\frac{2}{3}$, multiply both sides by the reciprocal of $\frac{2}{3}$.*

$$\frac{3}{2}\left(\frac{2}{3}r\right) < \frac{3}{2}(6)$$

$$r < 9$$ *The solution set is {r : r < 9}.*

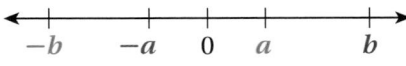

 **CHECK IT OUT!** Solve each inequality and graph the solutions. Check your answer.

1a. $4k > 24$ **1b.** $-50 \geq 5q$ **1c.** $\frac{3}{4}g > 27$

What happens when you multiply or divide both sides of an inequality by a negative number?

Look at the number line below.

$a < b$	$b > -a$
$-a \;\rule{1em}{0.6em}\; -b$ *Multiply both sides by -1.*	$-b \;\rule{1em}{0.6em}\; a$ *Multiply both sides by -1.*
$-a > -b$ *Use the number line to determine the direction of the inequality.*	$-b < a$ *Use the number line to determine the direction of the inequality.*

Notice that when you multiply (or divide) both sides of an inequality by a negative number, you must reverse the inequality symbol.

Know it! Note

Properties of Inequality

Multiplication and Division by Negative Numbers

WORDS	NUMBERS	ALGEBRA
Multiplication If you multiply both sides of an inequality by the same *negative* number, you must reverse the inequality symbol for the statement to still be true.	$8 > 4$ $8(-2) \;<\; 4(-2)$ $-16 \;<\; -8$ $-16 \;<\; -8$	If $a > b$ and $c < 0$, then $ac < bc$.
Division If you divide both sides of an inequality by the same *negative* number, you must reverse the inequality symbol for the statement to still be true.	$12 > 4$ $\dfrac{12}{-4} \;<\; \dfrac{4}{-4}$ $-3 \;<\; -1$ $-3 \;<\; -1$	If $a > b$ and $c < 0$, then $\dfrac{a}{c} < \dfrac{b}{c}$.

These properties are also true for inequalities that use the symbols $<$, $\geq$, and $\leq$.

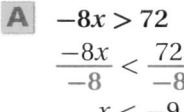

EXAMPLE 2 **Multiplying or Dividing by a Negative Number**

Solve each inequality and graph the solutions.

A $-8x > 72$

$$\frac{-8x}{-8} < \frac{72}{-8}$$

$$x < -9$$

Since x is multiplied by −8, divide both sides by −8.
Change > to <.

B $-3 \le \dfrac{x}{-5}$

$$-5(-3) \ge -5\left(\frac{x}{-5}\right)$$

$$15 \ge x$$

$$x \le 15$$

Since x is divided by −5, multiply both sides by −5.
Change ≤ to ≥.

> **Caution!**
>
> Do not change the direction of the inequality symbol just because you see a negative sign. For example, you do not change the symbol when solving $4x < -24$.

CHECK IT OUT! Solve each inequality and graph the solutions. Check your answer.

2a. $10 \ge -x$ **2b.** $4.25 > -0.25h$

EXAMPLE 3 *Consumer Application*

Ryan has a $16 gift card for a health store where a smoothie costs $2.50 with tax. What are the possible numbers of smoothies that Ryan can buy?

Let *s* represent the number of smoothies Ryan can buy.

$2.50	times	number of smoothies	is at most	$16.00.
2.50	•	*s*	≤	16.00

$$2.50s \le 16.00$$

$$\frac{2.50s}{2.50} \le \frac{16.00}{2.50}$$

Since s is multiplied by 2.50, divide both sides by 2.50. The symbol does not change.

$$s \le 6.4$$

Ryan can buy only a whole number of smoothies.

Ryan can buy 0, 1, 2, 3, 4, 5, or 6 smoothies.

CHECK IT OUT! **3.** A pitcher holds 128 ounces of juice. What are the possible numbers of 10-ounce servings that one pitcher can fill?

THINK AND DISCUSS

1. Compare the Multiplication and Division Properties of Inequality and the Multiplication and Division Properties of Equality.

2. GET ORGANIZED Copy and complete the graphic organizer. In each cell, write and solve an inequality.

Solving Inequalities by Using Multiplication and Division		
	By a Positive Number	**By a Negative Number**
Divide		
Multiply		

3-3

Exercises

California Standards Practice
Preparation for 🔑 5.0;
24.3, 25.1, 25.2

go.hrw.com
Homework Help Online
KEYWORD: MA8CA 3-3
Parent Resources Online
KEYWORD: MA8CA Parent

GUIDED PRACTICE

SEE EXAMPLE **1**
p. 148

Solve each inequality and graph the solutions. Check your answer.

1. $3b > 27$ **2.** $-40 \geq 8b$ **3.** $\dfrac{d}{3} > 6$ **4.** $24d \leq 6$

5. $1.1m \leq 1.21$ **6.** $\dfrac{2}{3}k > 6$ **7.** $9s > -18$ **8.** $\dfrac{4}{5} \geq \dfrac{r}{2}$

SEE EXAMPLE **2**
p. 150

9. $-2x < -10$ **10.** $\dfrac{b}{-2} \geq 8$ **11.** $-3.5n < 1.4$ **12.** $4 > -8g$

13. $\dfrac{d}{-6} < \dfrac{1}{2}$ **14.** $-10h \geq -6$ **15.** $12 > \dfrac{t}{-6}$ **16.** $-\dfrac{1}{2}m \geq -7$

SEE EXAMPLE **3**
p. 150

17. Travel Tom saved $550 to go on a school trip. The cost for a hotel room, including tax, is $80 per night. Write an inequality to show the number of nights Tom can stay at the hotel.

PRACTICE AND PROBLEM SOLVING

Independent Practice

For Exercises	See Example
18–29	1
30–41	2
42	3

Extra Practice
Skills Practice p. EP6
Application Practice p. EP26

Solve each inequality and graph the solutions. Check your answer.

18. $10 < 2t$ **19.** $\dfrac{1}{3}j \leq 4$ **20.** $-80 < 8c$ **21.** $21 > 3d$

22. $\dfrac{w}{4} \geq -2$ **23.** $\dfrac{h}{4} \leq \dfrac{2}{7}$ **24.** $6y < 4.2$ **25.** $12c \leq -144$

26. $\dfrac{4}{5}x \geq \dfrac{2}{5}$ **27.** $6b \geq \dfrac{3}{5}$ **28.** $-25 > 10p$ **29.** $\dfrac{b}{8} \leq -2$

30. $-9a > 81$ **31.** $\dfrac{1}{2} < \dfrac{r}{-3}$ **32.** $-6p > 0.6$ **33.** $\dfrac{y}{-4} > -\dfrac{1}{2}$

34. $-\dfrac{1}{6}f < 5$ **35.** $-2.25t < -9$ **36.** $24 \leq -10w$ **37.** $-11z > 121$

38. $\dfrac{3}{5} < \dfrac{f}{-5}$ **39.** $-k \geq 7$ **40.** $-2.2b < -7.7$ **41.** $16 \geq -\dfrac{4}{3}p$

42. Camping The rope Roz brought with her camping gear is 54 inches long. Roz needs to cut shorter pieces of rope that are each 18 inches long. What are the possible number of pieces Roz can cut?

Solve each inequality and graph the solutions. Check your answer.

43. $-8x < 24$ **44.** $3t \leq 24$ **45.** $\dfrac{1}{4}x < 5$ **46.** $\dfrac{4}{5}p \geq -24$

47. $54 \leq -9p$ **48.** $3t > -\dfrac{1}{2}$ **49.** $-\dfrac{3}{4}b > -\dfrac{3}{2}$ **50.** $216 > 3.6r$

Write an inequality for each statement. Solve the inequality and graph the solutions. Check your answer.

51. The product of a number and 7 is not less than 21.

52. The quotient of h and -6 is at least 5.

53. The product of $-\dfrac{4}{5}$ and b is at most -16.

54. Ten is no more than the quotient of t and 4.

 55. Write About It Explain how you know whether to reverse the inequality symbol when solving an inequality.

56. Geometry The area of a rectangle is at most 21 square inches. The width of the rectangle is 3.5 inches. What are the possible measurements for the length of the rectangle?

Solve each inequality and match the solution to the correct graph.

57. $-0.5t \geq 1.5$

A. ← number line from −5 to 5, shaded left with closed dot at 3

58. $\frac{1}{9}t \leq -3$

B. ← number line from −5 to 5, shaded right with closed dot at 3

59. $-13.5 \leq -4.5t$

C. ← number line from −5 to 5, shaded left with closed dot at −3

60. $\frac{t}{-6} \leq -\frac{1}{2}$

D. ← number line from −45 to 9, shaded left with closed dot at −27

61. Animals A wildlife shelter is home to native species of birds, mammals, and reptiles. If mixed seed is sold in 20 lb bags, what is the least number of bags of mixed seed needed for one year at this shelter?

Food Consumed at a Wildlife Shelter per Week	
Type of Food	Amount of Food (lb)
Grapes	4
Mixed seed	10
Peanuts	5
Raw meat	10
Grains	5

62. Education In order to earn an A in a college math class, a student must score no less than 90% of all possible points. One semester, students who earned an A had at least 567 points. Write an inequality to show the range of points possible.

63. Critical Thinking Explain why you cannot solve an inequality by multiplying both sides by zero.

64. ///**ERROR ANALYSIS**/// Two students have different answers for a homework problem. Which answer is incorrect? Explain the error.

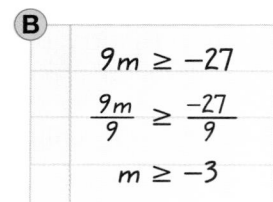

A
$9m \geq -27$
$\frac{9m}{9} \geq \frac{-27}{9}$
$m \leq -3$

B
$9m \geq -27$
$\frac{9m}{9} \geq \frac{-27}{9}$
$m \geq -3$

65. Jan has a budget of $800 for catering. The catering company charges $12.50 per guest. Write and solve an inequality to show the numbers of guests Jan can invite.

CONCEPT CONNECTION

66. This problem will prepare you for the Concept Connection on page 154.

a. The Swimming Club can spend a total of $250 for hotel rooms for its spring trip. One hotel costs $75 per night. Write an inequality to find the number of rooms the club can reserve at this hotel. Let *n* be the number of rooms.

b. Solve the inequality you wrote in part **a**. Graph the solutions on a number line. Make sure your answer is reasonable.

c. Another hotel offers a rate of $65 per night. Does this allow the club to reserve more rooms? Explain your reasoning.

Multiple Choice For Exercises 67–69, choose the best answer.

67. Which inequality does NOT have the same solutions as $-\frac{2}{3}y > 4$?

  (A) $12 < -2y$

  (B) $\frac{y}{2} < -12$

  (C) $-\frac{3}{4}y > \frac{9}{2}$

  (D) $-3y > 18$

68. The solutions of which inequality are NOT represented by the graph?

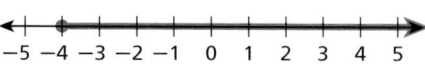

  (A) $\frac{x}{2} \geq -2$

  (B) $-5x \geq 20$

  (C) $3x \geq -12$

  (D) $-7x \leq 28$

69. Which inequality can be used to find the number of 39-cent stamps you can purchase for $4.00?

  (A) $0.39s \geq 4.00$

  (B) $0.39s \leq 4.00$

  (C) $\frac{s}{0.39} \leq 4.00$

  (D) $\frac{4.00}{0.39} \leq s$

70. **Short Response** Write three different inequalities that are equivalent to $x > 4$. Show your work and explain each step.

CHALLENGE AND EXTEND

Solve each inequality. Check your answer.

71. $2\frac{1}{3} \leq -\frac{5}{6}g$

72. $\frac{2x}{3} < 8.25$

73. $2\frac{5}{8}m > \frac{7}{10}$

74. $3\frac{3}{5}f \geq 14\frac{2}{5}$

75. **Estimation** What is the greatest possible integer solution of the inequality $3.806x < 19.902$?

76. **Reasoning** The Transitive Property of Equality states that if $a = b$ and $b = c$, then $a = c$. Is there a Transitive Property of Inequality using the symbol $<$? If so, explain. If not, give a counterexample.

77. **Reasoning** The Symmetric Property of Equality states that if $a = b$, then $b = a$. Is there a Symmetric Property of Inequality? If so, explain. If not, give a counterexample.

SPIRAL STANDARDS REVIEW   🔑 6AF1.1, 7AF2.1, 🔑 15.0

Write the power represented by each geometric model. *(Lesson 1-4)*

78.

79.

80.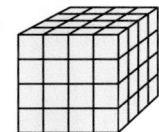

Find the unit rate. *(Lesson 2-5)*

81. Twelve gallons of gas cost $22.68.

82. A tree grows four feet in six years.

83. A student types 105 words in 3 minutes.

Solve each inequality and graph the solutions. Check your answer. *(Lesson 3-2)*

84. $x + 5 \geq 3$

85. $t - \frac{1}{4} < \frac{3}{4}$

86. $4 > x - 1$

87. $6 > b - 8$

CONCEPT CONNECTION

Simple Inequalities

Remember the Alamo! The Spanish Club is planning a trip for next summer. They plan to travel from Fort Worth, Texas, to San Antonio, Texas. They can spend only $550 for the entire trip.

1. The treasurer of the club budgets $90 for gasoline. The current gas price is $3.10/gallon. The school van gets an average of 20 miles per gallon of gasoline. Determine how many miles they can drive on this budget. Round your answer to the nearest mile.

2. The distance from Fort Worth to San Antonio is 266 miles. Write an inequality that can be used to solve for the number of miles m that they can drive while in San Antonio. Solve your inequality and graph the solutions. Check your answer.

3. The treasurer budgeted $200 for hotel rooms for one night. The club chose a hotel that charges $58 per night. Write an inequality that can be used to solve for the number of rooms they can reserve n. What is the maximum number of rooms that they can reserve in the hotel?

4. Use the maximum number of rooms you found in Problem **3.** How much will the club spend on hotel rooms?

5. The club members plan to spend $80 on food. They also want to see attractions in San Antonio, such as SeaWorld and the Alamo.

   Write an inequality that can be solved to find the amount of money available for seeing attractions. What is the maximum amount the club can spend seeing attractions?

6. Write a summary of the budget for the Spanish Club trip. Include the amount they plan to spend on gasoline, hotel rooms, food, and attractions.

READY TO GO ON?

Quiz for Lessons 3-1 Through 3-3

3-1 Graphing and Writing Inequalities

Describe the solutions of each inequality in words.

1. $-2 < r$ **2.** $t - 1 \leq 7$ **3.** $2s \geq 6$ **4.** $4 > 5 - x$

Graph each inequality.

5. $x > -2$ **6.** $m \leq 1\frac{1}{2}$ **7.** $g < \sqrt{8 + 1}$ **8.** $h \geq 2^3$

Write the inequality shown by each graph.

9.

```
←——┼——┼——●——┼——┼——┼——┼——┼——┼——┼——┼——→
  -5  -4  -3  -2  -1   0   1   2   3   4   5
```

10.

```
←——┼——┼——┼——┼——┼——┼——┼——┼——┼——○——┼——→
  -4  -3  -2  -1   0   1   2   3   4   5   6
```

11.

```
              -1.5
←——┼——┼——┼——┼——●——┼——┼——┼——┼——┼——→
  -6  -5  -4  -3  -2  -1   0   1   2   3   4
```

Write an inequality for each situation and graph the solutions.

12. You must purchase at least 5 tickets to receive a discount.

13. Children under 13 are not admitted to certain movies without an adult.

14. A cell phone plan allows up to 250 free minutes per month.

3-2 Solving Inequalities by Adding and Subtracting

Solve each inequality and graph the solutions. Check your answer.

15. $k + 5 \leq 7$ **16.** $4 > p - 3$ **17.** $r - 8 \geq -12$ **18.** $-3 + p < -6$

19. Allie must sell at least 50 gift baskets for the band fund-raiser. She already sold 36 baskets. Write and solve an inequality to determine how many more baskets Allie must sell for the fund-raiser.

20. Dante has at most $12 to spend on entertainment each week. So far this week, he spent $7.50. Write and solve an inequality to determine how much money Dante can spend on entertainment the rest of the week.

3-3 Solving Inequalities by Multiplying and Dividing

Solve each inequality and graph the solutions. Check your answer.

21. $-4x < 8$ **22.** $\frac{d}{3} \geq -3$ **23.** $\frac{3}{4}t \leq 12$ **24.** $8 > -16c$

25. A spool of ribbon is 80 inches long. Riley needs to cut strips of ribbon that are 14 inches long. What are the possible numbers of strips that Riley can cut?

California Standards

4.0 Students simplify expressions before solving **linear** equations and **inequalities in one variable**, such as $3(2x - 5) + 4(x - 2) = 12$.

5.0 Students solve **multi-step problems, including word problems, involving** linear equations and **linear inequalities in one variable** and provide justification for each step.

Why learn this?

Contestants at a county fair can solve an inequality to find how many pounds a prize-winning pumpkin must weigh. (See Example 3.)

At the county fair, contestants can enter contests that judge animals, recipes, crops, art projects, and more. Sometimes an average score or average weight is used to determine the winner of the blue ribbon. A contestant can use a multi-step inequality to determine what score or weight is needed in order to win.

Inequalities that contain more than one operation require more than one step to solve. Use inverse operations to undo the operations in the inequality one at a time.

EXAMPLE 1 | **Solving Multi-Step Inequalities**

Solve each inequality and graph the solutions.

A $160 + 4f \le 500$

$$
\begin{aligned}
160 + 4f &\le 500 \\
-160 \quad\quad &\quad -160 \\
\hline
4f &\le 340
\end{aligned}
$$

Since 160 is added to 4f, subtract 160 from both sides to undo the addition.

$$\frac{4f}{4} \le \frac{340}{4}$$

Since f is multiplied by 4, divide both sides by 4 to undo the multiplication.

$$f \le 85$$

The solution set is {f : f ≤ 85}.

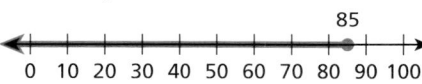

B $7 - 2t \le 21$

$$
\begin{aligned}
7 - 2t &\le 21 \\
-7 \quad\quad &\quad -7 \\
\hline
-2t &\le 14
\end{aligned}
$$

Since 7 is added to −2t, subtract 7 from both sides to undo the addition.

$$\frac{-2t}{-2} \ge \frac{14}{-2}$$

Since t is multiplied by −2, divide both sides by −2 to undo the multiplication.
Change ≤ to ≥.

$$t \ge -7$$

The solution set is {t : t ≥ −7}.

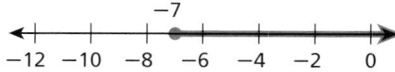

Remember!

Subtracting a number is the same as adding its opposite.
$7 - 2t = 7 + (-2t)$

Solve each inequality and graph the solutions. Check your answer.

1a. $-12 \ge 3x + 6$ **1b.** $\dfrac{x + 5}{-2} > 3$ **1c.** $\dfrac{1 - 2n}{3} \ge 7$

To solve more complicated inequalities, you may first need to simplify the expressions on one or both sides.

EXAMPLE 2   **Simplifying Before Solving Inequalities**

Solve each inequality and graph the solutions.

A $-4 + (-8) < -5c - 2$

$$-12 < -5c - 2$$

Combine like terms. Since 2 is subtracted from $-5c$,

$$\underline{+2 \qquad\qquad +2}$$
$$-10 < -5c$$

add 2 to both sides to undo the subtraction.

$$\frac{-10}{-5} > \frac{-5c}{-5}$$

Since c is multiplied by -5, divide both sides by -5 to undo the multiplication.

Change $<$ to $>$.

$$2 > c \ (\text{or } c < 2)$$

The solution set is $\{c : c < 2\}$.

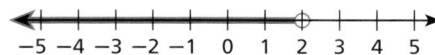

B $-3(3 - x) < 4^2$

$$-3(3 - x) < 4^2$$
$$-3(3) - 3(-x) < 4^2$$
$$-9 + 3x < 4^2$$

Distribute -3 on the left side.

$$-9 + 3x < 16$$

Simplify the right side.

$$-9 + 3x < 16$$

Since -9 is added to $3x$, add 9 to both sides

$$\underline{+9 \qquad\qquad +9}$$
$$3x < 25$$

to undo the addition.

$$\frac{3x}{3} < \frac{25}{3}$$

Since x is multiplied by 3, divide both sides by 3 to undo the multiplication.

$$x < 8\frac{1}{3}$$

The solution set is $\left\{x : x < 8\frac{1}{3}\right\}$.

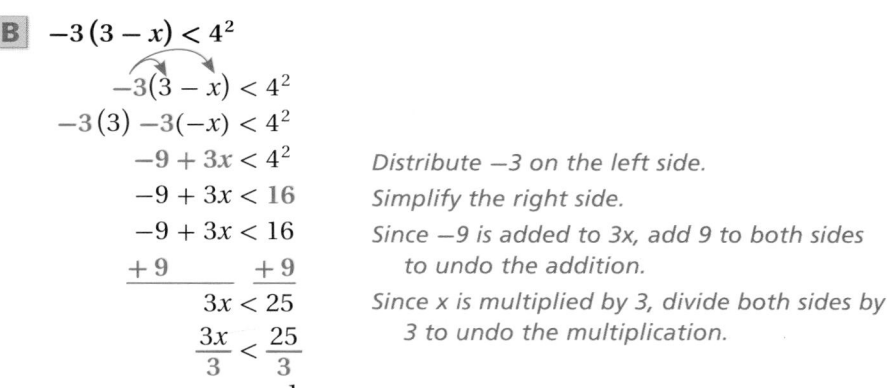

C $\dfrac{4}{5}x + \dfrac{1}{2} > \dfrac{3}{5}$

$$10\left(\frac{4}{5}x + \frac{1}{2}\right) > 10\left(\frac{3}{5}\right)$$

Multiply both sides by 10, the LCD of the fractions.

$$10\left(\frac{4}{5}x\right) + 10\left(\frac{1}{2}\right) > 10\left(\frac{3}{5}\right)$$

Distribute 10 on the left side.

$$8x + 5 > 6$$

Since 5 is added to $8x$, subtract 5 from

$$\underline{-5 \quad -5}$$
$$8x \quad > 1$$

both sides to undo the addition.

$$\frac{8x}{8} > \frac{1}{8}$$

Since x is multiplied by 8, divide both sides by 8 to undo the multiplication.

$$x > \frac{1}{8}$$

The solution set is $\left\{x : x > \frac{1}{8}\right\}$.

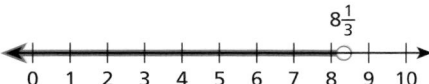

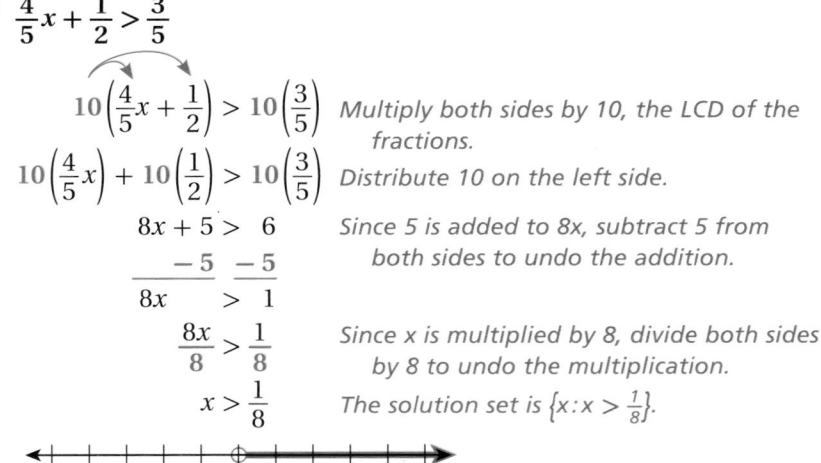

 Solve each inequality and graph the solutions. Check your answer.

2a. $2m + 5 > 5^2$ **2b.** $3 + 2(x + 4) > 3$ **2c.** $\dfrac{5}{8} < \dfrac{3}{8}x - \dfrac{1}{4}$

EXAMPLE 3 *Gardening Application*

To win the blue ribbon for the Heaviest Pumpkin Crop at the county fair, the average weight of John's two pumpkins must be greater than 819 lb. One of his pumpkins weighs 887 lb. What is the least number of pounds the second pumpkin could weigh in order for John to win the blue ribbon?

Let p represent the weight of the second pumpkin. The average weight of the pumpkins is the sum of each weight divided by 2.

(887	plus	p)	divided by	2	must be greater than	819.
(887	+	p)	÷	2	>	819

$$\frac{887 + p}{2} > 819$$ *Since 887 + p is divided by 2, multiply both sides by 2 to undo the division.*

$$2\left(\frac{887 + p}{2}\right) > 2(819)$$

$$887 + p > 1638$$ *Since 887 is added to p, subtract 887 from both sides to undo the addition.*

$$\underline{-887 \qquad\qquad -887}$$
$$p > \quad 751$$

The second pumpkin must weigh more than 751 pounds.

Check   Check the endpoint, 751.   Check a number greater than 751.

$$\frac{887 + p}{2} = 819$$

$\frac{887 + 751}{2}$	819
$\frac{1638}{2}$	819
819	819 ✓

$$\frac{887 + p}{2} > 819$$

$\frac{887 + 755}{2}$	>	819
$\frac{1642}{2}$	>	819
821	>	819 ✓

3. The average of Jim's two test scores must be at least 90 to make an A in the class. Jim got a 95 on his first test. What grades can Jim get on his second test to make an A in the class?

THINK AND DISCUSS

1. The inequality $v \geq 25$ states that 25 is the ___?___. (*value of v, minimum value of v,* or *maximum value of v*)

2. Describe two sets of steps for solving the inequality $\frac{x+5}{3} > 7$.

3. GET ORGANIZED Copy and complete the graphic organizer.

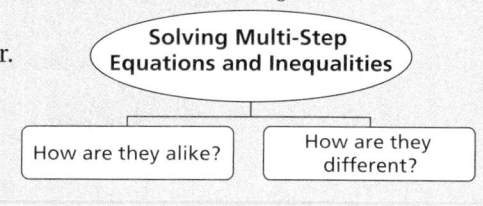

California Standards Practice
🔑 4.0, 🔑 5.0

go.hrw.com
Homework Help Online
KEYWORD: MA8CA 3-4
Parent Resources Online
KEYWORD: MA8CA Parent

GUIDED PRACTICE

SEE EXAMPLE 1
p. 156

Solve each inequality and graph the solutions. Check your answer.

1. $2m + 1 > 13$　　**2.** $2d + 21 \le 11$　　**3.** $6 \le -2x + 2$　　**4.** $4c - 7 > 5$

5. $\dfrac{4 + x}{3} > -4$　　**6.** $1 < 0.2x - 0.7$　　**7.** $\dfrac{3 - 2x}{3} \le 7$　　**8.** $2x + 5 \ge 2$

SEE EXAMPLE 2
p. 157

9. $4(x + 2) > 6$　　**10.** $\dfrac{1}{4}x + \dfrac{2}{3} < \dfrac{3}{4}$　　**11.** $4 - x + 6^2 \ge 21$

12. $4 - x > 3(4 - 2)$　　**13.** $0.2(x - 10) > -1.8$　　**14.** $3(j + 41) \le 35$

SEE EXAMPLE 3
p. 158

15. Business A sales representative is given a choice of two paycheck plans. One choice includes a monthly base pay of $300 plus 10% of his sales. The second choice is a monthly salary of $1200. For what amount of sales would the representative make more money with the first plan?

PRACTICE AND PROBLEM SOLVING

Independent Practice

For Exercises	See Example
16–27	1
28–36	2
37	3

Extra Practice
Skills Practice p. EP7
Application Practice p. EP26

Solve each inequality and graph the solutions. Check your answer.

16. $4r - 9 > 7$　　**17.** $3 \le 5 - 2x$　　**18.** $\dfrac{w + 3}{2} > 6$　　**19.** $11w + 99 < 77$

20. $9 \ge \dfrac{1}{2}v + 3$　　**21.** $-4x - 8 > 16$　　**22.** $8 - \dfrac{2}{3}z \le 2$　　**23.** $f + 2\dfrac{1}{2} < -2$

24. $\dfrac{3n - 8}{5} \ge 2$　　**25.** $-5 > -5 - 3w$　　**26.** $10 > \dfrac{5 - 3p}{2}$　　**27.** $2v + 1 > 2\dfrac{1}{3}$

28. $4(x + 3) > -24$　　**29.** $4 > x - 3(x + 2)$　　**30.** $-18 \ge 33 - 3h$

31. $-2 > 7x - 2(x - 4)$　　**32.** $9 - (9)^2 > 10x - x$　　**33.** $2a - (-3)^2 \ge 13$

34. $6 - \dfrac{x}{3} + 1 > \dfrac{2}{3}$　　**35.** $12(x - 3) + 2x > 6$　　**36.** $15 \ge 19 + 2(q - 18)$

37. Communications One cell phone company offers a plan that costs $29.99 and includes unlimited night and weekend minutes. Another company offers a plan that costs $19.99 and charges $0.35 per minute during nights and weekends. For what numbers of night and weekend minutes does the second company's plan cost more than the first company's plan?

Solve each inequality and graph the solutions. Check your answer.

38. $-12 > -4x - 8$　　**39.** $5x + 4 \le 14$　　**40.** $\dfrac{2}{3}x - 5 > 7$

41. $x - 3x > 2 - 10$　　**42.** $5 - x - 2 > 3$　　**43.** $3 < 2x - 5(x + 3)$

44. $\dfrac{1}{6} - \dfrac{2}{3}m \ge \dfrac{1}{4}$　　**45.** $4 - (r - 2) > 3 - 5$　　**46.** $0.3 - 0.5n + 1 \ge 0.4$

47. $6^2 > 4(x + 2)$　　**48.** $-4 - 2n + 4n > 7 - 2^2$　　**49.** $\dfrac{1}{4}(p - 10) \ge 6 - 4$

50. Use the inequality $-4t - 8 \le 12$ to fill in the missing numbers.

　　a. $t \ge$ ▨　　　　　**b.** $t + 4 \ge$ ▨　　　　　**c.** $t -$ ▨ ≥ 0

　　d. $t + 10 \ge$ ▨　　　**e.** $3t \ge$ ▨　　　　　**f.** $\dfrac{t}{▨} \ge -5$

Write an inequality for each statement. Solve the inequality and graph the solutions.

51. One-half of a number, increased by 9, is less than 33.

52. Six is less than or equal to the sum of 4 and $-2x$.

53. The product of 4 and the sum of a number and 12 is at most 16.

54. The sum of half a number and two-thirds of the number is less than 14.

Solve each inequality and match the solution to the correct graph.

55. $4x - 9 \geq 7$

A. ![number line from -5 to 5 with closed dot at -2, shaded left]

56. $-0.6 \geq 0.3(x - 2)$

B. ![number line from -5 to 5 with closed dot at 4, shaded right]

57. $-2x - 6 \geq -4 + 2$

C. ![number line from -5 to 5 with open dot at $-\frac{3}{2}$, shaded left]

58. $\frac{1}{2} - \frac{1}{3}x \leq \left(\frac{2}{3} + \frac{1}{3}\right)^2$

D. ![number line from -5 to 5 with closed dot at -2, shaded right]

59. Entertainment A digital video recorder (DVR) records television shows on an internal hard drive. To use a DVR, you need a subscription with a DVR service company. Two companies advertise their charges for a DVR machine and subscription service.

EASY ELECTRONICS

$225 for DVR machine

$400 for lifetime subscription

CABLE SOLUTIONS

$275 for DVR machine

$15 per month for service

For what numbers of months will a consumer pay less for the machine and subscription at Easy Electronics than at Cable Solutions?

60. Geometry The area of the triangle shown is less than 55 square inches.

   a. Write an inequality that can be used to find x.

   b. Solve the inequality you wrote in part **a.**

   c. What is the maximum height of the triangle?

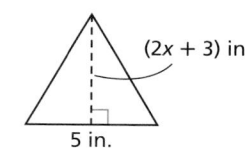

$(2x + 3)$ in.

5 in.

61. This problem will prepare you for the Concept Connection on page 184.

CONCEPT CONNECTION

   a. A band wants to create a CD of their last concert. They received a donation of $500 to cover the cost. The CDs cost $350 plus $3 per CD. Complete the table to find a relationship between the number of CDs and the total cost.

   b. Write an equation for the cost C of the CDs based on the number of CDs n.

   c. Write an inequality that can be used to determine how many CDs can be made with the $500 donation. Solve the inequality and determine how many CDs the band can have made from the $500 donation. Check your answer.

Number	Process	Cost
1	350 + 3	353
2		
3		
10		
n		

62. Critical Thinking What is the least whole number that is a solution of $4r - 4.9 > 14.95$?

63. Write About It Describe two sets of steps to solve $2(x + 3) > 10$.

Multiple Choice For Exercises 64–66, choose the best answer.

64. What are the solutions of $3y > 2x + 4$ when $y = 6$?

 Ⓐ $7 > x$ Ⓑ $x > 7$ Ⓒ $x > 11$ Ⓓ $11 > x$

65. Cecilia has $30 to spend at a carnival. Admission costs $5.00, lunch will cost $6.00, and each ride ticket costs $1.25. Which inequality represents the number of ride tickets x that Cecilia can buy?

 Ⓐ $30 - (5 - 6) + 1.25x \le 30$ Ⓒ $30 - (5 + 6) \le 1.25x$

 Ⓑ $5 + 6 + 1.25x \le 30$ Ⓓ $30 + 1.25x \le 5 + 6$

66. Which statement is modeled by $2p + 5 < 11$?

 Ⓐ The sum of 5 and 2 times p is at least 11.

 Ⓑ Five added to the product of 2 and p is less than 11.

 Ⓒ Two times p plus 5 is at most 11.

 Ⓓ The product of 2 and p added to 5 is 11.

67. Gridded Response A basketball team scored 8 points more in its second game than in its first. In its third game, the team scored 42 points. The total number of points scored in the three games was more than 150. What is the least number of points the team might have scored in its *second* game?

CHALLENGE AND EXTEND

Solve each inequality and graph the solutions. Check your answer.

68. $3(x + 2) - 6x + 6 \le 0$ **69.** $-18 > -(2x + 9) - 4 + x$ **70.** $\dfrac{2 + x}{2} - (x - 1) > 1$

Write an inequality for each statement. Graph the solutions.

71. x is a positive number.   **72.** x is a negative number.

73. x is a nonnegative number.   **74.** x is not a positive number.

75. x times negative 3 is positive.   **76.** The opposite of x is greater than 2.

 SPIRAL STANDARDS REVIEW    6AF1.1, 2.0, 5.0

Find each square root. *(Lesson 1-5)*

77. $\sqrt{49}$ **78.** $-\sqrt{144}$ **79.** $\sqrt{\dfrac{4}{9}}$

80. $\sqrt{196}$ **81.** $-\sqrt{1}$ **82.** $\sqrt{10{,}000}$

83. Video rental store A charges a membership fee of $25 and $2 for each movie rental. Video rental store B charges a membership fee of $10 and $2.50 for each movie. Find the number of movie rentals for which both stores' charges are the same. *(Lesson 2-4)*

Solve each inequality and graph the solutions. Check your answer. *(Lesson 3-3)*

84. $2x < -8$ **85.** $\dfrac{a}{-2} \le -3$ **86.** $\dfrac{1}{4} < \dfrac{t}{12}$

3-5 Solving Inequalities with Variables on Both Sides

California Standards

◆— **4.0** Students simplify expressions before solving linear equations and **inequalities in one variable,** such as $3(2x - 5) + 4(x - 2) = 12$.

◆— **5.0** Students solve multi-step problems, including word problems, involving linear equations and **linear inequalities in one variable** and provide justification for each step.

Who uses this?

Business owners can use inequalities to find the most cost-efficient services. (See Example 2.)

Some inequalities have variable terms on both sides of the inequality symbol. You can solve these inequalities like you solved equations with variables on both sides.

Use the properties of inequality to "collect" all the variable terms on one side and all the constant terms on the other side.

EXAMPLE 1 **Solving Inequalities with Variables on Both Sides**

Solve each inequality and graph the solutions.

A $3x + 8 > x$

$$\begin{array}{ll} 3x + 8 > x \\ \underline{-x -x} \\ 2x + 8 > 0 \\ \underline{-8 -8} \\ 2x > -8 \end{array}$$

To collect the variable terms on one side, subtract x from both sides.

Since 8 is added to 2x, subtract 8 from both sides to undo the addition.

$$\frac{2x}{2} > \frac{-8}{2}$$

Since x is multiplied by 2, divide both sides by 2 to undo the multiplication.

$$x > -4$$

The solution set is {x : x > −4}.

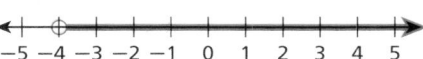

Helpful Hint

Your first step can also be to subtract 3x from both sides to get $8 > -2x$. When you divide by a negative number, remember to reverse the inequality symbol.

B $6x - 1 \le 3.5x + 4$

$$\begin{array}{ll} 6x - 1 \le 3.5x + 4 \\ \underline{-6x -6x} \\ -1 \le -2.5x + 4 \\ \underline{-4 -4} \\ -5 \le -2.5x \end{array}$$

Subtract 6x from both sides.

Since 4 is added to −2.5x, subtract 4 from both sides to undo the addition.

$$\frac{-5}{-2.5} \ge \frac{-2.5x}{-2.5}$$

Since x is multiplied by −2.5, divide both sides by −2.5 to undo the multiplication. Reverse the inequality symbol.

$$2 \ge x$$

The solution set is {x : x ≤ 2}.

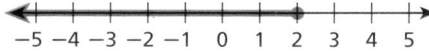

Solve each inequality and graph the solutions. Check your answer.

1a. $4x \ge 7x + 6$ **1b.** $5t + 1 < -2t - 6$

EXAMPLE 2 **Business Application**

The *Daily Info* charges a fee of $650 plus $80 per week to run an ad. The *People's Paper* charges $145 per week. For how many weeks will the total cost at *Daily Info* be less expensive than the cost at *People's Paper*?

Let w be the number of weeks the ad runs in the paper.

Daily Info fee	plus	$80 per week	times	number of weeks	is less expensive than	People's Paper charge per week	times	number of weeks.
$650	+	$80	·	w	<	$145	·	w

$$650 + 80w < 145w$$

$\underline{\quad -80w \quad\quad -80w \quad}$ Subtract 80w from both sides.

$$650 \quad\quad < \quad\quad 65w$$ Since w is multiplied by 65, divide both sides by 65 to undo the multiplication.

$$\frac{650}{65} < \frac{65w}{65}$$

$$10 < w$$

The total cost at *Daily Info* is less than the cost at *People's Paper* if the ad runs for more than 10 weeks.

 **CHECK IT OUT!**
2. A-Plus Advertising charges a fee of $24 plus $0.10 per flyer to print and deliver flyers. Print and More charges $0.25 per flyer. For how many flyers is the cost at A-Plus Advertising less than the cost at Print and More?

You may need to simplify one or both sides of an inequality before solving it. Look for like terms to combine and places to use Distributive Property.

EXAMPLE 3 **Simplifying Each Side Before Solving**

Solve each inequality and graph the solutions.

A $3x > 6(1 - x)$

$$3x > 6(1 - x)$$ Distribute 6 on the right side of the inequality.

$$3x > 6(1) - 6(x)$$

$$3x > 6 - 6x$$

$\underline{+6x \quad\quad +6x}$ Add 6x to both sides so that the coefficient of x is positive.

$$9x > 6$$

$$\frac{9x}{9} > \frac{6}{9}$$ Since x is multiplied by 9, divide both sides by 9 to undo the multiplication.

$$x > \frac{2}{3}$$ The solution set is $\{x : x > \frac{2}{3}\}$.

$$-\frac{1}{3} \quad 0 \quad \frac{1}{3} \quad \frac{2}{3} \quad 1 \quad 1\frac{1}{3} \quad 1\frac{2}{3} \quad 2 \quad 2\frac{1}{3} \quad 2\frac{2}{3} \quad 3$$

Helpful Hint

In Example 3B, you can also multiply each term in the inequality by the same power of 10 to clear the decimals.
$10(1.6x) \leq 10(-0.2x)$
$+ 10(0.9)$
$16x \leq -2x + 9$

Solve each inequality and graph the solutions.

B $1.6x \leq -0.2x + 0.9$

$$1.6x \leq -0.2x + 0.9$$

$$\underline{+\, 0.2x \quad\quad +\, 0.2x}$$

$$1.8x \leq \quad\quad\quad\quad 0.9$$

$$\frac{1.8x}{1.8} \leq \frac{0.9}{1.8}$$

$$x \leq \frac{1}{2}$$

Since −0.2x is added to 0.9, subtract −0.2x from both sides. Subtracting −0.2x is the same as adding 0.2x.

Since x is multiplied by 1.8, divide both sides by 1.8 to undo the multiplication.

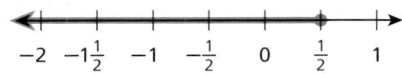

Solve each inequality and graph the solutions. Check your answer.

3a. $5(2 - r) \geq 3(r - 2)$ **3b.** $0.5x - 0.3 + 1.9x < 0.3x + 6$

Some inequalities are true no matter what value is substituted for the variable. For these inequalities, the solution set is all real numbers.

Some inequalities are false no matter what value is substituted for the variable. These inequalities have no solutions. Their solution set is the empty set, $\varnothing$.

If both sides of an inequality are fully simplified and the same variable term appears on both sides, then the inequality has all real numbers as solutions or it has no solutions. Look at the other terms in the inequality to decide which is the case.

EXAMPLE   **4**   **All Real Numbers as Solutions or No Solutions**

Solve each inequality.

A $x + 5 \geq x + 3$

$$x + 5 \geq x + 3$$

The same variable term (x) appears on both sides. Look at the other terms.

For any number x, adding **5** will always result in a greater number than adding **3**.

All values of x make the inequality true.
All real numbers are solutions.

B $2(x + 3) < 5 + 2x$

$$2x + 6 < 5 + 2x \quad\quad \textit{Distribute 2 on the left side.}$$

The same variable term ($2x$) appears on both sides. Look at the other terms.

For any number $2x$, adding **6** will never result in a lesser number than adding **5**.

No values of x make the inequality true.
There are no solutions. The solution set is $\varnothing$.

Solve each inequality.

4a. $4(y - 1) \geq 4y + 2$ **4b.** $x - 2 < x + 1$

THINK AND DISCUSS

1. Explain how you would collect the variable terms to solve the inequality $5c - 4 > 8c + 2$.

2. GET ORGANIZED Copy and complete the graphic organizer. In each box, give an example of an inequality of the indicated type.

Solutions of Inequalities with Variables on Both Sides

| All real numbers | No solutions |

3-5 Exercises

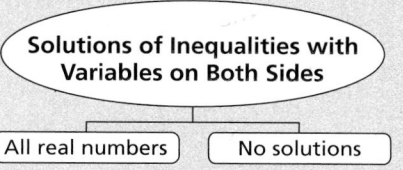

California Standards Practice

🔑 4.0, 🔑 5.0, 25.2

go.hrw.com
Homework Help Online
KEYWORD: MA8CA 3-5
Parent Resources Online
KEYWORD: MA8CA Parent

GUIDED PRACTICE

SEE EXAMPLE **1**
p. 162

Solve each inequality and graph the solutions. Check your answer.

1. $2x > 4x - 6$

2. $7y + 1 \leq y - 5$

3. $27x + 33 > 58x - 29$

4. $-3r < 10 - r$

5. $5c - 4 > 8c + 2$

6. $4.5x - 3.8 \geq 1.5x - 2.3$

SEE EXAMPLE **2**
p. 163

7. School The school band will sell pizzas to raise money for new uniforms. The supplier charges $100 plus $4 per pizza. If the band members sell the pizzas for $7 each, how many pizzas will they have to sell to make a profit?

SEE EXAMPLE **3**
p. 163

Solve each inequality and graph the solutions. Check your answer.

8. $5(4 + x) \leq 3(2 + x)$

9. $-4(3 - p) > 5(p + 1)$

10. $2(6 - x) < 4x$

11. $4x > 3(7 - x)$

12. $\frac{1}{2}f + \frac{3}{4} \geq \frac{1}{4}f$

13. $-36.72 + 5.65t < 0.25t$

SEE EXAMPLE **4**
p. 164

Solve each inequality.

14. $2(x - 2) \leq -2(1 - x)$

15. $4(y + 1) < 4y + 2$

16. $4v + 1 < 4v - 7$

17. $b - 4 \geq b - 6$

18. $3(x - 5) > 3x$

19. $2k + 7 \geq 2(k + 14)$

PRACTICE AND PROBLEM SOLVING

Solve each inequality and graph the solutions. Check your answer.

20. $3x \leq 5x + 8$

21. $9y + 3 > 4y - 7$

22. $1.5x - 1.2 < 3.1x - 2.8$

23. $7 + 4b \geq 3b$

24. $7 - 5t < 4t - 2$

25. $2.8m - 5.2 > 0.8m + 4.8$

 26. Geometry Write and solve an inequality to find the values of x for which the area of the rectangle is greater than the area of the triangle.

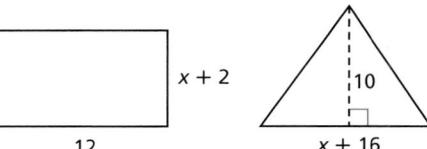

For Exercises	See Example
20–25	1
26	2
27–32	3
33–38	4

Independent Practice

Extra Practice
Skills Practice p. EP7
Application Practice p. EP26

Solve each inequality and graph the solutions. Check your answer.

27. $4(2 - x) \le 5(x - 2)$

28. $-3(n + 4) < 6(1 - n)$

29. $9(w + 2) \le 12w$

30. $4.5 + 1.3t > 3.8t - 3$

31. $\frac{1}{2}r + \frac{2}{3} \ge \frac{1}{3}r$

32. $2(4 - n) < 3n - 7$

Solve each inequality.

33. $3(2 - x) < -3(x - 1)$

34. $7 - y > 5 - y$

35. $3(10 + z) \le 3z + 36$

36. $-5(k - 1) \ge 5(2 - k)$

37. $4(x - 1) \le 4x$

38. $3(v - 9) \ge 15 + 3v$

Solve each inequality and graph the solutions. Check your answer.

39. $3t - 12 > 5t + 2$

40. $-5(y + 3) - 6 < y + 3$

41. $3x + 9 - 5x < x$

42. $18 + 9p > 12p - 31$

43. $2(x - 5) < -3x$

44. $-\frac{2}{5}x \le \frac{4}{5} - \frac{3}{5}x$

45. $-2(x - 7) - 4 - x < 8x + 32$

46. $-3(2r - 4) \ge 2(5 - 3r)$

47. $-7x - 10 + 5x \ge 3(x + 4) + 8$

48. $-\frac{1}{3}(n + 8) + \frac{1}{3}n \le 1 - n$

Recreation

The American Kitefliers Association has over 4000 members in 35 countries. Kitefliers participate in festivals, competitions, and kite-making workshops.

49. Recreation A red kite is 100 feet off the ground and is rising at 8 feet per second. A blue kite is 180 feet off the ground and is rising at 5 feet per second. How long will it take for the red kite to be higher than the blue kite? Round your answer to the nearest second.

50. Education The table shows the enrollment in Howard High School and Phillips High School for three school years.

School Enrollment			
	Year 1	Year 2	Year 3
Howard High School	1192	1188	1184
Phillips High School	921	941	961

  a. How much did the enrollment change each year at Howard?

  b. Use the enrollment in year 1 and your answer from part **a** to write an expression for the enrollment at Howard in any year x.

  c. How much did the enrollment change each year at Phillips?

  d. Use the enrollment in year 1 and your answer from part **c** to write an expression for the enrollment at Phillips in any year x.

  e. Assume that the pattern in the table continues. Use your expressions from parts **b** and **d** to write an inequality that can be solved to find the year in which the enrollment at Phillips High School will be greater than the enrollment at Howard High School. Solve your inequality.

CONCEPT CONNECTION

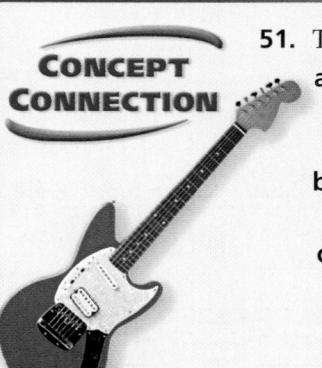

51. This problem will prepare you for the Concept Connection on page 184.

  a. The school orchestra is creating a CD of their last concert. To create the CDs, there is a fee of $400 and a charge of $4.50 per CD. Write an expression for the cost of creating the CDs based on the number of CDs n.

  b. The orchestra plans to sell the CDs for $12. Write an expression for the amount the orchestra earns from the sale of n CDs.

  c. In order for the orchestra to make a profit, the amount they make selling the CDs must be greater than the cost of creating the CDs. Write an inequality that can be solved to find the number of CDs the orchestra must sell in order to make a profit. Solve your inequality. Check your answer.

Write an inequality to represent each relationship. Solve your inequality.

52. Four more than twice a number is greater than two-thirds of the number.

53. Ten less than five times a number is less than six times the number decreased by eight.

54. The sum of a number and twenty is less than four times the number decreased by one.

55. Three-fourths of a number is greater than or equal to five less than the number.

56. Entertainment Use the table to determine how many movies you would have to rent for Video View to be less expensive than Movie Place.

	Membership Fee ($)	Cost per Rental ($)
Movie Place	None	2.99
Video View	19.99	1.99

57. Geometry In an acute triangle, all angles measure less than 90°. Also, the sum of the measures of any two angles is greater than the measure of the third angle. Can the measures of an acute triangle be x, $x - 1$, and $2x$? Explain.

58. Write About It Compare the steps you would follow to solve an inequality to the steps you would follow to solve an equation.

59. Critical Thinking How can you tell just by looking at the inequality $x > x + 1$ that it has no solutions?

60. ///**ERROR ANALYSIS**/// Two students solved the inequality $5x < 3 - 4x$. Which is incorrect? Explain the error.

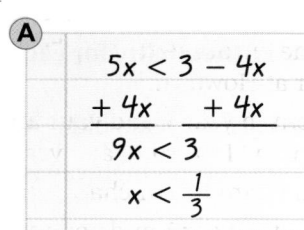

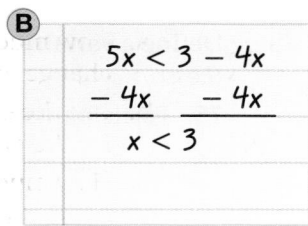

Multiple Choice For Exercises 61–64, choose the best answer.

61. If $a - b > a + b$, which statement is true?

    (A) The value of a is positive.   **(C)** The value of a is negative.

    (B) The value of b is positive.   **(D)** The value of b is negative.

62. If $-a < b$, which statement is always true?

    (A) $a < b$ **(B)** $a > b$ **(C)** $a < -b$ **(D)** $a > -b$

63. Which is a solution of the inequality $7(2 - x) > 4(x - 2)$?

    (A) −2   **(B)** 2   **(C)** 4   **(D)** 7

64. Which is the graph of $-3x < -6$?

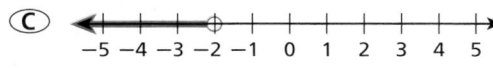

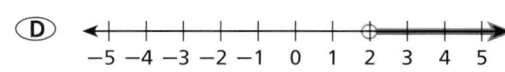

65. Short Response Write a real-world situation that could be modeled by the inequality $7x + 4 > 4x + 13$. Explain how the inequality relates to your situation.

CHALLENGE AND EXTEND

Solve each inequality. Check your answer.

66. $2\frac{1}{2} + 2x \geq 5\frac{1}{2} + 2\frac{1}{2}x$

67. $1.6x - 20.7 > 6.3x - (-2.2x)$

68. $1.3x - 7.5x < 8.5x - 29.4$

69. $-4w + \dfrac{-8 - 37}{9} \leq \dfrac{75 - 3}{9} + 3w$

70. Replace the square and circle with numbers so that all real numbers are solutions of the inequality. $\square - 2x < \bigcirc - 2x$

71. Replace the square and circle with numbers so that the inequality has no solutions. $\square - 2x < \bigcirc - 2x$

72. Critical Thinking Explain whether there are any numbers that can replace the square and circle so that all real numbers are solutions of the inequality. $\square + 2x < \bigcirc + x$

 SPIRAL STANDARDS REVIEW   **7AF1.1, 3.0, ⚷ 5.0**

73. The ratio of the width of a rectangle to the length is $2:5$. The length is 65 inches. Find the width. *(Lesson 2-5)*

74. Roman recorded the temperature for the last 7 days. The average temperature was 82 degrees and rose or fell by 8 degrees. Write and solve an absolute-value equation to find the minimum and maximum temperatures over the last 7 days. *(Lesson 2-7)*

Define a variable and write an inequality for each situation. Graph the solutions. *(Lesson 3-1)*

75. Participants must be at least 14 years old.

76. The maximum speed on a certain highway is 60 miles per hour.

Career Path

Katie Flannigan
Culinary Arts program

go.hrw.com
Career Resources Online
KEYWORD: MA8CA Career

Q: What math classes did you take in high school?
A: Algebra 1, Geometry, and Algebra 2

Q: What math classes have you taken since high school?
A: I have taken a basic accounting class and a business math class.

Q: How do you use math?
A: I use math to estimate how much food I need to buy. I also use math when adjusting recipe amounts to feed large groups of people.

Q: What are your future plans?
A: I plan to start my own catering business. The math classes I took will help me manage the financial aspects of my business.

LOGICAL REASONING

Deductive Reasoning and Inequalities

Use with Lessons 3-1 through 3-5

Just as you do solving equations, you use deductive reasoning every time you solve an inequality.

California Standards

← **5.0** Students solve multi-step **problems,** including word problems, **involving** linear equations and **linear inequalities in one variable and provide justification for each step.**
Also covered: ← **4.0, 24.2, 25.1, 25.2**

Example

Solve $2(x - 3) - 5x \geq -18$. Give a reason for each step in your solution process. Identify the conditional statement that is proved and its hypothesis and conclusion.

Statements	Reasons
1. $2(x - 3) - 5x \geq -18$	Given
2. $2x - 6 - 5x \geq -18$	Distributive Property
3. $(2x - 5x) - 6 \geq -18$	Commutative and Associative Properties of Addition
4. $-3x - 6 \geq -18$	Combine like terms.
5. $-3x \geq -12$	Addition Property of Inequality (Add 6 to both sides.)
6. $x \leq 4$	Division Property of Inequality (Divide both sides by -3. Reverse the inequality symbol.)

The above proves the conditional statement "If $2(x - 3) - 5x \geq -18$, then $x \leq 4$."

Hypothesis: $2(x - 3) - 5x \geq -18$ Conclusion: $x \leq 4$

Try This

Solve each inequality. Give a reason for each step in your solution process. Identify the conditional statement that is proved and its hypothesis and conclusion.

1. $x + 5 < 9$ **2.** $x - 9 \leq -12$ **3.** $8x > 64$ **4.** $\dfrac{x}{12} \leq -7$

5. $2x + 15 < 29$ **6.** $5(3 + x) < 20$ **7.** $16 - x \geq 3x + 8 - 5x$ **8.** $-4(x + 3) > 6(3 - x)$

9. What is the error in the solution below? Write a correct solution.

Statements	Reasons
1. $3x + 9 - 4x \geq 15$	Given
2. $x + 9 \geq 15$	Combine like terms.
3. $x \geq 6$	Subtraction Property of Inequality (Subtract 9 from both sides.)

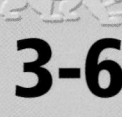

3-6 Solving Compound Inequalities

California Standards

5.0 Students solve multi-step problems, including word problems, involving linear equations and **linear inequalities in one variable** and provide justification for each step.

Vocabulary
compound inequality
intersection
union

Who uses this?
A lifeguard can use compound inequalities to describe the safe pH levels in a swimming pool. (See Example 1.)

The inequalities you have seen so far are simple inequalities. When two simple inequalities are combined into one statement by the words AND or OR, the result is called a **compound inequality** .

Know it! Note

Compound Inequalities

WORDS	ALGEBRA	GRAPH
All real numbers greater than 2 AND less than 6	$x > 2$ AND $x < 6$ $2 < x < 6$	(number line: open circles at 2 and 6) 0 2 4 6 8
All real numbers greater than or equal to 2 AND less than or equal to 6	$x \geq 2$ AND $x \leq 6$ $2 \leq x \leq 6$	(number line: solid circles at 2 and 6) 0 2 4 6 8
All real numbers less than 2 OR greater than 6	$x < 2$ OR $x > 6$	(number line: open circles at 2 and 6) 0 2 4 6 8
All real numbers less than or equal to 2 OR greater than or equal to 6	$x \leq 2$ OR $x \geq 6$	(number line: solid circles at 2 and 6) 0 2 4 6 8

EXAMPLE 1 *Chemistry Application*

A water analyst recommends that the pH level of swimming pool water be between 7.2 and 7.6 inclusive. Write a compound inequality to show the pH levels that are within the recommended range. Graph the solutions.

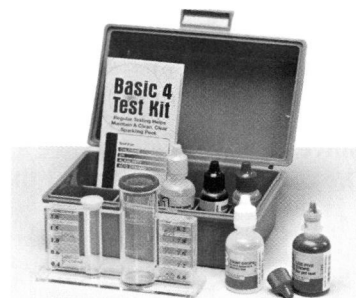

Reading Math

The phrase "between 7.2 and 7.6 *inclusive*" means that the numbers 7.2 and 7.6 are included in the solutions. Use a solid circle for endpoints that are solutions.

Let p be the pH level of swimming pool water.

7.2	is less than or equal to	pH level	is less than or equal to	7.6
7.2	$\leq$	p	$\leq$	7.6

$7.2 \leq p \leq 7.6$

(number line with solid circles at 7.2 and 7.6)
7.1 7.2 7.3 7.4 7.5 7.6 7.7

1. The free chlorine level in a pool should be between 1.0 and 3.0 parts per million inclusive. Write a compound inequality to show the levels that are within this range. Graph the solutions.

In this diagram, oval *A* represents some integer solutions of $x < 10$, and oval *B* represents some integer solutions of $x > 0$. The overlapping region represents numbers that belong in both ovals. Those numbers are solutions of *both x < 10 and x > 0*.

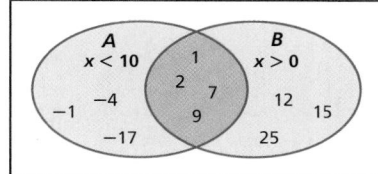

You can graph the solutions of a compound inequality involving AND by using the idea of an overlapping region. The overlapping region is called the **intersection** and shows the numbers that are solutions of both inequalities.

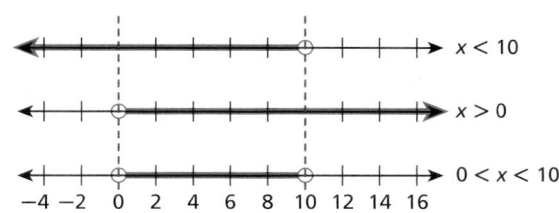

EXAMPLE 2

Solving Compound Inequalities Involving AND

Solve each compound inequality and graph the solutions.

A $4 \le x + 2 \le 8$

$$4 \le x + 2 \quad \text{AND} \quad x + 2 \le 8 \qquad \textit{Write the compound inequality using AND.}$$
$$\underline{-2 \quad\quad -2} \qquad\qquad \underline{-2 \quad -2} \qquad \textit{Solve each simple inequality.}$$
$$2 \le x \quad\quad \text{AND} \quad x \quad\quad \le 6 \qquad \textit{The solution set is } \{x : 2 \le x \text{ AND } x \le 6\}.$$

Graph $2 \le x$.

Graph $x \le 6$.

Graph the intersection by finding where the two graphs overlap.

Remember!

The statement $-5 \le 2x + 3 \le 9$ consists of two inequalities connected by AND. Example 2B shows a "shorthand" method.

B $-5 \le 2x + 3 < 9$

$$-5 \le 2x + 3 < 9 \qquad \textit{Since 3 is added to 2x, subtract 3 from each part}$$
$$\underline{-3 \quad\quad -3 \quad -3} \qquad\qquad \textit{of the inequality.}$$
$$-8 \le 2x \quad\quad < 6$$

$$\frac{-8}{2} \le \frac{2x}{2} < \frac{6}{2} \qquad \textit{Since x is multiplied by 2, divide each part of the}$$
$$\qquad\qquad\qquad\qquad \textit{inequality by 2.}$$
$$-4 \le x < 3 \qquad \textit{The solution set is } \{x : -4 \le x < 3\}.$$

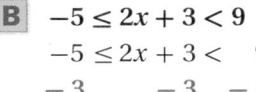

Graph $-4 \le x$.

Graph $x < 3$.

Graph the intersection by finding where the two graphs overlap.

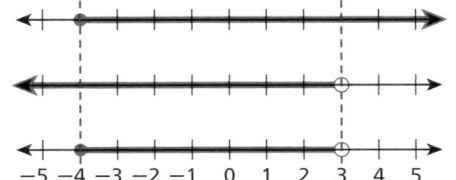

Solve each compound inequality and graph the solutions.

2a. $-9 < x - 10 < -5$ **2b.** $-4 \le 3n + 5 < 11$

In this diagram, circle A represents some integer solutions of $x < 0$, and circle B represents some integer solutions of $x > 10$. The combined shaded regions represent numbers that are solutions of *either* $x < 0$ *or* $x > 10$.

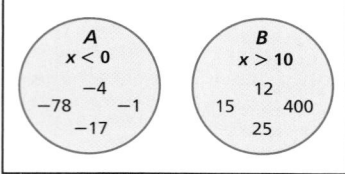

You can graph the solutions of a compound inequality involving OR by using the idea of combining regions. The combined regions are called the **union** and show the numbers that are solutions of either inequality.

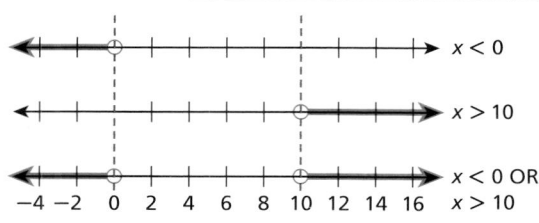

EXAMPLE **3** **Solving Compound Inequalities Involving OR**

Solve each compound inequality and graph the solutions.

A $-4 + a > 1$ OR $-4 + a < -3$

$$-4 + a > 1 \text{ OR} -4 + a < -3$$
$$\underline{+4 +4} \quad \underline{+4 +4}$$
$$a > 5 \text{ OR} a < 1$$

Solve each simple inequality.
The solution set is {a : a > 5 OR a < 1}.

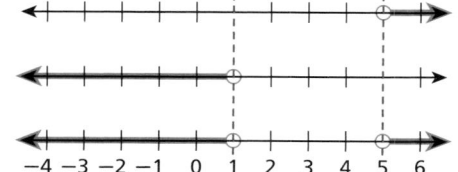

Graph a > 5.

Graph a < 1.

Graph the union by combining the regions.

Helpful Hint

AND inequalities can sometimes be combined into one expression.
$$1 < x < 5$$
OR inequalities cannot be combined as one expression.
$$x < 1 \text{ OR } x > 5$$

B $2x \le 6$ OR $3x > 12$

$$2x \le 6 \text{ OR } 3x > 12$$
$$\frac{2x}{2} \le \frac{6}{2} \qquad \frac{3x}{3} > \frac{12}{3}$$
$$x \le 3 \text{ OR } \quad x > 4$$

Solve each simple inequality.
The solution set is {x : x ≤ 3 OR x > 4}.

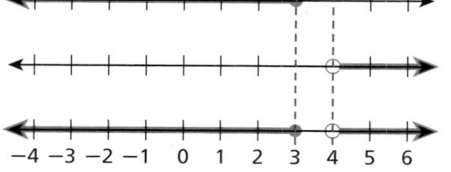

Graph x ≤ 3.

Graph x > 4.

Graph the union by combining the regions.

 Solve each compound inequality and graph the solutions.

3a. $2 + r < 12$ OR $r + 5 > 19$

3b. $7x \ge 21$ OR $2x < -2$

Every solution of a compound inequality involving AND must be a solution of both parts of the compound inequality. If no numbers are solutions of *both* simple inequalities, then the compound inequality has no solutions.

The solutions of a compound inequality involving OR are not always two separate sets of numbers. Some numbers may be solutions of both parts of the compound inequality.

EXAMPLE 4 **Writing a Compound Inequality from a Graph**

Write the compound inequality shown by each graph.

A

The shaded portion of the graph is not between two values, so the compound inequality involves OR.

> *On the left, the graph shows an arrow pointing left, so use either < or ≤. The solid circle at −1 means −1 is a solution, so use ≤.*

$x \leq -1$

> *On the right, the graph shows an arrow pointing right, so use either > or ≥. The solid circle at 7 means 7 is a solution, so use ≥.*

$x \geq 7$

The compound inequality is $x \leq -1$ OR $x \geq 7$.

B

The shaded portion of the graph is between the values 0 and 6, so the compound inequality involves AND.

> *The shaded values are to the right of 0, so use > or ≥. The solid circle at 0 means 0 is a solution, so use ≥.*

$x \geq 0$

> *The shaded values are to the left of 6, so use < or ≤. The empty circle at 6 means 6 is not a solution, so use <.*

$x < 6$

The compound inequality is $x \geq 0$ AND $x < 6$ or $0 \leq x \leq 6$.

CHECK IT OUT! Write the compound inequality shown by each graph.

4a.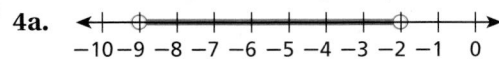

4b.

THINK AND DISCUSS

1. Describe how to write the compound inequality $y > 4$ AND $y \leq 12$ without using the joining word AND.

Know it! Note

2. GET ORGANIZED Copy and complete the graphic organizers. Write three solutions in each of the three sections of the diagram. Then write each of your nine solutions in the appropriate column or columns of the table.

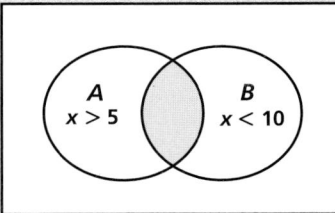

$x > 5$ AND $x < 10$	$x > 5$ OR $x < 10$

3-6

Exercises

California Standards Practice
🔑 5.0

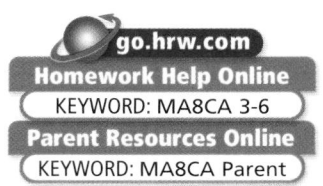
go.hrw.com
Homework Help Online
KEYWORD: MA8CA 3-6
Parent Resources Online
KEYWORD: MA8CA Parent

GUIDED PRACTICE

1. **Vocabulary** The graph of a(n) ____?____ shows all values that are solutions to both simple inequalities that make a compound inequality. (*union* or *intersection*)

SEE EXAMPLE **1**
p. 170

2. **Biology** An iguana needs to live in a warm environment. The temperature in a pet iguana's cage should be between 70° F and 95°F inclusive. Write a compound inequality to show the temperatures that are within the recommended range. Graph the solutions.

SEE EXAMPLE **2**
p. 171

Solve each compound inequality and graph the solutions.

3. $-3 < x + 2 < 7$

4. $5 \le 4x + 1 \le 13$

5. $2 < x + 2 < 5$

6. $11 < 2x + 3 < 21$

SEE EXAMPLE **3**
p. 172

7. $x + 2 < -6 \text{ OR } x + 2 > 6$

8. $r - 1 < 0 \text{ OR } r - 1 > 4$

9. $n + 2 < 3 \text{ OR } n + 3 > 7$

10. $x - 1 < -1 \text{ OR } x - 5 > -1$

SEE EXAMPLE **4**
p. 173

Write the compound inequality shown by each graph.

11.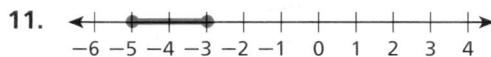

12.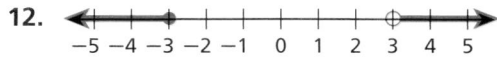

13.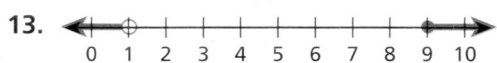

14.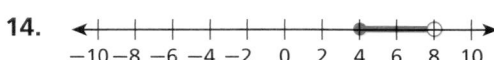

PRACTICE AND PROBLEM SOLVING

Independent Practice	
For Exercises	See Example
15	1
16–19	2
20–23	3
24–27	4

Extra Practice
Skills Practice p. EP7
Application Practice p. EP26

15. **Meteorology** Earth's atmosphere is made of several layers. A layer called the stratosphere extends from about 16 km above Earth's surface to about 50 km above Earth's surface. Write a compound inequality to show the altitudes that are within the range of the stratosphere. Graph the solutions.

Solve each compound inequality and graph the solutions.

16. $-1 < x + 1 < 1$

17. $1 \le 2n - 5 \le 7$

18. $-2 < x - 2 < 2$

19. $5 < 3x - 1 < 17$

20. $x - 4 < -7 \text{ OR } x + 3 > 4$

21. $2x + 1 < 1 \text{ OR } x + 5 > 8$

22. $x + 1 < 2 \text{ OR } x + 5 > 8$

23. $x + 3 < 0 \text{ OR } x - 2 > 0$

Write the compound inequality shown by each graph.

24.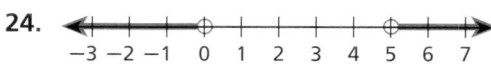

25.

26.

27.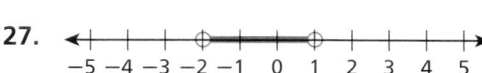

28. **Music** A typical acoustic guitar has a range of three octaves. When the guitar is tuned to "concert pitch," the range of frequencies for those three octaves is between 82.4 Hz and 659.2 Hz inclusive. Write a compound inequality to show the frequencies that are within the range of a typical acoustic guitar. Graph the solutions.

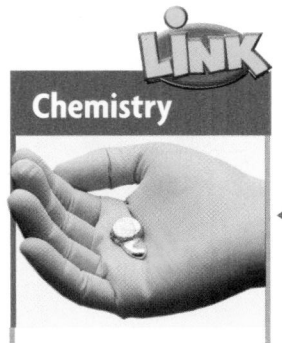

CONCEPT CONNECTION

29. This problem will prepare you for the Concept Connection on page 184.

Jenna's band is going to record a CD at a recording studio. They will pay $225 to use the studio for one day and $80 per hour for sound technicians. Jenna has $200 and hopes to raise an additional $350 by taking pre-orders for the CDs.

a. Explain how the inequality $200 \leq 225 + 80n \leq 550$ can be used to find the number of hours Jenna and her band can afford to use the studio and sound technicians.

b. Solve the inequality. Are there any numbers in the solution set that are not reasonable in this situation?

c. How much more money does Jenna need to raise if she wants to use the studio and sound technicians for 6 hours?

Write and graph a compound inequality for the numbers described.

30. all real numbers between -6 and 6

31. all real numbers less than or equal to 2 and greater than or equal to 1

32. all real numbers greater than 0 and less than 15

33. all real numbers between -10 and 10 inclusive

Chemistry

34. **Transportation** The cruise-control function on Georgina's car should keep the speed of the car within 3 mi/h of the set speed. Write a compound inequality to show the acceptable speeds s if the set speed is 55 mi/h. Graph the solutions.

35. **Chemistry** Water is not a liquid if its temperature is above 100°C or below 0°C. Write a compound inequality for the temperatures t when water is not a liquid.

The element gallium is in a solid state at room temperature but becomes a liquid at about 30°C. Gallium stays in a liquid state until it reaches a temperature of about 2204°C.

Solve each compound inequality and graph the solutions.

36. $5 \leq 4b - 3 \leq 9$

37. $-3 < x - 1 < 4$

38. $r + 2 < -2 \text{ OR } r - 2 > 2$

39. $2a - 5 < -5 \text{ OR } 3a - 2 > 1$

40. $x - 4 \geq 5 \text{ AND } x - 4 \leq 5$

41. $n - 4 < -2 \text{ OR } n + 1 > 6$

42. **Sports** The ball used in a soccer game may not weigh more than 16 ounces or less than 14 ounces at the start of the match. After $1\frac{1}{2}$ ounces of air was added to a ball, the ball was approved for use in a game. Write and solve a compound inequality to show how much the ball might have weighed before the air was added.

43. **Meteorology** Tornado damage is rated using the Fujita scale shown in the table. A tornado has a wind speed of 200 miles per hour. Write and solve a compound inequality to show how many miles per hour the wind speed would need to increase for the tornado to be rated "devastating" but not "incredible."

Fujita Tornado Scale		
Category	**Type**	**Wind Speed (mi/h)**
F0	Weak	40 to 72
F1	Moderate	73 to 112
F2	Significant	113 to 157
F3	Severe	158 to 206
F4	Devastating	207 to 260
F5	Incredible	261 to 318

44. Give a real world situation that can be described by a compound inequality. Write the inequality that describes your situation.

45. **Write About It** How are the graphs of the compound inequality $x < 3$ AND $x < 7$ and the compound inequality $x < 3$ OR $x < 7$ different? How are the graphs alike? Explain.

46. Critical Thinking If there is no solution to a compound inequality, does the compound inequality involve OR or AND? Explain.

Multiple Choice For Exercises 47–50, choose the best answer.

47. Which of the following describes the solutions of $-x + 1 > 2$ OR $x - 1 > 2$?

   (A) all real numbers greater than 1 or less than 3

   (B) all real numbers greater than 3 or less than 1

   (C) all real numbers greater than -1 or less than 3

   (D) all real numbers greater than 3 or less than -1

48. Which of the following describes the solutions of $x - 3 < 2$ AND $x + 3 > 2$?

   (A) $\{x : x > -1\}$

   (C)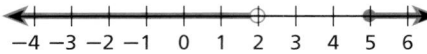

   (B) (number line from -6 to 4)

   (D) $\{x : x < -1$ OR $x > 5\}$

49. Which compound inequality is shown by the graph?

(number line from -4 to 6)

   (A) $x \leq 2$ OR $x > 5$ (C) $x \leq 2$ OR $x \geq 5$

   (B) $x < 2$ OR $x \geq 5$ (D) $x < 2$ OR $x > 5$

50. Which of the following is a solution of $x + 1 \geq 3$ AND $x + 1 \leq 3$?

   (A) 0   (B) 1   (C) 2   (D) 3

CHALLENGE AND EXTEND

Solve and graph each compound inequality.

51. $2c - 10 < 5 - 3c < 7c$ **52.** $5p - 10 < p + 6 < 3p$

53. $2s \leq 18 - s$ OR $5s \geq s + 36$ **54.** $9 - x \geq 5x$ OR $20 - 3x \leq 17$

55. Write a compound inequality that represents all values of x that are NOT solutions to $x < -1$ OR $x > 3$.

56. For the compound inequality $x + 2 \geq a$ AND $x - 7 \leq b$, find values of a and b for which the only solution is $x = 1$.

Use properties and operations to show that the first expression simplifies to the second expression. *(Lesson 1-7)*

57. $4(x - 3) + 7, 4x - 5$ **58.** $5x - 4y - x + 3y, 4x - y$ **59.** $6a - 3(a - 1), 3a + 3$

Solve each equation. Check your answer. *(Lesson 2-4)*

60. $7x + 3 = 4x$ **61.** $19 - 5t = t + 1$ **62.** $k - \frac{1}{2} = 6k + \frac{3}{4}$

63. Solve the formula $\frac{d}{r} = t$ for d. Find the distance in miles that a car would travel in 4 hours if its average speed was 31.71 mi/h. Round to the nearest tenth. *(Lesson 2-6)*

Solve each inequality and graph the solutions. Check your answer. *(Lesson 3-4)*

64. $3m - 5 < 1$ **65.** $2(x + 4) > 6$ **66.** $11 \leq 7 - 2x$

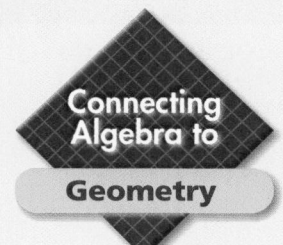

Triangle Inequality

For any triangle, the sum of the lengths of any two sides is greater than the length of the third side.

California Standards

Reinforcement of 7NS1.1 Read, write, and compare rational numbers in scientific notation (positive and negative powers of 10), **compare rational numbers in general.**

The sides of this triangle are labeled a, b, and c. You can use the Triangle Inequality to write three statements about the triangle.

$$a + b > c \qquad a + c > b \qquad b + c > a$$

Unless all three of the inequalities are true, the lengths a, b, and c cannot form a triangle.

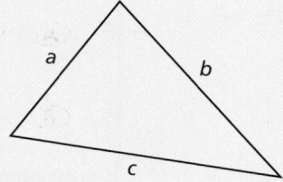

Example 1

Can three side lengths of 25 cm, 15 cm, and 5 cm form a triangle?

a. $25 + 15 > 5$ **b.** $25 + 5 > 15$ **c.** $15 + 5 > 25$
      $40 > 5$ *True* $30 > 15$ *True* $20 > 25$ *False*

One of the inequalities is false, so the three lengths will not make a triangle. The situation is shown in the figure to the right.

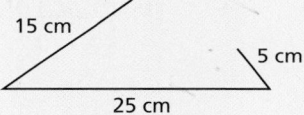

Example 2

Two sides of a triangle measure 8 ft and 10 ft. What is the range of lengths of the third side?

Start by writing three statements about the triangle. Use x for the unknown side length.

a. $8 + 10 > x$ **b.** $8 + x > 10$ **c.** $x + 10 > 8$
      $18 > x$ $8 + x - 8 > 10 - 8$ $x + 10 - 10 > 8 - 10$
                                              $x > 2$ $x > -2$

The third side must be   *The third side must be*   *This provides no new*
shorter than 18 ft.   *longer than 2 ft.*   *useful information.*

From part **a**, the third side must be shorter than 18 ft. And from part **b**, it must be longer than 2 ft. An inequality showing this is $2 < x < 18$.

Try This

Decide whether the three lengths given can form a triangle. If not, explain.

1. 14 ft, 30 ft, 10 ft   **2.** 11 cm, 8 cm, 17 cm   **3.** $6\frac{1}{2}$ yd, 3 yd, $2\frac{3}{4}$ yd

Write a compound inequality for the range of lengths of the third side of each triangle.

4. 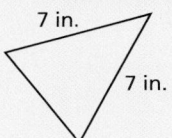   **5.** 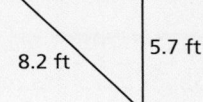   **6.**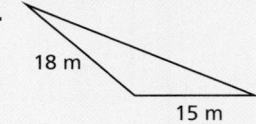

3-7 Solving Absolute-Value Inequalities

California Standards

3.0 Students solve equations and **inequalities involving absolute values.**

Also covered: 🔑 **5.0**

Why learn this?

You can solve an absolute-value inequality to determine the safe range for the pressure of a fire extinguisher. (See Example 3.)

When an inequality contains an absolute-value expression, it can be rewritten as a compound inequality. The inequality $|x| < 5$ describes all real numbers whose distance from 0 is less than 5 units. The solutions are all numbers between -5 and 5, so $|x| < 5$ can be rewritten as $-5 < x < 5$ or as $x > -5$ AND $x < 5$.

Know it! Note

Absolute-Value Inequalities Involving <

WORDS	NUMBERS
The inequality $|x| < a$ (when $a > 0$) asks, "What values of x have an absolute value less than a?" The solutions are numbers between $-a$ *and* a.	$|x| < 5$ $-5 < x < 5$ $x > -5$ AND $x < 5$
GRAPH	**ALGEBRA**
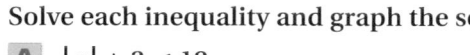	$|x| < a$ (when $a > 0$) $-a < x < a$ $x > -a$ AND $x < a$

The same properties are true for inequalities that use the symbol $\leq$.

EXAMPLE **1** **Solving Absolute-Value Inequalities Involving <**

Solve each inequality and graph the solutions.

A $|x| + 3 < 12$

$$|x| + 3 < \quad 12$$
$$\underline{\quad -3 \quad\quad -3}$$
$$|x| \quad < \quad 9$$

Since 3 is added to $|x|$, subtract 3 from both sides to undo the addition.

$x > -9$ AND $x < 9$

Write as a compound inequality. The solution set is $\{x: -9 < x < 9\}$.

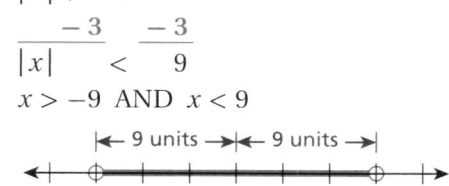

B $|x + 4| \leq 2$

$$x + 4 \geq -2 \text{ AND } x + 4 \leq \quad 2$$
$$\underline{\quad -4 \quad -4 \quad\quad\quad -4 \quad -4}$$
$$x \quad\quad \geq -6 \text{ AND } x \quad\quad \leq -2$$

Write as a compound inequality.

Solve each inequality.

Write as a compound inequality. The solution set is $\{x: -6 \leq x \leq -2\}$.

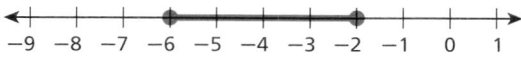

 **CHECK IT OUT!** Solve each inequality and graph the solutions.

1a. $2|x| \le 6$ **1b.** $|x + 3| - 4.5 \le 7.5$

The inequality $|x| > 5$ describes all real numbers whose distance from 0 is greater than 5 units. The solutions are all numbers less than -5 or greater than 5. The inequality $|x| > 5$ can be rewritten as the compound inequality $x < -5$ OR $x > 5$.

Absolute-Value Inequalities Involving >

WORDS	NUMBERS
The inequality $|x| > a$ (when $a > 0$) asks, "What values of x have an absolute value greater than a?" The solutions are numbers less than $-a$ or greater than a.	$|x| > 5$ $x < -5$ OR $x > 5$
GRAPH	**ALGEBRA**
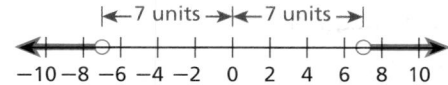	$|x| > a$ (when $a > 0$) $x < -a$ OR $x > a$

The same properties are true for inequalities that use the symbol $\ge$.

EXAMPLE 2 **Solving Absolute-Value Inequalities Involving >**

Solve each inequality and graph the solutions.

A $|x| - 20 > -13$

$|x| - 20 > -13$

$\underline{+20+20}$ *Since 20 is subtracted from $|x|$, add 20 to both sides to undo the subtraction.*

$|x| > 7$

$x < -7$ OR $x > 7$ *Write as a compound inequality. The solution set is {x: x < −7 OR x > 7}.*

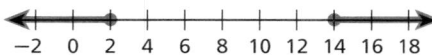

B $|x - 8| + 5 \ge 11$

$|x - 8| + 5 \ge 11$

$\underline{-5-5}$ *Since 5 is added to $|x - 8|$, subtract 5 from both sides to undo the addition.*

$|x - 8| \ge 6$

$x - 8 \le -6$ OR $x - 8 \ge 6$ *Write as a compound inequality. Solve each inequality.*

$\underline{+8 +8 +8 +8}$

$x \le 2$ OR $x \ge 14$ *Write as a compound inequality. The solution set is {x: x ≤ 2 OR x ≥ 14}.*

 **CHECK IT OUT!** Solve each inequality and graph the solutions.

2a. $|x| + 10 \ge 12$ **2b.** $\left| x + 2\frac{1}{2} \right| + \frac{1}{2} \ge 4$

EXAMPLE 3 **Safety Application**

Some fire extinguishers contain pressurized water. The water pressure should be 162.5 psi (pounds per square inch), but it is acceptable for the pressure to differ from this value by at most 12.5 psi. Write and solve an absolute-value inequality to find the range of acceptable pressures. Graph the solutions.

Let p represent the actual water pressure of a fire extinguisher.

The difference between p and the ideal pressure is at most 12.5 psi.

$$p - 162.5 \quad \leq \quad 12.5$$

$$|p - 162.5| \leq 12.5$$

$p - 162.5 \geq \quad -12.5 \quad \text{AND} \quad p - 162.5 \leq \quad 12.5$ *Solve the two inequalities.*

$$\underline{+\,162.5 \quad +\,162.5} \qquad \qquad \underline{+\,162.5 \quad +\,162.5}$$

$p \qquad \geq \qquad 150 \quad \text{AND} \quad p \qquad \leq \qquad 175$

The range of acceptable pressures is $150 \leq p \leq 175$.

3. A dry-chemical fire extinguisher should be pressurized to 125 psi, but it is acceptable for the pressure to differ from this value by at most 75 psi. Write and solve an absolute-value inequality to find the range of acceptable pressures. Graph the solution.

When solving an absolute-value inequality, you may get a statement that is true for all values of the variable. In this case, all real numbers are solutions of the original inequality. If you get a false statement when solving an absolute-value inequality, the original inequality has no solutions. Its solution set is ∅.

EXAMPLE 4 **Special Cases of Absolute-Value Inequalities**

Solve each inequality.

A $|x - 6| + 7 > 2$

$$|x - 6| + 7 > \quad 2$$

$$\underline{-\,7 \quad -\,7} \qquad$$ *Subtract 7 from both sides.*

$$|x - 6| \quad > -5 \qquad$$ *Absolute-value expressions are always nonnegative. Therefore, the statement is true for all values of x.*

The solution set is all real numbers.

> **Remember!**
>
> An absolute value represents a distance, and distance cannot be less than 0.

B $|x + 12| - 5 \leq -6$

$$|x + 12| - 5 \leq -6$$

$$\underline{+\,5 \quad +\,5} \qquad$$ *Add 5 to both sides.*

$$|x + 12| \quad \leq -1 \qquad$$ *Absolute-value expressions are always nonnegative. Therefore, the statement is false for all values of x.*

The inequality has no solutions. The solution set is ∅.

Solve each inequality.

4a. $|x| - 9 \geq -11$ **4b.** $4|x - 3.5| \leq -8$

THINK AND DISCUSS

1. Describe how the solutions of $7|x| \leq 21$ are different from the solutions of $7|x| < 21$.

2. **GET ORGANIZED** Copy and complete the graphic organizer. In each box, write an example of the indicated type of absolute-value inequality and then solve.

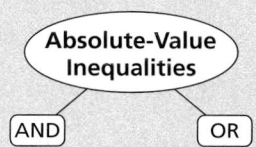

Absolute-Value Inequalities
AND   OR

3-7 Exercises

California Standards Practice
3.0, ⚷ 5.0, 25.1, 25.3

go.hrw.com
Homework Help Online
KEYWORD: MA8CA 3-7
Parent Resources Online
KEYWORD: MA8CA Parent

GUIDED PRACTICE

Solve each inequality and graph the solutions.

SEE EXAMPLE **1**
p. 178

1. $|x| - 5 \leq -2$
2. $|x + 1| - 7.8 < 6.2$
3. $|3x| + 2 < 8$
4. $4|x| \leq 20$
5. $|x - 5| + 1 < 2$
6. $\left|x + \frac{1}{2}\right| - \frac{1}{2} \leq 3\frac{1}{2}$

SEE EXAMPLE **2**
p. 179

7. $|x| - 6 > 16$
8. $|x| + 2.9 > 8.6$
9. $2|x| \geq 8$
10. $|x + 2| > 7$
11. $|x - 3| + 2 \geq 4$
12. $|x + 5| - 4\frac{1}{2} \geq 7\frac{1}{2}$

SEE EXAMPLE **3**
p. 180

13. **Nutrition** A nutritionist recommends that an adult male consume 55 grams of fat per day. It is acceptable for the fat intake to differ from this amount by at most 25 grams. Write and solve an absolute-value inequality to find the range of fat intake that is acceptable. Graph the solutions.

SEE EXAMPLE **4**
p. 180

Solve each inequality.

14. $|x| + 8 \leq 2$
15. $|x + 3| < -5$
16. $|x + 4| \geq -8$
17. $|x - 5| + \frac{1}{3} > -1$
18. $|3x| + 7 > 2$
19. $|x - 7| + 3.5 \leq 2$

PRACTICE AND PROBLEM SOLVING

Independent Practice

For Exercises	See Example
20–25	1
26–31	2
32	3
33–38	4

Extra Practice

Skills Practice p. EP7

Application Practice p. EP26

Solve each inequality and graph the solutions.

20. $|x| + 6 \leq 10$
21. $|x - 3| < 1$
22. $|x - 2| - 8 \leq -3$
23. $|5x| < 15$
24. $|x - 2.4| + 4 \leq 6.4$
25. $4 + |x + 3| < 7$
26. $|x - 1| > 2$
27. $6|x| \geq 60$
28. $|x - 4| + 3 > 8$
29. $2|x + 2| \geq 16$
30. $3 + |x - 4| > 4$
31. $\left|x - \frac{1}{2}\right| + 9 > 10\frac{1}{2}$

32. The thermostat for a sauna is set to 175°F, but the actual temperature of the sauna may vary by as much as 12°F. Write and solve an absolute-value inequality to find the range of possible temperatures. Graph the solutions.

Solve each inequality.

33. $12 + |x| \leq 10$
34. $\left|x + \frac{3}{5}\right| - 2 > -4$
35. $|x + 1| + 5 \geq 4$
36. $|4x| - 3 < -6$
37. $3|x - 4| \leq -9$
38. $|2x| + 9 \geq 9$

Reasoning Tell whether each statement is sometimes, always, or never true. Explain.

39. The value of $|x + 1|$ is greater than -5.

40. The value of $|x - 7|$ is less than 0.

41. An absolute-value inequality has all real numbers as solutions.

Write and solve an absolute-value inequality for each expression. Graph the solutions on a number line.

42. All numbers whose absolute value is less than or equal to 15

43. All numbers less than or equal to 3 units from 2 on the number line

44. All numbers at least 2 units from 8 on the number line

Write an absolute-value inequality for each graph.

45. 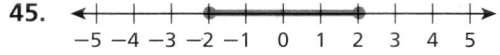   **46.**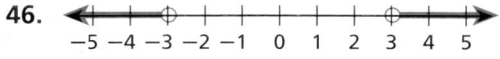

47. 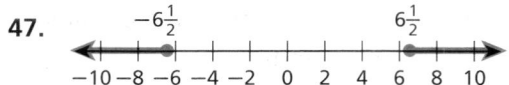   **48.**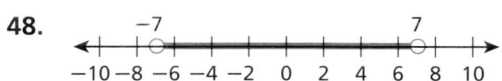

49. Multi-Step The frequency of a sound wave determines its pitch. The human ear can detect a wide range of frequencies, from 20 Hz (very low notes) to 20,000 Hz (very high notes).

   a. What frequency is at the middle of the range?

   b. Write an inequality for the range of frequencies the human ear can detect.

50. Biology The diagram shows the temperature range at which several fish species can survive. For each species, write an absolute-value inequality that gives the range of temperatures at which it can survive.

51. Entertainment On a game show, a contestant must guess a secret two-digit number. The secret number is 23. Write an inequality that shows that the contestant's guess is more than 12 numbers away from the secret number.

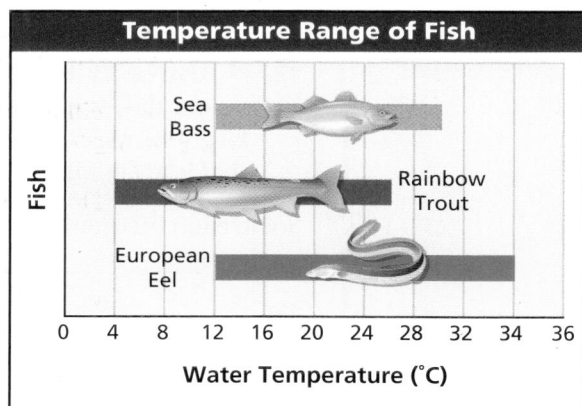

52. This problem will help prepare you for the Concept Connection on page 184.

The manager of a band recommends that the band sell its CDs for $8.75. The band decides to sell the CDs for p dollars.

   a. Write an absolute-value expression that tells how far the band's price is from the recommended price.

   b. The band wants the price of its CD to be no more than $1.25 from the recommended price. Write an absolute-value inequality that gives the range of possible prices for the CD.

   c. Solve inequality. Write the solution as a compound inequality.

CONCEPT CONNECTION

53. Critical Thinking For which values of k does the inequality $|x| + 1 < k$ have no solutions? Explain.

 54. Write About It Describe how to use an absolute-value inequality to find all the values on a number line that are within 5 units of -6.

Multiple Choice For Exercises 55–57, choose the best answer.

55. What is the solution set of the inequality $3 + |x + 4| < 6$?

   Ⓐ $\{x: -13 < x < 5\}$ Ⓒ $\{x: -6 < x < -2\}$

   Ⓑ $\{x: -7 < x < -1\}$ Ⓓ $\{x: 1 < x < 7\}$

56. A thermometer gives temperature readings that may be inaccurate by at most 2°F. The actual temperature is 75°F. Which absolute-value inequality describes the range of temperatures that may be shown on the thermometer?

   Ⓐ $|x - 75| \le 2$ Ⓑ $|x + 75| \le 2$ Ⓒ $|x - 75| \ge 2$ Ⓓ $|x + 75| \ge 2$

57. The inequality $|w - 156| \le 3$ describes the weights of members of a wrestling team. Which statement is NOT true?

   Ⓐ All of the team members weigh no more than 159 pounds.

   Ⓑ A team member may weigh 152 pounds.

   Ⓒ Every member of the team is at most 3 pounds away from 156 pounds.

   Ⓓ There are no team members who weigh 160 pounds.

CHALLENGE AND EXTEND

Write an absolute-value inequality for each graph.

58. 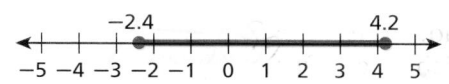   **59.**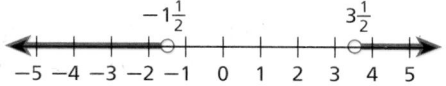

60. Reasoning Fill in the missing reasons to justify each step in solving $|2x - 6| + 5 \le 7$.

	Statements	Reasons
1.	$|2x - 6| + 5 \le 7$	Given
2.	$|2x - 6| \le 2$	?
3.	$2x - 6 \ge -2$ AND $2x - 6 \le 2$	Definition of absolute value
4.	$2x \ge 4$ AND $2x \le 8$	?
5.	$x \ge 2$ AND $x \le 4$	?

 SPIRAL STANDARDS REVIEW   **7AF1.4, 5.0**

Solve each proportion. Check your answer. *(Lesson 2-5)*

61. $\dfrac{x + 1}{4} = \dfrac{5}{8}$ **62.** $\dfrac{2}{15} = \dfrac{6}{y - 5}$ **63.** $\dfrac{12}{m + 2} = \dfrac{8}{3}$ **64.** $\dfrac{7 + g}{10} = \dfrac{6}{8}$

Describe the solutions of each inequality in words. *(Lesson 3-1)*

65. $16 > 8m$ **66.** $c + 4 < 11$ **67.** $-4 \le x + 2$ **68.** $0 \ge x + 7$

Solve each compound inequality and graph the solutions. *(Lesson 3-6)*

69. $-3 < x - 3 < 1$ **70.** $-3 \le 2x + 1 \le 9$

71. $x - 2 < -1$ OR $x - 2 > 2$ **72.** $x + 4 \le 3$ OR $x + 4 \ge 6$

3-7 Solving Absolute-Value Inequalities   **183**

CONCEPT CONNECTION

Multi-Step and Compound Inequalities

Guitar Picks Cullen and his band are interested in recording a CD of their music. The recording studio charges $450 to record the music and then charges $5 for each CD. The band is required to spend at least $1000 for the total of the recording and CD charges.

1. Write an equation for the cost C of the CDs based on the number of CDs n.

2. Write an inequality that can be used to determine the minimum number of CDs that must be burned at this studio to meet the $1000 total.

3. Solve your inequality from Problem 2. Check your answer.

4. The band orders the minimum number of CDs found in Problem 3. They want to sell the CDs and make at least as much money as they spent for the recording studio and making the CDs. Write an inequality that can be solved to determine the minimum amount the band should charge for their CDs.

5. Solve your inequality from Problem 4. Check your answer.

6. If the band has 30 more CDs made than the minimum number found in Problem 4 and charges the minimum price found in Problem 5, will they make a profit? If so, how much profit will the band make?

READY TO GO ON?

Quiz for Lessons 3-4 Through 3-7

3-4 Solving Two-Step and Multi-Step Inequalities

Solve each inequality and graph the solutions. Check your answer.

1. $2x + 3 < 9$ **2.** $3t - 2 > 10$ **3.** $7 \geq 1 - 6r$

Solve each inequality.

4. $2(x - 3) > -1$

5. $\frac{1}{3}a + \frac{1}{2} > \frac{2}{3}$

6. $15 < 5(m - 7)$

7. $2 + (-6) > 0.8p$

8. The average of Mindy's two test scores must be at least 92 to make an A in the class. Mindy got an 88 on her first test. What scores can she get on her second test to make an A in the class?

3-5 Solving Inequalities with Variables on Both Sides

Solve each inequality and graph the solutions. Check your answer.

9. $5x < 3x + 8$ **10.** $6p - 3 > 9p$ **11.** $r - 8 \geq 3r - 12$

Solve each inequality.

12. $3(y + 6) > 2(y + 4)$

13. $4(5 - g) \geq g$

14. $4x < 4(x - 1)$

15. $3(1 - x) \geq -3(x + 2)$

16. Phillip has $100 in the bank and deposits $18 per month. Gil has $145 in the bank and deposits $15 per month. For how many months will Gil have a larger bank balance than Phillip?

3-6 Solving Compound Inequalities

Solve each compound inequality and graph the solutions.

17. $-2 \leq x + 3 < 9$

18. $m + 2 < -1$ OR $m - 2 > 6$

19. $-3 \geq x - 1 > 2$

20. $-2 > r + 2$ OR $r + 4 < 5$

21. It is recommended that a certain medicine be stored in temperatures above 32° F and below 70° F. Write a compound inequality to show the acceptable storage temperatures for this medicine.

3-7 Solving Absolute-Value Inequalities

Solve each inequality and graph the solutions.

22. $|x| + 9 \leq 12$ **23.** $|x + 7| - 15 < 6$ **24.** $4.5|x| \geq 31.5$

Solve each inequality.

25. $|x - 2| \leq 14$

26. $|x| - 9.2 < -5.7$

27. $\frac{1}{2} + 2|x| > -4$

28. $7 + |3x| > 13$

29. Eli attended a concert. The decibel level of the music averaged 110 decibels but varied by 22 decibels from the average. Write and solve an absolute-value inequality to find the decibel range. Graph the solutions.

Study Guide: Review

Vocabulary

Complete the sentences below with vocabulary words from the list above.

1. A(n) ____?____ is a mathematical statement that two quantities are not equal.

2. The numbers that are solutions to either inequality of a compound inequality is the ____?____ .

3. A statement formed by combining two simple inequalities with the words AND or OR is a(n) ____?____ .

4. The numbers that are solutions to both inequalities of a compound inequality is the ____?____ .

5. Any value that makes the inequality true is a(n) ____?____ .

3-1 Graphing and Writing Inequalities (pp. 136–141)

 Prep for ⚿ 5.0

EXAMPLES

■ Graph the inequality $y > -1$.

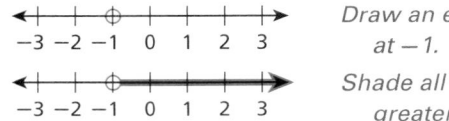

Draw an empty circle at −1.

Shade all the numbers greater than −1.

■ Write the inequality shown by the graph.

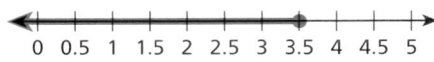

$n \leq 3.5$ *Use the variable n.*
The arrow points left, so use either < or ≤. The closed circle means 3.5 is a solution, so use ≤.

■ Write an inequality for the situation and graph the solutions.

Applicants for a driver's permit must be at least 16 years old.

age	must be at least	16 years
a	$\geq$	16

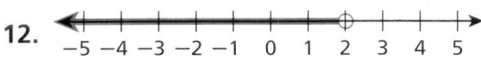

EXERCISES

Graph each inequality.

6. $x > -3$

7. $p \leq 4$

8. $-1 > t$

9. $r \geq 9.5$

10. $2(3 - 5) < k$

11. $w < 3$

Write the inequality shown by each graph.

12.
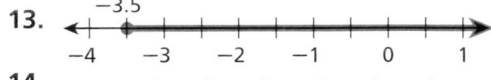

13.

14.

Define a variable and write an inequality for each situation. Graph the solutions.

15. The temperature must be at least 72°F.

16. No more than 12 students were present.

17. It takes less than 30 minutes to complete the lab activity.

3-2 Solving Inequalities by Adding or Subtracting (pp. 142–147)

 Prep for 5.0

EXAMPLES

Solve each inequality and graph the solutions.

■ $x + 6 > 2$

$$x + 6 > \quad 2$$ *Since 6 is added to x,*
$$\underline{-6 \quad -6}$$ *subtract 6 from both sides.*
$$x > -4$$

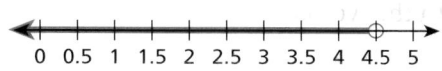

$$-5 \ -4 \ -3 \ -2 \ -1 \ \ 0 \ \ 1 \ \ 2 \ \ 3 \ \ 4 \ \ 5$$

■ $n - 1.3 < 3.2$

$$n - 1.3 < \quad 3.2$$ *Since 1.3 is subtracted from x,*
$$\underline{+1.3 \quad +1.3}$$ *add 1.3 to both sides.*
$$n < \quad 4.5$$

$$0 \ \ 0.5 \ \ 1 \ \ 1.5 \ \ 2 \ \ 2.5 \ \ 3 \ \ 3.5 \ \ 4 \ \ 4.5 \ \ 5$$

EXERCISES

Solve each inequality and graph the solutions. Check your answer.

18. $t + 3 < 10$

19. $k - 7 \le -5$

20. $-1 < m + 4$

21. $x + 2.3 \ge 6.8$

22. $w - 3 < 6.5$

23. $4 > a - 1$

24. $h - \dfrac{1}{4} < \dfrac{3}{4}$

25. $5 > 7 + v$

26. Tammy wants to run at least 10 miles per week. So far this week, she ran 4.5 miles. Write and solve an inequality to determine how many more miles Tammy must run this week to reach her goal.

27. Rob has a gift card for $50. So far, he has selected a shirt that costs $32. Write and solve an inequality to determine the amount Rob could spend without exceeding the gift card limit.

3-3 Solving Inequalities by Multiplying or Dividing (pp. 148–153)

 Prep for 5.0

EXAMPLES

■ Solve $\dfrac{p}{-3} \le 6$ and graph the solutions.

$$\dfrac{p}{-3} \le 6$$ *Since p is divided by −3,*
    multiply both sides by −3.
$$-3 \cdot \dfrac{p}{-3} \ge -3 \cdot 6$$
$$p \ge -18$$ *Change ≤ to ≥.*

$$-21 \ -18 \ -15 \ -12 \ \ -9 \ \ -6 \ \ -3$$

■ What possible numbers of pizzas that cost $5.50 each can be purchased with $30?

Let n represent the number of pizzas that can be purchased.

$5.50	times	number of pizzas	is at most	$30.
5.50	•	n	≤	30

$$5.50n \le 30$$
$$\dfrac{5.50n}{5.50} \le \dfrac{30}{5.50}$$ *Since n is multiplied by 5.50,*
    divide both sides by 5.50.
$$n \le 5\dfrac{5}{11}$$

Only a whole number of pizzas can be purchased, so 0, 1, 2, 3, 4, or 5 pizzas can be purchased.

EXERCISES

Solve each inequality and graph the solutions. Check your answer.

28. $3a \le 15$

29. $-18 < 6t$

30. $\dfrac{p}{4} > 2$

31. $\dfrac{2}{5}x \le -10$

32. $-3n < -18$

33. $\dfrac{g}{-2} > 6$

34. $-2k < 14$

35. $-3 > \dfrac{1}{3}r$

36. $27 < -9h$

37. $-0.4g > -1$

38. What are the possible numbers of notebooks costing $1.39 that can be purchased with $10?

39. The senior class is selling lanyards as a fundraiser. The profit for each lanyard is $0.75. Write and solve an inequality to determine the number of lanyards the class must sell to make a profit of at least $250.

3-4 Solving Two-Step and Multi-Step Inequalities (pp. 156–161)

EXAMPLES

Solve each inequality and graph the solution.

■ $18 + 3t > -12$

$$\begin{array}{ll} 18 + 3t > -12 & \text{Since 18 is added to 3t,} \\ \underline{-18 \qquad -18} & \text{subtract 18 from both} \\ 3t > -30 & \text{sides.} \end{array}$$

$$\begin{array}{ll} \dfrac{3t}{3} > \dfrac{-30}{3} & \text{Since t is multiplied by 3,} \\ & \text{divide both sides by 3.} \\ t > -10 \end{array}$$

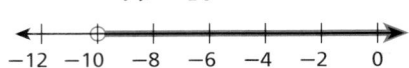

■ $3^2 - 5 \le 2(1 + x)$

$$\begin{array}{ll} 3^2 - 5 \le 2(1 + x) & \text{Simplify the left side using} \\ 9 - 5 \le 2(1 + x) & \text{order of operations.} \\ 4 \le 2(1 + x) & \text{Distribute 2 on the right} \\ 4 \le 2(1) + 2(x) & \text{side.} \\ 4 \le 2 + 2x & \text{Since 2 is added to 2x,} \\ \underline{-2 \qquad -2} & \text{subtract 2 from both} \\ 2 \le 2x & \text{sides} \\ \dfrac{2}{2} \le \dfrac{2x}{2} & \text{Since x is multiplied by 2,} \\ & \text{divide both sides by 2.} \\ 1 \le x \end{array}$$

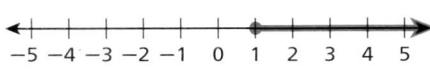

EXERCISES

Solve each inequality and graph the solutions. Check your answer.

40. $3x + 4 < 19$

41. $7 \le 2t - 5$

42. $\dfrac{m + 3}{2} > -4$

43. $2(x + 5) < 8$

44. $-4(2 - 5) > (-3)^2 - h$

45. $\dfrac{1}{5}x + \dfrac{1}{2} > \dfrac{4}{5}$

46. $0.5(b - 2) \le 4$

47. $\dfrac{1}{3}y - \dfrac{1}{2} > \dfrac{2}{3}$

48. $6 - 0.2n < 9$

49. Carl's Cable Company charges $55 for monthly service plus $4 for each pay-per-view movie. Teleview Cable Company charges $110 per month with no fee for movies. For what number of movies is the cost of Carl's Cable Company less than the cost of Teleview?

3-5 Solving Inequalities with Variables on Both Sides (pp. 162–168)

EXAMPLES

■ Solve $b + 16 < 3b$ and graph the solutions.

$$\begin{array}{ll} b + 16 > 3b & \text{Subtract b from both sides so} \\ \underline{-b \qquad -b} & \text{that the coefficient of b is} \\ 16 > 2b & \text{positive.} \\ \dfrac{16}{2} > \dfrac{2b}{2} & \text{Since b is multiplied by 2,} \\ & \text{divide both sides by 2.} \\ 8 > b \end{array}$$

Solve each inequality.

■ $3(1 - k) > 4 - 3k$

$$\begin{array}{ll} 3(1) - 3(k) > 4 - 3k & \text{Distribute the 3.} \\ 3 - 3k > 4 - 3k & \\ \underline{+ 3k \qquad + 3k} & \text{Add 3k to both sides.} \\ 3 > 4 & \text{False statement} \end{array}$$

There are no solutions.

EXERCISES

Solve the inequality and graph the solutions.

50. $5 + 2m < -3m$ **51.** $y \le 6 + 4y$

52. $4c - 7 > 9c + 8$ **53.** $-3(2 - q) \ge 6(q + 1)$

54. $2(5 - x) < 3x$ **55.** $3.5t - 1.8 < 1.6t + 3.9$

Solve each inequality.

56. $d - 2 < d - 4$ **57.** $2(1 - x) > -2(1 + x)$

58. $4(1 - p) < 4(2 + p)$ **59.** $3w + 1 > 3(w - 1)$

60. $5(4 - k) < 5k$ **61.** $3(c + 1) > 3c + 5$

62. Hanna has a savings account with a balance of $210 and deposits $16 per month. Faith has a savings account with a balance of $175 and deposits $20 per month. Write and solve an inequality to determine the number of months Hanna's account balance will be greater than Faith's account balance.

3-6 Solving Compound Inequalities (pp. 170–176)

EXAMPLES

Solve each compound inequality and graph the solutions.

■ $-3 < c + 5 \leq 11$ *Since 5 is added to c, subtract*
  $\underline{-5 \qquad -5 \quad -5}$ *5 from each part of the*
  $-8 < c \qquad \leq 6$ *inequality.*

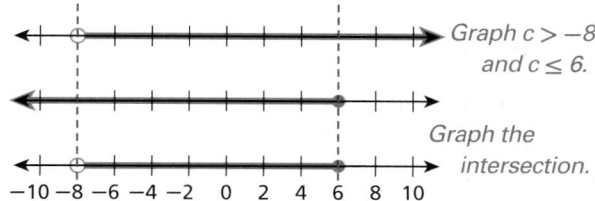

Graph $c > -8$ and $c \leq 6$.

Graph the intersection.

■ $-2 + t \geq 2$ OR $t + 3 < 1$
  $\underline{+2 \qquad +2 \qquad -3 \quad -3}$ *Solve the simple*
  $t \geq 4$ OR $t < -2$ *inequalities.*

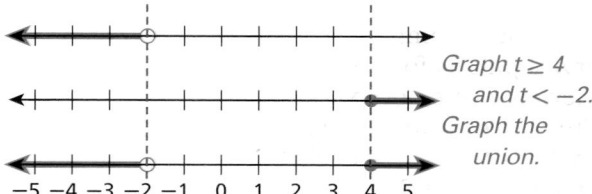

Graph $t \geq 4$ and $t < -2$.
Graph the union.

EXERCISES

Solve each compound inequality and graph the solutions.

63. $-4 < t + 6 < 10$ **64.** $-8 < k - 2 \leq 5$

65. $-3 + r > 4$ OR $r + 1 < -1$

66. $2 > n + 3 > 5$

67. $12 \geq p + 7 > 5$

68. $3 < s + 9$ OR $1 > s - 4$

69. One day, the high temperature was 84°F and the low temperature was 68°F. Write a compound inequality to represent the day's temperatures.

70. The table shows formulas for the recommended heart rates during exercise for a person who is a years old. Write and solve a compound inequality to determine the heart rate range for a 16-year-old person.

Recommended Heart Rate Range	
Lower Limit	$0.5 \times (220 - a)$
Upper Limit	$0.9 \times (220 - a)$

3-7 Solving Absolute-Value Inequalities (pp. 178–183)

EXAMPLES

Solve each inequality and graph the solutions.

■ $|x| + 4 < 9$
  $|x| + 4 < 9$
  $\underline{\quad -4 \quad -4}$ *Subtract 4 from both sides.*
  $|x| \qquad < 5$

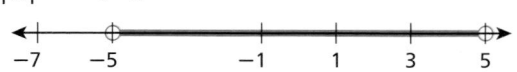

$x > -5$ AND $x < 5$ *Write as a compound inequality.*

■ $|x - 3| + 7 \geq 13$
  $\underline{\qquad -7 \quad -7}$ *Subtract 7 from both sides.*
  $|x - 3| \qquad \geq 6$
  $x - 3 \leq -6$ OR $x - 3 \geq 6$ *Solve the two*
  $\underline{+3 \quad +3 \qquad +3 \quad +3}$ *inequalities.*
  $x \qquad \leq -3$ OR $x \qquad \geq 9$

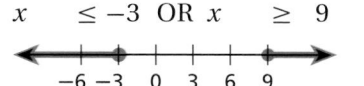

EXERCISES

Solve the inequality and graph the solutions.

71. $|x| - 7 \leq 15$ **72.** $|x + 4| > 8$

73. $6|x| \leq 24$ **74.** $|x + 9| + 11 < 20$

75. $3|x| \geq 9$ **76.** $4|2x| < 24$

Solve the inequality.

77. $|x| - 5.4 > 8.5$ **78.** $|5.2 + x| < 7.3$

79. $|x - 7| + 10 \geq 12$ **80.** $14|x| - 15 \geq 41$

81. $\left|x - \dfrac{1}{2}\right| + 4 \leq \dfrac{5}{2}$ **82.** $|x + 5.5| - 6.4 \leq 4.9$

83. The water depth for a pool is set to 6 ft, but the actual depth of the pool may vary by as much as 4 in. Write and solve an absolute-value inequality to find the range of possible water depths in inches. Graph the solutions.

CHAPTER TEST

Describe the solutions of each inequality in words.

1. $-6 \le m$

2. $3t > 12$

3. $-x \ge 2$

4. $2 + b \le 10$

Graph each inequality.

5. $b > -3$

6. $2.5 < c$

7. $y \le -\sqrt{25}$

8. $3 - (4 + 7) \ge h$

Write the inequality shown by each graph.

9.
```
←+——+——+——+——+——+——⊕——+——+——+——+——→
  -5  -4  -3  -2  -1   0   1   2   3   4   5
```

10.
```
        -4.5
←+——————◆——+——————+——————+——————+——→
 -5     -4    -3       -2      -1      0
```

Write an inequality for the situation and graph the solutions.

11. Madison must run a mile in no more than 9 minutes to qualify for the race.

Solve each inequality and graph the solutions.

12. $d - 5 > -7$

13. $f + 4 < -3$

14. $4.5 \ge s + 3.2$

15. $g + (-2) \le 9$

16. Students need at least 75 hours of volunteer service to meet their graduation requirement. Samir has already completed 48 hours. Write and solve an inequality to determine how many more hours he needs to complete.

Solve each inequality and graph the solutions.

17. $-2c \le 2$

18. $3 > \dfrac{k}{2}$

19. $\dfrac{4}{5}x \le -8$

20. $\dfrac{b}{3} > -7$

21. Marco needs to buy premium gasoline for his car. He has $20 in his wallet. Write and solve an inequality to determine how many gallons of gas Marco can buy.

Gasoline Prices ($)		
Regular	Plus	Premium
2.05	2.12	2.25

Solve each inequality and graph the solutions.

22. $3x - 8 < 4$

23. $-2(c - 3) > 4$

24. $5 \le \dfrac{3}{4}n - 2^4$

25. $3 - 2a \le -15 + (-9)$

Solve each inequality.

26. $2k - 6 > 3k + 2$

27. $2(5 - f) \le f + 12$

28. $\dfrac{3}{2}d \le -\dfrac{1}{2}d + 6$

Solve each compound inequality and graph the solutions.

29. $-1 \le x - 3 < 3$

30. $t + 7 < 3 \text{ OR } t - 1 > 4$

31. $4 \le d - 2 < 5$

32. The driving school instructor has asked Lina to stay within 2 miles of the posted speed limits. The current road has a speed limit of 45 mi/h. Write a compound inequality to show Lina's acceptable speeds s.

Solve each inequality.

33. $|x - 3| + 7 < 17$

34. $6|x| + 4 \ge 16$

35. $|x + 12| \le 23$

COLLEGE ENTRANCE EXAM PRACTICE

FOCUS ON SAT STUDENT-PRODUCED RESPONSES

Ten questions on the SAT require you to enter your answer in a special grid like the one shown. You do not have to write your answer in the boxes at the top of the grid, but doing this may help you avoid errors when filling in the grid. The circles must be filled in correctly for you to receive credit.

 You cannot enter a zero in the first column of the grid. This is to encourage you to give a more accurate answer when you need to round. For example, $\frac{1}{16}$ written as a decimal is 0.0625. This should be entered in the grid as .063 instead of 0.06.

You may want to time yourself as you take this practice test. It should take you about 9 minutes to complete.

1. Mailing a standard-sized letter in 2005 by first-class mail cost $0.37 for a letter weighing 1 ounce or less and $0.23 for each additional ounce. How much did it cost, in dollars, to send a standard-sized letter that weighed 3 ounces?

2. If $p = q - 2$ and $\frac{q}{3} = 9$, what is the value of p?

3. Give the maximum value of x if $12 - 3(x + 1) \geq \frac{1}{2}(3 - 5)$.

4. Give the minimum value of x if $2x + y \leq 7x - 9$ and $y = -3$.

5. For what integer value of x is $2x - 9 < 5$ and $x - 1 > 4$?

6. What is the minimum value of z that satisfies the inequality $z - 7.3 \geq 4.1$?

7. To be eligible for financial aid, Alisa must work at least 15 hours per week in a work-study program. She wants to spend at least 5 more hours studying than working each week. What is the minimum number of hours per day (Monday through Friday) that she must study to meet this goal and be eligible for financial aid?

8. For all real numbers a and b, define the operation # as follows:
$$a \# b = 2a - b$$
Given $a = 3$ and $a \# b = 1$, what is the value of b?

STRATEGIES FOR SUCCESS

Short Response: Understand Short Response Scores

To answer a short-response question completely, you must show how you solved the problem and explain your answer. Short response questions are scored using a 2-point scoring rubric. A sample scoring rubric is provided below.

EXAMPLE 1

Short Response An online company offers free shipping if the cost of the order is at least $35. Your order currently totals $26.50. Write an inequality to show how much more you need to spend to qualify for free shipping. Solve the inequality and explain what your answer means.

2-point response:

Let c be the amount I must add to my order.
c plus the amount I already ordered must be at least $35.
c +   26.50   ≥   35

$$c + 26.50 \geq 35$$
$$c + 26.50 - 26.50 \geq 35 - 26.50$$
$$c \geq 8.50$$

Check:
$8.50 + 26.50 \geq 35$ ✓

To get free shipping on the order, I must spend at least $8.50 more since $8.50 + $26.50 is at least $35.

The student wrote and solved an inequality correctly. The student defined the variable used in the inequality, answered the question in a complete sentence, and showed an explanation for the work done.

1-point response:

$$C + 26.50 > 35$$
$$C > 8.50$$
$$\$8.50$$

The student did not define the variable. The student gave a correct answer, but the inequality symbol shown in the student's work is incorrect. No explanation was given.

0-point response:

$9.25

The student gave an answer that satisfies the problem, but the student did not show any work or give explanation.

Scoring Rubric:

2 points: The student writes and correctly solves an inequality, showing all work. Student defines the variable, answers the question in a complete sentence, and provides an explanation.

1 point: The student writes and correctly solves an inequality but does not show all work, does not define the variable, or does not provide an explanation.

1 point: The student writes and solves an inequality but gives an incorrect answer. The student shows all work and provides an explanation for the answer.

0 points: The student gives no response or provides a solution without showing any work or explanation.

Read short-response test items carefully. If you are allowed to write in the test booklet, underline or circle the parts of the question that tell you what your answer must include. Be sure to explain how you get your answer in complete sentences.

Read each sample and answer the questions that follow by using the scoring rubric below.

Sample A
Short Response Write a real-world situation that can be modeled by the inequality $25s - 75 \geq 250$. Solve for s and explain how the value of s relates to your situation.

Student's Answer

A painter rents a booth at the county fair for $75. The artist sells his paintings for $25 each. If he makes at least $250 in profit, he can buy a new easel.

The artist has to sell at least 13 paintings.

1. What score should the student's answer receive? Explain your reasoning.

2. What additional information, if any, should the student's answer include in order to receive full credit?

Sample B
Short Response How do the solutions of $3s - 10 < 15 - 2s$ and $-34 + 9s \leq 4s - 9$ differ? How are the solutions alike? Include a graph in your explanation.

Student's Answer

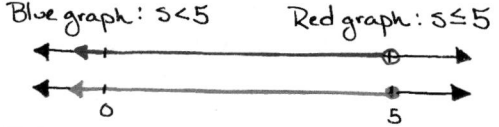

3. What score should the student's answer receive? Explain your reasoning.

4. What additional information, if any, should the student's answer include in order to receive full credit?

Sample C
Short Response Explain the difference between the solution of the equation $x - 6 = 2x + 9$ and the solutions of the inequality $x - 6 < 2x + 9$.

Student's Answer

The equation has a solution of x = –15, and the inequality has a solution of x > –15. The equation is true only when x equals –15. The inequality is true for all values greater than –15.

5. What score should the student's answer receive? Explain your reasoning.

6. What additional information, if any, should the student's answer include in order to receive full credit?

CUMULATIVE ASSESSMENT, CHAPTERS 1–3

Multiple Choice

1. Which algebraic expression means "5 less than y"?

   (A) $5 - y$

   (B) $y - 5$

   (C) $5 < y$

   (D) $5 \div y$

2. Which is a simplified expression for $5 + 2(x - 5)$?

   (A) $2x$

   (B) $2x + 5$

   (C) $2x - 5$

   (D) $7x - 35$

3. If $t + 8 = 2$, find the value of $2t$.

   (A) -12

   (B) -6

   (C) 12

   (D) 20

4. The length of the rectangle is $2(x + 1)$ meters and the perimeter is 60 meters. Find the length of the rectangle.

$$2(x + 1)$$
$$4$$

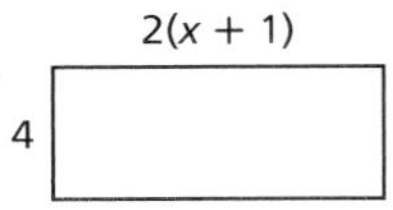

   (A) 12 meters

   (B) 26 meters

   (C) 28 meters

   (D) 56 meters

5. Samantha deposited some money in her account in June. She deposited twice that amount in August. Samantha has less than $600 in her account. If she made no other withdrawals or deposits, which inequality could be used to determine the maximum amount Samantha could have deposited in June?

   (A) $2x < 600$

   (B) $2x > 600$

   (C) $3x < 600$

   (D) $3x > 600$

6. A negative number is raised to a power, and the result is a positive number. Which of the following CANNOT be true?

   (A) The number is even.

   (B) The number is odd.

   (C) The exponent is even.

   (D) The exponent is odd.

7. For which inequality is -2 a solution?

   (A) $2x < -4$

   (B) $-2x < 4$

   (C) $-2x > -4$

   (D) $-2x < -4$

8. Which graph shows the solutions of $-2(1 - x) < 3(x - 2)$?

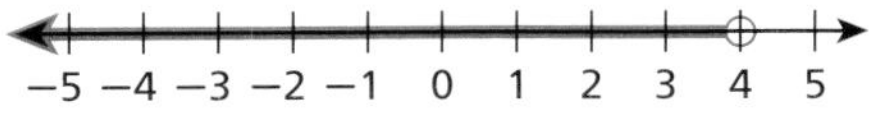

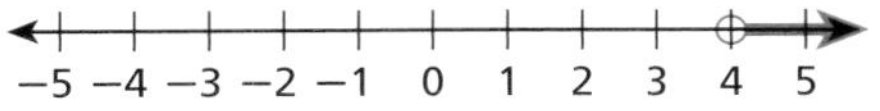

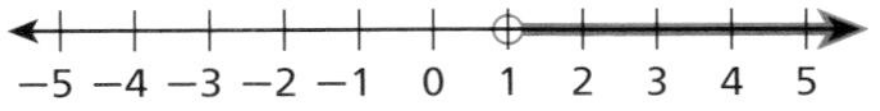

   (A) number line from −5 to 5, open circle at 4, shaded to the left

   (B) number line from −5 to 5, open circle at 4, shaded to the right

   (C) number line from −5 to 5, open circle at 1, shaded to the right

   (D) number line from −5 to 5, open circle at −4, shaded to the right

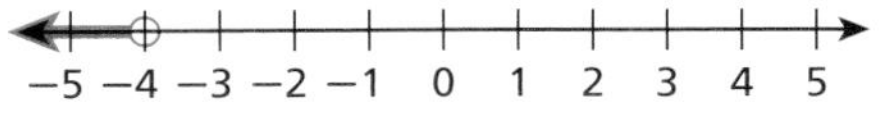

9. Which compound inequality has no solution?

   (A) $x > 1$ OR $x < -2$

   (B) $x < 1$ AND $x > -2$

   (C) $x < 1$ OR $x < -2$

   (D) $x > 1$ AND $x < -2$

10. Which expression describes the rate at which a bicycle rider is traveling if the rider has traveled 15 kilometers in 40 minutes? Round to the nearest tenth.

   (A) 0.5 kilometers/minute

   (B) 2.7 kilometers/minute

   (C) 0.4 kilometers/minute

   (D) 0.3 kilometers/minute

To check your answer, use a different method to solve the problem from the one you originally used. If you made a mistake the first time, you are unlikely to make the same mistake when you solve the problem a different way.

11. Which inequality is equivalent to $p < -2$?

(A) $p + 1 < -2$

(B) $p + 4 < 2$

(C) $2p + 1 < -4$

(D) $3p < -12$

12. What is the greatest integer solution of $5 - 3m > 11$?

(A) 0

(B) −1

(C) −2

(D) −3

Gridded Response

13. The sum of the measures of any two sides of a triangle must be greater than the measure of the third side. What is the greatest possible integer value for x?

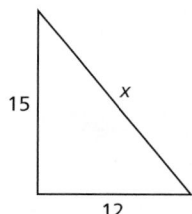

14. Brian plays basketball. In the past, he has made 4 out of every 5 free throws. What percent of his free throws has Brian made?

15. Amy's bowling score in her third game was 10 points less than her score in the first game and 5 points more than her score in the second game. The total points for all three games was no more than 275. What is the highest number of points Amy could have scored in her first game?

16. Trevor needs a 93 on his second quiz to have a quiz average of 90. What score did Trevor receive on his first quiz?

17. What is the length in meters of the radius of a circle that has area of 314 square meters? (Use 3.14 for π.)

Short Response

18. Write 2 different inequalities that are equivalent to $n > 3$ such that

a. the first inequality uses the symbol > and requires addition or subtraction to solve.

b. the second inequality uses the symbol < and requires multiplication or division to solve.

19. Alison has twice as many videogames as Kyle. Maurice has 5 more videogames than Alison. The total number of videogames is less than 40.

a. Write an inequality to represent this situation.

b. Solve the inequality to determine the greatest number of videogames Maurice could have.

20. Donna's Deli delivers lunches for $7 per person plus a $35 delivery fee. Larry's Lunches delivers lunches for $11 per person.

a. Write an expression to represent the cost of x lunches from Donna's Deli. Write an expression to represent the cost of ordering x lunches from Larry's Lunches.

b. Write an inequality to determine the number of lunches for which the cost of Larry's Lunches is less than the cost of Donna's Deli.

c. Solve the inequality and explain what the answer means. Which restaurant charges less for an order of 10 lunches?

Extended Response

21. Aleya has two employment opportunities. Company A offered her a yearly salary of $31,000. Company B offered her a similar position with a yearly salary of $27,000 plus 2.5% of her total sales for the year.

a. Let x represent Aleya's total sales for the year at company B. Write an expression to represent the total income after one year at company B.

b. Use your expression from part **a** to write an inequality that could be solved to determine the amount of sales for which the yearly income at company A would be greater than that at company B.

c. Solve the inequality from part **b** and explain the meaning of the solution in relation to Aleya's decision to work for company A or company B.

d. How much more than the salary at company A would Aleya make after one year at company B if her total sales for the year was $200,000?

Functions

go.hrw.com
Chapter Project Online
KEYWORD: MA8CA ChProj

Scientists can use data along with functions to model and make predictions about populations and endangered species, such as this sea otter.

ARE YOU READY?

✓ Vocabulary

Match each term on the left with a definition on the right.

1. absolute value
2. algebraic expression
3. input
4. output
5. x-axis

A. a letter used to represent a value that can change

B. the value generated for y

C. a group of numbers, symbols, and variables with one or more operations

D. the distance of a number from zero on the number line

E. the horizontal number line in the coordinate plane

F. a value substituted for x

✓ Ordered Pairs

Graph each point on the same coordinate plane.

6. $(-2, 4)$
7. $(0, -5)$
8. $(1, -3)$
9. $(4, 2)$
10. $(3, -2)$
11. $(-1, -2)$
12. $(-1, 3)$
13. $(-4, 0)$

✓ Evaluate Expressions

Evaluate each expression for $x = -2$.

14. $-2x - 1$
15. $x + 1$
16. $-x^2$
17. $\frac{1}{2}x + 2$
18. $(x + 1)^2$
19. $(x - 1)^2$

✓ Solve Multi-Step Equations

Solve each equation. Check your answer.

20. $17x - 15 = 12$
21. $-7 + 2t = 7$
22. $-6 = \frac{p}{3} + 9$
23. $5n - 10 = 35$
24. $3r - 14 = 7$
25. $9 = \frac{x}{2} + 1$
26. $-2.4 + 1.6g = 5.6$
27. $34 - 2x = 12$
28. $2(x + 5) = -8$

✓ Solve for a Variable

Solve each equation for the indicated variable.

29. $A = \ell w$ for w
30. $V = \ell w h$ for w
31. $A = bh$ for h
32. $C = 2\pi r$ for r
33. $I = Prt$ for P
34. $V = \frac{1}{3}\ell w h$ for h

CHAPTER

4

Unpacking the Standards

The information below "unpacks" the standards. The Academic Vocabulary is highlighted and defined to help you understand the language of the standards. Refer to the lessons listed after each standard for help with the math terms and phrases. The Chapter Concept shows how the standard is applied in this chapter.

California Standard	Academic Vocabulary	Chapter Concept
16.0 Students understand the concepts of a relation and a function, determine whether a given relation defines a function, and give pertinent information about given relations and functions. (Lessons **4-2, 4-3**)	**concept(s)** the most basic meaning **pertinent** related to	You learn to determine if a relation is also a function given a graph, a table, and a mapping diagram. You find the domain and range of relations.
17.0 Students determine the domain of independent variables and the range of dependent variables defined by a graph, a set of ordered pairs, **or a symbolic expression.** (Lessons **4-2, 4-3**)	**determine** find out **symbolic** using a symbol or symbols to represent something else	You identify the domain of independent variables and the range of dependent variables defined by a graph, a table, and a mapping diagram.
18.0 Students determine whether a relation defined by a graph, a set of ordered pairs, **or a symbolic expression is a function and justify the conclusion.** (Lessons **4-2, 4-3**)	**defined by** to show something clearly **justify** to give a reason or explanation	You identify functions defined by a graph, a table, and a mapping diagram. You also graph equations and use the vertical-line test to determine whether the equation represents a function.

Reading Strategy: Read and Interpret Math Symbols

It is essential that as you read through each lesson of the textbook, you can interpret mathematical symbols.

Common Math Symbols

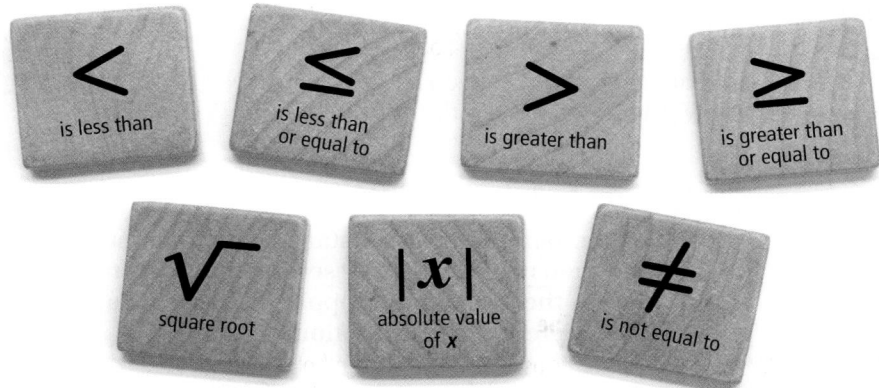

$<$ is less than

$\leq$ is less than or equal to

$>$ is greater than

$\geq$ is greater than or equal to

$\sqrt{}$ square root

$|x|$ absolute value of x

$\neq$ is not equal to

You must be able to translate symbols into words . . .

Using Symbols	Using Words
$3\left(\dfrac{x}{12}\right) - 1 = 21$	Three times the quotient of x and 12, minus 1 **equals** 21.
$25x + 6 \geq 17$	Twenty-five times x plus 6 **is greater than or equal** to 17.
$|x| > 14$	The **absolute value** of x **is greater than** 14.
$\sqrt{60 + x} \leq 40$	The **square root** of the sum of 60 and x **is less than or equal** to 40.

. . . and words into symbols.

Using Words	Using Symbols
The height of the shed **is at least** 9 feet.	$h \geq 9$ ft
The distance **is at most** one tenth of a mile.	$d \leq 0.1$ mi
The silo contains **more than** 600 cubic feet of corn.	$c > 600$ ft^3

Try This

Translate the symbols into words.

1. $x \leq \sqrt{10}$ **2.** $|x| + 2 > 45$ **3.** $-5 \leq x < 8$ **4.** $-6 - \dfrac{1}{5}x = -32$

Translate the words into symbols.

5. There are less than 15 seconds remaining. **6.** The tax is 8.25 percent of the cost.

7. Ann counted over 100 pennies.   **8.** Joe can spend at least $22 but no more than $30.

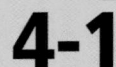

4-1 Graphing Relationships

California Standards

Review of Grade 7 AF1.5
Represent quantitative relationships graphically and interpret the meaning of a specific part of a graph in the situation represented by the graph.

Vocabulary
continuous graph
discrete graph

Who uses this?
Cardiologists can use graphs to analyze their patients' heartbeats. (See Example 2.)

Graphs can be used to illustrate many different situations. For example, trends shown on a cardiograph can help a doctor see how the patient's heart is functioning.

To relate a graph to a given situation, use key words in the description.

EXAMPLE 1 **Relating Graphs to Situations**

The air temperature was constant for several hours at the beginning of the day and then rose steadily for several hours. It stayed the same temperature for most of the day before dropping sharply at sundown. Choose the graph that best represents this situation.

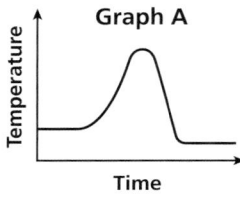
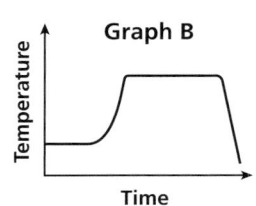
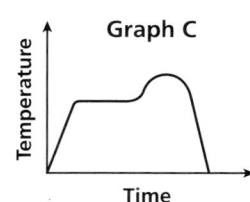

Step 1 Read the graphs from left to right to show time passing.

Step 2 List key words in order and decide which graph shows them.

Key Words	Segment Description...	Graphs...
Was constant	Horizontal	Graphs A and B
Rose steadily	Slanting upward	Graphs A and B
Stayed the same	Horizontal	Graph B
Dropped sharply	Slanting downward	Graph B

Step 3 Pick the graph that shows all the key phrases in order.

horizontal, **slanting upward,** horizontal, **slanting downward**

The correct graph is B.

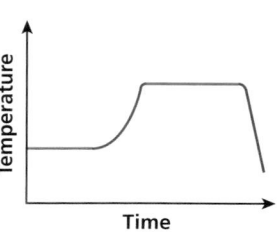

1. The air temperature increased steadily for several hours and then remained constant. At the end of the day, the temperature increased slightly again before dropping sharply. Choose the graph above that best represents this situation.

As seen in Example 1, some graphs are connected lines or curves called **continuous graphs**. Some graphs are only distinct points. These are called **discrete graphs**.

The graph on theme-park attendance is an example of a discrete graph. It consists of distinct points because each year is distinct and people are counted in whole numbers only. The values between the whole numbers are not included, since they have no meaning for the situation.

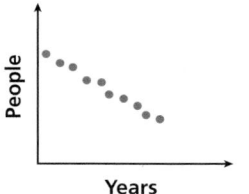

Theme Park Attendance

EXAMPLE 2 **Sketching Graphs for Situations**

Sketch a graph for each situation. Tell whether the graph is continuous or discrete.

A Simon is selling candles to raise money for the school dance. For each candle he sells, the school will get $2.50. He has 10 candles that he can sell.

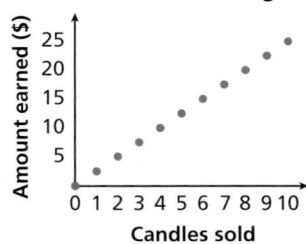

Simon's Earnings

The amount earned (y-axis) increases by $2.50 for each candle Simon sells (x-axis).

Since Simon can only sell whole candles or none at all, the graph is 11 distinct points.

The graph is discrete.

B Angelique's heart rate is being monitored while she exercises on a treadmill. While walking, her heart rate remains the same. As she increases her pace, her heart rate rises at a steady rate. When she begins to run, her heart rate increases more rapidly and then remains high while she runs. As she decreases her pace, her heart rate slows down and returns to her normal rate.

As time passes during her workout (moving left to right along the *x*-axis), her heart rate (*y*-axis) does the following:

- remains the same,
- rises at a steady rate,
- increases **more rapidly** (**steeper** than previous segment),
- remains high,
- slows down,
- and then returns to her normal rate.

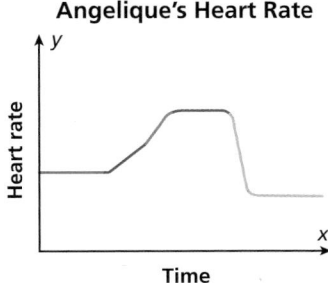

Angelique's Heart Rate

The graph is continuous.

Sketch a graph for each situation. Tell whether the graph is continuous or discrete.

2a. Jamie is taking an 8-week keyboarding class. At the end of each week, she takes a test to find the number of words she can type per minute. She improves each week.

2b. Henry begins to drain a water tank by opening a valve. Then he opens another valve. Then he closes the first valve. He leaves the second valve open until the tank is empty.

Both graphs below show a relationship about a child going down a slide. **Graph A** represents the child's *distance from the ground* related to time. **Graph B** represents the child's *speed* related to time.

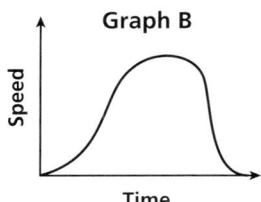

Graph A

Graph B

EXAMPLE **3** **Writing Situations for Graphs**

Write a possible situation for the given graph.

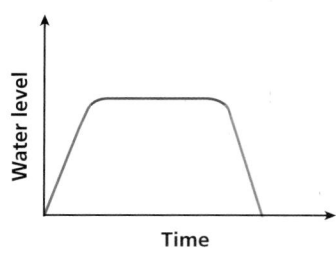

Step 1 Identify labels.
x-axis: time   *y*-axis: water level

Step 2 Analyze sections.
Over time, the water level does the following:
- **increases steadily**,
- **remains unchanged**,
- and then **decreases steadily**.

Possible Situation:

A watering can is **filled with water**. It **sits for a while** until the flowers are planted. The water in the can is then **emptied** on top of the planted flowers.

 **3.** Write a possible situation for the given graph.

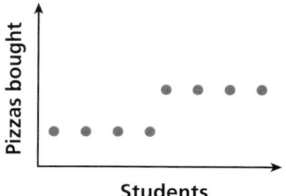

THINK AND DISCUSS

1. Should a graph of age related to height be a continuous graph or a discrete graph? Explain.

2. Give an example of a situation that, when graphed, would include a horizontal segment.

3. **GET ORGANIZED** Copy and complete the graphic organizer. Write an example of key words that suggest the given segments on a graph. One example for each segment is given for you.

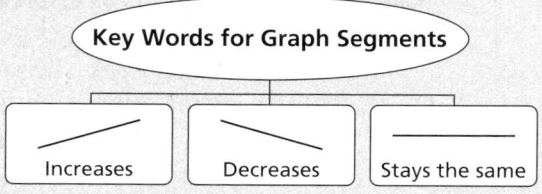

California
Standards Practice
Review of Grade 7 **AF1.5**

go.hrw.com
Homework Help Online
KEYWORD: MA8CA 4-1
Parent Resources Online
KEYWORD: MA8CA Parent

GUIDED PRACTICE

Vocabulary Apply the vocabulary from this lesson to answer each question.

1. A ___?___ graph is made of connected lines or curves. (*continuous* or *discrete*)

2. A ___?___ graph is made of only distinct points. (*continuous* or *discrete*)

SEE EXAMPLE 1
p. 200

Choose the graph that best represents each situation.

3. A person alternates between running and walking.

4. A person gradually speeds up to a constant running pace.

5. A person walks, gradually speeds up to a run, and then slows back down to a walk.

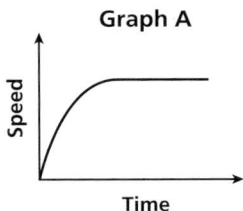
Graph A

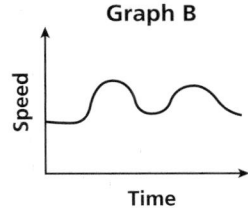
Graph B

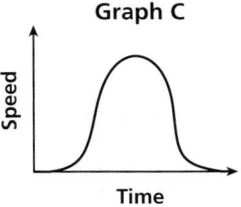
Graph C

SEE EXAMPLE 2
p. 201

6. Maxine is buying extra pages for her photo album. Each page holds exactly 8 photos. Sketch a graph to show the maximum number of photos she can add to her album if she buys 1, 2, 3, or 4 extra pages. Tell whether the graph is continuous or discrete.

SEE EXAMPLE 3
p. 202

Write a possible situation for each graph.

7.
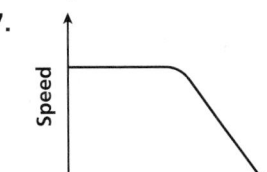

8.
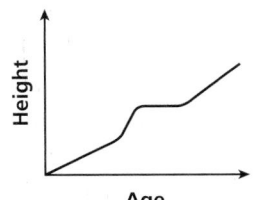

9.

PRACTICE AND PROBLEM SOLVING

Independent Practice

For Exercises	See Example
10–12	1
13	2
14–16	3

Extra Practice

Skills Practice p. EP8

Application Practice p. EP27

Choose the graph that best represents each situation.

10. A flag is raised up a flagpole quickly at the beginning and then more slowly near the top.

11. A flag is raised up a flagpole in a jerky motion, using a hand-over-hand method.

12. A flag is raised up a flagpole at a constant rate of speed.

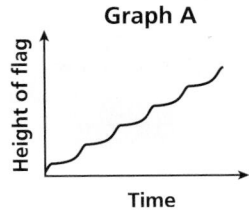
Graph A

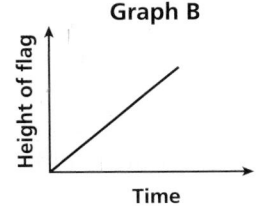
Graph B

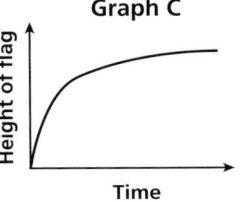
Graph C

13. For six months, a puppy gained weight at a steady rate. Sketch a graph to illustrate the weight of the puppy during that time period. Tell whether the graph is continuous or discrete.

Write a possible situation for each graph.

14.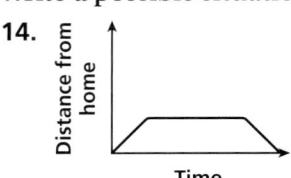

15.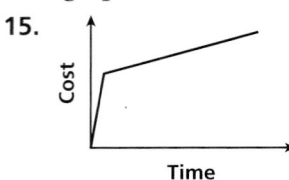

16.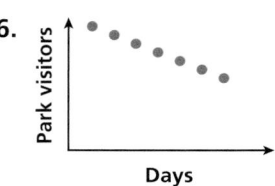

17. Data Collection Use a graphing calculator and motion detector for the following.

   a. On a coordinate plane, draw a graph relating distance away from a starting point walking at various speeds and time.

   b. Using the motion detector as the starting point, walk away from the motion detector to make a graph on the graphing calculator that matches the one you drew.

   c. Compare your walking speeds to each change in steepness on the graph.

18. Sports The graph shows the speed of a horse during and after a race. Use it to describe the changing pace of the horse.

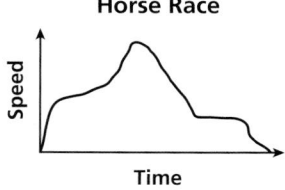

Horse Race

19. Recreation You hike up a mountain path starting at 10 A.M. You camp overnight and then walk back down the same path at the same pace at 10 A.M. the next morning. On the same set of axes, graph the relationship between distance from the top of the mountain and the time of day for both the hike up and the hike down. What does the point of intersection of the graphs represent?

20. Critical Thinking Suppose that you sketched a graph of speed related to time for a brick being dropped from the top of a building. Then you sketched a graph for speed related to time for a ball that was rolled down a hill and then came to rest. How would the graphs be the same? How would they be different?

 21. Write About It Describe a real-life situation that could be represented by a graph that has distinct points. Then describe a real-life situation that could be represented by a connected graph.

CONCEPT CONNECTION

22. This problem will prepare you for the Concept Connection on page 222.

A rectangular pool that is 4 feet deep at all places is being filled at a constant rate.

   a. Sketch a graph to show the depth of the water as it increases over time.

   b. The side view of another swimming pool is shown. If the pool is being filled at a constant rate, sketch a graph to show the depth of the water as it increases over time.

Multiple Choice For Exercises 23 and 24, choose the best answer.

23. Which situation would NOT be represented by a graph with distinct points?

(A) Amount of money earned based on the number of cereal bars sold

(B) Number of visitors per day for one week to a grocery store

(C) The amount of iced tea in a pitcher at a restaurant during the lunch hour

(D) The total cost of buying 1, 2, or 3 CDs at the music store

24. Which situation is best represented by the graph?

(A) A snowboarder starts at the bottom of the hill and takes a ski lift to the top.

(B) A cruise boat travels at a steady pace from the port to its destination.

(C) An object dropped from the top of a building gains speed at a rapid pace before hitting the ground.

(D) A marathon runner starts at a steady pace and then runs faster at the end of the race before stopping at the finish line.

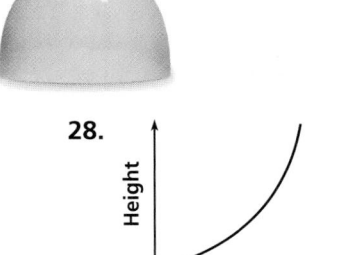

25. Short Response Marla participates in a triathlon consisting of swimming, biking, and running. Would a graph of Marla's speed during the triathlon be a connected graph or distinct points? Explain.

CHALLENGE AND EXTEND

Pictured are three vases and graphs representing the height of water as it is poured into each of the vases at a constant rate. Match each vase with the correct graph.

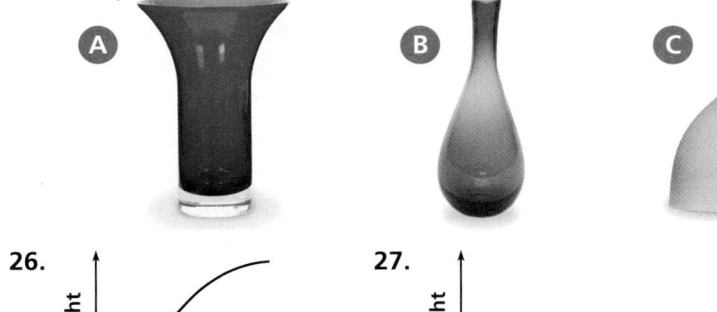

26. **27.** **28.**

 SPIRAL STANDARDS REVIEW 🔑 7NS1.2, 7AF1.1, 3.0

Evaluate each expression. *(Lesson 1-4)*

29. -2^3

30. 4^4

31. $\left(\dfrac{1}{3}\right)^2$

Write and solve an equation to represent each relationship. *(Lesson 2-1)*

32. A number increased by 11 is equal to 3.

33. Five less than a number is equal to -2.

Solve each equation. *(Lesson 2-7)*

34. $|x| = 7.2$

35. $19 = |x + 4|$

36. $|3x| + 2 = 8$

4-2

Relations and Functions

California Standards

16.0 Students understand the concepts of a relation and a function, determine whether a given relation defines a function, and give pertinent information about given relations and functions.

Also covered: **17.0, 18.0**

Vocabulary
relation
domain
range
function

Why learn this?
You can use a relation to show finishing positions and scores in a track meet.

In Lesson 4-1, you saw relationships represented by graphs. Relationships can also be represented by a set of ordered pairs, called a **relation** .

In the scoring system of some track meets, for **first place** you get **5** points, for **second place** you get **3** points, for **third place** you get **2** points, and for **fourth place** you get **1** point. This scoring system is a relation, so it can be shown as ordered pairs, $\{(1, 5), (2, 3), (3, 2), (4, 1)\}$. You can also show relations in other ways, such as tables, graphs, or *mapping diagrams*.

EXAMPLE **1** **Showing Multiple Representations of Relations**

Express the relation for the track meet scoring system, $\{(1, 5), (2, 3), (3, 2), (4, 1)\}$, as a table, as a graph, and as a mapping diagram.

Remember!

To review how to plot points in the coordinate plane, see Skills Bank p. SB23.

Table	Graph	Mapping Diagram
Track Scoring 	**Track Scoring**	

Place	Points
1	5
2	3
3	2
4	1

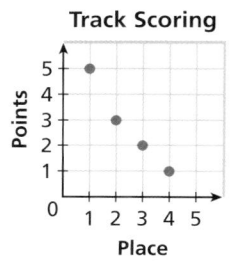

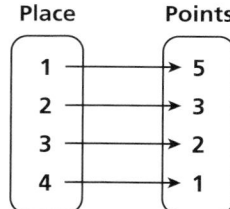

Write all x-values under "Place" and all y-values under "Points."

Use the x- and y-values to plot the ordered pairs.

Write all x-values under "Place" and all y-values under "Points." Draw an arrow from each x-value to its corresponding y-value.

 **1.** Express the relation $\{(1, 3) (2, 4), (3, 5)\}$ as a table, as a graph, and as a mapping diagram.

The **domain** of a relation is the set of first coordinates (or *x*-values) of the ordered pairs. The **range** of a relation is the set of second coordinates (or *y*-values) of the ordered pairs. The domain of the track meet scoring system is {1, 2, 3, 4}. The range is {1, 2, 3, 5}. Notice that domains and ranges can be written as sets.

EXAMPLE 2 Finding the Domain and Range of a Relation

Give the domain and range of the relation.

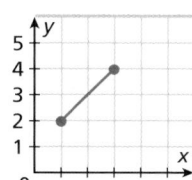

The domain is all *x*-values from 1 through 3, inclusive.

The range is all *y*-values from 2 through 4, inclusive.

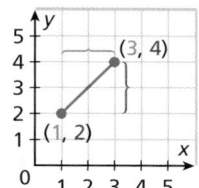

D: $1 \leq x \leq 3$ R: $2 \leq y \leq 4$

Writing Math

You can use set-builder notation to write domains and ranges. In Example 2, the domain is $\{x : 1 \leq x \leq 3\}$. The range is $\{y : 2 \leq y \leq 4\}$.

 Give the domain and range of each relation.

2a.
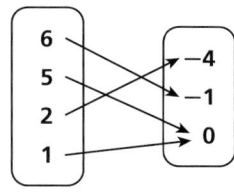

2b.

x	y
1	1
4	4
8	1

A **function** is a special type of relation that pairs each domain value with exactly one range value.

EXAMPLE 3 Identifying Functions

Give the domain and range of each relation. Tell whether the relation is a function. Explain.

 A

Field Trip	
Students x	**Buses y**
68	2
75	2
125	3

D: $\{68, 75, 125\}$

R: $\{2, 3\}$

Even though 2 is in the range twice, it is written only once when you are giving the range.

This relation is a function. Each domain value is paired with exactly one range value.

 B

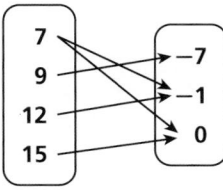

Use the arrows to determine which domain values correspond to each range value.

D: $\{7, 9, 12, 15\}$

R: $\{-7, -1, 0\}$

This relation is not a function. Each domain value does not have exactly one range value. The domain value 7 is paired with the range values -1 and 0.

Give the domain and range of each relation. Tell whether the relation is a function. Explain.

 C

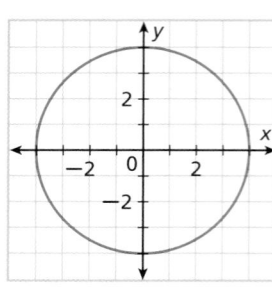

Draw in lines to see the domain and range values.

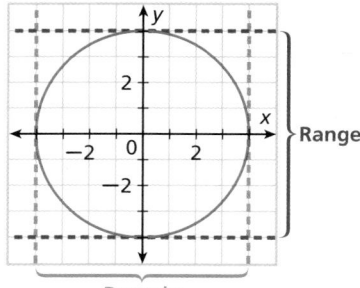

Range

Domain

D: $-4 \le x \le 4$ R: $-4 \le y \le 4$

x	4	0	0	-4
y	0	4	-4	0

To compare domain and range values, make a table using points from the graph.

This relation is not a function because there are several domain values that have more than one range value. For example, the domain value 0 is paired with both 4 and −4.

Helpful Hint

To find the domain and range from a graph, it may help to draw lines to see the *x*- and *y*-values.

CHECK IT OUT! Give the domain and range of each relation. Tell whether the relation is a function and explain.

3a. $\{(8, 2), (-4, 1), (-6, 2), (1, 9)\}$ **3b.**

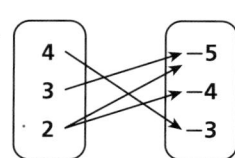

Student to Student   *Functions*

Eric Dawson
Boone High School

*I decide whether a list of ordered pairs is a function by looking at the **x-values**. If they're all different, then it's a function.*

(1, 6), (2, 5), (6, 5), (0, 8)
All different x-values
Function

(5, 6), (7, 2), (5, 8), (6, 3)
Same x-value (with different *y*-values)
Not a function

THINK AND DISCUSS

1. Describe how to tell whether a set of ordered pairs is a function.

2. Can the graph of a vertical line segment represent a function? Explain.

3. GET ORGANIZED Copy and complete the graphic organizer by explaining when a relation is a function and when it is not a function.

A relation is...	
A function if...	Not a function if...

4-2

Exercises

California Standards Practice
16.0, 17.0, 18.0

go.hrw.com
Homework Help Online
KEYWORD: MA8CA 4-2
Parent Resources Online
KEYWORD: MA8CA Parent

GUIDED PRACTICE

Vocabulary Apply the vocabulary from this lesson to answer each question.

1. Use a mapping diagram to show a relation that is not a *function*.

2. The set of *x*-values for a relation is also called the ____?____. (*domain* or *range*)

SEE EXAMPLE 1
p. 206

Express each relation as a table, as a graph, and as a mapping diagram.

3. $\{(1, 1), (1, 2)\}$

4. $\left\{(-1, 1), \left(-2, \frac{1}{2}\right), \left(-3, \frac{1}{3}\right), \left(-4, \frac{1}{4}\right)\right\}$

5. $\{(-1, 1), (-3, 3), (5, -5), (-7, 7)\}$

6. $\{(0, 0), (2, -4), (2, -2)\}$

SEE EXAMPLE 2
p. 207

Give the domain and range of each relation.

7. $\{(-5, 7), (0, 0), (2, -8), (5, -20)\}$

8. $\{(1, 2), (2, 4), (3, 6), (4, 8), (5, 10)\}$

9.
x	3	5	2	8	6
y	9	25	4	81	36

10.
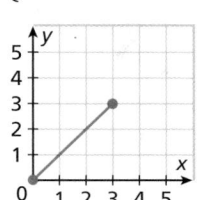

SEE EXAMPLE 3
p. 207

Multi-Step Give the domain and range of each relation. Tell whether the relation is a function. Explain.

11. $\{(1, 3), (1, 0), (1, -2), (1, 8)\}$

12. $\{(-2, 1), (-1, 2), (0, 3), (1, 4)\}$

13.
x	−2	−1	0	1	2
y	1	1	1	1	1

14.
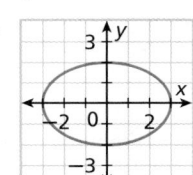

PRACTICE AND PROBLEM SOLVING

Independent Practice
For Exercises	See Example
15–16	1
17–18	2
19–20	3

Extra Practice
Skills Practice p. EP8
Application Practice p. EP27

Express each relation as a table, as a graph, and as a mapping diagram.

15. $\{(-2, -4), (-1, -1), (0, 0), (1, -1), (2, -4)\}$

16. $\left\{(2, 1), \left(2, \frac{1}{2}\right), (2, 2), \left(2, 2\frac{1}{2}\right)\right\}$

Give the domain and range of each relation.

17.
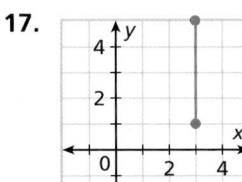

18.
x	y
4	4
5	5
6	6
7	7
8	8

Multi-Step Give the domain and range of each relation. Tell whether the relation is a function. Explain.

19.

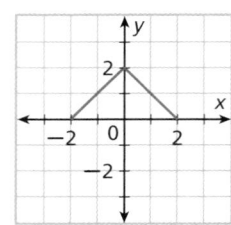

20.

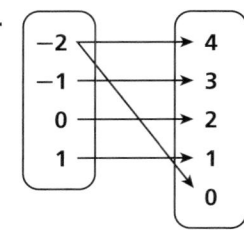

21. Consumer Application An electrician charges a base fee of $75 plus $50 for each hour of work. Create a table that shows the amount the electrician charges for 1, 2, 3, and 4 hours of work. Let x represent the number of hours and y represent the amount charged for x hours. Is this relation a function? Explain.

22. Geometry Write a relation as a set of ordered pairs in which the x-value represents the length of a side of a square and the y-value represents the area of the square. Use a domain of 2, 4, 6, 9, and 11.

23. Multi-Step Create a mapping diagram to display the numbers of days in 1, 2, 3, and 4 weeks. Is this relation a function? Explain.

24. Nutrition The illustrations list the number of grams of fat and the number of Calories from fat for selected foods.
  a. Create a graph for the relation between grams of fat and Calories from fat.
  b. Is this relation a function? Explain.

Hamburger
Fat (g): 14
Fat (Cal): 126

Cheeseburger
Fat (g): 18
Fat (Cal): 162

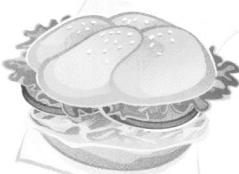

Grilled chicken filet
Fat (g): 3.5
Fat (Cal): 31.5

Breaded chicken filet
Fat (g): 11
Fat (Cal): 99

Taco salad
Fat (g): 19
Fat (Cal): 171

25. Recreation A shop rents canoes for a $7 equipment fee and $2 per hour, with a maximum cost of $15 per day. Express the number of hours x and the cost y as a relation in table form, and find the cost to rent a canoe for 1, 2, 3, 4, and 5 hours. Is this relation a function? Explain.

26. Health You can burn about 6 Calories a minute bicycling. Let x represent the number of minutes bicycled, and let y represent the number of Calories burned.
  a. Write ordered pairs to show the number of Calories burned if you bicycle for 60, 120, 180, 240, or 300 minutes. Graph the ordered pairs.
  b. Find the domain and range of the relation.
  c. Does this graph represent a function? Explain.

27. Critical Thinking For a function, can the number of elements in the range be greater than the number of elements in the domain? Explain.

28. Reasoning Tell whether each statement is true or false. Explain your answers.
  a. All relations are functions.   **b.** All functions are relations.

29. This problem will prepare you for the Concept Connection on page 222.

   a. The graph shows the number of gallons being pumped into a pool over a 5-hour time period. Find the domain and range of the graph.

   b. Does the graph represent a function? Explain.

   c. Give the time and volume as ordered pairs at 2 hours and at 3 hours 30 minutes.

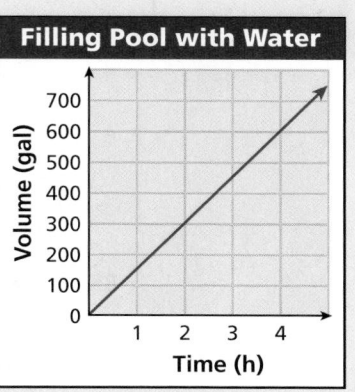

Filling Pool with Water

30. **///ERROR ANALYSIS///** When asked whether the relation $\{(-4, 16), (-2, 4), (0, 0), (2, 4)\}$ is a function, a student stated that the relation is not a function because 4 appears twice. What error did the student make? How would you explain to the student why this relation is a function?

 31. **Write About It** Describe a real-world situation using a relation that is NOT a function. Create a mapping diagram to show why the relation is not a function.

Multiple Choice For Exercises 32–34, choose the best answer.

32. Which of the following relations is NOT a function?

   Ⓐ $\{(6, 2), (-1, 2), (-3, 2), (-5, 2)\}$

   Ⓒ
x	3	5	7
y	1	15	30

   Ⓑ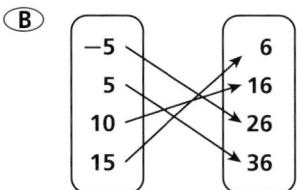

   Ⓓ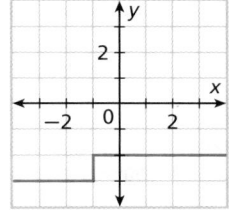

33. Which is NOT a correct way to describe the function $\{(-3, 2), (1, 8), (-1, 5), (3, 11)\}$?

   Ⓐ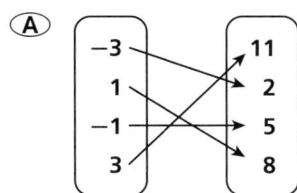

   Ⓒ Domain: $\{-3, -1, 1, 3\}$

   Range: $\{2, 5, 8, 11\}$

   Ⓑ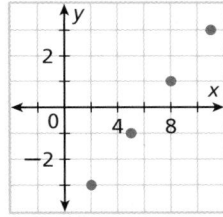

   Ⓓ
x	y
-3	2
-1	5
1	8
3	11

34. Which graph represents a function?

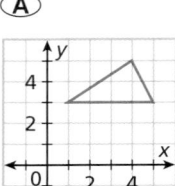

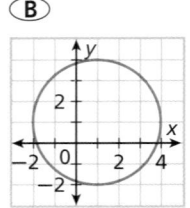

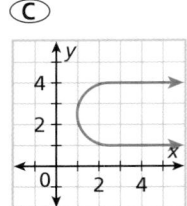

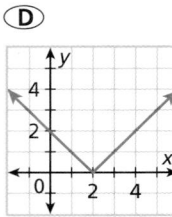

35. Extended Response Use the table for the following.

x	−3	−1	0	1	3
y	5	7	9	11	13

   a. Express the relation as ordered pairs.

   b. Give the domain and range of the relation.

   c. Does the relation represent a function? Explain your answer.

CHALLENGE AND EXTEND

36. What values of a make the relation $\{(a, 1), (2, 3), (4, 5)\}$ a function? Explain.

37. What values of b make the relation $\{(5, 6), (7, 8), (9, b)\}$ a function? Explain.

38. The *inverse* of a relation is created by interchanging the x- and y-coordinates of each ordered pair in the relation.

   a. Find the inverse of the following relation: $\{(-2, 5), (0, 4), (3, -8), (7, 5)\}$.

   b. Is the original relation a function? Why or why not? Is the inverse of the relation a function? Why or why not?

   c. Reasoning The statement "If a relation is a function, then the inverse of the relation is also a function" is sometimes true. Give an example of a relation and its inverse that are both functions. Also give an example of a relation and its inverse that are both not functions.

 SPIRAL STANDARDS REVIEW   7SDAP1.2, 🗝 5.0

39. The ratio of the width of a rectangle to its length is $3:4$. The length of the rectangle is 36 cm. Write and solve a proportion to find the rectangle's width. *(Lesson 2-5)*

40. A scale drawing of a house is drawn with a scale of 1 in: 16 ft. Find the actual length of a hallway that is $\frac{5}{8}$ in. on the scale drawing. *(Lesson 2-5)*

41. Penny wants to drink at least 64 ounces of water today. She has consumed 45 ounces of water so far. Write, solve, and graph an inequality to determine how many more ounces of water Penny must drink to reach her goal. *(Lesson 3-2)*

42. The local pizza parlor sold the following number of pizzas over 10 days. Sketch a graph for the situation. Tell whether the graph is continuous or discrete. *(Lesson 4-1)*

Time (days)	1	2	3	4	5	6	7	8	9	10
Pizzas Sold	5	11	2	4	8	10	3	6	12	1

4-3 Writing and Graphing Functions

California Standards

16.0 Students understand the concepts of a relation and a function, determine whether a given relation defines a function, and give pertinent information about given relations and functions.

17.0 Students determine the domain of independent variables and the range of dependent variables defined by a graph, a set of ordered pairs, **or a** symbolic expression.

Also covered: **18.0**

Vocabulary
dependent variable
independent variable
function notation

Why learn this?
You can use a function to calculate how much money you will earn for working specific amounts of time.

Suppose Tasha baby-sits and charges $5 per hour.

Time Worked (h) x	1	2	3	4
Amount Earned ($) y	5	10	15	20

The amount of money Tasha earns is $5 times the number of hours she works. You can write an equation using two variables to show this relationship.

Amount earned is $5 times the number of hours worked.

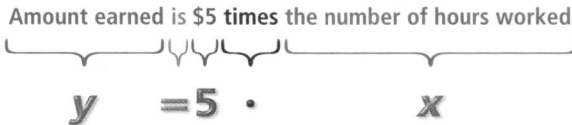

$$y = 5 \cdot x$$

EXAMPLE 1 **Using a Table to Write an Equation**

Determine a relationship between the x- and y-values. Write an equation.

x	1	2	3	4
y	−2	−1	0	1

Step 1 List possible relationships between the first x- and y-values.

$1 - 3 = -2$ or $1(-2) = -2$

Step 2 Determine whether one relationship works for the remaining values.

$2 - 3 = -1$ ✓ $2(-2) \neq -1$ ✗

$3 - 3 = 0$ ✓ $3(-2) \neq 0$ ✗

$4 - 3 = 1$ ✓ $4(-2) \neq 1$ ✗

The first relationship works. The value of y is 3 less than x.

Step 3 Write an equation.

$y = x - 3$ *The value of y is 3 less than x.*

 **1.** Determine a relationship between the x- and y-values in the relation $\{(1, 3), (2, 6), (3, 9), (4, 12)\}$. Write an equation.

When an equation has two variables, its solutions will be all ordered pairs (x, y) that make the equation true. Since the solutions are ordered pairs, it is possible to represent them on a graph. When you represent all solutions of an equation on a graph, you are *graphing the equation.*

Since the solutions of an equation that has two variables are a set of ordered pairs, they are a relation. One way to tell if this relation is a function is to graph the equation and use the *vertical-line test*.

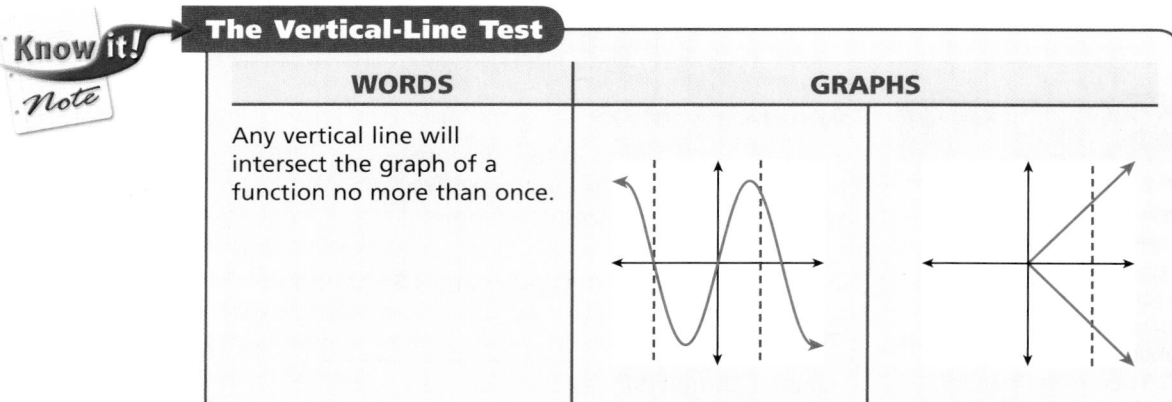

Know it!
Note

The Vertical-Line Test

WORDS	GRAPHS	
Any vertical line will intersect the graph of a function no more than once.		
	Function	Not a function

EXAMPLE **2** **Graphing Functions**

Graph each equation. Then tell whether the equation represents a function.

A $2x + 1 = y$

Step 1 Choose several values of x and generate ordered pairs.

Step 2 Plot enough points to see a pattern.

x	$2x + 1 = y$	(x, y)
-3	$2(-3) + 1 = -5$	$(-3, -5)$
-2	$2(-2) + 1 = -3$	$(-2, -3)$
-1	$2(-1) + 1 = -1$	$(-1, -1)$
0	$2(0) + 1 = 1$	$(0, 1)$
1	$2(1) + 1 = 3$	$(1, 3)$
2	$2(2) + 1 = 5$	$(2, 5)$
3	$2(3) + 1 = 7$	$(3, 7)$

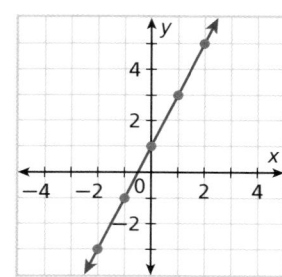

Helpful Hint

When choosing values of x, be sure to choose both positive and negative values.

Step 3 The points appear to form a line. **Draw a line** through all the points to show all the ordered pairs that satisfy the function. Draw arrowheads on both "ends" of the line.

Step 4 Use the vertical-line test on the graph.

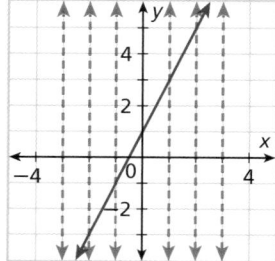

No vertical line will intersect the graph more than once. The equation $y = 2x + 1$ represents a function.

Graph each equation. Then tell whether the equation represents a function.

B $y = x^2$

Step 1 Choose several values of x and generate ordered pairs.

x	$y = x^2$	(x, y)
-3	$y = (-3)^2 = 9$	$(-3, 9)$
-2	$y = (-2)^2 = 4$	$(-2, 4)$
-1	$y = (-1)^2 = 1$	$(-1, 1)$
0	$y = (0)^2 = 0$	$(0, 0)$
1	$y = (1)^2 = 1$	$(1, 1)$
2	$y = (2)^2 = 4$	$(2, 4)$

Step 2 Plot enough points to see a pattern.

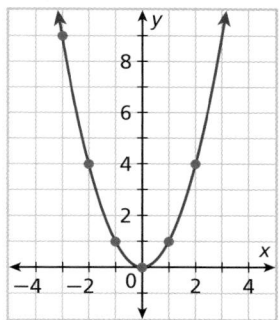

Step 3 The points appear to form an almost U-shaped graph. **Draw a smooth curve** through the points to show all the ordered pairs that satisfy the function. Draw arrowheads on the "ends" of the curve.

Step 4 Use the vertical-line test on the graph.

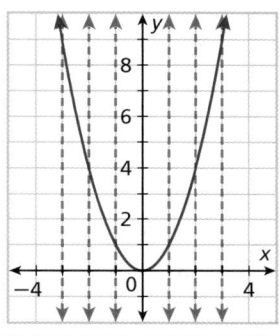

No vertical line will intersect the graph more than once. The equation $y = x^2$ represents a function.

 **Graph each equation. Then tell whether the equation represents a function.**

2a. $y = 3x - 2$ **2b.** $y = |x - 1|$

Looking at the graph of a function can help you determine its domain and range.

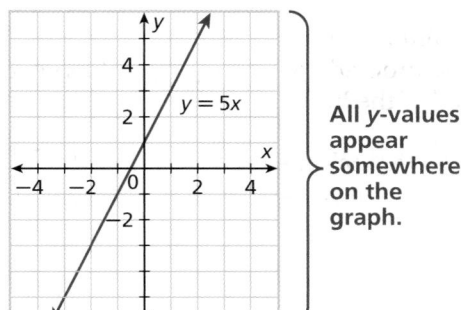

All y-values appear somewhere on the graph.

All x-values appear somewhere on the graph.

For $y = 5x$, the domain is all real numbers and **the range is all real numbers.**

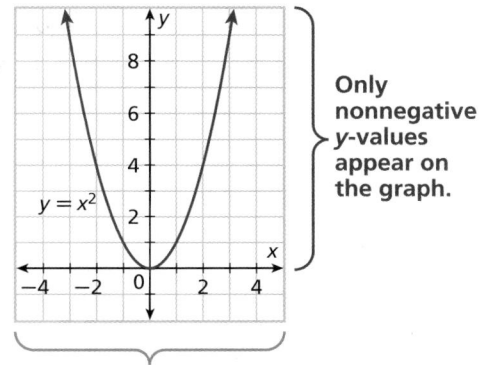

Only nonnegative y-values appear on the graph.

All x-values appear somewhere on the graph.

For $y = x^2$, the domain is all real numbers and **the range is $y \geq 0$.**

In a function, one variable (usually denoted by x) is the *independent variable* and the other variable (usually y) is the *dependent variable*. The value of the **dependent variable** *depends* on, or is a function of, the value of the **independent variable.** For Tasha, who earns $5 per hour, the amount she earns depends on, or is a function of, the amount of time she works.

When an equation represents a function, you can write the equation using *function notation*. If x is independent and y is dependent, the **function notation** for y is $f(x)$, read "f of x," where f names the function.

The dependent variable is a function of the independent variable .

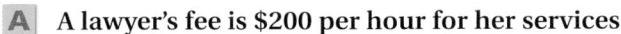

y		is a function of		x .
y	$=$	f		(x)

Tasha's earnings, $y = 5x$, can be rewritten in function notation by substituting $f(x)$ for y—$f(x) = 5x$. Note that function notation always defines the dependent variable in terms of the independent variable.

EXAMPLE **3** **Writing Functions**

Identify the independent and dependent variables. Write a rule in function notation for each situation.

A **A lawyer's fee is $200 per hour for her services.**

The **fee** for the lawyer depends on how many hours she works.
Dependent: **fee**   Independent: hours

Let h represent the number of hours the lawyer works.

The function for the lawyer's fee is $f(h) = 200h$.

B **Apples cost $0.99 per pound.**

The **cost** depends on the number of pounds purchased.
Dependent: **cost**   Independent: pounds

Let p represent the number of pounds of apples purchased.

The function for the cost of the apples is $f(p) = 0.99p$.

C **The admission fee to a local carnival is $8. Each ride costs $1.50.**

The **total cost** depends on the number of rides ridden, plus $8.
Dependent: **total cost**   Independent: number of rides

Let r represent the number of rides ridden.

The function for the total cost of the carnival is $f(r) = 1.50r + 8$.

 **Identify the independent and dependent variables. Write a rule in function notation for each situation.**

3a. A tutor's fee for music lessons is $28 per hour for private lessons.

3b. Steven buys lettuce that costs $1.69/lb.

3c. An amusement park charges a $6.00 parking fee plus $29.99 per person.

You can think of a function rule as an **input-output** machine. For Tasha's earnings, $f(x) = 5x$, if you input a value x, the output is $5x$.

If Tasha wanted to know how much money she would earn by working 6 hours, she could input 6 for x and find the output. This is called *evaluating the function*.

Input
× 6 2
Function
$f(x) = 5x$
30 5x
10
Output

EXAMPLE 4 **Evaluating Functions**

Evaluate each function for the given input values.

A For $f(x) = 5x$, find $f(x)$ when $x = 6$ and when $x = 7.5$.

$f(x) = 5x$ $f(x) = 5x$

$f(6) = 5(6)$ *Substitute 6 for x.* $f(7.5) = 5(7.5)$ *Substitute 7.5 for x.*

      $= 30$ *Simplify.* $= 37.5$ *Simplify.*

B For $g(t) = 2.30t + 10$, find $g(t)$ when $t = 2$ and when $t = -5$.

$g(t) = 2.30t + 10$ $g(t) = 2.30t + 10$

$g(2) = 2.30(2) + 10$ $g(-5) = 2.30(-5) + 10$

     $= 4.6 + 10$ $= -11.5 + 10$

     $= 14.6$ $= -1.5$

C For $h(x) = \frac{1}{2}x - 3$, find $h(x)$ when $x = 12$ and when $x = -8$.

$h(x) = \frac{1}{2}x - 3$ $h(x) = \frac{1}{2}x - 3$

$h(12) = \frac{1}{2}(12) - 3$ $h(-8) = \frac{1}{2}(-8) - 3$

      $= 6 - 3$ $= -4 - 3$

      $= 3$ $= -7$

 **CHECK IT OUT!**   **4.** Evaluate $h(c) = 2c - 1$ when $c = 1$ and when $c = -3$.

THINK AND DISCUSS

1. For the function $f(x) = 2x$, what is the domain? What is the range?

2. How do you identify independent and dependent variables?

3. When you input water into an ice machine, the output is ice cubes. Name another real-world object that has an input and an output.

4. GET ORGANIZED Copy and complete the graphic organizer using the equation $y = x + 3$.

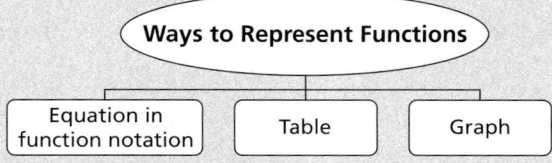

Ways to Represent Functions

| Equation in function notation | Table | Graph |

California Standards Practice
16.0, 17.0, 18.0

go.hrw.com
Homework Help Online
KEYWORD: MA8CA 4-3
Parent Resources Online
KEYWORD: MA8CA Parent

GUIDED PRACTICE

Vocabulary Apply the vocabulary from this lesson to answer each question.

1. The output of a function is the ___?___ variable.

2. To show that an equation is a function, you can write it using ___?___.

SEE EXAMPLE **1**
p. 213

Determine a relationship between the x- and y-values. Write an equation.

3.

x	1	2	3	4
y	−1	0	1	2

4. $\{(1, 4), (2, 7), (3, 10), (4, 13)\}$

SEE EXAMPLE **2**
p. 214

Graph each equation. Then tell whether the equation represents a function.

5. $y = 6x + 4$

6. $y = \frac{1}{2}x + 4$

7. $x + y = 0$

8. $y = |x| - 4$

9. $y = 2x^2 - 7$

10. $y = -x^2 + 5$

SEE EXAMPLE **3**
p. 216

Identify the independent and dependent variables. Write a rule in function notation for each situation.

11. An air-conditioning technician charges customers $75 per hour.

12. An ice rink charges $3.50 for skates and $1.25 per hour.

SEE EXAMPLE **4**
p. 217

Evaluate each function for the given input values.

13. For $f(x) = 7x + 2$, find $f(x)$ when $x = 0$ and when $x = 1$.

14. For $g(x) = 4x - 9$, find $g(x)$ when $x = 3$ and when $x = 5$.

15. For $h(t) = \frac{1}{3}t - 10$, find $h(t)$ when $t = 27$ and when $t = -15$.

PRACTICE AND PROBLEM SOLVING

Independent Practice

For Exercises	See Example
16–17	1
18–26	2
27–29	3
30–32	4

Extra Practice

Skills Practice p. EP8
Application Practice p. EP27

Determine a relationship between the x- and y-values. Write an equation.

16.

x	1	2	3	4
y	−2	−4	−6	−8

17. $\{(1, -1), (2, -2), (3, -3), (4, -4)\}$

Graph each equation. Then tell whether the equation represents a function.

18. $y = -3x + 5$

19. $y = 3x$

20. $x + y = 8$

21. $y = 2x + 2$

22. $y = -|x| + 10$

23. $y = -5 + x^2$

24. $y = |x + 1| + 1$

25. $y = (x - 2)^2 - 1$

26. $x^2 + 2 = y$

Identify the independent and dependent variables. Write a rule in function notation for each situation.

27. A movie rental store charges $3.99 to rent a DVD plus $0.99 for every day that it is late.

28. Stephen charges $25 for each lawn he mows.

29. A car can travel 28 miles per gallon of gas.

Evaluate each function for the given input values.

30. For $f(x) = x^2 - 5$, find $f(x)$ when $x = 0$ and when $x = 3$.

31. For $g(x) = x^2 + 6$, find $g(x)$ when $x = 1$ and when $x = 2$.

32. For $f(x) = \frac{2}{3}x + 3$, find $f(x)$ when $x = 9$ and when $x = -3$.

For each function, determine whether the given points are on the graph.

33. $y = 7x - 2$; (1, 5) and (2, 10)

34. $y = |x| + 2$; (3, 5) and (−1, 3)

35. $y = x^2$; (1, 1) and (−3, −9)

36. $y = \frac{1}{4}x - 2$; $\left(1, -\frac{3}{4}\right)$ and (4, −1)

Transportation

Air Force One refers to two specially configured Boeing 747-200B airplanes. The radio call sign when the president is aboard either aircraft or any Air Force aircraft is "Air Force One."

37. **Transportation** Air Force One can travel 630 miles per hour. Let h be the number of hours traveled. The equation $d = 630h$ gives the distance d in miles that Air Force One travels in h hours.

   a. Is the equation $d = 630h$ a function? If so, identify the independent and dependent variables and write $d = 630h$ in function notation. If not, explain why not.

   b. How far can Air Force One travel in 12 hours?

38. Complete the table for $h(x) = x^2 + x$.

x	0	1	2	3
h(x)				

39. Complete the table for $g(z) = 2z - 5$.

z	1	2	3	4
g(z)				

Give the domain and range of each function.

40. $-6 = 3x + 2y$

41. $y = 1.1x + 2$

42. $y = \frac{4}{5}x$

43. $y = 3x - 1$

44. $y = |x| + 6$

45. $y = x^2 - 5$

46. Find the value of x so that $(x, 12)$ satisfies $y = 4x + 8$.

47. Find the value of x so that $(x, 6)$ satisfies $y = -x - 4$.

48. Find the value of y so that $(-2, y)$ satisfies $y = -2x^2$.

49. **/// ERROR ANALYSIS ///** Rashid saves $150 each month. He wants to know how much he will have saved in 2 years. He writes the equation $s = m + 150$ to help him figure out how much he will save, where s is the amount saved and m is the number of months he saves. Explain why his equation is incorrect.

50. **Write About It** Give a real-life situation that can be described by a function. Explain which is the independent variable and which is the dependent variable.

CONCEPT CONNECTION

51. This problem will prepare you for the Concept Connection on page 222.

The table shows the volume v of water pumped into a pool after t hours.

   a. Determine a relationship between the time and the volume of water and write an equation.

   b. Identify the independent and dependent variables.

   c. If the pool holds 10,000 gallons, how long will it take to fill?

Amount of Water in Pool	
Time (h)	Volume (gal)
0	0
1	1250
2	2500
3	3750
4	5000

Multiple Choice For Exercises 52 and 53, choose the best answer.

52. Marsha buys x pens at \$0.70 per pen and one pencil for \$0.10. Which equation gives the total amount c that Marsha spends?

(A) $c = 0.70x + 0.10x$

(B) $c = 0.70x + 1$

(C) $c = (0.70 + 0.10)x$

(D) $c = 0.70x + 0.10$

53. Belle is buying pizzas for her daughter's birthday party, using the prices in the table. Which equation best describes the relationship between the total cost c and the number of pizzas p?

Pizzas	Total Cost ($)
5	26.25
10	52.50
15	78.75

(A) $c = 26.25p$

(B) $c = 5.25p$

(C) $c = p + 26.25$

(D) $c = 6p - 3.75$

54. Gridded Response What is the value of $f(x) = 5 - \frac{1}{2}x$ when $x = 3$?

CHALLENGE AND EXTEND

55. Reasoning Complete the following argument, which explains why the vertical-line test can be used to identify functions.

The x-values of all of the points on a vertical line are _____?_____ . For a relation to be a function, there cannot be a(n) _____?_____ that is paired with more than one y-value. If there are two or more points on a vertical line that are also on the graph of a relation, then these points have the same _____?_____ but different _____?_____. In other words, there is a(n) _____?_____ paired with _____?_____ y-value. So, the graph cannot represent a function.

56. Does the equation $x = |y|$ represent a function? Explain.

57. Write an equation that does NOT represent a function.

Show that each equation does not represent a function. (*Hint:* Try to find a domain value that is paired with more than one range value.)

58. $x^2 + y^2 = 4$

59. $y^2 = x^2 + 36$

60. $x = |y| + 1$

 SPIRAL STANDARDS REVIEW   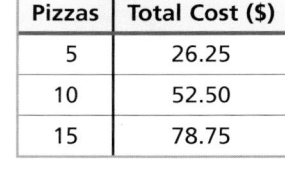 4.0,  5.0, 16.0, 17.0, 18.0

Solve each equation. Check your answer. (*Lesson 2-3*)

61. $5x + 2 - 7x = -10$

62. $3(2 - y) = 15$

63. $\frac{2}{3}p - \frac{1}{2} = \frac{1}{6}$

Solve each inequality. (*Lesson 3-5*)

64. $21 + 7x \leq 7(3 + x)$

65. $9(w + 2) < 9w + 17$

66. $13(r + 1) < 13r - 6$

67. $2a - 16 \geq 2a - 17$

68. $3t - 12 > 3t + 2$

69. $2 - 3g + 7 \geq 3(2 - g)$

Give the domain and range of each relation. Tell whether the relation is a function and explain. (*Lesson 4-2*)

70.

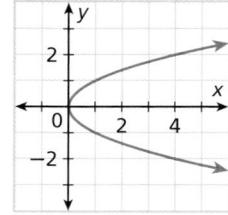

71.

x	y
−3	4
−1	2
0	0
1	2
3	−4

4-3 Technology LAB

Connect Equations, Tables, and Graphs

You can use a graphing calculator to understand the connections among equations, tables, and graphs.

Use with Lesson 4-3

Activity

Make a table of values for the equation $y = 4x + 3$.
Then graph.

1. Press **Y=** and enter **4x + 3**.

2. Press **2nd** **WINDOW** (TBLSET). Make sure **Indpnt: Auto** and **Depend: Auto** are selected.

3. To view the table, press **2nd** **GRAPH** (TABLE). The x-values and the corresponding y-values appear in table form. Use the up and down arrow keys to scroll through the table.

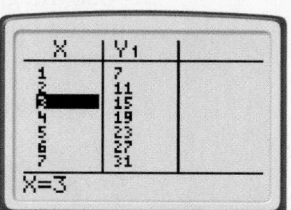

4. To view the table with the graph, press **MODE** and select **G-T** (Graph-Table) view. Press **ENTER**. Be sure to use the standard window.

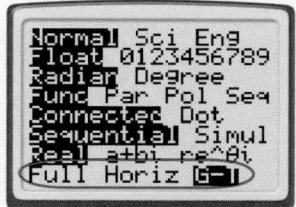

5. Press **TRACE** to see both the graph and a table of values.

6. Press the left arrow key several times to move the cursor. Notice how the point on the graph and the values in the table correspond.

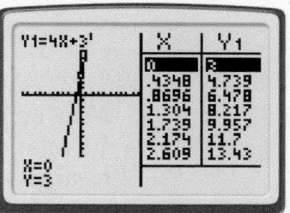

Try This

Make a table of values for each equation. Then graph.

1. $f(x) = 2x - 1$ 2. $f(x) = 1.5x$ 3. $f(x) = \frac{1}{2}x + 2$

4. Explain the relationship between an equation and its table of values and the graph of the equation.

CONCEPT CONNECTION

Function Concepts

Down the Drain The graph shows the relationship between the number of hours that have passed since a pool began to drain and the amount of water in the pool.

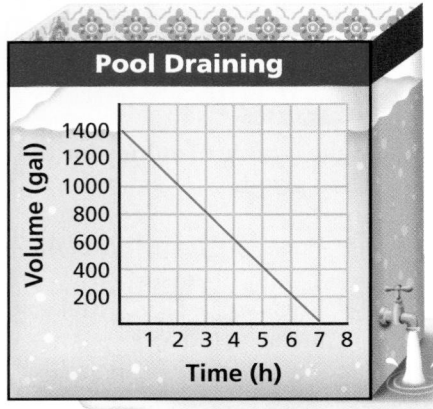

Pool Draining

1. Describe in words the relationship between the amount of water in the pool and the number of hours that have passed since the pool began to drain.

2. What are the domain and range for the graph?

3. Use the graph to determine how much water is in the pool after 3 hours. How much water is in the pool after $4\frac{1}{2}$ hours?

4. Copy and complete the table.

Draining Pool	
Time (h)	Volume (gal)
0	1400
1	
2	
3	
4	
5	
6	
7	

5. Write an equation to describe the relationship between the volume V and the number of hours h. Use the equation to find how much water is in the pool after 5.2 hours.

READY TO GO ON?

Quiz for Lessons 4-1 Through 4-3

4-1 Graphing Relationships

Choose the graph that best represents each situation.

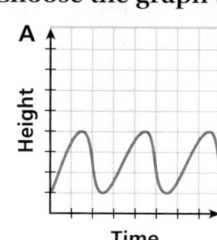 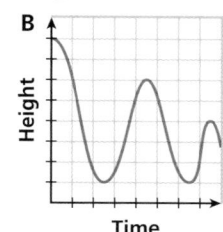

1. A person bungee jumps from a high platform.

2. A person jumps on a trampoline in a steady motion.

3. Xander takes a quiz worth 100 points. Each question is worth 20 points. Sketch a graph to show his possible score if he misses 1, 2, 3, 4, or 5 questions.

4-2 Relations and Functions

Give the domain and range of each relation. Tell whether the relation is a function. Explain.

4.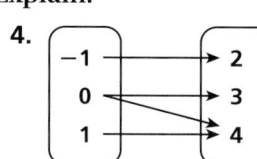

5.

x	−1	−2	0	2	3
y	3	3	3	3	3

6.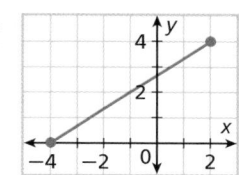

4-3 Writing and Graphing Functions

Determine a relationship between the x- and y-values. Write an equation.

7.

x	y
1	−6
2	−5
3	−4
4	−3

8.

x	y
1	−3
2	−6
3	−9
4	−12

9. A printer can print 8 pages per minute. Identify the dependent and independent variables for the situation. Write a rule in function notation.

Evaluate each function for the given input values.

10. For $f(x) = 3x - 1$, find $f(x)$ when $x = 2$.

11. For $g(x) = x^2 - x$, find $g(x)$ when $x = -2$.

Graph each equation. Then tell whether the equation represents a function.

12. $x + y = 6$ 13. $y = |x| - 3$ 14. $y = x^2 + 1$

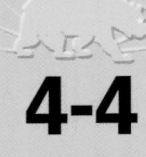

4-4 Scatter Plots and Trend Lines

California Standards

Review of Grade 7
SDAP 1.2 Represent two numerical variables on a scatter plot and informally describe how the data points are distributed and any apparent relationship that exists between the two variables (e.g., between time spent on homework and grade level).

Who uses this?
Ecologists can use scatter plots to help them analyze data about endangered species, such as ocelots. (See Example 1.)

In this chapter, you have examined relationships between sets of ordered pairs, or data. Displaying data visually can help you see relationships.

A **scatter plot** is a graph with points plotted to show a possible relationship between two sets of data. A scatter plot is an effective way to display some types of data.

Vocabulary
scatter plot
correlation
positive correlation
negative correlation
no correlation
trend line

EXAMPLE 1 | **Graphing a Scatter Plot from Given Data**

The table shows the number of species added to the list of endangered and threatened species in the United States during the given years. Graph a scatter plot using the given data.

Increase in List							
Calendar Year	1996	1997	1998	1999	2000	2001	2002
Species Added	91	79	62	11	39	10	9

Source: U.S. Fish and Wildlife Service

Helpful Hint

The point (2000, 39) tells you that in the year 2000, the list increased by 39 species.

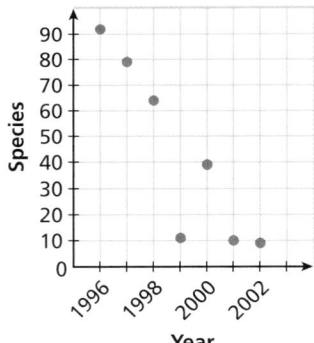

Species Added to List

Use the table to make ordered pairs for the scatter plot.

The x-value represents the calendar year and the y-value represents the number of species added.

Plot the ordered pairs.

 **1.** The table shows the number of points scored by a high school football team in the first four games of a season. Graph a scatter plot using the given data.

Game	1	2	3	4
Points Scored	6	21	46	34

A **correlation** describes a relationship between two data sets. A graph may show the correlation between data. The correlation can help you analyze trends and make predictions. There are three types of correlations between data.

Correlations

Positive Correlation	Negative Correlation	No Correlation
Both sets of data values increase.	One set of data values increases as the other set decreases.	There is no relationship between the data sets.
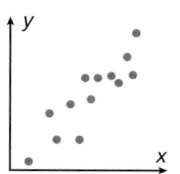	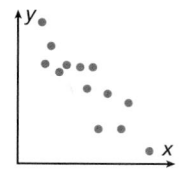	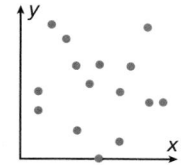

In the endangered species graph, as time increases, the number of new species added decreases. So the correlation between the data is negative.

EXAMPLE **2** **Describing Correlations from Scatter Plots**

Describe the correlation illustrated by the scatter plot.

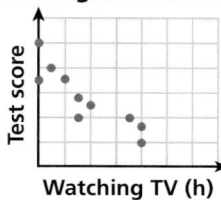

As the number of hours spent watching TV increased, test scores decreased.

There is a negative correlation between the two data sets.

 **2.** Describe the correlation illustrated by the scatter plot.

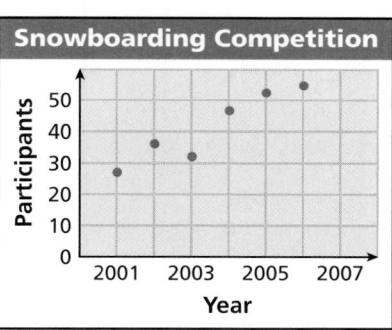

EXAMPLE **3** **Identifying Correlations**

Identify the correlation you would expect between each pair of data sets. Explain.

A the number of empty seats in a classroom and the number of students seated in the class

You would expect a negative correlation. As the number of students increases, the number of empty seats decreases.

B the number of pets a person owns and the number of books that person read last year

You would expect no correlation. The number of pets a person owns has nothing to do with how many books the person has read.

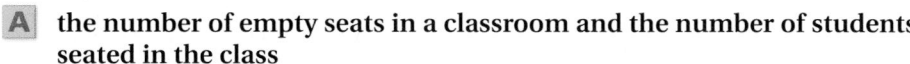

Identify the correlation you would expect between each pair of data sets. Explain.

 **the monthly rainfall and the depth of water in a reservoir**

You would expect a positive correlation. As more rain falls, there is more water in the reservoir.

CHECK IT OUT! Identify the correlation you would expect between each pair of data sets. Explain.

3a. the temperature in Houston and the number of cars sold in Boston

3b. the number of members in a family and the size of the family's grocery bill

3c. the number of times you sharpen your pencil and the length of your pencil

EXAMPLE 4 Matching Scatter Plots to Situations

Choose the scatter plot that best represents the relationship between the number of days since a sunflower seed was planted and the height of the plant. Explain.

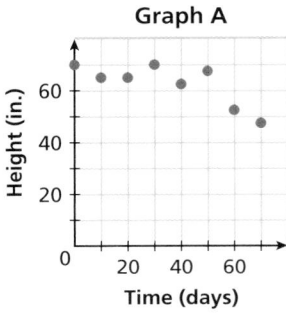

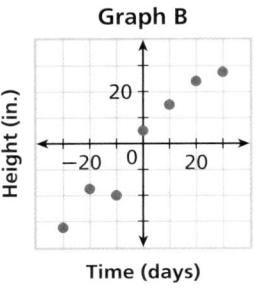

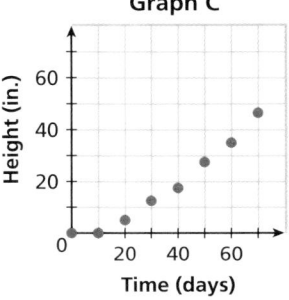

There will be a positive correlation between the number of days and the height because the plant will grow each day.

Neither the number of days nor the plant heights can be negative.

This graph shows all positive coordinates and a positive correlation, so it could represent the data sets.

Graph A has a negative correlation, so it is incorrect.

Graph B shows negative values, so it is incorrect.

Graph C is the correct scatter plot.

CHECK IT OUT! **4.** Choose the scatter plot that best represents the relationship between the number of minutes since an oven was turned off and the temperature of the oven. Explain.

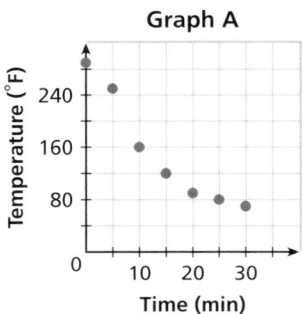

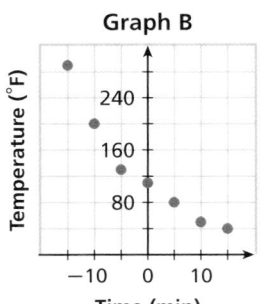

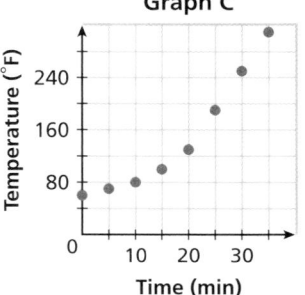

It is often helpful to add a line to better describe a scatter plot. This line, called a **trend line**, helps show the correlation between data sets more clearly. It can also be helpful when making predictions based on the data.

EXAMPLE 5 *Fund-raising Application*

The scatter plot shows a relationship between the total amount of money collected and the total number of rolls of wrapping paper sold as a school fund-raiser. Based on this relationship, predict how much money will be collected when 175 rolls have been sold.

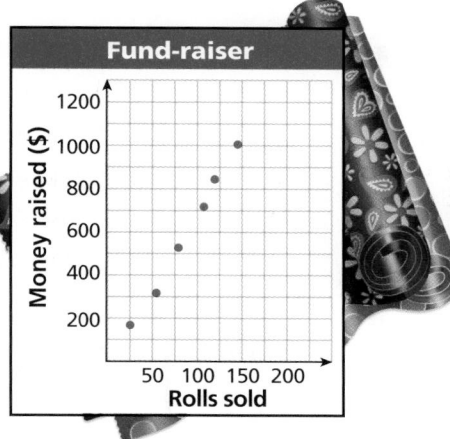
Fund-raiser

Draw a trend line and use it to make a prediction.

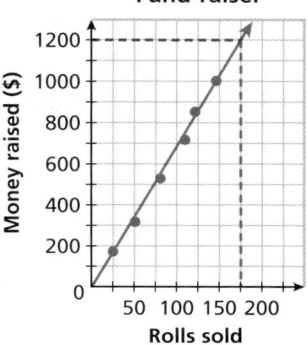
Fund-raiser

Draw a line that has about the same number of points above and below it. Your line may or may not go through data points.

Find the point on the line whose x-value is 175. The corresponding y-value is 1200.

Based on the data, $1200 is a reasonable prediction of how much money will be collected when 175 rolls have been sold.

5. Based on the trend line above, predict how many wrapping paper rolls need to be sold to raise $500.

THINK AND DISCUSS

1. Is it possible to make a prediction based on a scatter plot with no correlation? Explain your answer.

2. GET ORGANIZED Copy and complete the graphic organizer with either a scatter plot, or a real-world example, or both.

	Graph	Example
Positive Correlation		
Negative Correlation		The amount of water in a watering can and the number of flowers watered
No Correlation		

California Standards Practice
Review of Grade 7 **SDAP1.2**

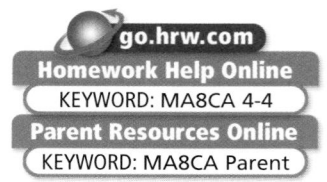

go.hrw.com
Homework Help Online
KEYWORD: MA8CA 4-4
Parent Resources Online
KEYWORD: MA8CA Parent

GUIDED PRACTICE

Vocabulary Apply the vocabulary from this lesson to answer each question.

1. Give an example of a graph that is not a *scatter plot*.

2. How is a scatter plot that shows *no correlation* different from a scatter plot that shows a *negative correlation*?

3. Does a *trend line* always pass through every point on a scatter plot? Explain.

SEE EXAMPLE 1
p. 224

Graph a scatter plot using the given data.

4.

Garden Statue	Cupid	Gnome	Lion	Flamingo	Wishing well
Height (in.)	32	18	35	28	40
Price ($)	50	25	80	15	75

SEE EXAMPLE 2
p. 225

Describe the correlation illustrated by each scatter plot.

5.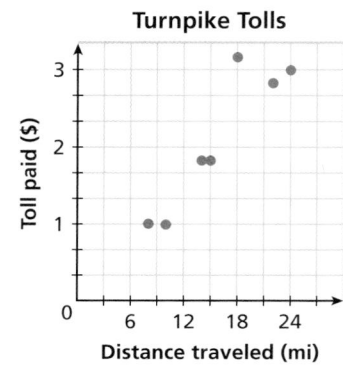

6.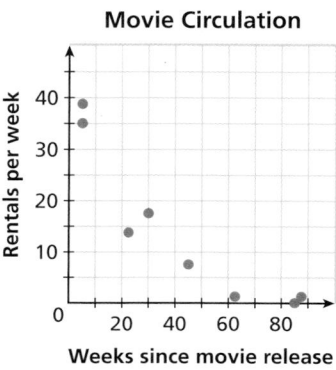

SEE EXAMPLE 3
p. 225

Identify the correlation you would expect between each pair of data sets. Explain.

7. the volume of water poured into a container and the amount of empty space left in the container

8. a person's shoe size and the length of the person's hair

9. the outside temperature and the number of people at the beach

SEE EXAMPLE 4
p. 226

Choose the scatter plot that best represents the described relationship. Explain.

10. age of car and number of miles traveled

11. age of car and resale value of the car

12. age of car and number of states traveled to

Graph A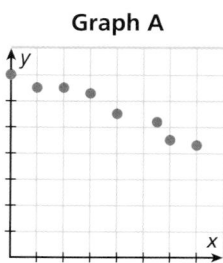

Graph B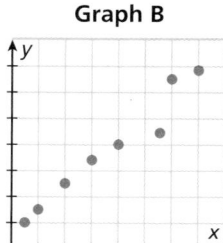

Graph C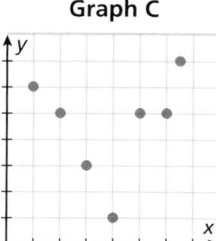

13. **Transportation** The scatter plot shows the total number of miles passengers flew on U.S. domestic flights in the month of April for the years 1997–2004. Based on this relationship, predict how many miles passengers will fly in April 2008.

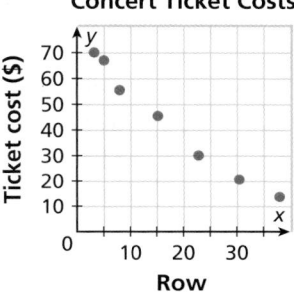

PRACTICE AND PROBLEM SOLVING

Independent Practice

For Exercises	See Example
14	1
15–16	2
17–18	3
19–20	4
21	5

Extra Practice

Skills Practice p. EP9

Application Practice p. EP27

Graph a scatter plot using the given data.

14.

Train Arrival Time	6:45 A.M.	7:30 A.M.	8:15 A.M.	9:45 A.M.	10:30 A.M.
Passengers	160	148	194	152	64

Describe the correlation illustrated by each scatter plot.

15.

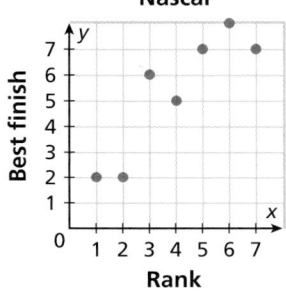

16.

Concert Ticket Costs

Identify the correlation you would expect between each pair of data sets. Explain.

17. the speed of a runner and the distance she can cover in 10 minutes

18. the year a car was made and the total mileage

Choose the scatter plot that best represents the described relationship. Explain.

19. the number of college classes taken and the number of roommates

20. the number of college classes taken and the hours of free time.

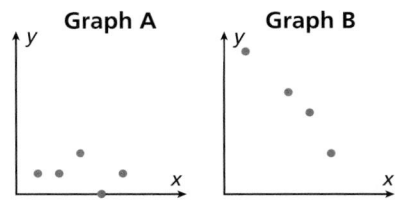

21. **Ecology** The scatter plot shows a projection of the average ocelot population living in Laguna Atascosa National Wildlife Refuge near Brownsville, Texas. Based on this relationship, predict the number of ocelots living at the wildlife refuge in 2014 if nothing is done to help manage the ocelot population.

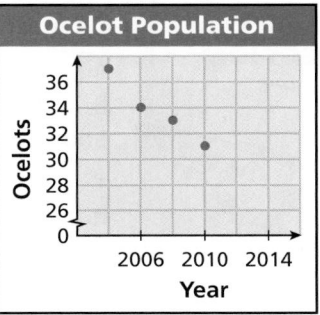

22. **Estimation** Angie enjoys putting jigsaw puzzles together. The scatter plot shows the number of puzzle pieces and the time in minutes it took her to complete each of her last six puzzles. Use the trend line to estimate the time in minutes it will take Angie to complete a 1200-piece puzzle.

Puzzle Completion

23. **Critical Thinking** Describe the correlation between the number of left shoes sold and the number of right shoes sold.

24. Roma had guests for dinner at her house eight times and has recorded the number of guests and the total cost for each meal in the table.

Guests	3	4	4	6	6	7	8	8
Cost ($)	30	65	88	90	115	160	150	162

a. Graph a scatter plot of the data.

b. Describe the correlation.

c. Draw a trend line.

d. Based on the trend line you drew, predict the cost of dinner for 11 guests.

e. **What if...?** Suppose that each cost in the table increased by $5. How will this affect the cost of dinner for 11 guests?

25. **///ERROR ANALYSIS///** Students graphed a scatter plot for the temperature of hot bath water over time if no new water is added. Which graph is incorrect? Explain the error.

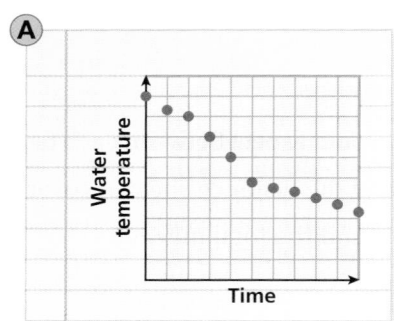

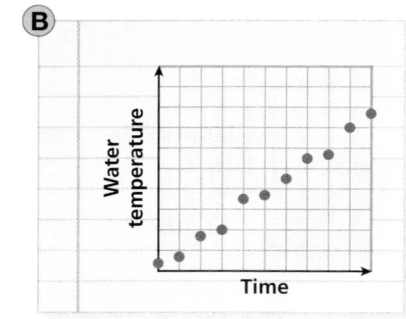

26. **Critical Thinking** Do you think more people or fewer people will buy an item if the price goes up? Describe the correlation you would expect.

27. This problem will prepare you for the Concept Connection on page 240.

CONCEPT CONNECTION

Juan and his parents are visiting a university 205 miles from their home. As they travel, Juan uses the car odometer and his watch to keep track of the distance.

a. Make a scatter plot for this data set.

b. Describe the correlation. Explain.

c. Draw a trend line for the data and predict the distance Juan would have traveled going to a university 4 hours away.

Time (min)	Distance (mi)
0	0
30	28
60	58
90	87
120	117
150	148
180	178
210	205

28. Write About It Predict whether there will be a positive, negative, or no correlation between the number of siblings a person has and the number of pets that person has. Then conduct a survey of your classmates to find the number of siblings they have and the number of pets they have. Graph the data in a scatter plot. What is the relationship between the two data sets? Was your prediction correct?

Multiple Choice For Exercises 29 and 30, choose the best answer.

29. Which graph is the best example of a negative correlation?

(A) 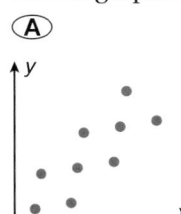   (B) 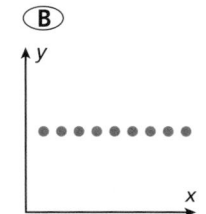   (C) 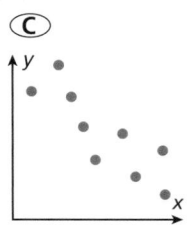   (D)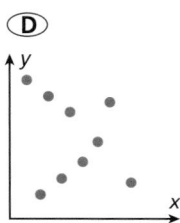

30. Which situation best describes a positive correlation?

(A) The amount of rainfall on Fridays

(B) The height of a candle and the amount of time it stays lit

(C) The price of a pizza and the number of toppings added

(D) The temperature of a cup of hot chocolate and the length of time it sits

31. Short Response Write a real-world situation for the graph. Explain your answer.

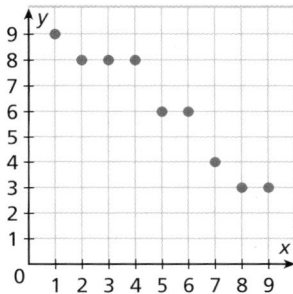

CHALLENGE AND EXTEND

32. Describe a situation that involves a positive correlation. Gather data on the situation. Make a scatter plot showing the correlation. Use the scatter plot to make a prediction. Repeat for a negative correlation and for no correlation.

33. Research an endangered or threatened species in your state. Gather information on its population for several years. Make a scatter plot using the data you gather. Is there a positive or negative correlation? Explain. Draw a trend line and make a prediction about the species population over the next 5 years.

 SPIRAL STANDARDS REVIEW  4.0, 5.0, 18.0

Write an equation to represent each relationship. Then solve the equation. *(Lesson 2-4)*

34. Five times a number increased by 2 is equal to twice the number decreased by 4.

35. Five times the sum of a number and 2 is equal to 8 less than twice the number.

Solve each inequality. *(Lesson 3-5)*

36. $4(6 + x) \geq -2x$ **37.** $3(x - 1) > 3x$ **38.** $2(3 - x) < 2(1 + x)$

Graph each equation. Then tell whether the equation represents a function. *(Lesson 4-3)*

39. $y = 2x - 3$ **40.** $y = -|x| + 3$ **41.** $y = x^2 - 4$

Median-Fit Line

You have learned about trend lines. Now you will learn about another line of fit called the median-fit line.

California Standards

Reinforcement of 6SDAP1.1
Compute the range, mean, **median,** and mode **of data sets.**
Also covered: **Reinforcement of 7SDAP1.2**

Example

At a water raft rental shop, a group of up to four people can rent a single raft. The table shows the number of rafts rented to different groups of people one morning. Find the median-fit line for the data.

People x	1	2	4	5	5	5	7	9	10	11	12	15
Rafts Rented y	1	1	1	3	4	5	4	7	5	3	4	6

1 Plot the points on a coordinate plane.

2 Divide the data into three sections of equal size. Find the medians of the x-values and the y-values for each section. Plot the three median points with an X.

1	2	4	5	5	5	7	9	10	11	12	15
1	1	1	3	4	5	4	7	5	3	4	6

Median point: (3, 1)   Median point: (6, 4.5)   Median point: (11.5, 4.5)

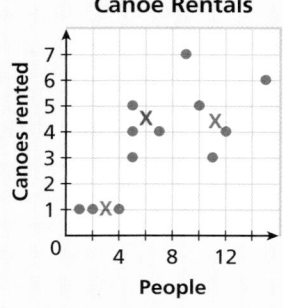
Canoe Rentals

3 Connect the outside, or first and third, median points with a line.

4 Lightly draw a dashed line straight down from the middle median point to the line just drawn. Mark the dashed line to create three equal segments.

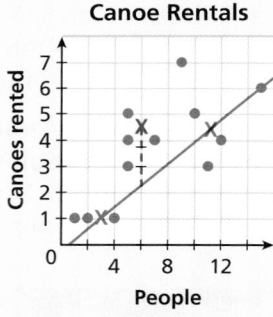
Canoe Rentals

5 Keeping your ruler parallel to the first line you drew, move your ruler to the mark closest to the line. Draw the line. This is the median-fit line.

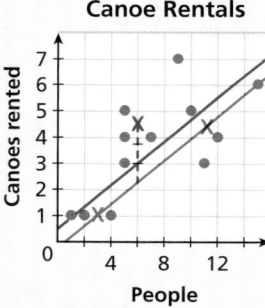
Canoe Rentals

Try This

1. A manager at a restaurant kept track one afternoon of the number of people in a party and the time it took to seat them. Graph the data and find the median-fit line.

People x	3	7	8	8	10	12
Wait Time y (min)	1	5	3	9	6	6

2. Use your median-fit line to predict the time it took to seat a party of 6.

Inductive Reasoning

Inductive reasoning is the process of reasoning that a rule or statement is true because specific cases are true. A common example of inductive reasoning is drawing a conclusion based on a pattern.

A statement you believe to be true based on inductive reasoning is a **conjecture**.

24.1 Students explain the difference between inductive and deductive reasoning and identify and **provide examples** of each.

The diagrams below represent the side views of tables. Each has a tabletop and a base. Copy and complete the chart using the pattern shown in the diagrams.

Tabletop →
Base →

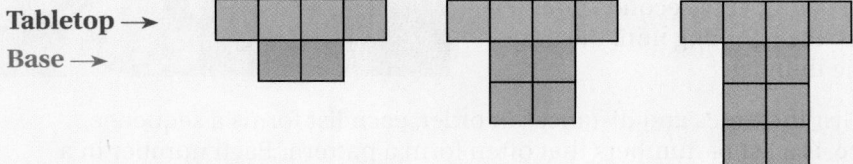

TABLE NUMBER	FIGURE	DESCRIPTION OF FIGURE	NUMBER OF BLOCKS
1		width of table top = **4** height of base = **1**	6
2		width of table top = **4** height of base = **2**	8
3		width of table top = **4** height of base = **3**	10
4	▪	▪	▪
5	▪	▪	▪

Try This

1. Explain any patterns you see in the table.
2. **Make a Conjecture** How many blocks do you think there will be in the 25th table?
3. **Make a Conjecture** Write an expression that you think you can use to find the number of blocks in the *n*th table. Explain why you think your expression is correct.

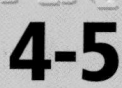

4-5 Arithmetic Sequences

California Standards

Preparation for Algebra II
22.0 Students find the general term and the sums of arithmetic **series** and of both finite and infinite geometric series.

Vocabulary
sequence
term
arithmetic sequence
common difference

Why learn this?

The distance between you and a lightning strike can be approximated by using an arithmetic sequence.

During a thunderstorm, you can estimate your distance from a lightning strike by counting the number of seconds from the time you see the lightning until the time you hear the thunder.

When you list the times and distances in order, each list forms a sequence. A **sequence** is a list of numbers that often form a pattern. Each number in a sequence is a **term**.

Time (s)	1	2	3	4	5	6	7	8
Distance (mi)	0.2	0.4	0.6	0.8	1.0	1.2	1.4	1.6

+ 0.2   + 0.2   + 0.2   + 0.2   + 0.2   + 0.2   + 0.2

Notice that in the distance sequence, you can find the next term by adding 0.2 to the previous term. When the terms of a sequence differ by the same nonzero number d, the sequence is an **arithmetic sequence** and d is the **common difference**. So the distances in the table form an arithmetic sequence with common difference 0.2.

EXAMPLE **Identifying Arithmetic Sequences**

Determine whether each sequence appears to be an arithmetic sequence. If so, find the common difference and the next three terms in the sequence.

A 12, 8, 4, 0, …

Step 1 Find the difference between successive terms.

12,   8,   4,   0, …
      − 4 − 4 − 4

You add −4 to each term to find the next term. The common difference is −4.

Step 2 Use the common difference to find the next 3 terms.

12, 8, 4, 0,   −4,   −8,   −12
            − 4   − 4   − 4

The sequence appears to be an arithmetic sequence with a common difference of −4. If so, the next 3 terms would be −4, −8, −12.

B 1, 4, 9, 16, …

Find the difference between successive terms.

1,   4,   9,   16, …
  + 3 + 5 + 7

The difference between successive terms is not the same.

This sequence is not an arithmetic sequence.

Reading Math

The three dots at the end of a sequence are called an ellipsis. They mean that the sequence continues and can be read as "and so on."

 **Determine whether each sequence appears to be an arithmetic sequence. If so, find the common difference and the next three terms.**

1a. $-\dfrac{3}{4}, -\dfrac{1}{4}, \dfrac{1}{4}, \dfrac{3}{4}, \ldots$ **1b.** $\dfrac{2}{3}, \dfrac{1}{3}, -\dfrac{1}{3}, -\dfrac{2}{3}, \ldots$ **1c.** $4, 1, -2, -5, \ldots$

The variable a is often used to represent terms in a sequence. The variable a_9, read "a sub 9," is the ninth term in a sequence. To designate any term, or the nth term, in a sequence, you write a_n, where n can be any number.

1	2	3	4...		n	← Position
↓	↓	↓	↓			
3,	**5,**	**7,**	**9...**			← Term
a_1	a_2	a_3	a_4	a_n		

The sequence above starts with the first term, 3. The common difference d is 2. You can use the first term, 3, and the common difference, 2, to write a rule for finding a_n.

Words	Numbers	Algebra
1st term	3	a_1
2nd term = 1st term plus common difference	$3 + (1)2 = 5$	$a_1 + 1d$
3nd term = 1st term plus 2 common differences	$3 + (2)2 = 7$	$a_1 + 2d$
4th term = 1st term plus 3 common differences	$3 + (3)2 = 9$	$a_1 + 3d$
$\vdots$	$\vdots$	$\vdots$
nth term = 1st term plus $(n-1)$ common differences	$3 + (n-1)2$	$a_1 + (n-1)d$

The pattern in the table shows that to find the nth term, add the **first term** to the product of $(n-1)$ and the **common difference**.

 **Finding the nth Term of an Arithmetic Sequence**

The nth term of an arithmetic sequence with **common difference d** and **first term a_1** is

$$a_n = a_1 + (n-1)d.$$

EXAMPLE 2   **Finding the nth Term of an Arithmetic Sequence**

Find the indicated term of each arithmetic sequence.

A 22nd term: $5, 2, -1, -4, \ldots$

   Step 1 Find the common difference.

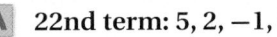
   $5,\quad 2,\quad -1,\quad -4, \ldots$ *The common difference is −3.*

   $-3\quad -3\quad -3$

   Step 2 Write a rule to find the 22nd term.

   $a_n = a_1 + (n-1)d$ *Write the rule to find the nth term.*
   $a_{22} = 5 + (22-1)(-3)$ *Substitute 5 for a_1, 22 for n, and −3 for d.*
   $\quad\ \ = 5 + (21)(-3)$ *Simplify the expression in parentheses.*
   $\quad\ \ = 5 - 63$ *Multiply.*
   $\quad\ \ = -58$ *Add.*

   The 22nd term is -58.

Find the indicated term of each arithmetic sequence.

B 15th term: $a_1 = 7; d = 3$

$a_n = a_1 + (n - 1)d$ *Write the rule to find the nth term.*

$a_{15} = 7 + (15 - 1)3$ *Substitute 7 for a_1, 15 for n, and 3 for d.*

$\phantom{a_{15}} = 7 + (14)3$ *Simplify the expression in parentheses.*

$\phantom{a_{15}} = 7 + 42$ *Multiply.*

$\phantom{a_{15}} = 49$ *Add.*

The 15th term is 49.

 **CHECK IT OUT!** Find the indicated term of each arithmetic sequence.
2a. 60th term: 11, 5, −1, −7, …   **2b.** 12th term: $a_1 = 4.2; d = 1.4$

EXAMPLE 3   *Travel Application*

The odometer on a car reads 60,473 on day 1. Every day, the car is driven 54 miles. If this pattern continues, what will be the odometer reading on day 20?

Step 1 Determine whether the situation appears to be arithmetic.

The sequence for the situation is arithmetic because the odometer reading will increase by 54 miles per day.

Step 2 Find d, a_1, and n.

Since the odometer reading will increase by 54 miles per day, $d = 54$.
Since the odometer reading on day 1 is 60,473 miles, $a_1 = 60{,}473$.
Since you want to find the odometer reading on day 20, you will need to find the 20th term of the sequence, so $n = 20$.

Step 3 Find the odometer reading for a_n.

$a_n = a_1 + (n - 1)d$ *Write the rule to find the nth term.*

$a_{21} = 60{,}473 + (20 - 1)54$ *Substitute 60,473 for a_1, 54 for d, and 20 for n.*

$\phantom{a_{21}} = 60{,}473 + (19)54$ *Simplify the expression in parentheses.*

$\phantom{a_{21}} = 60{,}473 + 1026$ *Multiply.*

$\phantom{a_{21}} = 61{,}499$ *Add.*

The odometer will read 61,499 miles on day 20.

 **CHECK IT OUT!** **3.** Each time a truck stops, it drops off 250 pounds of cargo. At stop 1, it started with a load of 2000 pounds. How much does the load weigh on stop 6?

THINK AND DISCUSS

1. Explain how to determine if a sequence appears to be arithmetic.

2. GET ORGANIZED Copy and complete the graphic organizer with steps for finding the *n*th term of an arithmetic sequence.

Finding the *n*th Term of an Arithmetic Sequence $\rightarrow$ 1. $\rightarrow$ 2.

4-5

Exercises

California
Standards Practice
Preparation for Algebra II 22.0

go.hrw.com
Homework Help Online
KEYWORD: MA8CA 4-5
Parent Resources Online
KEYWORD: MA8CA Parent

GUIDED PRACTICE

1. **Vocabulary** When trying to find the nth term of an arithmetic sequence you must first know the _____?_____. (*common difference* or *sequence*)

SEE EXAMPLE 1
p. 234

Multi-Step Determine whether each sequence appears to be an arithmetic sequence. If so, find the common difference and the next three terms.

2. 2, 8, 14, 20, …

3. 2.1, 1.4, 0.7, 0, …

4. 1, 1, 2, 3, …

5. 0.1, 0.3, 0.9, 2.7, …

SEE EXAMPLE 2
p. 235

Find the indicated term of each arithmetic sequence.

6. 21st term: 3, 8, 13, 18, …

7. 18th term: $a_1 = -2$; $d = -3$

SEE EXAMPLE 3
p. 236

8. **Shipping** To package and ship an item, it costs $5 for shipping supplies and $0.75 for each pound the package weighs. What is the cost of shipping a 12-pound package?

PRACTICE AND PROBLEM SOLVING

Independent Practice	
For Exercises	See Example
9–12	1
13–14	2
15	3

Extra Practice
Skills Practice p. EP9
Application Practice p. EP27

Multi-Step Determine whether each sequence appears to be an arithmetic sequence. If so, find the common difference and the next three terms.

9. −1, 10, −100, 1,100, …

10. 0, −2, −4, −6, …

11. −22, −31, −40, −49, …

12. 0.2, 0.5, 0.9, 1.1, …

Find the indicated term of each arithmetic sequence.

13. 31st term: 1.40, 1.55, 1.70, …

14. 50th term: $a_1 = 2.2$; $d = 1.1$

15. **Travel** Rachel signed up for a frequent-flier program and received 3000 bonus miles. She earns 1300 frequent-flier miles each time she purchases a round-trip ticket. How many frequent-flier miles will she have after 5 round-trips?

Find the common difference for each arithmetic sequence.

16. 0, 6, 12, 18, …

17. $\frac{1}{2}, \frac{3}{4}, 1, \frac{5}{4}, \ldots$

18. 107, 105, 103, 101, …

19. 7.9, 5.7, 3.5, 1.3, …

20. $\frac{1}{5}, \frac{2}{5}, \frac{3}{5}, \frac{4}{5}, \ldots$

21. 4.25, 4.32, 4.39, 4.46, …

Find the next four terms in each arithmetic sequence.

22. −4, −7, −10, −13, …

23. $\frac{1}{8}, 0, -\frac{1}{8}, -\frac{1}{4}, \ldots$

24. 505, 512, 519, 526, …

25. 1.8, 1.3, 0.8, 0.3, …

26. $\frac{2}{3}, \frac{4}{3}, 2, \frac{8}{3}, \ldots$

27. −1.1, −0.9, −0.7, −0.5

Find the given term of each arithmetic sequence.

28. 5, 10, 15, 20, …; 17th term

29. 121, 110, 99, 88, …; 10th term

30. −2, −5, −8, −11, …; 41st term

31. −30, −22, −14, −6, …; 20th term

32. **Critical Thinking** For the arithmetic sequence $5a - 1, 3a - 1, a - 1, -a - 1, \ldots$ find the common difference and the next three terms.

33. **Recreation** The rates for a go-cart course are shown.

   a. Explain why the relationship described on the flyer could be an arithmetic sequence.

   b. Find the cost for 1, 2, 3, and 4 laps. Write a rule to find the nth term of the sequence.

   c. How much would 15 laps cost?

   d. **What if...?** After 9 laps, you get the 10th one free. Will the sequence still be arithmetic? Explain.

JESSIKA'S SPEEDWAY
License: $7
Per Lap: $2

Find the given term of each arithmetic sequence.

34. 2.5, 8.5, 14.5, 20.5, …; 30th term

35. 189.6, 172.3, 155, 137.7, …; 18th term

36. $\frac{1}{4}, \frac{3}{4}, \frac{5}{4}, \frac{7}{4}, …$; 15th term

37. $\frac{2}{3}, \frac{11}{12}, \frac{7}{6}, \frac{17}{12}, …$; 25th term

38. **Number Theory** The sequence 1, 1, 2, 3, 5, 8, 13, … is a famous sequence called the Fibonacci sequence. After the first two terms, each term is the sum of the previous two terms.

   a. Write the first 10 terms of the Fibonacci sequence. Is the Fibonacci sequence arithmetic? Explain.

   b. Notice that the third term is divisible by 2. Are the 6th and 9th terms also divisible by 2? What conclusion can you draw about every third term? Why is this true?

   c. Can you find any other patterns? (*Hint:* Look at every 4th and 5th term.)

39. **Entertainment** Seats in a concert hall are arranged in the pattern shown.

   a. The numbers of seats in the rows form an arithmetic sequence. Write a rule for the arithmetic sequence.

   b. How many seats are in the 15th row?

   c. A ticket costs $40. Suppose every seat in the first 10 rows is filled. What is the total revenue from those seats?

   d. **What if...?** An extra chair is added to each row. Write the new rule for the arithmetic sequence and find the new total revenue from the first 10 rows.

Row 1
Row 2
Row 3
Row 4

40. **Write About It** Explain how to find the common difference of an arithmetic sequence. How can you determine whether the arithmetic sequence has a positive common difference or a negative common difference?

CONCEPT CONNECTION

STATE

41. This problem will prepare you for the Concept Connection on page 240.

   Juan is traveling to visit universities. He notices mile markers along the road. He records the mile marker every 10 minutes. His father is driving at a constant speed.

   a. Copy and complete the table.

   b. Write the rule for the sequence.

   c. What does the common difference represent?

   d. If this sequence continues, find the mile marker for time interval 10.

Time Interval	Mile Marker
1	520
2	509
3	498
4	
5	
6	

Multiple Choice For Exercises 42–44, choose the best answer.

42. What are the next three terms in the arithmetic sequence −21, −12, −3, 6, … ?

    (A) 9, 12, 15   (B) 15, 24, 33   (C) 12, 21, 27   (D) 13, 20, 27

43. What is the common difference for the data listed in the second column?

    (A) −1.8   (C) 2.8

    (B) 1.8   (D) −3.6

Altitude (ft)	Boiling Point of Water (°F)
1000	210.2
2000	208.4
3000	206.6

44. Which of the following sequences CANNOT be arithmetic?

    (A) −4, 2, 8, 14, …   (B) 9, 4, −1, −6, …   (C) 2, 4, 8, 16, …   (D) $\frac{1}{3}$, $1\frac{1}{3}$, $2\frac{1}{3}$, $3\frac{1}{3}$ …

CHALLENGE AND EXTEND

45. The first term of an arithmetic sequence is 2, and the common difference is 9. Find two consecutive terms of the sequence that have a sum of 355. What positions in the sequence are the terms?

46. The 60th term of an arithmetic sequence is 106.5, and the common difference is 1.5. What is the first term of the sequence?

47. Athletics Verona is training for a marathon. The first part of her training schedule is shown below.

Session	1	2	3	4	5	6
Distance Run (mi)	3.5	5	6.5	8	9.5	11

    a. If Verona continues this pattern, during which training session will she run 26 miles? Is her training schedule an arithmetic sequence? Explain.

    b. If Verona's training schedule starts on a Monday and she runs every third day, on which day will she run 26 miles?

SPIRAL STANDARDS REVIEW   7SDAP1.2, ⚷ 4.0, ⚷ 5.0

48. Three sides of a triangle are represented by x, $x + 3$ and $x + 5$. The perimeter of the triangle is 35 units. Solve for x. *(Lesson 2-3)*

49. The length of a rectangle is 2 and the width is represented by $x + 4$. The area of the rectangle is 40 square units. Solve for x. *(Lesson 2-3)*

Solve each compound inequality and graph the solutions. *(Lesson 3-6)*

50. $4 < 2n + 6 \leq 20$ **51.** $t + 5 > 7$ OR $2t − 8 < −12$

Describe the correlation illustrated by each scatter plot. *(Lesson 4-4)*

52. Household Televisions

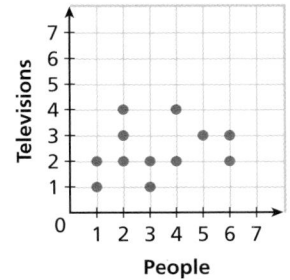

53. Safe Heart Rate

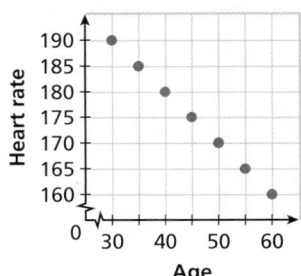

CONCEPT CONNECTION

Applying Functions

College Knowledge Myra is helping her brother plan a college visit 10 hours away from their home. She creates a table listing approximate travel times and distances from their home.

1. Create a scatter plot for the data.

2. Draw a trend line through the data.

3. Based on the trend line, how many miles will they have traveled after 5 hours?

4. If Myra's brother decided to visit a college 13 hours away from their home, approximately how many miles will they travel?

5. To find the average speed for the entire trip, find $\frac{\text{change in distance}}{\text{change in time}}$ between the initial ordered pair and the final ordered pair. Include the units.

Time (h)	Distance (mi)
0	0
2	123
3	190
4	207
6	355
8	472
10	657

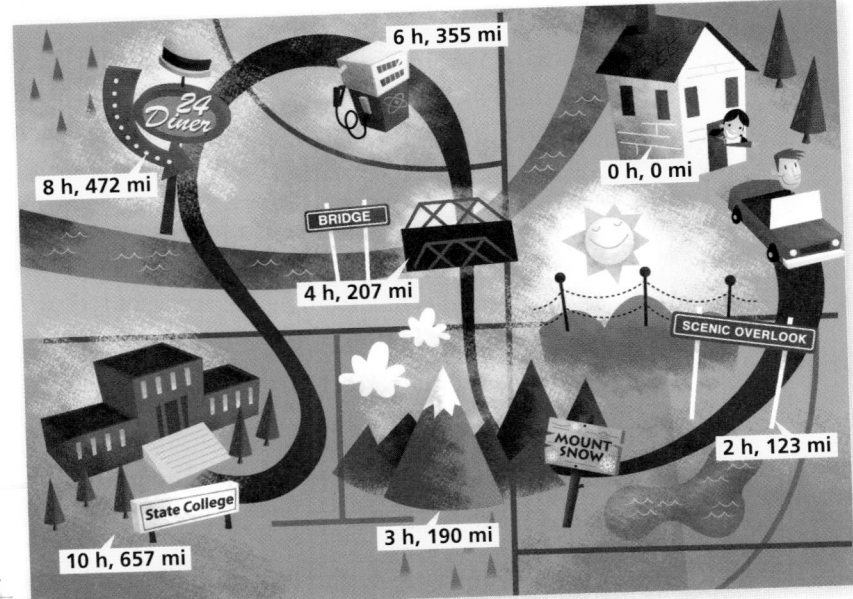

READY TO GO ON?

Quiz for Lessons 4-4 and 4-5

4-4 Scatter Plots and Trend Lines

The table shows the time it takes different people to read a given number of pages.

Pages Read	2	6	6	8	8	10	10
Time (min)	10	15	20	15	30	25	30

1. Graph a scatter plot using the given data.

2. Describe the correlation illustrated by the scatter plot.

Choose the scatter plot that best represents the described relationship. Explain.

3. number of movie tickets sold and number of empty seats

4. number of movie tickets sold and amount of concession sales

5. number of movie tickets sold and length of movie

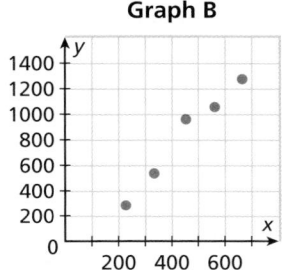

6. The scatter plot shows the estimated annual sales for an electronics and appliance chain of stores for the years 2004–2009. Based on this relationship, predict the annual sales in 2012.

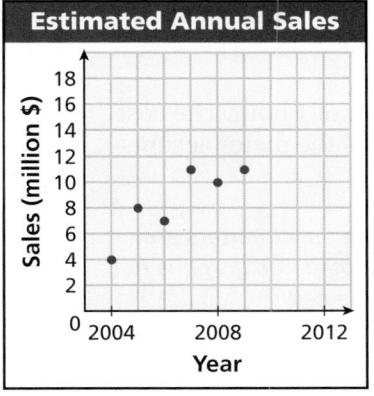

4-5 Arithmetic Sequences

Determine whether each sequence appears to be an arithmetic sequence. If so, find the common difference and the next three terms.

7. $7, 3, -1, -5, \ldots$ 8. $3, 6, 12, 24, \ldots$ 9. $-3.5, -2, -0.5, 1, \ldots$

Find the indicated term of the arithmetic sequence.

10. 31st term: $12, 7, 2, -3, \ldots$ 11. 22nd term: $a_1 = 6; d = 4$

12. With no air resistance, an object would fall 16 feet during the first second, 48 feet during the second second, 80 feet during the third second, 112 feet during the fourth second, and so on. How many feet will the object fall during the ninth second?

CHAPTER 4

Study Guide: Review

Vocabulary

Complete the sentences below with vocabulary words from the list above.

1. The set of *x*-coordinates of the ordered pairs of a relation is called the ___?___ .

2. If one set of data values increases as another set of data values decreases, the relationship can be described as having a(n) ___?___ .

3. A sequence is an ordered list of numbers where each number is a(n) ___?___ .

4-1 Graphing Relationships *(pp. 200–205)*

Review of Grade 7 AF1.5

EXAMPLES

Sketch a graph for each situation. Tell whether the graph is continuous or discrete.

■ A parking meter has a limit of 1 hour. The cost is $0.25 per 15 minutes and the meter accepts quarters only.

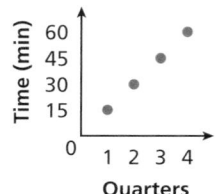

Since only quarters are accepted, the graph is not connected.

The graph is discrete.

■ Ian bought a cup of coffee. At first, he sipped slowly. As it cooled, he drank more quickly. The last bit was cold, and he dumped it out.

As time passes the coffee was **sipped slowly**, **drank more quickly**, and then **dumped out**.

The graph is continuous.

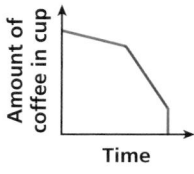

EXERCISES

Sketch a graph for each situation. Tell whether the graph is continuous or discrete.

4. A girl was walking home at a steady pace. Then she stopped to talk to a friend. After her friend left, she jogged the rest of the way home.

5. A ball is dropped from a second story window and bounces to a stop on the patio below.

6. Jason was on the second floor when he got a call to attend a meeting on the sixth floor. He took the stairs. After the meeting, he took the elevator to the first floor.

Write a possible situation for each graph.

7.   **8.**

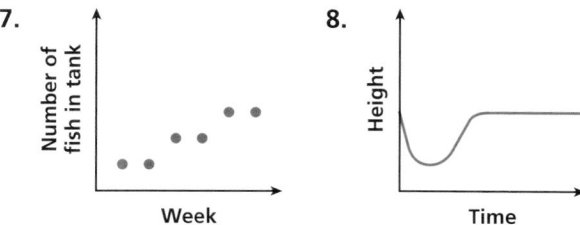

4-2 Relations and Functions (pp. 206–212)

16.0, 17.0, 18.0

EXAMPLES

■ Express the relation $\{(2, 15), (4, 12), (5, 7), (7, 2)\}$ as a table, as a graph, and as a mapping diagram.

Table

x	y
2	15
4	12
5	7
7	2

Graph

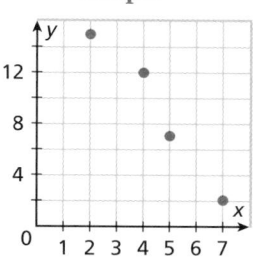

Mapping Diagram

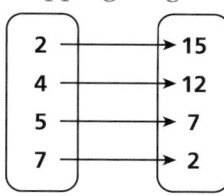

Give the domain and range of each relation. Tell whether the relation is a function. Explain.

■
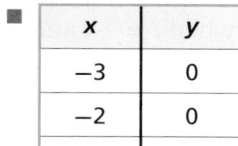

D: $\{-3, -2, -1\}$

R: $\{0, 1\}$

The relation is a function because each domain value is paired with exactly one range value.

■
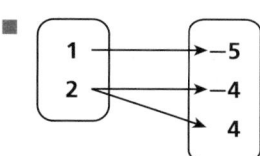

D: $\{1, 2\}$

R: $\{-5, -4, 4\}$

The relation is not a function because one domain value is paired with two range values.

■
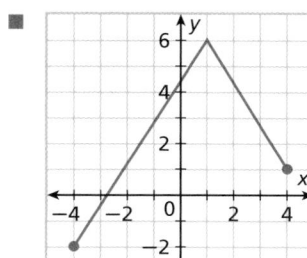

D: $-4 \le x \le 4$

R: $-2 \le y \le 6$

The relation is a function because every x-value is paired with exactly one y-value.

EXERCISES

Express each relation as a table, as a graph, and as a mapping diagram.

9. $\{(-1, 0), (0, 1), (2, 1)\}$

10. $\{(-2, -1), (-1, 1), (2, 3), (3, 4)\}$

Give the domain and range of each relation.

11. $\{(-4, 5), (-2, 3), (0, 1), (2, -1)\}$

12. $\{(-2, -1) (-1, 0), (0, -1), (1, 0), (2, -1)\}$

13.

x	0	1	4	1	4
y	0	−1	−2	1	2

14.
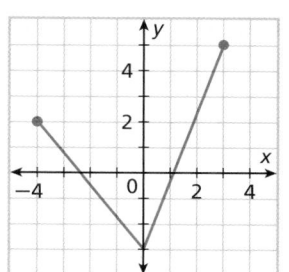

Give the domain and range of each relation. Tell whether the relation is a function. Explain.

15. $\{(-5, -3), (-3, -2), (-1, -1), (1, 0)\}$

16.
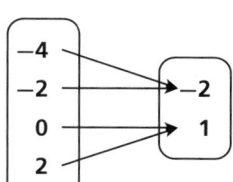

17.

x	1	2	3	4	1
y	3	2	1	0	−1

18. A local parking garage charges $5.00 for the first hour plus $1.50 for each additional hour or part of an hour. Write a relation as a set of ordered pairs in which the x-value represents the number of hours and the y-value represents the cost for x hours. Use a domain of 1, 2, 3, 4, 5. Is this relation a function? Explain.

19. A baseball coach is taking the team for ice cream. Four students can ride in each car. Create a mapping diagram to show the number of cars needed to transport 8, 10, 14, and 16 students. Is this relation a function? Explain.

4-3 Writing and Graphing Functions (pp. 213–220)

EXAMPLES

■ **Determine a relationship between the *x*- and *y*-values in the table. Write an equation.**

x	1	2	3	4
y	−3	−6	−9	−12

What are possible relationships between the x-values and the y-values?

$1 - 4 = -3$ $1(-3) = -3$
$2 - 4 \ne -6$ ✗ $2(-3) = -6$ ✓
     $3(-3) = -9$ ✓
     $4(-3) = -12$ ✓

$y = -3x$ *Write an equation.*

Identify the independent and dependent variables. Write a rule in function notation for the situation.

■ Nia earns $5.25 per hour.
Nia's **pay** depends on the **number of hours** she works.
  Dependent: **pay**
  Independent: **hours**

Let *h* represent the number of hours Nia works. The function for Nia's pay is $f(h) = 5.25h$.

■ **Graph the function $y = 3x - 1$.**

Step 1 Choose several values of *x* to generate ordered pairs.

x	y = 3x − 1	(x, y)
−1	$y = 3(-1) - 1 = -4$	(−1, −4)
0	$y = 3(0) - 1 = -1$	(0, −1)
1	$y = 3(1) - 1 = 2$	(1, 2)
2	$y = 3(2) - 1 = 5$	(2, 5)

Step 2 Plot enough points to see a pattern.

Step 3 Draw a line through the points to show all the ordered pairs that satisfy this function.

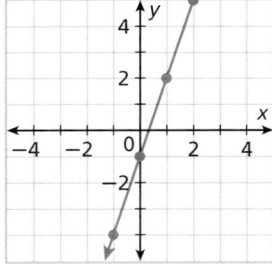

EXERCISES

Determine the relationship between the *x*- and *y*-values. Write an equation.

20.

x	y
1	−6
2	−5
3	−4
4	−3

21.

x	y
1	0.5
2	1
3	1.5
4	2

22. $\{(1, 9), (2, 18), (3, 27), (4, 36)\}$

Identify the independent and dependent variables. Write a rule in function notation for each situation.

23. A baker spends $6 on ingredients for each cake he bakes.

24. Tim will buy twice as many CDs as Raul.

Evaluate each function for the given input values.

25. For $f(x) = -2x + 4$, find $f(x)$ when $x = -5$.

26. For $g(n) = -n^2 - 2$, find $g(n)$ when $n = -3$.

27. For $h(t) = 7 - |t + 3|$, find $h(t)$ when $t = -4$ and when $t = 5$.

28. For $k(p) = \frac{1}{2}(p)^2 + 7$, find $k(p)$ when $p = 4$ and $p = -6$.

29. For $w(x) = \sqrt{x} - 5.5$, find $w(x)$ when $x = 16$ and $x = 12.25$.

Graph each equation. Then tell whether the equation represents a function.

30. $3x - y = 1$ **31.** $y = 2 - |x|$

32. $y = x^2 - 6$ **33.** $y = |x + 5| + 1$

Give the domain and range of each function.

34. $y = 2x + 7$ **35.** $y = 4x - 5$

36. $y = |x| - 6$ **37.** $y = x^2 + 5$

4-4 Scatter Plots and Trend Lines (pp. 224–231)

 Review of Grade 7 SDAP1.2

EXAMPLE

■ The graph shows the amount of money in a savings account. Based on this relationship, predict how much money will be in the account in month 7.

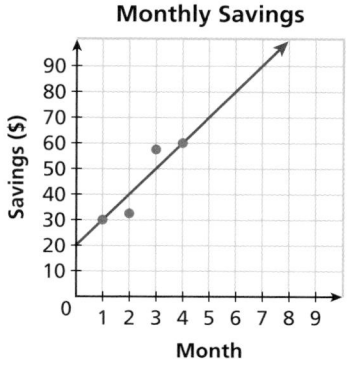

Monthly Savings

Draw a line that has about the same number of points above and below it. Your line may or may not go through data points.

Find the point on the line whose x-value is 7.

Based on the data, $90 is a reasonable prediction.

EXERCISES

38. The table shows the value of a car for the given years. Graph a scatter plot using the given data. Describe the correlation illustrated by the scatter plot.

Year	2000	2001	2002	2003
Value (thousand $)	28	25	23	20

39. The graph shows the results of a 2003–2004 survey on class size at the given grade levels. Based on this relationship, predict the class size for the 9th grade.

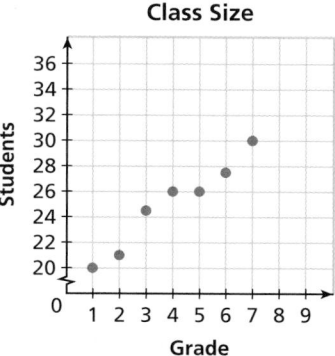

Class Size

4-5 Arithmetic Sequences (pp. 234–239)

Prep for Algebra II 22.0

EXAMPLES

■ Determine whether the sequence appears to be arithmetic. If so, find the common difference and the next three terms.

$-8, -5, -2, 1,\ldots$

Step 1 Find the difference between successive terms.

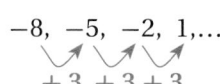

$-8, -5, -2, 1,\ldots$ *The common difference is 3.*

$+3 \ +3 \ +3$

Step 2 Use the common difference to find the next 3 terms.

$-8, -5, -2, 1, \ 4, \ 7, \ 10$

$+3 \ +3 \ +3$

■ Find the indicated term of the arithmetic sequence. 18th term: $a_1 = -4; d = 6$

$a_n = a_1 + (n-1)d$ *Write the rule.*
$a_{18} = -4 + (18-1)6$ *Substitute.*
$= -4 + (17)6$ *Simplify.*
$= -4 + 102$ *Simplify.*
$= 98$

The 18th term is 98.

EXERCISES

Determine whether each sequence appears to be arithmetic. If so, find the common difference and the next three terms.

40. $20, 14, 8, 2,\ldots$ **41.** $-15, -12, -9, -4,\ldots$

42. $5, 4, 2, -1,\ldots$ **43.** $-8, -5.5, -3, -0.5,\ldots$

Find the indicated term of each arithmetic sequence.

44. 31st term: $-15, -11, -7, -3,\ldots$

45. 24th term: $a_1 = 7; d = -3$

46. 17th term: $a_1 = -20; d = 2.5$

47. Marie has $180 in a savings account. She plans to deposit $12 per week. Assuming that she does not withdraw any money from her account, what will her balance be at week 20?

48. The table shows the temperature at the given heights above sea level. Find the temperature at 8000 feet above sea level.

Height Above Sea Level (thousand feet)	1	2	3	4
Temperature (°C)	30	23.5	17	10.5

CHAPTER TEST

Choose the graph that best represents each situation.

1. A person walks leisurely, stops, and then continues walking.

2. A person jogs, then runs, and then jogs again.

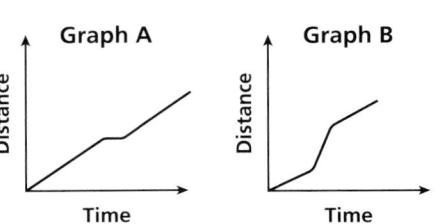

Graph A

Graph B

Give the domain and range for each relation.
Tell whether the relation is a function. Explain.

3.

x	y
−2	3
1	2
0	1
1	0
3	−1

4.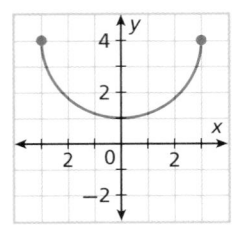

5. Bowling costs $3 per game plus $2.50 for shoe rental. Identify the independent and dependent variables. Write a rule in function notation for the situation.

Evaluate each function for the given input values.

6. For $f(x) = -3x + 4$, find $f(x)$ when $x = -2$.

7. For $f(x) = 2x^2$, find $f(x)$ when $x = -3$.

Graph each equation. Then tell whether the equation represents a function.

8. $y = x - 5$

9. $y = x^2 - 5$

10. $y = |x| + 3$

The table shows possible recommendations for the number of hours of sleep that children should get every day.

Age (yr)	1	2	3	4	5	14
Sleep Needed (h)	14	13	12	12	11	9

11. Graph a scatter plot of the given data.

12. Describe the correlation illustrated by the scatter plot.

13. Predict how many hours of sleep are recommended for a 16-year-old.

Determine whether each sequence appears to be an arithmetic sequence. If so, find the common difference and the next three terms.

14. $11, 6, 1, -4, \ldots$

15. $-4, -3, -1, 2, \ldots$

16. $7, 21, 30, 45, \ldots$

Find the indicated term of each arithmetic sequence.

17. 32nd term: $18, 11, 4, -3, \ldots$

18. 24th term: $a_1 = 4; d = 6$

19. Mandy's new job has a starting salary of $16,000 and annual increases of $800. How much will she earn during her fifth year?

COLLEGE ENTRANCE EXAM PRACTICE

FOCUS ON ACT

Questions on the ACT Mathematics Test do not require the use of a calculator, but you may bring one to use with the test. Make sure that it is a calculator that is on the approved list for the ACT.

You may want to time yourself as you take this practice test. It should take you about 6 minutes to complete.

When taking the test, you will be more comfortable using a calculator that you are used to. If you already have a calculator, make sure it is one of the permitted calculators. If you plan to use a new one, make sure to practice using it before the test.

---

1. The soccer team is ordering new uniforms. There is a one-time setup charge of $50.00, and each uniform costs $23.50. Which of the following best describes the total cost C for ordering uniforms for p players?

(A) $C = 23.50p$

(B) $C = 50p$

(C) $C = 73.50p$

(D) $C = 23.50p + 50$

(E) $C = 50p + 23.50$

---

2. In the given relation, what domain value corresponds to the range value -2?
$\{(-1, 2), (-2, 4), (2, 5), (0, -2), (2, 0)\}$

(F) -2

(G) 0

(H) 2

(J) 4

(K) 5

---

3. Evaluate $h(x) = \frac{1}{2}(5 - 6x) + 9x$ when $x = \frac{2}{3}$.

(A) $\frac{9}{2}$

(B) $\frac{13}{2}$

(C) 7

(D) $\frac{19}{2}$

(E) $\frac{23}{2}$

---

4. What is the seventh term of the arithmetic sequence $-4, -1, 2, \ldots$?

(F) 5

(G) 10

(H) 11

(J) 14

(K) 17

---

5. The graph of which function is shown below?

(A) $y = -3x - 5$

(B) $y = -\frac{1}{3}x - \frac{5}{3}$

(C) $y = -5x - 3$

(D) $y = 3x - 5$

(E) $y = 5x + 3$

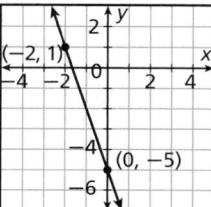

---

6. Which of the following relations is NOT a function?

(F) $\{(0, 1), (1, 2), (2, 3), (3, 4)\}$

(G) $\{(1, 2), (2, 2), (3, 3), (4, 3)\}$

(H) $\{(0, 2), (2, 4), (4, 1), (1, 3)\}$

(J) $\{(1, 3), (4, 2), (2, 0), (3, 4)\}$

(K) $\{(0, 2), (1, 3), (4, 3), (1, 2)\}$

STRATEGIES FOR SUCCESS

Extended Response: Understand the Scores

Extended response test items are typically multipart questions that require a high level of thinking. The responses are scored using a 4-point rubric. To receive full credit, you must correctly answer all parts of the question and provide a clear explanation. A partial answer is worth 2 to 3 points, an incorrect solution is worth 1 point, and no response is worth 0 points.

EXAMPLE 1

Extended Response A train traveling from Boston, Massachusetts, to Richmond, Virginia, averages about 55 miles per hour. Define the variables, write an equation, make a table, and draw a graph to show the distance the train travels in 0 to 5 hours.

Here are examples of four different responses and their scores using the rubric shown.

4-point response:

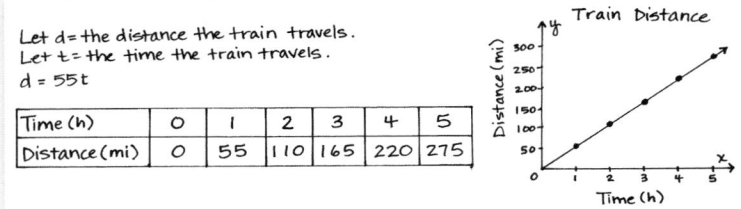

3-point response:

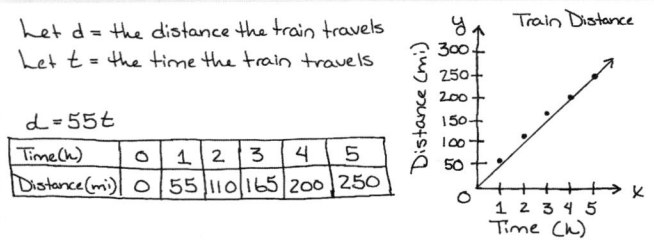

The student shows all of the work, but there are two minor computation errors when t = 4 and t = 5.

2-point response:

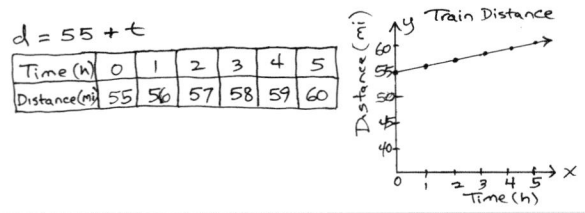

The student writes an incorrect equation and uses it to create an incorrect table and graph. However, the table and graph are correct for the student's equation.

1-point response:

$$d = 55t$$

The student does not answer two parts of the question.

Never leave an extended-response test item blank. At least try to define variables or write equations where appropriate. You will get some points just for trying.

Read each test item and answer the questions that follow using the rubric below.

Scoring Rubric:

4 points: The student shows all of the work, correctly answers all parts of the question, and provides a clear explanation.

3 points: The student shows most of the work and provides a clear explanation but has a minor computation error, or the student shows all of the work and arrives at a correct solution but does not provide a clear explanation.

2 points: The student makes major errors resulting in an incorrect solution, or the student gives a correct solution but does not show any work nor provide an explanation.

1 point: The student shows no work and gives an incorrect solution.

0 points: The student gives no response.

Item A
Extended Response Draw a graph that is a function. Explain why it is a function. Then draw a graph that is NOT a function. Explain why it is not a function.

1. What should be included in a 4-point response?

2. Explain how would you score the response below.

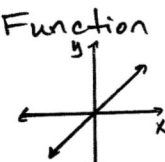

Function

Not a function

The first graph is a function because each x-value has exactly one y-value. When x=1, y=1. The second graph is not a function because there is more than one y-value for each x-value. When x=1, y=1, and y=-1. Therefore, the second graph is not a function.

Item B
Extended Response A car travels at a steady rate of 60 miles per hour. Identify the independent and dependent variables. Describe the domain and range. Write an equation to describe the situation.

3. Ana wrote the response below.

The equation is y = 60x. The independent variable is time and the dependent variable is distance. The domain and range are all real numbers.

Explain how would you score Ana's response.

4. If you did not give Ana full credit, what should be added to Ana's response, if anything, so that it receives full credit?

Item C
Extended Response Lara bought 8 notebooks and 4 binders. She spent $14 total without tax. How much did each notebook cost if each binder cost $2.50? Write an equation and find the solution.

5. Explain how would you score the response below.

Let s = the cost of each notebook.
Let b = the cost of each binder.
8s + 4b = 14
8s + 4(2.50) = 14
8s + 10 = 14
8s = 4
s = 2   The notebooks cost $2 each

6. If you did not give the response full credit, what should be added to the response, if anything, so that it receives full credit?

CUMULATIVE ASSESSMENT, CHAPTERS 1–4

Multiple Choice

1. How many different values of x are solutions of $|x - 2| = 3$?

A none   **C** two

B one   **D** three

2. Jemma is ordering DVDs. The DVDs cost $14 each and shipping costs $5, no matter how many she buys. Jemma can spend at most $75. Which inequality represents the number of DVDs she can buy?

A $14 + 5x \le 75$ **C** $14(x + 5) \le 75$

B $5 + 14x \le 75$ **D** $5(x + 14) \le 75$

3. Simplify the expression $2(m - 4) + 7m$.

A $-5m - 8$ **C** $9m - 4$

B $2m - 1$ **D** $9m - 8$

4. Which property is illustrated by the equation $(x + 4) + y = x + (4 + y)$?

A Associative Property of Addition

B Closure Property of the Real Numbers

C Commutative Property of Addition

D Distributive Property

5. Roberto is solving the equation $3(x - 5) + 1 = 10$. As a first step, he rewrites the equation as $3x - 15 + 1 = 10$. Which property justifies this step?

A Associative Property of Addition

B Closure Property of the Real Numbers

C Commutative Property of Addition

D Distributive Property

6. For which values of p is the inequality $2(p + 2) < 8$ true?

A $p < 1$ **C** $p < 4$

B $p < 2$ **D** $p < 6$

7. Which of the following is an example of the Distributive Property?

A $3 \cdot 4 \cdot 7 = (3 \cdot 4) \cdot 7$

B $7(6 + 1) = 7 \cdot 6 + 7 \cdot 1$

C $2 \cdot 9 = 9 \cdot 2$

D $(6 + 11) + 4 = 6 + (11 + 4)$

8. Jo Ann needs at least 3 pounds of peaches for a recipe. At the market, she calculates that she has enough money to buy 5 pounds at most. Which graph shows all possible numbers of pounds of peaches Jo Ann can buy so that she has enough for the recipe?

A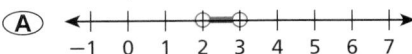

B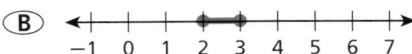

C

D

9. Mr. Jackson drew a graph on the board and said that the graph is an example of a relation that is *not* a function. Which graph could he have drawn?

10. Which relation is NOT a function?

A $\{(1, -5), (3, 1), (-5, 4), (4, -2)\}$

B $\{(2, 7), (3, 7), (4, 7), (5, 8)\}$

C $\{(1, -5), (-1, 6), (1, 5), (6, -3)\}$

D $\{(3, -2), (5, -6), (7, 7), (8, \ 8)\}$

Most test problems are written so that they can be solved without lengthy calculations. If you find yourself getting involved in a long, complicated calculation, check the information in the problem again to see if you might have missed something helpful.

11. The graph below shows a function.

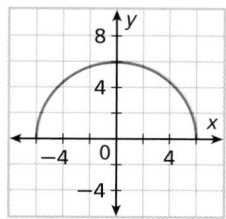

What is the domain of the function?

Ⓐ $x \geq 0$

Ⓑ $x \geq -6$

Ⓒ $0 \leq x \leq 6$

Ⓓ $-6 \leq x \leq 6$

12. Which of the following statements is true for every relation that is a function?

Ⓐ The domain is the set of all real numbers.

Ⓑ The range is the set of all real numbers.

Ⓒ Each domain value is paired with exactly one range value.

Ⓓ Each range value is paired with exactly one domain value.

13. Which of the following is a solution of $x + 1 \leq \frac{3}{2}$ AND $x - 1 \geq -\frac{5}{4}$?

Ⓐ $\frac{3}{2}$ Ⓒ $-\frac{1}{3}$

Ⓑ $\frac{1}{3}$ Ⓓ $-\frac{3}{2}$

Gridded Response

14. What is the value of x when $3(x + 7) - 6x = 4 - (x + 1)$?

15. Allie simplifies $5(4 + 3x) - 2x$. What value should she use for the coefficient of x in the simplified expression?

16. WalkieTalkie phone company charges $18.00 for basic phone service per month and $0.15 per minute for long distance calls. Arena Calls charges $80.00 per month with no fee for long distance calls. What is the minimum number of minutes of long distance calls for which the cost of WalkieTalkie is more than the cost of Arena Calls?

Short Response

17. A function is graphed below.

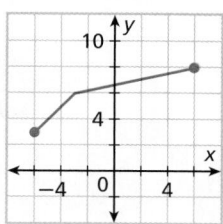

What is the domain and range of the function?

18. The figure gives the dimensions of a rectangular picture frame.

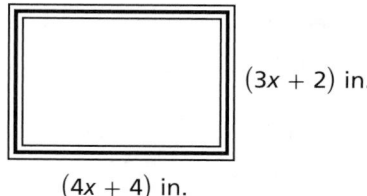

$(3x + 2)$ in.

$(4x + 4)$ in.

The frame has a perimeter of 40 inches. What is the value of x? Show your work.

19. A company prints custom t-shirts. There is a $25 set-up fee and the shirts cost $9 each. Ray wants to have n shirts printed and he must spend no more than $115.

a. Write an inequality that Ray can use to find the number of shirts he can have printed.

b. Solve the inequality. Show your work.

20. Consider the inequality $3|x| + 4 > 13$.

a. Solve the inequality. Write the solution as a compound inequality.

b. Graph the solutions on a number line.

Extended Response

21. A relation is shown in the table.

a. Express the relation as a mapping diagram.

b. Is the relation a function? Explain why or why not.

c. Write a possible real-life situation for the relation.

x	y
2	12
3	15
3	18
5	40
6	64

CHAPTER 5

Linear Functions

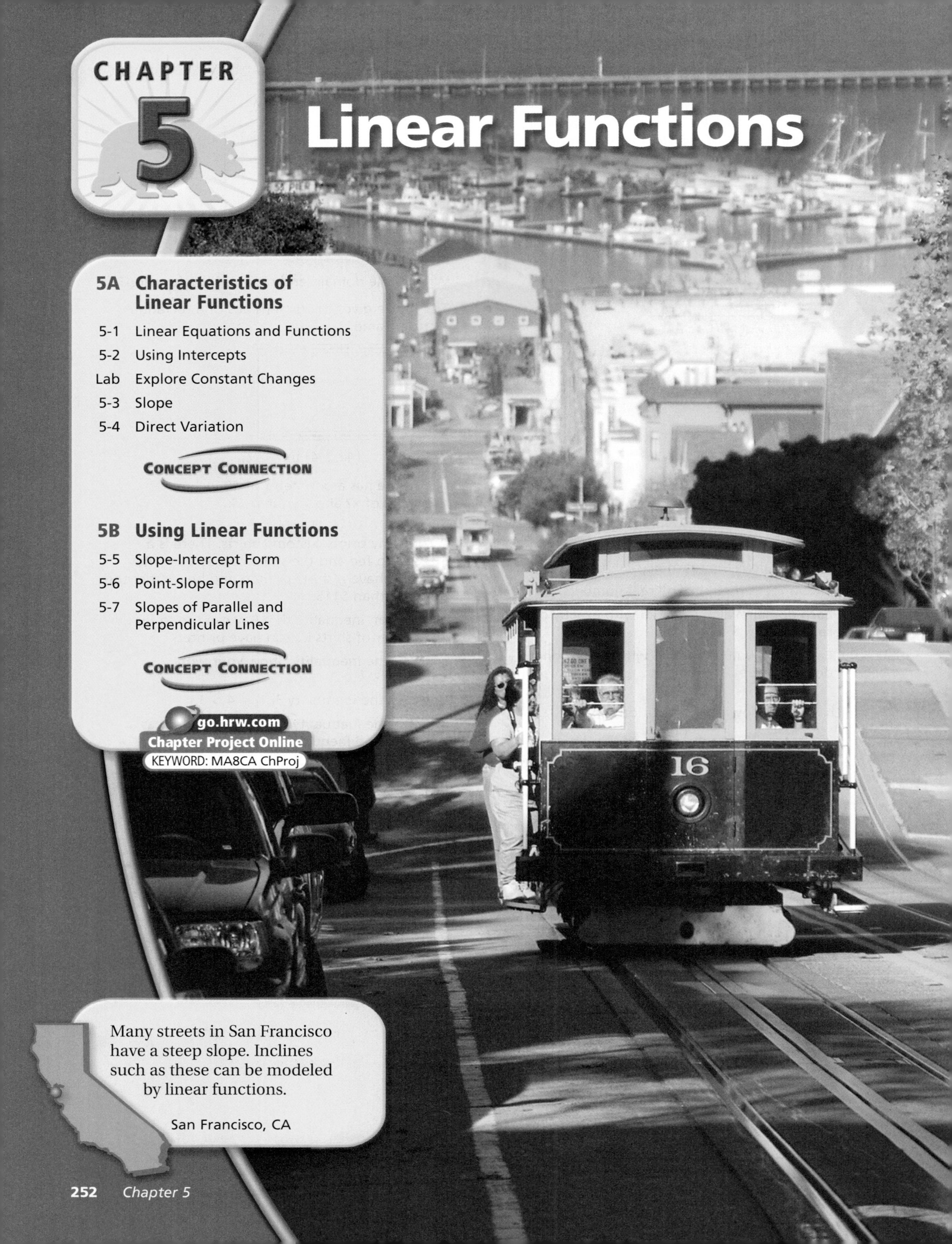

go.hrw.com
Chapter Project Online
KEYWORD: MA8CA ChProj

Many streets in San Francisco have a steep slope. Inclines such as these can be modeled by linear functions.

San Francisco, CA

ARE YOU READY?

✓ Vocabulary

Match each term on the left with a definition on the right.

1. coefficient
2. coordinate plane
3. coordinates
4. perpendicular

   A. a change in the size or position of a figure

   B. forming right angles

   C. a two-dimensional system formed by the intersection of a horizontal number line and a vertical number line

   D. an ordered pair of numbers that gives the location of a point

   E. a number multiplied by a variable

✓ Ordered Pairs

Graph each point on the same coordinate plane.

5. $A(2, 5)$
6. $B(-1, -3)$
7. $C(-5, 2)$
8. $D(4, -4)$
9. $E(-2, 0)$
10. $F(0, 3)$
11. $G(8, 7)$
12. $H(-8, -7)$

✓ Solve for a Variable

Solve each equation for y.

13. $2x + y = 8$
14. $5y = 5x - 10$
15. $2y = 6x - 8$
16. $10x + 25 = 5y$

✓ Evaluate Expressions

Evaluate each expression for the given value of the variable.

17. $4g - 3; g = -2$
18. $8p - 12; p = 4$
19. $4x + 8; x = -2$
20. $-5t - 15; t = 1$

✓ Connect Words and Algebra

21. The value of a stock begins at $0.05 and increases by $0.01 each month. Write an equation representing the value of the stock v in any month m.

22. Write a situation that could be modeled by the equation $b = 100 - s$.

✓ Rates and Unit Rates

Find each unit rate.

23. 322 miles on 14 gallons of gas
24. $14.25 for 3 pounds of deli meat
25. 32 grams of fat in 4 servings
26. 120 pictures on 5 rolls of film

Unpacking the Standards

The information below "unpacks" the standards. The Academic Vocabulary is highlighted and defined to help you understand the language of the standards. Refer to the lessons listed after each standard for help with the math terms and phrases. The Chapter Concept shows how the standard is applied in this chapter.

California Standard	Academic Vocabulary	Chapter Concept
6.0 Students graph a linear equation and compute the x- and y-intercepts (e.g., graph $2x + 6y = 4$). They are also able to sketch the region defined by linear inequalities (e.g., they sketch the region defined by $2x + 6y < 4$). (Lessons **5-1, 5-2, 5-3, 5-4, 5-5, 5-6**)	**graph** to represent data with a diagram **compute** to calculate an answer	You graph an equation of a line using various methods: • plotting points that are solutions of an equation and connecting them with a line. • finding the points where a line will intersect the x-axis and the y-axis, and then connecting those two points with a line.
7.0 Students verify that a point lies on a line, given an equation of the line. Students are able to derive linear equations by using the point-slope formula. (Lessons **5-1, 5-6**)	**verify** to check whether or not something is true **derive** to reach a conclusion by reasoning	You learn that all points on the graph of a line are solutions to the equation. You also write an equation of a line given a point on the line and its slope.
8.0 Students understand the concepts of parallel lines and perpendicular lines and how their slopes are related. Students are able to find the equation of a line perpendicular to a given line that passes through a given point. (Lesson **5-7**)	**related** connected by similarities **passes through** to move all the way through	You use slope to determine if lines are parallel or perpendicular. You also write equations for perpendicular lines. 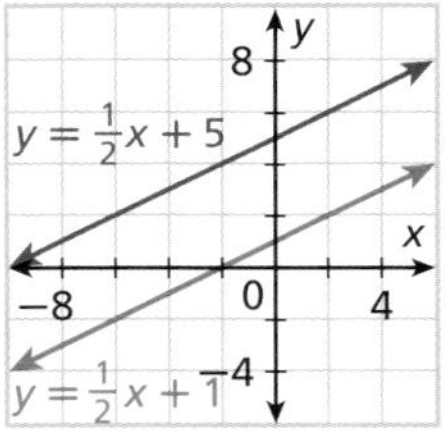 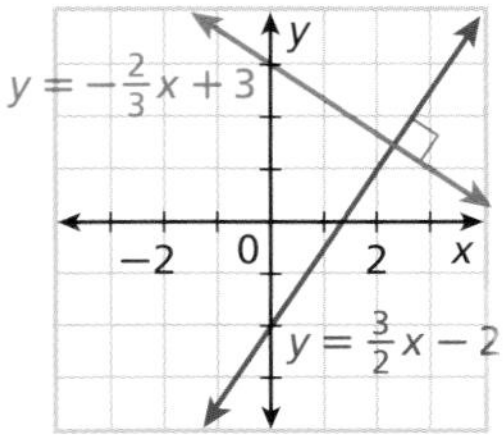

Reading and Writing Math

Study Strategy: Use Multiple Representations

Representing a math concept in more than one way can help you understand it more clearly. As you read the explanations and example problems in your text, note the use of tables, lists, graphs, diagrams, and symbols, as well as words to explain a concept.

From Lesson 4-3:

In this example from Chapter 4, the given function is described using an equation, a table, ordered pairs, and a graph.

Graphing Functions

Graph each equation. Then tell whether the equation represents a function.

A $2x + 1 = y$ ◁— **Equation**

Step 1 Choose several values of x and generate ordered pairs.

Step 2 Plot enough points to see a pattern.

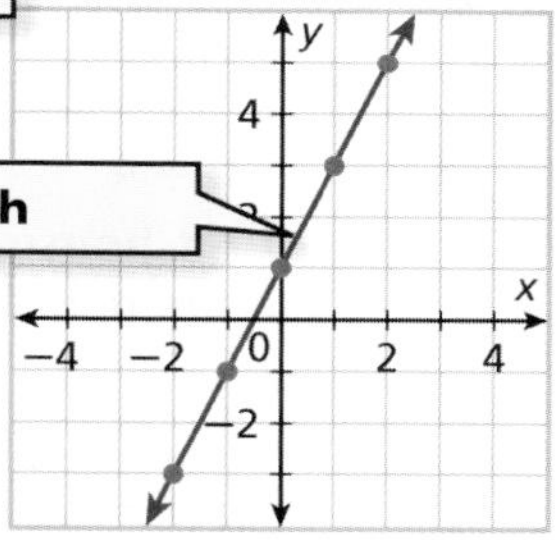

Table

Graph

x	2x + 1 = y	(x, y)
−3	2(−3) + 1 = −5	(−3, −5)
−2	2(−2) + 1 = −3	(−2, −3)
−1	2(−1) + 1 = −1	(−1, −1)
0	2(0) + 1 = 1	(0, 1)
1	2(1) + 1 = 3	(1, 3)
2	2(2) + 1 = 5	(2, 5)
3	2(3) + 1 = 7	(3, 7)

Ordered Pairs

Step 3 The points appear to form a line. **Draw a line** through all the points to show all the ordered pairs that satisfy the function. Draw arrowheads on both "ends" of the line.

Try This

1. If an employee earns $8.00 an hour, $y = 8x$ gives the total pay y the employee will earn for working x hours. For this equation, make a table of ordered pairs and a graph. Explain the relationships between the equation, the table, and the graph. How does each one describe the situation?

2. What situations might make one representation more useful than another?

5-1 Linear Equations and Functions

California Standards

🔑 **6.0** Students graph a **linear equation** and compute the x- and y-intercepts **(e.g., graph 2x + 6y = 4).** They are also able to sketch the region defined by linear inequalities (e.g., they sketch the region defined by 2x + 6y < 4). *Also covered:* 🔑 **7.0, 17.0, 18.0**

Vocabulary
linear equation
linear function

Why learn this?
Linear equations can describe many real-world situations, such as distances traveled at a constant speed.

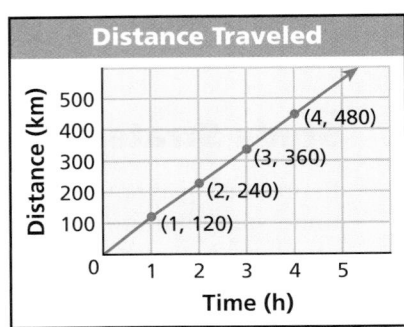

Many stretches on the German autobahn have a speed limit of 120 km/h. If a car travels continuously at this speed, $y = 120x$ gives the number of kilometers y that the car would travel in x hours.

Notice that the graph is a straight line. An equation whose graph forms a straight line is a **linear equation**. Also notice that this is a function. A function represented by a linear equation is a **linear function**.

For any two points, there is exactly one line that can be drawn through them both. This means you need only two ordered pairs to graph a line. However, graphing three points is a good way to check that your line is correct.

EXAMPLE 1 **Graphing Linear Equations**

Graph each linear equation. Then tell whether it represents a function.

A $y = -x + 4$

Step 1 Choose three values of x and generate ordered pairs.

x	y = −x + 4	(x, y)
−1	y = −(−1) + 4 = 5	(−1, 5)
0	y = −(0) + 4 = 4	(0, 4)
1	y = −(1) + 4 = 3	(1, 3)

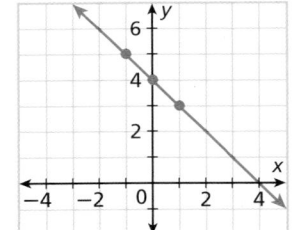

Step 2 Plot the points and connect them with a straight line.
No vertical line will intersect this graph more than once, so $y = -x + 4$ represents a function.

B $y - 2x = -1$

Step 1 Solve for y.

$$y - 2x = -1$$
$$\underline{+2x \quad +2x} \qquad \text{Add 2x to both sides.}$$
$$y \quad = 2x - 1$$

Step 2 Choose three values of x and generate ordered pairs.

x	y = 2x − 1	(x, y)
0	y = 2(0) − 1 = −1	(0, −1)
1	y = 2(1) − 1 = 1	(1, 1)
2	y = 2(2) − 1 = 3	(2, 3)

Helpful Hint

Sometimes solving for *y* first makes it easier to generate ordered pairs using values of *x*. To review solving for a variable, see Lesson 2-6.

For more on graphing linear equations, see the Function Builder on page MB2.

Step 3 Plot the points and connect them with a straight line.

No vertical line will intersect this graph more than once, so $2x + y = 1$ represents a function.

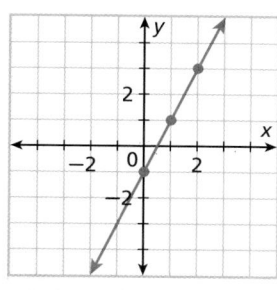

C $y = -3$

Any ordered pair with a y-coordinate of -3 will satisfy this equation.

Plot several points that have a y-coordinate of -3 and connect them with a straight line.

No vertical line will intersect this graph more than once, so $y = -3$ represents a function.

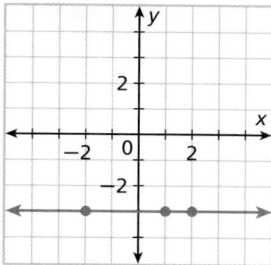

D $x = 2$

Any ordered pair with an x-coordinate of 2 will satisfy this equation.

Plot several points that have an x-coordinate of 2 and connect them with a straight line.

There is a vertical line that intersects this graph more than once, so $x = 2$ does *not* represent a function.

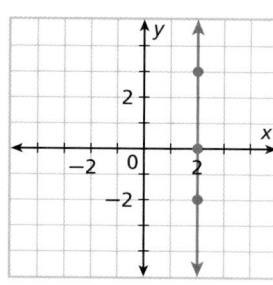

 Graph each linear equation. Then tell whether it represents a function.

1a. $y = 4x$ **1b.** $x + y = 7$ **1c.** $x = \frac{1}{2}$

Linear Equations and Their Graphs

For any linear equation in two variables,

- all points on its graph are solutions to the equation.
- all solutions to the equation appear on its graph.

EXAMPLE 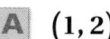 **Determining Whether a Point is on a Graph**

Without graphing, tell whether each point is on the graph of $y = -2x + 4$.

A $(1, 2)$

Substitute:

$$y = -2x + 4$$
$$2 \stackrel{?}{=} -2(1) + 4$$
$$2 \stackrel{?}{=} -2 + 4$$
$$2 = 2 \checkmark$$

Since $(1, 2)$ is a solution to $y = -2x + 4$, $(1, 2)$ is on the graph.

B $(-4, 0)$

Substitute:

$$y = -2x + 4$$
$$0 \stackrel{?}{=} -2(-4) + 4$$
$$0 \stackrel{?}{=} -8 + 4$$
$$0 \neq -4 \; \times$$

Since $(-4, 0)$ is not a solution to $y = -2x + 4$, $(-4, 0)$ is not on the graph.

 **CHECK IT OUT!** Without graphing, tell whether each point is on the graph of $x - 3y = 12$.

2a. $(5, 1)$ **2b.** $(0, -4)$ **2c.** $(1.5, -3.5)$

Linear equations can be written in the *standard form* shown below.

> **Know it! Note**
>
> ### Standard Form of a Linear Equation
>
> $Ax + By = C$ where A, B, and C are real numbers and A and B are not both 0
>
> | 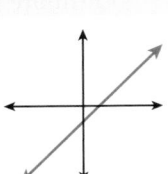 | 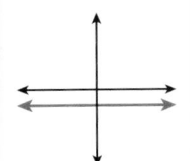 | 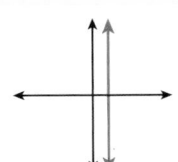 |
> |---|---|---|
> | When $A \neq 0$ and $B \neq 0$, the graph is a nonhorizontal, nonvertical line. | When $A = 0$, the graph is a horizontal line. | When $B = 0$, the graph is a vertical line. |

Notice that when a linear equation is written in standard form,
- x and y both have exponents of 1.
- x and y are not multiplied together.
- x and y do not appear in denominators, exponents, or radical signs.

Linear		Not Linear	
$3x + 2y = 10$	Standard form	$3xy + x = 1$	x and y are multiplied.
$y - 2 = 3x$	Can be written as $3x - y = -2$	$x^3 + y = -1$	x has an exponent other than 1.
$-y = 5x$	Can be written as $5x + y = 0$	$x + \dfrac{6}{y} = 12$	y is in a denominator.

EXAMPLE 3 **Writing Linear Equations in Standard Form**

Write $y = x + 3$ in standard form and give the values of A, B, and C. Then describe the graph.

> **Remember!**
> - $y - x = y + (-x)$
> - $y + (-x) = -x + y$
> - $-x = -1x$
> - $y = 1y$

$$y = x + 3$$
$$\underline{-x \qquad -x} \qquad \text{Subtract x from both sides.}$$
$$y - x = \qquad 3$$
$$-x + y = \qquad 3 \qquad \text{The equation is in standard form.}$$

$A = -1, B = 1, C = 3$

The graph is a line that is neither horizontal nor vertical.

 CHECK IT OUT! Write each equation in standard form and give the values of A, B, and C. Then describe the graph.

3a. $y = 5x - 9$ **3b.** $y = 12$ **3c.** $x = 2$

For linear functions whose graphs are not horizontal, the domain and range are all real numbers. However, in many real-world situations, the domain and range must be restricted. For example, some quantities cannot be negative, such as distance.

Sometimes domain and range are restricted even further to a set of points. For example, a quantity such as number of people can only be whole numbers. When this happens, the graph is not actually connected because every point on the line is not a solution. However, you may see these graphs shown connected to indicate that the linear pattern, or trend, continues.

EXAMPLE 4 *Career Application*

Sue rents a manicure station in a salon and pays the salon owner $5.50 for each manicure she gives. The amount Sue pays each day, in dollars, is given by $f(x) = 5.50x$, where x is the number of manicures. Graph this function and give its domain and range.

Choose several values of x and make a table of ordered pairs.

Graph the ordered pairs.

x	$f(x) = 5.50x$
0	$f(0) = 5.50(0) = 0$
1	$f(1) = 5.50(1) = 5.50$
2	$f(2) = 5.50(2) = 11.00$
3	$f(3) = 5.50(3) = 16.50$
4	$f(4) = 5.50(4) = 22.00$
5	$f(5) = 5.50(5) = 27.50$

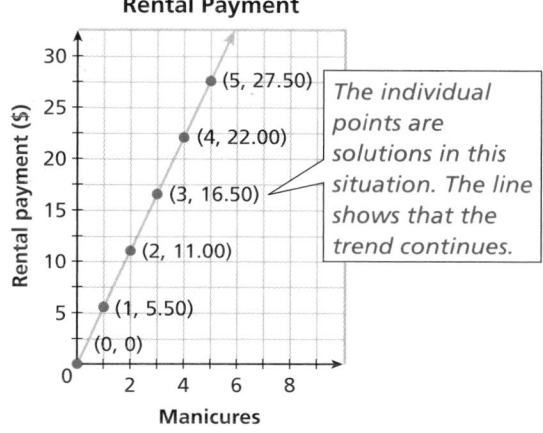

The individual points are solutions in this situation. The line shows that the trend continues.

The number of manicures must be a whole number, so the domain is $\{0, 1, 2, 3, \ldots\}$. The range is $\{0, 5.50, 11.00, 16.50, \ldots\}$.

4. What if...? At another salon, Sue can rent a station for $10.00 per day plus $3.00 per manicure. The amount she would pay each day is given by $f(x) = 3x + 10$, where x is the number of manicures. Graph this function and give its domain and range.

THINK AND DISCUSS

1. Suppose you are given five ordered pairs. When you graph them, four lie on a straight line, but the fifth does not. Are these ordered pairs solutions to one linear equation? Why or why not?

2. In Example 4, why is every point on the line not a solution?

3. GET ORGANIZED Copy and complete the graphic organizer. In each box, describe how to use the information to identify a linear function. Include an example.

Determining Whether a Function Is Linear
- From its graph
- From its equation
- From a list of ordered pairs

California Standards Practice
🔶 6.0, 🔶 7.0, 17.0, 18.0

go.hrw.com
Homework Help Online
KEYWORD: MA8CA 5-1
Parent Resources Online
KEYWORD: MA8CA Parent

GUIDED PRACTICE

1. **Vocabulary** Is the *linear equation* $3x - 2 = y$ in standard form? Explain.

SEE EXAMPLE **1**
p. 256

Graph each linear equation. Then tell whether it represents a function.

2. $y = 2x + 1$ 3. $x = 5$ 4. $-2x + y = 3$

SEE EXAMPLE **2**
p. 257

Without graphing, tell whether each point is on the graph of the given line.

5. $-4x + 2y = 8$; $(1, 6)$ 6. $12x + y = 16$; $\left(\frac{1}{2}, 3\right)$

7. $5x - 3y = 14$; $(-1, -6)$ 8. $\frac{1}{4}x - 2y = -6$; $(16, 5)$

9. $\frac{1}{3}x - 2y = 7$; $(9, -2)$ 10. $-6x - \frac{1}{4}y = 9$; $(-2, -12)$

SEE EXAMPLE **3**
p. 258

Write each equation in standard form and give the values of A, B, and C. Then describe the graph.

11. $2x + 3y = 5$ 12. $2y = 8$ 13. $\frac{x + 3}{5} = y$ 14. $\frac{x}{5} = \frac{y}{3}$

SEE EXAMPLE **4**
p. 259

15. **Transportation** A train travels at a constant speed of 75 mi/h. The function $f(x) = 75x$ gives the distance that the train travels in x hours. Graph this function and give its domain and range.

16. **Entertainment** A movie rental store charges a $6.00 membership fee plus $2.50 for each movie rented. The function $f(x) = 2.50x + 6$ gives the cost of renting x movies. Graph this function and give its domain and range.

PRACTICE AND PROBLEM SOLVING

Independent Practice

For Exercises	See Example
17–19	1
20–27	2
28–31	3
32	4

Extra Practice
Skills Practice p. EP10
Application Practice p. EP28

Graph each linear equation. Then tell whether it represents a function.

17. $3x + 2y = 4$ 18. $-x + 3 = y$ 19. $4.8x + 1.2y = 2.4$

Without graphing, tell whether each point is on the graph of the given line.

20. $12x + 3y = 6$; $(2, -4)$ 21. $-x + 6y = 24$; $(6, 5)$

22. $\frac{1}{2}y = -6x + 1$; $(2, -20)$ 23. $x - 2.7y = 5.4$; $(5.4, 2)$

24. $\frac{2}{3}x = \frac{1}{3}y - 2$; $(6, 18)$ 25. $6x + \frac{1}{2}y = -10\frac{1}{3}$; $\left(-\frac{5}{3}, \frac{2}{3}\right)$

26. $0.35y = 10x - 14$; $(1.4, 0)$ 27. $x - \frac{4}{5}y = -10$; $(0, 10)$

Write each equation in standard form and give the values of A, B, and C. Then describe the graph.

28. $y = 5$ 29. $4y - 2x = 0$ 30. $3 + 4y = 10$ 31. $5 + 3x = 8$

32. **Transportation** The gas tank in Tony's car holds 15 gallons, and the car can travel 25 miles for each gallon of gas. When Tony begins with a full tank of gas, the function $f(x) = -\frac{1}{25}x + 15$ gives the amount of gas $f(x)$ that will be left in the tank after traveling x miles (if he does not buy more gas). Graph this function and give its domain and range.

 33. **Reasoning** If you know that $AB = 0$ and $A \neq B$, what can you say about the equation $Ax + By = 1$? Describe the graph.

Tell whether the given ordered pairs all lie on the same line.

34.

x	2	2	2	2	2
y	5	4	3	2	1

35.

x	−8	−6	−4	−2	0
y	2	0	−2	−4	−6

36.

x	−12	−10	−6	−2	2	4	6
y	−0.25	0	0.25	0.50	0.75	1	1.25

37.

x	−5	−1	0	3	5	7	11
y	1	1	1	1	1	1	1

Tell whether each equation is linear. If so, write the equation in standard form and give the values of *A*, *B*, and *C*.

38. $2x - 8y = 16$ **39.** $y = 4x + 2$ **40.** $2x = \dfrac{y}{3} - 4$

41. $\dfrac{4}{x} = y$ **42.** $\dfrac{x+4}{2} = \dfrac{y-4}{3}$ **43.** $x = 7$

44. $xy = 6$ **45.** $3x - 5 + y = 2y - 4$ **46.** $y = -x + 2$

47. $5x = 2y - 3$ **48.** $2y = -6$ **49.** $y = \sqrt{x}$

Graph each linear equation.

50. $y = 3x + 7$ **51.** $y = x + 25$ **52.** $y = 8 - x$ **53.** $y = 2x$

54. $-2y = -3x + 6$ **55.** $y - x = 4$ **56.** $y - 2x = -3$ **57.** $x = 5 + y$

58. Measurement One inch is equal to approximately 2.5 centimeters. Let *x* represent inches and *y* represent centimeters. Write an equation in standard form relating *x* and *y*. Give the values of *A*, *B*, and *C*.

59. Wages Molly earns $8.00 an hour at her job.

   a. Let *x* represent the number of hours that Molly works. Write a function using *x* and $f(x)$ that describes Molly's pay for working *x* hours.

   b. Graph this function.

   c. Is this function a linear function? Explain.

 60. Write About It For $y = 2x - 1$, make a table of ordered pairs and a graph. Describe the relationships between the equation, the table, and the graph.

CONCEPT CONNECTION

61. This problem will prepare you for the Concept Connection on page 288.

Juan is running on a treadmill. The table shows the number of Calories Juan burns as a function of time.

   a. Create a graph of the data.

   b. How can you tell from the graph that the relationship is linear?

Time (min)	Calories
3	27
6	54
9	81
12	108
15	135
18	162
21	189

62. **Critical Thinking** Describe a real-world situation that can be represented by a linear function whose domain and range must be limited. Give your function and its domain and range.

63. **Physical Science** A ball was dropped from a height of 100 meters. Its height above the ground in meters at different times after its release is given in the table. Are all of these ordered pairs solutions to one linear equation? Explain.

Time (s)	0	1	2	3
Height (m)	100	90.2	60.8	11.8

64. **Critical Thinking** Is the equation $x = 9$ a linear equation? Does it describe a linear function? Explain.

Multiple Choice For Exercises 65 and 66, choose the best answer.

65. Which is NOT a linear equation?

    Ⓐ $y = 8x$ Ⓑ $y = x + 8$ Ⓒ $y = \dfrac{8}{x}$ Ⓓ $y = 8 - x$

66. The speed of sound in 0°C air is about 331 feet per second. Which equation could be used to describe the distance in feet d that sound will travel in air in s seconds?

    Ⓐ $d = s + 331$ Ⓑ $d = 331s$ Ⓒ $s = 331d$ Ⓓ $s = 331 - d$

67. **Extended Response** Write your own linear function. Show that it is a linear function in two different ways.

CHALLENGE AND EXTEND

68. What equation describes the x-axis? the y-axis? Do these equations represent linear functions?

Geometry Copy and complete each table below. Then tell whether the table shows a linear relationship.

69.

Perimeter of a Square	
Side Length	Perimeter
1	
2	
3	
4	

70.

Area of a Square	
Side Length	Area
1	
2	
3	
4	

71.

Volume of a Cube	
Side Length	Volume
1	
2	
3	
4	

SPIRAL STANDARDS REVIEW

3.0, 4.0

Solve each equation. Check your answer. *(Lesson 2-3)*

72. $4(t + 3) = 36$ 73. $3(2 - x) = 9$ 74. $k + 3k + 2 = -6$ 75. $3h - \dfrac{1}{6} + h = \dfrac{5}{18}$

Solve each equation. Check your answer. *(Lesson 2-4)*

76. $6m + 5 = 3m - 4$ 77. $2(t - 4) = 3 - (3t + 1)$ 78. $9y + 5 - 2y = 2y + 5 - y + 3$

Solve each inequality. *(Lesson 3-7)*

79. $|t| - 9 \le -10$ 80. $|z - 8| + 2 > 4$ 81. $|x - 1| - 11 \le 12$

82. $|x - 5| + 5.6 > 4.7$ 83. $|0.5x| + 7.4 < 4.5$ 84. $|x - 7| + \dfrac{1}{4} \ge \dfrac{1}{2}$

Using Intercepts

Vocabulary
y-intercept
x-intercept

Who uses this?

Divers can use intercepts to determine the time a safe ascent will take.

A diver explored the ocean floor 120 feet below the surface and then ascended at a rate of 30 feet per minute. The graph shows the diver's elevation below sea level during the ascent.

A **y-intercept** is the *y*-coordinate of any point where a graph intersects the *y*-axis. The *x*-coordinate of this point is always 0.

An **x-intercept** is the *x*-coordinate of any point where a graph intersects the *x*-axis. The *y*-coordinate of this point is always 0.

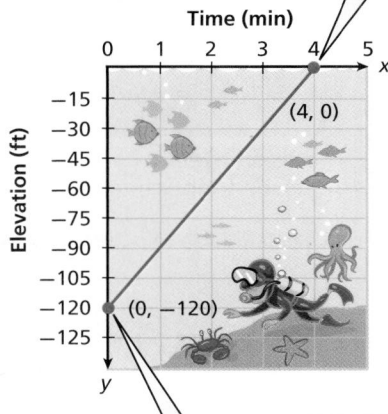

The *x*-intercept is 4. It represents the time that the diver reaches the surface, or when depth = 0.

The *y*-intercept is −120. It represents the diver's elevation at the start of the ascent, or when time = 0.

EXAMPLE **1** **Finding Intercepts**

Find the *x*- and *y*-intercepts.

A

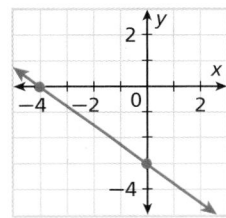

The graph intersects the *y*-axis at (0, −3).
The *y*-intercept is −3.

The graph intersects the *x*-axis at (−4, 0).
The *x*-intercept is −4.

B $3x - 2y = 12$

To find the *x*-intercept, replace *y* with 0 and solve for *x*.

$$3x - 2y = 12$$
$$3x - 2(0) = 12$$
$$3x - 0 = 12$$
$$3x = 12$$

$$\frac{3x}{3} = \frac{12}{3}$$

$$x = 4$$

The *x*-intercept is 4.

To find the *y*-intercept, replace *x* with 0 and solve for *y*.

$$3x - 2y = 12$$
$$3(0) - 2y = 12$$
$$0 - 2y = 12$$
$$-2y = 12$$

$$\frac{-2y}{-2} = \frac{12}{-2}$$

$$y = -6$$

The *y*-intercept is −6.

 **Find the *x*- and *y*-intercepts.**

1a.

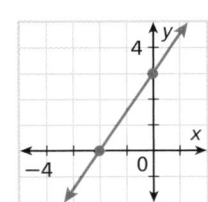

1b. $-3x + 5y = 30$

1c. $4x + 2y = 16$

Finding Intercepts

I use the "cover-up" method to find intercepts. To use this method, make sure the equation is in standard form first.

If I have $4x - 2y = 12$:

First, I cover $4x$ with my finger and solve the equation I can still see.

$$\text{(✋)} - 2y = 12$$
$$y = -6$$

The y-intercept is −6.

Then I cover $-2y$ with my finger and do the same thing.

$$4x \text{ (✋)} = 12$$
$$x = 3$$

The x-intercept is 3.

EXAMPLE 2 *Travel Application*

The Sandia Peak Tramway in Albuquerque, New Mexico, travels a distance of about 4500 meters to the top of Sandia Peak. Its speed is 300 meters per minute. The function $f(x) = 4500 - 300x$ gives the tram's distance in meters from the top of the peak after x minutes. Graph this function and find the intercepts. What does each intercept represent?

Neither time nor distance can be negative, so choose several nonnegative values for x. Use the function to generate ordered pairs.

x	0	2	5	10	15
$f(x) = 4500 - 300x$	4500	3900	3000	1500	0

Graph the ordered pairs. Connect the points with a line.

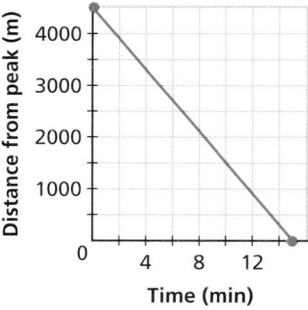

Sandia Peak Tramway

- y-intercept: 4500. This is the starting distance from the top (time = 0).
- x-intercept: 15. This the time when the tram reaches the peak (distance = 0).

Caution!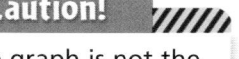

The graph is not the path of the tram. Even though the line is descending, the graph describes the distance from the peak as the tram goes *up* the mountain.

 **2.** The school store sells pens for $2.00 and notebooks for $3.00. The equation $2x + 3y = 60$ describes the number of pens x and notebooks y that you can buy for $60.

a. Graph the function and find its intercepts.

b. What does each intercept represent?

Remember, to graph a line, you need to plot only two ordered pairs.
It is often simplest to find the ordered pairs that contain the intercepts.

EXAMPLE **3** | **Graphing Linear Equations by Using Intercepts**

Use intercepts to graph the line given by each equation.

A $2x - 4y = 8$

Step 1 Find the intercepts.

x-intercept:	y-intercept:
$2x - 4y = 8$	$2x - 4y = 8$
$2x - 4(0) = 8$	$2(0) - 4y = 8$
$2x = 8$	$-4y = 8$
$\dfrac{2x}{2} = \dfrac{8}{2}$	$\dfrac{-4y}{-4} = \dfrac{8}{-4}$
$x = 4$	$y = -2$

Step 2 Graph the line.

Plot (4, 0) and (0, −2).
Connect with a straight line.

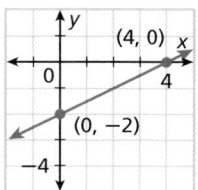

Helpful Hint

You can use a third point to check your line. Either choose a point from your graph and check it in the equation, or use the equation to generate a point and check that it is on your graph.

B $\dfrac{2}{3}y = 4 - \dfrac{1}{2}x$

Step 1 Write the equation in standard form.

$$6\left(\dfrac{2}{3}y\right) = 6\left(4 - \dfrac{1}{2}x\right)$$ *Multiply both sides by 6, the LCD of the fractions, to clear the fractions.*
$$4y = 24 - 3x$$
$$3x + 4y = 24$$ *Write the equation in standard form.*

Step 2 Find the intercepts.

x-intercept:	y-intercept:
$3x + 4y = 24$	$3x + 4y = 24$
$3x + 4(0) = 24$	$3(0) + 4y = 24$
$3x = 24$	$4y = 24$
$\dfrac{3x}{3} = \dfrac{24}{3}$	$\dfrac{4y}{4} = \dfrac{24}{4}$
$x = 8$	$y = 6$

Step 3 Graph the line.

Plot (8, 0) and (0, 6).
Connect with a straight line.

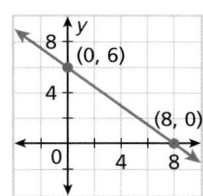

 Use intercepts to graph the line given by each equation.

3a. $-3x + 4y = -12$ **3b.** $y = \dfrac{1}{3}x - 2$

THINK AND DISCUSS

1. A function has x-intercept 4 and y-intercept 2. Name two points on the graph of this function.

2. What is the y-intercept of $2.304x + y = 4.318$? What is the x-intercept of $x - 92.4920y = -21.5489$?

3. GET ORGANIZED Copy and complete the graphic organizer.

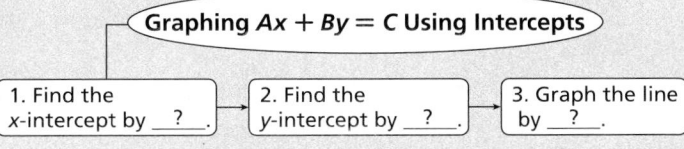

California Standards Practice
🔑 6.0, 24.1, 25.1

go.hrw.com
Homework Help Online
KEYWORD: MA8CA 5-2
Parent Resources Online
KEYWORD: MA8CA Parent

GUIDED PRACTICE

1. **Vocabulary** The ____?____ is the y-coordinate of the point where a graph crosses the y-axis. (*x-intercept* or *y-intercept*)

SEE EXAMPLE **1**
p. 263

Find the x- and y-intercepts.

2.
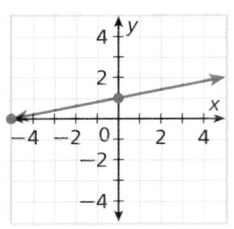

3.
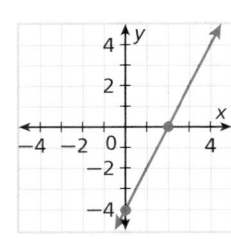

4.
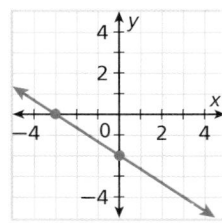

5. $2x - 4y = 4$ 6. $-2y = 3x - 6$ 7. $4y + 5x = 2y - 3x + 16$

SEE EXAMPLE **2**
p. 264

8. **Biology** To thaw a specimen stored at $-25°C$, the temperature of a refrigeration tank is raised $5°C$ every hour. The temperature in the tank after x hours can be described by the function $f(x) = -25 + 5x$.

   a. Graph the function and find its intercepts.

   b. What does each intercept represent?

SEE EXAMPLE **3**
p. 265

Use intercepts to graph the line given by each equation.

9. $4x - 5y = 20$ 10. $y = 2x + 4$ 11. $\frac{1}{3}x - \frac{1}{4}y = 2$ 12. $-5y + 2x = -10$

PRACTICE AND PROBLEM SOLVING

Independent Practice

For Exercises	See Example
13–21	1
22–23	2
24–29	3

Extra Practice
Skills Practice p. EP10
Application Practice p. EP28

Find the x- and y-intercepts.

13.
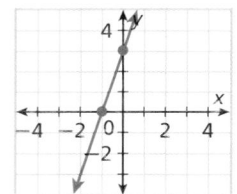

14.
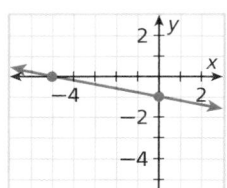

15.
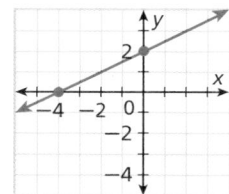

16. $6x + 3y = 12$ 17. $4y - 8 = 2x$ 18. $-2y + x = 2y - 8$

19. $4x + y = 8$ 20. $y - 3x = -15$ 21. $2x + y = 10x - 1$

22. **Environmental Science** A fishing lake was stocked with 300 bass. Each year, the population decreases by 25. The population of bass in the lake after x years is represented by the function $f(x) = 300 - 25x$.

   a. Graph the function and find its intercepts.

   b. What does each intercept represent?

23. **Sports** Julie is running a 5-kilometer race. She ran 1 kilometer every 5 minutes. Julie's distance from the finish line after x minutes is represented by the function $f(x) = 5 - \frac{1}{5}x$.

   a. Graph the function and find its intercepts.

   b. What does each intercept represent?

Use intercepts to graph the line given by each equation.

24. $4x - 6y = 12$
25. $2x + 3y = 18$
26. $\frac{1}{2}x - 4y = 4$
27. $y - x = -1$
28. $5x + 3y = 15$
29. $x - 3y = -1$

Biology

30. **Biology** A bamboo plant is growing 1 foot per day. When you first measure it, it is 4 feet tall.

  a. Write an equation to describe the height y, in feet, of the bamboo plant x days after you measure it.

  b. What is the y-intercept?

  c. What is the meaning of the y-intercept in this problem?

31. **Estimation** Look at the scatter plot and trend line.

  a. Estimate the x- and y-intercepts.

  b. What is the real-world meaning of each intercept?

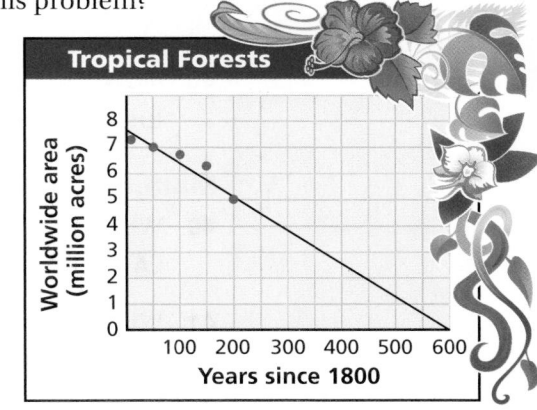

Bamboo is the world's fastest-growing woody plant. Some varieties can grow more than 30 centimeters a day and up to 40 meters tall.

32. **Personal Finance** A bank employee notices an abandoned checking account with a balance of $412. If the bank charges a $4 monthly fee for the account, the function $b = 412 - 4m$ shows the balance b in the account after m months.

  a. Graph the function.

  b. Find the intercepts. What does each intercept represent?

  c. When will the bank account balance be 0?

33. **Reasoning** Complete the following to learn about intercepts of horizontal and vertical lines.

  a. Graph $x = -6$, $x = 1$, and $x = 5$. Find the intercepts.

  b. Graph $y = -3$, $y = 2$, and $y = 7$. Find the intercepts.

  c. Based on your results in parts **a** and **b**, use inductive reasoning to make a conjecture about the intercepts of horizontal lines $x = k$ ($k \neq 0$) and vertical lines $y = c$ ($c \neq 0$). What happens when k and c are equal to 0?

For help with inductive reasoning, see p. 233.

Match each equation with a graph.

34. $-2x - y = 4$
35. $y = 4 - 2x$
36. $2y + 4x = 8$
37. $4x - 2y = 8$

A.

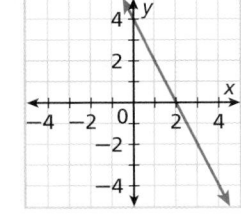

B.

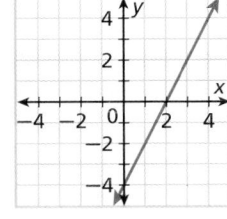

C.

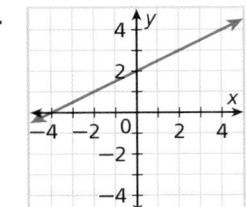

D.

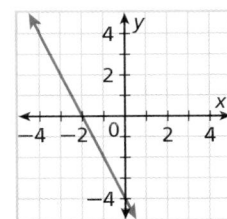

38. This problem will prepare you for the Concept Connection on page 288.

Kristyn rode a stationary bike at the gym. She programmed the timer for 20 minutes. The display counted backward to show how much time remained in her workout. It also showed her mileage.

   a. What are the intercepts?

   b. What do the intercepts represent?

Time Remaining (min)	Distance Covered (mi)
20	0
16	0.35
12	0.70
8	1.05
4	1.40
0	1.75

39. Write About It Write a real-world problem that could be modeled by a linear function whose x-intercept is 5 and whose y-intercept is 60.

Multiple Choice For Exercises 40 and 41, choose the best answer.

40. Which is the x-intercept of $-2x = 9y - 18$?

   (A) -9 (B) -2 (C) 2 (D) 9

41. Which situation could be represented by the graph?

   (A) Jamie owed her uncle $200. Each week for 40 weeks she paid him $5.

   (B) Jamie owed her uncle $200. Each week for 5 weeks she paid him $40.

   (C) Jamie owed her uncle $40. Each week for 5 weeks she paid him $200.

   (D) Jamie owed her uncle $40. Each week for 200 weeks she paid him $5.

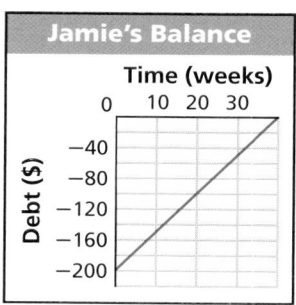

42. Gridded Response What is the y-intercept of $60x + 55y = 660$?

CHALLENGE AND EXTEND

Use intercepts to graph the line given by each equation.

43. $\frac{1}{2}x + \frac{1}{5}y = 1$ **44.** $0.5x - 0.2y = 0.75$ **45.** $y = \frac{3}{8}x + 6$

 **46. Reasoning** For any linear equation $Ax + By = C$, where $A \neq 0$ and $B \neq 0$, show that the x-intercept is $\frac{C}{A}$ and the y-intercept is $\frac{C}{B}$.

 SPIRAL STANDARDS REVIEW   🔑 4.0, 🔑 15.0

47. Marlon's fish tank is 80% filled with water. Based on the measurements shown, what volume of the tank is NOT filled with water? *(Lesson 2-5)*

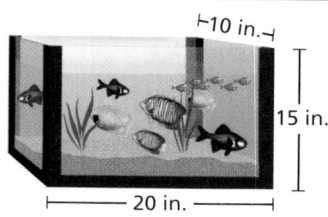

Solve each inequality and graph the solutions. *(Lesson 3-4)*

48. $2(t - 1) + 2 \leq -16$ **49.** $m + 4 \geq 2(-3 + 2)$ **50.** $-2(w + 2) > 10$

Tell whether the given ordered pairs all lie on the same line. *(Lesson 5-1)*

51. $\{(-2, 0), (0, 3), (2, 6), (4, 9), (6, 12)\}$ **52.** $\{(0, 0), (1, 1), (4, 2), (9, 3), (16, 4)\}$

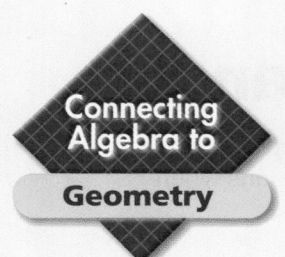

Connecting Algebra to Geometry

Area in the Coordinate Plane

Lines in the coordinate plane can form the sides of polygons. You can use points on these lines to help you find the areas of these polygons.

California Standards

Reinforcement of **7MG2.1 Use formulas routinely for finding the** perimeter and **area of basic two-dimensional figures** and the surface area and volume of basic three-dimensional figures, **including rectangles,** parallelograms, trapezoids, squares, **triangles,** circles, prisms, and cylinders.

Example

Find the area of the triangle formed by the x-axis, the y-axis, and the line given by $3x + 2y = 18$.

Step 1 Find the intercepts of $3x + 2y = 18$.

x-intercept: y-intercept:

$$3x + 2y = 18 \qquad\quad 3x + 2y = 18$$
$$3x + 2(0) = 18 \qquad 3(0) + 2y = 18$$
$$3x = 18 \qquad\qquad\quad 2y = 18$$
$$x = 6 \qquad\qquad\qquad y = 9$$

Step 2 Use the intercepts to graph the line. The x-intercept is 6, so plot $(6, 0)$. The y-intercept is 9, so plot $(0, 9)$. Connect with a straight line. Then shade the triangle formed by the line and the axes, as described.

Step 3 Recall that the area of a triangle is given by $A = \frac{1}{2}bh$.

- The length of the base is **6**.
- The height is **9**.

Step 4 Substitute these values into the formula.

$$A = \frac{1}{2}bh$$

$$A = \frac{1}{2}(6)(9) \qquad \textit{Substitute into the area formula.}$$

$$= \frac{1}{2}(54) \qquad \textit{Simplify.}$$

$$= 27$$

The area of the triangle is 27 square units.

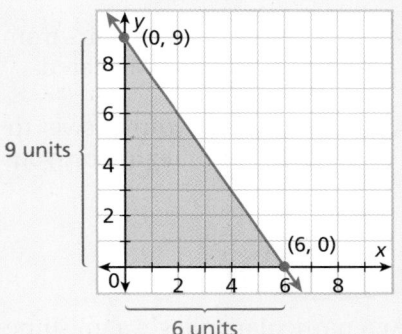

9 units

6 units

Try This

1. Find the area of the triangle formed by the x-axis, the y-axis, and the line given by $3x + 2y = 12$.

2. Find the area of the triangle formed by the x-axis, the y-axis, and the line given by $y = 6 - x$.

3. What polygon is formed by the x-axis, the y-axis, the line given by $y = 6$, and the line given by $x = 4$? What is its area?

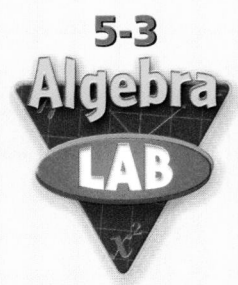

5-3

Algebra LAB

Explore Constant Changes

There are many real-life situations in which the amount of change is constant. In these activities, you will explore what happens when

- a quantity increases by a constant amount.
- a quantity decreases by a constant amount.

Use with Lesson 5-3

24.1 Students explain the difference between inductive and deductive reasoning and identify and **provide examples** of each.

Activity 1

Janice has read 7 books for her summer reading club. She plans to read 2 books each week for the rest of the summer. The table shows the total number of books that Janice will have read after different numbers of weeks have passed.

1 What number is added to the number of books in each row to get the number of books in the next row?

2 What does your answer to Problem 1 represent in Janice's situation? Describe the meaning of the constant change.

3 Graph the ordered pairs from the table. Describe how the points are related.

4 Look again at your answer to Problem 1. Explain how this number affects your graph.

Janice's Summer Reading	
Week	**Total Books Read**
0	7
1	9
2	11
3	13
4	15
5	17

Try This

At a particular college, a full-time student must take at least 12 credit hours per semester and may take up to 18 credit hours per semester. Tuition costs $200 per credit hour.

1. Copy and complete the table by using the information above.

2. What number is added to the cost in each row to get the cost in the next row?

3. What does your answer to Problem 2 above represent in the situation? Describe the meaning of the constant change.

4. Graph the ordered pairs from the table. Describe how the points are related.

5. Look again at your answer to Problem 2. Explain how this number affects the shape of your graph.

6. Compare your graphs from Activity 1 and Problem 4. How are they alike? How are they different?

7. Reasoning Make a conjecture about the graph of any situation that involves repeated addition of a positive number. Why do you think your conjecture is correct?

Tuition Costs	
Credit Hours	**Cost ($)**
12	
13	
14	
15	
16	
17	
18	

Activity 2

An airplane is 3000 miles from its destination. The plane is traveling at a rate of 540 miles per hour. The table shows how far the plane is from its destination after various amounts of time have passed.

1 What number is subtracted from the distance in each row to get the distance in the next row?

2 What does your answer to Problem 1 represent in the situation? Describe the meaning of the constant change.

3 Graph the ordered pairs from the table. Describe how the points are related.

4 Look again at your answer to Problem 1. Explain how this number affects your graph.

Airplane's Distance	
Time (h)	Distance to Destination (mi)
0	3000
1	2460
2	1920
3	1380
4	840

Try This

A television game show begins with 20 contestants. Each week, the players vote 2 contestants off the show.

8. Copy and complete the table by using the information above.

9. What number is subtracted from the number of contestants in each row to get the number of contestants in the next row?

10. What does your answer to Problem 9 represent in the situation? Describe the meaning of the constant change.

11. Graph the ordered pairs from the table. Describe how the points are related.

12. Look again at your answer to Problem 9. Explain how this number affects the shape of your graph.

13. Compare your graphs from Activity 2 and Problem 11. How are they alike? How are they different?

14. Reasoning Make a conjecture about the graph of any situation that involves repeated subtraction of a positive number. Why do you think your conjecture is correct?

15. Compare your two graphs from Activity 1 with your two graphs from Activity 2. How are they alike? How are they different?

16. Reasoning Make a conjecture to describe how the graphs of situations involving repeated subtraction differ from graphs of situations involving repeated addition. Explain your answer.

Game Show	
Week	Contestants Remaining
0	20
1	
2	
3	
4	
5	
6	

5-3 Slope

California Standards

Preparation for 8.0 Students understand the concepts of parallel lines and perpendicular lines and how their slopes are related. Students are able to find the equation of a line perpendicular to a given line that passes through a given point.

Also covered: **6.0**

Vocabulary
rate of change
rise
run
slope

Why learn this?

You can use the slope formula to find how quickly a quantity, such as the amount of water in a reservoir, is changing. (See Example 5.)

A **rate of change** is a ratio that compares the amount of change in a dependent variable to the amount of change in an independent variable.

$$\text{rate of change} = \frac{\text{change in dependent variable } (y)}{\text{change in independent variable } (x)}$$

For any two points on a nonvertical line, this ratio is constant. The constant rate of change of a nonvertical line is called the *slope* of the line.

Slope of a Line

The **rise** is the difference in the **y-values** of two points on a line.

The **run** is the difference in the **x-values** of two points on a line.

The **slope** of a line (*m*) is the ratio of **rise** to **run** for any two points on the line.

$$m = \frac{\text{rise}}{\text{run}}$$

If (x_1, y_1) and (x_2, y_2) are two points on a line, then the slope of the line can be found using the slope formula.

$$m = \frac{y_2 - y_1}{x_2 - x_1}$$

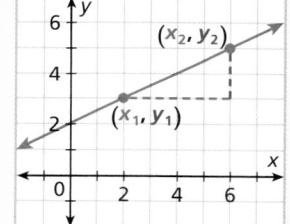

EXAMPLE 1 — Finding Slope from a Graph

Find the slope of the line.

Helpful Hint

Notice that it does not matter which point you start at. The slope is the same.

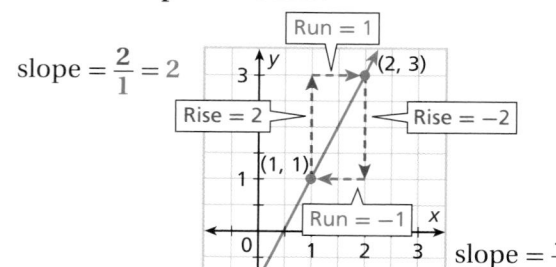

$$\text{slope} = \frac{2}{1} = 2$$

$$\text{slope} = \frac{-2}{-1} = 2$$

Begin at one point and count vertically to find the rise.

Then count horizontally to the second point to find the run.

1. Find the slope of the line.

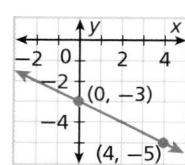

EXAMPLE 2 **Finding Slopes of Horizontal and Vertical Lines**

Find the slope of each line.

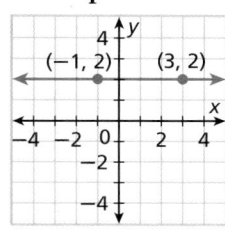 A

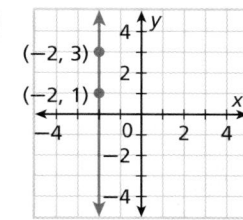 B

$$\frac{\text{rise}}{\text{run}} = \frac{0}{4} = 0$$

The slope is 0.

$$\frac{\text{rise}}{\text{run}} = \frac{2}{0}$$ *You cannot divide by 0.*

The slope is undefined.

 **Find the slope of each line.**

2a.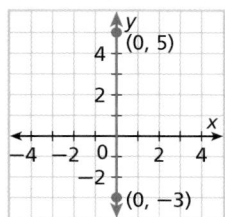

2b.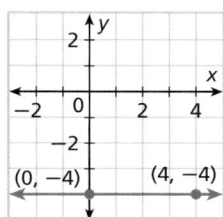

If you know 2 different points on a line, you can use the slope formula to find the slope of the line.

EXAMPLE 3 **Finding Slope by Using the Slope Formula**

Find the slope of the line that contains $(4, -2)$ and $(-1, 2)$.

$$m = \frac{y_2 - y_1}{x_2 - x_1}$$ *Use the slope formula.*

$$= \frac{2 - (-2)}{-1 - 4}$$ *Substitute $(4, -2)$ for (x_1, y_1) and $(-1, 2)$ for (x_2, y_2).*

$$= \frac{4}{-5} = -\frac{4}{5}$$ *Simplify.*

Reading Math

The small numbers to the bottom right of the variables are called subscripts. Read x_1 as "x sub one" and y_2 as "y sub two."

 **3a.** Find the slope of the line that contains $(-2, -2)$ and $(7, -2)$.

3b. Find the slope of the line that contains $(5, -7)$ and $(6, -4)$.

As shown in the previous examples, slope can be positive, negative, zero, or undefined.

 Know it! Note

Positive Slope	Negative Slope	Zero Slope	Undefined Slope
Line rises from left to right.	Line falls from left to right.	Horizontal line	Vertical line

EXAMPLE 4 **Describing Slope**

Tell whether the slope of each line is positive, negative, zero, or undefined.

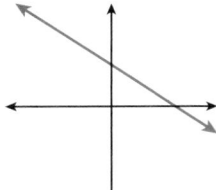 A

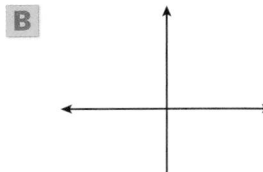 B

The line falls from left to right.
The slope is negative.

The line is horizontal.
The slope is 0.

 **CHECK IT OUT!** Tell whether the slope of each line is positive, negative, zero, or undefined.

4a. 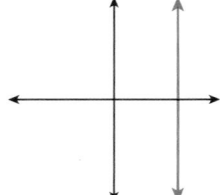 **4b.**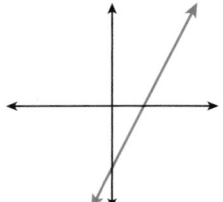

Remember that slope is a rate of change. In real-world problems, finding the slope can give you information about how a quantity is changing.

EXAMPLE 5 *Application*

Water is being released from a reservoir. The graph shows how much water is in the reservoir at different times. Find the slope of the line. Then tell what the slope represents.

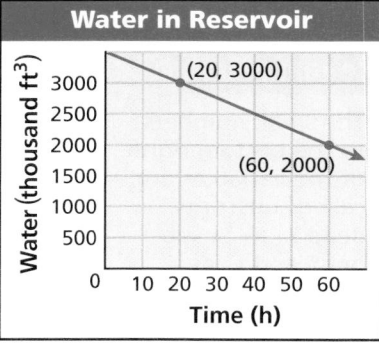

Step 1 Use the slope formula.

$$m = \frac{y_2 - y_1}{x_2 - x_1}$$

$$= \frac{2000 - 3000}{60 - 20}$$

$$= \frac{-1000}{40}$$

$$= -25$$

Caution! //////

Pay attention to the scales on the axes. One square on the grid may not represent 1 unit, as in Example 5. Also, one square on the x-axis may not represent the same quantity as one square on the y-axis.

Step 2 Tell what the slope represents.

In this situation, *y* represents **volume of water** and *x* represents **time**.

So slope represents $\frac{\textbf{change in volume}}{\text{change in time}}$ in units of

$\frac{\textbf{thousands of cubic feet}}{\text{hours}}$.

A slope of −25 means the amount of water in the reservoir is decreasing (negative change) at a rate of 25 thousand cubic feet each hour.

 **5.** The graph shows the height of a plant over a period of days. Find the slope of the line. Then tell what the slope represents.

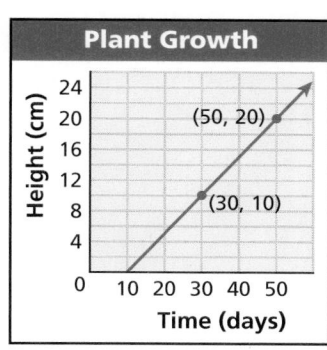

Plant Growth

If you know the equation of a line, you can find its slope by using any two ordered-pair solutions. It is often easiest to use the ordered pairs that contain the intercepts.

EXAMPLE 6   **Finding Slope from an Equation**

Find the slope of the line given by $6x - 5y = 30$.

Step 1 Find the x-intercept.

$$6x - 5y = 30$$
$$6x - 5(0) = 30 \quad \text{Let } y = 0.$$
$$6x = 30$$
$$\frac{6x}{6} = \frac{30}{6}$$
$$x = 5$$

Step 2 Find the y-intercept.

$$6x - 5y = 30$$
$$6(0) - 5y = 30 \quad \text{Let } x = 0.$$
$$-5y = 30$$
$$\frac{-5y}{-5} = \frac{30}{-5}$$
$$y = -6$$

Step 3 The line contains $(5, 0)$ and $(0, -6)$ Use the slope formula.

$$m = \frac{y_2 - y_1}{x_2 - x_1} = \frac{-6 - 0}{0 - 5} = \frac{-6}{-5} = \frac{6}{5}$$

 **6.** Find the slope of the line given by $2x + 3y = 12$.

A line's slope is a measure of its steepness. Some lines are steeper than others. As the absolute value of the slope increases, the line becomes steeper.

Comparing Slopes

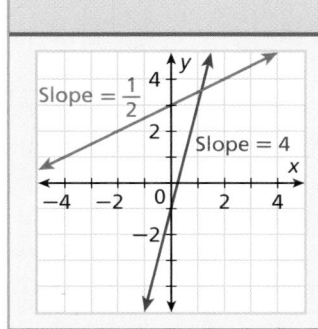

The line with slope **4** is steeper than the line with slope $\frac{1}{2}$.	The line with slope **−2** is steeper than the line with slope **−1**.	The line with slope **−3** is steeper than the line with slope $\frac{3}{4}$.
$\left\vert 4 \right\vert > \left\vert \frac{1}{2} \right\vert$	$\left\vert -2 \right\vert > \left\vert -1 \right\vert$	$\left\vert -3 \right\vert > \left\vert \frac{3}{4} \right\vert$

THINK AND DISCUSS

1. What is the rise shown in the graph? What is the run? What is the slope?

2. Two points lie on a line. When you substitute their coordinates into the slope formula, you get 0 in the denominator. Describe the graph of this line.

3. Would you rather climb a hill with a slope of 4 or a hill with a slope of 2.5? Explain your answer.

4. GET ORGANIZED Copy and complete the graphic organizer. In each box, show how to find slope using the given method.

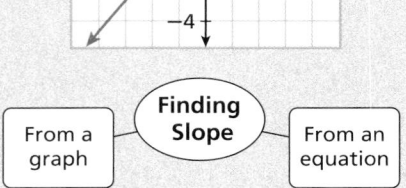

5-3 Exercises

California Standards Practice
Preparation for 8.0;
🔑 6.0, 24.1

go.hrw.com
Homework Help Online
KEYWORD: MA8CA 5-3
Parent Resources Online
KEYWORD: MA8CA Parent

GUIDED PRACTICE

Vocabulary Apply the vocabulary from this lesson to answer each question.

1. ____?____ is the difference in the y-values of two points on a line. (*Rise* or *Run*)

2. The *slope* of any nonvertical line is ____?____. (*positive* or *constant*)

SEE EXAMPLE **1**
p. 272

Find the slope of each line.

3.

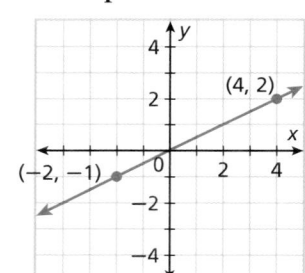

4.

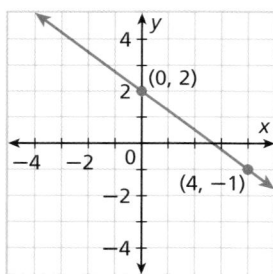

SEE EXAMPLE **2**
p. 273

5.

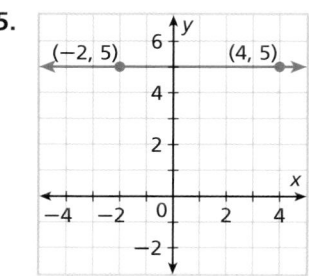

6.

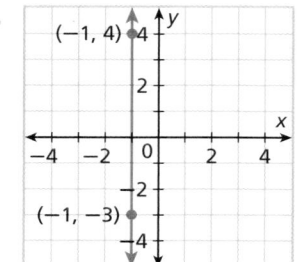

Find the slope of the line that contains each pair of points.

7. $(3, 6)$ and $(6, 9)$ **8.** $(2, 7)$ and $(4, 4)$ **9.** $(-1, -5)$ and $(-9, -1)$

10. $(5, 3)$ and $(-2, 0.5)$ **11.** $\left(\frac{3}{4}, \frac{7}{5}\right)$ and $\left(\frac{1}{4}, \frac{2}{5}\right)$ **12.** $(-2, 3)$ and $(2, -3)$

Tell whether the slope of each line is positive, negative, zero, or undefined.

13. 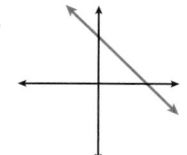   **14.**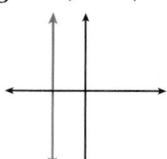

Find the slope of each line. Then tell what the slope represents.

15. 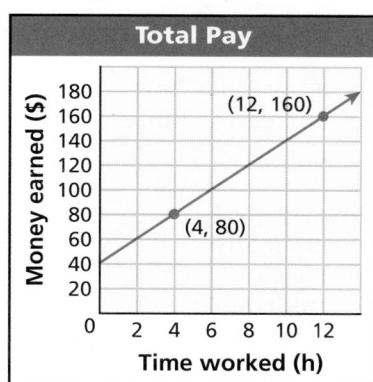   **16.**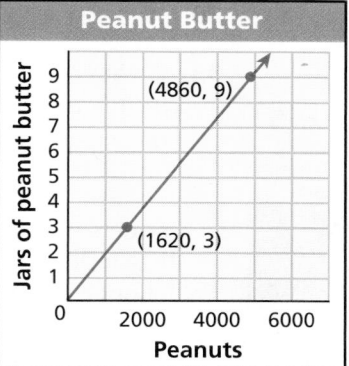

Find the slope of the line given by each equation.

17. $8x + 2y = 96$ **18.** $5x = 90 - 9y$ **19.** $5y = 160 + 9x$

PRACTICE AND PROBLEM SOLVING

Independent Practice

For Exercises	See Example
20	1
21	2
22–24	3
25–27	4
28–29	5
30–32	6

Extra Practice

Skills Practice p. EP10

Application Practice p. EP28

Find the slope of each line.

20. 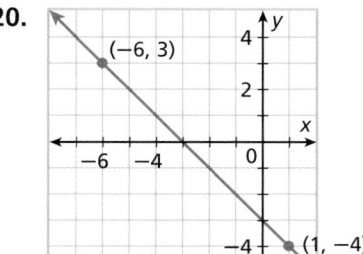   **21.**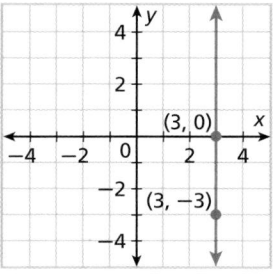

Find the slope of the line that contains each pair of points.

22. $(2, 5)$ and $(3, 1)$ **23.** $(-9, -5)$ and $(6, -5)$ **24.** $(3, 4)$ and $(3, -1)$

Tell whether the slope of each line is positive, negative, zero, or undefined.

25. 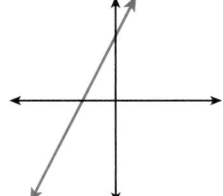   **26.** 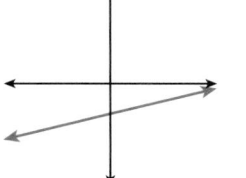   **27.**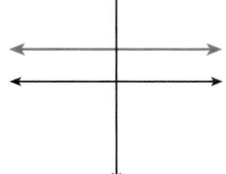

Find the slope of each line. Then tell what the slope represents.

28.

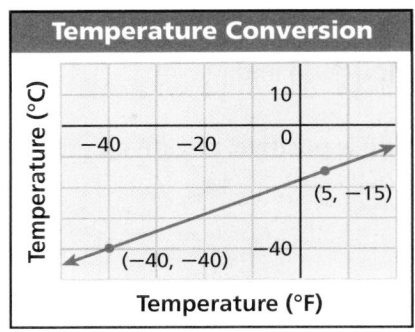

Temperature Conversion

(5, −15)

(−40, −40)

29.

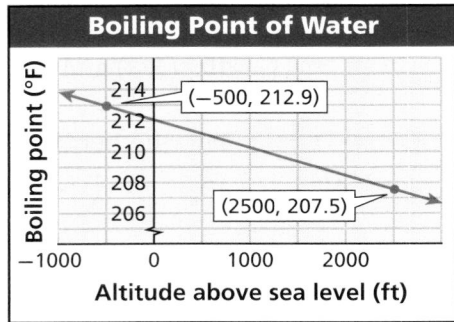

Boiling Point of Water

(−500, 212.9)

(2500, 207.5)

Find the slope of the line given by each equation.

30. $7x + 13y = 91$

31. $5y = 130 - 13x$

32. $7 - 3y = 9x$

California **LINK**

Travel

Lombard Street in San Francisco has 8 sharp, hair-pin turns to help make navigating the steep street easier for pedestrians and drivers.

33. Construction Most staircases in use today have 9-inch treads and $8\frac{1}{2}$-inch risers. What is the slope of a staircase with these measurements?

34. Travel Filbert Street is one of the steepest streets in San Francisco. Part of Filbert Street has a slope of 0.315. In this part, a vertical change of 1 unit corresponds to a horizontal change of about how many units? Round your answer to the nearest thousandth.

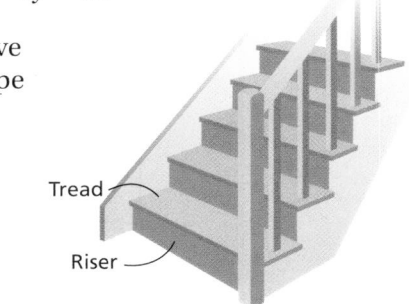

Tread

Riser

35. Estimation The graph shows the number of files scanned by a computer virus detection program over time.

   a. What does point A represent?

   b. Estimate the coordinates of point A.

   c. Estimate the coordinates of point B.

   d. Use your answers from parts **b** and **c** to estimate the rate of change (in files per second) between points A and B.

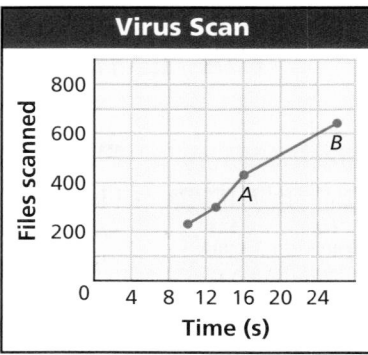

Virus Scan

Each table shows a linear relationship. Find the slope.

36.

x	y
1	18.5
2	22
3	25.5
4	29

37.

x	y
0	25
2	45
4	65
6	85

38. Reasoning Use deductive reasoning and the slope formula to prove that

   a. the slope of any horizontal line is 0.

   b. the slope of any vertical line is undefined.

39. Write About It You are given the coordinates of two points on a line. Describe two different ways to find the slope of that line.

40. What is the slope of the line given by $4x = 0$? by $5y = 0$?

CONCEPT CONNECTION

41. This problem will prepare you for the Concept Connection on page 288.

    a. The graph shows a relationship between a person's age and his or her maximum heart rate in beats per minute. Find the slope. Then tell what the slope represents.

    b. Describe the rate of change in this situation.

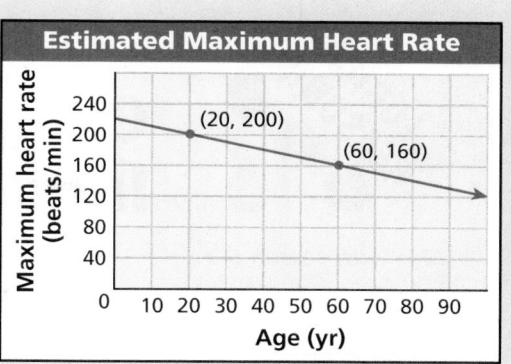

Multiple Choice For Exercises 42–44, choose the best answer.

42. A line with slope $-\dfrac{1}{3}$ could pass through which of the following pairs of points?

    Ⓐ $\left(0, -\dfrac{1}{3}\right)$ and $(1, 1)$ Ⓒ $(0, 0)$ and $\left(-\dfrac{1}{3}, -\dfrac{1}{3}\right)$

    Ⓑ $(-6, 5)$ and $(-3, 4)$ Ⓓ $(5, -6)$ and $(4, 3)$

43. The equation $2y + 3x = -6$ describes a line with what slope?

    Ⓐ $\dfrac{3}{2}$ Ⓑ 0 Ⓒ $\dfrac{1}{2}$ Ⓓ $-\dfrac{3}{2}$

44. What is the slope of a line that passes through the points $(-1, 2)$ and $(1, -3)$?

    Ⓐ $-\dfrac{5}{2}$ Ⓑ $-\dfrac{2}{5}$ Ⓒ $\dfrac{2}{5}$ Ⓓ $\dfrac{5}{2}$

CHALLENGE AND EXTEND

Find the slope of the line that contains each pair of points.

45. $(a, 0)$ and $(0, b)$ **46.** $(2x, y)$ and $(x, 3y)$ **47.** (x, y) and $(x + 2, 3 - y)$

48. Recreation Tara and Jade are hiking together up a hill with a constant slope. Each has a different stride. For Tara's stride, the run is 32 inches and the rise is 8 inches. The run for Jade's stride is 36 inches. What is the rise for Jade's stride?

Find the value of x so that the line that contains each pair of points has the given slope.

49. $(4, x)$ and $(6, 3x)$, $m = \dfrac{1}{2}$ **50.** $(x, 2)$ and $(-5, 8)$, $m = -1$

 SPIRAL STANDARDS REVIEW

Solve each equation. Check your answer. *(Lesson 2-1)*

51. $k - 3.14 = 1.71$ **52.** $-7 = p - 12$ **53.** $25 = f - 16$

Tell whether the given ordered pairs all lie on the same line. *(Lesson 5-1)*

54. $\{(1, 1), (2, 4), (3, 9), (4, 16)\}$ **55.** $\{(9, 0), (8, -5), (5, -20), (3, -30)\}$

Find the x- and y-intercepts. *(Lesson 5-2)*

56. $2x + y = 6$ **57.** $y = -3x - 9$ **58.** $2y = -4x + 1$

Comparing Deductive and Inductive Reasoning

Use with Lesson 5-3

California Standards

24.1 Students explain the difference between inductive and deductive reasoning and identify and provide examples of each.

Example

While doing her algebra homework, Adele came to the following problem:

Find the slope of the line that contains (2, 3) and (6, 9).

Adele wrote:

> Let $(x_1, y_1) = (2, 3)$ and $(x_2, y_2) = (6, 9)$.
>
> $$\frac{y_2 - y_1}{x_2 - x_1} = \frac{9 - 3}{6 - 2} = \frac{6}{4} = \frac{3}{2}$$
>
> The slope is $\frac{3}{2}$.

But Adele was not sure of her answer. She had missed class, and she wondered if it was important which point was (x_1, y_1) and which point was (x_2, y_2). She thought, "Maybe the answer is different if I switch the points." She decided to check.

> Let $(x_1, y_1) = (6, 9)$ and $(x_2, y_2) = (2, 3)$.
>
> $$\frac{y_2 - y_1}{x_2 - x_1} = \frac{3 - 9}{2 - 6} = \frac{-6}{-4} = \frac{3}{2}$$
>
> The slope is $\frac{3}{2}$.

Adele repeated the same process for the next three problems, and she found the same result. Then she said, "It doesn't matter which point is (x_1, y_1) and which point is (x_2, y_2). The slope is the same."

To make her conjecture, Adele used inductive reasoning. Remember that when you use inductive reasoning, you first note a pattern in specific cases and then make a conjecture about every case. Adele noticed something about several specific lines and made a conjecture about every line.

Conjectures based on inductive reasoning may or may not be true. In other words, you cannot use inductive reasoning to prove a statement.

In contrast, a statement reached through deductive reasoning is true. Once you have proven a statement through deductive reasoning, you can apply that statement to specific cases.

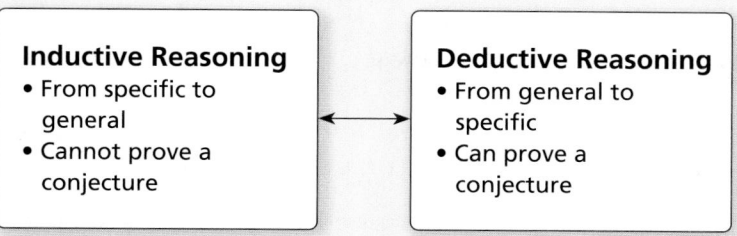

Inductive Reasoning
• From specific to general
• Cannot prove a conjecture

Deductive Reasoning
• From general to specific
• Can prove a conjecture

Try This

For each situation, tell whether the conclusion was reached through inductive or deductive reasoning.

1. It has been raining for three days. Andrew predicts that it will rain again tomorrow.

2. All Internal Revenue Service (IRS) workers are federal employees. John is an IRS worker. Carla concludes that John is a federal employee.

3. Jennifer is going to the beach this weekend. Her mother says, "I know you will come home with a sunburn because you always get a sunburn when you go to the beach."

4. Marc examined the sequence below.

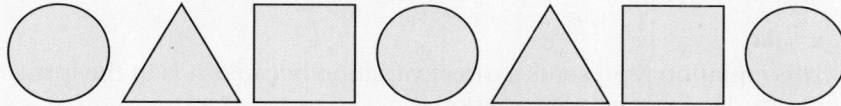

Then he said, "The next shape will be a triangle."

5. All numbers that end in 0 are divisible by 10. Therefore, 1,225,610 is divisible by 10.

6. All numbers that end in 0 are divisible by 10, and all numbers that are divisible by 10 are also divisible by 5. Therefore 1,225,610 is divisible by 5.

7. Morgan noticed that $3 + 5 = 8$, $7 + 15 = 22$, and $25 + 5 = 30$. He concludes that the sum of two odd numbers is always even.

8. Rachel looked at the scatter plot and concluded that a student who received a 75 on the math test probably received an 85 on the science test.

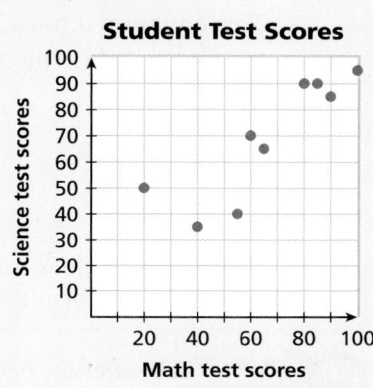

9. Create your own situations that illustrate inductive and deductive reasoning. Describe at least one situation for each type of reasoning.

10. In your own words, describe the difference between inductive and deductive reasoning.

5-4 Direct Variation

California Standards

🔑 **6.0 Students graph a linear equation** and compute the x- and y-intercepts (e.g., graph 2x + 6y = 4). They are also able to sketch the region defined by linear inequalities (e.g., they sketch the region defined by 2x + 6y < 4).

Vocabulary
direct variation
constant of variation

Who uses this?
Chefs can use direct variation to determine ingredients needed for a certain number of servings.

A recipe for paella calls for 1 cup of rice to make 5 servings. In other words, a chef needs 1 cup of rice for every 5 servings.

Paella is a rice dish that originated in Valencia, Spain.

Rice (c) x	1	2	3	4
Servings y	5	10	15	20

The equation $y = 5x$ describes this relationship. In this relationship, the number of servings *varies directly* with the number of cups of rice.

A **direct variation** is a special type of linear relationship that can be written in the form $y = kx$, where k is a nonzero constant called the **constant of variation**.

EXAMPLE 1 **Identifying Direct Variations from Equations**

Tell whether each equation represents a direct variation. If so, identify the constant of variation.

A $y = 4x$

This equation represents a direct variation because it is in the form $y = kx$. The constant of variation is 4.

B $-3x + 5y = 0$

$$-3x + 5y = 0 \qquad \textit{Solve the equation for y.}$$
$$\underline{+3x \qquad\qquad +3x} \qquad \textit{Since −3x is added to y, add 3x to both sides.}$$
$$5y = 3x$$
$$\frac{5y}{5} = \frac{3x}{5} \qquad \textit{Since y is multiplied by 5, divide both sides by 5.}$$
$$y = \frac{3}{5}x$$

This equation represents a direct variation because it can be written in the form $y = kx$. The constant of variation is $\frac{3}{5}$.

C $2x + y = 10$

$$2x + y = 10 \qquad \textit{Solve the equation for y.}$$
$$\underline{-2x \qquad -2x} \qquad \textit{Since 2x is added to y, subtract 2x from both sides.}$$
$$y = -2x + 10$$

This equation does not represent a direct variation because it cannot be written in the form $y = kx$.

Tell whether each equation represents a direct variation. If so, identify the constant of variation.

1a. $3y = 4x + 1$ **1b.** $3x = -4y$ **1c.** $y + 3x = 0$

What happens if you solve $y = kx$ for k?

$$y = kx$$

$$\frac{y}{x} = \frac{kx}{x} \qquad \text{Divide both sides by } x \ (x \neq 0).$$

$$\frac{y}{x} = k$$

So, in a direct variation, the ratio $\frac{y}{x}$ is equal to the constant of variation. Another way to identify a direct variation is to check whether $\frac{y}{x}$ is the same for each ordered pair (except where $x = 0$).

EXAMPLE 2   **Identifying Direct Variations from Ordered Pairs**

Tell whether each relationship is a direct variation. Explain.

x	1	3	5
y	6	18	30

Method 1 Write an equation.

$$y = 6x \qquad \text{Each y-value is 6 times the corresponding x-value.}$$

This is a direct variation because it can be written as $y = kx$, where $k = 6$.

Method 2 Find $\frac{y}{x}$ for each ordered pair.

$$\frac{6}{1} = 6 \qquad\qquad \frac{18}{3} = 6 \qquad\qquad \frac{30}{5} = 6$$

This is a direct variation because $\frac{y}{x}$ is the same for each ordered pair.

x	2	4	8
y	−2	0	4

Method 1 Write an equation.

$$y = x - 4 \qquad \text{Each y-value is 4 less than the corresponding x-value.}$$

This is not a direct variation because it cannot be written as $y = kx$.

Method 2 Find $\frac{y}{x}$ for each ordered pair.

$$\frac{-2}{2} = -1 \qquad\qquad \frac{0}{4} = 0 \qquad\qquad \frac{4}{8} = \frac{1}{2}$$

This is not a direct variation because $\frac{y}{x}$ is not the same for all ordered pairs.

Tell whether each relationship is a direct variation. Explain.

2a.

x	y
−3	0
1	3
3	6

2b.

x	y
2.5	−10
5	−20
7.5	−30

2c.

x	y
−2	5
1	3
4	1

If you know one ordered pair that satisfies a direct variation, you can write the equation. You can also find other ordered pairs that satisfy the direct variation.

EXAMPLE 3 **Writing and Solving Direct Variation Equations**

The value of y varies directly with x, and $y = 6$ when $x = 12$.
Find y when $x = 27$.

Method 1 Find the value of k and then write the equation.

$y = kx$	*Write the equation for a direct variation.*
$6 = k(12)$	*Substitute 6 for y and 12 for x. Solve for k.*
$\dfrac{1}{2} = k$	*Since k is multiplied by 12, divide both sides by 12.*

The equation is $y = \dfrac{1}{2}x$. When $x = 27$, $y = \dfrac{1}{2}(27) = 13.5$.

Method 2 Use a proportion.

$\dfrac{6}{12} \bowtie \dfrac{y}{27}$	*In a direct variation, $\dfrac{y}{x}$ is the same for all values of x and y.*
$12y = 162$	*Use cross products.*
$y = 13.5$	*Since y is multiplied by 12, divide both sides by 12.*

CHECK IT OUT! **3.** The value of y varies directly with x, and $y = 4.5$ when $x = 0.5$.
Find y when $x = 10$.

EXAMPLE 4 **Graphing Direct Variations**

The three-toed sloth is an extremely slow animal. On the ground, it travels at a speed of about 6 feet per minute. Write a direct variation equation for the distance y a sloth will travel in x minutes. Then graph.

Step 1 Write a direct variation equation.

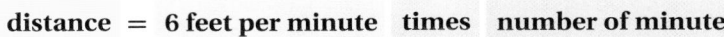

distance	=	6 feet per minute	times	number of minutes
y	=	6	•	x

Step 2 Choose values of x and generate ordered pairs.

x	$y = 6x$	(x, y)
0	$y = 6(0) = 0$	$(0, 0)$
1	$y = 6(1) = 6$	$(1, 6)$
2	$y = 6(2) = 12$	$(2, 12)$

Step 3 Graph the points and connect.

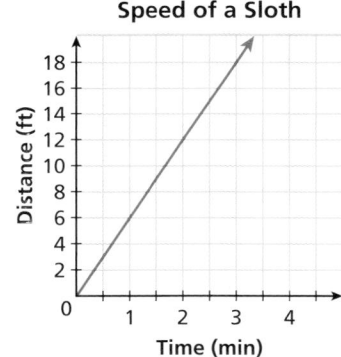

CHECK IT OUT! **4.** The perimeter y of a square varies directly with its side length x.
Write a direct variation equation for this relationship. Then graph.

Look at the graph in Example 4. It passes through $(0, 0)$ and has a slope of 6.
The graph of any direct variation $y = kx$
- contains $(0, 0)$.   - has a slope of k.

THINK AND DISCUSS

1. How do you know that a direct variation is linear?

2. Why does the graph of any direct variation contain $(0, 0)$?

3. GET ORGANIZED Copy and complete the graphic organizer. In each box, describe how you can use the given information to identify a direct variation.

Recognizing a Direct Variation		
From an Equation	From Ordered Pairs	From a Graph

5-4 Exercises

California Standards Practice
🔑 6.0, 24.1

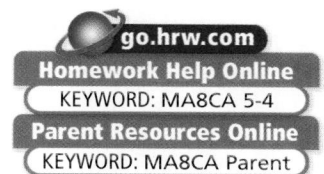
go.hrw.com
Homework Help Online
KEYWORD: MA8CA 5-4
Parent Resources Online
KEYWORD: MA8CA Parent

GUIDED PRACTICE

1. Vocabulary If x varies directly with y, then the relationship between the two variables is said to be a ___?___. (*direct variation* or *constant of variation*)

SEE EXAMPLE **1**
p. 282

Tell whether each equation represents a direct variation. If so, identify the constant of variation.

2. $y = 4x + 9$ **3.** $2y = -8x$ **4.** $x + y = 0$

SEE EXAMPLE **2**
p. 283

Tell whether each relationship is a direct variation. Explain.

5.

x	10	5	2
y	12	7	4

6.

x	3	−1	−4
y	−6	2	8

SEE EXAMPLE **3**
p. 284

7. The value of y varies directly with x, and $y = -3$ when $x = 1$. Find y when $x = -6$.

8. The value of y varies directly with x, and $y = 6$ when $x = 18$. Find y when $x = 12$.

SEE EXAMPLE **4**
p. 284

9. Wages Cameron earns $5 per hour at her after-school job. The total amount of her paycheck varies directly with the amount of time she works. Write a direct variation equation for the amount of money y that she earns for working x hours. Then graph.

PRACTICE AND PROBLEM SOLVING

Tell whether each equation represents a direct variation. If so, identify the constant of variation.

10. $y = \frac{1}{6}x$ **11.** $4y = x$ **12.** $x = 2y - 12$

Tell whether each relationship is a direct variation. Explain.

13.

x	6	9	17
y	13.2	19.8	37.4

14.

x	−6	3	12
y	4	−2	−8

Independent Practice

For Exercises	See Example
10–12	1
13–14	2
15–16	3
17	4

Extra Practice

Skills Practice p. EP10

Application Practice p. EP28

15. The value of y varies directly with x, and $y = 8$ when $x = -32$. Find y when $x = 64$.

16. The value of y varies directly with x, and $y = \frac{1}{2}$ when $x = 3$. Find y when $x = 1$.

17. While on his way to school, Norman saw that the cost of gasoline was $2.50 per gallon. Write a direct variation equation to describe the cost y of x gallons of gas. Then graph.

Tell whether each relationship is a direct variation. Explain your answer.

18. The equation $-15x + 4y = 0$ relates the length of a videotape in inches x to its approximate playing time in seconds y.

19. The equation $y - 2.00x = 2.50$ relates the cost y of a taxicab ride to distance x of the cab ride in miles.

Each ordered pair is a solution of a direct variation. Write the equation of direct variation. Then graph your equation and show that the slope of the line is equal to the constant of variation.

20. $(2, 10)$ **21.** $(-3, 9)$ **22.** $(8, 2)$ **23.** $(1.5, 6)$

24. $(7, 21)$ **25.** $(1, 2)$ **26.** $(2, -16)$ **27.** $\left(\frac{1}{7}, 1\right)$

28. $(-2, 9)$ **29.** $(9, -2)$ **30.** $(4, 6)$ **31.** $(3, 4)$

32. $(5, 1)$ **33.** $(1, -6)$ **34.** $\left(-1, \frac{1}{2}\right)$ **35.** $(7, 2)$

36. **Astronomy** Weight varies directly with gravity. A Mars lander weighed 767 pounds on Earth but only 291 pounds on Mars. Its accompanying Mars rover weighed 155 pounds on Mars. How much did it weigh on Earth? Round your answer to the nearest pound.

Astronomy

The Mars rover *Spirit* landed on Mars in January 2004 and immediately began sending photos of the planet's surface back to Earth.

37. **Environment** Mischa bought an energy-efficient washing machine. She will save about 15 gallons of water per wash load.

   a. Write an equation of direct variation to describe how many gallons of water y Mischa saves for x loads of laundry she washes.

   b. Graph your direct variation from part **a.** Is every point on the graph a solution in this situation? Why or why not?

   c. If Mischa does 2 loads of laundry per week, how many gallons of water will she have saved at the end of a year?

For help with deductive reasoning, see pp. 99, 108, and 169.

38. **Reasoning** Use deductive reasoning to show that if you double an x-value in a direct variation, then the corresponding y-value will also double.

39. **Write About It** In a direct variation $y = kx$, k is sometimes called the "constant of proportionality." How are proportions related to direct variations?

CONCEPT CONNECTION

40. This problem will prepare you for the Concept Connection on page 288.

Rhea exercised on a treadmill at the gym. When she was finished, the display showed that she had walked at an average speed of 3 miles per hour.

   a. Write an equation that gives the number of miles y that Rhea would cover in x hours if she walked at this speed.

   b. Explain why this is a direct variation and find the value of k. What does this value represent in Rhea's situation?

Multiple Choice For Exercises 41–43, choose the best answer.

41. Which equation does NOT represent a direct variation?

Ⓐ $y = \frac{1}{3}x$ 　　　Ⓑ $y = -2x$ 　　　Ⓒ $y = 4x + 1$ 　　　Ⓓ $6x - y = 0$

42. Identify which set of data represents a direct variation.

Ⓐ
x	1	2	3
y	1	2	3

Ⓒ
x	1	2	3
y	3	5	7

Ⓑ
x	1	2	3
y	0	1	2

Ⓓ
x	1	2	3
y	3	4	5

43. Two yards of fabric cost \$13, and 5 yards of fabric cost \$32.50. Which equation relates the cost of the fabric c to its length ℓ?

Ⓐ $c = 2.6\ell$ 　　　Ⓑ $c = 6.5\ell$ 　　　Ⓒ $c = 13\ell$ 　　　Ⓓ $c = 32.5\ell$

44. Gridded Response A car is traveling at a constant speed. After 3 hours, the car has traveled 180 miles. If the car continues to travel at the same constant speed, how many hours will it take to travel a total of 270 miles?

CHALLENGE AND EXTEND

45. Transportation The equation $y = 20x$ gives the number of miles y that a gasoline-powered sport-utility vehicle (SUV) can travel on x gallons of gas. The equation $y = 60x$ gives the number of miles y that a gas-electric hybrid car can travel on x gallons of gas.

a. If you drive 120 miles, how much gas will you save by driving the hybrid instead of the SUV?

b. Graph both equations on the same coordinate plane. Will the lines ever meet? Explain.

c. What if...? Shannon drives 15,000 miles in one year. How many gallons of gas will she use if she drives the SUV? the hybrid?

 46. Reasoning Suppose $Ax + By = C$, where A, B, and C are real numbers, $A \neq 0$, and $B \neq 0$, describes a direct variation. Use deductive reasoning to show that $C = 0$.

 SPIRAL STANDARDS REVIEW　　　　　　　　　　　🔑 4.0, 🔑 7.0, 17.0

Solve each equation. Check your answer. *(Lesson 2-3)*

47. $p(1 + 4) - 2(p + 6) = 6$ 　　　　　　**48.** $s - (s + 5) + 3(s - 1) = -2$

Give the domain and range of each relation. Tell whether the relation is a function. *(Lesson 4-2)*

49.
x	y
1	−5
2	−4
3	−3
4	−2

50.
x	y
1	−2
2	−4
3	−6
4	−8

51.
x	y
−3	9
−2	6
−1	3
−2	0

Without graphing, tell whether each point is on the graph of $2x - y = 5$. *(Lesson 5-1)*

52. $(3, 1)$ 　　　　　　**53.** $(1, -2)$ 　　　　　　**54.** $(4, -3)$

CONCEPT CONNECTION

Characteristics of Linear Functions

Heart Health People who exercise need to be aware of their maximum heart rate.

1. One way to estimate your maximum heart rate m is to subtract 85% of your age in years from 217. Create a table of values that shows the maximum heart rates for people ages 13 to 18. Then write an equation to describe the data in the table.

2. Use your table from Problem 1 to graph the relationship between age and maximum heart rate. What are the intercepts? What is the slope?

3. What do the intercepts represent in this situation?

4. What does the slope represent? Explain why the slope is negative.

5. Another formula for estimating maximum heart rate is $m = 206.3 - 0.711a$, where a represents age in years. Describe how this equation is different from your equation in Problem 1. Include slope and intercepts in your description.

6. Which equation gives a higher maximum heart rate?

7. To be exercising in your *aerobic training zone* means that your heart rate is 70% to 80% of your maximum heart rate. Write two equations that someone could use to estimate the range of heart rates that are within his or her aerobic training zone. Use your equation for maximum heart rate from Problem 1.

READY TO GO ON?

Quiz for Lessons 5-1 Through 5-4

5-1 Linear Equations and Functions

Graph each linear equation. Then tell whether it represents a function.

1. $x + y = 4$
2. $x = 6$
3. $\dfrac{x}{y} = 6$
4. $y - 2 = -\dfrac{1}{3}x$

Without graphing, tell whether each point is on the graph of $y = -4x - 1$.

5. $(0, 0)$
6. $(-1, 0)$
7. $(0, -1)$
8. $\left(-\dfrac{1}{2}, -1\right)$

5-2 Using Intercepts

9. A baby pool that held 120 gallons of water is draining at a rate of 6 gal/min. The function $f(x) = 120 - 6x$ gives the amount of water in the pool after x minutes. Graph the function and find its intercepts. What does each intercept represent?

Use intercepts to graph the line given by each equation.

10. $2x - 4y = 16$
11. $-3y + 6x = -18$
12. $y = -3x + 3$

5-3 Slope

Find the slope of each line. Then tell what the slope represents.

13.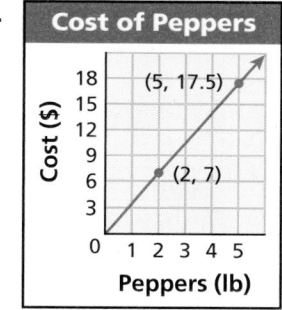

14.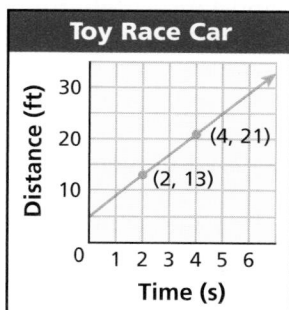

15.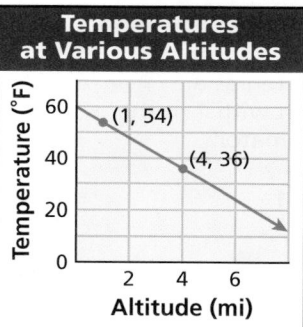

Find the slope of the line given by each equation.

16. $3x + y = 1$
17. $y + 4x = 8$
18. $x - 2y = 2$
19. $4x - 5y = -2$

5-4 Direct Variation

Tell whether each relationship is a direct variation. If so, identify the constant of variation.

20.

x	1	4	8	12
y	3	6	10	14

21.

x	−6	−2	0	3
y	−3	−1	0	1.5

22. The value of y varies directly with x, and $y = 10$ when $x = 4$. Find x when $y = 14$.

5-5 Slope-Intercept Form

Who uses this?

Consumers can use slope-intercept form to model and calculate costs, such as the cost of renting a moving van. (See Example 4.)

You have seen that you can graph a line if you know two points on the line. Another way is to use the point that contains the *y*-intercept and the slope of the line.

EXAMPLE 1 **Graphing by Using Slope and *y*-intercept**

Graph each line given the slope and *y*-intercept.

A slope $= \dfrac{3}{4}$; *y*-intercept $= -2$

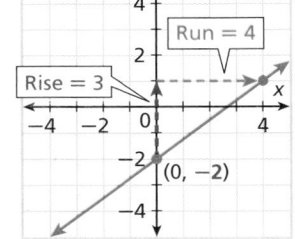

Step 1 The *y*-intercept is -2, so the line contains $(0, -2)$. Plot $(0, -2)$.

Step 2 Slope $= \dfrac{\text{rise}}{\text{run}} = \dfrac{3}{4}$. Count 3 units up and 4 units right from $(0, -2)$ and plot another point.

Step 3 Draw the line through the two points.

Writing Math

Any integer can be written as a fraction with 1 in the denominator.

$-2 = \dfrac{-2}{1}$

B slope $= -2$, *y*-intercept $= 4$

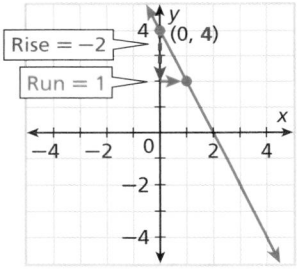

Step 1 The *y*-intercept is 4, so the line contains $(0, 4)$. Plot $(0, 4)$.

Step 2 Slope $= \dfrac{\text{rise}}{\text{run}} = \dfrac{-2}{1}$. Count 2 units down and 1 unit right from $(0, 4)$ and plot another point.

Step 3 Draw the line through the two points.

Graph each line given the slope and *y*-intercept.

1a. slope $= 2$, *y*-intercept $= -3$ **1b.** slope $= -\dfrac{2}{3}$, *y*-intercept $= 1$

If you know the slope of a line and the *y*-intercept, you can write an equation that describes the line.

Step 1 If a line has slope m and the *y*-intercept is b, then $(0, b)$ is on the line. Substitute these values into the slope formula.

Slope formula $\rightarrow m = \dfrac{y_2 - y_1}{x_2 - x_1}$ $m = \dfrac{y - b}{x - 0}$ $\leftarrow$ *Since you don't know (x_2, y_2), use (x, y).*

Step 2 Solve for y: $m = \dfrac{y - b}{x - 0}$

$$m = \frac{y - b}{x} \qquad \text{\textit{Simplify the denominator.}}$$

$$m \cdot x = \left(\frac{y - b}{x}\right) \cdot x \qquad \text{\textit{Multiply both sides by x.}}$$

$$mx = y - b$$

$$\underline{+\,b \qquad +\,b} \qquad \text{\textit{Add b to both sides.}}$$

$$mx + b = y, \text{ or } y = mx + b$$

> ### Slope-Intercept Form of a Linear Equation
>
> The slope-intercept form of a linear equation is $y = mx + b$, where m is the **slope** of the equation's graph and b is the **y-intercept**.

Any linear equation can be written in slope-intercept form by solving for y and simplifying. In this form, you can immediately see the slope and y-intercept. Also, you can quickly graph a line when the equation is written in slope-intercept form.

EXAMPLE 2 **Writing Linear Equations in Slope-Intercept Form**

Write the equation of each line in slope-intercept form.

Remember!

Subtraction is the same as addition of the opposite.

$$-12x - \frac{1}{2} =$$

$$-12x + \left(-\frac{1}{2}\right)$$

A slope $= \dfrac{1}{3}$, y-intercept $= 6$

$y = mx + b$ *Substitute the given*

$y = \dfrac{1}{3}x + 6$ *values for m and b.*

          Simplify if necessary.

B slope $= -12$, y-intercept $= -\dfrac{1}{2}$

$y = mx + b$

$y = -12x + \left(-\dfrac{1}{2}\right)$

$y = -12x - \dfrac{1}{2}$

C slope $= 1$, y-intercept $= 0$

$y = mx + b$ *Substitute the given*

$y = 1x + 0$ *values for m and b.*

$y = x$ *Simplify.*

D slope $= 0$, y-intercept $= -5$

$y = mx + b$

$y = 0x + (-5)$

$y = -5$

E slope $= 4$, $(2, 5)$ is on the line

Step 1 Find the y-intercept.

$y = mx + b$ *Write the slope-intercept form.*

$5 = 4(2) + b$ *Substitute 4 for m, 2 for x, and 5 for y.*

$5 = 8 + b$ *Solve for b. Since 8 is added to b, subtract 8 from both sides to undo the addition.*

$\underline{-8 \qquad -8}$

$-3 = b$

Step 2 Write the equation.

$y = mx + b$ *Write the slope-intercept form.*

$y = 4x + (-3)$ *Substitute 4 for m and −3 for b.*

$y = 4x - 3$

2. A line has slope 8 and $(3, -1)$ is on the line. Write the equation of this line in slope-intercept form.

EXAMPLE 3 **Using Slope-Intercept Form to Graph**

For more on graphing linear equations, see the Function Builder on page MB2.

Write each equation in slope-intercept form. Then graph the line given by the equation.

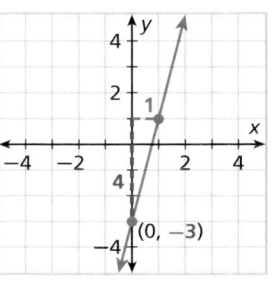

A $y = 4x - 3$

$y = 4x - 3$ is in the form $y = mx + b$.

slope: $m = 4 = \frac{4}{1}$

y-intercept: $b = -3$

Step 1 Plot $(0, -3)$.
Step 2 Count **4 units up** and **1 unit right** and plot another point.
Step 3 Draw the line connecting the two points.

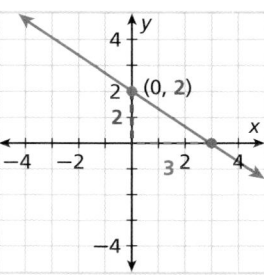

B $y = -\frac{2}{3}x + 2$

$y = -\frac{2}{3}x + 2$ is in the form $y = mx + b$.

slope: $m = -\frac{2}{3} = \frac{-2}{3}$

y-intercept: $b = 2$

Step 1 Plot $(0, 2)$
Step 2 Count **2 units down** and **3 units right** and plot another point.
Step 3 Draw the line connecting the two points.

Helpful Hint

To divide $(8 - 3x)$ by 2, you can multiply by $\frac{1}{2}$ and distribute.

$\frac{8 - 3x}{2} = \frac{1}{2}(8 - 3x)$

$= \frac{1}{2}(8) + \frac{1}{2}(-3x)$

$= 4 - \frac{3}{2}x$

C $3x + 2y = 8$

Step 1 Write the equation in slope-intercept form by solving for y.

$$3x + 2y = 8$$
$$\underline{-3x \qquad\quad -3x} \qquad \textit{Subtract 3x from both sides.}$$
$$2y = 8 - 3x$$
$$\frac{2y}{2} = \frac{8 - 3x}{2} \qquad \textit{Since y is multiplied by 2, divide both sides by 2.}$$
$$y = 4 - \frac{3}{2}x \qquad \frac{3x}{2} = \frac{3}{2}x$$
$$y = -\frac{3}{2}x + 4 \qquad \textit{Write the equation in the form y = mx + b.}$$

Step 2 Graph the line.

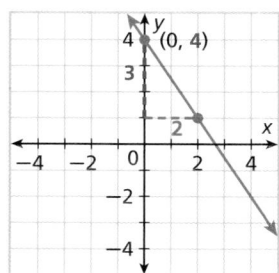

$y = -\frac{3}{2}x + 4$ is in the form $y = mx + b$.

slope: $m = -\frac{3}{2} = \frac{-3}{2}$

y-intercept: $b = 4$

- Plot $(0, 4)$.
- Then count **3 units down** and **2 units right** and plot another point.
- Draw the line connecting the two points.

Write each equation in slope-intercept form. Then graph the line given by the equation.

3a. $y = \frac{2}{3}x$ **3b.** $6x + 2y = 10$ **3c.** $y = -4$

EXAMPLE 4 *Consumer Application*

To rent a van, a moving company charges $30.00 plus $0.50 per mile. The cost as a function of the number of miles driven is shown in the graph.

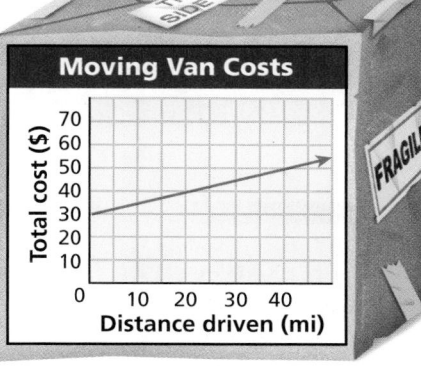

Moving Van Costs

a. Write an equation that represents the cost as a function of the number of miles.

Cost	is	$0.50 per mile	times	miles	plus	$30.00
y	$=$	0.5	$\cdot$	x	$+$	30

An equation is $y = 0.5x + 30$.

b. Identify the slope and *y*-intercept and describe their meanings.

The *y*-intercept is 30. This is the cost for 0 miles, or the initial fee of $30.00.

The slope is 0.5. This is the rate of change of the cost: $0.50 per mile.

c. Find the cost of the van for 150 miles.

$y = 0.5x + 30$

$= 0.5(150) + 30 = 105$ *Substitute 150 for x in the equation.*

The cost of the van for 150 miles is $105.

CHECK IT OUT!

4. A caterer charges a $200 fee plus $18 per person served. The cost as a function of the number of guests is shown in the graph.

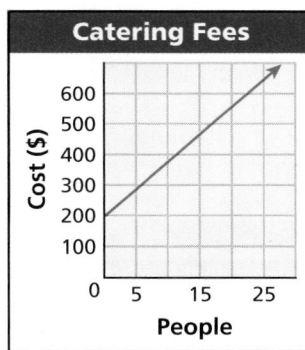

Catering Fees

a. Write an equation that represents the cost as a function of the number of guests.

b. Identify the slope and *y*-intercept and describe their meanings.

c. Find the cost of catering an event for 200 guests.

THINK AND DISCUSS

1. If a linear function has a *y*-intercept of *b*, at what point does its graph cross the *y*-axis?

2. Where does the line given by $y = 4.395x - 23.75$ cross the *y*-axis?

3. GET ORGANIZED Copy and complete the graphic organizer.

Graphing the Line Described by $y = mx + b$

| 1. Plot the point ___?___ . | 2. Find a second point on the line by ___?___ . | 3. Draw ___?___ . |

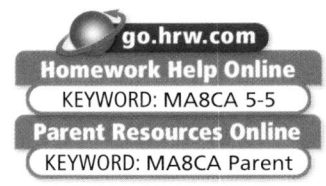

California Standards Practice
⚷ 6.0, ⚷ 7.0, 25.1, 25.2

go.hrw.com
Homework Help Online
KEYWORD: MA8CA 5-5
Parent Resources Online
KEYWORD: MA8CA Parent

GUIDED PRACTICE

SEE EXAMPLE 1
p. 290

Graph each line given the slope and y-intercept.

1. slope $= \frac{1}{3}$, y-intercept $= -3$

2. slope $= 0.5$, y-intercept $= 3.5$

3. slope $= 5$, y-intercept $= -1$

4. slope $= -2$, y-intercept $= 2$

SEE EXAMPLE 2
p. 291

Write the equation of each line in slope-intercept form.

5. slope $= 8$, y-intercept $= 2$

6. slope $= \frac{1}{2}$, y-intercept $= -6$

7. slope $= 0$, y-intercept $= -3$

8. slope $= 5$, the point $(2, 7)$ is on the line

SEE EXAMPLE 3
p. 292

Write each equation in slope-intercept form. Then graph the line given by the equation.

9. $y = \frac{2}{5}x - 6$

10. $3x - y = 1$

11. $2x + y = 4$

SEE EXAMPLE 4
p. 293

12. Helen is in a bicycle race. She has already biked 10 miles at a rate of 18 miles per hour. She keeps biking at the same rate throughout the race. Her distance as a function of time is shown in the graph.

  a. Write an equation that represents the distance Helen has biked as a function of time.

  b. Identify the slope and y-intercept and describe their meanings.

  c. How far will Helen have biked after 2 hours?

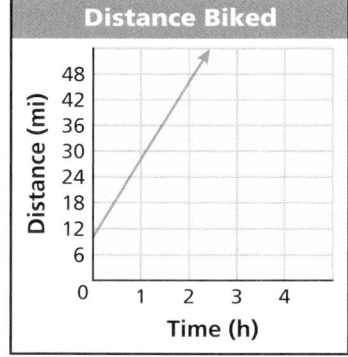

PRACTICE AND PROBLEM SOLVING

Independent Practice

For Exercises	See Example
13–16	1
17–20	2
21–29	3
30	4

Extra Practice
Skills Practice p. EP11
Application Practice p. EP28

Graph each line given the slope and y-intercept.

13. slope $= \frac{1}{4}$, y-intercept $= 7$

14. slope $= -6$, y-intercept $= -3$

15. slope $= 1$, y-intercept $= -4$

16. slope $= -\frac{4}{5}$, y-intercept $= 6$

Write the equation of each line in slope-intercept form.

17. slope $= 5$, y-intercept $= -9$

18. slope $= -\frac{2}{3}$, y-intercept $= 2$

19. slope $= -\frac{1}{2}$, $(6, 4)$ is on the line

20. slope $= 0$, $(6, -8)$ is on the line

Write each equation in slope-intercept form. Then graph the line given by the equation.

21. $y = -\frac{1}{2}x + 3$

22. $y = \frac{1}{3}x - 5$

23. $y = x + 6$

24. $6x + 3y = 12$

25. $y = \frac{7}{2}$

26. $4x + y = 9$

27. $-\frac{1}{2}x + y = 4$

28. $\frac{2}{3}x + y = 2$

29. $2x + y = 8$

30. Fitness Pauline's health club has an enrollment fee of $175 and costs $35 per month. Total cost as a function of number of membership months is shown in the graph.

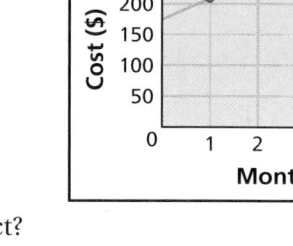

Health Club Membership Costs

a. Write an equation that represents the total cost as a function of months.

b. Identify the slope and *y*-intercept and describe their meanings.

c. Find the cost of one year of membership.

31. ///ERROR ANALYSIS/// Two students wrote $3x + 2y = 5$ in slope-intercept form. Who is incorrect? Describe the error.

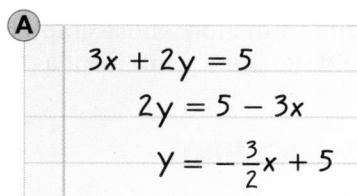

Ⓐ
$$3x + 2y = 5$$
$$2y = 5 - 3x$$
$$y = -\frac{3}{2}x + 5$$

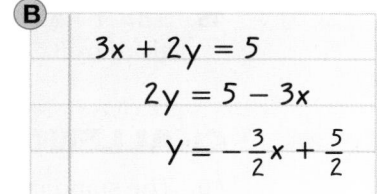

Ⓑ
$$3x + 2y = 5$$
$$2y = 5 - 3x$$
$$y = -\frac{3}{2}x + \frac{5}{2}$$

Reasoning Tell whether each situation is possible or impossible. If possible, draw a sketch of the graphs. If impossible, explain.

32. Two different lines have the same slope.

33. Two different linear functions have the same *y*-intercept.

34. Two different intersecting lines have the same slope.

35. A linear function does not have a *y*-intercept.

Match each equation with its corresponding graph.

36. $y = 2x - 1$

37. $y = \frac{1}{2}x - 1$

38. $y = -\frac{1}{2}x + 1$

A.

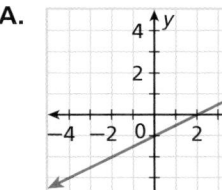

B.

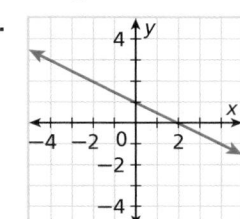

C.

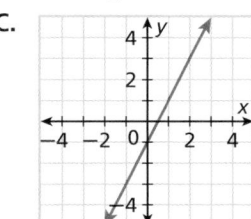

39. Write About It Write an equation for a vertical line. Can you write this equation in slope-intercept form? Why or why not?

CONCEPT CONNECTION

40. This problem will prepare you for the Concept Connection on page 312.

a. Ricardo and Sam walk from Sam's house to school. Sam lives 3 blocks from Ricardo's house. The graph shows their distance from Ricardo's house as they walk to school at specific times. Create a table of these values.

b. Find an equation for the distance as a function of time.

c. Using the equation, what are the slope and *y*-intercept? What do they represent in this situation?

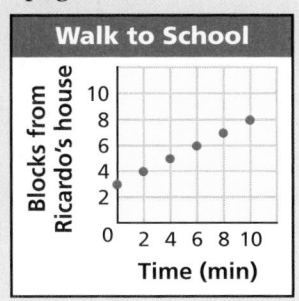

Walk to School

Multiple Choice For Exercises 41–43, choose the best answer.

41. Which function has the same y-intercept as $y = \frac{1}{2}x - 2$?

    Ⓐ $2x + 3y = 6$　　Ⓑ $x + 4y = -8$　　Ⓒ $-\frac{1}{2}x + y = 4$　　Ⓓ $\frac{1}{2}x - 2y = -2$

42. What is the slope-intercept form of $x - y = -8$?

    Ⓐ $y = -x - 8$　　Ⓑ $y = x - 8$　　Ⓒ $y = -x + 8$　　Ⓓ $y = x + 8$

43. Which function has a y-intercept of 3?

    Ⓐ $2x - y = 3$　　Ⓑ $2x + y = 3$　　Ⓒ $2x + y = 6$　　Ⓓ $y = 3x$

44. **Gridded Response** What is the slope of the line given by $-6x = -2y + 5$?

45. **Short Response** Write a function whose graph has the same slope as the line given by $3x - 9y = 9$ and the same y-intercept as $8x - 2y = 6$. Show your work.

CHALLENGE AND EXTEND

46. The standard form of a linear equation is $Ax + By = C$. Rewrite this equation in slope-intercept form. What is the slope? What is the y-intercept?

47. What value of n in the equation $nx + 5 = 3y$ would give a line with slope -2?

 48. **Reasoning** A line has slope 3 and $(1, 6)$ is on the line. Below are the steps to find the equation of this line. Fill in the missing reasons for each step.

Statements	Reasons
1. $y = mx + b$	a. _____?_____
2. $6 = 3(1) + b$	b. _____?_____
3. $6 = 3 + b$	c. _____?_____
4. $3 = b$	d. _____?_____
5. $y = mx + b$	e. _____?_____
6. $y = 3x + 3$	f. _____?_____

 SPIRAL STANDARDS REVIEW　　 4.0, ↞ 5.0, ↞ 6.0

Write an inequality for each statement. Solve the inequality and graph the solutions. *(Lesson 3-4)*

49. The sum of three times a number and four is less than or equal to 10.

50. One-half the difference of a number and 150 is greater than or equal to 75.

Solve each inequality. *(Lesson 3-5)*

51. $3n \le 2n + 8$　　　　52. $4x - 4 > 2(x + 5)$　　　　53. $2(2t + 1) > 6t + 8$

Find the x- and y-intercepts. *(Lesson 5-2)*

54. $12x = 3y$　　　　55. $y = -2x + 6$　　　　56. $y = -0.5x - 3.5$

5-6 Point-Slope Form

Why learn this?

You can use point-slope form to represent a cost function, such as the cost of placing a newspaper ad. (See Example 5.)

In Lesson 5-5, you saw that if you know the slope of a line and the *y*-intercept, you can graph the line. You can also graph a line if you know its slope and any point on the line.

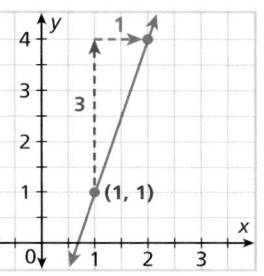

KITTENS AVAILABLE to good home. 2 mo. old, litter trained. Very cute and playful! $10 adoption fee.

EXAMPLE 1 Using Slope and a Point to Graph

Graph the line with the given slope that contains the given point.

A slope = 3; $(1, 1)$

Step 1 Plot $(1, 1)$.

Step 2 Use the slope to move from $(1, 1)$ to another point.

$$\text{slope} = \frac{\text{rise}}{\text{run}} = 3 = \frac{3}{1}$$

Move **3 units up** and **4 unit right** and plot another point.

Step 3 Draw the line connecting the two points.

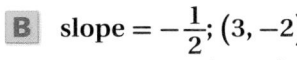

B slope = $-\frac{1}{2}$; $(3, -2)$

Step 1 Plot $(3, -2)$.

Step 2 Use the slope to move from $(3, -2)$ to another point.

$$\text{slope} = \frac{\text{rise}}{\text{run}} = \frac{1}{-2} = -\frac{1}{2}$$

Move **1 unit up** and **2 units left** and plot another point.

Step 3 Draw the line connecting the two points.

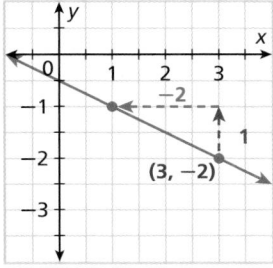

C slope = 0; $(3, 2)$

A line with slope of 0 is horizontal.
Draw the horizontal line through $(3, 2)$.

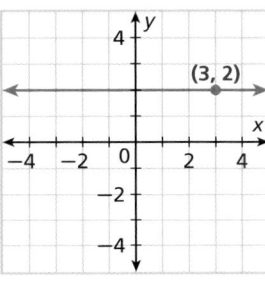

> **Helpful Hint**
>
> For a negative fraction, you can write the negative sign in one of three places.
>
> $$-\frac{1}{2} = \frac{-1}{2} = \frac{1}{-2}$$

 **CHECK IT OUT!**

1. Graph the line with slope −1 that contains $(2, -2)$.

If you know the slope and any point on the line, you can write an equation of the line by using the slope formula.

$$m = \frac{y_2 - y_1}{x_2 - x_1} \qquad \text{\textit{Slope formula}}$$

$$m(x_2 - x_1) = \left(\frac{y_2 - y_1}{x_2 - x_1}\right)(x_2 - x_1) \qquad \text{\textit{Multiply both sides by} } (x_2 - x_1).$$

$$m(x_2 - x_1) = y_2 - y_1 \qquad \text{\textit{Simplify.}}$$

$$y_2 - y_1 = m(x_2 - x_1)$$

Know it!
.Note

Point-Slope Form of a Linear Equation

The line with slope m that contains the point (x_1, y_1) can be described by the equation $y - y_1 = m(x - x_1)$.

EXAMPLE 2 **Writing Linear Equations in Point-Slope Form**

Write an equation in point-slope form for the line with the given slope that contains the given point.

A slope $= \frac{5}{2}; (-3, 0)$

$y - y_1 = m(x - x_1)$

$y - 0 = \frac{5}{2}[x - (-3)]$

$y - 0 = \frac{5}{2}(x + 3)$

B slope $= -7; (4, 2)$

$y - y_1 = m(x - x_1)$

$y - 2 = -7(x - 4)$

C slope $= 0; (-2, -3)$

$y - y_1 = m(x - x_1)$

$y - (-3) = 0[x - (-2)]$

$y + 3 = 0(x + 2)$

CHECK IT OUT! Write an equation in point-slope form for the line with the given slope that contains the given point.

2a. slope $= 2; \left(\frac{1}{2}, 1\right)$ **2b.** slope $= 0; (3, -4)$

EXAMPLE 3 **Writing Linear Equations in Slope-Intercept Form**

Write an equation in slope-intercept form for the line with slope -4 that contains $(-1, -2)$.

Step 1 Write the equation in point-slope form: $y - y_1 = m(x - x_1)$

$y - (-2) = -4[x - (-1)]$

Step 2 Write the equation in slope-intercept form by solving for y.

$y - (-2) = -4[x - (-1)]$

$y + 2 = -4(x + 1)$ *Rewrite subtraction of negative numbers as addition.*

$y + 2 = -4x - 4$ *Distribute -4 on the right side.*

$\underline{ -2 \qquad\qquad -2}$ *Subtract 2 from both sides.*

$y = -4x - 6$

CHECK IT OUT! **3.** Write an equation in slope-intercept form for the line with slope $\frac{1}{3}$ that contains $(-3, 1)$.

EXAMPLE 4 **Using Two Points to Write an Equation**

Write an equation in slope-intercept form for the line through the two points.

A $(1, -4)$ and $(3, 2)$

Step 1 Find the slope.

$$m = \frac{y_2 - y_1}{x_2 - x_1} = \frac{2 - (-4)}{3 - 1} = \frac{6}{2} = 3$$

Step 2 Substitute the slope and one of the points into the point-slope form.

$$y - y_1 = m(x - x_1)$$
$$y - 2 = 3(x - 3) \quad \textit{Choose (3, 2).}$$

Step 3 Write the equation in slope-intercept form.

$$y - 2 = 3(x - 3)$$
$$y - 2 = 3x - 9$$
$$\underline{ + 2 \quad\quad + 2}$$
$$y = 3x - 7$$

B $(4, -7)$ and $(0, 5)$

Step 1 Find the slope.

$$m = \frac{y_2 - y_1}{x_2 - x_1} = \frac{5 - (-7)}{0 - 4} = \frac{12}{-4} = -3$$

Step 2 Substitute the slope and one of the points into the point-slope form.

$$y - y_1 = m(x - x_1)$$
$$y - (-7) = -3(x - 4) \quad \textit{Choose (4, -7).}$$
$$y + 7 = -3(x - 4)$$

Step 3 Write the equation in slope-intercept form.

$$y + 7 = -3(x - 4)$$
$$y + 7 = -3x + 12$$
$$\underline{ - 7 \quad\quad - 7}$$
$$y = -3x + 5$$

Helpful Hint

After Step 1 of Example 4B, you could have written the equation in slope-intercept form immediately, because one of the given points contained the y-intercept.

 **CHECK IT OUT!** Write an equation in slope-intercept form for the line through the two points.

4a. $(1, -2)$ and $(3, 10)$ **4b.** $(6, 3)$ and $(0, -1)$

EXAMPLE 5 **Problem-Solving Application**

The cost to place an ad in a newspaper for one week is a linear function of the number of lines in the ad. The costs for 3, 5, and 10 lines are shown. Write an equation in slope-intercept form that represents the function. Then find the cost of an ad that is 18 lines long.

City Gazette

Newspaper Ad Costs

Lines	3	5	10
Cost ($)	13.50	18.50	31

1. Understand the Problem

• The **answer** will have two parts—an equation in slope-intercept form and the cost of an ad that is 18 lines long.
• The ordered pairs given in the table—$(3, 13.50)$, $(5, 18.50)$, and $(10, 31)$—satisfy the equation.

2. Make a Plan

You can use two of the ordered pairs to find the slope. Then use point-slope form to write the equation. Finally, write the equation in slope-intercept form.

3 Solve

Step 1 Choose any two ordered pairs from the table to find the slope.

$$m = \frac{y_2 - y_1}{x_2 - x_1} = \frac{18.50 - 13.50}{5 - 3} = \frac{5}{2} = 2.5 \quad \textit{Use (3, 13.50) and (5, 18.50).}$$

Step 2 Substitute the slope and any ordered pair from the table into the point-slope form.

$$y - y_1 = m(x - x_1)$$
$$y - 31 = 2.5(x - 10) \qquad\qquad \textit{Use (10, 31).}$$

Step 3 Write the equation in slope-intercept form by solving for y.

$$y - 31 = 2.5(x - 10)$$
$$y - 31 = 2.5x - 25 \qquad\qquad \textit{Distribute 2.5.}$$
$$y = 2.5x + 6 \qquad\qquad \textit{Add 31 to both sides.}$$

Step 4 Find the cost of an ad containing 18 lines by substituting 18 for x.

$$y = 2.5x + 6$$
$$y = 2.5(18) + 6 = 51$$

The cost of an ad containing 18 lines is $51.

 Look Back

If the equation is correct, the ordered pairs that you did not use in Step 2 will be solutions. Substitute (3, 13.50) and (5, 18.50) into the equation.

$y = 2.5x + 6$		$y = 2.5x + 6$	
13.50	$2.5(3) + 6$	18.50	$2.5(5) + 6$
13.5	$7.5 + 6$	18.5	$12.5 + 6$
13.5	13.5 ✓	18.5	18.5 ✓

 **5. What if...?** At a different newspaper, the costs to place an ad for one week are shown. Write an equation in slope-intercept form that represents this linear function. Then find the cost of an ad that is 21 lines long.

Lines	Cost ($)
3	12.75
5	17.25
10	28.50

THINK AND DISCUSS

1. How are point-slope form and slope-intercept form alike? different?

2. When is point-slope form useful? When is slope-intercept form useful?

 **3. GET ORGANIZED** Copy and complete the graphic organizer. In each box, describe how to find the equation of a line using each method.

Writing the Equation of a Line

If you know two points on the line	If you know the slope and y-intercept	If you know the slope and a point on the line

---

Math Builders

For more on using ordered pairs to write a linear equation, see the Function Builder on page MB2.

CHECK IT OUT!

Know it!
Note

5-6

Exercises

California
Standards Practice
6.0, 7.0, 25.2

go.hrw.com
Homework Help Online
KEYWORD: MA8CA 5-6
Parent Resources Online
KEYWORD: MA8CA Parent

GUIDED PRACTICE

SEE EXAMPLE 1
p. 297

Graph the line with the given slope that contains the given point.

1. slope = 1; $(1, 0)$ **2.** slope = −1; $(3, 1)$ **3.** slope = −2; $(−4, −2)$

SEE EXAMPLE 2
p. 298

Write an equation in point-slope form for the line with the given slope that contains the given point.

4. slope = $\frac{1}{5}$; $(2, −6)$ **5.** slope = −4; $(1, 5)$ **6.** slope = 0; $(3, −7)$

SEE EXAMPLE 3
p. 298

Write an equation in slope-intercept form for the line with the given slope that contains the given point.

7. slope = $−\frac{1}{3}$; $(−3, 8)$ **8.** slope = 2; $(1, 1)$ **9.** slope = $\frac{1}{3}$; $(−6, −2)$

10. slope = 2; $(−1, 1)$ **11.** slope = 3; $(2, −7)$ **12.** slope = −4; $(4, 2)$

SEE EXAMPLE 4
p. 299

Write an equation in slope-intercept form for the line through the two points.

13. $(−2, 2)$ and $(2, −2)$ **14.** $(0, −4)$ and $(1, −6)$ **15.** $(1, 1)$ and $(−5, 3)$

16. $(−3, 1)$ and $(0, 10)$ **17.** $(7, 8)$ and $(6, 9)$ **18.** $(0, −2)$ and $(2, 8)$

SEE EXAMPLE 5
p. 299

19. Measurement An oil tank is being filled at a constant rate. The depth of the oil is a function of the number of minutes the tank has been filling, as shown in the table. Write an equation in slope-intercept form that represents this linear function. Then find the depth of the oil after one-half hour.

Time (min)	Depth (ft)
0	3
10	5
15	6

PRACTICE AND PROBLEM SOLVING

Independent Practice

For Exercises	See Example
20–22	1
23–28	2
29–34	3
35–40	4
41	5

Extra Practice

Skills Practice p. EP11

Application Practice p. EP28

Graph the line with the given slope that contains the given point.

20. slope = $−\frac{1}{2}$; $(3, 1)$ **21.** slope = $\frac{3}{5}$; $(1, −2)$ **22.** slope = 4; $(−1, 0)$

Write an equation in point-slope form for the line with the given slope that contains the given point.

23. slope = $\frac{2}{9}$; $(−1, 5)$ **24.** slope = 0; $(4, −2)$ **25.** slope = 8; $(1, 8)$

26. slope = $\frac{1}{2}$; $(−8, 3)$ **27.** slope = 3; $(4, 7)$ **28.** slope = −2; $(−1, 3)$

Write an equation in slope-intercept form for the line with the given slope that contains the given point.

29. slope = $−\frac{2}{7}$; $(14, −3)$ **30.** slope = $\frac{4}{5}$; $(−15, 1)$ **31.** slope = $−\frac{1}{4}$; $(4, −1)$

32. slope = −6; $(9, 3)$ **33.** slope = −5; $(2, 3)$ **34.** slope = $\frac{1}{5}$; $(−5, −2)$

Write an equation in slope-intercept form for the line through the two points.

35. $(7, 8)$ and $(−7, 6)$ **36.** $(2, 7)$ and $(−4, 4)$ **37.** $(−1, 2)$ and $(4, −23)$

38. $(4, −1)$ and $(−8, −10)$ **39.** $(0, 11)$ and $(−7, −3)$ **40.** $(1, 27)$ and $(−2, 12)$

41. Science At higher altitudes, water boils at lower temperatures. This relationship between altitude and boiling point is linear. The table shows some altitudes and the corresponding boiling points. Write an equation in slope-intercept form that represents this linear function. Then find the boiling point at 6000 feet.

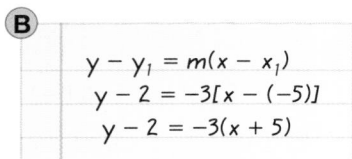

Boiling Point of Water	
Altitude (ft)	Temperature (°F)
1000	210
1500	209
3000	206

The tables show linear relationships between _x_ and _y_. Copy and complete the tables.

42.

x	−2	0	▧	7
y	−18	▧	12	27

43.

x	−4	1	0	▧
y	14	4	▧	−6

44. ///ERROR ANALYSIS/// Two students used point-slope form to find an equation that describes the line with slope −3 through $(-5, 2)$. Who is incorrect? Explain the error.

Ⓐ
$$y - y_1 = m(x - x_1)$$
$$y - 2 = -3(x - 5)$$

Ⓑ
$$y - y_1 = m(x - x_1)$$
$$y - 2 = -3[x - (-5)]$$
$$y - 2 = -3(x + 5)$$

45. Critical Thinking Compare the methods for finding the equation of a line when you know
- a point on the line and the slope of the line.
- two points on the line.

How are the methods alike? How are they different?

46. Write About It Explain why the first statement is false but the second is true.
- All linear equations can be written in point-slope form.
- All linear equations that describe functions can be written in point-slope form.

47. Multi-Step The table shows the mean scores on a standardized test for several different years.

Years Since 1980	0	5	10	17	21
Mean Score	994	1009	1001	1016	1020

a. Make a scatter plot of the data and add a trend line to your graph.
b. Use your trend line to estimate the slope and _y_-intercept, and write an equation in slope-intercept form.
c. What do the slope and _y_-intercept represent in this situation?

CONCEPT CONNECTION

48. This problem will prepare you for the Concept Connection on page 312.
a. Stephen is walking from his house to his friend Sharon's house. When he is 12 blocks away, he looks at his watch. He looks again when he is 8 blocks away and finds that 6 minutes have passed. Write two ordered pairs for these data in the form (time, blocks).
b. Write a linear equation for these two points.
c. What is the total amount of time it takes Stephen to reach Sharon's house?

Multiple Choice For Exercises 49 and 50, choose the best answer.

49. Which equation describes the line through $(-5, 1)$ with slope of 1?

Ⓐ $y + 1 = x - 5$ Ⓒ $y - 1 = -5(x - 1)$

Ⓑ $y + 5 = x - 1$ Ⓓ $y - 1 = x + 5$

50. A line contains $(4, 4)$ and $(5, 2)$. What are the slope and y-intercept?

Ⓐ slope $= -2$; y-intercept $= 2$ Ⓒ slope $= -2$; y-intercept $= 12$

Ⓑ slope $= 1.2$; y-intercept $= -2$ Ⓓ slope $= 12$; y-intercept $= 1.2$

CHALLENGE AND EXTEND

51. A linear function has the same y-intercept as $x + 4y = 8$ and its graph contains the point $(2, 7)$. Find the slope and y-intercept.

52. Write the equation of a line in slope-intercept form that contains $\left(\frac{3}{4}, \frac{1}{2}\right)$ and has the same slope as the line described by $y + 3x = 6$.

53. Write the equation of a line in slope-intercept form that contains $\left(-\frac{1}{2}, -\frac{1}{3}\right)$ and $\left(1\frac{1}{2}, 1\right)$.

 SPIRAL STANDARDS REVIEW    🔑 5.0, 🔑 6.0, 🔑 7.0

Solve each compound inequality and graph the solutions. *(Lesson 3-6)*

54. $-4 \le x + 2 \le 1$ **55.** $m - 5 > -7$ AND $m + 1 < 2$

Graph each function. *(Lesson 4-3)*

56. $y = x - 3$ **57.** $y = x^2 + 5$ **58.** $y = |2x|$

Write the equation of each line in slope-intercept form. *(Lesson 5-5)*

59. slope $= 3$, the point $(3, 4)$ is on the line   **60.** slope $= -2$, the point $(2, 4)$ is on the line

---

Career Path

 go.hrw.com

Career Resources Online

KEYWORD: MA8CA Career

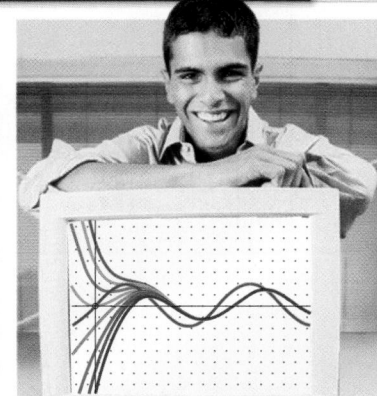

Michael Raynor
Data mining major

Q: **What math classes did you take in high school?**

A: Algebra 1 and 2, Geometry, and Statistics

Q: **What math classes have you taken in college?**

A: Applied Statistics, Data Mining Methods, Web Mining, and Artificial Intelligence

Q: **How do you use math?**

A: Once for a class, I used software to analyze basketball statistics. What I learned helped me develop strategies for our school team.

Q: **What are your future plans?**

A: There are many options for people with data mining skills. I could work in banking, pharmaceuticals, or even the military. But my dream job is to develop game strategies for an NBA team.

5-7 Slopes of Parallel and Perpendicular Lines

Vocabulary
parallel lines
perpendicular lines

Why learn this?
Parallel lines and their equations can be used to model costs, such as the cost of a booth at a farmers' market.

To sell at a particular farmers' market for a year, there is a $100 membership fee. Then you pay $3 for each hour that you sell at the market. However, if you were a member the previous year, the membership fee is reduced to $50.

- The red line shows the total cost if you are a new member.

- The blue line shows the total cost if you are a returning member.

These two lines are *parallel*. **Parallel lines** are lines in the same plane that have no points in common. In other words, they do not intersect.

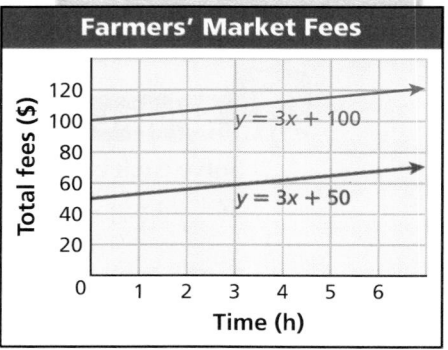

Know it! Note

Parallel Lines		
WORDS	Two different nonvertical lines are parallel if and only if they have the same slope.	All different vertical lines are parallel.
GRAPH	$y = \frac{1}{2}x + 5$ $y = \frac{1}{2}x + 1$	$x = -2$ $x = 4$

EXAMPLE 1 **Identifying Parallel Lines**

Identify which lines are parallel.

A $y = \frac{4}{3}x + 3$; $y = 2$; $y = \frac{4}{3}x - 5$; $y = -3$

The lines described by $y = \frac{4}{3}x + 3$ and $y = \frac{4}{3}x - 5$ both have slope $\frac{4}{3}$. These lines are parallel. The lines described by $y = 2$ and $y = -3$ both have slope 0. These lines are parallel.

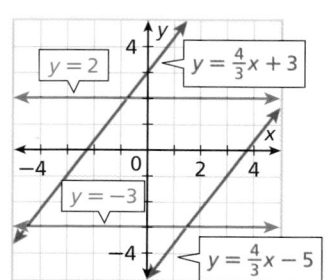

Identify which lines are parallel.

B $y = 3x + 2$; $y = -\frac{1}{2}x + 4$; $x + 2y = -4$; $y - 5 = 3(x - 1)$

Write all equations in slope-intercept form to determine the slopes.

$y = 3x + 2$	$y = -\frac{1}{2}x + 4$
slope-intercept form ✓	slope-intercept form ✓

$$x + 2y = -4$$
$$\underline{-x \qquad\qquad -x}$$
$$2y = -x - 4$$
$$\frac{2y}{2} = \frac{-x - 4}{2}$$
$$y = -\frac{1}{2}x - 2$$

$$y - 5 = 3(x - 1)$$
$$y - 5 = 3x - 3$$
$$\underline{+5 \qquad\qquad +5}$$
$$y = 3x + 2$$

The lines given by $y = 3x + 2$ and $y - 5 = 3(x - 1)$ have the same slope, but they are not parallel lines. They are the same line.

The lines given by $y = -\frac{1}{2}x + 4$ and $x + 2y = -4$ represent parallel lines. They each have slope $-\frac{1}{2}$.

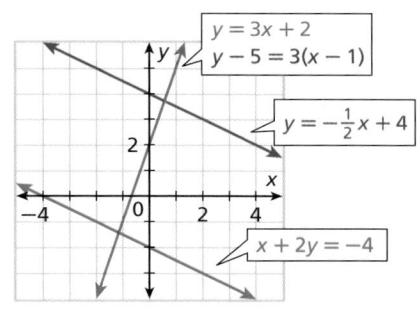

CHECK IT OUT!

Identify which lines are parallel.

1a. $y = 2x + 2$; $y = 2x + 1$; $y = -4$; $x = 1$

1b. $y = \frac{3}{4}x + 8$; $-3x + 4y = 32$; $y = 3x$; $y - 1 = 3(x + 2)$

EXAMPLE 2 *Geometry Application*

Reasoning

Show that *ABCD* is a parallelogram.

Use the ordered pairs and the slope formula to find the slopes of $\overline{AB}$ and $\overline{CD}$.

$$\text{slope of } \overline{AB} = \frac{7 - 5}{4 - (-1)} = \frac{2}{5}$$

$$\text{slope of } \overline{CD} = \frac{3 - 1}{4 - (-1)} = \frac{2}{5}$$

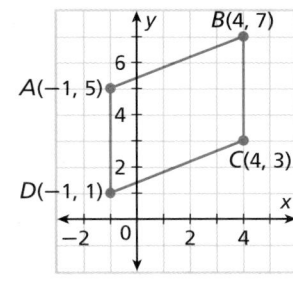

Remember!

In a parallelogram, opposite sides are parallel.

$\overline{AB}$ is parallel to $\overline{CD}$ because they have the same slope.

$\overline{AD}$ is parallel to $\overline{BC}$ because they are both vertical.

Therefore, *ABCD* is a parallelogram because both pairs of opposite sides are parallel.

CHECK IT OUT!

2. Show that the points $A(0, 2)$, $B(4, 2)$, $C(1, -3)$, and $D(-3, -3)$ are the vertices of a parallelogram.

Perpendicular lines are lines that intersect to form right angles (90°).

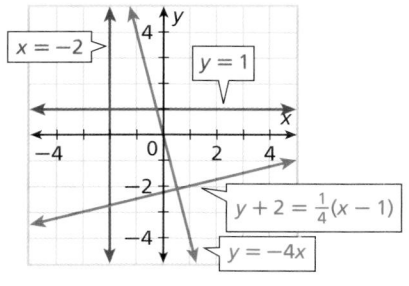

Know it!
Note

Perpendicular Lines		
WORDS	Two nonvertical lines are perpendicular if and only if the product of their slopes is −1.	Vertical lines are perpendicular to horizontal lines.
GRAPH	$y = -\frac{2}{3}x + 3$ $y = \frac{3}{2}x - 2$	$y = 3$ $x = 2$

E X A M P L E **3** **Identifying Perpendicular Lines**

Identify which lines are perpendicular: $x = -2$; $y = 1$; $y = -4x$;
$y + 2 = \frac{1}{4}(x + 1)$.

The line given by $x = -2$ is a vertical line, and the line given by $y = 1$ is a horizontal line. These lines are perpendicular.

The slope of the line given by $y = -4x$ is -4. The slope of the line given by $y + 2 = \frac{1}{4}(x - 1)$ is $\frac{1}{4}$.

$(-4)\left(\frac{1}{4}\right) = -1$

These lines are perpendicular because the product of their slopes is -1.

CHECK IT OUT! **3.** Identify which lines are perpendicular: $y = -4$; $y - 6 = 5(x + 4)$; $x = 3$; $y = -\frac{1}{5}x + 2$.

E X A M P L E **4** *Geometry Application*

Reasoning

Show that *PQR* is a right triangle.

If *PQR* is a right triangle, $\overline{PQ}$ will be perpendicular to $\overline{QR}$.

slope of $\overline{PQ} = \dfrac{3 - 1}{3 - 0} = \dfrac{2}{3}$

slope of $\overline{QR} = \dfrac{3 - 0}{3 - 5} = \dfrac{3}{-2} = -\dfrac{3}{2}$

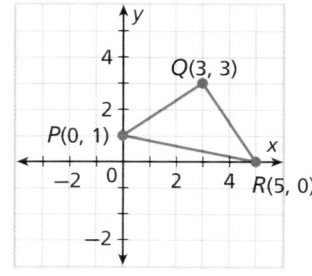

$\overline{PQ}$ is perpendicular to $\overline{QR}$ because $\dfrac{2}{3}\left(-\dfrac{3}{2}\right) = -1$.

Therefore, *PQR* is a right triangle because it contains a right angle.

Helpful Hint

A right triangle contains one right angle. In Example 4, $\angle P$ and $\angle R$ are clearly not right angles, so the only possibility is $\angle Q$.

CHECK IT OUT! **4.** Show that $P(1, 4)$, $Q(2, 6)$, and $R(7, 1)$ are the vertices of a right triangle.

EXAMPLE 5 | **Writing Equations of Parallel and Perpendicular Lines**

A **Write an equation in slope-intercept form for the line that passes through $(4, 5)$ and is parallel to the line given by $y = 5x + 10$.**

Step 1 Find the slope of the line.

$y = 5x + 10$ *The slope is 5.*

The parallel line also has a slope of 5.

Step 2 Write the equation in point-slope form.

$y - y_1 = m(x - x_1)$ *Use point-slope form.*

$y - 5 = 5(x - 4)$ *Substitute 5 for m, 4 for x_1, and 5 for y_1.*

Step 3 Write the equation in slope-intercept form.

$y - 5 = 5(x - 4)$

$y - 5 = 5x - 20$ *Distribute 5 on the right side.*

$y = 5x - 15$ *Add 5 to both sides.*

B **Write an equation in slope-intercept form for the line that passes through $(3, 2)$ and is perpendicular to the line given by $y = 3x - 1$.**

Step 1 Find the slope of the line.

$y = 3x - 1$ *The slope is 3.*

The perpendicular line has a slope of $-\frac{1}{3}$, because $3\left(-\frac{1}{3}\right) = -1$.

Step 2 Write the equation in point-slope form.

$y - y_1 = m(x - x_1)$ *Use point-slope form.*

$y - 2 = -\frac{1}{3}(x - 3)$ *Substitute $-\frac{1}{3}$ for m, 3 for x_1, and 2 for y_1.*

Step 3 Write the equation in slope-intercept form.

$y - 2 = -\frac{1}{3}(x - 3)$

$y - 2 = -\frac{1}{3}x + 1$ *Distribute $-\frac{1}{3}$ on the right side.*

$y = -\frac{1}{3}x + 3$ *Add 2 to both sides.*

> **Helpful Hint**
>
> If you know the slope of a line, the slope of a perpendicular line will be the "opposite reciprocal."
>
> $\frac{2}{3} \rightarrow -\frac{3}{2}$
>
> $\frac{1}{5} \rightarrow -5$
>
> $-7 \rightarrow \frac{1}{7}$

5a. Write an equation in slope-intercept form for the line that passes through $(5, 7)$ and is parallel to the line given by $y = \frac{4}{5}x - 6$.

5b. Write an equation in slope-intercept form for the line that passes through $(-5, 3)$ and is perpendicular to the line given by $y = 5x$.

THINK AND DISCUSS

1. Are the lines given by $y = \frac{1}{2}x$ and $y = 2x$ perpendicular? Explain.

2. Describe the slopes and y-intercepts when two nonvertical lines are parallel.

3. GET ORGANIZED Copy and complete the graphic organizer. In each box, sketch an example and describe the slopes.

Parallel lines	Perpendicular lines

5-7 Slopes of Parallel and Perpendicular Lines   **307**

5-7

Exercises

California Standards Practice
🔑 7.0, 8.0, 25.1

go.hrw.com
Homework Help Online
KEYWORD: MA8CA 5-7
Parent Resources Online
KEYWORD: MA8CA Parent

GUIDED PRACTICE

1. Vocabulary ___?___ lines have the same slope. (*Parallel* or *Perpendicular*)

SEE EXAMPLE **1**
p. 304

Identify which lines are parallel.

2. $y = 6$; $y = 6x + 5$; $y = 6x - 7$; $y = -8$

3. $y = \frac{3}{4}x - 1$; $y = -2x$; $y - 3 = \frac{3}{4}(x - 5)$; $y - 4 = -2(x + 2)$

SEE EXAMPLE **2**
p. 305

4. Reasoning Show that *ABCD* is a trapezoid. (*Hint:* In a trapezoid, exactly one pair of opposite sides is parallel.)

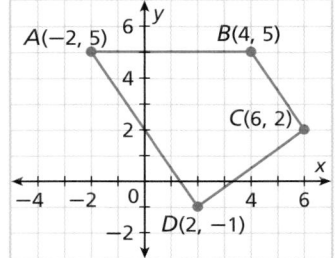

SEE EXAMPLE **3**
p. 306

Identify which lines are perpendicular.

5. $y = \frac{2}{3}x - 4$; $y = -\frac{3}{2}x + 2$; $y = -1$; $x = 3$

6. $y = -\frac{3}{7}x - 4$; $y - 4 = -7(x + 2)$;

$y - 1 = \frac{1}{7}(x - 4)$; $y - 7 = \frac{7}{3}(x - 3)$

SEE EXAMPLE **4**
p. 306

7. Reasoning Show that *PQRS* is a rectangle. (*Hint:* In a rectangle, all four angles are right angles.)

SEE EXAMPLE **5**
p. 307

8. Write an equation in slope-intercept form for the line that passes through (5, 0) and is perpendicular to the line given by $y = -\frac{5}{2}x + 6$.

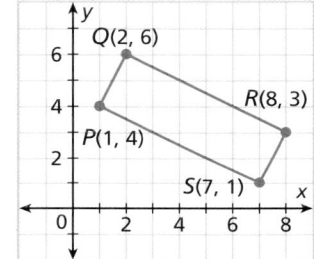

PRACTICE AND PROBLEM SOLVING

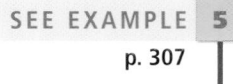

For Exercises	See Example
9–11	1
12	2
13–15	3
16	4
17	5

Extra Practice

Skills Practice p. EP11

Application Practice p. EP28

Identify which lines are parallel.

9. $x = 7$; $y = -\frac{5}{6}x + 8$; $y = -\frac{5}{6}x - 4$; $x = -9$

10. $y = -x$; $y - 3 = -1(x + 9)$; $y - 6 = \frac{1}{2}(x - 14)$; $y + 1 = \frac{1}{2}x$

11. $y = -3x + 2$; $y = \frac{1}{2}x - 1$; $-x + 2y = 17$; $3x + y = 27$

12. Reasoning Show that *LMNP* is a parallelogram.

Identify which lines are perpendicular.

13. $y = 6x$; $y = \frac{1}{6}x$; $y = -\frac{1}{6}x$; $y = -6x$

14. $y - 9 = 3(x + 1)$; $y = -\frac{1}{3}x + 5$; $y = 0$; $x = 6$

15. $x - 6y = 15$; $y = 3x - 2$; $y = -3x - 3$; $y = -6x - 8$;
$3y = -x - 11$

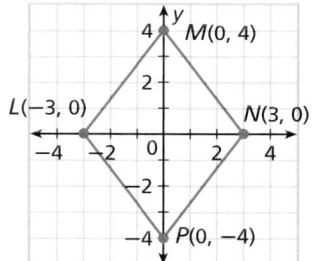

16. Reasoning Show that *ABC* is a right triangle.

17. Write an equation in slope-intercept form for the line that passes through $(0, 0)$ and is parallel to the line given by $y = -\frac{6}{7}x + 1$.

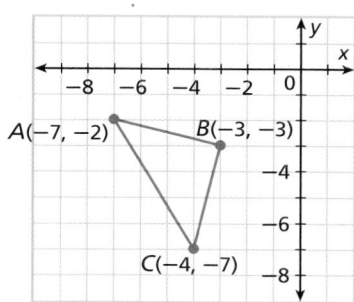
$A(-7, -2)$ $B(-3, -3)$
$C(-4, -7)$

Without graphing, tell whether each pair of lines is parallel, perpendicular, or neither.

18. $x = 2$ and $y = -5$

19. $y = 7x$ and $y - 28 = 7(x - 4)$

20. $y = 2x - 1$ and $y = \frac{1}{2}x + 2$

21. $y - 3 = \frac{1}{4}(x - 3)$ and $y + 13 = \frac{1}{4}(x + 1)$

Write an equation in slope-intercept form for the line that is parallel to the given line and that passes through the given point.

22. $y = 3x - 7; (0, 4)$

23. $y = \frac{1}{2}x + 5; (4, -3)$

24. $4y = x; (4, 0)$

25. $y = 2x + 3; (1, 7)$

26. $5x - 2y = 10; (3, -5)$

27. $y = 3x - 4; (-2, 7)$

28. $y = 7; (2, 4)$

29. $x + y = 1; (2, 3)$

30. $2x + 3y = 7; (4, 5)$

31. $y = 4x + 2; (5, -3)$

32. $y = \frac{1}{2}x - 1; (0, -4)$

33. $3x + 4y = 8; (4, -3)$

Write an equation in slope-intercept form for the line that is perpendicular to the given line and that passes through the given point.

34. $y = -3x + 4; (6, -2)$

35. $y = x - 6; (-1, 2)$

36. $3x - 4y = 8; (-6, 5)$

37. $5x + 2y = 10; (3, -5)$

38. $y = 5 - 3x; (2, -4)$

39. $-10x + 2y = 8; (4, -3)$

40. $2x + 3y = 7; (4, 5)$

41. $4x - 2y = -6; (3, -2)$

42. $-2x - 8y = 16; (4, 5)$

43. $y = -2x + 4; (-2, 5)$

44. $y = x - 5; (0, 5)$

45. $x + y = 2; (8, 5)$

46. Write an equation describing the line that is parallel to the *y*-axis and that is 6 units to the right of the *y*-axis.

47. Write an equation describing the line that is perpendicular to the *y*-axis and that is 4 units below the *x*-axis.

48. Critical Thinking Is it possible for two linear functions whose graphs are parallel lines to have the same *y*-intercept? Explain.

49. Estimation Estimate the slope of a line that is perpendicular to the line through $(2.07, 8.95)$ and $(-1.9, 25.07)$.

 50. Write About It Explain in words how to write an equation in slope-intercept form for a line parallel to $y - 3 = -6(x - 3)$.

CONCEPT CONNECTION

51. This problem will prepare you for the Concept Connection on page 312.
   a. Flora walks from her home to the bus stop at a rate of 50 steps per minute. Write a rule that gives her distance from home (in steps) as a function of time.
   b. Flora's neighbor Dan lives 30 steps closer to the bus stop. He begins walking at the same time and at the same pace as Flora. Write a rule that gives Dan's distance from *Flora's* house as a function of time.
   c. Will Flora meet Dan along the walk? Use a graph to help explain your answer.

Multiple Choice For Exercises 52 and 53, choose the best answer.

52. Which line is parallel to the line given by $y = -3x + 2$?

   Ⓐ $y = -3x$ Ⓑ $y = \frac{1}{3}x$ Ⓒ $y = 2 - 3x$ Ⓓ $y = \frac{1}{3}x + 2$

53. Which line passes through $(3, 3)$ and is perpendicular to the line given by $y = \frac{3}{5}x + 2$?

Ⓐ 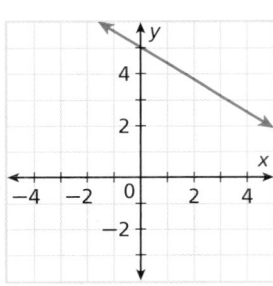   Ⓒ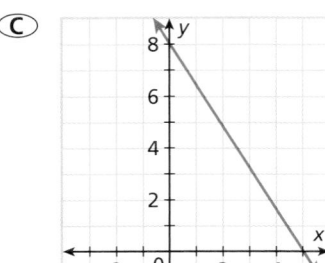

   Ⓑ $y = \frac{5}{3}x - 2$ Ⓓ $y = \frac{3}{5}x + \frac{6}{5}$

54. Gridded Response The graph of a linear function $f(x)$ is parallel to the line given by $2x + y = 5$ and contains the point $(6, -2)$. What is the y-intercept of $f(x)$?

CHALLENGE AND EXTEND

 55. Reasoning Three or more points that lie on the same line are called *collinear points*. Show that the points A, B, and C must be collinear if the line containing A and B has the same slope as the line containing B and C.

56. The lines given by $y = (a + 12)x + 3$ and $y = 4ax$ are parallel. What is the value of a?

57. The lines given by $y = (5a + 3)x$ and $y = -\frac{1}{2}x$ are perpendicular. What is the value of a?

 58. Geometry The diagram shows a square in the coordinate plane. Use the diagram and deductive reasoning to show that the diagonals of a square are perpendicular.

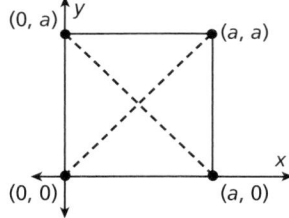

59. The record high temperature for a given city is $112°F + t$. The morning temperature today was $94°F$ and the temperature will increase $2t$ degrees. Write and solve an inequality to find all values of t that would break the record for the high temperature. *(Lesson 3-4)*

Graph each function. *(Lesson 4-3)*

60. $y = -3x + 5$ **61.** $y = x - 1$ **62.** $y = x^2 - 3$

Write an equation in slope-intercept form for the line with the given slope that contains the given point. *(Lesson 5-6)*

63. slope $= \frac{2}{3}$; $(6, -1)$ **64.** slope $= -5$; $(2, 4)$ **65.** slope $= -\frac{1}{2}$; $(-1, 0)$

66. slope $= -\frac{1}{3}$; $(2, 7)$ **67.** slope $= 0$; $(-3, 3)$ **68.** slope $= \frac{1}{5}$; $(-4, -2)$

Proving Conjectures

After working several math problems, Adele used inductive reasoning to conclude that when using two points to find the slope of a line, the order in which the points are substituted into the slope formula does not matter. (See pp. 280–281.)

California Standards

25.1 Students use properties of numbers to construct simple, valid arguments (**direct** and indirect) **for,** or formulate counterexamples to, **claimed assertions.** *Also covered:* **24.1**

Example

Inductive reasoning alone cannot prove a statement. However, inductive reasoning often leads to a conjecture that can be proved or disproved using deductive reasoning.

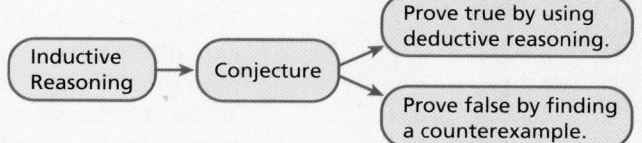

When Adele returned to class, she learned that her conjecture was correct. However, Adele wants to prove that her conjecture is true.

Adele's algebra teacher helped Adele write her conjecture as a conditional statement:

If (x_1, y_1) and (x_2, y_2) are two different points on a line, then $m = \dfrac{y_2 - y_1}{x_2 - x_1} = \dfrac{y_1 - y_2}{x_1 - x_2}$.

Try This

Adele wrote a proof of her conjecture, but she did not write reasons for her statements. Complete her proof by giving the reasons.

Statements	Reasons
1. (x_1, y_1) and (x_2, y_2) are two different points on a line.	?
2. $m = \dfrac{y_2 - y_1}{x_2 - x_1}$	?
3. $= \dfrac{y_2 - y_1}{x_2 - x_1}(1)$	?
4. $= \dfrac{y_2 - y_1}{x_2 - x_1}\left(\dfrac{-1}{-1}\right)$	?
5. $= \dfrac{-y_2 + y_1}{-x_2 + x_1}$	?
6. $= \dfrac{y_1 + (-y_2)}{x_1 + (-x_2)}$	?
7. $= \dfrac{y_1 - y_2}{x_1 - x_2}$	?

CONCEPT CONNECTION

Using Linear Functions

Take a Walk! All intersections in Durango, Colorado, have crossing signals with timers. Once the signal changes to walk, the timer begins at 28 seconds and counts down to show how much time pedestrians have to cross the street.

1. Pauline counted her steps as she crossed the street. She counted 15 steps with 19 seconds remaining. When she reached the opposite side of the street, she had counted a total of 30 steps and had 10 seconds remaining. Copy and complete the table below using these values.

Time Remaining (s)	28		
Steps Taken	0		

2. Find the average rate of change for Pauline's walk.

3. Sketch a graph of the points in the table, or plot them on your graphing calculator.

4. Find an equation for the line through the points.

5. How would the graph change if Pauline increased her speed? What if she decreased her speed?

READY TO GO ON?

Quiz for Lessons 5-5 Through 5-7

5-5 Slope-Intercept Form

Graph each line given the slope and y-intercept.

1. slope $= \frac{1}{4}$
  y-intercept $= 2$

2. slope $= -3$
  y-intercept $= 5$

3. slope $= -1$
  y-intercept $= -6$

Write each equation in slope-intercept form. Then graph the line given by the equation.

4. $2x + y = 5$

5. $2x - 6y = 6$

6. $3x + y = 3x - 4$

7. Entertainment At a chili cook-off, people pay a $3.00 entrance fee and $0.50 for each bowl of chili they taste. The graph shows the total cost per person as a function of the number of bowls of chili tasted.

  a. Write a rule that gives the total cost per person as a function of the number of bowls of chili tasted.

  b. Identify the slope and y-intercept and describe their meanings in this situation.

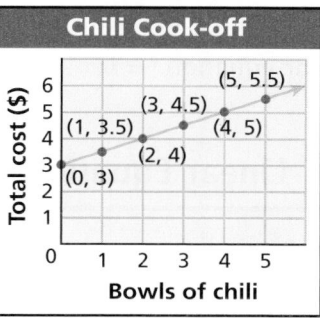

5-6 Point-Slope Form

Graph the line with the given slope that contains the given point.

8. slope $= -3$; $(0, 3)$

9. slope $= -\frac{2}{3}$; $(-3, 5)$

10. slope $= 2$; $(-3, -1)$

11. Write an equation in slope-intercept form for the line with slope -3 that contains $(2, -4)$.

Write an equation in slope-intercept form for the line through the two points.

12. $(3, 1)$ and $(4, 3)$

13. $(-1, -1)$ and $(1, 7)$

14. $(1, -4)$ and $(-2, 5)$

5-7 Slopes of Parallel and Perpendicular Lines

Identify which lines are parallel.

15. $y = -2x$; $y = 2x + 1$; $y = 2x$; $y = 2(x + 5)$

16. $-3y = x$; $y = -\frac{1}{3}x + 1$; $y = -3x$; $y + 2 = x + 4$

Identify which lines are perpendicular.

17. $y = -4x - 1$; $y = \frac{1}{4}x$; $y = 4x - 6$; $x = -4$

18. $y = -\frac{3}{4}x$; $y = \frac{3}{4}x - 3$; $y = \frac{4}{3}x$; $y = 4$; $x = 3$

19. Write an equation in slope-intercept form for the line that passes through $(5, 2)$ and is parallel to the line given by $3x - 5y = 15$.

20. Write an equation in slope-intercept form for the line that passes through $(3, 5)$ and is perpendicular to the line given by $y = -\frac{3}{2}x - 2$.

Study Guide: Review

Vocabulary

Complete the sentences below with vocabulary words from the list above. Words may be used more than once.

1. An equation that can be written in the form $y = kx$ is a(n) ___?___ .

2. The *x*-coordinate of the point that contains the ___?___ is always 0.

3. In the equation $y = mx + b$, the value of *m* is the ___?___ , and the value of *b* is the ___?___ .

5-1 Linear Equations and Functions (pp. 256–262)

 6.0, 7.0, 17.0, 18.0

EXAMPLES

■ Graph $y = -3x + 2$. Then tell whether it represents a function.

Generate ordered pairs.

x	y = -3x + 2	(x, y)
-2	y = -3(-2) + 2 = 8	(-2, 8)
0	y = -3(0) + 2 = 2	(0, 2)
2	y = -3(2) + 2 = -4	(2, -4)

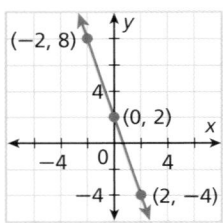

Plot the points and connect them with a straight line.

No vertical line will intersect this graph more than once, so $y = -3x + 2$ represents a function.

■ Write $y = 2x - 3$ in standard form and give the values of *A*, *B*, and *C*.

$$y = 2x - 3$$
$$\underline{-2x -2x}$$ *Subtract 2x from both sides.*
$$-2x + y = -3$$

$$A = -2 \quad B = 1 \quad C = -3$$

EXERCISES

Graph each linear equation. Then tell whether it describes a function.

4. $2x = y$

5. $5x - 2y = 10$

6. $y = 1$

7. $y + 5 = -4x$

Without graphing, tell whether each point is on the graph of $3x + 2y = 1$.

8. $(1, 6)$

9. $\left(0, \dfrac{1}{2}\right)$

10. $(3, -4)$

11. $(5, 1.5)$

Write each equation in standard form and give the values of *A*, *B*, and *C*. Then describe the graph.

12. $y = -5x + 1$

13. $\dfrac{x + 2}{2} = -3y$

14. $4y = 7x$

15. $9 = y$

5-2 Using Intercepts (pp. 263–268)

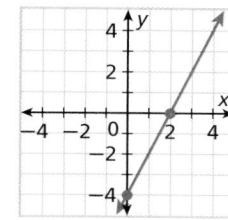

⬤─── 6.0

EXAMPLE

■ Find the x- and y-intercepts of $2x + 5y = 10$.

Let $y = 0$.	Let $x = 0$.
$2x + 5(0) = 10$	$2(0) + 5y = 10$
$2x + 0 = 10$	$0 + 5y = 10$
$2x = 10$	$5y = 10$
$\dfrac{2x}{2} = \dfrac{10}{2}$	$\dfrac{5y}{5} = \dfrac{10}{5}$
$x = 5$	$y = 2$

The x-intercept is 5.   The y-intercept is 2.

EXERCISES

Find the x- and y-intercepts.

16.

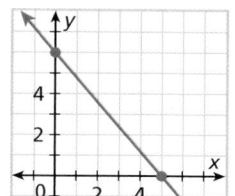

17.

18. $3x - y = 9$

19. $-2x + y = 1$

20. $-x + 6y = 18$

21. $3x - 4y = 1$

5-3 Slope (pp. 272–279)

Prep for 8.0, ⬤─── 6.0

EXAMPLES

■ Find the slope.

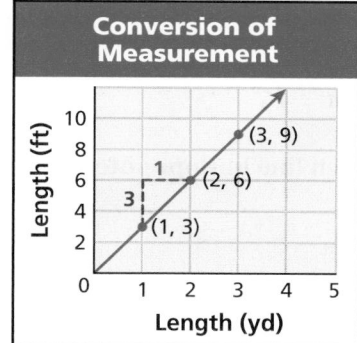

Conversion of Measurement

slope $= \dfrac{\text{change in } y}{\text{change in } x}$

$= \dfrac{3}{1} = 3$

■ Find the slope of the line given by $2x - 3y = 6$.

Step 1 Identify the x- and y-intercepts.

Let $y = 0$.	Let $x = 0$.
$2x - 3(0) = 6$	$2(0) - 3y = 6$
$2x = 6$	$-3y = 6$
$x = 3$	$y = -2$

The line contains $(3, 0)$ and $(0, -2)$.

Step 2 Use the slope formula.

$$m = \frac{y_2 - y_1}{x_2 - x_1} = \frac{-2 - 0}{0 - 3} = \frac{-2}{-3} = \frac{2}{3}$$

EXERCISES

22. Find the slope of the line graphed below.

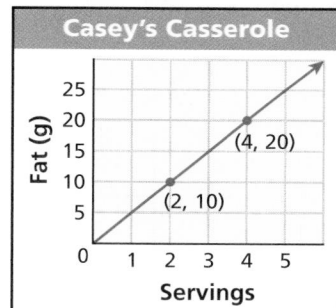

Casey's Casserole

Find the slope of the line described by each equation.

23. $4x + 3y = 24$ **24.** $y = -3x + 6$

25. $x + 2y = 10$ **26.** $3x = y + 3$

27. $y + 2 = 7x$ **28.** $16x = 4y + 1$

Find the slope of the line that contains each pair of points.

29. $(1, 2)$ and $(2, -3)$ **30.** $(4, -2)$ and $(-5, 7)$

31. $(-3, -6)$ and $(4, 1)$ **32.** $\left(\dfrac{1}{2}, 2\right)$ and $\left(\dfrac{3}{4}, \dfrac{5}{2}\right)$

33. $(2, 2)$ and $(2, 7)$ **34.** $(1, -3)$ and $(5, -3)$

5-4 Direct Variation *(pp. 282–287)*

 6.0

EXAMPLE

■ Tell whether $6x = -4y$ is a direct variation. If so, identify the constant of variation.

$$6x = -4y$$
$$\frac{6x}{-4} = \frac{-4y}{-4} \quad \text{Solve the equation for y.}$$
$$-\frac{6}{4}x = y$$
$$y = -\frac{3}{2}x \quad \text{Simplify.}$$

This equation is a direct variation because it can be written in the form $y = kx$, where $k = -\frac{3}{2}$.

EXERCISES

Tell whether each equation is a direct variation. If so, identify the constant of variation.

35. $y = -6x$

36. $x - y = 0$

37. $y + 4x = 3$

38. $2x = -4y$

39. The value of y varies directly with x, and $y = -8$ when $x = 2$. Find y when $x = 3$.

40. Maleka charges $8 per hour for baby-sitting. The amount of money she makes varies directly with the number of hours she baby-sits. The equation $y = 8x$ tells how much she earns y for baby-sitting x hours. Graph this direct variation.

5-5 Slope-Intercept Form *(pp. 290–296)*

 6.0

EXAMPLE

■ Graph the line with slope $= -\frac{4}{5}$ and y-intercept $= 8$.

Step 1 Plot $(0, 8)$.

Step 2 For a slope of $\frac{-4}{5}$, count 4 **down** and 5 **right** from $(0, 8)$. Plot another point.

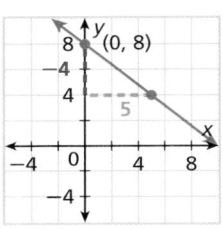

Step 3 Connect the two points with a line.

EXERCISES

Graph each line given the slope and y-intercept.

41. slope $= -\frac{1}{2}$; y-intercept $= 4$

42. slope $= 3$; y-intercept $= -7$

Write the equation of each line in slope-intercept form.

43. slope $= \frac{1}{3}$, y-intercept $= 5$

44. slope $= 4$, the point $(1, -5)$ is on the line

5-6 Point-Slope Form *(pp. 297–303)*

 6.0, 7.0

EXAMPLES

■ Graph the line with slope $\frac{1}{3}$ that passes through $(3, -4)$.

Step 1 Plot $(3, -4)$.

Step 2 For a slope of $\frac{1}{3}$, count 1 **up** and 3 **right** from $(3, -4)$. Plot another point.

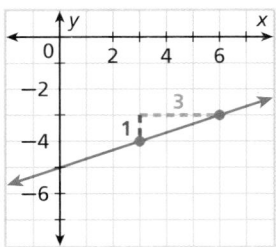

Step 3 Connect the two points with a line.

EXERCISES

Graph the line with the given slope that contains the given point.

45. slope $= \frac{1}{2}$; $(4, -3)$

46. slope $= -1$; $(-3, 1)$

Write an equation in point-slope form for the line with the given slope that contains the given point.

47. slope $= 2$; $(1, 3)$

48. slope $= -5$; $(-6, 4)$

■ Write an equation in slope-intercept form for the line through $(4, -1)$ and $(-2, 8)$.

$$m = \frac{y_2 - y_1}{x_2 - x_1}$$

$$= \frac{8 - (-1)}{-2 - 4} = \frac{9}{-6} = -\frac{3}{2} \quad \textit{Find the slope.}$$

$$y - y_1 = m(x - x_1) \qquad \textit{Substitute into the}$$
$$\qquad\qquad\qquad\qquad\qquad \textit{point-slope form.}$$

$$y - 8 = -\frac{3}{2}\big[x - (-2)\big]$$

$$y - 8 = -\frac{3}{2}(x + 2) \qquad \textit{Solve for y.}$$

$$y - 8 = -\frac{3}{2}x - 3$$

$$y = -\frac{3}{2}x + 5$$

Write an equation in slope-intercept form for the line through the two points.

49. $(1, 4)$ and $(3, 8)$ **50.** $(0, 3)$ and $(-2, 5)$

51. $(-2, 4)$ and $(-1, 6)$ **52.** $(-3, 2)$ and $(5, 2)$

53. A water tank at an aquarium is losing water. The depth of the water is a linear function of the number of minutes since the leak began, as shown in the table. Write an equation in slope-intercept form that represents this linear function. Then find the depth of the water after 2 hours.

Time (min)	Depth (in.)
0	48
30	38
60	28

5-7 Slopes of Parallel and Perpendicular Lines (pp. 304–310)

 8.0, 25.1

EXAMPLE

■ Write an equation in slope-intercept form for the line that passes through $(4, -2)$ and is perpendicular to the line given by $y = -4x + 3$.

Step 1 Find the slope of $y = -4x + 3$. The slope is -4. The perpendicular line has a slope of $\frac{1}{4}$.

Step 2 Write the equation. The perpendicular line has a slope of $\frac{1}{4}$ and contains $(4, -2)$.

$$y - y_1 = m(x - x_1)$$
$$y - (-2) = \frac{1}{4}(x - 4)$$
$$y + 2 = \frac{1}{4}(x - 4)$$

Step 3 Write the equation in slope-intercept form.

$$y + 2 = \frac{1}{4}(x - 4)$$

$$y + 2 = \frac{1}{4}x - 1 \qquad \textit{Distribute } \frac{1}{4}.$$

$$y = \frac{1}{4}x - 3 \qquad \textit{Subtract 2 from both}$$
$$\qquad\qquad\qquad\qquad \textit{sides.}$$

EXERCISES

Identify which lines are parallel.

54. $y = -\frac{1}{3}x$; $y = 3x + 2$;

$y = -\frac{1}{3}x - 6$; $y = 3$

55. $y - 2 = -4(x - 1)$; $y = 4x - 4$;

$y = \frac{1}{4}x$; $y = -4x - 2$

Identify which lines are perpendicular.

56. $y - 1 = -5(x - 6)$; $y = \frac{1}{5}x + 2$;

$y = 5$; $y = 5x + 8$

57. $y = 2x$; $y - 2 = 3(x + 1)$;

$y = \frac{2}{3}x - 4$; $y = -\frac{1}{3}x$

58. Show that ABC is a right triangle.

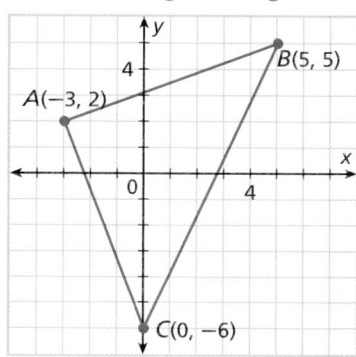

59. Write an equation in slope-intercept form for the line that passes through $(1, -1)$ and is parallel to the line given by $y = 2x - 4$.

CHAPTER TEST

Without graphing, tell whether each point is on the graph of the given line.

1. $-x + 8y = 22$; $(2, -3)$

2. $5x - 7y = -11$; $(2, 3)$

3. Lily plans to volunteer at the tutoring center for 45 hours. She can tutor 3 hours per week. The function $f(x) = 45 - 3x$ gives the number of hours she will have left to tutor after x weeks. Graph the function and find its intercepts. What does each intercept represent?

4. Use intercepts to graph the line given by $2x - 3y = 6$.

Find the slope of each line. Then tell what the slope represents.

5.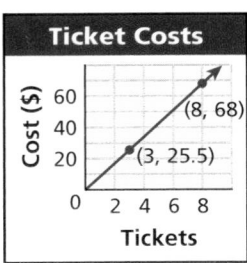

6.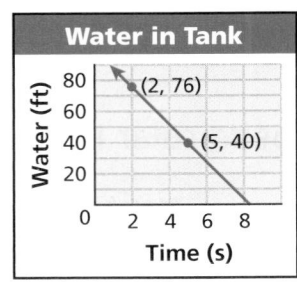

7.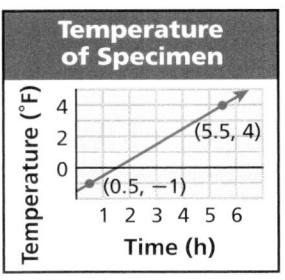

Tell whether each relationship is a direct variation. If so, identify the constant of variation.

8.

x	−1	2	5	9
y	4	7	10	14

9.

x	−2	2	6	10
y	1	−1	−3	−5

10.

x	4	−8	16	−24
y	1	−2	4	−6

11.

x	8	5	1	−2
y	4	2.5	1	−1

12. Write the equation $2x - 2y = 4$ in slope-intercept form. Then graph the line given by the equation.

13. Graph the line with slope $\frac{1}{3}$ that contains the point $(-4, -3)$.

14. Write an equation in slope-intercept form for the line through $(-1, 1)$ and $(0, 3)$.

15. Identify which lines are parallel: $y = -\frac{1}{2}x + 3$; $y = \frac{1}{2}x + 1$; $y = 2x$; $x + 2y = 4$.

16. Identify which lines are perpendicular: $y - 2 = 3x$; $y + 4x = -1$; $y = -\frac{1}{3}x + 5$; $y = \frac{1}{3}x - 4$.

17. Write an equation in slope-intercept form for the line that passes through $(0, 6)$ and is parallel to the line given by $y = 2x + 3$.

18. Write an equation in slope-intercept form for the line that passes through $(4, 6)$ and is perpendicular to the line given by $y = x - 3$.

19. Write an equation in slope-intercept form for the line parallel to $y = 3x - 4$ that passes through $(0, -1)$.

20. Write an equation in slope-intercept form for the line perpendicular to $y = \frac{1}{2}x + 7$ that passes through $(-1, 3)$.

FOCUS ON SAT

SAT scores are based on the total number of items answered correctly minus a fraction of the number of multiple-choice questions answered incorrectly. No points are subtracted for questions unanswered.

On the SAT, there is a penalty for incorrect answers. Guess only when you can eliminate at least one of the answer choices.

You may want to time yourself as you take this practice test. It should take you about 7 minutes to complete.

---

1. The line through $A(1, -3)$ and $B(-2, d)$ has slope -2. What is the value of d?

(A) $-\dfrac{3}{2}$

(B) -1

(C) $\dfrac{1}{2}$

(D) 3

(E) 5

---

2. The ordered pairs $\{(0, -3), (4, -1), (6, 0), (10, 2)\}$ satisfy a pattern. Which is NOT true?

(A) The pattern is linear.

(B) The pattern can be described by $2x - 4y = 12$.

(C) The ordered pairs lie on a line.

(D) $(-4, 1)$ satisfies the same pattern.

(E) The set of ordered pairs is a function.

---

3. If y varies directly as x, what is the value of x when $y = 72$?

x	7	12	
y	28	48	72

(A) 17

(B) 18

(C) 24

(D) 28

(E) 36

---

4. The line segment between the points $(4, 0)$ and $(2, -2)$ forms one side of a rectangle. Which of the following coordinates could determine another vertex of that rectangle?

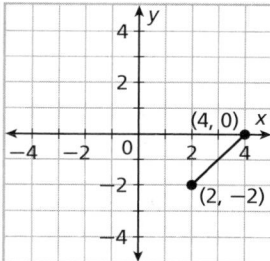

(A) $(-2, 6)$

(B) $(-2, -2)$

(C) $(0, 6)$

(D) $(1, 2)$

(E) $(4, 6)$

---

5. Which of the following has the same slope as the line given by $2x - 3y = 3$?

(A) $3x - 2y = 2$

(B) $\dfrac{2}{3}x - y = -2$

(C) $2x - 2y = 3$

(D) $\dfrac{1}{3}x - 2y = -2$

(E) $-2x - 3y = 2$

STRATEGIES FOR SUCCESS

Multiple Choice: Recognize Distracters

In multiple-choice items, the options that are incorrect are called *distracters*. This is an appropriate name, because these incorrect options can distract you from the correct answer.

Test writers create distracters by using common student errors. Beware! Even if the answer you get when you work the problem is one of the options, it may not be the correct answer.

EXAMPLE 1

What is the *y*-intercept of $4x + 10 = -2y$?

    Ⓐ 10   Ⓒ −2.5

    Ⓑ 5   Ⓓ −5

Look at each option carefully.

   A   This is a distracter. The *y*-intercept would be 10 if the function was $4x + 10 = y$. A common error is to ignore the coefficient of *y*.

   B   This is a distracter. Another common error is to divide by 2 instead of −2 when solving for *y*.

   C   This is a distracter. One of the most common errors students make is confusing the *x*-intercept and the *y*-intercept. This distracter is actually the *x-intercept* of the given line.

   D   This is the correct answer.

EXAMPLE 2

What is the equation of a line with a slope of −4 that contains (2, −3)?

    Ⓐ $y - 3 = -4(x - 2)$ Ⓒ $y + 3 = -4(x - 2)$

    Ⓑ $y - 2 = -4(x + 3)$ Ⓓ $y + 4 = -3(x - 2)$

Look at each option carefully.

   A   This is a distracter. Students often make errors with positive and negative signs. You would get this answer if you simplified $y - (-3)$ as $y - 3$.

   B   This is a distracter. You would get this answer if you switched the *x*-coordinate and the *y*-coordinate.

   C   This is the correct answer.

   D   This is a distracter. You would get this answer if you substituted the given values incorrectly into the point-slope formula.

HOT TIP! When you calculate an answer to a multiple-choice test item, try to solve the problem again with a different method to make sure your answer is correct.

Read each test item and answer the questions that follow.

Item A
A line contains $(1, 2)$ and $(-2, 14)$. What are the slope and y-intercept?

(A) Slope $= -4$; y-intercept $= -2$

(B) Slope $= 4$; y-intercept $= 6$

(C) Slope $= -\frac{1}{4}$; y-intercept $= 1$

(D) Slope $= -4$; y-intercept $= 6$

---

1. What common error does the slope in choice B represent?

2. The slope given in choice A is correct, but the y-intercept is not. What error was made when finding the y-intercept?

3. What formula can you use to find the slope of a line? How was this formula used incorrectly to get the slope in choice C?

Item B
Which of these equations has a graph that is NOT parallel to the line given by $y = \frac{1}{2}x + 4$?

(A) $y = 6 - \frac{1}{2}x$

(B) $y = \frac{1}{2}x + 6$

(C) $-2y = -x + 1$

(D) $2y = x$

---

4. When given two linear equations, describe how to determine whether their graphs are parallel.

5. Which is the correct answer? Describe the errors a student might make to get each of the distracters.

Item C
Which of these lines has a slope of -3?

(A) 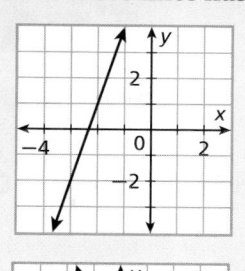 (C)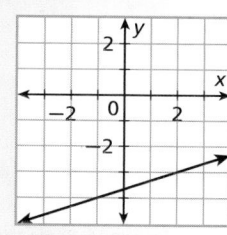

(B) 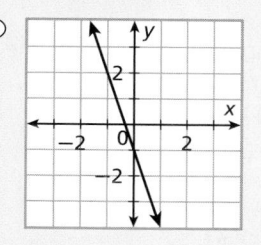 (D)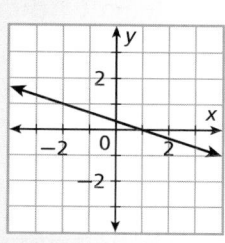

---

6. Which two answer choices can be eliminated immediately? Why?

7. Describe how to find the slope of a line from its graph.

8. What common error does choice A represent?

9. What common error does choice D represent?

10. Which is the correct answer?

Item D
Which is NOT a linear function?

(A) $f(x) = 4 + x$

(B) $f(x) = -x - 4$

(C) $f(x) = 4x^2$

(D) $f(x) = \frac{1}{4}x$

---

11. When given a function, how can you tell if it is linear?

12. What part of the function given in choice B might make someone think it is not linear?

13. What part of the function given in choice D might make someone think it is not linear?

14. What part of the function given in choice C makes it NOT linear?

MASTERING THE STANDARDS

go.hrw.com
Standards Practice Online
KEYWORD: MA8CA Practice

CUMULATIVE ASSESSMENT, CHAPTERS 1–5

Multiple Choice

1. Which of the following is an example of the Commutative Property of Multiplication?

Ⓐ $5 \cdot 2 \cdot 7 = (5 \cdot 2) \cdot 7$

Ⓑ $2(4 + 3) = 2 \cdot 4 + 2 \cdot 3$

Ⓒ $6 \cdot 8 = 8 \cdot 6$

Ⓓ $(2 + 4) + 6 = (4 + 2) + 6$

2. Which of these lines has an x-intercept of 4 and a y-intercept of 3?

Ⓐ $y = \frac{3}{4}x + 3$

Ⓑ $y = \frac{4}{3}x + 4$

Ⓒ $y = -\frac{3}{4}x + 3$

Ⓓ $y = -\frac{4}{3}x + 4$

3. Steven claims that the whole numbers are closed under division. Beth disagrees. Which of the following equations could Beth use as a counterexample to show that Steven's claim is false?

Ⓐ $12 \div 3 = 4$

Ⓑ $4 \div 8 = \frac{1}{2}$

Ⓒ $\frac{1}{2} \div \frac{1}{4} = 2$

Ⓓ $-10 \div 5 = -2$

4. The side length of a square s can be determined by the formula $s = \sqrt{A}$ where A represents the area of the square. What is the side length of a square with area 0.09 square meters?

Ⓐ 0.0081 meters

Ⓑ 0.81 meters

Ⓒ 0.03 meters

Ⓓ 0.3 meters

5. What is the value of x when $3x - 4(x + 5) = -18$?

Ⓐ -2

Ⓑ 2

Ⓒ 13

Ⓓ 23

6. Which relationship is a function?

Ⓐ
x	0	2	2	5
y	1	2	4	2

Ⓑ
x	1	1	1	1
y	1	2	3	4

Ⓒ
x	1	2	3	4
y	3	3	3	3

Ⓓ
x	0	5	5	5
y	-1	2	3	4

7. Which function has x-intercept -2 and y-intercept 4?

Ⓐ $2x - y = 4$

Ⓑ $2y - x = 4$

Ⓒ $y - 2x = 4$

Ⓓ $x - 2y = 4$

8. Keiko graphs the line $x - 3y + 3 = 0$. Then she plots the point $(4, 2)$. Which of the following describes the location of the point?

Ⓐ The point is below the line.

Ⓑ The point is above the line.

Ⓒ The point is to the left of the line.

Ⓓ The point is on the line.

9. Which graph is described by $x - 3y = -3$?

Ⓐ 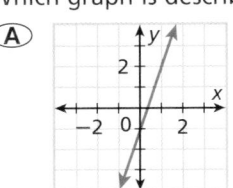 Ⓒ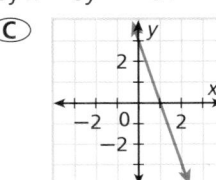

Ⓑ 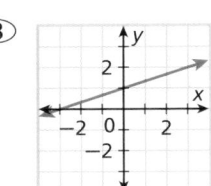 Ⓓ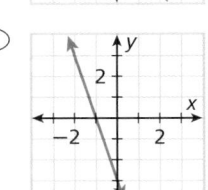

When answering multiple-choice test items, check that the test item number matches the number on your answer sheet, especially if you skip test items that you plan to come back to.

10. Which steps could you use to graph the line that has slope 2 and contains the point $(-1, 3)$?

   Ⓐ Plot $(-1, 3)$. Move 1 unit up and 2 units right and plot another point.

   Ⓑ Plot $(-1, 3)$. Move 2 units up and 1 unit right and plot another point.

   Ⓒ Plot $(-1, 3)$. Move 1 unit up and 2 units left and plot another point.

   Ⓓ Plot $(-1, 3)$. Move 2 units up and 1 unit left and plot another point.

11. Which line is parallel to the line described by $2x + 3y = 6$?

   Ⓐ $3x + 2y = 6$ Ⓒ $2x + 3y = -6$

   Ⓑ $3x - 2y = -6$ Ⓓ $2x - 3y = 6$

12. Which function's graph is NOT perpendicular to the line described by $4x - y = -2$?

   Ⓐ $y + \frac{1}{4}x = 0$ Ⓒ $3y = \frac{3}{4}x + 3$

   Ⓑ $\frac{1}{2}x = 10 - 2y$ Ⓓ $y = -\frac{1}{4}x + \frac{3}{2}$

13. Brent is solving the inequality $-5x + 3 + 2x > 9$. As a first step, he rewrites the inequality as $-5x + 2x + 3 > 9$. Which property justifies this step?

   Ⓐ Associative Property of Addition

   Ⓑ Closure Property of the Real Numbers

   Ⓒ Commutative Property of Addition

   Ⓓ Distributive Property

Gridded Response

14. What is the slope of a line that is perpendicular to the line shown?

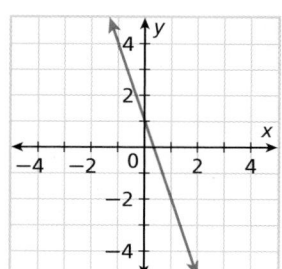

15. What is the x-intercept of $3x - 4y - 12 = 0$?

16. What is the y-intercept of $y - 2 = 3(x + 4)$?

Short Response

17. A video store charges a $10 membership fee plus $2 for each movie rental. The total cost for x movie rentals is given by $f(x) = 2x + 10$.

   a. Graph this function.

   b. Give a reasonable domain and range.

18. a. Write the equation of the line that has an x-intercept of -3 and a y-intercept of 6.

   b. Use your equation to help you decide whether or not the point $(-2, 2)$ lies on the line. Explain how you know.

19. a. Find the slope of the line below.

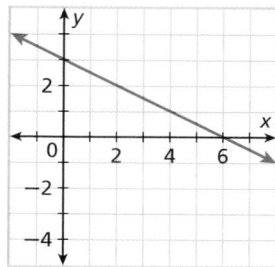

   b. Write an equation in slope-intercept form for a line that is perpendicular to the line in part **a** and has the same y-intercept as the function in part **a**. Show your work and explain how you got your answer.

Extended Response

20. A regional planner uses the coordinate plane shown below to design roads through the towns of Acorn, Bandon, and Chester.

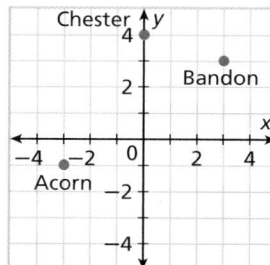

   a. Route 1 is a straight road that passes through Acorn and Bandon. Write an equation for Route 1.

   b. The planner uses the equation $2x - 3y = -12$ to lay out the path of Highway 205. Does Highway 205 pass through Chester? Why or why not?

   c. Show how the planner can use slopes to determine whether Route 1 and Highway 205 intersect.

CHAPTER 6

Systems of Equations and Inequalities

go.hrw.com
Chapter Project Online
KEYWORD: MA8CA ChProj

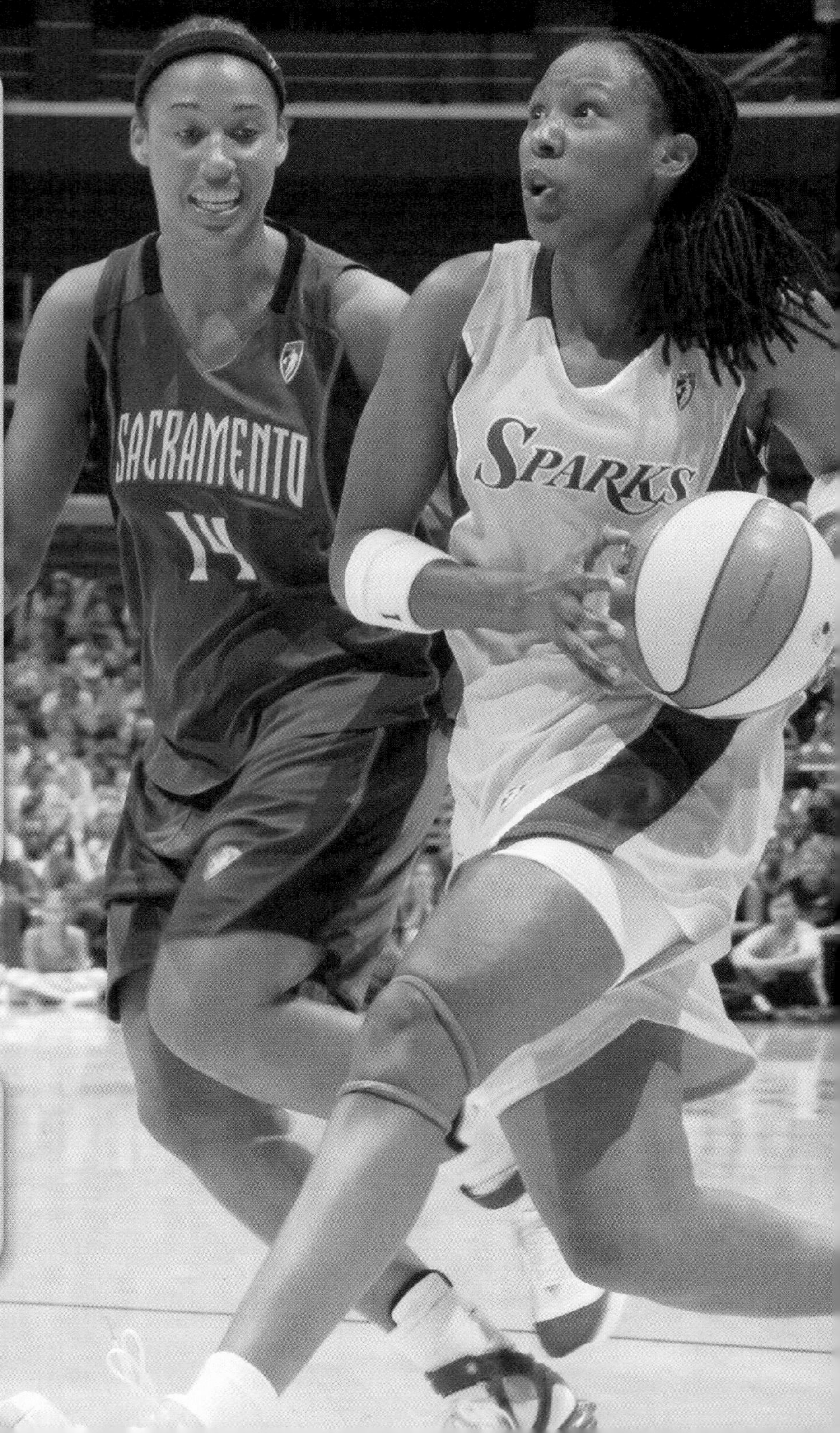

You can solve a system of equations to decide how many basketball game tickets you can buy at different prices.

Staples Center
Los Angeles, CA

ARE YOU READY?

✓ Vocabulary

Match each term on the left with a definition on the right.

1. inequality
2. linear equation
3. ordered pair
4. slope
5. solution of an equation

   A. a pair of numbers (x, y) that represent the coordinates of a point

   B. a statement that two quantities are not equal

   C. the y-value of the point at which the graph of an equation crosses the y-axis

   D. a value of the variable that makes the equation true

   E. the ratio of the vertical change to the horizontal change for a nonvertical line

   F. an equation whose graph is a straight line

✓ Graph Linear Functions

Graph each function.

6. $y = \frac{3}{4}x + 1$
7. $y = -3x + 5$
8. $y = x - 6$
9. $x + y = 4$
10. $y = -\frac{2}{3}x + 4$
11. $y = -5$

✓ Solve Multi-Step Equations

Solve each equation.

12. $-7x - 18 = 3$
13. $12 = -3n + 6$
14. $\frac{1}{2}d + 30 = 32$
15. $-2p + 9 = -3$
16. $33 = 5y + 8$
17. $-3 + 3x = 27$

✓ Solve for a Variable

Solve each equation for y.

18. $7x + y = 4$
19. $y + 2 = -4x$
20. $8 = x - y$
21. $x + 2 = y - 5$
22. $2y - 3 = 12x$
23. $y + \frac{3}{4}x = 4$

✓ Evaluate Expressions

Evaluate each expression for the given value of the variable.

24. $t - 5$ for $t = 7$
25. $9 - 2a$ for $a = 4$
26. $\frac{1}{2}x - 2$ for $x = 14$
27. $n + 15$ for $n = 37$
28. $9c + 4$ for $c = \frac{1}{3}$
29. $16 + 3d$ for $d = 5$

✓ Solve and Graph Inequalities

Solve and graph each inequality.

30. $b - 9 \geq 1$
31. $-2x < 10$
32. $3y \leq -3$
33. $\frac{1}{3}y \leq 5$

Unpacking the Standards

The information below "unpacks" the standards. The Academic Vocabulary is highlighted and defined to help you understand the language of the standards. Refer to the lessons listed after each standard for help with the math terms and phrases. The Chapter Concept shows how the standard is applied in this chapter.

California Standard	Academic Vocabulary	Chapter Concept
6.0 Students graph a linear equation and compute the x- and y-intercepts (e.g., graph $2x + 6y = 4$). **They are also able to sketch the region defined by linear inequalities (e.g., they sketch the region defined by $2x + 6y < 4$).** (Lessons **6-1, 6-6, 6-7**)	**define** to mark the limits of	You solve a linear inequality that contains two variables and graph the solutions on the coordinate plane.
8.0 Students understand the concepts of parallel lines and perpendicular lines **and how their slopes are related.** Students are able to find the equation of a line perpendicular to a given line that passes through a given point. (Lesson **6-4**)	**concept** idea or meaning	You understand parallel lines and how they are related in the coordinate plane.
9.0 Students solve a system of two linear equations in two variables algebraically and are able to interpret the answer graphically. Students are able to solve a system of two linear inequalities in two variables and to sketch the solution sets. (Lessons **6-1, 6-2, 6-3, 6-4, 6-5, 6-7**; Labs **6-2**, 6-7)	**algebraically** having to do with algebra **interpret** understand **graphically** having to do with a graph or graphs **in two variables** containing two variables	You use algebra to find solutions that satisfy two linear equations or inequalities, and you understand how the solutions are represented in the coordinate plane.
15.0 Students apply algebraic techniques to solve rate problems, work problems, **and percent mixture problems.** (Lesson **6-5**)	**algebraic** having to do with algebra **technique** a way of doing something	You use algebra to solve real-world problems about rates and mixtures.

Standard 5.0 is also covered in this chapter. To see this standard unpacked, go to Chapter 2, p. 70.

Reading and Writing Math

California Standards

English-Language Arts,
Writing 8.2.4.b

Writing Strategy: Write a Convincing Argument/Explanation

The Write About It icon ✎ appears throughout the book. These icons identify questions that require you to write a complete argument or explanation. Writing a convincing argument or explanation shows that you have a solid understanding of a concept.

To be effective, an argument or explanation should include

- reasoning, evidence, work, or facts.
- a complete response that will answer or explain.

From Lesson 3-7

✎ **54. Write About It** Describe how to use an absolute-value inequality to find all the values on a number line that are within 5 units of −6.

Step 1 **Identify what you need to answer or explain.**
Explain how an absolute-value inequality can help find values on a number line that are within 5 units of −6.

Step 2 **Give evidence, work, or facts that are needed to answer the question.**
The distance between two numbers can be found using subtraction. The inequality $|x| < 5$ describes all real numbers whose distance from 0 is less than 5 units. To find all real numbers whose distance from −6 is less than 5 units, you must subtract −6 from x.
$$|x - (-6)| < 5$$

Step 3 **Write a complete response that answers or explains.**
The difference between a number and −6 must be less than 5.
$$|x - (-6)| < 5$$
$$|x + 6| < 5$$

Try This

Write a convincing argument or explanation.

1. What is the least whole number that is a solution of $12x + 15.4 > 118.92$? Explain.

2. Which equation has an error? Explain the error.

    A. $4(6 \cdot 5) = (4)6 \cdot (4)5$ **B.** $4(6 \cdot 5) = (4 \cdot 6)5$

6-1 Technology Lab

Use with Lesson 6-1

Solve Linear Equations by Using a Spreadsheet

You can use a spreadsheet to answer "What if...?" questions. By changing one or more values, you can quickly model different scenarios.

go.hrw.com
Lab Resources Online
KEYWORD: MA8CA Lab6

Company Z makes DVD players. The company's costs are $400 per week plus $20 per DVD player. Each DVD player sells for $45. How many DVD players must company Z sell in one week to make a profit?

California Standards

5.0 Students solve multistep problems, including word problems involving linear equations and linear inequalities in one variable and provide justification for each step.

Let n represent the number of DVD players company Z sells in one week.

$c = 400 + 20n$ *The total cost is $400 plus $20 times the number of DVD players made.*

$s = 45n$ *The total sales income is $45 times the number of DVD players sold.*

$p = s - c$ *The total profit is the sales income minus the total cost.*

1 Set up your spreadsheet with columns for number of DVD players, total cost, total income, and profit.

2 Under Number of DVD Players, enter 1 in cell A2.

3 Use the equations above to enter the formulas for total cost, total sales, and total profit in row 2.
- In cell B2, enter the formula for total cost.
- In cell C2, enter the formula for total sales income.
- In cell D2, enter the formula for total profit.

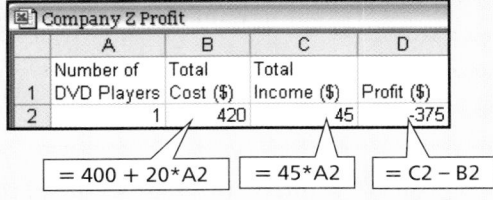

4 Fill columns A, B, C, and D by selecting cells A1 through D1, clicking the small box at the bottom right corner of cell D2, and dragging the box down through several rows.

5 Find the point where the profit is $0. This is known as the breakeven point, where total cost and total income are the same.

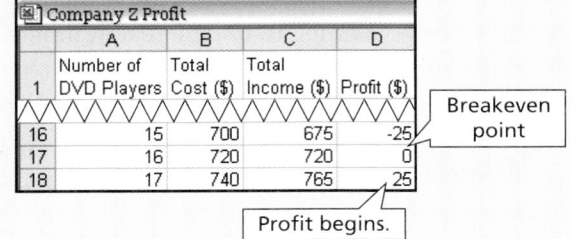

Try This

For Exercises 1 and 2, use the spreadsheet from the activity.

1. If company Z sells 10 DVD players, will they make a profit? Explain. What if they sell 16?

2. Company Z makes a profit of $225 dollars. How many DVD players did they sell?

For Exercise 3, make a spreadsheet.

3. Company Y's costs are $400 per week plus $20 per DVD player. They want the breakeven point to occur with sales of 8 DVD players. What should the sales price be?

6-1 Solving Systems by Graphing

California Standards

◆━ **9.0** Students solve a system of two linear equations in two variables algebraically and are able to interpret the answer graphically. Students are able to solve a system of two linear inequalities in two variables and to sketch the solution sets.

Also covered: ◆━ **6.0**

Why learn this?

You can compare costs by graphing a system of linear equations.

Sometimes there are different charges for the same service or product at different places. For example, Bowl-o-Rama charges $2.50 per game plus $2 for shoe rental while Bowling Pinz charges $2 per game plus $4 for shoe rental. A *system of linear equations* can be used to compare these charges.

A **system of linear equations** is a set of two or more linear equations containing two or more variables. A **solution of a system of linear equations** with two variables is an ordered pair that satisfies each equation in the system. So, if an ordered pair is a solution, it will make both equations true.

EXAMPLE **1** **Identifying Solutions of Systems**

Vocabulary
system of linear equations
solution of a system of linear equations

Tell whether the ordered pair is a solution of the given system.

A $(4, 1)$; $\begin{cases} x + 2y = 6 \\ x - y = 3 \end{cases}$

$x + 2y = 6$	
$4 + 2(1)$	6
$4 + 2$	6
6	6 ✓

Substitute 4 for x and 1 for y.

$x - y = 3$	
$4 - 1$	3
3	3 ✓

The ordered pair $(4, 1)$ makes both equations true.

$(4, 1)$ is a solution of the system.

Helpful Hint

If an ordered pair does not satisfy the first equation in the system, there is no need to check the other equations.

B $(-1, 2)$; $\begin{cases} 2x + 5y = 8 \\ 3x - 2y = 5 \end{cases}$

$2x + 5y = 8$	
$2(-1) + 5(2)$	8
$-2 + 10$	8
8	8 ✓

Substitute −1 for x and 2 for y.

$3x - 2y = 5$	
$3(-1) - 2(2)$	5
$-3 - 4$	5
-7	5 ✗

Substitute −1 for x and 2 for y.

The ordered pair $(-1, 2)$ makes one equation true, but not the other.

$(-1, 2)$ is not a solution of the system.

 Tell whether the ordered pair is a solution of the given system.

1a. $(1, 3)$; $\begin{cases} 2x + y = 5 \\ -2x + y = 1 \end{cases}$ **1b.** $(2, -1)$; $\begin{cases} x - 2y = 4 \\ 3x + y = 6 \end{cases}$

All solutions of a linear equation are on its graph. To find a solution of a system of linear equations, you need a point that each line has in common. In other words, you need their point of intersection.

$$\begin{cases} y = 2x - 1 \\ y = -x + 5 \end{cases}$$

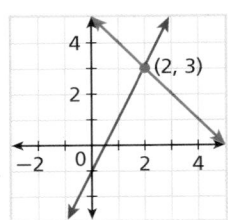

The point $(2, 3)$ is where the two lines intersect and is a solution of both equations, so $(2, 3)$ is the solution of the system.

EXAMPLE **2** **Solving a System of Linear Equations by Graphing**

Solve each system by graphing. Check your answer.

A $\begin{cases} y = x - 3 \\ y = -x - 1 \end{cases}$

Graph the system.

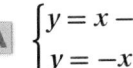

The solution appears to be at $(1, -2)$.

Check

Substitute $(1, -2)$ into the system.

$y = x - 3$	
-2	$1 - 3$
-2	$-2 ✓$

$y = -x - 1$	
-2	$-(1) - 1$
-2	$-2 ✓$

The solution is $(1, -2)$.

For more on graphing systems of equations, see the System Builder on page MB4.

B $\begin{cases} x + y = 0 \\ y = -\dfrac{1}{2}x + 1 \end{cases}$

$$\begin{array}{r} x + y = 0 \\ \underline{-x -x} \\ y = -x \end{array}$$

Rewrite the first equation in slope-intercept form.

Graph the system.

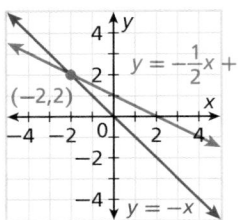

The solution appears to be at $(-2, 2)$.

Check

Substitute $(-2, 2)$ into the system.

$x + y = 0$	
$-2 + 2$	0
0	$0 ✓$

$y = -\dfrac{1}{2}x + 1$	
2	$-\dfrac{1}{2}(-2) + 1$
2	$1 + 1$
2	$2 ✓$

The solution is $(-2, 2)$.

CHECK IT OUT! **Solve each system by graphing. Check your answer.**

2a. $\begin{cases} y = -2x - 1 \\ y = x + 5 \end{cases}$

2b. $\begin{cases} y = \dfrac{1}{3}x - 3 \\ 2x + y = 4 \end{cases}$

EXAMPLE 3

Problem-Solving Application

Bowl-o-Rama charges $2.50 per game plus $2 for shoe rental, and Bowling Pinz charges $2 per game plus $4 for shoe rental. For how many games will the cost to bowl be the same at both places? What is that cost?

1 **Understand the Problem**

The **answer** will be the number of games played for which the total cost is the same at both bowling alleys. **List the important information:**
- Game price: Bowl-o-Rama $2.50   Bowling Pinz: $2
- Shoe-rental fee: Bowl-o-Rama $2   Bowling Pinz: $4

2 **Make a Plan**

Write a system of equations, one equation to represent the price at each company. Let x be the number of games played and y be the total cost.

	Total cost	is	price per game	times	games	plus	shoe-rental.
Bowl-o-Rama	y	=	2.5	$\bullet$	x	+	2
Bowling Pinz	y	=	2	$\bullet$	x	+	4

3 **Solve**

Graph $y = 2.5x + 2$ and $y = 2x + 4$. The lines appear to intersect at $(4, 12)$. So, the cost at both places will be the same for 4 games bowled and that cost will be $12.

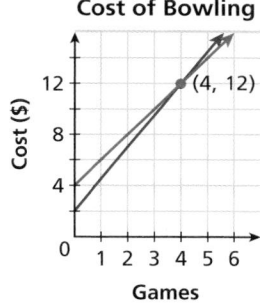

Cost of Bowling

4 **Look Back**

Check $(4, 12)$ using both equations.
Cost of bowling 4 games at Bowl-o-Rama:
$2.5(4) + \$2 = 10 + 2 = 12$ ✓
Cost of bowling 4 games at Bowling Pinz:
$2(4) + \$4 = 8 + 4 = 12$ ✓

3. Video club A charges $10 for membership and $3 per movie rental. Video club B charges $15 for membership and $2 per movie rental. For how many movie rentals will the cost be the same at both video clubs? What is that cost?

> **Writing Math**
>
> The solution set for Example 3 is written {(4, 12)}.

THINK AND DISCUSS

1. Explain how to use a graph to solve a system of linear equations.

2. Explain how to check a solution of a system of linear equations.

3. **GET ORGANIZED** Copy and complete the graphic organizer. In each box, write a step for solving a linear system by graphing. More boxes may be added.

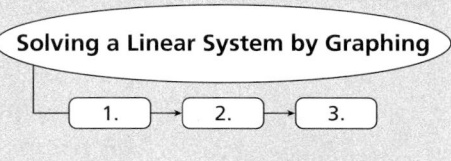

Solving a Linear System by Graphing

1. → 2. → 3.

6-1 **Exercises**

California
Standards Practice
🔑 6.0, 🔑 9.0

go.hrw.com
Homework Help Online
KEYWORD: MA8CA 6-1

Parent Resources Online
KEYWORD: MA8CA Parent

GUIDED PRACTICE

1. **Vocabulary** Describe a *solution of a system of linear equations.*

SEE EXAMPLE **1**
p. 329

Tell whether the ordered pair is a solution of the given system.

2. $(2, -2)$; $\begin{cases} 3x + y = 4 \\ x - 3y = -4 \end{cases}$

3. $(3, -1)$; $\begin{cases} x - 2y = 5 \\ 2x - y = 7 \end{cases}$

4. $(-1, 5)$; $\begin{cases} -x + y = 6 \\ 2x + 3y = 13 \end{cases}$

SEE EXAMPLE **2**
p. 330

Solve each system by graphing. Check your answer.

5. $\begin{cases} y = \dfrac{1}{2}x \\ y = -x + 3 \end{cases}$

6. $\begin{cases} y = x - 2 \\ 2x + y = 1 \end{cases}$

7. $\begin{cases} -2x - 1 = y \\ x + y = 3 \end{cases}$

SEE EXAMPLE **3**
p. 331

8. To deliver mulch, Lawn and Garden charges $30 per cubic yard of mulch plus a $30 delivery fee. Yard Depot charges $25 per cubic yard of mulch plus a $55 delivery fee. For how many cubic yards will the cost be the same? What will that cost be?

PRACTICE AND PROBLEM SOLVING

Independent Practice

For Exercises	See Example
9–11	1
12–15	2
16	3

Extra Practice
Skills Practice p. EP12
Application Practice p. EP29

Tell whether the ordered pair is a solution of the given system.

9. $(1, -4)$; $\begin{cases} x - 2y = 8 \\ 4x - y = 8 \end{cases}$

10. $(-2, 1)$; $\begin{cases} 2x - 3y = -7 \\ 3x + y = -5 \end{cases}$

11. $(5, 2)$; $\begin{cases} 2x + y = 12 \\ -3y - x = -11 \end{cases}$

Solve each system by graphing. Check your answer.

12. $\begin{cases} y = \dfrac{1}{2}x + 2 \\ y = -x - 1 \end{cases}$

13. $\begin{cases} y = x \\ y = -x + 6 \end{cases}$

14. $\begin{cases} -2x - 1 = y \\ x = -y + 3 \end{cases}$

15. $\begin{cases} x + y = 2 \\ y = x - 4 \end{cases}$

16. **Multi-Step** Angelo runs 7 miles per week and increases his distance by 1 mile each week. Marc runs 4 miles per week and increases his distance by 2 miles each week. In how many weeks will Angelo and Marc be running the same distance? What will that distance be?

17. **School** The school band sells carnations on Valentine's Day for $2 each. They buy the carnations from a florist for $0.50 each, plus a $16 delivery charge.

   a. Write a system of equations to describe the situation.

   b. Graph the system. What does the solution represent?

   c. Explain whether the solution shown on the graph makes sense in this situation. If not, give a reasonable solution.

CONCEPT CONNECTION

18. This problem will prepare you for the Concept Connection on page 362.

   a. The Warrior baseball team is selling hats as a fund-raiser. They contacted two companies. Hats Off charges a $50 design fee and $5 per hat. Top Stuff charges a $25 design fee and $6 per hat. Write an equation for each company's pricing.

   b. Graph the system of equations from part **a**. For how many hats will the cost be the same? What is that cost?

   c. Explain when it is cheaper for the baseball team to use Top Stuff and when it is cheaper to use Hats Off.

19. $\begin{cases} y = 4.7x + 2.1 \\ y = 1.6x - 5.4 \end{cases}$

20. $\begin{cases} 4.8x + 0.6y = 4 \\ y = -3.2x + 2.7 \end{cases}$

Landscaping

21. $\begin{cases} y = \dfrac{5}{4}x - \dfrac{2}{3} \\ \dfrac{8}{3}x + y = \dfrac{5}{9} \end{cases}$

22. $\begin{cases} y = 6.9x + 12.4 \\ y = -4.1x - 5.3 \end{cases}$

23. **Landscaping** The gardeners at Middleton Place Gardens want to plant a total of 45 white and pink hydrangeas in one flower bed. In another flower bed, they want to plant 120 hydrangeas. In this bed, they want 2 times the number of white hydrangeas and 3 times the number of pink hydrangeas as in the first bed. Use a system of equations to find how many white and how many pink hydrangeas the gardeners should buy altogether.

Middleton Place Gardens, South Carolina, are the United States' oldest landscaped gardens. The gardens were established in 1741 and opened to the public in the 1920s.

24. **Fitness** Rusty burns 5 Calories per minute swimming and 11 Calories per minute jogging. In the morning, Rusty burns 200 Calories walking and swims for x minutes. In the afternoon, Rusty will jog for x minutes. How many minutes must he jog to burn at least as many Calories y in the afternoon as he did in the morning? Round your answer up to the next whole number of minutes.

25. A tree that is 2 feet tall is growing at a rate of 1 foot per year. A 6-foot tall tree is growing at a rate of 0.5 foot per year. In how many years will the trees be the same height?

26. **Critical Thinking** Write a real-world situation that could be represented by the system $\begin{cases} y = 3x + 10 \\ y = 5x + 20 \end{cases}$.

27. **Write About It** When you graph a system of linear equations, why does the intersection of the two lines represent the solution of the system?

Multiple Choice For Exercises 28 and 29, choose the best answer.

28. Taxi company A charges $4 plus $0.50 per mile. Taxi company B charges $5 plus $0.25 per mile. Which system best represents this problem?

   Ⓐ $\begin{cases} y = 4x + 0.5 \\ y = 5x + 0.25 \end{cases}$

   Ⓒ $\begin{cases} y = -4x + 0.5 \\ y = -5x + 0.25 \end{cases}$

   Ⓑ $\begin{cases} y = 0.5x + 4 \\ y = 0.25x + 5 \end{cases}$

   Ⓓ $\begin{cases} y = -0.5x + 4 \\ y = -0.25x + 5 \end{cases}$

29. Which system of equations represents the given graph?

   Ⓐ $\begin{cases} y = 2x - 1 \\ y = \dfrac{1}{3}x + 3 \end{cases}$

   Ⓒ $\begin{cases} y = 2x + 1 \\ y = \dfrac{1}{3}x - 3 \end{cases}$

   Ⓑ $\begin{cases} y = -2x + 1 \\ y = 2x - 3 \end{cases}$

   Ⓓ $\begin{cases} y = -2x - 1 \\ y = 3x - 3 \end{cases}$

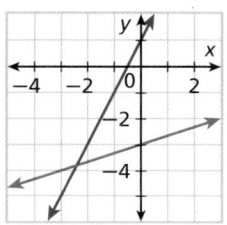

30. **Gridded Response** Which value of b will make the system $y = 2x + 2$ and $y = 2.5x + b$ intersect at the point $(2, 6)$?

CHALLENGE AND EXTEND

31. **Entertainment** If the pattern in the table continues, in what month will the number of sales of VCRs and DVD players be the same? What will that number be?

Total Number Sold				
Month	1	2	3	4
VCRs	500	490	480	470
DVD Players	250	265	280	295

32. Long Distance Inc. charges a $1.45 connection charge and $0.03 per minute. Far Away Calls charges a $1.52 connection charge and $0.02 per minute.

   a. For how many minutes will a call cost the same from both companies? What is that cost?

   b. When is it better to call using Long Distance Inc.? Far Away Calls? Explain.

   c. **What if...?** Long Distance Inc. raised its connection charge to $1.50 and Far Away Calls decreased its connection charge by 2 cents. How will this affect the graphs? Now which company is better to use for calling long distance? Why?

 SPIRAL STANDARDS REVIEW 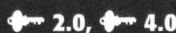 2.0, 4.0

Solve each equation. Check your answer. *(Lesson 2-1)*

33. $18 = \frac{3}{7}x$ **34.** $-\frac{x}{5} = 12$ **35.** $-6y = -13.2$ **36.** $\frac{2}{5} = \frac{y}{12}$

Solve each equation. Check your answer. *(Lesson 2-3)*

37. $5x + 6x + 5 = 16$ **38.** $6(x + 2) = -2(x + 10)$ **39.** $12 - 6z + 5z = 10$

Solve each inequality and graph the solutions. Check your answer. *(Lesson 3-4)*

40. $4(2x + 1) > 28$ **41.** $3^3 + 9 \le -4c$ **42.** $\frac{1}{8}x + \frac{3}{5} \le \frac{3}{8}$

Career Path

go.hrw.com
Career Resources Online
KEYWORD: MA8CA Career

Ethan Reynolds
Applied Sciences major

Q: What math classes did you take in high school?
A: Career Math, Algebra, and Geometry

Q: What are you studying and what math classes have you taken?
A: I am really interested in aviation. I am taking Statistics and Trigonometry. Next year I will take Calculus.

Q: How is math used in aviation?
A: I use math to interpret aeronautical charts. I also perform calculations involving wind movements, aircraft weight and balance, and fuel consumption. These skills are necessary for planning and executing safe air flights.

Q: What are your future plans?
A: I could work as a commercial or corporate pilot or even as a flight instructor. I could also work toward a bachelor's degree in aviation management, air traffic control, aviation electronics, aviation maintenance, or aviation computer science.

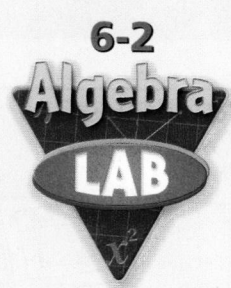

6-2

Algebra LAB

Model Systems of Linear Equations

You can use algebra tiles to model and solve some systems of linear equations.

Use with Lesson 6-2

 go.hrw.com
Lab Resources Online
KEYWORD: MA8CA Lab6

 California Standards

9.0 Students solve a system of two linear equations in two variables algebraically and are able to interpret the answer graphically. Students are able to solve a system of two linear inequalities in two variables and to sketch the solution sets.

KEY	REMEMBER
= 1 = −1 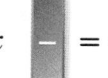 = x = $-x$	When two expressions are equal, you can substitute one for the other in any expression or equation.

Activity

Use algebra tiles to model and solve $\begin{cases} y = 2x - 3 \\ x + y = 9 \end{cases}$.

MODEL		ALGEBRA
	The first equation is solved for y. Model the second equation, $x + y = 9$, by substituting $2x - 3$ for y.	$x + y = 9$ $x + (2x - 3) = 9$ $3x - 3 = 9$
	Add 3 yellow tiles on both sides of the mat. This represents adding 3 to both sides of the equation. *Remove zero pairs.*	$\begin{array}{r} 3x - 3 = 9 \\ +3 +3 \\ \hline 3x = 12 \end{array}$
	Divide each group into 3 equal groups. Align one x-tile with each group on the right side. One x-tile is equivalent to 4 yellow tiles. $x = 4$	$\dfrac{3x}{3} = \dfrac{12}{3}$ $x = 4$

To solve for y, substitute 4 for x in one of the equations:

$$y = 2x - 3$$
$$= 2(4) - 3 = 5$$

The solution is (4, 5).

Try This

Use algebra tiles to model and solve each system of equations.

1. $\begin{cases} y = x + 3 \\ 2x + y = 6 \end{cases}$

2. $\begin{cases} 2x + 3 = y \\ x + y = 6 \end{cases}$

3. $\begin{cases} 2x + 3y = 1 \\ x = -1 - y \end{cases}$

4. $\begin{cases} y = x + 1 \\ 2x - y = -5 \end{cases}$

6-2 Solving Systems by Substitution

CAMPING OUT FOR THE BEST TICKETS ISN'T WHAT IT USED TO BE...

Why learn this?

You can solve systems of equations to help select the best value among high-speed Internet providers. (See Example 3.)

Sometimes it is difficult to identify the exact solution to a system by graphing. In this case, you can use a method called *substitution*.

Substitution is used to reduce the system to one equation that has only one variable. Then you can solve this equation by the methods taught in Chapter 2.

Solving Systems of Equations by Substitution
Step 1 Solve for one variable in at least one equation, if necessary.
Step 2 Substitute the resulting expression into the other equation.
Step 3 Solve that equation to get the value of the first variable.
Step 4 Substitute that value into one of the original equations and solve for the other variable.
Step 5 Write the values from Steps 3 and 4 as an ordered pair, (x, y), and check.

EXAMPLE 1 **Solving a System of Linear Equations by Substitution**

Solve each system by substitution.

A $\begin{cases} y = 2x \\ y = x + 5 \end{cases}$

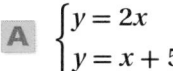

Helpful Hint

You can substitute the value of one variable into *either* of the original equations to find the value of the other variable.

Step 1 $y = 2x$ *Both equations are solved for y.*
 $y = x + 5$

Step 2 $y = x + 5$ *Substitute 2x for y in the second equation.*
 $2x = x + 5$

Step 3 $\underline{-x \quad\; -x}$ *Now solve this equation for x. Subtract x from*
 $x = 5$ *both sides to combine like terms.*

Step 4 $y = 2x$ *Write one of the original equations.*
 $y = 2(5)$ *Substitute 5 for x.*
 $y = 10$

Step 5 $(5, 10)$ *Write the solution as an ordered pair.*

Check Substitute $(5, 10)$ into both equations in the system.

$y = 2x$	
10	$2(5)$
10	$10 \checkmark$

$y = x + 5$	
10	$5 + 5$
10	$10 \checkmark$

Solve each system by substitution.

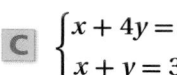 $\begin{cases} 2x + y = 5 \\ y = x - 4 \end{cases}$

Step 1 $y = x - 4$ *The second equation is solved for y.*

Step 2 $2x + y = 5$ *Write the first equation.*

$2x + (x - 4) = 5$ *Substitute x − 4 for y in the first equation.*

Step 3 $3x - 4 = 5$ *Simplify. Then solve for x.*

$\underline{+4 \quad +4}$ *Add 4 to both sides.*

$3x = 9$

$\dfrac{3x}{3} = \dfrac{9}{3}$ *Divide both sides by 3.*

$x = 3$

Step 4 $y = x - 4$ *Write one of the original equations.*

$y = 3 - 4$ *Substitute 3 for x.*

$y = -1$

Step 5 $(3, -1)$ *Write the solution as an ordered pair.*

C $\begin{cases} x + 4y = 6 \\ x + y = 3 \end{cases}$

Step 1 $x + 4y = 6$ *Solve the first equation for x by subtracting 4y from both sides.*

$\underline{-4y \quad -4y}$

$x = 6 - 4y$

Step 2 $x + y = 3$

$(6 - 4y) + y = 3$ *Substitute 6 − 4y for x in the second equation.*

Step 3 $6 - 3y = 3$ *Simplify. Then solve for y.*

$\underline{-6 -6}$ *Subtract 6 from both sides.*

$-3y = -3$

$\dfrac{-3y}{-3} = \dfrac{-3}{-3}$ *Divide both sides by −3.*

$y = 1$

Step 4 $x + y = 3$ *Write one of the original equations.*

$x + 1 = 3$ *Substitute 1 for y.*

$\underline{-1 \quad -1}$ *Subtract 1 from both sides.*

$x = 2$

Step 5 $(2, 1)$ *Write the solution as an ordered pair.*

> **Helpful Hint**
>
> Sometimes neither equation is solved for a variable. You can begin by solving either equation for either *x* or *y*.

 **Solve each system by substitution. Check your answer.**

1a. $\begin{cases} y = x + 3 \\ y = 2x + 5 \end{cases}$ **1b.** $\begin{cases} x = 2y - 4 \\ x + 8y = 16 \end{cases}$ **1c.** $\begin{cases} 2x + y = -4 \\ x + y = -7 \end{cases}$

Sometimes you substitute an expression for a variable that has a coefficient. When solving for the second variable in this situation, you can use the Distributive Property.

EXAMPLE 2 Using the Distributive Property

Solve $\begin{cases} 4y - 5x = 9 \\ x - 4y = 11 \end{cases}$ by substitution.

Step 1
$$x - 4y = \quad 11$$
$$\underline{\quad + 4y \quad + 4y}$$
$$x \quad = \quad 4y + 11$$

Solve the second equation for x by adding 4y to each side.

Caution! ⚠

When you solve one equation for a variable, you must substitute the value or expression into the *other* original equation, not the one that has just been solved.

Step 2
$$4y - 5x = 9$$
$$4y - 5(4y + 11) = 9$$

Substitute 4y + 11 for x in the first equation.

Step 3 $\quad 4y - 5(4y) - 5(11) = 9$
$$4y - 20y - 55 = 9$$
$$-16y - 55 = \quad 9$$
$$\underline{\quad\quad\quad + 55 \quad + 55}$$
$$-16y \quad = \quad 64$$

Distribute −5 to the expression in the parentheses. Simplify. Solve for y.

Add 55 to both sides.

$$\frac{-16y}{-16} = \frac{64}{-16}$$
$$y = -4$$

Divide both sides by −16.

Step 4
$$x - 4y = 11$$
$$x - 4(-4) = 11$$
$$x + 16 = \quad 11$$
$$\underline{\quad\quad - 16 \quad - 16}$$
$$x \quad = -5$$

Write one of the original equations.

Substitute −4 for y.

Simplify.

Subtract 16 from both sides.

Step 5 $(-5, -4)$

Write the solution as an ordered pair.

CHECK IT OUT! **2.** Solve $\begin{cases} -2x + y = 8 \\ 3x + 2y = 9 \end{cases}$ by substitution. Check your answer.

Student to Student

Solving Systems by Substitution

Erika Chu
Terrell High School

I always look for a variable with a coefficient of 1 or −1 when deciding which equation to solve for x or y.

For the system
$$\begin{cases} 2x + y = 14 \\ -3x + 4y = -10 \end{cases}$$

I would solve the first equation for y because it has a coefficient of 1.

$$2x + y = 14$$
$$y = -2x + 14$$

Then I use substitution to find the values of x and y.
$$-3x + 4y = -10$$
$$-3x + 4(-2x + 14) = -10$$
$$-3x + (-8x) + 56 = -10$$
$$-11x + 56 = -10$$
$$-11x = -66$$
$$x = 6$$

$$y = -2x + 14$$
$$y = -2(6) + 14 = 2$$

The solution is $(6, 2)$.

EXAMPLE 3 *Consumer Economics Application*

One high-speed Internet provider has a $50 setup fee and costs $30 per month. Another provider has no setup fee and costs $40 per month.

a. In how many months will both providers cost the same? What will that cost be?

Write an equation for each option. Let t represent the total amount paid and m represent the number of months.

	Total paid	is	setup fee	plus	cost per month	times	months.
Option 1	t	$=$	50	$+$	30	$\cdot$	m
Option 2	t	$=$	0	$+$	40	$\cdot$	m

Step 1 $t = 50 + 30m$ *Both equations are solved for t.*
$t = 40m$

Step 2 $50 + 30m = 40m$ *Substitute 50 + 30m for t in the second equation.*

Step 3 $\dfrac{-30m \quad\quad -30m}{50 \quad = \quad 10m}$ *Solve for m. Subtract 30m from both sides to combine like terms.*

$\dfrac{50}{10} = \dfrac{10m}{10}$ *Divide both sides by 10.*

$5 = m$

Step 4 $t = 40m$ *Write one of the original equations.*
$= 40(5)$ *Substitute 5 for m.*
$= 200$

Step 5 $(5, 200)$ *Write the solution as an ordered pair.*

In **5 months**, the total cost for each option will be the same—**$200**.

b. If you plan to cancel in 1 year, which is the cheaper provider? Explain.

Option 1: $t = 50 + 30(12) = 410$ Option 2: $t = 40(12) = 480$
Option 1 is cheaper.

 **3.** One cable television provider has a $60 setup fee and $80 per month, and the second has a $160 equipment fee and $70 per month.

a. In how many months will the cost be the same? What will that cost be?

b. If you plan to move in 6 months, which is the cheaper option? Explain.

THINK AND DISCUSS

1. If you graphed the equations in Example 1A, where would the lines intersect?

2. GET ORGANIZED Copy and complete the graphic organizer. In each box, solve the system by substitution using the first step given. Show that each method gives the same solution.

$\begin{cases} x + y = 8 \\ x - y = 2 \end{cases}$

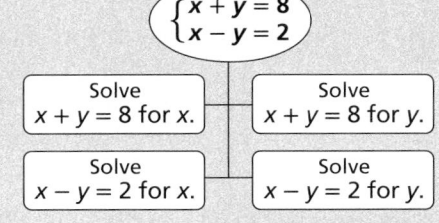

6-2

Exercises

California Standards Practice
🔑 6.0, 🔑 9.0

go.hrw.com
Homework Help Online
KEYWORD: MA8CA 6-2
Parent Resources Online
KEYWORD: MA8CA Parent

GUIDED PRACTICE

Solve each system by substitution. Check your answer.

SEE EXAMPLE 1
p. 336

1. $\begin{cases} y = 5x - 10 \\ y = 3x + 8 \end{cases}$

2. $\begin{cases} 3x + y = 2 \\ 4x + y = 20 \end{cases}$

3. $\begin{cases} y = x + 5 \\ 4x + y = 20 \end{cases}$

SEE EXAMPLE 2
p. 338

4. $\begin{cases} x - 2y = 10 \\ \frac{1}{2}x - 2y = 4 \end{cases}$

5. $\begin{cases} y - 2x = 3 \\ 2x - 3y = 21 \end{cases}$

6. $\begin{cases} x = y - 8 \\ -x - y = 0 \end{cases}$

SEE EXAMPLE 3
p. 339

7. Consumer Economics The Strauss family is deciding between two lawn-care services. Green Lawn charges a $49 startup fee, plus $29 per month. Grass Team charges a $25 startup fee, plus $37 per month.

a. In how many months will both lawn-care services cost the same? What will that cost be?

b. If the family will use the service for only 6 months, which is the better option? Explain.

PRACTICE AND PROBLEM SOLVING

Independent Practice

For Exercises	See Example
8–10	1
11–16	2
17	3

Extra Practice

Skills Practice p. EP12
Application Practice p. EP29

Solve each system by substitution. Check your answer.

8. $\begin{cases} y = x + 3 \\ y = 2x + 4 \end{cases}$

9. $\begin{cases} y = 2x + 10 \\ y = -2x - 6 \end{cases}$

10. $\begin{cases} x + 2y = 8 \\ x + 3y = 12 \end{cases}$

11. $\begin{cases} 2x + 2y = 2 \\ -4x + 4y = 12 \end{cases}$

12. $\begin{cases} y = 0.5x + 2 \\ -y = -2x + 4 \end{cases}$

13. $\begin{cases} -x + y = 4 \\ 3x - 2y = -7 \end{cases}$

14. $\begin{cases} 3x + y = -8 \\ -2x - y = 6 \end{cases}$

15. $\begin{cases} x + 2y = -1 \\ 4x - 4y = 20 \end{cases}$

16. $\begin{cases} 4x = y - 1 \\ 6x - 2y = -3 \end{cases}$

17. Recreation Casey wants to buy a gym membership. One gym has a $150 joining fee and costs $35 per month. Another gym has no joining fee and costs $60 per month.

a. In how many months will both gym memberships cost the same? What will that cost be?

b. If Casey plans to cancel in 5 months, which is the better option for him? Explain.

Solve each system by substitution. Check your answer.

18. $\begin{cases} x = 5 \\ x + y = 8 \end{cases}$

19. $\begin{cases} y = -3x + 4 \\ x = 2y + 6 \end{cases}$

20. $\begin{cases} 3x - y = 11 \\ 5y - 7x = 1 \end{cases}$

21. $\begin{cases} \frac{1}{2}x + \frac{1}{3}y = 6 \\ x - y = 2 \end{cases}$

22. $\begin{cases} x = 7 - 2y \\ 2x + y = 5 \end{cases}$

23. $\begin{cases} y = 1.2x - 4 \\ 2.2x + 5 = y \end{cases}$

24. Justin and Lacee are taking a walk. Justin walks at a rate of 6 ft/s, while Lacee walks at 4 ft/s. Lacee starts 10 ft ahead of Justin.

a. After how many seconds will Lacee and Justin be next to each other? What distance will they have walked?

b. How many seconds will it take for Justin to catch up to Lacee if she starts 32 ft ahead of Justin?

25. Ian and Jessica each save their quarters. Ian starts out with 34 quarters and saves 8 quarters a month. Jessica starts out with 2 quarters and saves 16 quarters a month. In how many months will Jessica have the same number of quarters as Ian? How many quarters will each of them have?

26. Multi-Step Use the receipts below to write and solve a system of equations to find the cost of a large popcorn and the cost of a small drink.

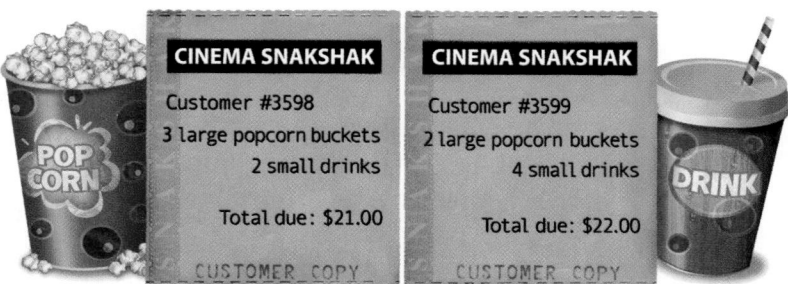

27. Finance Helene invested a total of $1000 in two simple-interest bank accounts. One account paid 5% annual interest; the other paid 6% annual interest. The total amount of interest she earned after one year was $58. Write and solve a system of equations to find the amount invested in each account. (*Hint:* Change the interest rates into decimals first.)

 Geometry Two angles whose measures have a sum of 90° are called complementary angles. For Exercises 28–31, *x* and *y* represent complementary angles. Find the measure of each angle.

28. $\begin{cases} x + y = 90 \\ y = 4x - 10 \end{cases}$

29. $\begin{cases} x = 2y \\ x + y = 90 \end{cases}$

30. $\begin{cases} y = 2(x - 15) \\ x + y = 90 \end{cases}$

31. $\begin{cases} x + y = 90 \\ y = 2x + 3 \end{cases}$

32. Tricia and Michael share a cell phone plan. Together, they made a total of 52 calls last month for a total of 620 min. Tricia averaged 15 min for each of her calls, while Michael averaged 10 min.

   a. How many calls did Tricia make last month? Michael?

   b. How many calls did Tricia make if the total number of calls was 60?

33. Write About It Explain how to solve a system of equations by substitution.

34. Critical Thinking Explain the connection between the solution of a system solved by graphing and the solution to the same system solved by substitution.

35. This problem will prepare you for the Concept Connection on page 362.

At the school store, Juanita bought 2 books and a backpack for a total of $26 before tax. Each book cost $8 less than the backpack.

   a. Write a system of equations that can be used to find the price of each book and the price of the backpack.

   b. Solve this system by substitution.

   c. Solve this system by graphing. Discuss advantages and disadvantages of solving by substitution and solving by graphing.

36. Estimation Use the graph to estimate the solution to
$$\begin{cases} 2x - y = 6 \\ x + y = -0.6 \end{cases}.$$

Round your answer to the nearest tenth.
Then solve the system by substitution.

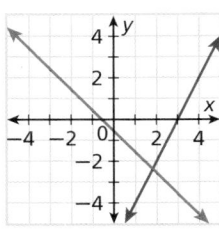

Multiple Choice For Exercises 37 and 38, choose the best answer.

37. Elizabeth met 24 of her cousins at a family reunion. The number of male cousins m was 6 less than twice the number of female cousins f. Which system can be used to find the number of male cousins and female cousins?

(A) $\begin{cases} m + f = 24 \\ f = 2m - 6 \end{cases}$ 　 (B) $\begin{cases} m + f = 24 \\ f = 2m \end{cases}$ 　 (C) $\begin{cases} m = 24 + f \\ m = f - 6 \end{cases}$ 　 (D) $\begin{cases} f = 24 - m \\ m = 2f - 6 \end{cases}$

38. Which problem is best represented by the system
$$\begin{cases} d = n + 5 \\ d + n = 12 \end{cases}?$$

(A) Roger has 12 coins in dimes and nickels. There are 5 more dimes than nickels.
(B) Roger has 5 coins in dimes and nickels. There are 12 more dimes than nickels.
(C) Roger has 12 coins in dimes and nickels. There are 5 more nickels than dimes.
(D) Roger has 5 coins in dimes and nickels. There are 12 more nickels than dimes.

CHALLENGE AND EXTEND

39. A car dealership has 378 cars on its lot. The ratio of new cars to used cars is 5:4. Write and solve a system of equations to find the number of new and used cars on the lot.

Solve each system by substitution. Check your answer.

40. $\begin{cases} 2r - 3s - t = 12 \\ s + 3t = 10 \\ t = 4 \end{cases}$ 　 **41.** $\begin{cases} x + y + z = 7 \\ y + z = 5 \\ 2y - 4z = -14 \end{cases}$ 　 **42.** $\begin{cases} a + 2b + c = 19 \\ -b + c = -5 \\ 3b + 2c = 15 \end{cases}$

 SPIRAL STANDARDS REVIEW 　　　  6.0, 7.0, 9.0

Without graphing, tell whether each point is on the graph of $y = 3x - 6x - 9$. *(Lesson 5-1)*

43. $(0, -9)$ 　　　 **44.** $(3, 0)$ 　　　 **45.** $\left(-\frac{1}{3}, -8\right)$

Find the x- and y-intercepts. *(Lesson 5-2)*

46. $6x - 2y = 12$ 　　　 **47.** $-3y + x = 15$ 　　　 **48.** $4y - 40 = -5x$

Tell whether each ordered pair is a solution of the given system. *(Lesson 6-1)*

49. $(3, 0)$; $\begin{cases} 2x - y = -6 \\ x + y = 3 \end{cases}$ 　 **50.** $(-1, 4)$; $\begin{cases} y - 2x = 6 \\ x + 4y = 15 \end{cases}$ 　 **51.** $(5, 6)$; $\begin{cases} \frac{1}{3}y + x = 7 \\ 2x = 12 \end{cases}$

6-3

Solving Systems by Elimination

![California Standards]
California Standards

🔑 **9.0** Students solve a system of two linear equations in two variables algebraically and are able to interpret the answer graphically. Students are able to solve a system of two linear inequalities in two variables and to sketch the solution sets.

Why learn this?

You can solve a system of linear equations to determine how many flowers of each type you can buy to make a bouquet. (See Example 4.)

Another method for solving systems of equations is *elimination*. Like substitution, the goal of elimination is to get one equation that has only one variable.

Remember that an equation stays balanced if you add equal amounts to both sides. Consider the system $\begin{cases} x - 2y = -19 \\ 5x + 2y = 1 \end{cases}$. Since $5x + 2y = 1$, you can add $5x + 2y$ to one side of the first equation and 1 to the other side and the balance is maintained.

$$\begin{array}{rr} x - 2y & -19 \\ + \; 5x + 2y & + \quad 1 \\ \hline 6x + 0 & -18 \end{array}$$

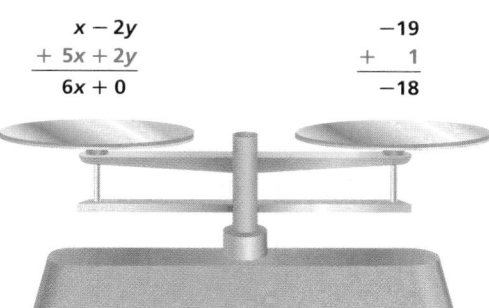

Since $-2y$ and $2y$ have **opposite coefficients**, you can eliminate the y-term by adding the two equations. The result is one equation that has only one variable: $6x = -18$.

Know it!
Note

Solving Systems of Equations by Elimination
Step 1 Write the system so that like terms are aligned.
Step 2 Eliminate one of the variables.
Step 3 Solve for the variable not eliminated in Step 2.
Step 4 Substitute the value of the variable into one of the original equations and solve for the other variable.
Step 5 Write the answers from Steps 3 and 4 as an ordered pair, (x, y), and check your answer.

Later in this lesson you will learn how to multiply one or more equations by a number in order to produce opposites that can be eliminated.

EXAMPLE 1 Elimination Using Addition

Solve $\begin{cases} x - 2y = -19 \\ 5x + 2y = 1 \end{cases}$ by elimination.

Step 1 $\quad x - 2y = -19 \qquad$ *Write the system so that like terms are aligned.*

Step 2 $\underline{+ 5x + 2y = \quad 1}$

$\qquad\qquad 6x \;\; + 0 = -18 \qquad$ *Add the equations to eliminate the y-terms.*

Step 3 $\qquad\qquad 6x = -18 \qquad$ *Simplify and solve for x.*

$\qquad\qquad \dfrac{6x}{6} = \dfrac{-18}{6} \qquad$ *Divide both sides by 6.*

$\qquad\qquad x = -3$

Step 4 $\qquad x - 2y = -19 \qquad$ *Write one of the original equations.*

$\qquad\quad -3 - 2y = -19 \qquad$ *Substitute −3 for x.*

$\qquad\underline{+ 3 \qquad\quad + 3} \qquad$ *Add 3 to both sides.*

$\qquad\qquad\quad -2y = -16$

$\qquad\qquad \dfrac{-2y}{-2} = \dfrac{-16}{-2} \qquad$ *Divide both sides by −2.*

$\qquad\qquad\quad y = 8$

Step 5 $(-3, 8) \qquad$ *Write the solution as an ordered pair.*

The helpful hint box on the left

Helpful Hint

Check your answer.

$$x - 2y = -19$$

$-3 - 2(8)$	-19
$-3 - 16$	-19
-19	$-19 \checkmark$

$$5x + 2y = 1$$

$5(-3) + 2(8)$	1
$-15 + 16$	1
1	$1 \checkmark$

CHECK IT OUT! **1.** Solve $\begin{cases} y + 3x = -2 \\ 2y - 3x = 14 \end{cases}$ by elimination. Check your answer.

When two equations each contain the same term, you can subtract one equation from the other to solve the system. To subtract an equation, add the opposite of *each* term.

EXAMPLE 2 Elimination Using Subtraction

Solve $\begin{cases} 3x + 4y = 18 \\ -2x + 4y = 8 \end{cases}$ by elimination.

Step 1 $\qquad 3x + 4y = 18$

Step 2 $\quad -(-2x + 4y = \;\; 8)$

$\qquad\qquad\;\; 3x + 4y = \;\; 18 \qquad$ *Add the opposite of each term*

$\qquad\underline{+ 2x - 4y = -8} \qquad$ *in the second equation.*

$\qquad\qquad 5x + \;\; 0 = 10 \qquad$ *Eliminate the y-term.*

Step 3 $\qquad\qquad\qquad 5x = 10 \qquad$ *Simplify and solve for x.*

$\qquad\qquad\qquad\quad x = 2$

Step 4 $\quad -2x + 4y = \;\; 8 \qquad$ *Write one of the original equations.*

$\qquad -2(2) + 4y = \;\; 8 \qquad$ *Substitute 2 for x.*

$\qquad\quad -4 + 4y = \;\; 8$

$\qquad\underline{+ 4 \qquad\quad + 4} \qquad$ *Add 4 to both sides.*

$\qquad\qquad\quad 4y = 12 \qquad$ *Simplify and solve for y.*

$\qquad\qquad\qquad y = 3$

Step 5 $\qquad\quad (2, 3) \qquad$ *Write the solution as an ordered pair.*

Remember!

Remember to check by substituting your answer into both original equations.

In some cases, you will first need to multiply one or both of the equations by a number so that one variable has opposite coefficients.

EXAMPLE 3 **Elimination Using Multiplication First**

Solve each system by elimination.

A $\begin{cases} 2x + y = 3 \\ -x + 3y = -12 \end{cases}$

Helpful Hint

In Step 1 of Example 3A, you could have also multiplied the first equation by −3 to eliminate the y-term.

Step 1 $\qquad 2x + y = 3$

Step 2 $\quad 2(-x + 3y = -12)$

$\qquad\qquad 2x + y = 3$ *Multiply each term in the second equation by 2 to get opposite x-coefficients.*

$\qquad\quad +(-2x + 6y = -24)$ *Add the new equation to the first equation.*

Step 3 $\qquad\qquad\quad 7y = -21$

$\qquad\qquad\qquad\quad y = -3$ *Simplify and solve for y.*

Step 4 $\quad 2x + y = 3$ *Write one of the original equations.*

$\qquad\quad 2x - 3 = 3$ *Substitute −3 for y.*

$\qquad\quad\underline{+3 \quad +3}$ *Add 3 to both sides.*

$\qquad\qquad 2x = 6$ *Simplify and solve for x.*

$\qquad\qquad\; x = 3$

Step 5 $(3, -3)$ *Write the solution as an ordered pair.*

B $\begin{cases} 7x - 12y = -22 \\ 5x - 8y = -14 \end{cases}$

Helpful Hint

Use the techniques for finding a common denominator when trying to find values to multiply each equation by. To review these techniques, see Skills Bank p. SB8.

Step 1 $\qquad 2(7x - 12y = -22)$

Step 2 $\quad (-3)(5x - 8y = -14)$

$\qquad\qquad 14x - 24y = -44$ *Multiply the first equation by 2 and the second equation by −3 to get opposite y-coefficients.*

$\qquad\quad +(-15x + 24y = 42)$ *Add the new equations.*

$\qquad\qquad -x + 0 = -2$

Step 3 $\qquad\qquad\quad x = 2$ *Simplify and solve for x.*

Step 4 $\qquad 7x - 12y = -22$ *Write one of the original equations.*

$\qquad\quad 7(2) - 12y = -22$ *Substitute 2 for x.*

$\qquad\qquad 14 - 12y = -22$

$\qquad\quad\underline{-14 \qquad\quad -14}$ *Subtract 14 from both sides.*

$\qquad\qquad\qquad -12y = -36$ *Simplify and solve for y.*

$\qquad\qquad\qquad\qquad y = 3$

Step 5 $\qquad\qquad (2, 3)$ *Write the solution as an ordered pair.*

 Solve each system by elimination. Check your answer.

3a. $\begin{cases} 3x + 2y = 6 \\ -x + y = -2 \end{cases}$ **3b.** $\begin{cases} 2x + 5y = 26 \\ -3x - 4y = -25 \end{cases}$

E X A M P L E **4** *Consumer Economics Application*

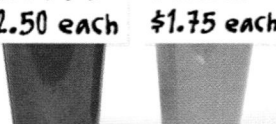

Sam spent $24.75 to buy 12 flowers for his mother. The bouquet contained roses and daisies. How many of each type of flower did Sam buy?

Write a system. Use r for the number of roses and d for the number of daisies.

Step 1 $2.50r + 1.75d = 24.75$ *The cost of roses and daisies totals $24.75.*

　　　　　$r + \quad d = 12$ *The total number of roses and daisies is 12.*

Step 2

$$2.50r + 1.75d = 24.75$$

$$(-2.50)(r + d = 12)$$ *Multiply the second equation by −2.50 to get opposite r-coefficients.*

$$2.50r + 1.75d = \quad 24.75$$

$$+ \underline{(-2.50r - 2.50d = -30.00)}$$ *Add this equation to the first equation to eliminate the r-term.*

Step 3 $-0.75d = \quad -5.25$

　　　　　　　$d = \quad 7$ *Simplify and solve for d.*

Step 4 $r + d = 12$ *Write one of the original equations.*

　　　　　$r + 7 = \quad 12$ *Substitute 7 for d.*

　　　　　$\underline{-7 \quad -7}$ *Subtract 7 from both sides.*

　　　　　$r \quad = \quad 5$

Step 5 $(5, 7)$ *Write the solution as an ordered pair.*

Sam can buy 5 roses and 7 daisies.

4. What if...? Sally spent $14.85 to buy 13 flowers. She bought lilies, which cost $1.25 each, and tulips, which cost $0.90 each. How many of each flower did Sally buy?

All systems can be solved in more than one way. For some systems, some methods may be more appropriate than others.

Know it!
Note

Systems of Linear Equations

METHOD	USE WHEN...	EXAMPLE
Graphing	• Both equations are solved for *y*. • You want to estimate a solution.	$\begin{cases} y = 3x + 2 \\ y = -2x + 6 \end{cases}$
Substitution	• A variable in either equation has a coefficient of 1 or −1. • Both equations are solved for the same variable. • Either equation is solved for a variable.	$\begin{cases} x + 2y = 7 \\ x = 10 - 5y \end{cases}$ or $\begin{cases} x = 2y + 10 \\ x = 3y + 5 \end{cases}$
Elimination	• Both equations have the same variable with the same or opposite coefficients. • A variable term in one equation is a multiple of the corresponding variable term in the other equation.	$\begin{cases} 3x + 2y = 8 \\ 5x + 2y = 12 \end{cases}$ or $\begin{cases} 6x + 5y = 10 \\ 3x + 2y = 15 \end{cases}$

THINK AND DISCUSS

1. Explain how multiplying the second equation in a system by −1 and eliminating by adding is the same as elimination by subtraction. Give an example of a system for which this applies.

2. Explain why it does not matter which variable you solve for first when solving a system by elimination.

3. GET ORGANIZED Copy and complete the graphic organizer. In each box, write an example of a system of equations that you could solve using the given method.

```
                              Solving Systems of
                              Linear Equations
          ┌───────────────────────┼───────────────────────┐
   ┌──────────────┐    ┌──────────────────┐    ┌──────────────────┐
   │ Substitution │    │ Elimination using │    │ Elimination using │
   └──────────────┘    │   addition or     │    │  multiplication   │
                       │   subtraction     │    └──────────────────┘
                       └──────────────────┘
```

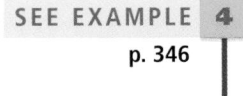
6-3 Exercises

California Standards Practice
🔑 9.0, 25.2

go.hrw.com
Homework Help Online
KEYWORD: MA8CA 6-3
Parent Resources Online
KEYWORD: MA8CA Parent

GUIDED PRACTICE

Solve each system by elimination. Check your answer.

SEE EXAMPLE 1
p. 344

1. $\begin{cases} -x + y = 5 \\ x - 5y = -9 \end{cases}$

2. $\begin{cases} x + y = 12 \\ x - y = 2 \end{cases}$

3. $\begin{cases} 2x + 5y = -24 \\ 3x - 5y = 14 \end{cases}$

SEE EXAMPLE 2
p. 344

4. $\begin{cases} x - 10y = 60 \\ x + 14y = 12 \end{cases}$

5. $\begin{cases} 5x + y = 0 \\ 5x + 2y = 30 \end{cases}$

6. $\begin{cases} -5x + 7y = 11 \\ -5x + 3y = 19 \end{cases}$

SEE EXAMPLE 3
p. 345

7. $\begin{cases} 2x + 3y = 12 \\ 5x - y = 13 \end{cases}$

8. $\begin{cases} -3x + 4y = 12 \\ 2x + y = -8 \end{cases}$

9. $\begin{cases} 2x + 4y = -4 \\ 3x + 5y = -3 \end{cases}$

SEE EXAMPLE 4
p. 346

10. Consumer Economics Each family in a neighborhood is contributing $20 worth of food to the neighborhood picnic. The Harlin family is bringing 12 packages of buns. The hamburger buns cost $2.00 per package. The hot-dog buns cost $1.50 per package. How many packages of each type of bun did they buy?

PRACTICE AND PROBLEM SOLVING

Independent Practice

For Exercises	See Example
11–13	1
14–16	2
17–19	3
20	4

Extra Practice
Skills Practice p. EP12
Application Practice p. EP29

Solve each system by elimination. Check your answer.

11. $\begin{cases} -x + y = -1 \\ 2x - y = 0 \end{cases}$

12. $\begin{cases} -2x + y = -20 \\ 2x + y = 48 \end{cases}$

13. $\begin{cases} 3x - y = -2 \\ -2x + y = 3 \end{cases}$

14. $\begin{cases} x - y = 4 \\ x - 2y = 10 \end{cases}$

15. $\begin{cases} x + 2y = 5 \\ 3x + 2y = 17 \end{cases}$

16. $\begin{cases} 3x - 2y = -1 \\ 3x - 4y = 9 \end{cases}$

17. $\begin{cases} x - y = -3 \\ 5x + 3y = 1 \end{cases}$

18. $\begin{cases} 9x - 3y = 3 \\ 3x + 8y = -17 \end{cases}$

19. $\begin{cases} 5x + 2y = -1 \\ 3x + 7y = 11 \end{cases}$

20. Multi-Step Mrs. Gonzalez bought centerpieces to put on each table at a graduation party. She spent $31.50. There are 8 tables each requiring either a candle or vase. Candles cost $3 and vases cost $4.25. How many of each type did she buy?

21. Geometry The difference between the length and width of a rectangle is 2 units. The perimeter is 40 units. Write and solve a system of equations to determine the length and width of the rectangle. (*Hint:* The perimeter of a rectangle is $2\ell + 2w$.)

22. /// **ERROR ANALYSIS** /// Which is incorrect? Explain the error.

Ⓐ
$$\begin{cases} x + y = -3 \\ 3x + y = 3 \end{cases}$$
$$\begin{aligned} x + y &= -3 \\ -(3x + y &= 3) \\ \hline -2x &= 0 \\ x &= 0 \end{aligned}$$

Ⓑ
$$\begin{cases} x + y = -3 \\ 3x + y = 3 \end{cases}$$
$$\begin{aligned} x + y &= -3 \\ -(3x + y &= 3) \\ \hline -2x &= -6 \\ x &= 3 \end{aligned}$$

Math History

In 1247, Qin Jiushao wrote *Mathematical Treatise in Nine Sections.* Its contents included solving systems of equations and the Chinese Remainder Theorem.

23. A music school Terry is interested in is offering a special for new students. If Terry enrolls in 2 classes, he has to pay a fee in addition to the price of classes for a total of $18. If he decides to take 6 classes, the fee is subtracted from his total for a total of $38. Follow the steps below to find the cost of each class and the price of the fee.

	Classes	+	Fee	=	Total Price
Price for 2 classes	2x	+	y	=	
Price for 6 classes	6x		y	=	38

a. Copy and complete the table.

b. Use the information in the table to write a system of equations.

c. Solve the system of equations to find the price of each class and the price of the fee that Terry has to pay.

Critical Thinking Solve each system. Which method did you use to solve each system? Explain.

24. $\begin{cases} \dfrac{1}{2}x - 5y = 30 \\ \dfrac{1}{2}x + 7y = 6 \end{cases}$

25. $\begin{cases} -x + 2y = 3 \\ 4x - 5y = -3 \end{cases}$

26. $\begin{cases} 3x - y = 10 \\ 2x - y = 7 \end{cases}$

27. $\begin{cases} 3y + x = 10 \\ x = 4y + 2 \end{cases}$

28. $\begin{cases} y = -4x \\ y = 2x + 3 \end{cases}$

29. $\begin{cases} 2x + 6y = 12 \\ 4x + 5y = 15 \end{cases}$

30. Business A local boys club sold 176 bags of mulch and made a total of $520. They did not sell any of the expensive cocoa mulch. Use the table to determine how many bags of each type of mulch they sold.

Mulch Prices ($)	
Cocoa	4.75
Hardwood	3.50
Pine Bark	2.75

CONCEPT CONNECTION

31. This problem will prepare you for the Concept Connection on page 362.

a. The school store is running a promotion on school supplies. Different supplies are placed on two shelves. You can purchase 3 items from shelf A and 2 from shelf B for $16. Or you can purchase 2 items from shelf A and 3 from shelf B for $14. Write a system of equations that can be used to find the individual prices for the supplies on shelf A and on shelf B.

b. Solve the system of equations by elimination. Check your answer.

c. If the supplies on shelf A are normally $6 each and the supplies on shelf B are normally $3 each, how much will you save on each package plan from part **a**?

32. Write About It Solve the system $\begin{cases} 3x + y = 1 \\ 2x + 4y = -6 \end{cases}$. Explain how you can check your solution algebraically and graphically.

Multiple Choice For Exercises 33 and 34, choose the best answer.

33. A math test has 25 problems. Some are worth 2 points, and some are worth 3 points. The test is worth 60 points total. Which system can be used to determine the number of 2-point problems and the number of 3-point problems on the test?

Ⓐ $\begin{cases} x + y = 25 \\ 2x + 3y = 60 \end{cases}$
Ⓑ $\begin{cases} x + y = 60 \\ 2x + 3y = 25 \end{cases}$
Ⓒ $\begin{cases} x - y = 25 \\ 2x + 3y = 60 \end{cases}$
Ⓓ $\begin{cases} x - y = 60 \\ 2x - 3y = 25 \end{cases}$

34. An electrician charges $15 plus $11 per hour. Another electrician charges $10 plus $15 per hour. For what amount of time will the cost be the same? What is that cost?

Ⓐ 1 hour; $25

Ⓒ $1\frac{1}{2}$ hours; $30

Ⓑ $1\frac{1}{4}$ hours; $28.75

Ⓓ $1\frac{3}{4}$ hours; $32.50

35. Short Response Three hundred and fifty-eight tickets to the school basketball game on Friday were sold. Student tickets were $1.50, and nonstudent tickets were $3.25. The school made $752.25.

a. Write a system of linear equations that could be used to determine how many student and how many nonstudent tickets were sold. Define the variables you use.

b. Solve the system you wrote in part **a.** How many student and how many nonstudent tickets were sold?

CHALLENGE AND EXTEND

Solve each system by any method. Check your answer.

36. $\begin{cases} x + 16\frac{1}{2} = -\frac{3}{4}y \\ y = \frac{1}{2}x \end{cases}$

37. $\begin{cases} 2x + y + z = 17 \\ \frac{1}{2}z = 5 \\ x - y = 5 \end{cases}$

38. $\begin{cases} x - 2y - z = -1 \\ -x + 2y + 4z = -11 \\ 2x + y + z = 1 \end{cases}$

39. Three students participated in a fund-raiser for school. Each sold a combination of pens, notebooks, and bags. The first student sold 2 pens, 7 notebooks, and 3 bags for a total of $73. The second student sold 10 pens, 2 notebooks, and 2 bags for a total of $50. The third student sold 1 pen, 4 notebooks, and 5 bags for a total of $71. Find the price of each item.

 SPIRAL STANDARDS REVIEW   ⟜ 7.0, ⟜ 9.0, 16.0

Determine whether each relation defines a function. Write an equation if possible. *(Lesson 4-3)*

40.

x	1	2	3	4
y	6	7	8	9

41.

x	1	2	3	4
y	3	6	9	12

42.

x	1	2	3	4
y	−9	−8	−7	−6

Write an equation in slope-intercept form for the line with the given slope that contains the given point. *(Lesson 5-6)*

43. slope = 2; (5, 1)

44. slope = −4; (3, −1)

45. slope = $\frac{1}{2}$; (−2, 9)

Solve each system by substitution. Check your answer. *(Lesson 6-2)*

46. $\begin{cases} y = x - 1 \\ x + y = 10 \end{cases}$

47. $\begin{cases} x = y - 5 \\ 2x + 1 = y \end{cases}$

48. $\begin{cases} y = 2x - 1 \\ x - y = 3 \end{cases}$

6-4 Solving Special Systems

California Standards

9.0 Students solve a system of two linear equations in two variables algebraically and are able to interpret the answer graphically. Students are able to solve a system of two linear inequalities in two variables and to sketch the solution sets.

Also covered: **8.0**

Vocabulary
consistent system
inconsistent system
independent system
dependent system

Why learn this?

Linear systems can be used to analyze business growth, such as comic book sales. (See Example 4.)

In Lesson 6-1, you saw that when two lines intersect at a point, there is exactly one solution to the system. Systems with at least one solution are **consistent systems**.

When the two lines in a system do not intersect, they are parallel lines. There are no ordered pairs that satisfy both equations, so there is no solution. A system that has no solution is an **inconsistent system**.

EXAMPLE 1 **Systems with No Solution**

Solve $\begin{cases} y = x - 1 \\ -x + y = 2 \end{cases}$.

Method 1 Compare slopes and y-intercepts.

$y = x - 1 \rightarrow y = 1x - 1$ *Write both equations in slope-intercept form.*
$-x + y = 2 \rightarrow y = 1x + 2$ *The lines are parallel because they have the same slope and different y-intercepts.*

These lines do not intersect so the system is an inconsistent system.

Method 2 Solve the system algebraically. Use the substitution method because the first equation is solved for y.

$-x + (x - 1) = 2$ *Substitute x − 1 for y in the second equation, and solve.*
$-1 = 2$ ✗   *False statement. The equation has no solutions.*

This system has no solution so it is an inconsistent system.

Check Graph the system to confirm that the lines are parallel.

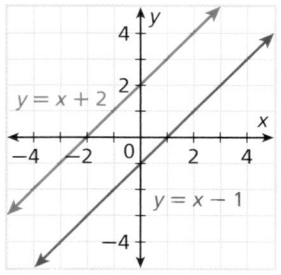

Remember!

To review slopes of parallel lines, see Lesson 5-7.

 **1.** Solve $\begin{cases} y = -2x + 5 \\ 2x + y = 1 \end{cases}$.

If two linear equations in a system have the same graph, the graphs are coincident lines, or the same line. There are infinitely many solutions of the system because every point on the line represents a solution of both equations.

EXAMPLE 2 **Systems with Infinitely Many Solutions**

Solve $\begin{cases} y = 2x + 1 \\ 2x - y + 1 = 0 \end{cases}$.

Compare slopes and y-intercepts.

$$y = 2x + 1 \rightarrow y = 2x + 1$$
$$2x - y + 1 = 0 \rightarrow y = 2x + 1$$

Write both equations in slope-intercept form. The lines have the same slope and the same y-intercept.

If this system were graphed, the graphs would be the same line. There are infinitely many solutions.

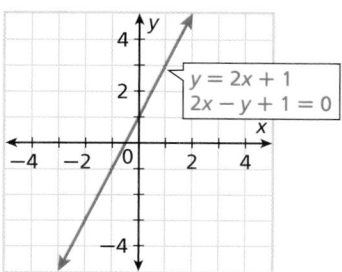

Every point on this line is a solution of the system.

 **2.** Solve $\begin{cases} y = x - 3 \\ x - y - 3 = 0 \end{cases}$.

Consistent systems can either be independent or dependent.

- An **independent system** has exactly one solution. The graph of an independent system consists of two intersecting lines.
- A **dependent system** has infinitely many solutions. The graph of a dependent system consists of two coincident lines.

Classification of Systems of Linear Equations

CLASSIFICATION	CONSISTENT AND INDEPENDENT	CONSISTENT AND DEPENDENT	INCONSISTENT
Number of Solutions	Exactly one	Infinitely many	None
Description	Different slopes	Same slope, same y-intercept	Same slope, different y-intercepts
Graph	Intersecting lines	Same line	Parallel lines

EXAMPLE 3 — Classifying Systems of Linear Equations

Classify each system. Give the number of solutions.

A $\begin{cases} 2y = x + 2 \\ -\dfrac{1}{2}x + y = 1 \end{cases}$

$2y = x + 2 \rightarrow y = \dfrac{1}{2}x + 1$ *Write both equations in slope-intercept form.*

$-\dfrac{1}{2}x + y = 1 \rightarrow y = \dfrac{1}{2}x + 1$ *The lines have the same slope and the same y-intercepts. They are the same.*

The system is consistent and dependent. It has infinitely many solutions.

B $\begin{cases} y = 2(x - 1) \\ y = x + 1 \end{cases}$

$y = 2(x - 1) \rightarrow y = 2x - 2$ *Write both equations in slope-intercept form.*

$y = x + 1 \rightarrow y = 1x + 1$ *The lines have different slopes. They intersect.*

The system is consistent and independent. It has one solution.

 Classify each system. Give the number of solutions.

3a. $\begin{cases} x + 2y = -4 \\ -2(y + 2) = x \end{cases}$ **3b.** $\begin{cases} y = -2(x - 1) \\ y = -x + 3 \end{cases}$ **3c.** $\begin{cases} 2x - 3y = 6 \\ y = \dfrac{2}{3}x \end{cases}$

EXAMPLE 4 — *Business Application*

The sales manager at Comics Now is comparing its sales with the sales of its competitor, Dynamo Comics. If the sales patterns continue, will the sales for Comics Now ever equal the sales for Dynamo Comics? Explain.

Comic Books Sold per Year (thousands)	2005	2006	2007	2008
Comics Now	130	170	210	250
Dynamo Comics	180	220	260	300

> **Helpful Hint**
>
> The increase in sales is the difference between sales each year.

Use the table to write a system of linear equations. Let y represent the sales total and x represent the increase in sales.

	Sales total	equals	increase in sales per year	times	years	plus	beginning sales.
Comics Now	y	$=$	40	$\cdot$	x	$+$	130
Dynamo Comics	y	$=$	40	$\cdot$	x	$+$	180

$\begin{cases} y = 40x + 130 \\ y = 40x + 180 \end{cases}$

$y = 40x + 130$ *Both equations are in slope-intercept form.*

$y = 40x + 180$ *The lines have the same slope, but different y-intercepts.*

The graphs of the two equations are parallel lines, so there is no solution. If the patterns continue, sales for the two companies will never be equal.

 **4.** Matt has $100 in a checking account and deposits $20 per month. Ben has $80 in a checking account and deposits $30 per month. Will the accounts ever have the same balance? Explain.

THINK AND DISCUSS

1. Describe the graph of a system of equations that has infinitely many solutions. Compare the slopes and *y*-intercepts.

2. What methods can be used to determine the number of solutions of a system of linear equations?

3. GET ORGANIZED Copy and complete the graphic organizer. In each box, write the word that describes a system with that number of solutions and sketch a graph.

Linear System of Equations

No solution

Exactly one   Infinitely many

6-4 Exercises

 California Standards Practice
8.0, 9.0, 24.1

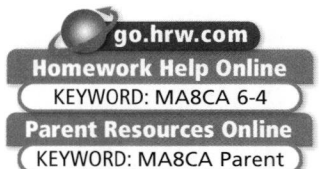 go.hrw.com
Homework Help Online
KEYWORD: MA8CA 6-4
Parent Resources Online
KEYWORD: MA8CA Parent

GUIDED PRACTICE

1. Vocabulary A ____?____ system can be independent or dependent. (*consistent* or *inconsistent*)

Solve each system of linear equations.

SEE EXAMPLE **1**
p. 350

2. $\begin{cases} y = x + 1 \\ -x + y = 3 \end{cases}$

3. $\begin{cases} 3x + y = 6 \\ y = -3x + 2 \end{cases}$

4. $\begin{cases} -y = 4x + 1 \\ 4x + y = 2 \end{cases}$

SEE EXAMPLE **2**
p. 351

5. $\begin{cases} y = -x + 3 \\ x + y - 3 = 0 \end{cases}$

6. $\begin{cases} y = 2x - 4 \\ 2x - y - 4 = 0 \end{cases}$

7. $\begin{cases} -7x + y = -2 \\ 7x - y = 2 \end{cases}$

SEE EXAMPLE **3**
p. 352

Classify each system. Give the number of solutions.

8. $\begin{cases} y = 2(x + 3) \\ -2y = 2x + 6 \end{cases}$

9. $\begin{cases} y = -3x - 1 \\ 3x + y = 1 \end{cases}$

10. $\begin{cases} 9y = 3x + 18 \\ \frac{1}{3}x - y = -2 \end{cases}$

SEE EXAMPLE **4**
p. 352

11. Athletics Micah walks on a treadmill at 4 miles per hour. He has walked 2 miles when Luke starts running at 6 miles per hour on the treadmill next to him. If their rates continue, will Luke's distance ever equal Micah's distance? Explain.

PRACTICE AND PROBLEM SOLVING

Solve each system of linear equations.

12. $\begin{cases} y = 2x - 2 \\ -2x + y = 1 \end{cases}$

13. $\begin{cases} x + y = 3 \\ y = -x - 1 \end{cases}$

14. $\begin{cases} x + 2y = -4 \\ y = -\frac{1}{2}x - 4 \end{cases}$

15. $\begin{cases} -6 + y = 2x \\ y = 2x - 36 \end{cases}$

16. $\begin{cases} y = -2x + 3 \\ 2x + y - 3 = 0 \end{cases}$

17. $\begin{cases} y = x - 2 \\ x - y - 2 = 0 \end{cases}$

18. $\begin{cases} x + y = -4 \\ y = -x - 4 \end{cases}$

19. $\begin{cases} -9x - 3y = -18 \\ 3x + y = 6 \end{cases}$

<table>
<tr><td colspan="2">**Independent Practice**</td></tr>
<tr><td>For
Exercises</td><td>See
Example</td></tr>
<tr><td>12–15</td><td>1</td></tr>
<tr><td>16–19</td><td>2</td></tr>
<tr><td>20–22</td><td>3</td></tr>
<tr><td>23</td><td>4</td></tr>
</table>

Extra Practice
Skills Practice p. EP12
Application Practice p. EP29

Classify each system. Give the number of solutions.

20. $\begin{cases} y = -x + 5 \\ x + y = 5 \end{cases}$

21. $\begin{cases} y = -3x + 2 \\ y = 3x \end{cases}$

22. $\begin{cases} y - 1 = 2x \\ y = 2x - 1 \end{cases}$

23. **Sports** Mandy is skating at 5 miles per hour. Nikki is skating at 6 miles per hour and started 1 mile behind Mandy. If their rates stay the same, will Mandy catch up with Nikki? Explain.

24. **Multi-Step** Photocopier A can print 35 copies per minute. Photocopier B can print 35 copies per minute. Copier B is started and makes 10 copies. Copier A is then started. If the copiers continue, will the number of copies from machine A ever equal the number of copies from machine B? Explain.

25. **Entertainment** One week Trey rented 4 DVDs and 2 video games for $18. The next week he rented 2 DVDs and 1 video game for $9. Find the rental costs for each video game and DVD. Explain your answer.

26. Rosa bought 1 pound of cashews and 2 pounds of peanuts for $10. At the same store, Sabrina bought 2 pounds of cashews and 1 pound of peanuts for $11. Find the cost per pound for cashews and peanuts.

California LINK

Geology

Geodes are rounded, hollow rock formations. Most are partially or completely filled with layers of colored quartz crystals. Geodes have been found at the Hauser Geode Beds near Blythe, CA, since the early 1930s.

27. **Geology** Pam and Tommy collect geodes. Pam's parents gave her 2 geodes to start her collection, and she buys 4 every year. Tommy has 2 geodes that were given to him for his birthday the same year Pam started her collection. He buys 4 every year. If Pam and Tommy continue to buy the same amount of geodes per year, when will Tommy have as many geodes as Pam? Explain your answer.

28. Use the data given in the tables.

x	3	4	5	6
y	6	8	10	12

x	12	13	14	15
y	24	26	28	30

 a. Write an equation to describe the data in each table.
 b. Graph the system of equations from part **a**. Describe the graph.
 c. How could you have predicted the graph by looking at the equations?
 d. **What if...?** Each y-value in the second table increases by 1. How does this affect the graphs of the two equations? How can you tell how the graphs would be affected without actually graphing?

29. **Critical Thinking** Describe the graphs of two equations if the result of solving the system by substitution or elimination is the statement $1 = 3$.

CONCEPT CONNECTION

30. This problem will prepare you for the Concept Connection on page 362.
The Crusader pep club is selling team buttons that support the sports teams. They contacted Buttons, Etc. which charges $50 plus $1.10 per button, and Logos, which charges $40 plus $1.10 per button.
 a. Write an equation for each company's cost.
 b. Use the system from part **a** to find when the price for both companies is the same. Explain.
 c. What part of the equation should the pep club negotiate to change so that the cost of Buttons, Etc. is the same as Logos? What part of the equation should change in order to get a better price?

31. **///ERROR ANALYSIS///** Student A says there is no solution to the graphed system of equations. Student B says there is one solution. Which student is incorrect? Explain the error.

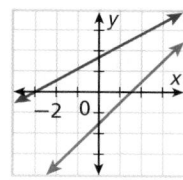

32. **Write About It** Compare the graph of a system that is consistent and independent with the graph of a system that is consistent and dependent.

Multiple Choice For Exercises 33 and 34, choose the best answer.

33. Which of the following classifications fit the following system?

$$\begin{cases} 2x - y = 3 \\ 6x - 3y = 9 \end{cases}$$

    Ⓐ Inconsistent and independent   Ⓒ Inconsistent and dependent

    Ⓑ Consistent and independent   Ⓓ Consistent and dependent

34. Which of the following would be enough information to classify a system of two linear equations?

    Ⓐ The graphs have the same slope.

    Ⓑ The y-intercepts are the same.

    Ⓒ The graphs have different slopes.

    Ⓓ The y-intercepts are different.

CHALLENGE AND EXTEND

35. What conditions are necessary for the system $\begin{cases} y = 2x + p \\ y = 2x + q \end{cases}$ to have infinitely many solutions? no solution?

36. **Reasoning** Solve the systems in parts **a** and **b**. Use this information to make a conjecture about all solutions that exist for the system in part **c**.

    a. $\begin{cases} 3x + 4y = 0 \\ 4x + 3y = 0 \end{cases}$ **b.** $\begin{cases} 2x + 5y = 0 \\ 5x + 2y = 0 \end{cases}$ **c.** $\begin{cases} ax + by = 0 \\ bx + ay = 0 \end{cases}$, for $a > 0, b > 0, a \neq b$

 SPIRAL STANDARDS REVIEW   3.0, ⚷ 5.0, ⚷ 6.0

Use the map to find the actual distances between each pair of cities. *(Lesson 2-5)*

37. from Hon to Averly

38. from Averly to Lewers

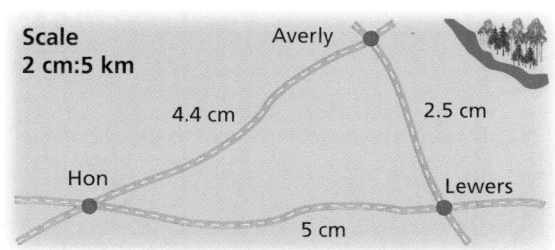

Scale
2 cm:5 km

Averly

4.4 cm   2.5 cm

Hon   Lewers

5 cm

Solve each equation. *(Lesson 2-7)*

39. $|x - 2.5| = 6$ 40. $|4x + 6| = -7$ 41. $|3z + 5| = 8$

Solve each system by graphing. *(Lesson 6-1)*

42. $\begin{cases} y = x - 2 \\ y = -x + 4 \end{cases}$ 43. $\begin{cases} y = 2x \\ x + y = -6 \end{cases}$ 44. $\begin{cases} y = -\frac{1}{2}x \\ y - x = 9 \end{cases}$

6-5 Applying Systems

California Standards

⚷ **9.0** Students solve a system of two linear equations in two variables algebraically and are able to interpret the answer graphically. Students are able to solve a system of two linear inequalities in two variables and to sketch the solution sets.

⚷ **15.0** Students apply algebraic techniques to solve rate problems, work problems, and percent mixture problems.

Who uses this?

Kayakers can calculate their rate of speed by solving a system of equations.

When a kayaker paddles downstream, the river's current helps the kayaker move faster, so the speed of the current is added to the kayaker's speed in still water to find the total speed. When a kayaker is going upstream, the speed of the current is subtracted from the kayaker's speed in still water.

You can use these ideas and a system of equations to solve problems about rates of speed.

E X A M P L E **1** **Solving Rate Problems**

Ben paddles his kayak 8 miles upstream in 4 hours. He turns around and paddles downstream to his starting point in 2 hours. What is the rate at which Ben paddles in still water? What is the rate of the river's current?

Let b be the rate at which Ben paddles in still water, and let c be the rate of the current.

Use a table to set up two equations—one for the upstream trip and one for the downstream trip.

	Rate	•	Time	=	Distance
Upstream	$b - c$	•	4	=	8
Downstream	$b + c$	•	2	=	8

> **Remember!**
>
> rate • time = distance

Solve the system $\begin{cases} 4(b - c) = 8 \\ 2(b + c) = 8 \end{cases}$. First write the system as $\begin{cases} 4b - 4c = 8 \\ 2b + 2c = 8 \end{cases}$, and then use elimination.

Step 1 $4b - 4c = 8$

Step 2 $2(2b + 2c = 8)$ *Multiply each term in the second equation by 2 to get opposite coefficients of c.*

$\rightarrow 4b - 4c = 8$

$\underline{+ (4b + 4c = 16)}$ *Add the new equation to the first equation.*

Step 3 $8b = 24$

$b = 3$ *Simplify and solve for b.*

Step 4 $4b - 4c = 8$ *Write one of the original equations.*

$4(3) - 4c = 8$ *Substitute 3 for b.*

$12 - 4c = 8$

$\underline{-12 -12}$ *Subtract 12 from both sides.*

$-4c = -4$ *Simplify and solve for c.*

$c = 1$

Step 5 $(3, 1)$ *Write the solution as an ordered pair.*

Ben paddles at 3 mi/h in still water. The rate of the current is 1 mi/h.

1. Ben paddles his kayak along a course on a different river. Going upstream, it takes him 6 hours to complete the course. Going downstream, it takes him 2 hours to complete the same course. What is the rate of the current, and how long is the course?

EXAMPLE 2

Solving Mixture Problems

Sun Block
Active
Ingredient:
Zinc Oxide
(10%)

A pharmacist wants to mix an ointment that is 6% zinc oxide with an ointment that is 12% zinc oxide to make 30 grams of an ointment that is 10% zinc oxide. How many grams of each ointment should the pharmacist mix together?

Let s be the number of grams of the 6% ointment, and let t be the number of grams of the 12% ointment.

Use a table to set up two equations—one for the amount of ointment and one for the amount of zinc oxide in the ointment.

	6% Ointment	+	12% Ointment	=	10% Ointment
Amount of Ointment (g)	s	+	t	=	30
Amount of Zinc Oxide (g)	$0.06s$	+	$0.12t$	=	$0.1(30) = 3$

Solve the system $\begin{cases} s + t = 30 \\ 0.06s + 0.12t = 3 \end{cases}$. Use substitution.

Step 1
$$s + t = 30$$
$$\underline{\quad -t \quad\quad -t \quad}$$
$$s \quad\quad = 30 - t$$
Solve the first equation for s by subtracting t from both sides.

Step 2
$$0.06s + 0.12t = 3$$
$$0.06(30 - t) + 0.12t = 3$$
Substitute $30 - t$ for s in the second equation.

$$\mathbf{0.06(30) - 0.06t + 0.12t = 3}$$
Distribute 0.06 to the expression in parentheses.

$$1.8 - 0.06t + 0.12t = 3$$

$$1.8 + 0.06t = 3$$
Simplify. Solve for t.

Step 3
$$\underline{-1.8 \quad\quad\quad -1.8 \quad}$$
$$0.06t = 1.2$$
Subtract 1.8 from both sides.

$$\frac{0.06t}{0.06} = \frac{1.2}{0.06}$$
Divide both sides by 0.06.

$$t = \mathbf{20}$$

Step 4
$$s + t = 30$$
Write one of the original equations.
$$s + 20 = 30$$
Substitute 20 for t.
$$\underline{\quad -20 \quad -20 \quad}$$
Subtract 20 from both sides.
$$s = 10$$

Step 5 $(10, 20)$
Write the solution as an ordered pair.

The pharmacist should use 10 grams of the 6% ointment and 20 grams of the 12% ointment.

2. Suppose the pharmacist wants to get the same result by mixing an ointment that is 9% zinc oxide with an ointment that is 15% zinc oxide. How many grams of each ointment should the pharmacist mix together?

EXAMPLE **3**   **Solving Number-Digit Problems**

The sum of the digits of a two-digit number is 7. When the digits are reversed, the new number is 45 less than the original number. What is the original number? Check your answer.

Helpful Hint

When you solve a number-digit problem, you must write numbers in expanded form.

Let t represent the tens digit of the original number, and let u represent the units digit. Write the original number and the new number in expanded form.

Original number: $10t + u$ New number: $10u + t$

Now set up two equations.

The sum of the digits in the original number is 7.

First equation: $t + u = 7$

The new number is 45 less than the original number.

Second equation: $10u + t = (10t + u) - 45$

Simplify the second equation, so that the variables are only on the left side.

$$\begin{aligned} 10u + t &= 10t + u - 45 \\ -10t \quad &\quad -10t \\ \hline 10u - 9t &= \qquad u - 45 \\ -u \quad &\qquad -u \\ \hline 9u - 9t &= \qquad -45 \end{aligned}$$ *Subtract 10t from both sides.*

   Subtract u from both sides.

$$\frac{9u}{9} - \frac{9t}{9} = \frac{-45}{9}$$ *Divide both sides by 9.*

$$u - t = -5$$

$$-t + u = -5$$ *Write the left side with the variable t first.*

Now solve the system $\begin{cases} t + u = 7 \\ -t + u = -5 \end{cases}$. Use elimination.

Step 1 $t + u = \quad 7$

Step 2 $\underline{-t + u = -5}$

Step 3 $\quad 2u = \quad 2$ *Add the equations to eliminate the t-terms.*

$$\frac{2u}{2} = \frac{2}{2}$$ *Divide both sides by 2.*

$$u = 1$$

Step 4 $t + u = 7$ *Write one of the original equations.*

$t + 1 = \quad 7$ *Substitute 1 for u.*

$\underline{-1 \quad -1}$ *Subtract 1 from both sides.*

$t \quad = \quad 6$

Step 5 $(6, 1)$ *Write the solution as an ordered pair.*

The original number is 61.

Check   Check the solution using the original problem.
The sum of the digits is $6 + 1 = 7$. ✓
When the digits are reversed, the new number is 16, and
$61 - 16 = 45$. ✓

3. The sum of the digits of a two-digit number is 17. When the digits are reversed, the new number is 9 more than the original number. What is the original number? Check your answer.

THINK AND DISCUSS

1. Explain how to set up the variables to solve a number-digit problem.

2. GET ORGANIZED Copy and complete the graphic organizer. In each box, write an example of each type of problem and find the solution.

Applications of Systems of Equations

Rate Problem | Mixture Problem | Number-Digit Problem

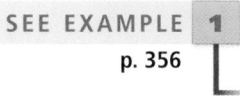 **Exercises**

California Standards Practice
🔑 9.0, 🔑 15.0, 25.2

go.hrw.com
Homework Help Online
KEYWORD: MA8CA 6-5
Parent Resources Online
KEYWORD: MA8CA Parent

GUIDED PRACTICE

SEE EXAMPLE **1**
p. 356

1. Recreation It takes Cathy 1.5 hours to paddle her canoe 6 miles upstream. Then she turns her canoe around and paddles 6 miles downstream in 1 hour. What is the rate of the current? What is Cathy's paddling rate in still water?

SEE EXAMPLE **2**
p. 357

2. Chemistry A chemist mixed a 15% glucose solution with a 35% glucose solution. This mixture produced 35 liters of a 19% glucose solution. How many liters of each solution did the chemist use in the mixture?

SEE EXAMPLE **3**
p. 358

3. The sum of the digits of a two-digit number is 14. When the digits are reversed, the new number is 36 more than the original number. What is the original number? Check your answer.

PRACTICE AND PROBLEM SOLVING

Independent Practice

For Exercises	See Example
4	1
5	2
6	3

Extra Practice
Skills Practice p. EP13
Application Practice p. EP29

4. Aviation With a tailwind, a jet flew 2000 miles in 4 hours. The jet's return trip against the same wind required 5 hours. Find the jet's speed and the wind speed.

5. Chemistry A 4% salt solution is mixed with a 16% salt solution. How many milliliters of each solution are needed to obtain 600 milliliters of a 10% salt solution?

6. The sum of the digits of a two-digit number is 10. If 18 is added to the number, the digits will be reversed. Find the number. Check your answer.

7. A coin bank contains 250 dimes and quarters worth a total of $39.25.

   a. Let q be the number of quarters, and let d be the number of dimes. Copy and complete the table.

	Quarters	+	Dimes	=	Total
Number of Coins	q	+		=	250
Value in Dollars	0.25q	+		=	

   b. Use the information in the table to write a system of equations.

   c. Find the number of quarters and the number of dimes in the bank.

8. **Business** A grocery store sells a mixture of peanuts and raisins for $1.75 per pound. Peanuts cost $1.25 per pound, and raisins cost $2.75 per pound. Follow the steps below to find the amount of raisins and peanuts that go into one pound of the mixture.

   a. Let p be the amount of peanuts, and let r be the amount of raisins in one pound of the mixture. Copy and complete the table.

	Peanuts	+	Raisins	=	Total
Weight (lb)	p	+	r	=	
Cost ($)	1.25p	+		=	1.75

   b. Use the information in the table to write a system of equations.

   c. Solve to find the amount of peanuts and raisins in the one-pound mixture.

9. A father is 32 years older than his daughter. In 4 years, the father will be 5 times as old as his daughter. Follow these steps to find their present ages.

   a. Let f be the father's present age, and let d be the daughter's present age. Write expressions that give the father's age and the daughter's age in 4 years.

   b. Write a system of equations based on the information in the problem.

   c. Solve the system to find the present age of the father and daughter.

10. **Multi-Step** The manager of a food store wants to create a blend of herbs that she can sell for $1 per ounce. She decides to make 8 ounces of a blend of oregano and sage. What will be the ratio of oregano to sage in the mixture?

11. The sum of the digits of a two-digit number is 13. Twice the first digit is 1 less than the second digit. What is the two-digit number?

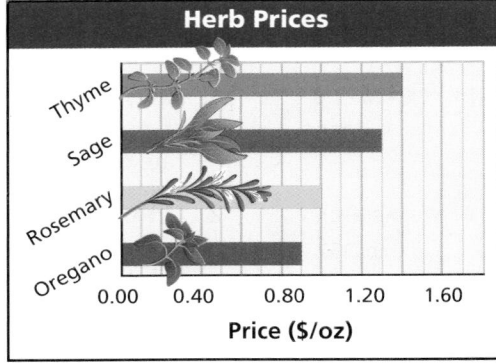

12. ///ERROR ANALYSIS/// The sum of Anna's age and Mario's age is 30. Mario is 6 years older than Anna. Two students found Anna's age a as shown. Which solution is incorrect? Explain.

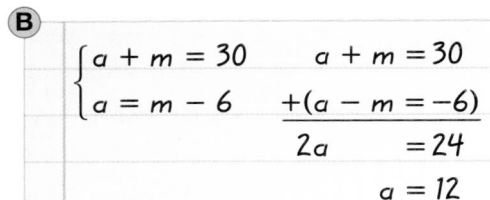

13. This problem will prepare you for the Concept Connection on page 362.

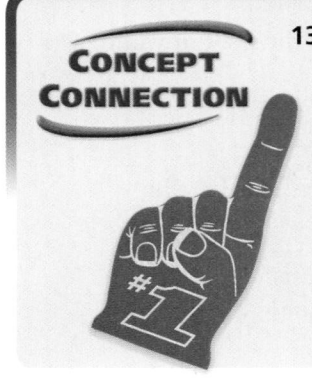

CONCEPT CONNECTION

A pep club is planning to sell adults' T-shirts and children's T-shirts as a fund-raiser. The club will order a total of 100 shirts. The club's president wants to raise $1100 from the sale of the shirts and proposes selling adults' shirts for $13 each and children's shirts for $8 each.

   a. Write a system of equations that the president could use to determine the number of each type of shirt to order.

   b. How many adults' shirts and children's shirts should the club order?

   c. How many of each type of shirt should the club order to be able to raise $1200?

14. Critical Thinking A chemist wants to mix a 10% saline solution with a 15% saline solution to make 20 milliliters of an 18% saline solution. What happens when you try to solve a system of equations to determine the amount of each saline solution that the chemist should use? Why does this happen?

 15. Write About It Write your own number-digit problem. Include a complete solution to the problem.

Multiple Choice For Exercises 16–18, choose the best answer.

16. With a tailwind, a plane makes a 3000-mile trip in 5 hours. On the return trip, the plane flies against the same wind and covers the 3000 miles in 6 hours. What is the speed of the wind?

Ⓐ 40 mi/h Ⓑ 50 mi/h Ⓒ 100 mi/h Ⓓ 550 mi/h

17. A jar contains quarters and dimes. There are 15 more quarters than dimes. The total value of the coins is $23. Which system of equations can be used to find the number of quarters q and the number of dimes d?

Ⓐ $\begin{cases} q = d - 15 \\ 0.25q + 0.1d = 0.23 \end{cases}$

Ⓒ $\begin{cases} d = q + 15 \\ 0.25q + 0.1d = 23 \end{cases}$

Ⓑ $\begin{cases} q = d + 15 \\ 0.25q + 0.1d = 0.23 \end{cases}$

Ⓓ $\begin{cases} q = d + 15 \\ 0.25q + 0.1d = 23 \end{cases}$

18. Donnell wants to make a 2-pound mixture of cashews and pecans that costs $2.60 per pound. How many pounds of cashews should he use?

Ⓐ 0.4 pound Ⓒ 1.2 pounds
Ⓑ 0.8 pound Ⓓ 1.6 pounds

Item	Price per Pound ($)
Cashews	2.50
Pecans	3.00

CHALLENGE AND EXTEND

19. In 15 years, Maya will be twice as old as David is now. In 15 years, David will be as old as Maya will be 10 years from now. How old are Maya and David now?

20. To train for a marathon, Mei runs an 18-mile course at a constant speed. If she doubles her usual speed, she can complete the course in an hour and a half less than her usual time. What is Mei's usual speed and her usual time to complete the course?

21. Write a word problem that can be solved by solving this system of equations.
$$\begin{cases} a + b = 20 \\ 0.25a + 0.5b = 6 \end{cases}$$

 SPIRAL STANDARDS REVIEW 1.1, 3.0, ⚷ 9.0

Use properties and operations to show that the first expression simplifies to the second expression. *(Lesson 1-7)*

22. $4(x - 1) + x, 5x - 4$ **23.** $7a - 2(a + 1), 5a - 2$ **24.** $4x + 5x + x^2 - 3x, 6x + x^2$

Solve each equation. Check your answer. *(Lesson 2-7)*

25. $2|x| + 5 = 11$ **26.** $3 + 4|x| = 3$ **27.** $|2x + 1| = 7$ **28.** $12 = 3|x + 2|$

Solve each system of linear equations. Check your answer. *(Lesson 6-4)*

29. $\begin{cases} 2x - y = 1 \\ x = \frac{1}{2}y + 1 \end{cases}$ **30.** $\begin{cases} -2y = x - 1 \\ x + 2y = 1 \end{cases}$ **31.** $\begin{cases} x - y = 2 \\ 2x = 2y + 4 \end{cases}$ **32.** $\begin{cases} x + y = 3 \\ x + 1 = -y \end{cases}$

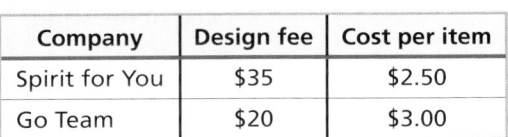

CONCEPT CONNECTION

Systems of Equations

We've Got Spirit Some cheerleaders are going to sell spirit bracelets and foam fingers to raise money for traveling to away games.

1. Two companies, Spirit for You and Go Team, are interested in providing the foam fingers. The cheerleaders plan to sell 100 foam fingers. Based on this information, which company should they choose? Explain your reasoning.

Company	Design fee	Cost per item
Spirit for You	$35	$2.50
Go Team	$20	$3.00

2. The cheerleaders sold foam fingers for $5 and spirit bracelets for $4. They sold 40 more foam fingers than bracelets, and they earned $965. Write a system of equations to describe this situation.

3. Solve this system using at least two different methods. Explain each method.

4. Using the company you chose in Problem 1, how much profit did the cheerleaders make from the foam fingers alone? (*Hint:* profit = amount earned − expenses)

5. What is the maximum price the cheerleaders could pay for each spirit bracelet in order to make a total profit of $500?

READY TO GO ON?

Quiz for Lessons 6-1 Through 6-5

6-1 Solving Systems by Graphing

Tell whether the ordered pair is a solution of the given system.

1. $(-2, 1)$; $\begin{cases} y = -2x - 3 \\ y = x + 3 \end{cases}$

2. $(9, 2)$; $\begin{cases} x - 4y = 1 \\ 2x - 3y = 3 \end{cases}$

3. $(3, -1)$; $\begin{cases} y = -\dfrac{1}{3}x \\ y + 2x = 5 \end{cases}$

Solve each system by graphing. Check your answer.

4. $\begin{cases} y = x + 5 \\ y = \dfrac{1}{2}x + 4 \end{cases}$

5. $\begin{cases} y = -x - 2 \\ 2x - y = 2 \end{cases}$

6. $\begin{cases} \dfrac{2}{3}x + y = -3 \\ 4x + y = 7 \end{cases}$

7. Banking Christiana and Marlena opened their first savings accounts on the same day. Christiana opened her account with $50 and plans to deposit $10 every month. Marlena opened her account with $30 and plans to deposit $15 every month. After how many months will their two accounts have the same amount of money? What will that amount be?

6-2 Solving Systems by Substitution

Solve each system by substitution. Check your answer.

8. $\begin{cases} y = -x + 5 \\ 2x + y = 11 \end{cases}$

9. $\begin{cases} 4x - 3y = -1 \\ 3x - y = -2 \end{cases}$

10. $\begin{cases} y = -x \\ y = -2x - 5 \end{cases}$

6-3 Solving Systems by Elimination

Solve each system by elimination. Check your answer.

11. $\begin{cases} x + 3y = 15 \\ 2x - 3y = -6 \end{cases}$

12. $\begin{cases} x + y = 2 \\ 2x + y = -1 \end{cases}$

13. $\begin{cases} -2x + 5y = -1 \\ 3x + 2y = 11 \end{cases}$

14. It takes Akira 10 minutes to make a black and white drawing and 25 minutes for a color drawing. On Saturday he made a total of 9 drawings in 2 hours. Write and solve a system of equations to determine how many drawings of each type Akira made.

6-4 Solving Special Systems

Classify each system. Give the number of solutions.

15. $\begin{cases} 3x = -6y + 3 \\ 2y = -x + 1 \end{cases}$

16. $\begin{cases} y = -4x + 2 \\ 4x + y = -2 \end{cases}$

17. $\begin{cases} 4x - 3y = 8 \\ y = 4(x + 2) \end{cases}$

6-5 Applying Systems

18. The sum of the digits of a two-digit number is 6. When the digits are reversed, the new number is 18 more than the original number. What is the original number? Check your answer.

6-6 Solving Linear Inequalities

California Standards

🔑 **6.0** Students graph a linear equation and compute the *x*- and *y*-intercepts (e.g., graph $2x + 6y = 4$). **They are also able to sketch the region defined by linear inequality (e.g., they sketch the region defined by $2x + 6y < 4$).**

Who uses this?

Consumers can use linear inequalities to determine how much food they can buy for an event. (See Example 3.)

A **linear inequality** is similar to a linear equation, but the equal sign is replaced with an inequality symbol. A **solution of a linear inequality** is any ordered pair that makes the inequality true.

EXAMPLE 1 **Identifying Solutions of Inequalities**

Tell whether the ordered pair is a solution of the inequality.

Vocabulary
linear inequality
solution of a linear inequality

A $(7, 3); y < x - 1$

$$y < x - 1$$

3	7 − 1
3	< 6 ✓

Substitute (7, 3) for (x, y).

$(7, 3)$ is a solution.

B $(4, 5); y > 3x + 2$

$$y > 3x + 2$$

5	3(4) + 2
5	12 + 2
5	> 14 ✗

Substitute (4, 5) for (x, y).

$(4, 5)$ is not a solution.

 Tell whether the ordered pair is a solution of the inequality.

1a. $(4, 5); y < x + 1$ **1b.** $(1, 1); y > x - 7$

A linear inequality describes a region of a coordinate plane called a *half-plane*. All points in the region are solutions of the linear inequality. The boundary line of the region is the graph of the related equation.

When the inequality is written as $y \leq$ or $y \geq$, the points on the boundary line are solutions, and the line is **solid**.

When the inequality is written as $y <$ or $y >$, the points on the boundary line are not solutions, and the line is **dashed**.

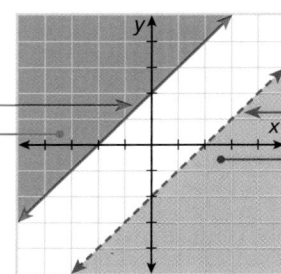

When the inequality is written as $y >$ or $y \geq$, the points **above** the boundary line are also solutions.

When the inequality is written as $y <$ or $y \leq$, the points **below** the boundary line are also solutions.

Graphing Linear Inequalities	
Step 1	Solve the inequality for y (slope-intercept form).
Step 2	Graph the boundary line. Use a solid line for $\leq$ or $\geq$. Use a dashed line for $<$ or $>$.
Step 3	Shade the half-plane above the line for $y >$ or $y \geq$. Shade the half-plane below the line for $y <$ or $y \leq$. Check your answer.

E X A M P L E 2 **Graphing Linear Inequalities in Two Variables**

Graph the solutions of each linear inequality. Check your answer.

A $y < 3x + 4$

    Step 1 The inequality is already solved for y.

    Step 2 Graph the boundary line $y = 3x + 4$.
          Use a dashed line for $<$.

    Step 3 The inequality is $<$, so shade below the line.

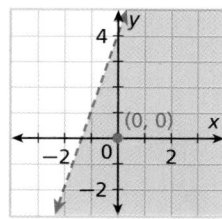

Check
$$
\begin{array}{c|c}
y & < 3x + 4 \\
\hline
0 & 3(0) + 4 \\
0 & 0 + 4 \\
0 & < 4 \checkmark
\end{array}
$$

Substitute (0, 0) for (x, y) because it is not on the boundary line.

The point (0, 0) satisfies the inequality, so the graph is shaded correctly.

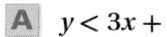

B $3x + 2y \geq 6$

    Step 1 Solve the inequality for y.
$$
\begin{array}{rcl}
3x + 2y & \geq & 6 \\
\underline{-3x} & & \underline{-3x} \\
2y & \geq & -3x + 6 \\
y & \geq & -\dfrac{3}{2}x + 3
\end{array}
$$

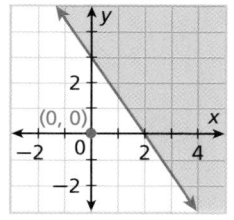

    Step 2 Graph the boundary line $y = -\dfrac{3}{2}x + 3$.
          Use a solid line for $\geq$.

    Step 3 The inequality is $\geq$, so shade above
          the line.

Check
$$
\begin{array}{c|c}
y & \geq \dfrac{3}{2}x + 3 \\
\hline
0 & \dfrac{3}{2}(0) + 3 \\
0 & 0 + 3 \\
0 & \geq 3 \; \text{✗}
\end{array}
$$

A false statement means that the half-plane containing (0, 0) should NOT be shaded. (0, 0) is not one of the solutions, so the graph is shaded correctly.

<aside>
Helpful Hint

Use the "test point" method shown in Example 2 to check your answers. The point (0, 0) is a good test point to use if it does not lie on the boundary line. However, be aware that this method will check only that your shading is correct. It will not check the boundary line.
</aside>

Graph the solutions of each linear inequality. Check your answer.

    2a. $4x - 3y > 12$ **2b.** $2x - y - 4 > 0$ **2c.** $y \geq -\dfrac{2}{3}x + 1$

EXAMPLE **3** *Consumer Economics Application*

Sarah can spend at most $7.50 on vegetables. Broccoli costs $1.25 per bunch and carrots cost $0.75 per package.

a. Write a linear inequality to describe the situation.

Let x represent the number of bunches of broccoli and let y represent the number of packages of carrots.

Write an inequality. Use ≤ for "at most."

Cost of broccoli	plus	cost of carrots	is at most	$7.50.
1.25x	+	0.75y	≤	7.50

Solve the inequality for y.

$$1.25x + 0.75y \leq 7.50$$

$$100(1.25x + 0.75y) \leq 100(7.50)$$ *You can multiply both sides of the inequality by 100 to eliminate the decimals.*

$$125x + 75y \leq 750$$

$$\underline{-125x \qquad\qquad -125x}$$ *Subtract 125x from both sides.*

$$75y \leq 750 - 125x$$

$$\frac{75y}{75} \leq \frac{750 - 125x}{75}$$ *Divide both sides by 75.*

$$y \leq 10 - \frac{5}{3}x$$

b. Graph the solutions.

Step 1 Since Sarah cannot buy a negative amount of vegetables, the system is graphed only in Quadrant I. Graph the boundary line $y = -\frac{5}{3}x + 10$. Use a solid line for ≤.

Step 2 Shade below the line. Sarah must buy whole numbers of bunches or packages. All the points on or below the line with whole number coordinates are the different combinations of broccoli and carrots that Sarah can buy.

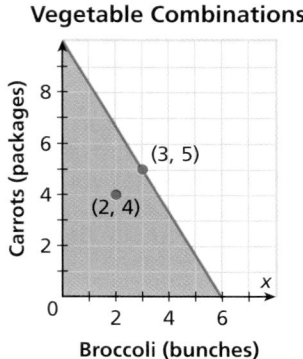

Vegetable Combinations

y-axis: Carrots (packages)
x-axis: Broccoli (bunches)

(3, 5)
(2, 4)

c. Give two combinations of vegetables that Sarah can buy.

Two different combinations that Sarah could buy for $7.50 or less are 2 bunches of broccoli and 4 packages of carrots, or 3 bunches of broccoli and 5 packages of carrots.

3. What if...? Dirk is going to bring two types of olives to the Honor Society induction and can spend no more than $6. Green olives cost $2 per pound and black olives cost $2.50 per pound.

a. Write a linear inequality to describe the situation.

b. Graph the solutions.

c. Give two combinations of olives that Dirk could buy.

EXAMPLE **4** **Writing an Inequality from a Graph**

Write an inequality to represent each graph.

A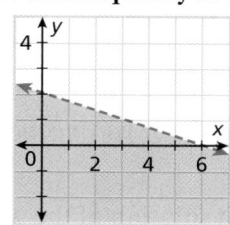

y-intercept: **2**; slope: $-\dfrac{1}{3}$

Write an equation in slope-intercept form.

$$y = mx + b \longrightarrow y = -\dfrac{1}{3}x + 2$$

The graph is shaded *below* a *dashed* boundary line.

Replace = with < to write the inequality $y < -\dfrac{1}{3}x + 2$.

B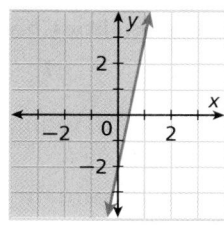

y-intercept: **−2**; slope: **5**

Write an equation in slope-intercept form.

$$y = mx + b \longrightarrow y = 5x + (-2)$$

The graph is shaded *above* a *solid* boundary line.

Replace = with ≥ to write the inequality $y \geq 5x - 2$.

C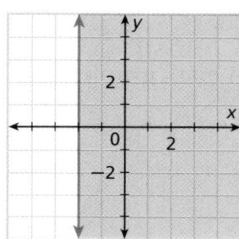

y-intercept: **none**; slope: **undefined**

The graph is a vertical line at $x = -2$.

The graph is shaded on the *right* side of a *solid* boundary line.

Replace = with ≥ to write the inequality $x \geq -2$.

 **Write an inequality to represent each graph.**

4a.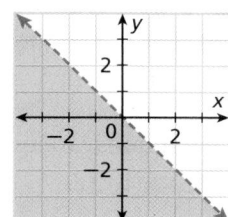

4b.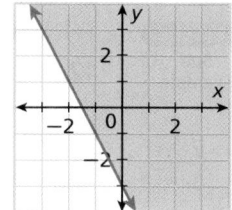

THINK AND DISCUSS

1. Tell how graphing a linear inequality is the same as graphing a linear equation. Tell how it is different.

2. Explain how you would write a linear inequality from a graph.

3. GET ORGANIZED Copy and complete the graphic organizer.

Inequality	$y < 5x + 2$	$y > 7x - 3$	$y \leq 9x + 1$	$y \geq -3x - 2$
Symbol	<			
Boundary Line	Dashed			
Shading	Below			

GUIDED PRACTICE

1. **Vocabulary** Can a *solution of a linear inequality* lie on a dashed boundary line? Explain.

SEE EXAMPLE 1
p. 364

Tell whether the ordered pair is a solution of the given inequality.

2. $(0, 3)$; $y \leq -x + 3$ **3.** $(2, 0)$; $y > -2x - 2$ **4.** $(-2, 1)$; $y < 2x + 4$

SEE EXAMPLE 2
p. 365

Graph the solutions of each linear inequality. Check your answer.

5. $y \leq -x$ **6.** $y > 3x + 1$ **7.** $-y < -x + 4$ **8.** $-y \geq x + 1$

SEE EXAMPLE 3
p. 366

9. **Multi-Step** Jack is making punch with orange juice and pineapple juice. He can make at most 16 cups of punch.

   a. Write an inequality to describe the situation.

   b. Graph the solutions.

   c. Give two possible combinations of cups of orange juice and pineapple juice that Jack can use in his punch.

SEE EXAMPLE 4
p. 367

Write an inequality to represent each graph.

10.

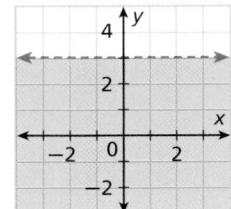

11.

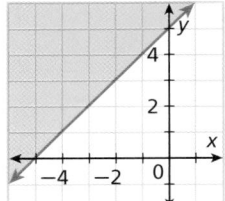

PRACTICE AND PROBLEM SOLVING

Independent Practice

For Exercises	See Example
12–14	1
15–18	2
19	3
20–21	4

Extra Practice

Skills Practice p. EP13

Application Practice p. EP29

Tell whether the ordered pair is a solution of the given inequality.

12. $(2, 3)$; $y \geq 2x + 3$ **13.** $(1, -1)$; $y < 3x - 3$ **14.** $(0, 7)$; $y > 4x + 7$

Graph the solutions of each linear inequality. Check your answer.

15. $y > -2x + 6$ **16.** $-y \geq 2x$ **17.** $x + y \leq 2$ **18.** $x - y \geq 0$

19. **Multi-Step** Beverly is serving hamburgers and hot dogs at her cookout. Hamburger meat costs $3 per pound, and hot dogs cost $2 per pound. She wants to spend no more than $30.

   a. Write an inequality to describe the situation.

   b. Graph the solutions.

   c. Give two possible combinations of pounds of hamburger and hot dogs that Beverly can buy.

Write an inequality to represent each graph.

20.

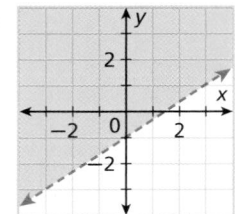

21.

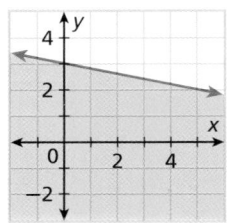

22. **Business** An electronics store makes $125 profit on every DVD player it sells and $100 on every CD player it sells. The store owner wants to make a profit of at least $500 a day selling DVD players and CD players.

    a. Write a linear inequality to determine the number of DVD players x and the number of CD players y that the owner needs to sell to meet his goal.

    b. Graph the linear inequality.

    c. Describe the possible values of x. Describe the possible values of y.

    d. List three possible combinations of DVD players and CD players that the owner could sell to meet his goal.

Graph the solutions of each linear inequality. Check your answer.

23. $y \le 2 - 3x$ 24. $-y < 7 + x$ 25. $2x - y \le 4$ 26. $3x - 2y > 6$

 27. **Geometry** Marvin has 18 yards of fencing that he can use to put around a rectangular garden.

    a. Write a linear inequality that describes the possible lengths and widths of the garden.

    b. Graph the inequality and list three possible solutions to the problem.

    c. What are the dimensions of the largest *square* garden that can be fenced in with whole-number dimensions?

28. **Hobbies** Stephen wants to buy yellow tangs and clown fish for his saltwater aquarium. He wants to spend no more than $77 on fish. At the store, yellow tangs cost $15 each and clown fish cost $11 each. Write and graph a linear inequality to find the number of yellow tangs x and the number of clown fish y that Stephen could purchase. Name a solution of your inequality that is not reasonable for the situation. Explain.

Graph each inequality on a coordinate plane.

29. $y > 1$ 30. $-2 < x$ 31. $x \ge -3$ 32. $y \le 0$

33. $0 \ge x$ 34. $-12 + y > 0$ 35. $x + 7 < 7$ 36. $-4 \ge x - y$

37. **School** At a high school football game, tickets at the gate cost $7 per adult and $4 per student. Write a linear inequality to determine the number of adult and student tickets that need to be sold so that the amount of money taken in at the gate is at least $280. Graph the inequality and list three possible solutions.

38. **Critical Thinking** Why must a region of a coordinate plane be shaded to show all solutions of a linear inequality?

39. **Write About It** Give a real-world situation that can be described by a linear inequality. Then graph the inequality and give two solutions.

CONCEPT CONNECTION

40. This problem will prepare you for the Concept Connection on page 378.

Gloria is making teddy bears. She is making boy and girl bears. She has enough stuffing to create 50 bears. Let x represent the number of girl bears and y represent the number of boy bears.

    a. Write an inequality that shows the possible number of boy and girl bears Jenna can make.

    b. Graph the inequality.

    c. Give three possible solutions for the numbers of boy and girl bears that can be made.

41. **///ERROR ANALYSIS///** Student A wrote $y < 2x - 1$ as the inequality represented by the graph. Student B wrote $y \leq 2x - 1$ as the inequality represented by the graph. Which student is incorrect? Explain the error.

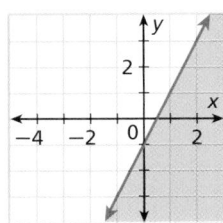

42. **Write About It** How do you decide to shade above or below an inequality? What does this shading represent?

Multiple Choice For Exercises 43–45, choose the best answer.

43. Which point is a solution of the inequality $y > -x + 3$?

   Ⓐ $(0, 3)$ Ⓑ $(1, 4)$ Ⓒ $(-1, 4)$ Ⓓ $(0, -3)$

44. Which inequality is represented by the graph at right?

   Ⓐ $2x + y \geq 3$ Ⓒ $2x + y \leq 3$
   Ⓑ $2x + y > 3$ Ⓓ $2x + y < 3$

45. Which of the following describes the graph of $3 \leq x$?

   Ⓐ The boundary line is dashed, and the shading is to the right.
   Ⓑ The boundary line is dashed, and the shading is to the left.
   Ⓒ The boundary line is solid, and the shading is to the right.
   Ⓓ The boundary line is solid, and the shading is to the left.

CHALLENGE AND EXTEND

Graph each inequality. Check your answer.

46. $0 \geq -6 - 2x - 5y$ 47. $y > |x|$ 48. $y \geq |x - 3|$

49. A linear inequality has the points $(0, 3)$ and $(-3, 1.5)$ as solutions on the boundary line. Also, the point $(1, 1)$ is not a solution. Write the linear inequality.

50. Two linear inequalities are graphed on the same coordinate plane. The point $(0, 0)$ is a solution of both inequalities. The entire coordinate plane is shaded except for Quadrant I. What are the two inequalities?

 SPIRAL STANDARDS REVIEW    6.0, 7.0, 9.0, 18.0

Graph each equation. Then tell whether the equation represents a function.
(Lesson 4-3)

51. $y = 2x - 4$ 52. $y = x^2 + 2$ 53. $y = 3$

Write an equation in slope-intercept form for the line through the two points.
(Lesson 5-6)

54. $(0, 9)$ and $(5, 2)$ 55. $(-5, -2)$ and $(7, 7)$ 56. $(0, 0)$ and $(-8, -10)$

57. $(-1, -2)$ and $(1, 4)$ 58. $(2, 2)$ and $(6, 5)$ 59. $(-3, 2)$ and $(3, -1)$

Solve each system by elimination. Check your answer. *(Lesson 6-3)*

60. $\begin{cases} x + 6y = 14 \\ x - 6y = -10 \end{cases}$ 61. $\begin{cases} x + y = 13 \\ 3x + y = 9 \end{cases}$ 62. $\begin{cases} 2x - 4y = 18 \\ 5x - y = 36 \end{cases}$

63. $\begin{cases} 2y + x = 12 \\ y - 2x = 1 \end{cases}$ 64. $\begin{cases} 2y - 6x = -8 \\ y = -5x + 12 \end{cases}$ 65. $\begin{cases} 2x + 3y = 33 \\ y = \frac{1}{4}x \end{cases}$

6-7

Solving Systems of Linear Inequalities

California Standards

9.0 Students solve a system of two linear equations in two variables algebraically and are able to interpret the answer graphically. **Students are able to solve a system of two linear inequalities in two variables and to sketch the solution sets.**

Also covered: **6.0**

Vocabulary
system of linear inequalities
solution of a system of linear inequalities

Who uses this?
The owner of a surf shop can use systems of linear inequalities to determine how many surfboards and wakeboards need to be sold to make a certain profit. (See Example 4.)

A **system of linear inequalities** is a set of two or more linear inequalities containing two or more variables. The **solutions of a system of linear inequalities** consists of all the ordered pairs that satisfy all the linear inequalities in the system.

EXAMPLE 1 Identifying Solutions of Systems of Linear Inequalities

Tell whether the ordered pair is a solution of the given system.

Remember!

An ordered pair must be a solution of all inequalities to be a solution of the system.

A $(2, 1);$ $\begin{cases} y < -x + 4 \\ y \le x + 1 \end{cases}$

$(2, 1)$

$y < -x + 4$	
1	$-2 + 4$
1	< 2 ✓

$(2, 1)$

$y \le x + 1$	
1	$2 + 1$
1	≤ 3 ✓

$(2, 1)$ is a solution to the system because it satisfies both inequalities.

B $(2, 0);$ $\begin{cases} y \ge 2x \\ y < x + 1 \end{cases}$

$(2, 0)$

$y \ge 2x$	
0	$2(2)$
0	≥ 4 ✗

$(2, 0)$

$y < x + 1$	
0	$2 + 1$
0	< 3 ✓

$(2, 0)$ is not a solution to the system because it does not satisfy both inequalities.

 Tell whether the ordered pair is a solution of the given system.

1a. $(0, 1);$ $\begin{cases} y < -3x + 2 \\ y \ge x - 1 \end{cases}$

1b. $(0, 0);$ $\begin{cases} y > -x + 1 \\ y > x - 1 \end{cases}$

To show all the solutions of a system of linear inequalities, graph the solutions of each inequality. The solutions of the system are represented by the overlapping shaded regions. Below are graphs of Examples 1A and 1B.

Math Builders

For more on graphing systems of linear inequalities, see the System Builder on page MB4.

Example 1A

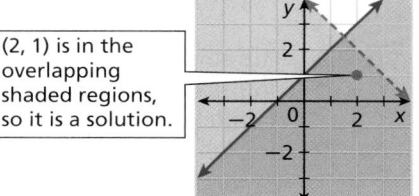

(2, 1) is in the overlapping shaded regions, so it is a solution.

Example 1B

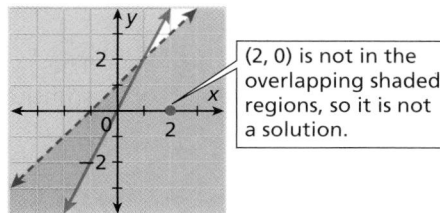

(2, 0) is not in the overlapping shaded regions, so it is not a solution.

6-7 Solving Systems of Linear Inequalities   **371**

EXAMPLE **2**   **Solving a System of Linear Inequalities by Graphing**

Graph the system of linear inequalities. Give two ordered pairs that are solutions and two that are not solutions.

$$\begin{cases} 8x + 4y \le 12 \\ y > \dfrac{1}{2}x - 2 \end{cases}$$

$8x + 4y \le 12$ *Write the first inequality in slope-intercept form.*
$\quad\quad 4y \le -8x + 12$
$\quad\quad\quad y \le -2x + 3$

Graph the system.

$$\begin{cases} y \le -2x + 3 \\ y > \dfrac{1}{2}x - 2 \end{cases}$$

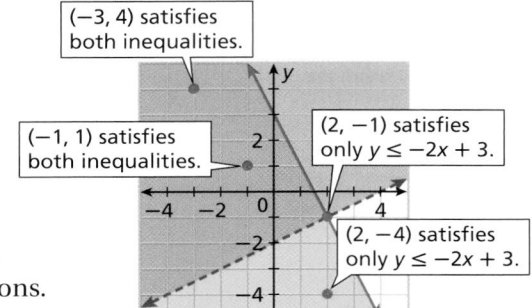

(−3, 4) satisfies both inequalities.

(−1, 1) satisfies both inequalities.

(2, −1) satisfies only $y \le -2x + 3$.

(2, −4) satisfies only $y \le -2x + 3$.

$(-1, 1)$ and $(-3, 4)$ are solutions.
$(2, -1)$ and $(2, -4)$ are not solutions.

 **Graph each system of linear inequalities. Give two ordered pairs that are solutions and two that are not solutions.**

2a. $\begin{cases} y \le x + 1 \\ y > 2 \end{cases}$ **2b.** $\begin{cases} y > x - 7 \\ 3x + 6y \le 12 \end{cases}$

In Lesson 6-4, you saw that in systems of linear equations, if the lines are parallel, there are no solutions. With systems of linear inequalities, that is not always true.

EXAMPLE **3**   **Graphing Systems with Parallel Boundary Lines**

Graph each system of linear inequalities.

A $\begin{cases} y < 2x - 3 \\ y > 2x + 2 \end{cases}$ **B** $\begin{cases} y > x - 3 \\ y \le x + 1 \end{cases}$ **C** $\begin{cases} y \le -3x - 2 \\ y \le -3x + 4 \end{cases}$

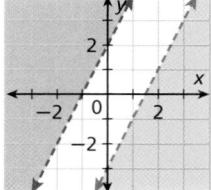   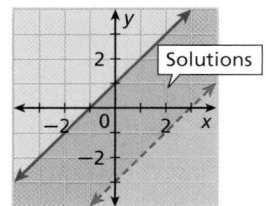   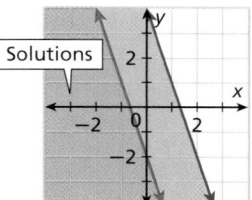

This system has no solution.

The solutions are all points between the parallel lines and on the solid line.

The solutions are the same as the solutions of $y \le -3x - 2$.

 **Graph each system of linear inequalities.**

3a. $\begin{cases} y > x + 1 \\ y \le x - 3 \end{cases}$ **3b.** $\begin{cases} y \ge 4x - 2 \\ y \le 4x + 2 \end{cases}$ **3c.** $\begin{cases} y > -2x + 3 \\ y > -2x \end{cases}$

EXAMPLE 4   *Business Application*

A surf shop makes the profits given in the table. The shop owner sells at least 10 surfboards and at least 20 wakeboards per month. He wants to earn at least $2000 a month. Show and describe all possible combinations of surfboards and wakeboards that the store owner needs to sell to meet his goals. List two possible combinations.

Profit per Board Sold ($)	
Surfboard	150
Wakeboard	100

Step 1 Write a system of inequalities.

Let x represent the number of surfboards and y represent the number of wakeboards.

$x \ge 10$	*He sells at least 10 surfboards.*
$y \ge 20$	*He sells at least 20 wakeboards.*
$150x + 100y \ge 2000$	*He wants to earn a total of at least $2000.*

Step 2 Graph the system.

The graph should be in only the first quadrant because sales are not negative.

Caution! ////////

An ordered pair solution of the system need not have whole numbers, but answers to many application problems may be restricted to whole numbers.

Step 3 Describe all possible combinations.
To meet the sales goals, the shop could sell any combination represented by an ordered pair of whole numbers in the solution region. Answers must be whole numbers because the shop cannot sell part of a surfboard or wakeboard.

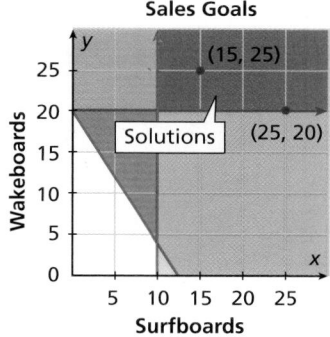

Step 4 List two possible combinations.
Two possible combinations are:
15 surfboards and 25 wakeboards
25 surfboards and 20 wakeboards

 **4.** At her party, Alice is serving pepper jack cheese and cheddar cheese. She wants to have at least 2 pounds of each. Alice wants to spend at most $20 on cheese. Show and describe all possible combinations of the two cheeses Alice could buy. List two possible combinations.

Price per Pound ($)	
Pepper Jack	4
Cheddar	2

THINK AND DISCUSS

1. How would you write a system of linear inequalities from a graph?

2. GET ORGANIZED Copy and complete each part of the graphic organizer. In each box, draw a graph and list one solution.

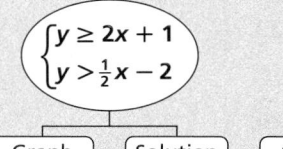

$\begin{cases} y \ge 2x + 1 \\ y > \frac{1}{2}x - 2 \end{cases}$ $\begin{cases} y < 2x + 1 \\ y \ge \frac{1}{2}x - 2 \end{cases}$

| Graph | Solution | | Graph | Solution |

California
Standards Practice
6.0, 9.0

go.hrw.com
Homework Help Online
KEYWORD: MA8CA 6-7
Parent Resources Online
KEYWORD: MA8CA Parent

GUIDED PRACTICE

1. **Vocabulary** A solution of a system of inequalities is a solution of _____?_____ of the inequalities in the system. (*at least one* or *all*)

SEE EXAMPLE 1
p. 371

Tell whether the ordered pair is a solution of the given system.

2. $(0, 0)$; $\begin{cases} y < -x + 3 \\ y < x + 2 \end{cases}$

3. $(0, 0)$; $\begin{cases} y < 3 \\ y > x - 2 \end{cases}$

4. $(1, 0)$; $\begin{cases} y > 3x \\ y \le x + 1 \end{cases}$

SEE EXAMPLE 2
p. 372

Graph each system of linear inequalities. Give two ordered pairs that are solutions and two that are not solutions.

5. $\begin{cases} y < 2x - 1 \\ y > 2 \end{cases}$

6. $\begin{cases} x < 3 \\ y > x - 2 \end{cases}$

7. $\begin{cases} y \ge 3x \\ 3x + y \ge 3 \end{cases}$

8. $\begin{cases} 2x - 4y \le 8 \\ y > x - 2 \end{cases}$

SEE EXAMPLE 3
p. 372

Graph each system of linear inequalities.

9. $\begin{cases} y > 2x + 3 \\ y < 2x \end{cases}$

10. $\begin{cases} y \le -3x - 1 \\ y \ge -3x + 1 \end{cases}$

11. $\begin{cases} y > 4x - 1 \\ y \le 4x + 1 \end{cases}$

12. $\begin{cases} y < -x + 3 \\ y > -x + 2 \end{cases}$

13. $\begin{cases} y > 2x - 1 \\ y > 2x - 4 \end{cases}$

14. $\begin{cases} y \le -3x + 4 \\ y \le -3x - 3 \end{cases}$

SEE EXAMPLE 4
p. 373

15. **Business** Sandy makes \$2 profit on every cup of lemonade that she sells and \$1 on every cupcake that she sells. Sandy wants to sell at least 5 cups of lemonade and at least 5 cupcakes per day. She wants to earn at least \$25 per day. Show and describe all the possible combinations of lemonade and cupcakes that Sandy needs to sell to meet her goals. List two possible combinations.

PRACTICE AND PROBLEM SOLVING

Independent Practice

For Exercises	See Example
16–18	1
19–22	2
23–28	3
29	4

Extra Practice
Skills Practice p. EP13
Application Practice p. EP29

Tell whether the ordered pair is a solution of the given system.

16. $(0, 0)$; $\begin{cases} y > -x - 1 \\ y < 2x + 4 \end{cases}$

17. $(0, 0)$; $\begin{cases} x + y < 3 \\ y > 3x - 4 \end{cases}$

18. $(1, 0)$; $\begin{cases} y > 3x \\ y > 3x + 1 \end{cases}$

Graph each system of linear inequalities. Give two ordered pairs that are solutions and two that are not solutions.

19. $\begin{cases} y < -3x - 3 \\ y \ge 0 \end{cases}$

20. $\begin{cases} y < -1 \\ y > 2x - 1 \end{cases}$

21. $\begin{cases} y > 2x + 4 \\ 6x + 2y \ge -2 \end{cases}$

22. $\begin{cases} 9x + 3y \le 6 \\ y > x \end{cases}$

Graph each system of linear inequalities.

23. $\begin{cases} y < 3 \\ y > 5 \end{cases}$

24. $\begin{cases} y < x - 1 \\ y > x - 2 \end{cases}$

25. $\begin{cases} x \ge 2 \\ x \le 2 \end{cases}$

26. $\begin{cases} y > -4x - 3 \\ y < -4x + 2 \end{cases}$

27. $\begin{cases} y > -1 \\ y > 2 \end{cases}$

28. $\begin{cases} y \le 2x + 1 \\ y \le 2x - 4 \end{cases}$

29. Multi-Step Linda works at a pharmacy for $15 an hour. She also baby-sits for $10 an hour. Linda needs to earn at least $90 per week, but she does not want to work more than 20 hours per week. Show and describe the number of hours Linda could work at each job to meet her goals. List two possible solutions.

30. Farming Tony wants to plant at least 40 acres of corn and at least 50 acres of soybeans. He wants no more than 200 acres of corn and soybeans. Show and describe all the possible combinations of the number of acres of corn and of soybeans Tony could plant. List two possible combinations.

Graph each system of linear inequalities.

31. $\begin{cases} y \geq -3 \\ y \geq 2 \end{cases}$

32. $\begin{cases} y > -2x - 1 \\ y > -2x - 3 \end{cases}$

33. $\begin{cases} x \leq -3 \\ x \geq 1 \end{cases}$

34. $\begin{cases} y < 4 \\ y > 0 \end{cases}$

Write a system of linear inequalities to represent each graph.

35.

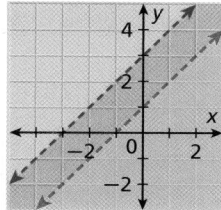

36.

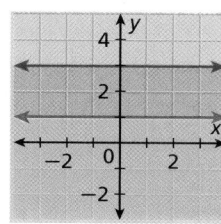

37.

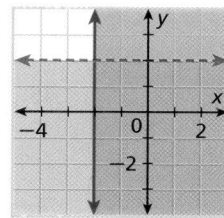

38. Military For males to enter the United States Air Force Academy, located in Colorado Springs, CO, they must be at least 17 but less than 23 years of age. Their standing height must be not less than 60 inches and not greater than 80 inches. Graph all possible heights and ages for eligible male candidates. Give three possible combinations.

39. ///ERROR ANALYSIS/// Two students wrote a system of linear inequalities to describe the graph. Which student is incorrect? Explain the error.

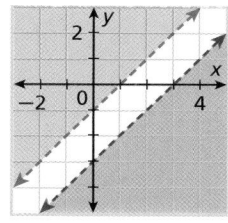

A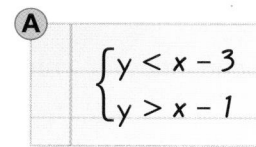
$\begin{cases} y < x - 3 \\ y > x - 1 \end{cases}$

B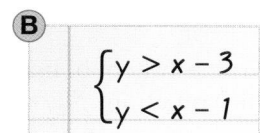
$\begin{cases} y > x - 3 \\ y < x - 1 \end{cases}$

40. Recreation Vance wants to fence in a rectangular area for his dog. He wants the length of the rectangle to be at least 30 feet and the perimeter to be no more than 150 feet. Graph all possible dimensions of the rectangle.

41. Reasoning Can the solutions of a system of linear inequalities be the points on a line? Explain.

42. This problem will prepare you for the Concept Connection on page 378.

Gloria is starting her own company making teddy bears. She has enough bear bodies to create 40 bears. She will make girl bears and boy bears.

a. Write an inequality to show this situation.

b. Gloria will charge $15 for girl bears and $12 for boy bears. She wants to earn at least $540 a week. Write an inequality to describe this situation.

c. Graph this situation and locate the solution region.

CONCEPT CONNECTION

43. Write About It What must be true of the boundary lines in a system of two linear inequalities if there is no solution of the system? Explain.

Multiple Choice For Exercises 44 and 45, choose the best answer.

44. Which point is a solution of $\begin{cases} 2x + y \geq 3 \\ y \geq -2x + 1 \end{cases}$?

    A $(0, 0)$ **B** $(0, 1)$ **C** $(1, 0)$ **D** $(1, 1)$

45. Which system of inequalities best describes the graph?

   A $\begin{cases} y < 2x - 3 \\ y > 2x + 1 \end{cases}$ **C** $\begin{cases} y < 2x - 3 \\ y < 2x + 1 \end{cases}$

   B $\begin{cases} y > 2x - 3 \\ y < 2x + 1 \end{cases}$ **D** $\begin{cases} y > 2x - 3 \\ y > 2x + 1 \end{cases}$

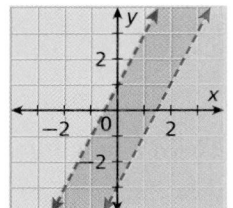

46. Short Response Graph and describe $\begin{cases} y + x > 2 \\ y \leq -3x + 4 \end{cases}$. Give two possible solutions of the system.

CHALLENGE AND EXTEND

47. Estimation Graph the given system of inequalities. Estimate the area of the overlapping solution regions.

$$\begin{cases} y \geq 0 \\ y \leq x + 3.5 \\ y \leq -x + 3.5 \end{cases}$$

48. Write a system of linear inequalities for which $(-1, 1)$ and $(1, 4)$ are solutions and $(0, 0)$ and $(2, -1)$ are not solutions.

49. Graph $|y| < 1$.

50. Write a system of linear inequalities for which the solutions are all the points in the third quadrant.

Use the diagram to find each of the following. *(Lesson 1-4)*

51. area of the square

52. area of the yellow triangle

53. combined area of the blue triangles

5 cm

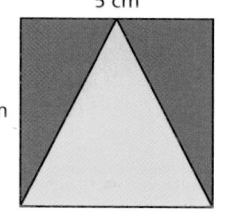
5 cm

Tell whether the given ordered pairs satisfy a linear function. *(Lesson 5-1)*

54. $\{(3, 8), (4, 6), (5, 4), (6, 2), (7, 0)\}$ **55.** $\{(6, 1), (7, 2), (8, 4), (9, 7), (10, 11)\}$

56. $\{(2, 10), (7, 9), (12, 8), (17, 7), (22, 6)\}$ **57.** $\{(1, -9), (3, -7), (5, -5), (7, -3), (9, -1)\}$

Graph the solutions of each linear inequality. Check your answer. *(Lesson 6-6)*

58. $y \leq 2x - 1$ **59.** $-\frac{1}{4}x + y > 6$ **60.** $5 - x \geq 0$

6-7
Technology LAB

Solve Systems of Linear Inequalities

A graphing calculator gives a visual solution to a system of linear inequalities.

California Standards

🔑 **9.0** Students solve a system of two linear equations in two variables algebraically and are able to interpret the answer graphically. **Students are able to solve a system of two linear inequalities in two variables and to sketch the solution sets.**

Use with Lesson 6-7

Activity

Graph the system $\begin{cases} y > 2x - 4 \\ 2.75y - x < 6 \end{cases}$. Give two ordered pairs that are solutions.

1 Write the first boundary line in slope-intercept form.

$$y > 2x - 4 \qquad \longrightarrow \qquad y = 2x - 4$$

2 Press [Y=] and enter $2x - 4$ for **Y1**.

The inequality contains the symbol $>$. The solution region is above the boundary line. Press ◄ to move the cursor to the left of **Y1**. Press [ENTER] until the icon that looks like a region above a line appears. Press [GRAPH].

3 Solve the second inequality for y.

$$2.75y - x < 6$$
$$2.75y < x + 6$$
$$y < \frac{x + 6}{2.75} \qquad \longrightarrow \qquad y = \frac{x + 6}{2.75}$$

4 Press [Y=] and enter $(x + 6)/2.75$ for **Y2**.

The inequality contains the symbol $<$. The solution region is below the boundary line. Press ◄ to move the cursor to the left of **Y2**. Press [ENTER] until the icon that looks like a region below a line appears. Press [GRAPH].

5 The solutions of the system are represented by the overlapping shaded regions. The points $(0, 0)$ and $(-1, 0)$ are in the shaded region.

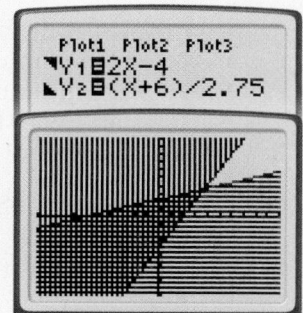

Check   Test $(0, 0)$ in both inequalities.   Test $(-1, 0)$ in both inequalities.

$y > 2x - 4$			$2.75y - x < 6$	
0		$2(0) - 4$	$2.75(0) - 0$	6
0	$>$	-4 ✓	0 $<$	6 ✓

$y > 2x - 4$			$2.75y - x < 6$	
0		$2(-1) - 4$	$2.75(0) - (-1)$	6
0	$>$	-6 ✓	1 $<$	6 ✓

Try This

Graph each system. Give two ordered pairs that are solutions.

1. $\begin{cases} x + 5y > -10 \\ x - y < 4 \end{cases}$ **2.** $\begin{cases} y > x - 2 \\ y \le x + 2 \end{cases}$ **3.** $\begin{cases} y > x - 2 \\ y \le 3 \end{cases}$ **4.** $\begin{cases} y < x - 3 \\ y - 3 > x \end{cases}$

CONCEPT CONNECTION

Equations and Formulas

Bearable Sales Gloria makes teddy bears. She dresses some as girl bears with dresses and bows and some as boy bears with bow ties. She is running low on supplies. She has only 100 eyes, 30 dresses, and 60 ties that can be used as bows on the girls and bow ties on the boys.

1. Write the inequalities that describe this situation. Let x represent the number of boy bears and y represent the number of girl bears.

2. Graph the inequalities and locate the region showing the number of boy and girl bears Gloria can make.

3. List at least three combinations of girl and boy bears that Gloria can make.

For 4 and 5, use the table.

4. Using the boundary line in your graph from Problem 2, copy and complete the table with the corresponding number of girl bears.

5. Gloria sells the bears for profit. She makes a profit of $8 for the girl bears and $5 for the boy bears. Use the table from Problem 4 to find the profit she makes for each given combination.

6. Which combination is the most profitable? Explain. Where does it lie on the graph?

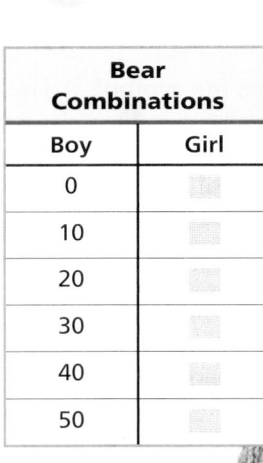

Bear Combinations	
Boy	Girl
0	
10	
20	
30	
40	
50	

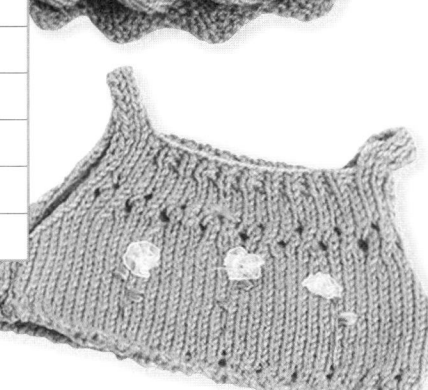

READY TO GO ON?

Quiz for Lessons 6-6 Through 6-7

6-6 Solving Linear Inequalities

Tell whether the ordered pair is a solution of the inequality.

1. $(3, -2); y < -2x + 1$ **2.** $(2, 1); y \geq 3x - 5$ **3.** $(1, -6); y \leq 4x - 10$

Graph the solutions of each linear inequality. Check your answers.

4. $y \geq 4x - 3$ **5.** $3x - y < 5$ **6.** $2x + 3y < 9$ **7.** $y \leq -\frac{1}{2}x$

8. Theo's mother has given him at most $150 to buy clothes for school. The pants cost $30 each and the shirts cost $15 each. How many of each can he buy? Write a linear inequality to describe the situation. Graph the linear inequality and give three possible combinations of pants and shirts Theo could buy.

Write an inequality to represent each graph.

9.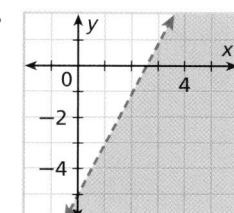

10.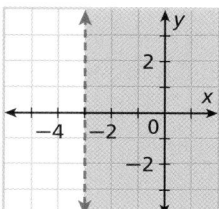

11.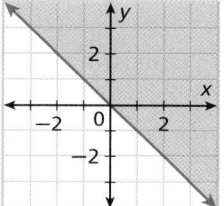

6-7 Solving Systems of Linear Inequalities

Tell whether the ordered pair is a solution of the given system.

12. $(-3, -1); \begin{cases} y > -2 \\ y < x + 4 \end{cases}$ **13.** $(-3, 0); \begin{cases} y \leq x + 4 \\ y \geq -2x - 6 \end{cases}$ **14.** $(0, 0); \begin{cases} y \geq 3x \\ 2x + y < -1 \end{cases}$

Graph each system of linear inequalities. Give two ordered pairs that are solutions and two that are not solutions.

15. $\begin{cases} y > -2 \\ y < x + 3 \end{cases}$ **16.** $\begin{cases} x + y \leq 2 \\ 2x + y \geq -1 \end{cases}$ **17.** $\begin{cases} 2x - 5y \leq -5 \\ 3x + 2y < 10 \end{cases}$

Graph each system of linear inequalities and describe the solutions.

18. $\begin{cases} y \geq x + 1 \\ y \geq x - 4 \end{cases}$ **19.** $\begin{cases} y \geq 2x - 1 \\ y < 2x - 3 \end{cases}$ **20.** $\begin{cases} y < -3x + 5 \\ y > -3x - 2 \end{cases}$

21. A grocer sells mangos for $4/lb and apples for $3/lb. The grocer starts with 45 lb of mangos and 50 lb of apples each day. The grocer's goal is to make at least $300 by selling mangos and apples each day. Show and describe all possible combinations of mangos and apples that could be sold to meet the goal. List two possible combinations.

Vocabulary

Complete the sentences below with vocabulary words from the list above.

1. A(n) ____?____ is a system that has exactly one solution.

2. A set of two or more linear equations that contain the same variable(s) is a(n) ____?____.

3. The ____?____ consists of all the ordered pairs that satisfy all the inequalities in the system.

4. A system consisting of equations of parallel lines with different y-intercepts is a(n) ____?____.

5. A(n) ____?____ consists of two intersecting lines.

6-1 Solving Systems by Graphing (pp. 329–334)

 **6.0, 9.0**

EXAMPLE

■ Solve $\begin{cases} y = 2x - 2 \\ x + 2y = 16 \end{cases}$ by graphing.

Check your answer.

$\begin{cases} y = 2x - 2 \\ y = -\dfrac{1}{2}x + 8 \end{cases}$ *Write the second equation in slope-intercept form.*

The solution appears to be at $(4, 6)$.

$\begin{array}{c|c} y = 2x - 2 \\ \hline 6 & 2(4) - 2 \\ 6 & 6 \checkmark \end{array}$ $\begin{array}{c|c} x + 2y = 16 \\ \hline 4 + 2(6) & 16 \\ & 16 & 16 \checkmark \end{array}$

The ordered pair $(4, 6)$ makes both equations true, so it is a solution of the system.

EXERCISES

Tell whether the ordered pair is a solution of the given system.

6. $(0, -5); \begin{cases} y = -6x + 5 \\ x - y = 5 \end{cases}$ **7.** $(4, 3); \begin{cases} x - 2y = -2 \\ y = \dfrac{1}{2}x + 1 \end{cases}$

8. $\left(1\dfrac{3}{4}, 7\dfrac{1}{4}\right); \begin{cases} x + y = 9 \\ 2y = 6x + 4 \end{cases}$ **9.** $(-1, -1); \begin{cases} y = -2x + 5 \\ 3y = 6x + 3 \end{cases}$

Solve each system by graphing. Check your answer.

10. $\begin{cases} y = 3x + 2 \\ y = -2x - 3 \end{cases}$ **11.** $\begin{cases} y = -\dfrac{1}{3}x + 5 \\ 2x - 2y = -2 \end{cases}$

12. Raheel is comparing the cost of two parking garages. Garage A charges a flat fee of $6 per car plus $0.50 per hour. Garage B charges a flat fee of $2 per car plus $1 per hour. After how many hours will the cost at garage A be the same as the cost at garage B? What will that cost be?

6-2 Solving Systems by Substitution (pp. 336–342)

EXAMPLE

■ Solve $\begin{cases} 2x - 3y = -2 \\ y - 3x = 10 \end{cases}$ by substitution.

Step 1 $y - 3x = 10$ *Solve the second*
         $y = 3x + 10$ *equation for y.*

Step 2 $2x - 3y = -2$ *Substitute 3x + 10*
    $2x - 3(3x + 10) = -2$ *for y in the first*
                         equation.

Step 3 $2x - 9x - 30 = -2$ *Solve for x.*
         $-7x - 30 = -2$
            $-7x = 28$
               $x = -4$

Step 4 $y - 3x = 10$ *Substitute −4 for x.*
    $y - 3(-4) = 10$
      $y + 12 = 10$ *Find the value of y.*
          $y = -2$

Step 5 $(-4, -2)$ *Write the solution as an*
                         ordered pair.

To check the solution, substitute $(-4, -2)$ into both equations in the system.

EXERCISES

Solve each system by substitution. Check your answer.

13. $\begin{cases} y = x + 3 \\ y = 2x + 12 \end{cases}$ **14.** $\begin{cases} y = -4x \\ y = 2x - 3 \end{cases}$

15. $\begin{cases} 2x + y = 4 \\ 3x + y = 3 \end{cases}$ **16.** $\begin{cases} x + y = -1 \\ y = -2x + 3 \end{cases}$

17. $\begin{cases} x = y - 7 \\ -y - 2x = 8 \end{cases}$ **18.** $\begin{cases} \frac{1}{2}x + y = 9 \\ 3x - 4y = -6 \end{cases}$

19. The Nash family's car needs repairs. Estimates for parts and labor from two garages are shown below.

Garage	Parts ($)	Labor ($ per hour)
Motor Works	650	70
Jim's Car Care	800	55

For how many hours of labor will the total cost of fixing the car be the same at both garages? What will that cost be? Which garage will be cheaper if the repairs require 8 hours of labor? Explain.

6-3 Solving Systems by Elimination (pp. 343–349)

EXAMPLE

■ Solve $\begin{cases} 2x - 3y = -8 \\ x + 4y = 7 \end{cases}$ by elimination.

Step 1 $2x - 3y = -8$ *Multiply the*
Step 2 $(-2)(x + 4y = 7)$ *second*
                             equation by −2.
      $2x - 3y = -8$ *Eliminate the*
   $+(-2x - 8y = -14)$ *x-term.*

         $0x - 11y = -22$
Step 3 $y = 2$ *Solve for y.*

Step 4 $2x - 3y = -8$
       $2x - 3(2) = -8$ *Substitute 2 for y.*
         $2x - 6 = -8$ *Simplify and solve*
            $2x = -2$ *for x.*
              $x = -1$

Step 5 $(-1, 2)$ *Write the solution as*
                       an ordered pair.

To check the solution, substitute $(-1, 2)$ into both equations in the system.

EXERCISES

Solve each system by elimination. Check your answer.

20. $\begin{cases} 4x + y = -1 \\ 2x - y = -5 \end{cases}$ **21.** $\begin{cases} x + 2y = -1 \\ x + y = 2 \end{cases}$

22. $\begin{cases} x + y = 12 \\ 2x + 5y = 27 \end{cases}$ **23.** $\begin{cases} 3x - 2y = -6 \\ \frac{1}{3}x + 3y = 9 \end{cases}$

Solve each system by any method. Explain why you chose each method. Check your answer.

24. $\begin{cases} 3x + y = 2 \\ y = -4x \end{cases}$ **25.** $\begin{cases} y = \frac{1}{3}x - 6 \\ y = -2x + 1 \end{cases}$

26. $\begin{cases} 2y = -3x \\ y = -2x + 2 \end{cases}$ **27.** $\begin{cases} x - y = 0 \\ 3x + y = 8 \end{cases}$

6-4 Solving Special Systems (pp. 350–355)

8.0, 9.0

EXAMPLE

■ Classify the system. Give the number of solutions.

$$\begin{cases} y = 3x + 4 \\ 6x - 2y = -8 \end{cases}$$

Use the substitution method.

$6x - 2(3x + 4) = -8$ *Substitute 3x + 4 for y in*
$6x - 6x - 8 = -8$ *the second equation.*
$-8 = -8$ ✓   *True.*

The equation is an identity. There are infinitely many solutions.

This system is **consistent** and **dependent**. The two lines are coincident because they have identical slopes and y-intercepts.

If the lines never intersect, the system is **inconsistent**. It has **no solution**. The system is **consistent** and **independent** when there is **one solution**.

EXERCISES

Classify each system. Give the number of solutions.

28. $\begin{cases} y = \dfrac{1}{2}x + 2 \\ y = \dfrac{1}{4}x - 8 \end{cases}$
   29. $\begin{cases} y = 3x - 7 \\ y = 3x + 2 \end{cases}$

30. $\begin{cases} 2x + y = 2 \\ y - 2 = -2x \end{cases}$
   31. $\begin{cases} -3x - y = -5 \\ y = -3x - 5 \end{cases}$

32. $\begin{cases} 2x + 3y = 1 \\ 3x + 2y = 1 \end{cases}$
   33. $\begin{cases} x + \dfrac{1}{2}y = 3 \\ 2x = 6 - y \end{cases}$

34. The two parallel lines graphed below represent a system of equations. Classify the system and give the number of solutions.

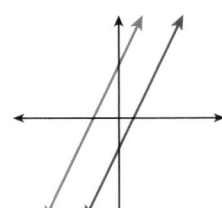

6-5 Applying Systems (pp. 356–361)

9.0, 15.0

EXAMPLE

■ Against the wind, Devin skated 200 meters in 50 seconds. With the wind, he skated the same distance in 25 seconds. What is the rate at which Devin skated? What is the rate of the wind?

Solve the system $\begin{cases} 50(d - w) = 200 \\ 25(d + w) = 200 \end{cases}$.

Step 1 $50d - 50w = 200$
Step 2 $2(25d + 25w = 200)$ *Multiply each*
                      term by 2.
     $50d - 50w = 200$
   $+(50d + 50w = 400)$ *Add.*

Step 3 $100d = 600$ *Simplify and*
             $d = 6$ *solve for d.*

Step 4 $50d - 50w = \;\;\;200$
     $50(6) - 50w = \;\;\;200$ *Substitute 6 for d.*
      $300 - 50w = \;\;\;200$ *Subtract 300 from*
    $\underline{-300 \qquad\qquad -300}$ *both sides.*
         $-50w = -100$ *Simplify and*
             $w = 2$ *solve for w.*

Step 5 $(6, 2)$ *Write the solution as an ordered pair.*

Devin's skating rate is 6 m/s. The rate of the wind is 2 m/s.

EXERCISES

35. Gena walked 160 feet in 40 seconds on a moving walkway. Against the walkway, she was able to walk the same distance in 80 seconds. What is the rate at which Gena walked, and what is the rate of the walkway?

36. Blake rows his boat against a current 90 yards in 15 minutes. With a current, he rows 90 yards in 9 minutes. What is the rate at which Blake rows, and what is the rate of the current?

37. Cole has a solution that is 20% water and another solution that is 60% water. He wants to mix these to make a 40 mL solution that is 30% water. How many mL of each solution should Cole mix together?

38. The sum of the digits of a two-digit number is 11. When the digits are reversed, the new number is 63 more than the original number. What is the original number?

6-6 Solving Linear Inequalities (pp. 364–370)

EXAMPLE

■ Graph the solutions of $x - 2y < 6$.

Step 1 Solve the inequality for y.

$$x - 2y < 6$$
$$-2y < -x + 6$$
$$y > \frac{1}{2}x - 3$$

Step 2 Graph $y = \frac{1}{2}x - 3$. Use a dashed line for $>$.

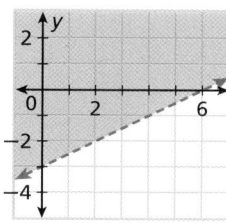

Step 3 The inequality is $>$, so shade above the boundary line.

Check Substitute $(0, 0)$ for (x, y) because it is not on the boundary line.

$$\begin{array}{c|c} x - 2y & < 6 \\ \hline 0 - 2(0) & 6 \\ 0 & < 6 \checkmark \end{array}$$

$(0, 0)$ satisfies the inequality, so the graph is shaded correctly.

EXERCISES

Tell whether the ordered pair is a solution of the inequality.

39. $(0, -3)$; $y < 2x - 3$

40. $(2, -1)$; $y \geq x - 3$

41. $(6, 0)$; $y > -3x + 4$

42. $(10, 10)$; $y \leq x - 3$

Graph the solutions of each linear inequality.

43. $y < -2x + 5$ **44.** $x - y \geq 2$

45. $-x + 2y \geq 6$ **46.** $y > -4x$

47. $x + y + 4 > 0$ **48.** $5 - y \geq 2x$

49. The Mathematics Club is selling pizza and lemonade to raise money for a trip. They estimate that the trip will cost at least $450. If they make $2 on each slice of pizza and $1 on each bottle of lemonade, how many of each do they need to sell to have enough money for their trip? Write an inequality to describe the situation. Graph and then give two combinations of the number of pizza slices and number of lemonade bottles they need to sell.

6-7 Solving Systems of Linear Inequalities (pp. 371–376)

EXAMPLE

■ Graph $\begin{cases} y < -x + 5 \\ y \geq 2x - 3 \end{cases}$. Give two ordered pairs that are solutions and two that are not solutions.

Graph both inequalities.

The solutions of the system are represented by the overlapping shaded regions.

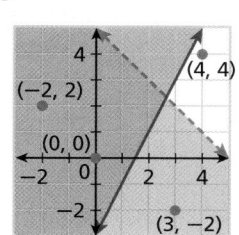

The points $(0, 0)$ and $(-2, 2)$ are solutions of the system.

The points $(3, -2)$ and $(4, 4)$ are not solutions.

EXERCISES

Tell whether the ordered pair is a solution of the given system.

50. $(3, 3)$; $\begin{cases} y > -2x + 9 \\ y \geq x \end{cases}$ **51.** $(-1, 0)$; $\begin{cases} 2x - y > -5 \\ y \leq -3x - 3 \end{cases}$

Graph each system of linear inequalities. Give two ordered pairs that are solutions and two that are not solutions.

52. $\begin{cases} y \geq x + 4 \\ y > 6x - 3 \end{cases}$ **53.** $\begin{cases} y \leq -2x + 8 \\ y > 3x - 5 \end{cases}$

54. $\begin{cases} -x + 2y > 6 \\ x + y < 4 \end{cases}$ **55.** $\begin{cases} x - y > 7 \\ x + 3y \leq 15 \end{cases}$

Graph each system of linear inequalities.

56. $\begin{cases} y > -x - 6 \\ y < -x + 5 \end{cases}$ **57.** $\begin{cases} 4x + 2y \geq 10 \\ 6x + 3y < -9 \end{cases}$

CHAPTER TEST

Tell whether the ordered pair is a solution of the given system.

1. $(1, -4);$ $\begin{cases} y = -4x \\ y = 2x - 2 \end{cases}$

2. $(0, -1);$ $\begin{cases} 3x - y = 1 \\ x + 5y = -5 \end{cases}$

3. $(3, 2);$ $\begin{cases} x - 2y = -1 \\ -3x + 2y = 5 \end{cases}$

Solve each system by graphing.

4. $\begin{cases} y = x - 3 \\ y = -2x - 3 \end{cases}$

5. $\begin{cases} 2x + y = -8 \\ y = \frac{1}{3}x - 1 \end{cases}$

6. $\begin{cases} y = -x + 4 \\ x = y + 2 \end{cases}$

Solve each system by substitution.

7. $\begin{cases} y = -6 \\ y = -2x - 2 \end{cases}$

8. $\begin{cases} -x + y = -4 \\ y = 2x - 11 \end{cases}$

9. $\begin{cases} x - 3y = 3 \\ 2x = 3y \end{cases}$

10. The costs for services at two kennels are shown in the table. Joslyn plans to board her dog and have him bathed once during his stay. For what number of days will the cost for boarding and bathing her dog at each kennel be the same? What will that cost be? If Joslyn plans a week-long vacation, which is the cheaper service? Explain.

Kennel Costs		
	Boarding ($ per day)	Bathing ($)
Pet Care	30	15
Fido's	28	27

Solve each system by elimination.

11. $\begin{cases} 3x - y = 7 \\ 2x + y = 3 \end{cases}$

12. $\begin{cases} 4x + y = 0 \\ x + y = -3 \end{cases}$

13. $\begin{cases} 2x + y = 3 \\ x - 2y = -1 \end{cases}$

Classify each system. Give the number of solutions.

14. $\begin{cases} y = 6x - 1 \\ 6x - y = 1 \end{cases}$

15. $\begin{cases} y = -3x - 3 \\ 3x + y = 3 \end{cases}$

16. $\begin{cases} 2x - y = 1 \\ -4x + y = 1 \end{cases}$

17. The sum of the digits of a two-digit number is 13. When the digits are reversed, the new number is 27 less than the original number. What is the original number?

Graph the solutions of each linear inequality.

18. $y < 2x - 5$

19. $-y \geq 8$

20. $y > \frac{1}{3}x$

Graph each system of linear inequalities. Give two ordered pairs that are solutions and two that are not solutions.

21. $\begin{cases} y > \frac{1}{2}x - 5 \\ y \leq 4x - 1 \end{cases}$

22. $\begin{cases} y > -x + 4 \\ 3x - y > 3 \end{cases}$

23. $\begin{cases} y \geq 2x \\ y - 2x < 6 \end{cases}$

24. Ezra and Tava sold at least 150 coupon books. Ezra sold at most 30 books more than twice the number Tava sold. Show and describe all possible combinations of the numbers of coupon books Ezra and Tava sold. List two possible combinations.

COLLEGE ENTRANCE
EXAM PRACTICE

FOCUS ON ACT

Four scores are reported for the ACT Mathematics Test: one score based on all 60 problems and one for each content area. The three content areas are: Pre-Algebra/ Elementary Algebra, Intermediate Algebra/Coordinate Geometry, and Plane Geometry/Trigonometry.

Taking classes that cover the content areas on the ACT is a good idea. This way you will have skills from each area of the test. Preparation over a long term is better than cramming at the last minute.

You may want to time yourself as you take this practice test. It should take you about 5 minutes to complete.

---

1. Which system of inequalities is represented by the graph?

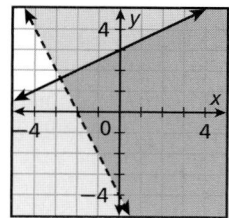

(A) $\begin{cases} -x + 2y < 6 \\ 2x + y > -4 \end{cases}$

(B) $\begin{cases} x - 2y \le 6 \\ 2x - y \ge 4 \end{cases}$

(C) $\begin{cases} -x + 2y \le 6 \\ 2x + y \ge 4 \end{cases}$

(D) $\begin{cases} -x + 2y \le 6 \\ 2x + y > -4 \end{cases}$

(E) $\begin{cases} x - 2y \le 6 \\ 2x - y > 4 \end{cases}$

---

2. What is the solution for y in the given system?

$\begin{cases} 4x + 3y = 1 \\ -4x + 3y = -7 \end{cases}$

(F) -1

(G) 0

(H) 1

(J) 2

(K) 6

---

3. Wireless phone company A charges $20 per month plus $0.12 per minute. Wireless phone company B charges $50 per month plus $0.06 per minute. For how many minutes of calls will the monthly bills be the same?

(A) 80 minutes

(B) 100 minutes

(C) 160 minutes

(D) 250 minutes

(E) 500 minutes

---

4. Which of the following systems of equations does NOT have a solution?

(F) $\begin{cases} x + 5y = 30 \\ -4x + 5y = 10 \end{cases}$

(G) $\begin{cases} x + 5y = -30 \\ -4x + 5y = 10 \end{cases}$

(H) $\begin{cases} x + 5y = -30 \\ -4x + 5y = -10 \end{cases}$

(J) $\begin{cases} -4x + 5y = -10 \\ -8x + 10y = -20 \end{cases}$

(K) $\begin{cases} -4x + 5y = -10 \\ -4x + 5y = -30 \end{cases}$

STRATEGIES FOR SUCCESS

Any Question Type: Read the Problem for Understanding

Standardized test questions may vary in format including multiple choice, gridded response, and short or extended response. No matter what format the test uses, read each question carefully and critically. Do not rush. Be sure you completely understand what you are asked to do and what your response should include.

EXAMPLE 1

Extended Response

An interior decorator charges a consultation fee of $50 plus $12 per hour. Another interior decorator charges a consultation fee of $5 plus $22 per hour. Write a system of equations to find the amount of time for which the cost of both decorators will be the same. Graph the system. After how many hours will the cost be the same for both decorators? What will the cost be?

Read the problem again.

What information are you given?

the consultation fees and hourly rates of two decorators

What are you asked to do?

1. Write a system of equations.
2. Graph the system.
3. Interpret the solution to the system.

What should your response include?

1. a system of equations with variables defined
2. a graph of the system
3. the time when the cost is the same for both decorators
4. the cost at that time

Read each test item and answer the questions that follow.

After you answer each item, read the item again to be sure your response includes everything that is asked for.

Item A
Short Response Which value of b will make the lines intersect at the point $(-2, 14)$?
$$\begin{cases} y = -6x + 2 \\ y = 4x + b \end{cases}$$

1. What information are you given?

2. What are you asked to do?

3. Ming's answer to this test problem was $y = 4x + 22$. Did Ming answer correctly? Explain.

Item B
Extended Response Solve the system by using elimination. Explain how you can check your solution algebraically and graphically.
$$\begin{cases} 4x + 10y = -48 \\ 6x - 10y = 28 \end{cases}$$

4. What method does the problem ask you to use to solve the system of equations?

5. What methods does the problem ask you to use to check your solution?

6. How many parts are there to this problem? List what needs to be included in your response.

Item C
Gridded Response What is the x-coordinate of the solution to this

system? $\begin{cases} y = 6x + 9 \\ y = 12x - 15 \end{cases}$

7. What question is being asked?

8. A student correctly found the solution of the system to be $(4, 33)$. What should the student mark on the grid so that the answer is correct?

Item D
Short Response Write an inequality to represent the graph below. Give a real-world situation that this inequality could describe.

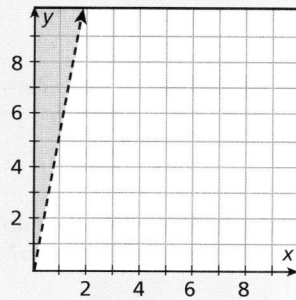

9. As part of his answer, a student wrote the following response:

The point $(1, 5)$ is not a solution to the inequality because it lies on the line, but $(2, 12)$ is a solution because it lies above the line.

Is his response appropriate? Explain.

10. What should the response include so that it answers all parts of the problem?

Item E
Multiple Choice Taylor bikes 50 miles per week and increases her distance by 2 miles each week. Josie bikes 30 miles per week and increases her distance by 10 miles each week. In how many weeks will Taylor and Josie be biking the same distance?

Ⓐ 2.5 weeks   Ⓒ 55 weeks

Ⓑ 7.5 weeks   Ⓓ 110 weeks

11. What question is being asked?

12. Carson incorrectly selected option C as his answer. What question did he most likely answer?

CUMULATIVE ASSESSMENT, CHAPTERS 1–6

Multiple Choice

1. What is the x-intercept of $3x + 2y = -6$?

  (A) -3 (C) 2

  (B) -2 (D) 3

2. Which of the problems below could be solved by finding the solution of this system?

$$\begin{cases} 2x + 2y = 56 \\ y = \dfrac{1}{3}x \end{cases}$$

  (A) The area of a rectangle is 56. The width is one-third the length. Find the length of the rectangle.

  (B) The area of a rectangle is 56. The length is one-third the perimeter. Find the length of the rectangle.

  (C) The perimeter of a rectangle is 56. The length is one-third more than the width. Find the length of the rectangle.

  (D) The perimeter of a rectangle is 56. The width is one-third the length. Find the length of the rectangle.

3. What is the slope of a line perpendicular to a line that passes through $(3, 8)$ and $(1, -4)$?

  (A) $-\dfrac{1}{6}$ (C) 2

  (B) $-\dfrac{1}{2}$ (D) 6

4. Which inequality is graphed below?

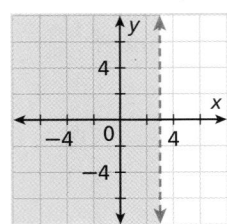

  (A) $-x > -3$ (C) $2x < -6$

  (B) $-y > -3$ (D) $3y < 9$

5. A chemist has a bottle of a 10% acid solution and a bottle of a 30% acid solution. He mixes the solutions together to get 500 mL of a 25% acid solution. How much of the 30% solution did he use?

  (A) 125 mL   (C) 375 mL

  (B) 150 mL   (D) 450 mL

6. Which ordered pair is NOT a solution of the system graphed below?

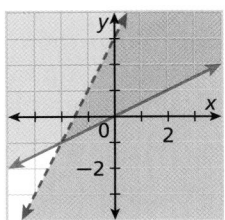

  (A) $(0, 0)$ (C) $(1, 1)$

  (B) $(0, 3)$ (D) $(2, 1)$

7. Which of the following best classifies a system of linear equations whose graph is two intersecting lines?

  (A) inconsistent and dependent

  (B) inconsistent and independent

  (C) consistent and dependent

  (D) consistent and independent

8. Which ordered pair is a solution of this system?

$$\begin{cases} 2x - y = -2 \\ \dfrac{1}{3}y = x \end{cases}$$

  (A) $(0, 2)$ (C) $(2, 6)$

  (B) $(1, 3)$ (D) $(3, 8)$

9. Where does the graph of $5x - 10y = 30$ cross the y-axis?

  (A) $(0, -3)$ (C) $(6, 0)$

  (B) $\left(0, \dfrac{1}{2}\right)$ (D) $(0, -6)$

10. Hillary needs markers and poster board for a project. The markers are $0.79 each and the poster board is $1.89 per sheet. She needs at least 4 sheets of poster board. Hillary has $15 to spend on project materials. Which system models this information?

(A) $\begin{cases} p \geq 4 \\ 0.79m + 1.89p \leq 15 \end{cases}$

(B) $\begin{cases} 0.79m \geq 1.89p \\ 4p \leq 15 \end{cases}$

(C) $\begin{cases} 4p \geq 1.89 \\ m + 4p \leq 15 \end{cases}$

(D) $\begin{cases} p + m \leq 15 \\ 0.79m + 1.89p \geq 4 \end{cases}$

11. How many different values of x are solutions of $|x - 2| + 5 = 5$?

(A) 0   (C) 2

(B) 1   (D) 3

Gridded Response

12. Kendra graphs the line shown below. Then she finds the equation of the line passing through $(-2, 2)$ that is perpendicular to this line. She writes the equation in slope-intercept form, $y = mx + b$. What is the value of b?

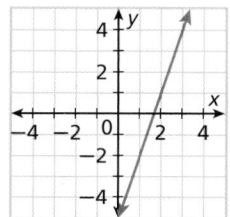

13. What value of y will make the line passing through $(4, -4)$ and $(-8, y)$ have a slope of $-\frac{1}{2}$?

14. What value of k will make the system $y - 5x = -1$ and $y = kx + 3$ inconsistent?

Short Response

15. What is the domain and range of the function shown in the graph?

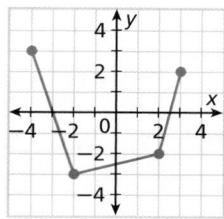

16. Graph $y > \frac{-x}{3} - 1$ on a coordinate plane. Name one point that is a solution of the inequality.

17. Marc and his brother Ty start saving money at the same time. Marc has $145 and will add $10 to his savings every week. Ty has $20 and will add $15 to his savings every week. After how many weeks will Marc and Ty have the same amount saved? What is that amount? Show your work.

18. A movie producer is looking for extras to act as office employees in his next movie. The producer needs extras that are at least 40 years old but less than 70 years old. They should be at least 60 inches tall but less than 75 inches tall. Graph all the possible combinations of ages and heights for extras that match the producer's needs. Let x represent age and y represent height. Show your work.

19. Graph the system $\begin{cases} y < -2x + 3 \\ y \geq 6x + 6 \end{cases}$.

   a. Is $(0, 0)$ a solution of the system you graphed? Explain why or why not.

   b. Is $(-4, 5)$ a solution of the system you graphed? Explain why or why not.

Extended Response

20. Every year, Erin knits scarves and sells them at the craft fair. This year she used $6 worth of yarn for each scarf. She also paid $50 to rent a table at the fair. She sold every scarf for $10.

   a. Write a system of linear equations to represent the amount Erin spent and the amount she collected. Tell what your variables represent. Tell what each equation in the system represents.

   b. Use any method to solve the system you wrote in part **a**. Show your work. How many scarves did Erin need to sell to make a profit? Explain.

   c. Describe two ways you could check your solution to part **b**. Check your solution by using one of those ways. Show your work.

Exponents and Polynomials

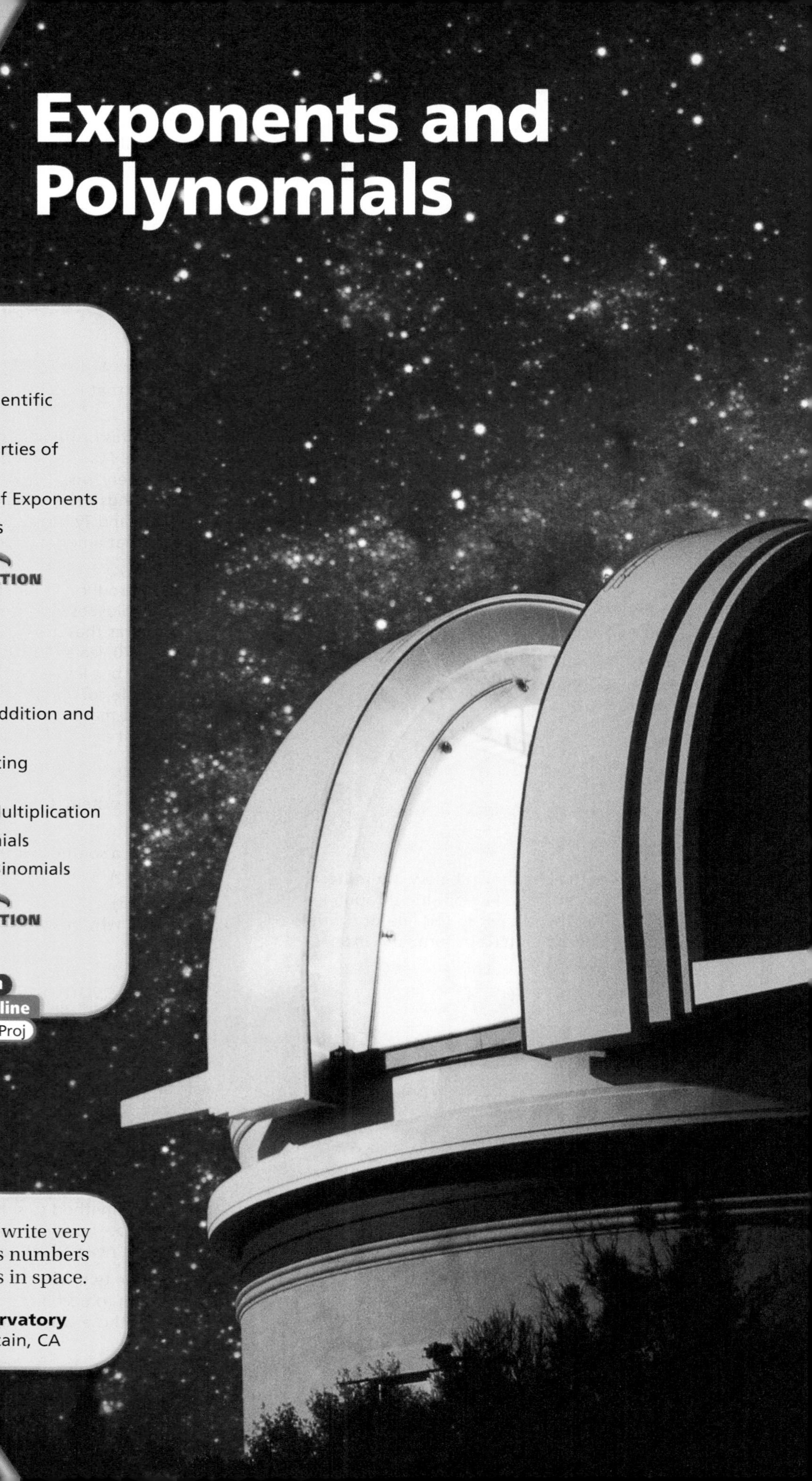

go.hrw.com

Chapter Project Online

KEYWORD: MA8CA ChProj

Exponents are used to write very large numbers, such as numbers that describe distances in space.

Palomar Observatory
Palomar Mountain, CA

ARE YOU READY?

✓ Vocabulary

Match each term on the left with a definition on the right.

1. Associative Property

2. coefficient

3. Commutative Property

4. exponent

5. like terms

A. a number that is raised to a power

B. a number multiplied by a variable

C. a property of addition and multiplication that states you can add or multiply numbers in any order

D. the number of times a base is used as a factor

E. terms that consist of the same variables raised to the same powers

F. a property of addition and multiplication that states you can group the numbers in any order

✓ Exponents

Write each expression using a base and an exponent.

6. $4 \cdot 4 \cdot 4 \cdot 4 \cdot 4 \cdot 4 \cdot 4$

7. $5 \cdot 5$

8. $(-10)(-10)(-10)(-10)$

9. $x \cdot x \cdot x$

10. $k \cdot k \cdot k \cdot k \cdot k$

11. 9

✓ Evaluate Powers

Evaluate each expression.

12. 3^4

13. -12^2

14. 5^3

15. 2^5

16. 4^3

17. $(-1)^6$

✓ Multiply Decimals

Multiply.

18. 0.006×10

19. $25{,}250 \times 100$

20. 2.4×6.5

✓ Combine Like Terms

Simplify each expression.

21. $6 + 3p + 14 + 9p$

22. $8y - 4x + 2y + 7x - x$

23. $(12 + 3w - 5) + 6w - 3 - 5w$

24. $6n - 14 + 5n$

✓ Squares and Square Roots

Tell whether each number is a perfect square. If so, identify its positive square root.

25. 42

26. 81

27. 36

28. 50

29. 100

30. 4

31. 1

32. 12

Unpacking the Standards

The information below "unpacks" the standards. The Academic Vocabulary is highlighted and defined to help you understand the language of the standards. Refer to the lessons listed after each standard for help with the math terms and phrases. The Chapter Concept shows how the standard is applied in this chapter.

California Standard	Academic Vocabulary	Chapter Concept
2.0 Students understand and use such operations as taking the opposite, finding the reciprocal, **taking a root, and raising to a fractional power. They understand and use the rules of exponents.** (Lessons **7-1, 7-2, 7-3, 7-4, 7-5**)	**fractional** having to do with fractions	You evaluate and simplify expressions containing exponents and/or roots. You understand what it means when an exponent is a fraction. ***Example:*** You simplify expressions such as $3^4 \cdot 3^2$. You will evaluate expressions like $16^{\frac{1}{4}}$.
10.0 Students add, subtract, multiply, and divide **monomials and polynomials. Students solve multistep problems, including word problems, by using these techniques.** (Lessons **7-7, 7-8, 7-9**; Labs **7-7, 7-8**)	**multistep** more than one step **technique** a way of doing something	You use your knowledge of exponents to add, subtract, and multiply polynomials, and you use polynomials to solve problems. ***Example:*** You simplify expressions such as $2x^2 - 2x + 5x^2 - 2$ and $x(2x^4 - 5x^3 - x^2)$.

Reading and Writing Math

Reading Strategy: Read and Understand the Problem

Follow this strategy when solving word problems.

- Read the problem through once.
- Identify exactly what the problem asks you to do.
- Read the problem again, slowly and carefully, to break it into parts.
- Highlight or underline the important information.
- Make a plan to solve the problem.

From Lesson 6-7

29. Multi-Step Linda works at a pharmacy for $15 an hour. She also baby-sits for $10 an hour. Linda needs to earn at least $90 per week, but she does not want to work more than 20 hours per week. Show and describe the number of hours Linda could work at each job to meet her goals. List two possible solutions.

Step 1	Identify exactly what the problem asks you to do.	• Show and describe the number of hours Linda can work at each job and earn at least $90 per week, without working more than 20 hours per week. • List two possible solutions of the system.
Step 2	Break the problem into parts. Highlight or underline the important information.	• Linda has two jobs. She makes **$15 per hour** at one job and **$10 per hour** at the other job. • She wants to earn **at least $90 per week.** • She does **not** want to work **more than 20 hours per week.**
Step 3	Make a plan to solve the problem.	• Write a system of inequalities. • Solve the system. • Identify two possible solutions of the system.

Try This

For the problem below,

    a. identify exactly what the problem asks you to do.

    b. break the problem into parts. Highlight or underline the important information.

    c. make a plan to solve the problem.

1. The difference between the length and the width of a rectangle is 14 units. The area is 120 square units. Write and solve a system of equations to determine the length and the width of the rectangle. (*Hint:* The formula for the area of a rectangle is $A = \ell w$.)

7-1 Integer Exponents

California Standards

🔑 **2.0** Students understand and use such operations as taking the opposite, finding the reciprocal, taking a root, and raising to a fractional power. **They understand and use the rules of exponents.**

Who uses this?

Manufacturers can use negative exponents to express very small measurements.

In 1930, the Model A Ford was one of the first cars to boast precise craftsmanship in mass production. The car's pistons had a diameter of $3\frac{7}{8}$ inches; this measurement could vary by at most 10^{-3} inch.

You have seen positive exponents. Recall that to simplify 3^2, use 3 as a factor 2 times: $3^2 = 3 \cdot 3 = 9$.

But what does it mean for an exponent to be negative or 0? You can use a table and look for a pattern to make a conjecture.

Remember!

Exponent

x^4

Base

Power	5^5	5^4	5^3	5^2	5^1	5^0	5^{-1}	5^{-2}
Value	3125	625	125	25	5			

$\div 5 \quad \div 5 \quad \div 5 \quad \div 5$

When the exponent decreases by one, the value of the power is divided by 5. Continue the pattern of dividing by 5:

$$5^0 = \frac{5}{5} = 1 \qquad 5^{-1} = \frac{1}{5} = \frac{1}{5^1} \qquad 5^{-2} = \frac{1}{5} \div 5 = \frac{1}{25} = \frac{1}{5^2}$$

Know it! Note

Integer Exponents

WORDS	NUMBERS	ALGEBRA
Zero exponent—Any nonzero number raised to the zero power is 1.	$3^0 = 1 \quad 123^0 = 1$ $(-16)^0 = 1 \quad \left(\frac{3}{7}\right)^0 = 1$	If $x \neq 0$, then $x^0 = 1$.
Negative exponent—A nonzero number raised to a negative exponent is equal to 1 divided by that number raised to the opposite (positive) exponent.	$3^{-2} = \frac{1}{3^2} = \frac{1}{9}$ $2^{-4} = \frac{1}{2^4} = \frac{1}{16}$	If $x \neq 0$ and n is an integer, then $x^{-n} = \frac{1}{x^n}$.

Reading Math

2^{-4} is read "2 to the negative fourth power."

Notice the phrase "nonzero number" in the table above. This is because 0^0 and 0 raised to a negative power are both undefined. For example, if you use the pattern given above the table with a base of 0 instead of 5, you would get $0^0 = \frac{0}{0}$. Also, 0^{-6} would be $\frac{1}{0^6} = \frac{1}{0}$. Since division by 0 is undefined, neither value exists.

EXAMPLE  **Manufacturing Application**

The diameter for the Model A Ford piston could vary by at most 10^{-3} inch. Simplify this expression.

$$10^{-3} = \frac{1}{10^3} = \frac{1}{10 \cdot 10 \cdot 10} = \frac{1}{1000}$$

10^{-3} inch is equal to $\frac{1}{1000}$ inch, or 0.001 inch.

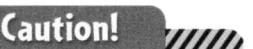 **1.** A sand fly may have a wingspan up to 5^{-3} m. Simplify this expression.

EXAMPLE **2** **Zero and Negative Exponents**

Simplify.

Caution! ⁄⁄⁄⁄⁄

In $(-3)^{-4}$, the base is negative because the negative sign is inside the parentheses.

In -3^{-4} the base (3) is positive.

A 2^{-3}

$$2^{-3} = \frac{1}{2^3} = \frac{1}{2 \cdot 2 \cdot 2} = \frac{1}{8}$$

B 5^0

$5^0 = 1$ *Any nonzero number raised to the zero power is 1.*

C $(-3)^{-4}$

$$(-3)^{-4} = \frac{1}{(-3)^4} = \frac{1}{(-3)(-3)(-3)(-3)} = \frac{1}{81}$$

D -3^{-4}

$$-3^{-4} = -\frac{1}{3^4} = -\frac{1}{3 \cdot 3 \cdot 3 \cdot 3} = -\frac{1}{81}$$

CHECK IT OUT! Simplify.

2a. 10^{-4} **2b.** $(-2)^{-4}$ **2c.** $(-2)^{-5}$ **2d.** -2^{-5}

EXAMPLE **3** **Evaluating Expressions with Zero and Negative Exponents**

Evaluate each expression for the given value(s) of the variable(s).

A x^{-1} for $x = 2$

2^{-1} *Substitute 2 for x.*

$2^{-1} = \frac{1}{2^1} = \frac{1}{2}$ *Use the definition $x^{-n} = \frac{1}{x^n}$.*

B $a^0 b^{-3}$ for $a = 8$ and $b = -2$

$8^0 \cdot (-2)^{-3}$ *Substitute 8 for a and −2 for b.*

$1 \cdot \dfrac{1}{(-2)^3}$ *Evaluate expressions with exponents.*

$1 \cdot \dfrac{1}{(-2)(-2)(-2)}$ *Write the power in the denominator as a product.*

$1 \cdot \dfrac{1}{-8}$ *Evaluate the power in the denominator.*

$-\dfrac{1}{8}$ *Simplify.*

 Evaluate each expression for the given value(s) of the variable(s).

3a. p^{-3} for $p = 4$ **3b.** $8a^{-2}b^0$ for $a = -2$ and $b = 6$

What if you have an expression with a negative exponent in a denominator, such as $\frac{1}{x^{-8}}$?

$$x^{-n} = \frac{1}{x^n}, \text{ or } \frac{1}{x^n} = x^{-n} \qquad \textit{Definition of negative exponent}$$

$$\frac{1}{x^{-8}} = x^{-(-8)} \qquad \textit{Substitute } -8 \text{ for } n.$$

$$= x^8 \qquad \textit{Simplify the exponent on the right side.}$$

If a base with a negative exponent is in a denominator, it is equivalent to the same base with the opposite (positive) exponent in the numerator.

An expression that contains negative or zero exponents is not considered to be simplified. Expressions should be rewritten with only positive exponents.

EXAMPLE **4** **Simplifying Expressions with Zero and Negative Exponents**

Simplify.

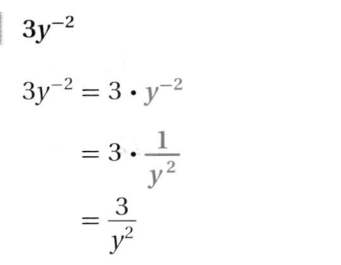
A $3y^{-2}$

$$3y^{-2} = 3 \cdot y^{-2}$$

$$= 3 \cdot \frac{1}{y^2}$$

$$= \frac{3}{y^2}$$

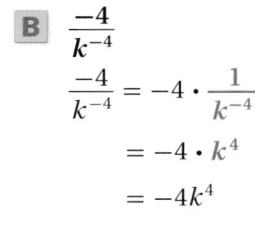
B $\frac{-4}{k^{-4}}$

$$\frac{-4}{k^{-4}} = -4 \cdot \frac{1}{k^{-4}}$$

$$= -4 \cdot k^4$$

$$= -4k^4$$

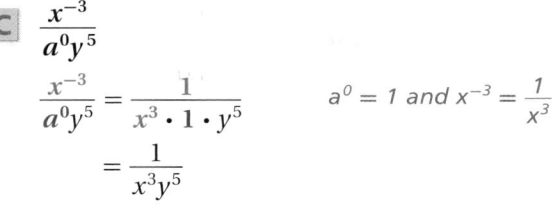
C $\frac{x^{-3}}{a^0 y^5}$

$$\frac{x^{-3}}{a^0 y^5} = \frac{1}{x^3 \cdot 1 \cdot y^5} \qquad a^0 = 1 \text{ and } x^{-3} = \frac{1}{x^3}.$$

$$= \frac{1}{x^3 y^5}$$

CHECK IT OUT! Simplify.

4a. $2r^0 m^{-3}$ **4b.** $\frac{r^{-3}}{7}$ **4c.** $\frac{g^4}{h^{-6}}$

THINK AND DISCUSS

1. Complete each equation: $2b^? = \frac{2}{b^2}$, $\frac{s^{-3}}{k^?} = \frac{1}{s^3}$, $?^{-2} = \frac{1}{t^2}$

2. GET ORGANIZED Copy and complete the graphic organizer. In each box, describe how to simplify, and give an example.

Simplifying Expressions with Negative Exponents

For a negative exponent in the numerator . . .

For a negative exponent in the denominator . . .

7-1

Exercises

California
Standards Practice
🔑 2.0, 25.2

go.hrw.com
Homework Help Online
KEYWORD: MA8CA 7-1
Parent Resources Online
KEYWORD: MA8CA Parent

GUIDED PRACTICE

SEE EXAMPLE **1**
p. 395

1. **Medicine** A typical virus is about 10^{-7} m in size. Simplify this expression.

SEE EXAMPLE **2**
p. 395

Simplify.

2. 6^{-2} 3. 3^0 4. -5^{-2} 5. 3^{-3} 6. 1^{-8}

7. -8^{-3} 8. 10^{-2} 9. $(4.2)^0$ 10. $(-3)^{-3}$ 11. 4^{-2}

SEE EXAMPLE **3**
p. 395

Evaluate each expression for the given value(s) of the variable(s).

12. b^{-2} for $b = -3$ 13. $(2t)^{-4}$ for $t = 2$

14. $(m-4)^{-5}$ for $m = 6$ 15. $2x^0y^{-3}$ for $x = 7$ and $y = -4$

SEE EXAMPLE **4**
p. 396

Simplify.

16. $4m^0$ 17. $3k^{-4}$ 18. $\dfrac{7}{r^{-7}}$ 19. $\dfrac{x^{10}}{d^{-3}}$

20. $2x^0y^{-4}$ 21. $\dfrac{f^{-4}}{g^{-6}}$ 22. $\dfrac{c^4}{d^{-3}}$ 23. p^7q^{-1}

PRACTICE AND PROBLEM SOLVING

Independent Practice

For Exercises	See Example
24	1
25–36	2
37–42	3
43–57	4

Extra Practice

Skills Practice p. EP14

Application Practice p. EP30

24. **Biology** One of the smallest bats is the northern blossom bat, which is found from Southeast Asia to Australia. This bat weighs about 2^{-1} ounce. Simplify this expression.

Simplify.

25. 8^0 26. 5^{-4} 27. 3^{-4} 28. -9^{-2}

29. -6^{-2} 30. 7^{-2} 31. $\left(\dfrac{2}{5}\right)^0$ 32. 13^{-2}

33. $(-3)^{-1}$ 34. $(-4)^2$ 35. $\left(\dfrac{1}{2}\right)^{-2}$ 36. -7^{-1}

Evaluate each expression for the given value(s) of the variable(s).

37. x^{-4} for $x = 4$ 38. $\left(\dfrac{2}{3}v\right)^{-3}$ for $v = 9$

39. $(10 - d)^0$ for $d = 11$ 40. $10m^{-1}n^{-5}$ for $m = 10$ and $n = -2$

41. $(3ab)^{-2}$ for $a = \dfrac{1}{2}$ and $b = 8$ 42. $4w^vx^v$ for $w = 3$, $v = 0$, and $x = -5$

Simplify.

43. k^{-4} 44. $2z^{-8}$ 45. $\dfrac{1}{2b^{-3}}$ 46. $c^{-2}d$ 47. $-5x^{-3}$

48. $4x^{-6}y^{-2}$ 49. $\dfrac{2f^0}{7g^{-10}}$ 50. $\dfrac{r^{-5}}{s^{-1}}$ 51. $\dfrac{s^5}{t^{-12}}$ 52. $\dfrac{3w^{-5}}{x^{-6}}$

53. b^0c^0 54. $\dfrac{2}{3}m^{-1}n^5$ 55. $\dfrac{q^{-2}r^0}{s^0}$ 56. $\dfrac{a^{-7}b^2}{c^3d^{-4}}$ 57. $\dfrac{h^3k^{-1}}{6m^2}$

Evaluate each expression for $x = 3$, $y = -1$, and $z = 2$.

58. z^{-5} **59.** $(x + y)^{-4}$ **60.** $(yz)^0$ **61.** $(xyz)^{-1}$

62. $(xy - 3)^{-2}$ **63.** x^{-y} **64.** $(yz)^{-x}$ **65.** xy^{-4}

66. ///**ERROR ANALYSIS**/// Look at the two equations below. Which is incorrect? Explain the error.

Ⓐ $5x^{-3} = \dfrac{1}{5x^3}$

Ⓑ $5x^{-3} = \dfrac{5}{x^3}$

Biology

Simplify.

67. a^3b^{-2} **68.** $c^{-4}d^3$ **69.** $v^0w^2y^{-1}$ **70.** $\left(a^2b^{-7}\right)^0$ **71.** $-5y^{-6}$

72. $\dfrac{2a^{-5}}{b^{-6}}$ **73.** $\dfrac{2a^3}{b^{-1}}$ **74.** $\dfrac{m^2}{n^{-3}}$ **75.** $\dfrac{x^{-8}}{3y^{12}}$ **76.** $-\dfrac{20p^{-1}}{5q^{-3}}$

77. Biology Human blood contains red blood cells, white blood cells, and platelets. The table shows the sizes of these components. Simplify each expression.

Blood Components	
Part	**Size (m)**
Red blood cell	$125{,}000^{-1}$
White blood cell	$3(500)^{-2}$
Platelet	$3(1000)^{-2}$

When bleeding occurs, platelets (which appear green in the image above) help to form a clot to reduce blood loss. Calcium and vitamin K are also necessary for clot formation.

Tell whether each statement is sometimes, always, or never true. Explain.

78. If n is a positive integer, then $x^{-n} = \dfrac{1}{x^n}$.

79. If x is positive, then $x^{-n} < 0$.

80. If n is zero, then x^{-n} is 1.

81. If n is a negative integer, then $x^{-n} = 1$.

82. If x is zero, then $x^{-n} = 1$.

83. If n is an integer, then $x^{-n} > 1$.

84. Reasoning Find the value of $2^3 \cdot 2^{-3}$. Then find the value of $3^2 \cdot 3^{-2}$. Make a conjecture about the value of $a^n \cdot a^{-n}$.

85. Write About It Explain in your own words why 2^{-3} is the same as $\dfrac{1}{2^3}$.

Find the missing value.

86. $\dfrac{1}{4} = 2^{\blacksquare}$ **87.** $9^{-2} = \dfrac{1}{\blacksquare}$ **88.** $\dfrac{1}{64} = \blacksquare^{-2}$ **89.** $\dfrac{\blacksquare}{3} = 3^{-1}$

90. $7^{-2} = \dfrac{1}{\blacksquare}$ **91.** $10^{\blacksquare} = \dfrac{1}{1000}$ **92.** $3 \cdot 4^{-2} = \dfrac{3}{\blacksquare}$ **93.** $2 \cdot \dfrac{1}{5} = 2 \cdot 5^{\blacksquare}$

CONCEPT CONNECTION

94. This problem will prepare you for the Concept Connection on page 428.

  a. The product of the frequency f and the wavelength w of light in air is a constant v. Write an equation for this relationship.

  b. Solve this equation for wavelength. Then write this equation as an equation with f raised to a negative exponent.

  c. The units for frequency are hertz (Hz). One hertz is one cycle per second, which is often written as $\frac{1}{s}$. Rewrite this expression using a negative exponent.

Multiple Choice For Exercises 95–97, choose the best answer.

95. Which is NOT equivalent to the other three?

Ⓐ $\dfrac{1}{25}$ Ⓑ 5^{-2} Ⓒ 0.04 Ⓓ -25

96. Which is equal to 6^{-2}?

Ⓐ $6(-2)$ Ⓑ $(-6)(-6)$ Ⓒ $-\dfrac{1}{6 \cdot 6}$ Ⓓ $\dfrac{1}{6 \cdot 6}$

97. Simplify $\dfrac{a^3 b^{-2}}{c^{-1}}$.

Ⓐ $\dfrac{a^3 c}{b^2}$ Ⓑ $\dfrac{a^3 b^2}{-c}$ Ⓒ $\dfrac{a^3}{-b^2 c}$ Ⓓ $\dfrac{c}{a^3 b^2}$

98. Gridded Response Simplify $\left[2^{-2} + (6 + 2)^0 \right]$.

99. Short Response If a and b are real numbers and n is a positive integer, write a simplified expression for the product $a^{-n} \cdot b^0$ that contains only positive exponents. Explain your answer.

CHALLENGE AND EXTEND

100. Multi-Step Copy and complete the table of values below. Then graph the ordered pairs and describe the shape of the graph.

x	−4	−3	−2	−1	0	1	2	3	4
$y = 2^x$									

 101. Reasoning Copy and complete the table. Then use inductive reasoning to make a conjecture about the values of 1^n and $(-1)^n$ when n is any negative integer.

For help with inductive reasoning, see p. 233.

n	−1	−2	−3	−4	−5
1^n					
$(-1)^n$					

SPIRAL STANDARDS REVIEW

🔑 4.0, 🔑 7.0, 16.0

Solve each equation. *(Lesson 2-3)*

102. $2(3x - 2) = 8$

103. $-9 = 3(p - 1)$

104. $\dfrac{y}{5} - 6 - 2 = -14 + 2$

105. $1.5h - 5 + 6h = 1 + 6h$

106. $2w + 6 - 3w = -10$

107. $-12 = \dfrac{1}{2}n + 2 - n$

Identify the independent and dependent variables. Write a rule in function notation for each situation. *(Lesson 4-3)*

108. Pink roses cost $1.50 per stem.

109. For dog-sitting, Beth charges a $30 flat fee plus $10 a day.

Write an equation in slope-intercept form for the line with the given slope that contains the given point. *(Lesson 5-6)*

110. slope $= 3$, $(3, 5)$

111. slope $= \dfrac{1}{3}$, $(6, 7)$

7-1 Integer Exponents   **399**

Powers of 10 and Scientific Notation

Nucleus of a silicon atom

California Standards

🔑 **2.0** Students understand and use such operations as taking the opposite, finding the reciprocal, taking a root, and raising to a fractional power. **They understand and use the rules of exponents.**

Vocabulary
scientific notation

Why learn this?

Powers of 10 can be used to read and write very large and very small numbers, such as the masses of atomic particles. (See Exercise 44.)

The table shows relationships between several powers of 10.

$\div 10 \quad \div 10 \quad \div 10 \quad \div 10 \quad \div 10 \quad \div 10$

Power	10^3	10^2	10^1	10^0	10^{-1}	10^{-2}	10^{-3}
Value	1000	100	10	1	$\frac{1}{10} = 0.1$	$\frac{1}{100} = 0.01$	$\frac{1}{1000} = 0.001$

$\times 10 \quad \times 10 \quad \times 10 \quad \times 10 \quad \times 10 \quad \times 10$

- Each time you **divide by 10**, the exponent decreases by 1 and the decimal point moves one place to the left.
- Each time you **multiply by 10**, the exponent increases by 1 and the decimal point moves one place to the right.

Know it!
Note

Powers of 10	
WORDS	**NUMBERS**
Positive Integer Exponent If n is a positive integer, find the value of 10^n by starting with 1 and moving the decimal point n places to the right.	$10^4 = 1\,0,0\,0\,0$ 4 places
Negative Integer Exponent If n is a positive integer, find the value of 10^{-n} by starting with 1 and moving the decimal point n places to the left.	$10^{-6} = \frac{1}{10^6} = 0.0\,0\,0\,0\,0\,1$ 6 places

EXAMPLE 1 **Evaluating Powers of 10**

Find the value of each power of 10.

A 10^{-3}

Start with 1 and move the decimal point three places to the left.

$0.\,0\,0\,1$

0.001

B 10^2

Start with 1 and move the decimal point two places to the right.

$1\,0\,0$

100

C 10^0

Start with 1 and move the decimal point zero places.

1

Writing Math

You may need to add zeros to the right or left of a number in order to move the decimal point in that direction.

 **Find the value of each power of 10.**

1a. 10^{-2} **1b.** 10^5 **1c.** 10^{10}

EXAMPLE 2 **Writing Powers of 10**

Reading Math

If you do not see a decimal point in a number, it is understood to be at the end of the number.

Write each number as a power of 10.

A 10,000,000	**B** 0.001	**C** 10
The decimal point is seven places to the right of 1, so the exponent is 7.	*The decimal point is three places to the left of 1, so the exponent is −3.*	*The decimal point is one place to the right of 1, so the exponent is 1.*
10^7	10^{-3}	10^1

 **Write each number as a power of 10.**

2a. 100,000,000   **2b.** 0.0001   **2c.** 0.1

You can also move the decimal point to find the product of any number and a power of 10. You start with the number instead of starting with 1.

Know it! Note

Multiplying by Powers of 10	
If the exponent is a positive integer, move the decimal point to the right.	$125 \times 10^5 = 12{,}5\ 0\ 0{,}\ 0\ 0\ 0$ 5 places
If the exponent is a negative integer, move the decimal point to the left.	$36.2 \times 10^{-3} = 0.0\ 3\ 6\ 2$ 3 places

EXAMPLE 3 **Multiplying by Powers of 10**

Find the value of each expression.

A 97.86×10^6

$97.8\ 6\ 0\ 0\ 0\ 0$ *Move the decimal point 6 places to the right.*

97,860,000

B 19.5×10^{-4}

$0\ 0\ 1\ 9.5$ *Move the decimal point 4 places to the left.*

0.00195

 **Find the value of each expression.**

3a. 853.4×10^5 **3b.** 0.163×10^{-2}

Scientific notation is a method of writing numbers that are very large or very small. A number written in scientific notation has two parts that are multiplied.

The first part is a number that is greater than or equal to 1 and less than 10.

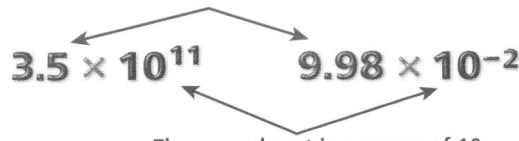

3.5×10^{11} 9.98×10^{-2}

The second part is a power of 10.

EXAMPLE 4 *Astronomy Application*

Jupiter has a diameter of about 143,000 km. Its shortest distance from Earth is about 5.91×10^8 km, and its average distance from the Sun is about 778,400,000 km. Jupiter's orbital speed is approximately 1.3×10^4 m/s.

143,000 km

Reading Math

Standard form refers to the usual way that numbers are written—not in scientific notation.

A Write Jupiter's shortest distance from Earth in standard form.

5.91×10^8

5.9 1 0 0 0 0 0 0   *Move the decimal point 8 places to the right.*

591,000,000 km

B Write Jupiter's average distance from the Sun in scientific notation.

778,400,000

7 7 8, 4 0 0, 0 0 0   *Count the number of places you need to move the decimal point to get a number between 1 and 10.*

8 places

7.784×10^8 km   *Use that number as the exponent of 10.*

 **4a.** Use the information above to write Jupiter's diameter in scientific notation.

4b. Use the information above to write Jupiter's orbital speed in standard form.

EXAMPLE 5 **Comparing and Ordering Numbers in Scientific Notation**

Order the list of numbers from least to greatest.

$1.2 \times 10^{-1}, 8.2 \times 10^4, 6.2 \times 10^5, 2.4 \times 10^5, 1 \times 10^{-1}, 9.9 \times 10^{-4}$

Step 1 List the numbers in order by powers of 10.

$9.9 \times 10^{-4}, 1.2 \times 10^{-1}, 1 \times 10^{-1}, 8.2 \times 10^4, 6.2 \times 10^5, 2.4 \times 10^5$

Step 2 Order the numbers that have the same power of 10.

$9.9 \times 10^{-4}, 1 \times 10^{-1}, 1.2 \times 10^{-1}, 8.2 \times 10^4, 2.4 \times 10^5, 6.2 \times 10^5$

 **5.** Order the list of numbers from least to greatest.
$5.2 \times 10^{-3}, 3 \times 10^{14}, 4 \times 10^{-3}, 2 \times 10^{-12}, 4.5 \times 10^{30}, 4.5 \times 10^{14}$

THINK AND DISCUSS

1. Tell why 34.56×10^4 is not correctly written in scientific notation.

2. GET ORGANIZED Copy and complete the graphic organizer.

Powers of 10 and Scientific Notation

| A negative exponent corresponds to moving the decimal point ___?___. | A positive exponent corresponds to moving the decimal point ___?___. |

7-2

Exercises

California Standards Practice
🔑 2.0

go.hrw.com
Homework Help Online
KEYWORD: MA8CA 7-2
Parent Resources Online
KEYWORD: MA8CA Parent

GUIDED PRACTICE

1. **Vocabulary** Explain how you can tell whether a number is written in *scientific notation*.

SEE EXAMPLE **1**
p. 400

Find the value of each power of 10.

2. 10^6 **3.** 10^{-5} **4.** 10^{-4} **5.** 10^8

SEE EXAMPLE **2**
p. 401

Write each number as a power of 10.

6. 10,000   **7.** 0.000001   **8.** 100,000,000,000,000,000

SEE EXAMPLE **3**
p. 401

Find the value of each expression.

9. 650.3×10^6 **10.** 48.3×10^{-4} **11.** 92×10^{-3}

SEE EXAMPLE **4**
p. 402

12. **Astronomy** A light-year is the distance that light travels in a year and is equivalent to 9.461×10^{12} km. Write this distance in standard form.

SEE EXAMPLE **5**
p. 402

13. Order the list of numbers from least to greatest.
8.5×10^{-1}, 3.6×10^8, 5.85×10^{-3}, 2.5×10^{-1}, 8.5×10^8

PRACTICE AND PROBLEM SOLVING

Independent Practice	
For Exercises	See Example
14–17	1
18–20	2
21–24	3
25–26	4
27	5

Extra Practice
Skills Practice p. EP14
Application Practice p. EP30

Find the value of each power of 10.

14. 10^3 **15.** 10^{-9} **16.** 10^{-12} **17.** 10^{14}

Write each number as a power of 10.

18. 0.01   **19.** 1,000,000   **20.** 0.000000000000001

Find the value of each expression.

21. 9.2×10^4 **22.** 1.25×10^{-7} **23.** 42×10^{-5} **24.** 0.05×10^7

25. **Biology** The human body is made of about 1×10^{13} cells. Write this number in standard form.

26. **Statistics** At the beginning of the twenty-first century, the population of China was about 1,287,000,000. Write this number in scientific notation.

27. Order the list of numbers from least to greatest.
2.13×10^{-1}, 3.12×10^2, 1.23×10^{-3}, 2.13×10^1, 1.32×10^{-3}, 3.12×10^{-3}

28. **Health** Donnell is allergic to pollen. The diameter of a grain of pollen is between 1.2×10^{-5} m and 9×10^{-5} m. Donnell's air conditioner has a filter that removes particles larger than 3×10^{-7} m. Will the filter remove pollen? Explain.

29. **Entertainment** In the United States, a CD is certified platinum if it sells 1,000,000 copies. A CD that has gone 2 times platinum has sold 2,000,000 copies. How many copies has a CD sold if it has gone 27 times platinum? Write your answer in scientific notation.

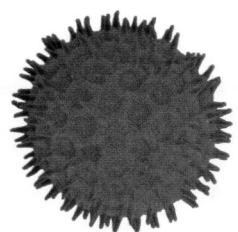

Grain of pollen, enlarged 1050 times

Write each number in scientific notation.

30. 40,080,000   **31.** 235,000   **32.** 170,000,000,000

33. 0.0000006   **34.** 0.000077   **35.** 0.0412

State whether each number is written in scientific notation. If not, write it in scientific notation.

36. 50×10^{-5} **37.** 8.1×10^{-2} **38.** $1,200,000$ **39.** 0.25×10^{3}

40. 0.1 **41.** 7×10^{8} **42.** $48,000$ **43.** 3.5×10^{-6}

44. **Chemistry** Atoms are made of three elementary particles: protons, electrons, and neutrons. The mass of a proton is about 1.67×10^{-27} kg. The mass of an electron is about $0.00000000000000000000000000000911$ kg. The mass of a neutron is about 1.68×10^{-27} kg. Which particle has the least mass?

45. **Communication** This bar graph shows the increase of cellular telephone subscribers worldwide.

    a. Write the number of subscribers for the following years in standard form: 1999, 2000, and 2003.

    b. Zorah looks at the bar graph and says, "It looks like the number of cell phone subscribers nearly doubled from 2000 to 2003." Do you agree with Zorah? Use scientific notation to explain.

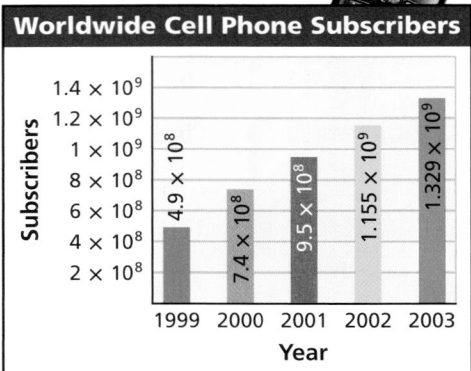

Worldwide Cell Phone Subscribers

46. **Measurement** In the metric system, the basic unit for measuring length is the meter (m). Other units for measuring length are based on the meter and powers of 10, as shown in the table.

Selected Metric Lengths	
1 millimeter (mm) = 10^{-3} m	1 dekameter (dam) = 10^{1} m
1 centimeter (cm) = 10^{-2} m	1 hectometer (hm) = 10^{2} m
1 decimeter (dm) = 10^{-1} m	1 kilometer (km) = 10^{3} m

    a. Which lengths in the table are longer than a meter? Which are shorter than a meter? How do you know?

    b. Evaluate each power of 10 in the table to check your answers to part **a.**

47. **Critical Thinking** Recall that $\frac{1}{10^{3}} = 10^{-3}$. Based on this information, complete the following statement: Dividing a number by 10^{3} is equivalent to multiplying by ▨.

 48. **Write About It** When you change a number from scientific notation to standard form, explain how you know which way to move the decimal point and how many places to move it.

CONCEPT CONNECTION

49. This problem will prepare you for the Concept Connection on page 428.

    a. The speed of light is approximately 3×10^{8} m/s. Write this number in standard form.

    b. Why do you think it would be better to express this number in scientific notation rather than standard form?

    c. The wavelength of a shade of red light is 0.00000068 meters. Write this number in scientific notation.

Multiple Choice For Exercises 50–52, choose the best answer.

50. There are about 3.2×10^7 seconds in one year. What is this number in standard form?

    Ⓐ 0.000000032

    Ⓑ 0.00000032

    Ⓒ 32,000,000

    Ⓓ 320,000,000

51. Which expression is the scientific notation for 82.35?

    Ⓐ 8.235×10^1 Ⓑ 823.5×10^{-1} Ⓒ 8.235×10^{-1} Ⓓ 0.8235×10^2

52. Which statement is correct for the list of numbers below?
2.35×10^{-8}, 0.000000029, 1.82×10^8, 1,290,000,000, 1.05×10^9

    Ⓐ The list is in increasing order.

    Ⓑ If 0.000000029 is removed, the list will be in increasing order.

    Ⓒ If 1,290,000,000 is removed, the list will be in increasing order.

    Ⓓ The list is in decreasing order.

CHALLENGE AND EXTEND

53. **Technology** The table shows estimates of computer storage. A CD-ROM holds 700 MB. A DVD-ROM holds 4.7 GB. Estimate how many times more storage a DVD has than a CD. Explain how you found your answer.

Computer Storage
1 kilobyte (KB) $\approx$ 1000 bytes
1 megabyte (MB) $\approx$ 1 million bytes
1 gigabyte (GB) $\approx$ 1 billion bytes

54. For parts **a–d,** use what you know about multiplying by powers of 10 and the Commutative and Associative Properties of Multiplication to find each product. Write each answer in scientific notation.

    a. $(3 \times 10^2)(2 \times 10^3)$ **b.** $(5 \times 10^8)(1.5 \times 10^{-6})$

    c. $(2.2 \times 10^{-8})(4 \times 10^{-3})$ **d.** $(2.5 \times 10^{-12})(2 \times 10^6)$

    e. Reasoning Based on your answers to parts **a–d,** write a rule for multiplying numbers in scientific notation.

    f. Does your rule work when you multiply $(6 \times 10^3)(8 \times 10^5)$? Explain.

SPIRAL STANDARDS REVIEW    2.0, ⟜ 4.0, ⟜ 9.0

Solve each inequality and graph the solutions. *(Lesson 3-4)*

55. $3(m - 2) \geq 39 + 2m$ 56. $4(p + 12) \leq 80 + 3p$ 57. $n(2 \cdot 7) > 7(100)$

Solve each system by elimination. Check your answer. *(Lesson 6-3)*

58. $\begin{cases} x + y = 8 \\ x - y = 2 \end{cases}$ 59. $\begin{cases} 2x + y = -3 \\ 2x + 3y = -1 \end{cases}$ 60. $\begin{cases} x - 6y = -3 \\ 3x + 4y = 13 \end{cases}$

61. $\begin{cases} 3x + y = -10 \\ 2x - y = -10 \end{cases}$ 62. $\begin{cases} 4x - 3y = 17 \\ -4x + y = -11 \end{cases}$ 63. $\begin{cases} x + 5y = 12 \\ 3x + 2y = 23 \end{cases}$

Evaluate each expression for the given value(s) of the variable(s). *(Lesson 7-1)*

64. t^{-4} for $t = 2$ 65. $(-8m)^0$ for $m = -5$ 66. $3a^{-3}b^0$ for $a = 5$ and $b = 6$

LOGICAL REASONING

Inductive Reasoning and Properties of Exponents

Use with Lesson 7-3   You can use inductive reasoning to find some properties of exponents.

California Standards

24.1 Students explain the difference between inductive and deductive reasoning and identify and **provide examples** of each. *Also covered:* **2.0**

Activity 1

1 Copy and complete the table below.

$3^2 \cdot 3^3 = (3 \cdot 3)(3 \cdot 3 \cdot 3) = 3^{\blacksquare}$

$5^4 \cdot 5^2 = (\blacksquare \cdot \blacksquare \cdot \blacksquare \cdot \blacksquare)(\blacksquare \cdot \blacksquare) = 5^{\blacksquare}$

$4^3 \cdot 4^3 = (\blacksquare \cdot \blacksquare \cdot \blacksquare)(\blacksquare \cdot \blacksquare \cdot \blacksquare) = \blacksquare^{\blacksquare}$

$2^3 \cdot 2^2 = (\blacksquare \cdot \blacksquare \cdot \blacksquare)(\blacksquare \cdot \blacksquare) = \blacksquare^{\blacksquare}$

$6^3 \cdot 6^4 = (\quad)(\quad) =$

2 Examine your completed table. Look at the two exponents in each factor and the exponent in the final answer. What pattern do you notice?

3 Use inductive reasoning to make a conjecture: $a^m \cdot a^n = a^{\blacksquare}$.

Try This

Use your conjecture to write each product below as a single power.

1. $5^3 \cdot 5^5$ **2.** $7^2 \cdot 7^2$ **3.** $10^8 \cdot 10^4$ **4.** $8^7 \cdot 8^3$

5. Make a table similar to the one above to explore what happens when you multiply more than two powers that have the same base. Then write a conjecture in words to summarize what you find.

Activity 2

1 Copy and complete the table below.

$(2^3)^2 = 2^3 \cdot 2^3 = (\blacksquare \cdot \blacksquare \cdot \blacksquare)(\blacksquare \cdot \blacksquare \cdot \blacksquare) = 2^{\blacksquare}$

$(2^2)^3 = \blacksquare \cdot \blacksquare \cdot \blacksquare = (\blacksquare \cdot \blacksquare)(\blacksquare \cdot \blacksquare)(\blacksquare \cdot \blacksquare) = \blacksquare^{\blacksquare}$

$(4^2)^4 = \blacksquare \cdot \blacksquare \cdot \blacksquare \cdot \blacksquare = (\blacksquare \cdot \blacksquare)(\blacksquare \cdot \blacksquare)(\blacksquare \cdot \blacksquare)(\blacksquare \cdot \blacksquare) = \blacksquare^{\blacksquare}$

$(3^4)^2 = \blacksquare \cdot \blacksquare = (\blacksquare \cdot \blacksquare \cdot \blacksquare \cdot \blacksquare)(\blacksquare \cdot \blacksquare \cdot \blacksquare \cdot \blacksquare) = \blacksquare^{\blacksquare}$

$(6^3)^4 =$

2 Examine your completed table. Look at the two exponents in the original expression and the exponent in the final answer. What pattern do you notice?

3 Use inductive reasoning to make a conjecture: $(a^m)^n = a^{\blacksquare}$.

Use your conjecture to write each product below as a single power.

6. $\left(5^3\right)^2$　　　　**7.** $\left(7^2\right)^2$　　　　**8.** $\left(3^3\right)^4$　　　　**9.** $\left(9^7\right)^3$

10. Make a table similar to the one in Activity 2 to explore what happens when you raise a power to two powers, for example, $\left[\left(4^2\right)^3\right]^3$. Then write a conjecture in words to summarize what you find.

Activity 3

1 Copy and complete the table below.

$(ab)^3 = (ab)(ab)(ab) = (a \cdot a \cdot a)(b \cdot b \cdot b) = a^{\blacksquare} b^{\blacksquare}$

$(mn)^4 = (\boxed{})(\boxed{})(\boxed{})(\boxed{}) = (\blacksquare \cdot \blacksquare \cdot \blacksquare \cdot \blacksquare)(\blacksquare \cdot \blacksquare \cdot \blacksquare \cdot \blacksquare) = \blacksquare^{\blacksquare} \blacksquare^{\blacksquare}$

$(xy)^2 = (\boxed{})(\boxed{}) = (\blacksquare \cdot \blacksquare)(\blacksquare \cdot \blacksquare) = \blacksquare^{\blacksquare} \blacksquare^{\blacksquare}$

$(cd)^5 = (\boxed{})(\boxed{})(\boxed{})(\boxed{})(\boxed{}) = (\blacksquare \cdot \blacksquare \cdot \blacksquare \cdot \blacksquare \cdot \blacksquare)(\blacksquare \cdot \blacksquare \cdot \blacksquare \cdot \blacksquare \cdot \blacksquare) = \blacksquare^{\blacksquare} \blacksquare^{\blacksquare}$

$(pq)^6 =$

2 Examine your completed table. Look at the original expression and the final answer. What pattern do you notice?

3 Use inductive reasoning to make a conjecture: $(ab)^n = a^{\blacksquare} b^{\blacksquare}$.

Try This

Use your conjecture to write each power below as a product.

11. $(rs)^8$　　　　**12.** $(yz)^9$　　　　**13.** $(ab)^7$　　　　**14.** $(xz)^{12}$

15. Look at the first row of your table. What property or properties allow you to write $(ab)(ab)(ab)$ as $(a \cdot a \cdot a)(b \cdot b \cdot b)$?

16. Make a table similar to the one above to explore what happens when you raise a product containing more than two factors to a power, for example, $(xyz)^7$. Then write a conjecture in words to summarize what you find.

7-3 Multiplication Properties of Exponents

Who uses this?

Astronomers can multiply expressions with exponents to find the distance between objects in space. (See Example 2.)

You have seen that exponential expressions are useful when writing very small or very large numbers. To perform operations on these numbers, you can use properties of exponents. You can also use these properties to simplify your answer.

In this lesson, you will learn some properties that will help you simplify exponential expressions containing multiplication.

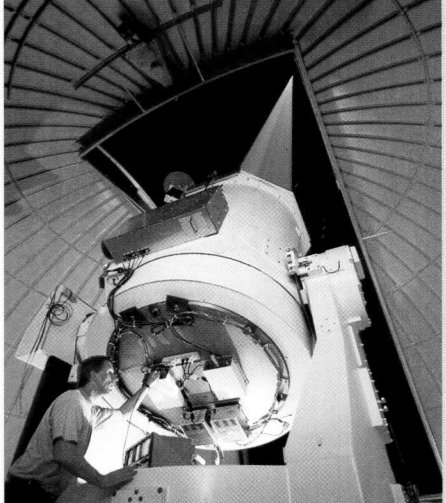

Know it! Note

Simplifying Exponential Expressions

An exponential expression is completely simplified if...
- There are no negative exponents.
- The same base does not appear more than once in a product or quotient.
- No powers are raised to powers.
- No products are raised to powers.
- No quotients are raised to powers.
- Numerical coefficients in a quotient do not have any common factor other than 1.

Examples	Nonexamples
$\frac{b}{a}$ x^3 z^{12} a^4b^4 $\frac{s^5}{t^5}$ $\frac{5a^2}{2b}$	$a^{-2}ba$ $x \cdot x^2$ $(z^3)^4$ $(ab)^4$ $\left(\frac{s}{t}\right)^5$ $\frac{10a^2}{4b}$

Products of powers with the same base can be found by writing each power as repeated multiplication.

$$a^m \cdot a^n = \underbrace{(a \cdot a \cdot \ldots \cdot a)}_{m \text{ factors}} \cdot \underbrace{(a \cdot a \cdot \ldots \cdot a)}_{n \text{ factors}}$$

$$= \underbrace{a \cdot a \cdot \ldots \cdot a}_{m + n \text{ factors}} = a^{m+n}$$

Know it! Note

Product of Powers Property

WORDS	NUMBERS	ALGEBRA
The product of two powers with the same base equals that base raised to the sum of the exponents.	$6^7 \cdot 6^4 = 6^{7+4} = 6^{11}$	If a is any nonzero real number and m and n are integers, then $a^m \cdot a^n = a^{m+n}$.

EXAMPLE 1 **Finding Products of Powers**

Simplify.

A $2^5 \cdot 2^6$

$2^5 \cdot 2^6$

2^{5+6}

2^{11} *Since the powers have the same base, keep the base and add the exponents.*

B $4^2 \cdot 3^{-2} \cdot 4^5 \cdot 3^6$

$4^2 \cdot 3^{-2} \cdot 4^5 \cdot 3^6$ *Group powers with the same base together.*

$(4^2 \cdot 4^5) \cdot (3^{-2} \cdot 3^6)$

$4^{2+5} \cdot 3^{-2+6}$ *Add the exponents of powers with the same base.*

$4^7 \cdot 3^4$

C $a^4 \cdot b^5 \cdot a^2$

$a^4 \cdot b^5 \cdot a^2$

$(a^4 \cdot a^2) \cdot b^5$ *Group powers with the same base together.*

$a^6 \cdot b^5$ *Add the exponents of powers with the same base.*

$a^6 b^5$

D $y^2 \cdot y \cdot y^{-4}$

$(y^2 \cdot y^1) \cdot y^{-4}$ *Group the first two powers.*

$y^3 \cdot y^{-4}$ *The first two powers have the same base, so add the exponents.*

y^{-1} *The two remaining powers have the same base, so add the exponents.*

$\dfrac{1}{y}$ *Write with a positive exponent.*

> **Remember!**
>
> A number or variable written without an exponent actually has an exponent of 1.
> $$10 = 10^1$$
> $$y = y^1$$

 **Simplify.**

1a. $7^8 \cdot 7^4$ **1b.** $3^{-3} \cdot 5^8 \cdot 3^4 \cdot 5^2$

1c. $m \cdot n^{-4} \cdot m^4$ **1d.** $x \cdot x^{-1} \cdot x^{-3} \cdot x^{-4}$

EXAMPLE 2 *Astronomy Application*

Light from the Sun travels at about 1.86×10^5 miles per second. It takes about 500 seconds for the light to reach Earth. Find the approximate distance from the Sun to Earth. Write your answer in scientific notation.

distance = rate × time

$= (1.86 \times 10^5) \times 500$

$= (1.86 \times 10^5) \times (5 \times 10^2)$ *Write 500 in scientific notation.*

$= (1.86 \times 5) \times (10^5 \times 10^2)$ *Use the Commutative and Associative Properties to group.*

$= 9.3 \times 10^7$ *Multiply within each group.*

The Sun is about 9.3×10^7 miles from Earth.

 **2.** Light travels at about 1.86×10^5 miles per second. Find the approximate distance that light travels in one hour. Write your answer in scientific notation.

To find a power of a power, you can use the meaning of exponents.

$$\left(a^m\right)^n = \underbrace{a^m \cdot a^m \cdot \ldots \cdot a^m}_{n \text{ factors}} = \underbrace{a \cdot a \cdot \ldots \cdot a}_{m \text{ factors}} \cdot \underbrace{a \cdot a \cdot \ldots \cdot a}_{m \text{ factors}} \cdot \ldots \cdot \underbrace{a \cdot a \cdot \ldots \cdot a}_{m \text{ factors}} = a^{mn}$$

n groups of m factors

Power of a Power Property

WORDS	NUMBERS	ALGEBRA
A power raised to another power equals that base raised to the product of the exponents.	$\left(6^7\right)^4 = 6^{7 \cdot 4} = 6^{28}$	If a is any nonzero real number and m and n are integers, then $\left(a^m\right)^n = a^{mn}$.

EXAMPLE 3   **Finding Powers of Powers**

Simplify.

A $\left(7^4\right)^3$

$7^{4 \cdot 3}$ *Use the Power of a Power Property.*

7^{12} *Simplify.*

B $\left(3^6\right)^0$

$3^{6 \cdot 0}$ *Use the Power of a Power Property.*

3^0 *Zero multiplied by any number is zero.*

1 *Any number raised to the zero power is 1.*

C $\left(x^2\right)^{-4} \cdot x^5$

$x^{2 \cdot (-4)} \, x^5$ *Use the Power of a Power Property.*

$x^{-8} \cdot x^5$ *Simplify the exponent of the first term.*

x^{-8+5} *Since the powers have the same base, add the exponents.*

x^{-3}

$\dfrac{1}{x^3}$ *Write with a positive exponent.*

 **Simplify.**

3a. $\left(3^4\right)^5$ **3b.** $\left(6^0\right)^3$ **3c.** $\left(a^3\right)^4 \cdot \left(a^{-2}\right)^{-3}$

Student to Student   *Multiplication Properties of Exponents*

Briana Tyler
Memorial High School

Sometimes I can't remember when to add exponents and when to multiply them. When this happens, I write everything in expanded form.

For example, I would write $x^2 \cdot x^3$ as $(x \cdot x)(x \cdot x \cdot x) = x^5$. Then $x^2 \cdot x^3 = x^{2+3} = x^5$.

I would write $\left(x^2\right)^3$ as $x^2 \cdot x^2 \cdot x^2$, which is $(x \cdot x)(x \cdot x)(x \cdot x) = x^6$.

Then $\left(x^2\right)^3 = x^{2 \cdot 3} = x^6$.

This way I get the right answer even if I forget the properties.

Powers of products can be found by using the meaning of an exponent.

$$(ab)^n = \underbrace{ab \cdot ab \cdot \ldots \cdot ab}_{n \text{ factors}} = \underbrace{a \cdot a \cdot \ldots \cdot a}_{n \text{ factors}} \cdot \underbrace{b \cdot b \cdot \ldots \cdot b}_{n \text{ factors}} = a^n b^n$$

Power of a Product Property

WORDS	NUMBERS	ALGEBRA
A product raised to a power equals the product of each factor raised to that power.	$(2 \cdot 4)^3 = 2^3 \cdot 4^3$	If a and b are any nonzero real numbers and n is any integer, then $(ab)^n = a^n b^n$.

EXAMPLE 4 **Finding Powers of Products**

Simplify.

A $(-3x)^2$

$(-3)^2 \cdot x^2$ *Use the Power of a Product Property.*

$9x^2$ *Simplify.*

Caution!

In Example 4B, the negative sign is not part of the base.

$-(3x)^2 = -1 \cdot (3x)^2$

B $-(3x)^2$

$-(3^2 \cdot x^2)$ *Use the Power of a Product Property.*

$-(9 \cdot x^2)$ *Simplify.*

$-9x^2$

C $(x^{-2} \cdot y^0)^3$

$(x^{-2})^3 \cdot (y^0)^3$ *Use the Power of a Product Property.*

$x^{-2 \cdot 3} \cdot y^{0 \cdot 3}$ *Use the Power of a Power Property.*

$x^{-6} \cdot y^0$ *Simplify.*

$x^{-6} \cdot 1$ *Write y^0 as 1.*

$\dfrac{1}{x^6}$ *Write with a positive exponent.*

CHECK IT OUT! **Simplify.**

4a. $(4p)^3$ **4b.** $(-5t^2)^2$ **4c.** $(x^2 y^3)^4 \cdot (x^2 y^4)^{-4}$

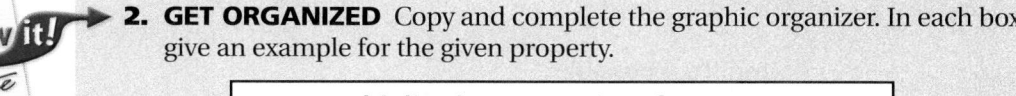

THINK AND DISCUSS

1. Explain why $(a^2)^3$ and $a^2 \cdot a^3$ are not equivalent expressions.

2. GET ORGANIZED Copy and complete the graphic organizer. In each box, give an example for the given property.

Multiplication Properties of Exponents		
Product of Powers Property	Power of a Power Property	Power of a Product Property

7-3 **Exercises**

California Standards Practice
🔑 2.0, 25.2

go.hrw.com
Homework Help Online
KEYWORD: MA8CA 7-3
Parent Resources Online
KEYWORD: MA8CA Parent

GUIDED PRACTICE

SEE EXAMPLE **1**
p. 409

Simplify.

1. $2^2 \cdot 2^3$ **2.** $5^3 \cdot 5^3$ **3.** $n^6 \cdot n^2$ **4.** $x^2 \cdot x^{-3} \cdot x^4$

SEE EXAMPLE **2**
p. 409

5. Physical Science If you traveled in space at a speed of 1000 miles per hour, how far would you travel in 7.5×10^5 hours? Write your answer in scientific notation.

SEE EXAMPLE **3**
p. 410

Simplify.

6. $\left(x^2\right)^5$ **7.** $\left(y^4\right)^8$ **8.** $\left(p^3\right)^3$

9. $\left(3^{-2}\right)^2$ **10.** $\left(a^{-3}\right)^4 \cdot \left(a^7\right)^2$ **11.** $xy \cdot \left(x^2\right)^3 \cdot \left(y^3\right)^4$

SEE EXAMPLE **4**
p. 411

12. $(2t)^5$ **13.** $(6k)^2$ **14.** $\left(r^2s\right)^7$

15. $\left(-2x^5\right)^3$ **16.** $-\left(2x^5\right)^3$ **17.** $\left(a^2b^2\right)^5 \cdot \left(a^{-5}\right)^2$

PRACTICE AND PROBLEM SOLVING

Independent Practice

For Exercises	See Example
18–21	1
22	2
23–28	3
29–34	4

Extra Practice

Skills Practice p. EP14

Application Practice p. EP30

Simplify.

18. $3^3 \cdot 2^3 \cdot 3$ **19.** $6 \cdot 6^2 \cdot 6^3 \cdot 6^2$ **20.** $a^5 \cdot a^0 \cdot a^{-5}$ **21.** $x^7 \cdot x^{-6} \cdot y^{-3}$

22. Geography Rhode Island is the smallest state in the United States. Its land area is about 2.9×10^{10} square feet. Alaska, the largest state, is about 5.5×10^2 times as large as Rhode Island. What is the land area of Alaska in square feet? Write your answer in scientific notation.

Simplify.

23. $\left(2^3\right)^3$ **24.** $\left(3^6\right)^0$ **25.** $\left(x^2\right)^{-1}$

26. $\left(b^4\right)^6 \cdot b$ **27.** $b \cdot \left(a^3\right)^4 \cdot \left(b^{-2}\right)^3$ **28.** $\left(x^4\right)^2 \cdot \left(x^{-1}\right)^{-4}$

29. $(3x)^3$ **30.** $\left(5w^8\right)^2$ **31.** $\left(p^4q^2\right)^7$

32. $\left(-4x^3\right)^4$ **33.** $-\left(4x^3\right)^4$ **34.** $\left(x^3y^4\right)^3 \cdot \left(xy^3\right)^{-2}$

Find the missing exponent in each expression.

35. $a^\blacksquare a^4 = a^{10}$ **36.** $\left(a^\blacksquare\right)^4 = a^{12}$ **37.** $\left(a^2b^\blacksquare\right)^4 = a^8b^{12}$

38. $\left(a^3b^6\right)^\blacksquare = \dfrac{1}{a^9b^{18}}$ **39.** $\left(b^2\right)^{-4} = \dfrac{1}{b^\blacksquare}$ **40.** $a^\blacksquare \cdot a^6 = a^6$

Geometry Write an expression for the area of each figure.

41.

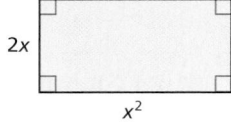

42.

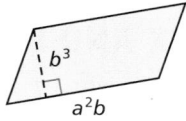

43.

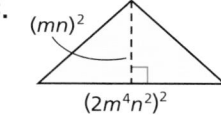

Simplify, if possible.

44. x^6y^5 **45.** $\left(2x^2\right)^2 \cdot \left(3x^3\right)^3$ **46.** $x^2 \cdot y^{-3} \cdot x^{-2} \cdot y^{-3}$

47. $\left(5x^2\right)\left(5x^2\right)^2$ **48.** $-\left(x^2\right)^4\left(-x^2\right)^4$ **49.** $a^3 \cdot a^0 \cdot 3a^3$

50. $(ab)^3(ab)^{-2}$ **51.** $10^2 \cdot 10^{-4} \cdot 10^5$ **52.** $\left(x^2y^2\right)^2\left(x^2y\right)^{-2}$

53. Astronomy The graph shows the approximate time it takes light from the Sun, which travels at a speed of 1.86×10^5 miles per second, to reach several planets. Find the approximate distance from the Sun to each planet in the graph. Write your answers in scientific notation. (*Hint:* Remember $d = rt$.)

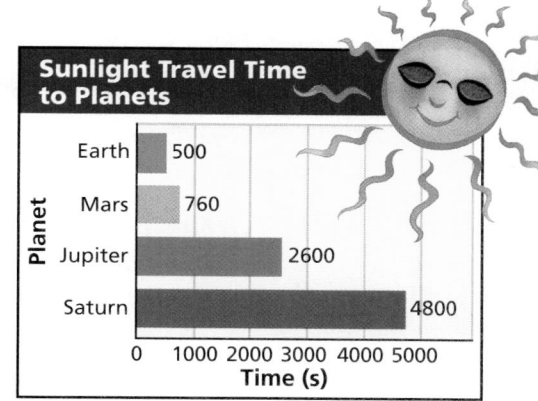

Sunlight Travel Time to Planets

Planet	Time (s)
Earth	500
Mars	760
Jupiter	2600
Saturn	4800

0 1000 2000 3000 4000 5000
Time (s)

 54. Geometry The volume of a rectangular prism can be found by using the formula $V = \ell wh$ where ℓ, w, and h represent the length, width, and height of the prism. Find the volume of a rectangular prism whose dimensions are $3a^2$, $4a^5$, and $4a^2b^2$.

55. ///ERROR ANALYSIS/// Explain the error in each simplification below. What is the correct answer in each case?

a. $x^2 \cdot x^4 = x^8$

b. $\left(x^4\right)^5 = x^9$

c. $\left(x^2\right)^3 = x^{2^3} = x^8$

Simplify.

56. $\left(-3x^2\right)\left(5x^{-3}\right)$

57. $\left(a^4b\right)\left(a^3b^{-6}\right)$

58. $\left(6w^5\right)\left(2v^2\right)\left(w^6\right)$

59. $\left(3m^7\right)\left(m^2n\right)\left(5m^3n^8\right)$

60. $\left(b^2\right)^{-2}\left(b^4\right)^5$

61. $\left(3st\right)^2t^5$

62. $\left(2^2\right)^2\left(x^5y\right)^3$

63. $(-t)(-t)^2\left(-t^4\right)$

64. $\left(2m^2\right)\left(4m^4\right)(8n)^2$

65. Estimation Estimate the value of each expression. Explain how you estimated.

a. $\left[(-3.031)^2\right]^3$

b. $\left(6.2085 \times 10^2\right) \times \left(3.819 \times 10^{-5}\right)$

66. Physical Science The speed of sound at sea level is about 344 meters per second. The speed of light is about 8.7×10^5 times faster than the speed of sound. What is the speed of light in meters per second? Write your answer in scientific notation and in standard form.

67. Write About It Is $\left(x^2\right)^3$ equal to $\left(x^3\right)^2$? Explain.

68. Biology A newborn baby has about 26,000,000,000 cells. An adult has about 1.9×10^3 times as many cells as a baby. About how many cells does an adult have? Write your answer in scientific notation.

Simplify.

69. $(-4k)^2 + k^2$

70. $-3z^3 + (-3z)^3$

71. $\left(2x^2\right)^2 + 2\left(x^2\right)^2$

72. $(2r)^2s^2 + 6(rs)^2 + 1$

73. $(3a)^2b^3 + 3(ab)^2(2b)$

74. $\left(x^2\right)\left(x^2\right)\left(x^2\right) + 3x^2$

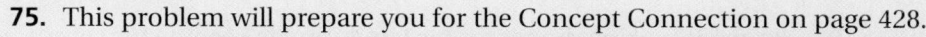

CONCEPT CONNECTION

75. This problem will prepare you for the Concept Connection on page 428.

a. The speed of light v is the product of the frequency f and the wavelength w: ($v = fw$). Wavelengths are often measured in *nanometers*. *Nano* means 10^{-9}, so 1 nanometer = 10^{-9} meters. What is 600 nanometers in meters? Write your answer in scientific notation.

b. Use your answer from part **a** to find the speed of light in meters per second if $f = 5 \times 10^{14}$ Hz.

c. Explain why you can rewrite $\left(6 \times 10^{-7}\right)\left(5 \times 10^{14}\right)$ as $(6 \times 5)\left(10^{-7}\right)\left(10^{14}\right)$.

Critical Thinking Rewrite each expression so that it has only one exponent. (*Hint:* You may use parentheses.)

76. $c^3 d^3$

77. $36a^2 b^2$

78. $\dfrac{8a^3}{b^3}$

79. $\dfrac{k^{-2}}{4m^2 n^2}$

Multiple Choice For Exercises 80–83, choose the best answer.

80. Which of the following is equivalent to $x^2 \cdot x^0$?

Ⓐ 0　　　　Ⓑ 1　　　　Ⓒ x^2　　　　Ⓓ x^{20}

81. Which of the following is equivalent to $(3 \times 10^5)(4 \times 10^2)$?

Ⓐ 7×10^7　　Ⓑ 7×10^{10}　　Ⓒ 1.2×10^8　　Ⓓ 1.2×10^{11}

82. What is the value of n^3 when $n = 4 \times 10^5$?

Ⓐ 1.2×10^9　　Ⓑ 1.2×10^{16}　　Ⓒ 6.4×10^9　　Ⓓ 6.4×10^{16}

83. Which represents the area of the triangle?

Ⓐ $6x^2$　　　　Ⓒ $7x^2$

Ⓑ $12x^2$　　　Ⓓ $24x^2$

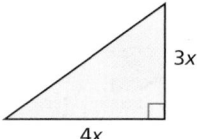

3x

4x

CHALLENGE AND EXTEND

Simplify.

84. $3^2 \cdot 3^x$

85. $(3^2)^x$

86. $(x^y z)^2$

87. $(x+1)^{-2}(x+1)^3$

88. $(x+1)^2(x+1)^{-3}$

89. $(x^y \cdot x^z)^3$

90. $(4^x)^x$

91. $(x^x)^x$

92. $(3x)^{2y}$

Find the value of x.

93. $5^x \cdot 5^4 = 5^8$

94. $7^3 \cdot 7^x = 7^{12}$

95. $(4^x)^3 = 4^{12}$

96. $(6^2)^x = 6^{16}$

97. Multi-Step The edge of a cube measures 1.2×10^{-2} m. What is the volume of the cube in cubic centimeters?

 SPIRAL STANDARDS REVIEW  🔑 2.0, 3.0, 🔑 4.0

Write an equation to represent each relationship. Then solve. *(Lesson 2-3)*

98. Three times the sum of a number and nine plus one equals 24.

99. Eight increased by 6 times a number equals 71 plus three.

100. Keenan sets up the sound for his band. He uses a tool to keep the sound level of his amplifiers within 15 decibels of 95 decibels. Write and solve an absolute-value equation to find the maximum and minimum decibel levels. *(Lesson 2-7)*

101. Jimmy is making dinner for his family and is keeping his soup at a warm temperature. He has the stove set to keep the soup at 120°F. Jimmy needs to make sure the temperature stays within 12°F of its current temperature. Write and solve an absolute-value equation to find the maximum and minimum temperatures. *(Lesson 2-7)*

Write each number in standard form. *(Lesson 7-2)*

102. 7.8×10^6

103. 4.95×10^{-4}

104. 983×10^{-1}

105. 0.06×10^8

7-4

Division Properties of Exponents

California Standards

2.0 Students understand and use such operations as taking the opposite, finding the reciprocal, taking a root, and raising to a fractional power. **They understand and use the rules of exponents.**

Who uses this?

Economists can use expressions with exponents to calculate national debt statistics. (See Example 3.)

A quotient of powers with the same base can be found by writing the powers in factored form and dividing out common factors.

$$\frac{a^m}{a^n} = \frac{\overbrace{a \cdot a \cdot \ldots \cdot a}^{m \text{ factors}}}{\underbrace{a \cdot a \cdot \ldots \cdot a}_{n \text{ factors}}} = a^{m-n}$$

Quotient of Powers Property

WORDS	NUMBERS	ALGEBRA
The quotient of two nonzero powers with the same base equals the base raised to the difference of the exponents.	$\dfrac{6^7}{6^4} = 6^{7-4} = 6^3$	If a is a nonzero real number and m and n are integers, then $\dfrac{a^m}{a^n} = a^{m-n}$.

EXAMPLE 1 **Finding Quotients of Powers**

Simplify.

A $\dfrac{3^8}{3^2}$

$\dfrac{3^8}{3^2} = 3^{8-2}$

$= 3^6$

$= 729$

B $\dfrac{x^5}{x^5}$

$\dfrac{x^5}{x^5} = x^{5-5}$

$= x^0$

$= 1$

Helpful Hint

$3^6 = 729$
Both 3^6 and 729 are considered to be simplified.

C $\dfrac{a^5 b^9}{(ab)^4}$

$\dfrac{a^5 b^9}{(ab)^4} = \dfrac{a^5 b^9}{a^4 b^4}$

$= a^{5-4} \cdot b^{9-4}$

$= a^1 \cdot b^5$

$= ab^5$

D $\dfrac{2^3 \cdot 3^2 \cdot 5^7}{2 \cdot 3^4 \cdot 5^5}$

$\dfrac{2^3 \cdot 3^2 \cdot 5^7}{2 \cdot 3^4 \cdot 5^5} = 2^{3-1} \cdot 3^{2-4} \cdot 5^{7-5}$

$= 2^2 \cdot 3^{-2} \cdot 5^2$

$= \dfrac{2^2 \cdot 5^2}{3^2}$

$= \dfrac{4 \cdot 25}{9}$

$= \dfrac{100}{9}$

 **Simplify.**

1a. $\dfrac{2^9}{2^7}$ **1b.** $\dfrac{y}{y^4}$ **1c.** $\dfrac{m^5 n^4}{(m^5)^2 n}$ **1d.** $\dfrac{3^5 \cdot 2^4 \cdot 4^3}{3^4 \cdot 2^2 \cdot 4^6}$

EXAMPLE **2** **Dividing Numbers in Scientific Notation**

Simplify $(2 \times 10^8) \div (8 \times 10^5)$ and write the answer in scientific notation.

$$(2 \times 10^8) \div (8 \times 10^5) = \frac{2 \times 10^8}{8 \times 10^5}$$

$$= \frac{2}{8} \times \frac{10^8}{10^5} \qquad \textit{Write as a product of quotients.}$$

$$= 0.25 \times 10^{8-5} \qquad \textit{Simplify each quotient.}$$

$$= 0.25 \times 10^3 \qquad \textit{Simplify the exponent.}$$

$$= 2.5 \times 10^{-1} \times 10^3 \qquad \textit{Write 0.25 in scientific notation as } 2.5 \times 10^{-1}.$$

$$= 2.5 \times 10^{-1+3} \qquad \textit{The second two terms have the same base, so add the exponents.}$$

$$= 2.5 \times 10^2 \qquad \textit{Simplify the exponent.}$$

 **2.** Simplify $(3.3 \times 10^6) \div (3 \times 10^8)$ and write the answer in scientific notation.

> **Writing Math**
>
> You can "split up" a quotient of products into a product of quotients:
>
> $$\frac{a \times c}{b \times d} = \frac{a}{b} \times \frac{c}{d}$$
>
> Example:
>
> $$\frac{3 \times 4}{5 \times 7} = \frac{3}{5} \times \frac{4}{7} = \frac{12}{35}$$

EXAMPLE **3** *Economics Application*

In the year 2000, the United States public debt was about 5.6×10^{12} dollars. The population of the United States in that year was about 2.8×10^8 people. What was the average debt per person? Give your answer in standard form.

To find the average debt per person, divide the total debt by the number of people.

$$\frac{\text{total debt}}{\text{number of people}} = \frac{5.6 \times 10^{12}}{2.8 \times 10^8}$$

$$= \frac{5.6}{2.8} \times \frac{10^{12}}{10^8} \qquad \textit{Write as a product of quotients.}$$

$$= 2 \times 10^{12-8} \qquad \textit{Simplify each quotient.}$$

$$= 2 \times 10^4 \qquad \textit{Simplify the exponent.}$$

$$= 20,000 \qquad \textit{Write in standard form.}$$

The average debt per person was about \$20,000.

 **3.** In 1990, the United States public debt was about 3.2×10^{12} dollars. The population of the United States in 1990 was about 2.5×10^8 people. What was the average debt per person? Write your answer in standard form.

A power of a quotient can be found by first writing factors and then writing the numerator and denominator as powers.

$$\left(\frac{a}{b}\right)^n = \underbrace{\frac{a}{b} \cdot \frac{a}{b} \cdot \ldots \cdot \frac{a}{b}}_{n \text{ factors}}$$

$$= \frac{\overbrace{a \cdot a \cdot \ldots \cdot a}^{n \text{ factors}}}{\underbrace{b \cdot b \cdot \ldots \cdot b}_{n \text{ factors}}} = \frac{a^n}{b^n}$$

Positive Power of a Quotient Property

WORDS	NUMBERS	ALGEBRA
A quotient raised to a positive power equals the quotient of each base raised to that power.	$\left(\dfrac{3}{5}\right)^4 = \dfrac{3}{5}\cdot\dfrac{3}{5}\cdot\dfrac{3}{5}\cdot\dfrac{3}{5} = \dfrac{3\cdot3\cdot3\cdot3}{5\cdot5\cdot5\cdot5} = \dfrac{3^4}{5^4}$	If a and b are nonzero real numbers and n is a positive integer, then $\left(\dfrac{a}{b}\right)^n = \dfrac{a^n}{b^n}$.

EXAMPLE 4 **Finding Positive Powers of Quotients**

Simplify.

A $\left(\dfrac{3}{4}\right)^3$

$\left(\dfrac{3}{4}\right)^3 = \dfrac{3^3}{4^3}$ *Use the Power of a Quotient Property.*

$= \dfrac{27}{64}$ *Simplify.*

B $\left(\dfrac{2x^3}{yz}\right)^3$

$\left(\dfrac{2x^3}{yz}\right)^3 = \dfrac{\left(2x^3\right)^3}{(yz)^3}$ *Use the Power of a Quotient Property.*

$= \dfrac{2^3\left(x^3\right)^3}{y^3z^3}$ *Use the Power of a Product Property:*
  $\left(2x^3\right)^3 = 2^3\left(x^3\right)^3$ *and* $(yz)^3 = y^3z^3$.

$= \dfrac{8x^9}{y^3z^3}$ *Simplify 2^3 and use the Power of a Power Property:* $\left(x^3\right)^3 = x^{3\cdot3} = x^9$.

CHECK IT OUT! **Simplify.**

4a. $\left(\dfrac{2^3}{3^2}\right)^2$ **4b.** $\left(\dfrac{ab^4}{c^2d^3}\right)^5$ **4c.** $\left(\dfrac{a^3b}{a^2b^2}\right)^3$

Remember that $x^{-n} = \dfrac{1}{x^n}$. What if x is a fraction?

$\left(\dfrac{a}{b}\right)^{-n} = \dfrac{1}{\left(\dfrac{a}{b}\right)^n} = 1 \div \left(\dfrac{a}{b}\right)^n$ *Write the fraction as division.*

$= 1 \div \dfrac{a^n}{b^n}$ *Use the Power of a Quotient Property.*

$= 1 \cdot \dfrac{b^n}{a^n}$ *Multiply by the reciprocal.*

$= \dfrac{b^n}{a^n}$ *Simplify.*

$= \left(\dfrac{b}{a}\right)^n$ *Use the Power of a Quotient Property.*

Therefore, $\left(\dfrac{a}{b}\right)^{-n} = \left(\dfrac{b}{a}\right)^n$.

Negative Power of a Quotient Property

WORDS	NUMBERS	ALGEBRA
A quotient raised to a negative power equals the reciprocal of the quotient raised to the opposite (positive) power.	$\left(\dfrac{2}{3}\right)^{-4} = \left(\dfrac{3}{2}\right)^{4} = \dfrac{3^4}{2^4}$	If a and b are nonzero real numbers and n is a positive integer, then $\left(\dfrac{a}{b}\right)^{-n} = \left(\dfrac{b}{a}\right)^{n} = \dfrac{b^n}{a^n}$.

EXAMPLE 5 **Finding Negative Powers of Quotients**

Simplify.

A $\left(\dfrac{2}{5}\right)^{-3}$

$$\left(\dfrac{2}{5}\right)^{-3} = \left(\dfrac{5}{2}\right)^{3}$$ *Rewrite with a positive exponent.*

$$= \dfrac{5^3}{2^3}$$ *Use the Power of a Quotient Property.*

$$= \dfrac{125}{8}$$ $5^3 = 125$ *and* $2^3 = 8$.

B $\left(\dfrac{3x}{y^2}\right)^{-3}$

$$\left(\dfrac{3x}{y^2}\right)^{-3} = \left(\dfrac{y^2}{3x}\right)^{3}$$ *Rewrite with a positive exponent.*

$$= \dfrac{\left(y^2\right)^3}{(3x)^3}$$ *Use the Power of a Quotient Property.*

    Use the Power of a Power Property:

$$= \dfrac{y^6}{3^3 x^3}$$ $\left(y^2\right)^3 = y^{2 \cdot 3} = y^6$.

    Use the Power of a Product Property:

    $(3x)^3 = 3^3 x^3$.

$$= \dfrac{y^6}{27x^3}$$ *Simplify the denominator.*

C $\left(\dfrac{3}{4}\right)^{-1}\left(\dfrac{2x}{3y}\right)^{-2}$

$$\left(\dfrac{3}{4}\right)^{-1}\left(\dfrac{2x}{3y}\right)^{-2} = \left(\dfrac{4}{3}\right)^{1}\left(\dfrac{3y}{2x}\right)^{2}$$ *Rewrite each fraction with a positive exponent.*

$$= \dfrac{4}{3} \cdot \dfrac{(3y)^2}{(2x)^2}$$ *Use the Power of a Quotient Property.*

$$= \dfrac{4}{3} \cdot \dfrac{3^2 y^2}{2^2 x^2}$$ *Use the Power of a Product Property:* $(3y)^2 = 3^2 y^2$ *and* $(2x)^2 = 2^2 x^2$.

$$= \dfrac{{}^1\cancel{4}}{{}_1\cancel{3}} \cdot \dfrac{\overset{3}{\cancel{9}}{}^{} y^2}{{}_1\cancel{4} x^2}$$ *Divide out common factors.*

$$= \dfrac{3y^2}{x^2}$$

Helpful Hint

Whenever all of the factors in the numerator or the denominator divide out, replace them with 1.

Simplify.

5a. $\left(\dfrac{4}{3^2}\right)^{-3}$ **5b.** $\left(\dfrac{2a}{b^2 c^3}\right)^{-4}$ **5c.** $\left(\dfrac{s}{3}\right)^{-2}\left(\dfrac{9s^2}{t}\right)^{-1}$

THINK AND DISCUSS

1. Compare the Quotient of Powers Property and the Product of Powers Property. Then compare the Power of a Quotient Property and the Power of a Product Property.

2. **GET ORGANIZED** Copy and complete the graphic organizer. In each cell, supply the missing information. Then give an example for each property.

If a and b are nonzero real numbers and m and n are integers, then...		
$\dfrac{a^m}{a^n} = \blacksquare$	$\left(\dfrac{a}{b}\right)^n = \dfrac{\blacksquare}{\blacksquare}$	$\left(\dfrac{a}{b}\right)^{-n} = \left(\dfrac{\blacksquare}{\blacksquare}\right)$

7-4 Exercises

California Standards Practice
🔑 2.0, 25.1

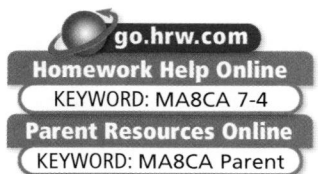

go.hrw.com
Homework Help Online
KEYWORD: MA8CA 7-4
Parent Resources Online
KEYWORD: MA8CA Parent

GUIDED PRACTICE

SEE EXAMPLE 1
p. 415

Simplify.

1. $\dfrac{5^8}{5^6}$

2. $\dfrac{2^2 \cdot 3^4 \cdot 4^4}{2^9 \cdot 3^5}$

3. $\dfrac{15x^6}{5x^6}$

4. $\dfrac{a^5 b^6}{a^3 b^7}$

SEE EXAMPLE 2
p. 416

Simplify each quotient and write the answer in scientific notation.

5. $\left(2.8 \times 10^{11}\right) \div \left(4 \times 10^8\right)$

6. $\left(5.5 \times 10^3\right) \div \left(5 \times 10^8\right)$

7. $\left(1.9 \times 10^4\right) \div \left(1.9 \times 10^4\right)$

SEE EXAMPLE 3
p. 416

8. **Sports** A star baseball player earns an annual salary of $\$8.1 \times 10^6$. There are 162 games in a baseball season. How much does this player earn per game? Write your answer in standard form.

SEE EXAMPLE 4
p. 417

Simplify.

9. $\left(\dfrac{2}{5}\right)^2$

10. $\left(\dfrac{x^2}{xy^3}\right)^3$

11. $\left(\dfrac{a^3}{(a^3 b)^2}\right)^2$

12. $\dfrac{y^{10}}{y}$

SEE EXAMPLE 5
p. 418

13. $\left(\dfrac{3}{4}\right)^{-2}$

14. $\left(\dfrac{2x}{y^3}\right)^{-4}$

15. $\left(\dfrac{2}{3}\right)^{-1} \left(\dfrac{3a}{2b}\right)^{-2}$

16. $\left(\dfrac{x^3}{y^2}\right)^{-4}$

PRACTICE AND PROBLEM SOLVING

Simplify.

17. $\dfrac{3^9}{3^6}$

18. $\dfrac{5^4 \cdot 3^3}{5^2 \cdot 3^2}$

19. $\dfrac{x^8 y^3}{x^3 y^3}$

20. $\dfrac{x^8 y^4}{x^9 yz}$

Simplify each quotient and write the answer in scientific notation.

21. $\left(4.7 \times 10^{-3}\right) \div \left(9.4 \times 10^3\right)$

22. $\left(8.4 \times 10^9\right) \div \left(4 \times 10^{-5}\right)$

23. $\left(4.2 \times 10^{-5}\right) \div \left(6 \times 10^{-3}\right)$

24. $\left(2.1 \times 10^2\right) \div \left(8.4 \times 10^5\right)$

Extra Practice

Skills Practice p. EP14

Application Practice p. EP30

25. Astronomy The mass of Earth is about 3×10^{-3} times the mass of Jupiter. The mass of Earth is about 6×10^{24} kg. What is the mass of Jupiter? Give your answer in scientific notation.

Simplify.

26. $\left(\dfrac{2}{3}\right)^4$

27. $\left(\dfrac{a^4}{b^2}\right)^3$

28. $\left(\dfrac{a^3b^2}{ab^3}\right)^6$

29. $\left(\dfrac{xy^2}{x^3y}\right)^3$

30. $\left(\dfrac{1}{7}\right)^{-3}$

31. $\left(\dfrac{x^2}{y^5}\right)^{-5}$

32. $\left(\dfrac{8w^7}{16}\right)^{-1}$

33. $\left(\dfrac{1}{4}\right)^{-2}\left(\dfrac{6x}{7}\right)^{-2}$

Simplify, if possible.

34. $\dfrac{x^6}{x^5}$

35. $\dfrac{8d^5}{4d^3}$

36. $\dfrac{x^2y^3}{a^2b^3}$

37. $\dfrac{(3x^3)^3}{(6x^2)^2}$

38. $\dfrac{(5x^2)^3}{5x^2}$

39. $\left(\dfrac{c^2a^3}{a^5}\right)^2$

40. $\left(\dfrac{3a}{a^3 \cdot a^0}\right)^3$

41. $\left(\dfrac{-p^4}{-5p^3}\right)^{-2}$

42. $\left(\dfrac{b^{-2}}{b^3}\right)^2$

43. $\left(\dfrac{10^2}{10^{-5} \cdot 10^5}\right)^{-1}$

44. $\left(\dfrac{x^2y^2}{x^2y}\right)^{-3}$

45. $\dfrac{(-x^2)^4}{-(x^2)^4}$

 46. Reasoning Use the Quotient of a Power Property to explain the definition of x^{-n}. (*Hint:* Think of $\dfrac{1}{x^n}$ as $\dfrac{x^0}{x^n}$.)

47. Geography *Population density* is the number of people per unit of area. The area of the United States is approximately 9.37×10^6 square kilometers. The table shows population data from the U. S. Census Bureau.

United States Population	
Year	**Population (to nearest million)**
2000	2.81×10^8
1995	2.66×10^8
1990	2.48×10^8

Write the approximate population density (people per square kilometer) for each of the given years in scientific notation. Round decimals to the nearest hundredth.

48. Chemistry The pH of a solution is a number that describes the concentration of hydrogen ions in that solution. For example, if the concentration of hydrogen ions in a solution is 10^{-4}, that solution has a pH of 4.

Lemon juice
pH 2

Apples
pH 3

Water
pH 7

Ammonia
pH 11

a. What is the concentration of hydrogen ions in lemon juice?

b. What is the concentration of hydrogen ions in water?

c. How many times more concentrated are the hydrogen ions in lemon juice than in water?

 49. Write About It Explain how to simplify $\dfrac{4^5}{4^2}$. How is it different from simplifying $\dfrac{4^2}{4^5}$?

Find the missing exponent(s).

50. $\dfrac{x^{\square}}{x^4} = x^2$

51. $\dfrac{x^7}{x^{\square}} = x^4$

52. $\left(\dfrac{a^2}{b^{\square}}\right)^4 = \dfrac{a^8}{b^{12}}$

53. $\left(\dfrac{x^4}{y}\right)^{-1} = \dfrac{y^3}{x^{\square}}$

54. This problem will prepare you for the Concept Connection on page 428.

    a. Yellow light has a wavelength of 589 nm. A nanometer (nm) is 10^{-9} m. What is 589 nm in meters? Write your answer in scientific notation.

    b. The speed of light in air, v, is 3×10^8 m/s, and $v = fw$, where f represents the frequency in hertz (Hz) and w represents the wavelength in meters. What is the frequency of yellow light?

Multiple Choice For Exercises 55–57, choose the best answer.

55. Which of the following is equivalent to $(8 \times 10^6) \div (4 \times 10^2)$?

    Ⓐ 2×10^3 Ⓑ 2×10^4 Ⓒ 4×10^3 Ⓓ 4×10^4

56. Which of the following is equivalent to $\left(\dfrac{x^{12}}{3xy^4}\right)^{-2}$?

    Ⓐ $\dfrac{9y^8}{x^{22}}$ Ⓑ $\dfrac{3y^8}{x^{22}}$ Ⓒ $\dfrac{3y^6}{x^{12}}$ Ⓓ $\dfrac{6y^8}{x^{26}}$

57. Which of the following is equivalent to $\dfrac{(-3x)^4}{-(3x)^4}$?

    Ⓐ -1 Ⓑ 1 Ⓒ $-81x^4$ Ⓓ $\dfrac{1}{81x^4}$

CHALLENGE AND EXTEND

 58. **Geometry** The volume of the prism at right is $V = 30x^4y^3$. Write and simplify an expression for the prism's height in terms of x and y.

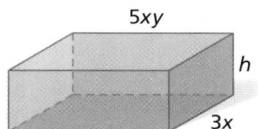

59. Simplify $\dfrac{3^{2x}}{3^{2x-1}}$.   **60.** Simplify $\dfrac{(x+1)^2}{(x+1)^3}$.

 61. **Reasoning** Copy and complete the table below to show how the Quotient of Powers Property can be found by using the Product of Powers Property.

Statements	Reasons
1. $a^{m-n} = a^{\blacksquare + \blacksquare}$	Subtraction is addition of the opposite.
2. $\phantom{a^{m-n}} = a^{\blacksquare} \cdot a^{\blacksquare}$	Product of Powers Property
3. $\phantom{a^{m-n}} = a^m \cdot \dfrac{1}{a^n}$	?
4. $\phantom{a^{m-n}} = \dfrac{a^m}{\blacksquare}$	Multiplication can be written as division.

SPIRAL STANDARDS REVIEW   ⚷ 2.0, ⚷ 4.0

Find each square root. *(Lesson 1-5)*

62. $\sqrt{36}$ **63.** $\sqrt{1}$ **64.** $-\sqrt{49}$ **65.** $\sqrt{144}$

Solve each equation. Check your answer. *(Lesson 2-4)*

66. $-2(x-1) + 4x = 5x + 3$ **67.** $x - 1 - (4x + 3) = 5x$

Simplify. *(Lesson 7-3)*

68. $3^2 \cdot 3^3$ **69.** $k^5 \cdot k^{-2} \cdot k^{-3}$ **70.** $(4t^5)^2$ **71.** $-(5x^4)^3$

7-5 Fractional Exponents

Vocabulary
index

Why learn this?

You can use fractional exponents to find the number of Calories animals need to consume each day to maintain health. (See Example 3.)

Recall that the radical symbol $\sqrt{}$ is used to indicate roots. The **index** is the small number to the left of the radical symbol that tells which root to take. For example, $\sqrt[3]{}$ represents a cube root. Since $2^3 = 2 \cdot 2 \cdot 2 = 8$, $\sqrt[3]{8} = 2$.

Another way to write nth roots is by using fractional exponents. For example, for $b > 1$, suppose $\sqrt{b} = b^k$.

$$\sqrt{b} = b^k$$
$$\left(\sqrt{b}\right)^2 = \left(b^k\right)^2 \qquad \textit{Square both sides.}$$
$$b^1 = b^{2k} \qquad \textit{Power of a Power Property}$$
$$1 = 2k \qquad \textit{If } b^m = b^n, \text{ then } m = n.$$
$$\frac{1}{2} = k \qquad \textit{Divide both sides by 2.}$$

So for all $b > 1$, $\sqrt{b} = b^{\frac{1}{2}}$.

> **Helpful Hint**
>
> When $b = 0$, $\sqrt[n]{b} = 0$.
> When $b = 1$, $\sqrt[n]{b} = 1$.

Know it!
.note

Definition of $b^{\frac{1}{n}}$

WORDS	NUMBERS	ALGEBRA
A number raised to the power of $\frac{1}{n}$ is equal to the nth root of that number.	$3^{\frac{1}{2}} = \sqrt{3}$ $5^{\frac{1}{4}} = \sqrt[4]{5}$ $2^{\frac{1}{7}} = \sqrt[7]{2}$	If $b > 1$ and n is an integer, where $n \geq 2$, then $b^{\frac{1}{n}} = \sqrt[n]{b}$. $b^{\frac{1}{2}} = \sqrt{b}$, $b^{\frac{1}{3}} = \sqrt[3]{b}$, $b^{\frac{1}{4}} = \sqrt[4]{b}$, and so on.

EXAMPLE 1 Simplifying $b^{\frac{1}{n}}$

Simplify each expression.

A $125^{\frac{1}{3}}$

$125^{\frac{1}{3}} = \sqrt[3]{125} = \sqrt[3]{5^3}$ *Use the definition of $b^{\frac{1}{n}}$.*
$= 5$

B $64^{\frac{1}{6}} + 25^{\frac{1}{2}}$

$64^{\frac{1}{6}} + 25^{\frac{1}{2}} = \sqrt[6]{64} + \sqrt{25}$ *Use the definition of $b^{\frac{1}{n}}$.*
$= \sqrt[6]{2^6} + \sqrt{5^2}$
$= \quad 2 \ + \ 5 \ = 7$

> **Remember!**
>
> $\sqrt{}$ is equivalent to $\sqrt[2]{}$.
> See Lesson 1-5.

 **Simplify each expression.**

1a. $81^{\frac{1}{4}}$

1b. $121^{\frac{1}{2}} + 256^{\frac{1}{4}}$

A fractional exponent can have a numerator other than 1, as in the expression $b^{\frac{2}{3}}$. You can write the exponent as a product in two different ways.

$$b^{\frac{2}{3}} = b^{\frac{1}{3} \cdot 2}$$
$$= \left(b^{\frac{1}{3}}\right)^2 \quad \text{Power of a Power Property}$$
$$= \left(\sqrt[3]{b}\right)^2 \quad \text{Definition of } b^{\frac{1}{n}}$$

$$b^{\frac{2}{3}} = b^{2 \cdot \frac{1}{3}}$$
$$= \left(b^2\right)^{\frac{1}{3}}$$
$$= \sqrt[3]{b^2}$$

Definition of $b^{\frac{m}{n}}$

WORDS	NUMBERS	ALGEBRA
A number raised to the power of $\frac{m}{n}$ is equal to the nth root of the number raised to the mth power.	$8^{\frac{2}{3}} = \left(\sqrt[3]{8}\right)^2 = 2^2 = 4$ $8^{\frac{2}{3}} = \sqrt[3]{8^2} = \sqrt[3]{64} = 4$	If $b > 1$ and m and n are integers, where $m \geq 1$ and $n \geq 2$, then $b^{\frac{m}{n}} = \left(\sqrt[n]{b}\right)^m = \sqrt[n]{b^m}$.

EXAMPLE 2 **Simplifying Expressions with Fractional Exponents**

Simplify each expression.

A $216^{\frac{2}{3}}$

$$216^{\frac{2}{3}} = \left(\sqrt[3]{216}\right)^2 \quad \text{Definition of } b^{\frac{m}{n}}$$
$$= \left(\sqrt[3]{6^3}\right)^2$$
$$= (6)^2 = 36$$

B $32^{\frac{4}{5}}$

$$32^{\frac{4}{5}} = \left(\sqrt[5]{32}\right)^4$$
$$= \left(\sqrt[5]{2^5}\right)^4$$
$$= (2)^4 = 16$$

 **Simplify each expression.**

2a. $16^{\frac{3}{4}}$

2b. $1^{\frac{2}{5}}$

2c. $27^{\frac{4}{3}}$

EXAMPLE 3 *Biology Application*

The approximate number of Calories C that an animal needs each day is given by $C = 72m^{\frac{3}{4}}$, where m is the animal's mass in kilograms. Find the number of Calories that a 16 kg dog needs each day.

$$C = 72m^{\frac{3}{4}}$$
$$= 72(16)^{\frac{3}{4}} \quad \text{Substitute 16 for } m.$$
$$= 72 \cdot \left(\sqrt[4]{16}\right)^3 \quad \text{Definition of } b^{\frac{m}{n}}$$
$$= 72 \cdot \left(\sqrt[4]{2^4}\right)^3$$
$$= 72 \cdot (2)^3$$
$$= 72 \cdot 8 = 576$$

The dog needs 576 Calories per day to maintain health.

 **3.** Find the number of Calories that an 81 kg panda needs each day.

Remember that $\sqrt{}$ always indicates a nonnegative square root. When you simplify variable expressions that contain $\sqrt{}$, such as $\sqrt{x^2}$, the answer cannot be negative. But x may be negative. Therefore you simplify $\sqrt{x^2}$ as $|x|$ to ensure the answer is nonnegative.

When x is...	and n is...	x^n is...	and $\sqrt[n]{x^n}$ is...
Positive	Even	Positive	Positive
Negative	Even	Positive	Positive
Positive	Odd	Positive	Positive
Negative	Odd	Negative	Negative

When n is even, you must simplify $\sqrt[n]{x^n}$ to $|x|$, because you do not know whether x is positive or negative. When n is odd, simplify $\sqrt[n]{x^n}$ to x.

EXAMPLE **Using Properties of Exponents to Simplify Expressions**

Simplify. All variables represent nonnegative numbers.

A $\sqrt[3]{x^9 y^3}$

$$\sqrt[3]{x^9 y^3} = \left(x^9 y^3\right)^{\frac{1}{3}} \qquad \textit{Definition of } b^{\frac{1}{n}}$$

$$= \left(x^9\right)^{\frac{1}{3}} \cdot \left(y^3\right)^{\frac{1}{3}} \qquad \textit{Power of a Product Property}$$

$$= \left(x^{9 \cdot \frac{1}{3}}\right) \cdot \left(y^{3 \cdot \frac{1}{3}}\right) \qquad \textit{Power of a Power Property}$$

$$= \left(x^3\right) \cdot \left(y^1\right) = x^3 y \qquad \textit{Simplify exponents.}$$

Helpful Hint

When you are told that all variables represent non-negative numbers, you do not need to use absolute values in your answers.

B $\left(x^2 y^{\frac{1}{2}}\right)^4 \sqrt[3]{y^3}$

$$\left(x^2 y^{\frac{1}{2}}\right)^4 \sqrt[3]{y^3} = \left(x^2 y^{\frac{1}{2}}\right)^4 \cdot y \qquad \sqrt[3]{y^3} = y$$

$$= \left(x^{2 \cdot 4}\right) \cdot \left(y^{\frac{1}{2} \cdot 4}\right) \cdot y \qquad \textit{Power of a Product Property}$$

$$= \left(x^8\right) \cdot \left(y^2\right) \cdot y \qquad \textit{Simplify exponents.}$$

$$= x^8 \cdot y^{2+1} = x^8 y^3 \qquad \textit{Product of Powers Property}$$

 Simplify. All variables represent nonnegative numbers.

4a. $\sqrt[4]{x^4 y^{12}}$

4b. $\dfrac{\left(xy^{\frac{1}{2}}\right)^2}{\sqrt[5]{x^5}}$

THINK AND DISCUSS

1. Explain how to find the value of $\left(\sqrt[10]{25}\right)^5$.

2. GET ORGANIZED Copy and complete the graphic organizer. In each cell, provide the definition and a numerical example of each type of fractional exponent.

Fractional Exponent	Definition	Numerical Example
$b^{\frac{1}{n}}$		
$b^{\frac{m}{n}}$		

7-5	Exercises

California Standards Practice
🔑 2.0, 25.1, 25.2

go.hrw.com
Homework Help Online
KEYWORD: MA8CA 7-5
Parent Resources Online
KEYWORD: MA8CA Parent

GUIDED PRACTICE

1. **Vocabulary** In the expression $\sqrt[5]{3x}$, what is the *index*?

SEE EXAMPLE 1
p. 422

Simplify each expression.

2. $8^{\frac{1}{3}}$

3. $16^{\frac{1}{2}}$

4. $0^{\frac{1}{6}}$

5. $27^{\frac{1}{3}}$

6. $81^{\frac{1}{2}}$

7. $216^{\frac{1}{3}}$

8. $1^{\frac{1}{9}}$

9. $625^{\frac{1}{4}}$

10. $36^{\frac{1}{2}} + 1^{\frac{1}{3}}$

11. $8^{\frac{1}{3}} + 64^{\frac{1}{2}}$

12. $81^{\frac{1}{4}} + 8^{\frac{1}{3}}$

13. $25^{\frac{1}{2}} - 1^{\frac{1}{4}}$

SEE EXAMPLE 2
p. 423

14. $81^{\frac{3}{4}}$

15. $8^{\frac{5}{3}}$

16. $125^{\frac{2}{3}}$

17. $25^{\frac{3}{2}}$

18. $36^{\frac{3}{2}}$

19. $64^{\frac{4}{3}}$

20. $1^{\frac{3}{4}}$

21. $0^{\frac{2}{3}}$

SEE EXAMPLE 3
p. 423

22. **Geometry** Given a square with area a, you can use the formula $P = 4a^{\frac{1}{2}}$ to find the perimeter P of the square. Find the perimeter of a square that has an area of 64 m².

SEE EXAMPLE 4
p. 424

Simplify. All variables represent nonnegative numbers.

23. $\sqrt{x^4y^2}$

24. $\sqrt[4]{z^4}$

25. $\sqrt{x^6y^6}$

26. $\sqrt[3]{a^{12}b^6}$

27. $\left(a^{\frac{1}{2}}\right)^2 \sqrt{a^2}$

28. $\left(x^{\frac{1}{3}}\right)^6 \sqrt[4]{y^4}$

29. $\dfrac{\left(z^{\frac{1}{3}}\right)^3}{\sqrt{z^2}}$

30. $\dfrac{\sqrt[3]{x^6y^9}}{x^2}$

PRACTICE AND PROBLEM SOLVING

Independent Practice

For Exercises	See Example
31–42	1
43–50	2
51	3
52–59	4

Extra Practice
Skills Practice p. EP15
Application Practice p. EP30

Simplify each expression.

31. $100^{\frac{1}{2}}$

32. $1^{\frac{1}{5}}$

33. $512^{\frac{1}{3}}$

34. $729^{\frac{1}{2}}$

35. $32^{\frac{1}{5}}$

36. $196^{\frac{1}{2}}$

37. $256^{\frac{1}{8}}$

38. $400^{\frac{1}{2}}$

39. $125^{\frac{1}{3}} + 81^{\frac{1}{2}}$

40. $25^{\frac{1}{2}} - 81^{\frac{1}{4}}$

41. $121^{\frac{1}{2}} - 243^{\frac{1}{5}}$

42. $256^{\frac{1}{4}} + 0^{\frac{1}{3}}$

43. $4^{\frac{3}{2}}$

44. $27^{\frac{2}{3}}$

45. $256^{\frac{3}{4}}$

46. $64^{\frac{5}{6}}$

47. $100^{\frac{3}{2}}$

48. $1^{\frac{5}{3}}$

49. $9^{\frac{5}{2}}$

50. $243^{\frac{2}{5}}$

51. **Biology** Biologists use a formula to estimate the mass of a mammal's brain. For a mammal with a mass of m grams, the approximate mass B of the brain, also in grams, is given by $B = \frac{1}{8}m^{\frac{2}{3}}$. Find the approximate mass of the brain of a mouse that has a mass of 64 grams.

Simplify. All variables represent nonnegative numbers.

52. $\sqrt[3]{a^6c^9}$

53. $\sqrt[3]{8m^3}$

54. $\sqrt[4]{x^{16}y^4}$

55. $\sqrt[3]{27x^6}$

56. $\left(x^{\frac{1}{2}}y^3\right)^2 \sqrt{x^2}$

57. $\left(a^2b^4\right)^{\frac{1}{2}} \sqrt[3]{b^6}$

58. $\dfrac{\sqrt[3]{x^6y^6}}{yx^2}$

59. $\dfrac{\left(a^2b^{\frac{1}{2}}\right)^4}{\sqrt{b^2}}$

Fill in the boxes to make each statement true.

60. $256^{\frac{\blacksquare}{4}} = 4$

61. $\blacksquare^{\frac{1}{5}} = 1$

62. $225^{\frac{1}{\blacksquare}} = 15$

63. $\blacksquare^{\frac{1}{6}} = 0$

64. $64^{\frac{\blacksquare}{3}} = 16$

65. $\blacksquare^{\frac{3}{4}} = 125$

66. $27^{\frac{4}{\blacksquare}} = 81$

67. $36^{\frac{\blacksquare}{2}} = 216$

Simplify each expression.

68. $\left(\dfrac{81}{169}\right)^{\frac{1}{2}}$

69. $\left(\dfrac{8}{27}\right)^{\frac{1}{3}}$

70. $\left(\dfrac{256}{81}\right)^{\frac{1}{4}}$

71. $\left(\dfrac{1}{16}\right)^{\frac{1}{2}}$

72. $\left(\dfrac{9}{16}\right)^{\frac{3}{2}}$

73. $\left(\dfrac{8}{27}\right)^{\frac{2}{3}}$

74. $\left(\dfrac{16}{81}\right)^{\frac{3}{4}}$

75. $\left(\dfrac{4}{49}\right)^{\frac{3}{2}}$

76. $\left(\dfrac{4}{25}\right)^{\frac{3}{2}}$

77. $\left(\dfrac{1}{81}\right)^{\frac{3}{4}}$

78. $\left(\dfrac{27}{64}\right)^{\frac{2}{3}}$

79. $\left(\dfrac{8}{125}\right)^{\frac{4}{3}}$

80. Multi-Step Scientists have found that the life span of a mammal living in captivity is related to the mammal's mass. The life span in years L can be approximated by the formula $L = 12m^{\frac{1}{5}}$, where m is the mammal's mass in kilograms. How much longer is the life span of a lion compared with that of a wolf?

Typical Mass of Mammals	
Mammal	Mass (kg)
Koala	8
Wolf	32
Lion	243
Giraffe	1024

81. Geometry Given a sphere with volume V, the formula $r = 0.62V^{\frac{1}{3}}$ may be used to approximate the sphere's radius r. Find the approximate radius of a sphere that has a volume of 27 in³.

82. Reasoning Show that a number raised to the power $\frac{1}{3}$ is the same as the cube root of that number. (*Hint:* Use properties of exponents to find the cube of $b^{\frac{1}{3}}$. Then compare this with the cube of $\sqrt[3]{b}$. Use the fact that if two numbers have the same cube, then they are equal.)

83. Critical Thinking Compare $n^{\frac{2}{3}}$ and $n^{\frac{3}{2}}$ for values of n greater than 1. When simplifying each of these expressions, will the result be greater than n or less than n? Explain.

84. /// ERROR ANALYSIS /// Two students simplified $64^{\frac{3}{2}}$. Which solution is incorrect? Explain the error.

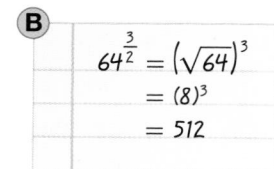

A
$$64^{\frac{3}{2}} = \left(\sqrt[3]{64}\right)^2$$
$$= (4)^2$$
$$= 16$$

B
$$64^{\frac{3}{2}} = \left(\sqrt{64}\right)^3$$
$$= (8)^3$$
$$= 512$$

CONCEPT CONNECTION

85. This problem will prepare you for the Concept Connection on page 428.
You can estimate an object's distance in inches from a light source by using the formula $d = \left(0.8\dfrac{L}{B}\right)^{\frac{1}{2}}$, where L is the light's luminosity in lumens and B is the light's brightness in lumens per square inch.

a. Find an object's distance to a light source with a luminosity of 4000 lumens and a brightness of 32 lumens per square inch.

b. Suppose the brightness of this light source decreases to 8 lumens per square inch. How does the object's distance from the source change?

86. Write About It You can write $4^{\frac{3}{2}}$ as $4^{3 \cdot \frac{1}{2}}$ or as $4^{\frac{1}{2} \cdot 3}$. Use the Power of a Power Property to show that both expressions are equal. Is one method easier than the other? Explain.

Multiple Choice For Exercises 87–90, choose the best answer.

87. What is $9^{\frac{1}{2}} + 8^{\frac{1}{3}}$?

   Ⓐ 4   Ⓑ 5   Ⓒ 6   Ⓓ 10

88. Which expression is equal to 8?

   Ⓐ $4^{\frac{3}{2}}$ Ⓑ $16^{\frac{1}{2}}$ Ⓒ $32^{\frac{4}{5}}$ Ⓓ $64^{\frac{3}{2}}$

89. Which expression is equivalent to $\sqrt[3]{a^9 b^3}$?

   Ⓐ $a^2 b$ Ⓑ a^3 Ⓒ $a^3 b$ Ⓓ $a^3 b^3$

90. Which of the following is NOT equal to $16^{\frac{3}{2}}$?

   Ⓐ $\left(\sqrt{16}\right)^3$ Ⓑ 4^3 Ⓒ $\left(\sqrt[3]{16}\right)^2$ Ⓓ $\sqrt{16^3}$

CHALLENGE AND EXTEND

Use properties of exponents to simplify each expression.

91. $\left(a^{\frac{1}{3}}\right)\left(a^{\frac{1}{3}}\right)\left(a^{\frac{1}{3}}\right)$ **92.** $\left(x^{\frac{1}{2}}\right)^5\left(x^{\frac{3}{2}}\right)$ **93.** $\left(x^{\frac{1}{3}}\right)^4\left(x^5\right)^{\frac{1}{3}}$

You can use properties of exponents to help you solve equations. For example, to solve $x^3 = 64$, raise both sides to the $\frac{1}{3}$ power to get $\left(x^3\right)^{\frac{1}{3}} = 64^{\frac{1}{3}}$. Simplifying both sides gives $x = 4$. Use this method to solve each equation. Check your answer.

94. $y^5 = 32$ **95.** $27x^3 = 729$ **96.** $1 = \frac{1}{8}x^3$

 97. Geometry The formula for the surface area of a sphere S in terms of its volume V is $S = (4\pi)^{\frac{1}{3}}(3V)^{\frac{2}{3}}$. What is the surface area of a sphere that has a volume of 36π cm^3? Leave the symbol π in your answer. What do you notice?

Solve each equation. *(Lesson 2-7)*

98. $|x + 6| = 2$ **99.** $|5x + 5| = 0$ **100.** $|2x - 1| = 3$

Solve each inequality and graph the solutions. *(Lesson 3-4)*

101. $3n + 5 < 14$ **102.** $4 \le \frac{1}{2}x + 3$ **103.** $7 \ge 2y + 11$

Give the domain and range of each relation. Tell whether the relation is a function. Explain. *(Lesson 4-2)*

104. $\{(2, 3), (2, 4), (2, 5), (2, 6)\}$ **105.** $\{(-2, 0), (-1, 1), (0, 2), (1, 3)\}$

106.

x	y
5	2
7	2
9	2
11	2

107.

CONCEPT CONNECTION

Exponents

I See the Light! The speed of light is the product of its frequency f and its wavelength w. In air, the speed of light is 3×10^8 m/s.

1. Write an equation for the relationship described above, and then solve this equation for frequency. Write this equation as an equation with w raised to a negative exponent.

2. Wavelengths of visible light range from 400 to 700 nanometers (10^{-9} meters). Use a graphing calculator and the relationship you found in Problem 1 to graph frequency as a function of wavelength. Sketch the graph with the axes clearly labeled. Describe your graph.

3. The speed of light in water is $\frac{3}{4}$ of its speed in air. Find the speed of light in water.

4. When light enters water, some colors bend more than others. How much the light bends depends on its wavelength. This is what creates a rainbow. The frequency of green light is about 5.9×10^{14} cycles per second. Find the wavelength of green light in water.

5. When light enters water, colors with shorter wavelengths bend more than colors with longer wavelengths. Violet light has a frequency of 7.5×10^{14} cycles per second, and red light has a frequency of 4.6×10^{14} cycles per second. Which of these colors of light will bend more when it enters water? Justify your answer.

READY TO GO ON?

Quiz for Lessons 7-1 Through 7-5

7-1 Integer Exponents

Evaluate each expression for the given value(s) of the variable(s).

1. t^{-6} for $t = 2$
2. n^{-3} for $n = -5$
3. $r^0 s^{-2}$ for $r = 8$ and $s = 10$

Simplify.

4. $5k^{-3}$
5. $\dfrac{x^4}{y^{-6}}$
6. $8f^{-4} g^0$
7. $\dfrac{a^{-3}}{b^{-2}}$

8. Measurement Metric units can be written in terms of a base unit. The table shows some of these equivalencies. Simplify each expression.

Selected Metric Prefixes					
Milli-	Centi-	Deci-	Deka-	Hecto-	Kilo-
10^{-3}	10^{-2}	10^{-1}	10^1	10^2	10^3

7-2 Powers of 10 and Scientific Notation

9. Find the value of 10^4.
10. Write 0.0000001 as a power of 10.
11. Write 100,000,000,000 as a power of 10.
12. Find the value of 82.1×10^4.

13. Measurement The lead in a mechanical pencil has a diameter of 0.5 mm. Write this number in scientific notation.

7-3 Multiplication Properties of Exponents

Simplify.

14. $2^2 \cdot 2^5$
15. $3^5 \cdot 3^{-3}$
16. $p^4 \cdot p^5$
17. $a^3 \cdot a^{-6} \cdot a^{-2}$

18. Biology A swarm of locusts was estimated to contain 2.8×10^{10} individual insects. If each locust weighs about 2.5 grams, how much did this entire swarm weigh? Write your answer in scientific notation.

Simplify.

19. $\left(3x^4\right)^3$
20. $\left(m^3 n^2\right)^5$
21. $\left(-4d^7\right)^2$
22. $\left(cd^6\right)^3 \cdot \left(c^5 d^2\right)^2$

7-4 Division Properties of Exponents

Simplify.

23. $\dfrac{6^9}{6^7}$
24. $\dfrac{12a^5}{3a^2}$
25. $\left(\dfrac{3}{5}\right)^3$
26. $\left(\dfrac{4p^3}{2pq^4}\right)^2$

Simplify each quotient and write the answer in scientific notation.

27. $\left(8 \times 10^9\right) \div \left(2 \times 10^6\right)$
28. $\left(3.5 \times 10^5\right) \div \left(7 \times 10^8\right)$
29. $\left(1 \times 10^4\right) \div \left(4 \times 10^4\right)$

7-5 Fractional Exponents

Simplify each expression. All variables represent nonnegative numbers.

30. $81^{\frac{1}{2}}$
31. $125^{\frac{1}{3}}$
32. $4^{\frac{3}{2}}$
33. $0^{\frac{2}{9}}$
34. $\sqrt{x^8 y^4}$
35. $\sqrt[3]{r^9}$
36. $\sqrt[6]{z^{12}}$
37. $\sqrt[3]{p^3 q^{12}}$

7-6 Polynomials

California Standards

Preparation for ⚷ **10.0**
Students add, subtract, multiply, and divide monomials and polynomials. Students solve multistep problems, including word problems, by using these techniques.

Vocabulary
monomial
degree of a monomial
polynomial
degree of a polynomial
standard form of a
    polynomial
leading coefficient
quadratic
cubic   trinomial
binomial   root

Who uses this?
Pyrotechnicians can use polynomials to plan complex fireworks displays. (See Example 4.)

A **monomial** is a number, a variable, or a product of numbers and variables with whole-number exponents. A monomial may be a constant or a single variable.

Monomials	Not Monomials
5 x $-7xy$ $0.5x^4$	$-0.3x^{-2}$ $4x - y$ $\dfrac{2}{x^3}$

The **degree of a monomial** is the sum of the exponents of the variables. A constant has degree 0.

EXAMPLE 1 Finding the Degree of a Monomial

Find the degree of each monomial.

A $-2a^2b^4$
The degree is 6.   *Add the exponents of the variables: $2 + 4 = 6$*

B 4
$4x^0$ *There is no variable, but you can write 4 as $4x^0$.*
The degree is 0.

C $8y$
$8y^1$ *A variable written without an exponent has exponent 1.*
The degree is 1.

Remember!

The *terms* of an expression are the parts being added or subtracted. See Lesson 1-7.

 Find the degree of each monomial.
1a. $1.5k^2m$ **1b.** $4x$ **1c.** $2c^3$

A **polynomial** is a monomial or a sum or difference of monomials. The **degree of a polynomial** is the degree of the term with the greatest degree.

The terms of a polynomial may be written in any order. However, polynomials that contain only one variable are usually written in *standard form*.

The **standard form of a polynomial** that contains one variable is written with the terms in order from greatest degree to least degree. When written in standard form, the coefficient of the first term is called the **leading coefficient**.

EXAMPLE 2 | **Writing Polynomials in Standard Form**

Write each polynomial in standard form. Then give the leading coefficient.

A $20x - 4x^3 + 2 - x^2$

Find the degree of each term. Then arrange them in descending order.

$$\underbrace{20x}_{1} \underbrace{-4x^3}_{3} \underbrace{+2}_{0} \underbrace{-x^2}_{2} \longrightarrow \underbrace{-4x^3}_{3} \underbrace{-x^2}_{2} \underbrace{+20x}_{1} \underbrace{+2}_{0}$$

Degree:

The standard form is $-4x^3 - x^2 + 20x + 2$. The leading coefficient is -4.

B $y^3 + y^5 + 4y$

Find the degree of each term. Then arrange them in descending order.

$$\underbrace{y^3}_{3} \underbrace{+y^5}_{5} \underbrace{+4y}_{1} \longrightarrow \underbrace{y^5}_{5} \underbrace{+y^3}_{3} \underbrace{+4y}_{1}$$

Degree:

The standard form is $y^5 + y^3 + 4y$. The leading coefficient is 1.

> **Remember!**
>
> A variable written without a coefficient has a coefficient of 1.
> $$y^5 = 1y^5$$

 **CHECK IT OUT!** Write each polynomial in standard form. Then give the leading coefficient.

2a. $16 - 4x^2 + x^5 + 9x^3$ **2b.** $18y^5 - 3y^8 + 14y$

Some polynomials have special names based on their degree and the number of terms they have.

Degree	Name
0	Constant
1	Linear
2	**Quadratic**
3	**Cubic**
4	Quartic
5	Quintic
6 or more	6th degree, 7th degree, and so on

Terms	Name
1	Monomial
2	**Binomial**
3	**Trinomial**
4 or more	Polynomial

EXAMPLE 3 | **Classifying Polynomials**

Classify each polynomial according to its degree and number of terms.

A $5x - 6$

Degree: 1   Terms: 2 $5x - 6$ is a linear binomial.

B $y + y^2 + 4$

Degree: 2   Terms: 3 $y + y^2 + 4$ is a quadratic trinomial.

C $6x^7 + 9x^2 - x + 3$

Degree: 7   Terms: 4 $6x^7 + 9x^2 - x + 3$ is a 7th-degree polynomial.

D n^3

Degree: 3   Terms: 1 n^3 is a cubic monomial.

 **CHECK IT OUT!** Classify each polynomial according to its degree and number of terms.

3a. $x^3 + x^2 - x + 2$ **3b.** 6 **3c.** $-3y^8 + 18y^5 + 14y$

EXAMPLE *Physical Science Application*

A firework is launched from a platform 6 feet above the ground at a speed of 200 feet per second. The firework has a 5-second fuse. The height of the firework in feet is given by the polynomial $-16t^2 + 200t + 6$, where t is the time in seconds. How high will the firework be when it explodes?

Substitute the time for t to find the firework's height.

$-16t^2 + 200t + 6$

$-16(5)^2 + 200(5) + 6$ *The time is 5 seconds.*

$-16(25) + 200(5) + 6$

$-400 + 1000 + 6$ *Evaluate the polynomial by using the order of operations.*

606

When the firework explodes, it will be 606 feet above the ground.

 **4. What if...?** Another firework with a 5-second fuse is launched from the same platform at a speed of 400 feet per second. Its height is given by $-16t^2 + 400t + 6$. How high will this firework be when it explodes?

A **root** of a polynomial in one variable is a value of the variable for which the polynomial is equal to 0.

EXAMPLE **Identifying Roots of Polynomials**

Tell whether each number is a root of $2k^2 - k - 3$.

A   4

$2k^2 - k - 3$

$2(4)^2 - 4 - 3$ *Substitute for k.*

$2(16) - 4 - 3$

$32 - 4 - 3$ *Simplify.*

25 ✗

$25 \neq 0$, so 4 is not a root of $2k^2 - k - 3$.

B -1

$2k^2 - k - 3$

$2(-1)^2 - (-1) - 3$

$2(1) + 1 - 3$

$2 + 1 - 3$

0 ✓

-1 is a root of $2k^2 - k - 3$.

 **5.** Tell whether 1 is a root of $3x^3 + x - 4$.

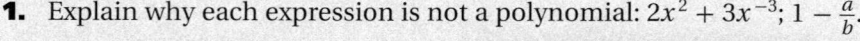

THINK AND DISCUSS

1. Explain why each expression is not a polynomial: $2x^2 + 3x^{-3}$; $1 - \frac{a}{b}$.

2. GET ORGANIZED Copy and complete the graphic organizer. In each circle, write an example of the given type of polynomial.

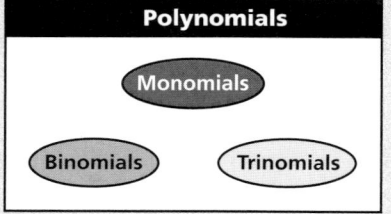

7-6

Exercises

California Standards Practice
Preparation for ⬦ 10.0; 25.2

go.hrw.com
Homework Help Online
KEYWORD: MA8CA 7-6
Parent Resources Online
KEYWORD: MA8CA Parent

GUIDED PRACTICE

Vocabulary Match each polynomial on the left with its classification on the right.

1. $2x^3 + 6$
2. $3x^3 + 4x^2 - 7$
3. $5x^2 - 2x + 3x^4 - 6$

   a. quartic polynomial
   b. quadratic polynomial
   c. cubic trinomial
   d. cubic binomial

SEE EXAMPLE 1
p. 430

Find the degree of each monomial.

4. 10^6
5. $-7xy^2$
6. $0.4n^8$
7. 2

SEE EXAMPLE 2
p. 431

Write each polynomial in standard form. Then give the leading coefficient.

8. $-2b + 5 + b^2$
9. $9a^8 - 8a^9$
10. $5s^2 - 3s + 3 - s^7$
11. $2x + 3x^2 - 1$
12. $5g - 7 + g^2$
13. $3c^2 + 5c^4 + 5c^3 - 4$

SEE EXAMPLE 3
p. 431

Classify each polynomial according to its degree and number of terms.

14. $x^2 + 2x + 3$
15. $7 - x$
16. $8 + k + 5k^4$
17. $q^2 + 6 - q^3 + 3q^4$
18. $7k^3 + 5k^2$
19. $2a^3 + 4a^2 - a^4$

SEE EXAMPLE 4
p. 432

20. **Geometry** The surface area of a cone is approximated by the polynomial $3.14r^2 + 3.14r\ell$, where r is the radius and ℓ is the slant height. Find the approximate surface area of this cone.

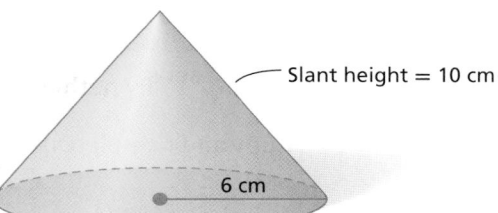
Slant height = 10 cm
6 cm

SEE EXAMPLE 5
p. 432

Tell whether each number is a root of the polynomial.

21. $4x^2 + 3;\ 0$
22. $-2n + 4;\ -2$
23. $a^2 + 6a + 9;\ -3$
24. $m^3 + 2m - 1;\ 1$
25. $x^2 - 4x + 3;\ 3$
26. $x^2 - 4x + 3;\ 1$

PRACTICE AND PROBLEM SOLVING

Independent Practice

For Exercises	See Example
27–34	1
35–43	2
44–51	3
52	4
53–58	5

Extra Practice
Skills Practice p. EP15
Application Practice p. EP30

Find the degree of each monomial.

27. $3y^4$
28. $6k$
29. $2a^3b^2c$
30. 325
31. $2y^4z^3$
32. $9m^5$
33. p
34. 5

Write each polynomial in standard form. Then give the leading coefficient.

35. $2.5 + 4.9t^3 - 4t^2 + t$
36. $8a - 10a^2 + 2$
37. $x^7 - x + x^3 - x^5 + x^{10}$
38. $-m + 7 - 3m^2$
39. $3x^2 + 5x - 4 + 5x^3$
40. $-2n + 1 - n^2$
41. $4d + 3d^2 - d^3 + 5$
42. $3s^2 + 12s^3 + 6$
43. $4x^2 - x^5 - x^3 + 1$

Classify each polynomial according to its degree and number of terms.

44. 12
45. $6k$
46. $3.5x^3 - 4.1x - 6$
47. $4g + 2g^2 - 3$
48. $2x^2 - 6x$
49. $6 - s^3 - 3s^4$
50. $c^2 + 7 - 2c^3$
51. $-y^2$

52. Transportation The polynomial $3.675v + 0.096v^2$ is used by transportation officials to estimate the stopping distance in feet for a car whose speed is v miles per hour on flat, dry pavement. What is the stopping distance for a car traveling at 30 miles per hour?

Tell whether each number is a root of the polynomial.

53. $6x; 0$

54. $-r^3 + 2r - 2; 1$

55. $3x^4 - 48; 2$

56. $125 - d^3; 5$

57. $2n^2 - 3n; 3$

58. $5t^2 + 3t - 4; -2$

Tell whether each statement is sometimes, always, or never true. Explain.

59. A monomial is a polynomial.

60. A trinomial is a 3rd-degree polynomial.

61. A binomial is a trinomial.

62. A polynomial has two or more terms.

63. Geometry A piece of 8.5-by-11-inch cardboard has identical squares cut from its corners. It is then folded into a box with no lid. The volume of the box in cubic inches is $4c^3 - 39c^2 + 93.5c$, where c is the side length of the missing squares in inches.

a. What is the volume of the box if $c = 1$ in.?

b. What is the volume of the box if $c = 1.5$ in.?

c. What is the volume of the box if $c = 4.25$ in.?

d. Critical Thinking Does your answer to part **c** make sense? Explain why or why not.

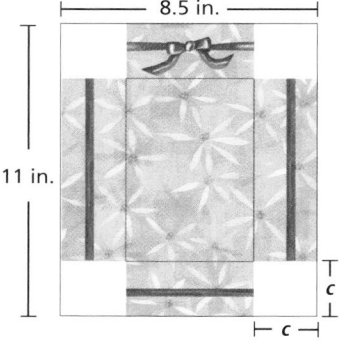

Copy and complete the table by evaluating each polynomial for the given values of x.

	Polynomial	$x = -2$	$x = 0$	$x = 5$
64.	$5x - 6$	$5(-2) - 6 = -16$	$5(0) - 6 = -6$	
65.	$x^5 + x^3 + 4x$			
66.	$-10x^2$			

Give one example of each type of polynomial.

67. quadratic trinomial

68. linear binomial

69. constant monomial

70. cubic monomial

71. quintic binomial

72. 12th-degree trinomial

73. Write About It Explain the steps you would follow to write the polynomial $4x^3 - 3 + 5x^2 - 2x^4 - x$ in standard form.

CONCEPT CONNECTION

74. This problem will prepare you for the Concept Connection on page 462.

a. The perimeter of the rectangle shown is $12x + 6$. What is the degree of this polynomial?

b. The area of the rectangle is $8x^2 + 12x$. What is the degree of this polynomial?

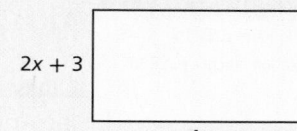

2x + 3

4x

75. ///**ERROR ANALYSIS**/// Two students evaluated $4x - 3x^5$ for $x = -2$. Which is incorrect? Explain the error.

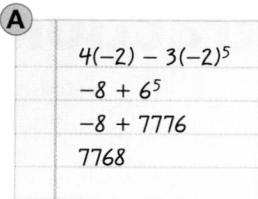

A	
$4(-2) - 3(-2)^5$	
$-8 + 6^5$	
$-8 + 7776$	
7768	

B	
$4(-2) - 3(-2)^5$	
$-8 - 3(-32)$	
$-8 + 96$	
88	

Multiple Choice For Exercises 76 and 77, choose the best answer.

76. Which polynomial has the highest degree?

  (A) $3x^8 - 2x^7 + x^6$ (B) $5x - 100$ (C) $25x^{10} + 3x^5 - 15$ (D) $134x^2$

77. Which is NOT a root of $x^3 - x^2 - 2x$?

  (A) -1 (B) 0 (C) 1 (D) 2

78. Short Response A toy rocket is launched from the ground at 75 feet per second. The polynomial $-16t^2 + 75t$ gives the rocket's height in feet after t seconds. Make a table showing the rocket's height after 1 second, 2 seconds, 3 seconds, and 4 seconds. At which of these times will the rocket be the highest?

CHALLENGE AND EXTEND

79. Medicine Doctors and nurses use growth charts and formulas to tell whether a baby is developing normally. The polynomial $0.016m^3 - 0.390m^2 + 4.562m + 50.310$ gives the average length in centimeters of a baby boy between 0 and 10 months of age, where m is the baby's age in months.

  a. What is the average length of a 2-month-old baby boy? a 5-month-old baby boy? Round your answers to the nearest centimeter.

  b. What is the average length of a newborn (0-month-old) baby boy?

  c. How could you find the answer to part **b** without doing any calculations?

80. Consider the binomials $4x^5 + x$, $4x^4 + x$, and $4x^3 + x$.

  a. Without calculating, which binomial has the greatest value for $x = 5$?

  b. Are there any values of x for $4x^3 + x$ which will have the greatest value? Explain.

 SPIRAL STANDARDS REVIEW 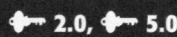 2.0, 5.0

81. Jordan is allowed 90 minutes of screen time per week. He used m minutes yesterday, and today he has already used $2m$ minutes, leaving 45 minutes for the week. Write and solve an equation for the number of minutes Jordan used yesterday. *(Lesson 2-3)*

82. Blue pens cost $0.50 each and red pens cost $0.75 each. Giselle bought the same number of each color pen p and an eraser for $0.45, for a total of $6.70. Write and solve an equation for the number of pens of each color that Giselle bought. *(Lesson 2-3)*

Classify each system. Give the number of solutions. *(Lesson 6-4)*

83. $\begin{cases} y = -4x + 5 \\ 4x + y = 2 \end{cases}$ **84.** $\begin{cases} 2x + 8y = 10 \\ 4y = -x + 5 \end{cases}$ **85.** $\begin{cases} y = 3x + 2 \\ y = -5x - 6 \end{cases}$

Simplify. *(Lesson 7-4)*

86. $\dfrac{4^7}{4^4}$ **87.** $\dfrac{x^6y^4}{x^4y^9}$ **88.** $\left(\dfrac{2v^4}{vw^5}\right)^2$ **89.** $\left(\dfrac{2p}{p^3}\right)^{-4}$

7-7
Algebra LAB

Model Polynomial Addition and Subtraction

You can use algebra tiles to model polynomial addition and subtraction.

Use with Lesson 7-7

go.hrw.com
Lab Resources Online
KEYWORD: MA8CA LAB7

KEY

 = 1

 = −1

 = x 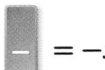 = −x  = x^2 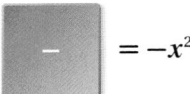 = −x^2

California Standards

10.0 Students add, subtract, multiply, and divide **monomials and polynomials.** Students solve multistep problems, including word problems, by using these techniques.

Activity 1

Use algebra tiles to find $(2x^2 - x) + (x^2 + 3x - 1)$.

MODEL		ALGEBRA
	Use tiles to represent all terms from both expressions.	$(2x^2 - x) + (x^2 + 3x - 1)$
	Rearrange tiles so that like tiles are together. Like tiles are the same size and shape.	$(2x^2 + x^2) + (-x + 3x) - 1$
	Remove any zero pairs.	$3x^2 - x + x + 2x - 1$
	The remaining tiles represent the sum.	$3x^2 + 2x - 1$

Try This

Use algebra tiles to find each sum.

1. $(-2x^2 + 1) + (-x^2)$

2. $(3x^2 + 2x + 5) + (x^2 - x - 4)$

3. $(x - 3) + (2x - 2)$

4. $(5x^2 - 3x - 6) + (x^2 + 3x + 6)$

5. $-5x^2 + (2x^2 + 5x)$

6. $(x^2 - x - 1) + (6x - 3)$

Activity 2

Use algebra tiles to find $(2x^2 + 6) - 4x^2$.

MODEL		ALGEBRA
	Use tiles to represent the terms in the first expression.	$2x^2 + 6$

To subtract $4x^2$, you would remove 4 yellow x^2-tiles, but there are not enough to do this. Remember that subtraction is the same as adding the opposite, so rewrite $(2x^2 + 6) - 4x^2$ as $(2x^2 + 6) + (-4x^2)$.

MODEL		ALGEBRA
	Add 4 red x^2-tiles.	$2x^2 + 6 + (-4x^2)$
	Rearrange tiles so that like tiles are together.	$2x^2 + (-4x^2) + 6$
	Remove zero pairs.	$2x^2 + (-2x^2) + (-2x^2) + 6$
	The remaining tiles represent the difference.	$-2x^2 + 6$

Try This

Use algebra tiles to find each difference.

7. $(6x^2 + 4x) - 3x^2$ **8.** $(2x^2 + x - 7) - 5x$ **9.** $(3x + 6) - 6$

10. $(8x + 5) - (-2x)$ **11.** $(x^2 + 2x) - (-4x^2 + x)$ **12.** $(3x^2 - 4) - (x^2 + 6x)$

13. ⊞ ⊟ represents a zero pair. Use algebra tiles to model two other zero pairs.

14. When is it not necessary to "add the opposite" for polynomial subtraction using algebra tiles?

7-7 Adding and Subtracting Polynomials

Who uses this?

Business owners can add and subtract polynomials that model profit. (See Example 4.)

Just as you can perform operations on numbers, you can perform operations on polynomials. To add or subtract polynomials, combine like terms.

EXAMPLE **1** **Adding and Subtracting Monomials**

Add or subtract.

A $15m^3 + 6m^2 + 2m^3$

$15m^3 + 6m^2 + 2m^3$	*Identify like terms.*
$15m^3 + 2m^3 + 6m^2$	*Rearrange terms so that like terms are together.*
$17m^3 + 6m^2$	*Combine like terms.*

B $3x^2 + 5 - 7x^2 + 12$

$3x^2 + 5 - 7x^2 + 12$	*Identify like terms.*
$3x^2 - 7x^2 + 5 + 12$	*Rearrange terms so that like terms are together.*
$-4x^2 + 17$	*Combine like terms.*

C $0.9y^5 - 0.4y^5 + 0.5x^5 + y^5$

$0.9y^5 - 0.4y^5 + 0.5x^5 + y^5$	*Identify like terms.*
$0.9y^5 - 0.4y^5 + y^5 + 0.5x^5$	*Rearrange terms so that like terms are together.*
$1.5y^5 + 0.5x^5$	*Combine like terms.*

D $2x^2y - x^2y - x^2y$

$2x^2y - x^2y - x^2y$	*All terms are like terms.*
0	*Combine like terms.*

Remember!

Like terms are constants or terms with the same variable(s) raised to the same power(s). To review combining like terms, see Lesson 1-7.

Add or subtract.

1a. $2s^2 + 3s^2 + s$ **1b.** $4z^4 - 8 + 16z^4 + 2$

1c. $2x^8 + 7y^8 - x^8 - y^8$ **1d.** $9b^3c^2 + 5b^3c^2 - 13b^3c^2$

Polynomials can be added in either vertical or horizontal form.

In vertical form, align the like terms and add:

$$\begin{array}{r} 5x^2 + 4x + 1 \\ + \; 2x^2 + 5x + 2 \\ \hline 7x^2 + 9x + 3 \end{array}$$

In horizontal form, use the Associative and Commutative Properties to regroup and combine like terms:

$$\left(5x^2 + 4x + 1\right) + \left(2x^2 + 5x + 2\right)$$
$$= \left(5x^2 + 2x^2\right) + \left(4x + 5x\right) + \left(1 + 2\right)$$
$$= 7x^2 + 9x + 3$$

EXAMPLE 2 Adding Polynomials

Add.

A $(2x^2 - x) + (x^2 + 3x - 1)$

$(2x^2 - x) + (x^2 + 3x - 1)$ *Identify like terms.*

$(2x^2 + x^2) + (-x + 3x) + (-1)$ *Group like terms together.*

$3x^2 + 2x - 1$ *Combine like terms.*

B $(-2ab + b) + (2ab + a)$

$(-2ab + b) + (2ab + a)$ *Identify like terms.*

$(-2ab + 2ab) + b + a$ *Group like terms together.*

$0 + b + a$ *Combine like terms.*

$b + a$ *Simplify.*

C $(4b^5 + 8b) + (3b^5 + 6b - 7b^5 + b)$

$(4b^5 + 8b) + (3b^5 + 6b - 7b^5 + b)$ *Identify like terms.*

$(4b^5 + 8b) + (-4b^5 + 7b)$ *Combine like terms in the second polynomial.*

$ 4b^5 + 8b$ *Use the vertical method.*

$\underline{+\ -4b^5 + 7b}$

$ 0 \quad + 15b$ *Combine like terms.*

$ 15b$ *Simplify.*

D $(20.2y^2 + 6y + 5) + (1.7y^2 - 8)$

$(20.2y^2 + 6y + 5) + (1.7y^2 - 8)$ *Identify like terms.*

$ 20.2y^2 + 6y + 5$ *Use the vertical method.*

$\underline{+\ 1.7y^2 + 0y - 8}$ *Write 0y as a placeholder in the second polynomial.*

$ 21.9y^2 + 6y - 3$ *Combine like terms.*

 **2.** Add $(5a^3 + 3a^2 - 6a + 12a^2) + (7a^3 - 10a)$.

> **Writing Math**
> When you use the Associative and Commutative Properties to rearrange the terms, the sign in front of each term must stay with that term.

To subtract polynomials, remember that subtracting is the same as adding the opposite. To find the opposite of a polynomial, you must write the opposite of *each* term in the polynomial:

$$-(2x^3 - 3x + 7) = -2x^3 + 3x - 7$$

EXAMPLE 3 Subtracting Polynomials

Subtract.

A $(2x^2 + 6) - (4x^2)$

$(2x^2 + 6) + (-4x^2)$ *Rewrite subtraction as addition of the opposite.*

$(2x^2 + 6) + (-4x^2)$ *Identify like terms.*

$(2x^2 - 4x^2) + 6$ *Group like terms together.*

$-2x^2 + 6$ *Combine like terms.*

B $(a^4 - 2a) - (3a^4 - 3a)$

$(a^4 - 2a) + (-3a^4 + 3a)$ *Rewrite subtraction as addition of the opposite.*

$(a^4 - 2a) + (-3a^4 + 3a)$ *Identify like terms.*

$(a^4 - 3a^4) + (-2a + 3a)$ *Group like terms together.*

$-2a^4 + a$ *Combine like terms.*

Subtract.

C $\left(3x^2 - 2x + 8\right) - \left(x^2 - 4\right)$

    $\left(3x^2 - 2x + 8\right) + \left(-x^2 + 4\right)$ *Rewrite subtraction as addition of the opposite.*

    $\left(3x^2 - 2x + 8\right) + \left(-x^2 + 4\right)$ *Identify like terms.*

$$
\begin{array}{l}
3x^2 - 2x\ + 8 \\
\underline{+\ -x^2 + 0x\ + 4} \\
2x^2 - 2x + 12
\end{array}
$$
    Use the vertical method.
    Write 0x as a placeholder.
    Combine like terms.

D $\left(11z^3 - 2z\right) - \left(z^3 - 5\right)$

    $\left(11z^3 - 2z\right) + \left(-z^3 + 5\right)$ *Rewrite subtraction as addition of the opposite.*

    $\left(11z^3 - 2z\right) + \left(-z^3 + 5\right)$ *Identify like terms.*

$$
\begin{array}{l}
11z^3 - 2z + 0 \\
\underline{+\ -z^3 + 0z + 5} \\
10z^3 - 2z + 5
\end{array}
$$
    Use the vertical method.
    Write 0 and 0z as placeholders.
    Combine like terms.

 **3.** Subtract $\left(2x^2 - 3x^2 + 1\right) - \left(x^2 + x + 1\right)$.

E X A M P L E   **4**   **Business Application**

The profits of two different manufacturing plants can be modeled as shown, where x is the number of units produced at each plant.

Eastern:
$-0.03x^2 + 25x - 1500$

Southern:
$-0.02x^2 + 21x - 1700$

Write a polynomial that represents the difference of the profits at the eastern plant and the profits at the southern plant.

$$
\begin{array}{l}
\left(-0.03x^2 + 25x - 1500\right) \\
-\left(-0.02x^2 + 21x - 1700\right)
\end{array}
$$
    Eastern plant profits
    Southern plant profits

$$
\begin{array}{l}
\left(-0.03x^2 + 25x - 1500\right) \\
\underline{+\left(+0.02x^2 - 21x + 1700\right)} \\
-0.01x^2 +\ \ 4x +\ \ 200
\end{array}
$$
    Write subtraction as addition of the opposite.
    Combine like terms.

 **4.** Use the information above to write a polynomial that represents the total profits from both plants.

THINK AND DISCUSS

1. Identify the like terms in the following list: $-12x^2$, $-4.7y$, $\frac{1}{5}x^2y$, y, $3xy^2$, $-9x^2$, $5x^2y$, $-12x$

2. Describe how to find the opposite of $9t^2 - 5t + 8$.

 **3.** **GET ORGANIZED** Copy and complete the graphic organizer. In each box, write an example that shows how to perform the given operation.

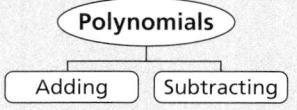

California
Standards Practice
🔑 10.0, 25.2

go.hrw.com
Homework Help Online
KEYWORD: MA8CA 7-7
Parent Resources Online
KEYWORD: MA8CA Parent

GUIDED PRACTICE

SEE EXAMPLE **1**
p. 438

Add or subtract.

1. $7a^2 - 10a^2 + 9a$
2. $13x^2 + 9y^2 - 6x^2$
3. $0.07r^4 + 0.32r^3 + 0.19r^4$
4. $\frac{1}{4}p^3 + \frac{2}{3}p^3$
5. $5b^3c + b^3c - 3b^3c$
6. $-8m + 5 - 16 + 11m$

SEE EXAMPLE **2**
p. 439

Add.

7. $(5n^3 + 3n + 6) + (18n^3 + 9)$
8. $(3.7q^2 - 8q + 3.7) + (4.3q^2 - 2.9q + 1.6)$
9. $(-3x + 12) + (9x^2 + 2x - 18)$
10. $(9x^4 + x^3) + (2x^4 + 6x^3 - 8x^4 + x^3)$

SEE EXAMPLE **3**
p. 439

Subtract.

11. $(6c^4 + 8c + 6) - (2c^4)$
12. $(16y^2 - 8y + 9) - (6y^2 - 2y + 7y)$
13. $(2r + 5) - (5r - 6)$
14. $(-7k^2 + 3) - (2k^2 + 5k - 1)$

SEE EXAMPLE **4**
p. 440

15. **Geometry** Write a polynomial that represents the measure of angle ABD.

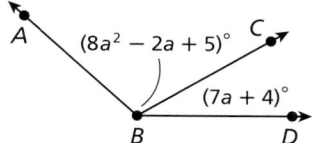

PRACTICE AND PROBLEM SOLVING

Independent Practice	
For Exercises	See Example
16–24	1
25–28	2
29–32	3
33–34	4

Extra Practice
Skills Practice p. EP15
Application Practice p. EP30

Add or subtract.

16. $4k^3 + 6k^2 + 9k^3$
17. $5m + 12n^2 + 6n - 8m$
18. $2.5a^4 - 8.1b^4 - 3.6b^4$
19. $2d^5 + 1 - d^5$
20. $7xy - 4x^2y - 2xy$
21. $-6x^3 + 5x + 2x^3 + 4x^3$
22. $x^2 + x + 3x + 2x^2$
23. $3x^3 - 4 - x^3 - 1$
24. $3b^3 - 2b - 1 - b^3 - b$

Add.

25. $(2t^2 - 8t) + (8t^2 + 9t)$
26. $(-7x^2 - 2x + 3) + (4x^2 - 9x)$
27. $(x^5 - x) + (x^4 + x)$
28. $(-2z^3 + z + 2z^3 + z) + (3z^3 - 5z^2)$

Subtract.

29. $(t^3 + 8t^2) - (3t^3)$
30. $(3x^2 - x) - (x^2 + 3x - x)$
31. $(5m + 3) - (6m^3 - 2m^2)$
32. $(3s^2 + 4s) - (-10s^2 + 6s)$

33. **Photography** The measurements of a photo and its frame are shown in the diagram. Write a polynomial that represents the width of the photo.

34. **Geometry** The length of a rectangle is represented by $4a + 3b$, and its width is represented by $7a - 2b$. Write a polynomial for the perimeter of the rectangle.

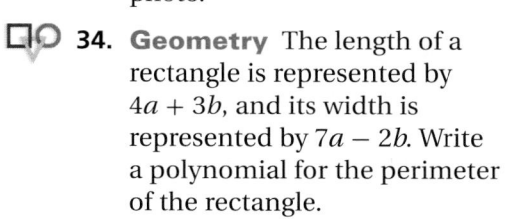

$6w^2 + 8$

$w^2 - 3w + 2$

Add or subtract.

35. $(2t - 7) + (-t + 2)$

36. $(4m^2 + 3m) + (-2m^2)$

37. $(4n - 2) - 2n$

38. $(-v - 7) - (-2v)$

39. $(4x^2 + 3x - 6) + (2x^2 - 4x + 5)$

40. $(2z^2 - 3z - 3) + (2z^2 - 7z - 1)$

41. $(5u^2 + 3u + 7) - (u^3 + 2u^2 + 1)$

42. $(-7h^2 - 4h + 7) - (7h^2 - 4h + 11)$

 43. Geometry The length of a rectangle is represented by $2x + 3$, and its width is represented by $3x + 7$. The perimeter of the rectangle is 35 units. Find the value of x.

44. Write About It If the parentheses are removed from $(3m^2 - 5m) + (12m^2 + 7m - 10)$, is the new expression equivalent to the original? If the parentheses are removed from $(3m^2 - 5m) - (12m^2 + 7m - 10)$, is the new expression equivalent to the original? Explain.

45. ///**ERROR ANALYSIS**/// Two students found the sum of the polynomials $(-3n^4 + 6n^3 + 4n^2)$ and $(8n^4 - 3n^2 + 9n)$. Which is incorrect? Explain the error.

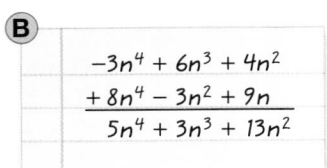

Ⓐ

$-3n^4 + 6n^3 + 4n^2 + 0n$
$+8n^4 + 0n^3 - 3n^2 + 9n$
$\overline{5n^4 + 6n^3 + n^2 + 9n}$

Ⓑ

$-3n^4 + 6n^3 + 4n^2$
$+8n^4 - 3n^2 + 9n$
$\overline{5n^4 + 3n^3 + 13n^2}$

Copy and complete the table by finding the missing polynomials.

	Polynomial 1	Polynomial 2	Sum
46.	$x^2 - 6$	$3x^2 - 10x + 2$	
47.	$12x + 5$		$15x + 11$
48.		$5x^4 + 8$	$6x^4 - 3x^2 - 1$
49.	$7x^3 - 6x - 3$		$7x^3 + 11$
50.	$2x^3 + 5x^2$	$7x^3 - 5x^2 + 1$	
51.		$x + x^2 + 6$	$3x^2 + 2x + 1$

52. Critical Thinking Does the order in which you add polynomials affect the sum? Does the order in which you subtract polynomials affect the difference? Explain.

CONCEPT CONNECTION

53. This problem will prepare you for the Concept Connection on page 462.

  a. Ian plans to build a fenced dog pen. At first, he planned for the pen to be a square of length x on each side, but then he decided that a square may not be best. He added 4 to the length and subtracted 3 from the width. Draw a diagram to show the dimensions of the new pen.

  b. Write a polynomial that represents the amount of fencing that Ian will need for the new dog pen.

  c. How much fencing will Ian need if $x = 15$?

Multiple Choice For Exercises 54 and 55, choose the best answer.

54. What is the missing term?

$$\left(-14y^2 + 9y^2 - 12y + 3\right) + \left(2y^2 + \boxed{} - 6y - 2\right) = \left(-3y^2 - 15y + 1\right)$$

   Ⓐ $-6y$ Ⓑ $-3y$ Ⓒ $3y$ Ⓓ $6y$

55. Which is NOT equivalent to $-5t^3 - t$?

   Ⓐ $-\left(5t^3 + t\right)$ Ⓒ $\left(t^3 + 6t\right) - \left(6t^3 + 7t\right)$

   Ⓑ $\left(2t^3 - 4t\right) - \left(-7t - 3t\right)$ Ⓓ $\left(2t^3 - 3t^2 + t\right) - \left(7t^3 - 3t^2 + 2t\right)$

56. Extended Response Tammy plans to put a wallpaper border around the perimeter of her room. She will not put the border across the doorway, which is 3 feet wide.

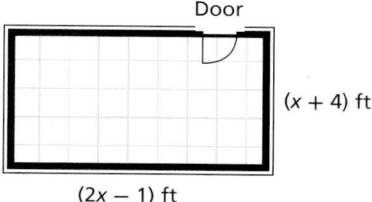

Door

$(x + 4)$ ft

$(2x - 1)$ ft

  a. Write a polynomial that represents the number of feet of wallpaper border that Tammy will need.

  b. A local store has 50 feet of the border that Tammy has chosen. What is the greatest whole-number value of x for which this amount would be enough for Tammy's room? Justify your answer.

  c. Determine the dimensions of Tammy's room for the value of x that you found in part **b**.

CHALLENGE AND EXTEND

57. Geometry The legs of the isosceles triangle at right measure $\left(x^3 + 5\right)$ units. The perimeter of the triangle is $\left(2x^3 + 3x^2 + 8\right)$ units. Write a polynomial that represents the measure of the base of the triangle.

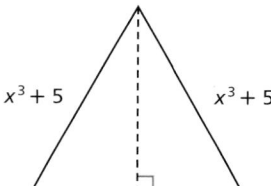

$x^3 + 5$ $x^3 + 5$

58. Write two polynomials whose sum is $4m^3 + 3m$.

59. Write two polynomials whose difference is $4m^3 + 3m$.

60. Write three polynomials whose sum is $4m^3 + 3m$.

61. Write three trinomials whose sum is $4m^3 + 3m$.

62. Write two monomials whose sum is $4m^3 + 3m$.

Solve each inequality and graph the solutions. Check your answer. *(Lesson 3-2)*

63. $d + 5 \geq -2$ **64.** $15 < m - 11$ **65.** $-6 + t < -6$

Write each equation in slope-intercept form. Then graph the line described by each equation. *(Lesson 5-6)*

66. $3x + y = 8$ **67.** $2y = \dfrac{1}{2}x + 6$ **68.** $y = 4(-x + 1)$

Simplify. *(Lesson 7-3)*

69. $b^4 \cdot b^7$ **70.** $cd^4 \cdot \left(c^{-5}\right)^3$ **71.** $\left(-3z^6\right)^2$ **72.** $\left(j^3k^{-5}\right)^3 \cdot \left(k^2\right)^4$

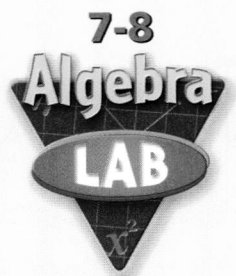

7-8
Algebra LAB

Use with Lesson 7-8

Model Polynomial Multiplication

You can use algebra tiles to multiply polynomials. Use the length and width of a rectangle to represent the factors. The area of the rectangle represents the product.

California Standards

10.0 Students add, subtract, **multiply,** and divide **monomials and polynomials.** Students solve multistep problems, including word problems, by using these techniques.

KEY

$\boxed{+} = 1$

$\boxed{-} = -1$

$\boxed{+} = x$ $\boxed{-} = -x$ $\boxed{+} = x^2$

REMEMBER
- The product of two values with the same sign is positive.
- The product of two values with different signs is negative.

Activity 1

Use algebra tiles to find $2(x + 1)$.

MODEL		ALGEBRA
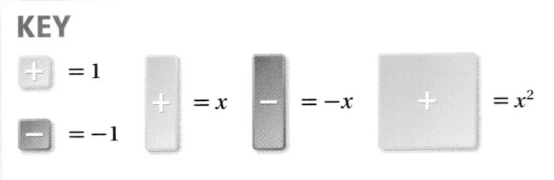	*Place the first factor in a column along the left side of the grid. This will be the width of the rectangle.* *Place the second factor across the top of the grid. This will be the length of the rectangle.*	$2(x + 1)$
	*Fill in the grid with tiles that have the same width as the tiles in the left column and the same length as the tiles in the top row.*	
	The area of the rectangle inside the grid represents the product.	$x + x + 1 + 1$ $2x + 2$

The rectangle has an area of $2x + 2$, so $2(x + 1) = 2x + 2$. Notice that this is the same product you would get by using the Distributive Property to multiply $2(x + 1)$.

Try This

Use algebra tiles to find each product.

1. $3(x + 2)$ **2.** $2(2x + 1)$ **3.** $3(x + 1)$ **4.** $3(2x + 2)$

Activity 2

Use algebra tiles to find $2x(x - 3)$.

MODEL		ALGEBRA
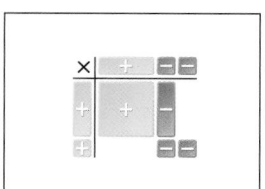	Place tiles to form the length and width of a rectangle and fill in the rectangle. The product of two values with the same sign (same color) is positive (yellow). The product of two values with different signs (different colors) is negative (red).	$2x(x - 3)$
	The area of the rectangle inside the grid represents the product. The rectangle has an area of $2x^2 - 6x$, so $2x(x - 3) = 2x^2 - 6x$.	$x^2 + x^2 - x - x - x - x - x - x$ $2x^2 - 6x$

Try This

Use algebra tiles to find each product.

5. $3x(x - 2)$　　　　**6.** $x(2x - 1)$　　　　**7.** $x(x + 1)$　　　　**8.** $(8x + 5)(-2x)$

Activity 3

Use algebra tiles to find $(x + 1)(x - 2)$.

MODEL		ALGEBRA
	Place tiles for each factor to form the length and width of a rectangle. Fill in the grid and remove any zero pairs.	$(x + 1)(x - 2)$ $x^2 - x - x + x - 1 - 1$
	The area inside the grid represents the product. The remaining area is $x^2 - x - 2$, so $(x + 1)(x - 2) = x^2 - x - 2$.	$x^2 - x - 1 - 1$ $x^2 - x - 2$

Try This

Use algebra tiles to find each product.

9. $(x + 2)(x - 3)$　　　　**10.** $(x - 1)(x + 3)$　　　　**11.** $(x - 2)(x - 3)$　　　　**12.** $(x + 1)(x + 2)$

7-8 Multiplying Polynomials

California Standards

🔑 **10.0** Students add, subtract, **multiply,** and divide **monomials** and **polynomials. Students solve multistep problems, including word problems, by using these techniques.**

Why learn this?
You can multiply polynomials to write expressions for areas, such as the area of a dulcimer. (See Example 5.)

To multiply monomials and polynomials, you will use some of the properties of exponents that you learned earlier in this chapter.

EXAMPLE 1 **Multiplying Monomials**

Multiply.

A $(5x^2)(4x^3)$

$(5x^2)(4x^3)$

$(5 \cdot 4)(x^2 \cdot x^3)$ *Group factors with like bases together.*

$20x^5$ *Multiply.*

B $(-3x^3y^2)(4xy^5)$

$(-3x^3y^2)(4xy^5)$

$(-3 \cdot 4)(x^3 \cdot x)(y^2 \cdot y^5)$ *Group factors with like bases together.*

$-12x^4y^7$ *Multiply.*

C $\left(\frac{1}{2}a^3b\right)(a^2c^2)(6b^2)$

$\left(\frac{1}{2}a^3b\right)(a^2c^2)(6b^2)$

$\left(\frac{1}{2} \cdot 6\right)(a^3 \cdot a^2)(b \cdot b^2)(c^2)$ *Group factors with like bases together.*

$3a^5b^3c^2$ *Multiply.*

> **Remember!**
>
> When multiplying powers with the same base, keep the base and add the exponents.
>
> $x^2 \cdot x^3 = x^{2+3} = x^5$

 Multiply.

1a. $(3x^3)(6x^2)$ **1b.** $(2r^2t)(5t^3)$ **1c.** $\left(\frac{1}{3}x^2y\right)(12x^3z^2)(y^4z^5)$

To multiply a polynomial by a monomial, use the Distributive Property.

EXAMPLE 2 **Multiplying a Polynomial by a Monomial**

Multiply.

A $5(2x^2 + x + 4)$

$5\,(2x^2 + x + 4)$

$(5)2x^2 + (5)x + (5)4$ *Distribute 5.*

$10x^2 + 5x + 20$ *Multiply.*

446   *Chapter 7 Exponents and Polynomials*

Multiply.

B $2x^2y(3x - y)$

$(2x^2y)(3x - y)$

$(2x^2y)3x + (2x^2y)(-y)$ *Distribute $2x^2y$.*

$(2 \cdot 3)(x^2 \cdot x)y + 2\,(-1)(x^2)(y \cdot y)$ *Group like bases together.*

$6x^3y - 2x^2y^2$ *Multiply.*

C $4a(a^2b + 2b^2)$

$4a(a^2b + 2b^2)$

$(4a)a^2b + (4a)2b^2$ *Distribute $4a$.*

$(4)(a \cdot a^2)(b) + (4 \cdot 2)(a)(b^2)$ *Group like bases together.*

$4a^3b + 8ab^2$ *Multiply.*

CHECK IT OUT! **Multiply.**

2a. $2(4x^2 + x + 3)$ **2b.** $3ab(5a^2 + b)$ **2c.** $5r^2s^2(r - 3s)$

To multiply a binomial by a binomial, you can apply the Distributive Property more than once:

$(x + 3)(x + 2) = x(x + 2) + 3(x + 2)$ *Distribute x and 3.*

$ = x(x + 2) + 3(x + 2)$

$ = x(x) + x(2) + 3(x) + 3(2)$ *Distribute x and 3 again.*

$ = x^2 + 2x + 3x + 6$ *Multiply.*

$ = x^2 + 5x + 6$ *Combine like terms.*

Another method for multiplying binomials is called the FOIL method.

1. Multiply the **F**irst terms. $(x+3)(x+2) \rightarrow x \cdot x = x^2$

2. Multiply the **O**uter terms. $(x+3)(x+2) \rightarrow x \cdot 2 = 2x$

3. Multiply the **I**nner terms. $(x+3)(x+2) \rightarrow 3 \cdot x = 3x$

4. Multiply the **L**ast terms. $(x+3)(x+2) \rightarrow 3 \cdot 2 = 6$

$$(x+3)(x+2) = x^2 + 2x + 3x + 6 = x^2 + 5x + 6$$

$$\text{F} \quad\quad \text{O} \quad\quad \text{I} \quad\quad \text{L}$$

EXAMPLE 3 **Multiplying Binomials**

Multiply.

A $(x+2)(x-5)$

$(x+2)(x-5)$

$x(x-5) + 2(x-5)$ *Distribute x and 2.*

$x(x) + x(-5) + 2(x) + 2(-5)$ *Distribute x and 2 again.*

$x^2 - 5x + 2x - 10$ *Multiply.*

$x^2 - 3x - 10$ *Combine like terms.*

B $(x+5)^2$

$(x+5)(x+5)$ *Write as a product of two binomials.*

$(x \cdot x) + (x \cdot 5) + (5 \cdot x) + (5 \cdot 5)$ *Use the FOIL method.*

$x^2 + 5x + 5x + 25$ *Multiply.*

$x^2 + 10x + 25$ *Combine like terms.*

C $(3a^2 - b)(a^2 - 2b)$

$3a^2(a^2) + 3a^2(-2b) - b(a^2) - b(-2b)$ *Use the FOIL method.*

$3a^4 - 6a^2b - a^2b + 2b^2$ *Multiply.*

$3a^4 - 7a^2b + 2b^2$ *Combine like terms.*

> **Helpful Hint**
>
> In the expression $(x+5)^2$, the base is $(x+5)$.
> $(x+5)^2 =$
> $(x+5)(x+5)$

 **CHECK IT OUT!**   **3a.** $(a+3)(a-4)$ **3b.** $(x-3)^2$ **3c.** $(2a - b^2)(a + 4b^2)$

To multiply polynomials with more than two terms, you can use the Distributive Property several times. Multiply $(5x + 3)$ by $(2x^2 + 10x - 6)$:

$$(5x + 3)(2x^2 + 10x - 6) = 5x(2x^2 + 10x - 6) + 3(2x^2 + 10x - 6)$$

$$= 5x(2x^2 + 10x - 6) + 3(2x^2 + 10x - 6)$$

$$= 5x(2x^2) + 5x(10x) + 5x(-6) + 3(2x^2) + 3(10x) + 3(-6)$$

$$= 10x^3 + 50x^2 - 30x + 6x^2 + 30x - 18$$

$$= 10x^3 + 56x^2 - 18$$

You can also use a rectangle model to multiply polynomials with more than two terms. This is similar to finding the area of a rectangle with length $(2x^2 + 10x - 6)$ and width $(5x + 3)$:

	$2x^2$	$+ 10x$	$- 6$
$5x$	$10x^3$	$50x^2$	$-30x$
$+ 3$	$6x^2$	$30x$	-18

Write the product of the monomials in each row and column.

To find the product, add all of the terms inside the rectangle by combining like terms and simplifying if necessary.

$$10x^3 + 6x^2 + 50x^2 + 30x - 30x - 18$$

$$10x^3 + 56x^2 - 18$$

Another method that can be used to multiply polynomials with more than two terms is the vertical method. This is similar to methods used to multiply whole numbers.

$$2x^2 + 10x - 6$$

$$\underline{\times 5x + 3}$$

$$6x^2 + 30x - 18 \qquad \textit{Multiply each term in the top polynomial by 3.}$$

$$\underline{+ \, 10x^3 + 50x^2 - 30x} \qquad \textit{Multiply each term in the top polynomial by 5x,}$$
and align like terms.

$$10x^3 + 56x^2 + 0x - 18 \qquad \textit{Combine like terms by adding vertically.}$$

$$10x^3 + 56x^2 - 18 \qquad \textit{Simplify.}$$

EXAMPLE 4 Multiplying Polynomials

Multiply.

Helpful Hint

A polynomial with *m* terms multiplied by a polynomial with *n* terms has a product that, before simplifying, has *mn* terms. In Example 4A, there are 2 · 3, or 6, terms before simplifying.

A $(x + 2)(x^2 - 5x + 4)$

$(x + 2)(x^2 - 5x + 4)$

$x(x^2 - 5x + 4) + 2(x^2 - 5x + 4)$ *Distribute x and 2.*

$x(x^2) + x(-5x) + x(4) + 2(x^2) + 2(-5x) + 2(4)$ *Distribute x and 2 again.*

$x^3 + 2x^2 - 5x^2 - 10x + 4x + 8$ *Simplify.*

$x^3 - 3x^2 - 6x + 8$ *Combine like terms.*

B $(3x - 4)(-2x^3 + 5x - 6)$

$(3x - 4)(-2x^3 + 5x - 6)$

$$-2x^3 + 0x^2 + 5x - 6 \qquad \textit{Add } 0x^2 \textit{ as a placeholder.}$$

$$\underline{\times 3x - 4}$$

$$8x^3 + 0x^2 - 20x + 24 \qquad \textit{Multiply each term in the top}$$
polynomial by −4.

$$\underline{+ \, -6x^4 + 0x^3 + 15x^2 - 18x} \qquad \textit{Multiply each term in the top polynomial}$$
by 3x, and align like terms.

$$-6x^4 + 8x^3 + 15x^2 - 38x + 24 \qquad \textit{Combine like terms by adding vertically.}$$

C $(x - 2)^3$

$[(x - 2)(x - 2)](x - 2)$ *Write as the product of three binomials.*

$[x \cdot x + x(-2) - 2 \cdot x - 2(-2)](x - 2)$ *Use the FOIL method on the first two factors.*

$(x^2 - 2x - 2x + 4)(x - 2)$ *Multiply.*

$(x^2 - 4x + 4)(x - 2)$ *Combine like terms.*

$(x - 2)(x^2 - 4x + 4)$ *Use the Commutative Property of Multiplication.*

$x(x^2 - 4x + 4) + (-2)(x^2 - 4x + 4)$ *Distribute x and −2.*

$x(x^2) + x(-4x) + x(4) + (-2)(x^2)$ *Distribute x and −2 again.*

$ + (-2)(-4x) + (-2)(4)$

$x^3 - 4x^2 + 4x - 2x^2 + 8x - 8$ *Simplify.*

$x^3 - 6x^2 + 12x - 8$ *Combine like terms.*

Multiply.

D $(2x + 3)(x^2 - 6x + 5)$

	x^2	$-6x$	$+5$
$2x$	$2x^3$	$-12x^2$	$10x$
$+3$	$3x^2$	$-18x$	15

Write the product of the monomials in each row and column.

$2x^3 + 3x^2 - 12x^2 - 18x + 10x + 15$ *Add all terms inside the rectangle.*
$2x^3 - 9x^2 - 8x + 15$ *Combine like terms.*

CHECK IT OUT! **Multiply.**
4a. $(x + 3)(x^2 - 4x + 6)$
4b. $(3x + 2)(x^2 - 2x + 5)$

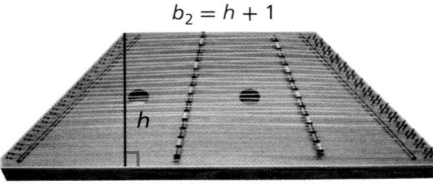

$b_2 = h + 1$
h
$b_1 = 2h - 1$

EXAMPLE 5 *Music Application*

A dulcimer is a musical instrument that is sometimes shaped like a trapezoid.

A Write a polynomial that represents the area of the dulcimer shown.

$A = \dfrac{1}{2}h\left(b_1 + b_2\right)$ *Write the formula for area of a trapezoid.*

$= \dfrac{1}{2}h\left[(2h - 1) + (h + 1)\right]$ *Substitute $2h - 1$ for b_1 and $h + 1$ for b_2.*

$= \dfrac{1}{2}h(3h)$ *Combine like terms.*

$= \dfrac{3}{2}h^2$ *Simplify.*

The area is represented by $\dfrac{3}{2}h^2$.

B Find the area of the dulcimer when the height is 22 inches.

$A = \dfrac{3}{2}h^2$ *Use the polynomial from part **a**.*

$= \dfrac{3}{2}(22)^2$ *Substitute 22 for h.*

$= \dfrac{3}{2}(484) = 726$

The area is 726 square inches.

CHECK IT OUT! **5.** The length of a rectangle is 4 meters shorter than its width.
    a. Write a polynomial that represents the area of the rectangle.
    b. Find the area of the rectangle when the width is 6 meters.

THINK AND DISCUSS

1. Compare the vertical method for multiplying polynomials with the vertical method for multiplying whole numbers.

2. GET ORGANIZED Copy and complete the graphic organizer. In each box, multiply two polynomials using the given method.

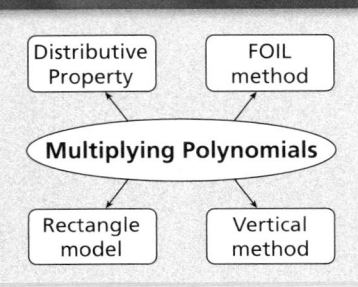

Distributive Property   FOIL method

Multiplying Polynomials

Rectangle model   Vertical method

7-8

Exercises

California
Standards Practice

🔑 10.0

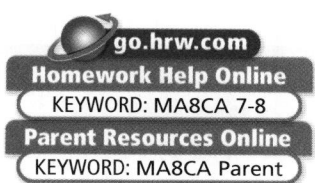
go.hrw.com
Homework Help Online
KEYWORD: MA8CA 7-8
Parent Resources Online
KEYWORD: MA8CA Parent

GUIDED PRACTICE

Multiply.

SEE EXAMPLE **1**
p. 446

1. $(2x^2)(7x^4)$

2. $(-5mn^3)(4m^2n^2)$

3. $(6rs^2)(s^3t^2)(\frac{1}{2}r^4t^3)$

4. $(\frac{1}{3}a^5)(12a)$

5. $(-3x^4y^2)(-7x^3y)$

6. $(-2pq^3)(5p^2q^2)(-3q^4)$

SEE EXAMPLE **2**
p. 446

7. $4(x^2 + 2x + 1)$

8. $3ab(2a^2 + 3b^3)$

9. $2a^3b(3a^2b + ab^2)$

10. $-3x(x^2 - 4x + 6)$

11. $5x^2y(2xy^3 - y)$

12. $5m^2n^3 \cdot mn^2(4m - n)$

SEE EXAMPLE **3**
p. 448

13. $(x + 1)(x - 2)$

14. $(x + 1)^2$

15. $(x - 2)^2$

16. $(y - 3)(y - 5)$

17. $(4a^3 - 2b)(a - 3b^2)$

18. $(m^2 - 2mn)(3mn + n^2)$

SEE EXAMPLE **4**
p. 449

19. $(x + 5)(x^2 - 2x + 3)$

20. $(3x + 4)(x^2 - 5x + 2)$

21. $(2x - 4)(-3x^3 + 2x - 5)$

22. $(-4x + 6)(2x^3 - x^2 + 1)$

23. $(x - 5)(x^2 + x + 1)$

24. $(a + b)(a - b)(b - a)$

SEE EXAMPLE **5**
p. 450

25. **Photography** The length of a rectangular photograph is 3 inches less than twice the width.

a. Write a polynomial that represents the area of the photograph.

b. Find the area of the photograph when the width is 4 inches.

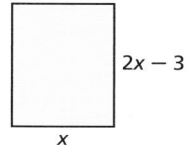
$2x - 3$
x

PRACTICE AND PROBLEM SOLVING

Multiply.

Independent Practice

For Exercises	See Example
26–34	1
35–43	2
44–52	3
53–61	4
62	5

Extra Practice
Skills Practice p. EP15
Application Practice p. EP30

26. $(3x^2)(8x^5)$

27. $(-2r^3s^4)(6r^2s)$

28. $(15xy^2)(\frac{1}{3}x^2z^3)(y^3z^4)$

29. $(-2a^3)(-5a)$

30. $(6x^3y^2)(-2x^2y)$

31. $(-3a^2b)(-2b^3)(-a^3b^2)$

32. $(7x^2)(xy^5)(2x^3y^2)$

33. $(-4a^3bc^2)(a^3b^2c)(3ab^4c^5)$

34. $(12mn^2)(2m^2n)(mn)$

35. $9s(s + 6)$

36. $9(2x^2 - 5x)$

37. $3x(9x^2 - 4x)$

38. $3(2x^2 + 5x + 4)$

39. $5s^2t^3(2s - 3t^2)$

40. $x^2y^3 \cdot 5x^2y(6x + y^2)$

41. $-5x(2x^2 - 3x - 1)$

42. $-2a^2b^3(3ab^2 - a^2b)$

43. $-7x^3y \cdot x^2y^2(2x - y)$

44. $(x + 5)(x - 3)$

45. $(x + 4)^2$

46. $(m - 5)^2$

47. $(5x - 2)(x + 3)$

48. $(3x - 4)^2$

49. $(5x + 2)(2x - 1)$

50. $(x - 1)(x - 2)$

51. $(x - 8)(7x + 4)$

52. $(2x + 7)(3x + 7)$

53. $(x + 2)(x^2 - 3x + 5)$

54. $(x^2 - 4x + 3)(2x + 5)$

55. $(5x - 1)(-2x^3 + 4x - 3)$

56. $(x - 3)(x^2 - 5x + 6)$

57. $(4x^3 - x^2 + 7)(2x^2 - 3)$

58. $(x - 4)^3$

59. $(x - 2)(x^2 + 2x + 1)$

60. $(2x + 10)(4 - x + 6x^3)$

61. $(1 - x)^3$

62. **Geometry** The length of the rectangle at right is 3 feet longer than its width.

a. Write a polynomial that represents the area of the rectangle.

b. Find the area of the rectangle when the width is 5 feet.

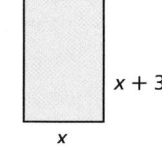
$x + 3$
x

63. A square tabletop has side lengths of $(4x - 6)$ units. Write a polynomial that represents the area of the tabletop.

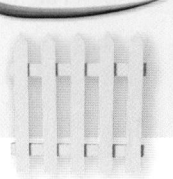

64. This problem will prepare you for the Concept Connection on page 462.

  a. Marie is creating a garden. She designs a rectangular garden with a length of $(x + 4)$ feet and a width of $(x + 1)$ feet. Draw a diagram of Marie's garden with the length and width labeled.

  b. Write a polynomial that represents the area of Marie's garden.

  c. What is the area when $x = 4$?

65. Copy and complete the table below.

	A	Degree of A	B	Degree of B	A · B	Degree of A · B
	$2x^2$	2	$3x^5$	5	$6x^7$	7
a.	$5x^3$		$2x^2 + 1$			
b.	$x^2 + 2$		$x^2 - x$			
c.	$x - 3$		$x^3 - 2x^2 + 1$			

  d. Use the results from the table to complete the following: The product of a polynomial of degree m and a polynomial of degree n has a degree of ▦.

 Geometry Write a polynomial that represents the area of each rectangle.

66. $2x + 3$ $4x$

67. $3(2x + 1)$ $2x + 1$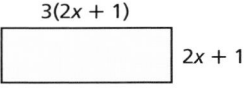

68. $x - 5$ $x - 5$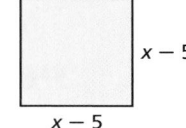

69. **Sports** The length of a regulation team handball court is twice its width.

  a. Write a polynomial that represents the area of the court.

  b. The width of a team handball court is 20 meters. Find the area of the court.

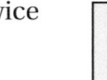 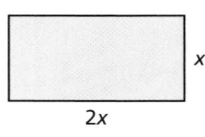

Team handball is a game with elements of soccer and basketball. It originated in Europe in the 1900s and was first played at the Olympics in 1936 with teams of 11 players. Today, a handball team consists of seven players—six court players and one goalie.

Multiply.

70. $(1.5a^3)(4a^6)$

71. $(2x + 5)(x - 6)$

72. $(3g - 1)(g + 5)$

73. $(4x - 2y)(2x - 3y)$

74. $(x + 3)(x - 3)$

75. $(1.5x - 3)(4x + 2)$

76. $(x - 10)(x + 4)$

77. $x^2(x + 3)$

78. $(x + 1)(x^2 + 2x)$

79. $(x - 4)(2x^2 + x - 6)$

80. $(a + b)(a - b)^2$

81. $(2p - 3q)^3$

82. **Multi-Step** A rectangular swimming pool is 25 feet long and 10 feet wide. It is surrounded by a fence that is x feet from each side of the pool.

  a. Draw a diagram of this situation.

  b. Write expressions for the length and width of the fenced region. (*Hint:* How much longer is one side of the fenced region than the corresponding side of the pool?)

  c. Write an expression for the area of the fenced region.

83. **Write About It** Explain why the FOIL method can be used to multiply only two binomials at a time.

84. Geometry Write a polynomial that represents the volume of the rectangular prism.

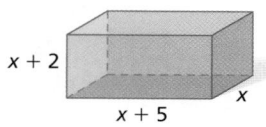

85. Critical Thinking Is there any value for x that would make the statement $(x + 3)^3 = x^3 + 3^3$ true? Give an example to justify your answer.

86. Estimation The length of a rectangle is 1 foot more than its width. Write a polynomial that represents the area of the rectangle. Estimate the width of the rectangle if its area is 25 square feet.

Multiple Choice For Exercises 87–89, choose the best answer.

87. Which of the following products is equal to $a^2 - 5a - 6$?

Ⓐ $(a - 1)(a - 5)$ Ⓑ $(a - 2)(a - 3)$ Ⓒ $(a + 1)(a - 6)$ Ⓓ $(a + 2)(a - 3)$

88. Which of the following is equal to $2a(a^2 - 1)$?

Ⓐ $2a^2 - 2a$ Ⓑ $2a^3 - 1$ Ⓒ $2a^3 - 2a$ Ⓓ $2a^2 - 1$

89. What is the degree of the product of $3x^3y^2z$ and x^2yz?

Ⓐ 5   Ⓑ 6   Ⓒ 7   Ⓓ 10

CHALLENGE AND EXTEND

Simplify.

90. $6x^2 - 2(3x^2 - 2x + 4)$ **91.** $x^2 - 2x(x + 3)$ **92.** $x(4x - 2) + 3x(x + 1)$

93. The diagram shows a sandbox and the frame that surrounds it.

    a. Write a polynomial that represents the area of the sandbox.

    b. Write a polynomial that represents the area of the frame that surrounds the sandbox.

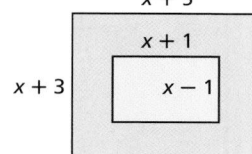

94. Geometry The side length of a square is $(8 + 2x)$ units. The area of this square is the same as the perimeter of another square with a side length of $(x^2 + 48)$ units. Find the value of x.

95. Write a polynomial that represents the product of three consecutive integers. Let x represent the first integer.

96. Find m and n so that $x^m(x^n + x^{n-2}) = x^5 + x^3$.

97. Find a so that $2x^a(5x^{2a-3} + 2x^{2a+2}) = 10x^3 + 4x^8$

98. A stop sign is 2.5 meters tall and casts a shadow that is 3.5 meters long. At the same time, a flagpole casts a shadow that is 28 meters long. If the height of each object is proportional to the length of its shadow, how tall is the flagpole? *(Lesson 2-5)*

Graph the solutions of each linear inequality. *(Lesson 6-6)*

99. $y \le x - 2$ **100.** $4x - 2y < 10$ **101.** $-y \ge -3x + 1$

Simplify. All variables represent nonnegative numbers. *(Lesson 7-5)*

102. $\sqrt{x^6 y^{12}}$ **103.** $\left(x^{\frac{1}{2}}\right)^8 \sqrt[3]{y^9}$ **104.** $\dfrac{\sqrt{x^4 y^{10}}}{x^2}$ **105.** $\sqrt[4]{a^{16} b^{24}}$

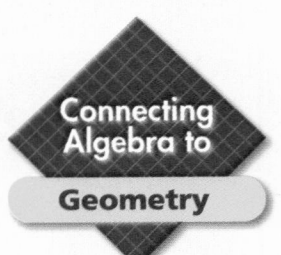

Volume and Surface Area

The volume V of a three-dimensional figure is the amount of space it occupies. The surface area S is the total area of the two-dimensional surfaces that make up the figure.

California Standards

Reinforcement of **7MG2.1** Use formulas routinely for finding the perimeter and area of basic two-dimensional figures and the surface area and volume of basic three-dimensional figures, including rectangles, parallelograms, trapezoids, squares, triangles, circles, **prisms, and cylinders.**

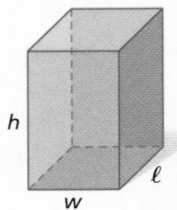
Rectangular Prism
$V = \ell wh$
$S = 2(\ell w + \ell h + wh)$

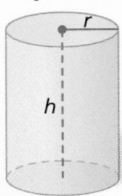
Cylinder
$V = \pi r^2 h$
$S = 2\pi r^2 + 2\pi rh$

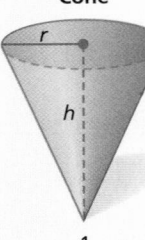
Cone
$V = \frac{1}{3}\pi r^2 h$

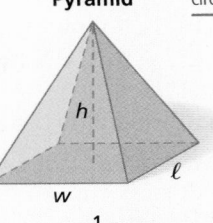
Pyramid
$V = \frac{1}{3}\ell wh$

Example

Write and simplify a polynomial expression for the volume of the cone. Leave the symbol π in your answer.

$V = \frac{1}{3}\pi r^2 \boldsymbol{h}$ *Choose the correct formula.*

$= \frac{1}{3}\pi(6p)^2(p+1)$ *Substitute 6p for r and p + 1 for h.*

$= \frac{1}{3}\pi(36p^2)(p+1)$ *Use the Power of a Product Property.*

$= \frac{1}{3}(36)\pi[p^2(p+1)]$ *Use the Associative Property of Multiplication.*

$= 12\pi p^2(p+1)$ *Distribute 12π p².*

$= 12\pi p^3 + 12\pi p^2$

(cone labeled $p + 1$, $6p$)

Try This

Write and simplify a polynomial expression for the volume of each figure.

1.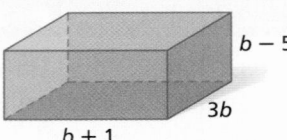
$b - 5$
$3b$
$b + 1$

2.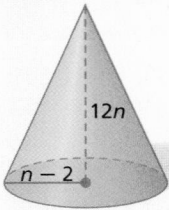
$12n$
$n - 2$

3.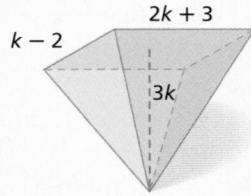
$2k + 3$
$k - 2$
$3k$

Write and simplify a polynomial expression for the surface area of each figure.

4.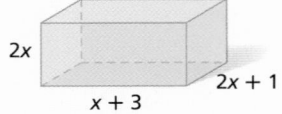
$2x$
$2x + 1$
$x + 3$

5.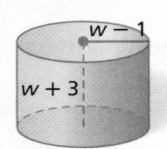
$w - 1$
$w + 3$

6.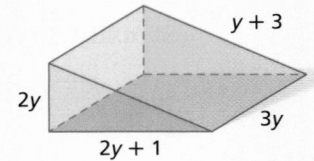
$y + 3$
$2y$
$3y$
$2y + 1$

7-9 Special Products of Binomials

California Standards

◆ **10.0** Students add, subtract, multiply, and divide monomials and polynomials. Students solve multistep problems, including word problems, by using these techniques.

Vocabulary
perfect-square trinomial
difference of two squares

Why learn this?
You can use special products to find areas, such as the area of a path around a pond. (See Example 4.)

Imagine a square with sides of length $(a + b)$:

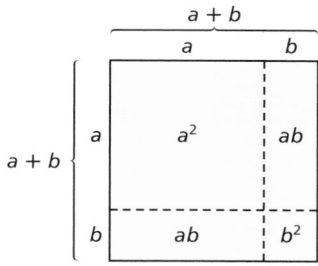

The area of this square is $(a + b)(a + b)$, or $(a + b)^2$. The area of this square can also be found by adding the areas of the smaller squares and rectangles inside. The sum of the areas inside is $a^2 + ab + ab + b^2$.

This means that $(a + b)^2 = a^2 + 2ab + b^2$.

You can use the FOIL method to verify this:

$$(a + b)^2 = (a + b)(a + b) = a^2 + ab + ab + b^2$$
$$= a^2 + 2ab + b^2$$

A trinomial of the form $a^2 + 2ab + b^2$ is called a *perfect-square trinomial*. A **perfect-square trinomial** is a trinomial that is the result of squaring a binomial.

EXAMPLE 1 | **Finding Products in the Form $(a + b)^2$**

Multiply.

A $(x + 4)^2$

$(a + b)^2 = a^2 + 2ab + b^2$ *Use the rule for $(a + b)^2$.*

$(x + 4)^2 = x^2 + 2(x)(4) + 4^2$ *Identify a and b: a = x and b = 4.*

$\quad\quad\quad = x^2 + 8x + 16$ *Simplify.*

B $(3x + 2y)^2$

$(a + b)^2 = a^2 + 2ab + b^2$ *Use the rule for $(a + b)^2$.*

$(3x + 2y)^2 = (3x)^2 + 2(3x)(2y) + (2y)^2$ *Identify a and b: a = 3x and b = 2y.*

$\quad\quad\quad = 9x^2 + 12xy + 4y^2$ *Simplify.*

Multiply.

C $\left(4 + s^2\right)^2$

$(a + b)^2 = a^2 + 2ab + b^2$ *Use the rule for $(a + b)^2$.*

$\left(4 + s^2\right)^2 = (4)^2 + 2(4)\left(s^2\right) + \left(s^2\right)^2$ *Identify a and b: a = 4 and b = s^2.*

$= 16 + 8s^2 + s^4$ *Simplify.*

D $(-m + 3)^2$

$(a + b)^2 = a^2 + 2ab + b^2$ *Use the rule for $(a + b)^2$.*

$(-m + 3)^2 = (-m)^2 + 2(-m)(3) + 3^2$ *Identify a and b: a = −m and b = 3.*

$= m^2 - 6m + 9$ *Simplify.*

 **Multiply.**

1a. $(x + 6)^2$ **1b.** $(5a + b)^2$ **1c.** $\left(1 + c^3\right)^2$

You can use the FOIL method to find products in the form $(a - b)^2$:

$$(a - b)^2 = (a - b)(a - b) = a^2 - ab - ab + b^2$$
$$= a^2 - 2ab + b^2$$

A trinomial of the form $a^2 - 2ab + b^2$ is also a perfect-square trinomial because it is the result of squaring the binomial $(a - b)$.

EXAMPLE 2   **Finding Products in the Form $(a - b)^2$**

Multiply.

A $(x - 5)^2$

$(a - b)^2 = a^2 - 2ab + b^2$ *Use the rule for $(a - b)^2$.*

$(x - 5)^2 = x^2 - 2(x)(5) + 5^2$ *Identify a and b: a = x and b = 5.*

$= x^2 - 10x + 25$ *Simplify.*

B $(6a - 1)^2$

$(a - b)^2 = a^2 - 2ab + b^2$ *Use the rule for $(a - b)^2$.*

$(6a - 1)^2 = (6a)^2 - 2(6a)(1) + (1)^2$ *Identify a and b: a = 6a and b = 1.*

$= 36a^2 - 12a + 1$ *Simplify.*

C $(4c - 3d)^2$

$(a - b)^2 = a^2 - 2ab + b^2$ *Use the rule for $(a - b)^2$.*

$(4c - 3d)^2 = (4c)^2 - 2(4c)(3d) + (3d)^2$ *Identify a and b: a = 4c and b = 3d.*

$= 16c^2 - 24cd + 9d^2$ *Simplify.*

D $\left(3 - x^2\right)^2$

$(a - b)^2 = (a)^2 - 2ab + b^2$ *Use the rule for $(a - b)^2$.*

$\left(3 - x^2\right)^2 = (3)^2 - 2(3)\left(x^2\right) + \left(x^2\right)^2$ *Identify a and b: a = 3 and b = x^2.*

$= 9 - 6x^2 + x^4$ *Simplify.*

 **Multiply.**

2a. $(x - 7)^2$ **2b.** $(3b - 2c)^2$ **2c.** $\left(a^2 - 4\right)^2$

You can use an area model to see that $(a + b)(a - b) = a^2 - b^2$.

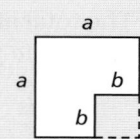

Begin with a square with area a^2. Remove a square with area b^2. The area of the new figure is $a^2 - b^2$.

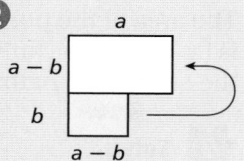

Then remove the smaller rectangle on the bottom. Turn it 90° and slide it up next to the top rectangle.

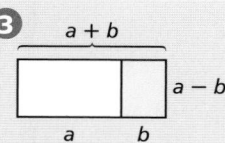

The new arrangement is a rectangle with length $a + b$ and width $a - b$. Its area is $(a + b)(a - b)$.

So $(a + b)(a - b) = a^2 - b^2$. A binomial of the form $a^2 - b^2$ is called a **difference of two squares**.

EXAMPLE **3** **Finding Products in the Form $(a + b)(a - b)$**

Multiply.

A $(x + 6)(x - 6)$

$(a + b)(a - b) = a^2 - b^2$ *Use the rule for $(a + b)(a - b)$.*

$(x + 6)(x - 6) = x^2 - 6^2$ *Identify a and b: a = x and b = 6.*

$= x^2 - 36$ *Simplify.*

B $(x^2 + 2y)(x^2 - 2y)$

$(a + b)(a - b) = a^2 - b^2$ *Use the rule for $(a + b)(a - b)$.*

$(x^2 + 2y)(x^2 - 2y) = (x^2)^2 - (2y)^2$ *Identify a and b: a = x² and b = 2y.*

$= x^4 - 4y^2$ *Simplify.*

C $(7 + n)(7 - n)$

$(a + b)(a - b) = a^2 - b^2$ *Use the rule for $(a + b)(a - b)$.*

$(7 + n)(7 - n) = 7^2 - n^2$ *Identify a and b: a = 7 and b = n.*

$= 49 - n^2$ *Simplify.*

 **Multiply.**

3a. $(x + 8)(x - 8)$ **3b.** $(3 + 2y^2)(3 - 2y^2)$ **3c.** $(9 + r)(9 - r)$

EXAMPLE **4** *Problem-Solving Application*

A square koi pond is surrounded by a gravel path. Write an expression that represents the area of the path.

1 **Understand the Problem**

The **answer** will be an expression that represents the area of the path.

List the important information:

• The pond is a square with a side length of $x - 2$.

• The path has a side length of $x + 2$.

2 Make a Plan

The area of the pond is $(x - 2)^2$. The total area of the path plus the pond is $(x + 2)^2$. You can subtract the area of the pond from the total area to find the area of the path.

3 Solve

Step 1 Find the total area.

$$(x + 2)^2 = x^2 + 2(x)(2) + 2^2$$

Use the rule for $(a + b)^2$: $a = x$ and $b = 2$.

$$= x^2 + 4x + 4$$

Step 2 Find the area of the pond.

$$(x - 2)^2 = x^2 - 2(x)(2) + 2^2$$

Use the rule for $(a - b)^2$: $a = x$ and $b = 2$.

$$= x^2 - 4x + 4$$

Step 3 Find the area of the path.

area of path	=	**total area**	−	**area of pond**

$$a = x^2 + 4x + 4 - (x^2 - 4x + 4)$$

$$= x^2 + 4x + 4 - x^2 + 4x - 4 \qquad \textit{Identify like terms.}$$
$$= (x^2 - x^2) + (4x + 4x) + (4 - 4) \quad \textit{Group like terms together.}$$
$$= 8x$$

The area of the path is $8x$.   *Combine like terms.*

4 Look Back

Suppose that $x = 10$. Then one side of the path is 12, and the total area is 12^2, or 144. Also, if $x = 10$, one side of the pond is 8, and the area of the pond is 8^2, or 64. This means the area of the path is $144 - 64 = 80$.

According to the solution above, the area of the path is $8x$. If $x = 10$, then $8x = 8(10) = 80$. ✓

 CHECK IT OUT!

4. Write an expression that represents the area of the swimming pool at right.

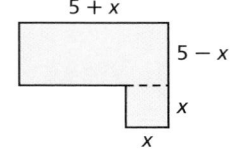

 **Know it! Note**

Special Products of Binomials

Perfect-Square Trinomials

$$(a + b)^2 = (a + b)(a + b) = a^2 + 2ab + b^2$$
$$(a - b)^2 = (a - b)(a - b) = a^2 - 2ab + b^2$$

Difference of Two Squares

$$(a + b)(a - b) = a^2 - b^2$$

 California LINK

Gardens

The Huntington Botanical Gardens in San Marino, CA, include a Japanese garden, several other theme gardens, and a botanical conservatory. The Huntington Botanical Gardens have approximately 15,000 plants from all over the world.

THINK AND DISCUSS

1. Use the FOIL method to verify that $(a + b)(a - b) = a^2 - b^2$.

2. When a binomial is squared, the middle term of the resulting trinomial is twice the _____?_____ of the first and last terms.

3. GET ORGANIZED Copy and complete the graphic organizer. Complete the special product rules and give an example of each.

Special Products of Binomials		
Perfect-Square Trinomials		Difference of Two Squares
$(a + b)^2 = ?$	$(a - b)^2 = ?$	$(a + b)(a - b) = ?$

7-9 Exercises

California Standards Practice
🔑 10.0, 25.2

go.hrw.com
Homework Help Online
KEYWORD: MA8CA 7-9
Parent Resources Online
KEYWORD: MA8CA Parent

GUIDED PRACTICE

1. Vocabulary In your own words, describe a *perfect-square trinomial*.

SEE EXAMPLE **1**
p. 455

Multiply.

2. $(x + 7)^2$ **3.** $(2 + x)^2$ **4.** $(x + 1)^2$

5. $(2x + 6)^2$ **6.** $(5x + 9)^2$ **7.** $(2a + 7b)^2$

SEE EXAMPLE **2**
p. 456

8. $(x - 6)^2$ **9.** $(x - 2)^2$ **10.** $(2x - 1)^2$

11. $(8 - x)^2$ **12.** $(6p - q)^2$ **13.** $(7a - 2b)^2$

SEE EXAMPLE **3**
p. 457

14. $(x + 5)(x - 5)$ **15.** $(x + 6)(x - 6)$ **16.** $(5x + 1)(5x - 1)$

17. $(2x^2 + 3)(2x^2 - 3)$ **18.** $(9 - x^3)(9 + x^3)$ **19.** $(2x - 5y)(2x + 5y)$

SEE EXAMPLE **4**
p. 457

20. Geometry Write a polynomial that represents the area of the figure.

$x + 3$
$x + 1$
$x + 3$
$x + 1$

PRACTICE AND PROBLEM SOLVING

Independent Practice
For Exercises	See Example
21–26	1
27–32	2
33–38	3
39	4

Extra Practice
Skills Practice p. EP15
Application Practice p. EP30

Multiply.

21. $(x + 3)^2$ **22.** $(4 + z)^2$ **23.** $(x^2 + y^2)^2$

24. $(p + 2q^3)^2$ **25.** $(2 + 3x)^2$ **26.** $(r^2 + 5t)^2$

27. $(s^2 - 7)^2$ **28.** $(2c - d^3)^2$ **29.** $(a - 8)^2$

30. $(5 - w)^2$ **31.** $(3x - 4)^2$ **32.** $(1 - x^2)^2$

33. $(a - 10)(a + 10)$ **34.** $(y + 4)(y - 4)$ **35.** $(7x + 3)(7x - 3)$

36. $(x^2 - 2)(x^2 + 2)$ **37.** $(5a^2 + 9)(5a^2 - 9)$ **38.** $(x^3 + y^2)(x^3 - y^2)$

39. Entertainment Write a polynomial that represents the area of the circular puzzle. Remember that the formula for area of a circle is $A = \pi r^2$, where r is the radius of the circle. Leave the symbol π in your answer.

$r = x + 4$

40. Multi-Step A square has sides that are $(x - 1)$ units long and a rectangle has a length of x units and a width of $(x - 2)$ units.

  a. What are the possible values of x? Explain.

  b. Which has the greater area, the square or the rectangle?

  c. What is the difference in the areas?

Multiply.

41. $(x + y)^2$ **42.** $(x - y)^2$ **43.** $(x^2 + 4)(x^2 - 4)$

44. $(x^2 + 4)^2$ **45.** $(x^2 - 4)^2$ **46.** $(1 - x)^2$

47. $(1 + x)^2$ **48.** $(1 - x)(1 + x)$ **49.** $(x^3 - a^3)(x^3 - a^3)$

50. $(5 + n)(5 + n)$ **51.** $(6a - 5b)(6a + 5b)$ **52.** $(r - 4t^4)(r - 4t^4)$

Copy and complete the tables to verify the special products of binomials.

	a	b	$(a - b)^2$	$a^2 - 2ab + b^2$
	1	4	$(1 - 4)^2 = 9$	$1^2 - 2(1)(4) + 4^2 = 9$
53.	2	4		
54.	3	2		

	a	b	$(a + b)^2$	$a^2 + 2ab + b^2$
55.	1	4		
56.	2	5		
57.	3	0		

	a	b	$(a + b)(a - b)$	$a^2 - b^2$
58.	1	4		
59.	2	3		
60.	3	2		

Math History

Beginning about 3000 B.C.E., the Babylonians lived in what is now Iraq and Turkey. Around 575 B.C.E., they built the Ishtar Gate to serve as one of eight main entrances into the city of Babylon. The image above is a relief sculpture from a restoration of the Ishtar Gate.

61. Math History The Babylonians used tables of squares and the formula $ab = \dfrac{(a + b)^2 - (a - b)^2}{4}$ to multiply two numbers. Use this formula to find the product $35 \cdot 24$.

62. Critical Thinking Find a value of c that makes $16x^2 - 24x + c$ a perfect-square trinomial.

63. /// ERROR ANALYSIS /// Explain the error below. What is the correct product?
$(a - b)^2 = a^2 - b^2$

64. This problem will prepare you for the Concept Connection on page 462.

   a. Michael is fencing part of his yard. He started with a square of length x on each side. He then added 3 feet to the length and subtracted 3 feet from the width. Make a sketch to show the fenced area with the length and width labeled.

   b. Write a polynomial that represents the area of the fenced region.

   c. Michael bought a total of 48 feet of fencing. What is the area of his fenced region?

65. Critical Thinking The polynomial $ax^2 - 49$ is a difference of two squares. Find all possible values of a between 1 and 100 inclusive.

66. Write About It When is the product of two binomials also a binomial? Explain and give an example.

Multiple Choice For Exercises 67–70, choose the best answer.

67. What is $(5x - 6y)(5x - 6y)$?

  Ⓐ $25x^2 - 22xy + 36y^2$ Ⓒ $25x^2 + 22xy + 36y^2$

  Ⓑ $25x^2 - 60xy + 36y^2$ Ⓓ $25x^2 + 60xy + 36y^2$

68. Which product is represented by the model?

  Ⓐ $(2x + 5)(2x + 5)$ Ⓒ $(5x + 2)(5x - 2)$

  Ⓑ $(5x - 2)(5x - 2)$ Ⓓ $(5x + 2)(5x + 2)$

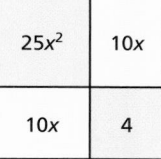

69. If $a + b = 12$ and $a^2 - b^2 = 96$ what is the value of a?

  Ⓐ 2   Ⓑ 4   Ⓒ 8   Ⓓ 10

70. If $rs = 15$ and $(r + s)^2 = 64$, what is the value of $r^2 + s^2$?

  Ⓐ 25   Ⓑ 30   Ⓒ 34   Ⓓ 49

CHALLENGE AND EXTEND

71. Multiply $(x + 4)(x + 4)(x - 4)$.   **72.** Multiply $(x + 4)(x - 4)(x - 4)$.

73. Reasoning If $x^2 + bx + c$ is a perfect-square trinomial, show that $b = \pm 2\sqrt{c}$.

74. You can multiply two numbers by rewriting the numbers as the difference of two squares. For example:

$$36 \cdot 24 = (30 + 6)(30 - 6) = 30^2 - 6^2 = 900 - 36 = 864$$

Use this method to multiply $27 \cdot 19$. Explain how you rewrote the numbers.

SPIRAL STANDARDS REVIEW   2.0,   6.0,   10.0

75. The square paper that Yuki is using to make an origami frog has an area of 165 cm^2. Find the side length of the paper to the nearest centimeter. *(Lesson 1-5)*

Use intercepts to graph the line described by each equation. *(Lesson 5-2)*

76. $2x + 3y = 6$ **77.** $y = -3x + 9$ **78.** $\frac{1}{2}x + y = 4$

Add or subtract. *(Lesson 7-7)*

79. $3x^2 + 8x - 2x + 9x^2$ **80.** $(8m^4 + 2n - 3m^3 + 6) + (9m^3 + 5 - 4m^4)$

81. $(2p^3 + p) - (5p^3 + 9p)$ **82.** $(12t - 3t^2 + 10) - (-5t^2 - 7 - 4t)$

7-9 Special Products of Binomials   **461**

Polynomials

Don't Fence Me In James has 500 feet of fencing to enclose a rectangular region on his farm for some sheep.

1. Make a sketch of three possible regions that James could enclose and give the corresponding areas.

2. If the length of the region is x, find an expression for the width.

3. Use your answer to Problem 2 to write an equation for the area of the region.

4. Graph your equation from Problem 3 on your calculator. Sketch the graph.

5. James wants his fenced region to have the largest area possible using 500 feet of fencing. Find this area using the graph or a table of values.

6. What are the length and width of the region with the area from Problem 5? Describe this region.

Quiz for Lessons 7-6 Through 7-9

7-6 Polynomials

Write each polynomial in standard form. Then give the leading coefficient.

1. $4r^2 + 2r^6 - 3r$
2. $y^2 + 7 - 8y^3 + 2y$
3. $-12t^3 - 4t + t^4$

Classify each polynomial according to its degree and number of terms.

4. $5b^2$
5. $-2x^3 - 5 + x - 2x^7$
6. $5 - 6b^2 + b - 4b^4$

Tell whether the number is a root of the polynomial.

7. $3x^2 - 27$; 3
8. $g^2 - 2g - 8$; 4
9. $6x^3 - 49$; 2

10. **Business** The function $C(x) = x^3 - 15x + 14$ gives the cost to manufacture x units of a product. What is the cost to manufacture 900 units?

7-7 Adding and Subtracting Polynomials

Add or subtract.

11. $(10m^3 + 4m^2) + (7m^2 + 3m)$
12. $(3t^2 - 2t) + (9t^2 + 4t - 6)$
13. $(12d^6 - 3d^2) + (2d^4 + 1)$
14. $(6y^3 + 4y^2) - (2y^2 + 3y)$
15. $(7n^2 - 3n) - (5n^2 + 5n)$
16. $(b^2 - 10) - (-5b^3 + 4b)$

17. **Geometry** The measures of the sides of a triangle are shown as polynomials. Write a polynomial to represent the perimeter of the triangle.

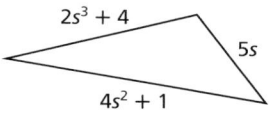

$2s^3 + 4$

$5s$

$4s^2 + 1$

7-8 Multiplying Polynomials

Multiply.

18. $2h^3 \cdot 5h^5$
19. $(s^8t^4)(-6st^3)$
20. $2ab(5a^3 + 3a^2b)$
21. $(3k + 5)^2$
22. $(2x^3 + 3y)(4x^2 + y)$
23. $(p^2 + 3p)(9p^2 - 6p - 5)$

24. **Geometry** Write a polynomial expression for the area of a parallelogram whose base is $(x + 7)$ units and whose height is $(x - 3)$ units.

7-9 Special Products of Binomials

Multiply.

25. $(d + 9)^2$
26. $(3 + 2t)^2$
27. $(2x + 5y)^2$
28. $(m - 4)^2$
29. $(a - b)^2$
30. $(3w - 1)^2$
31. $(c + 2)(c - 2)$
32. $(5r + 6)(5r - 6)$

33. **Sports** A child's basketball has a radius of $(x - 5)$ inches. Write a polynomial that represents the surface area of the basketball. (The formula for the surface area of a sphere is $S = 4\pi r^2$, where r represents the radius of the sphere.) Leave the symbol π in your answer.

Study Guide: Review

Vocabulary

Complete the sentences below with vocabulary words from the list above.

1. A(n) ____?____ polynomial is a polynomial of degree 3.

2. When a polynomial is written with the terms in order from highest to lowest degree, it is in ____?____ .

3. A(n) ____?____ is a number, a variable, or a product of numbers and variables with whole-number exponents.

4. A(n) ____?____ is a polynomial with three terms.

5. ____?____ is a method of writing numbers that are very large or very small.

7-1 Integer Exponents (pp. 394–399)

 2.0

EXAMPLES

Simplify.

■ -2^{-4}

$-2^{-4} = -\dfrac{1}{2^4} = -\dfrac{1}{2 \cdot 2 \cdot 2 \cdot 2} = -\dfrac{1}{16}$

■ 3^0

$3^0 = 1$ *Any nonzero number raised to the zero power is 1.*

■ Evaluate $r^3 s^{-4}$ for $r = -3$ and $s = 2$.

$r^3 s^{-4}$

$(-3)^3(2)^{-4} = \dfrac{(-3)(-3)(-3)}{2 \cdot 2 \cdot 2 \cdot 2} = -\dfrac{27}{16}$

■ Simplify $\dfrac{a^{-3}b^4}{c^{-2}}$.

$\dfrac{a^{-3}b^4}{c^{-2}} = \dfrac{b^4 c^2}{a^3}$

EXERCISES

6. The diameter of a certain bearing is 2^{-5} in. Evaluate this expression.

Simplify.

7. $(3.6)^0$

8. $(-1)^{-4}$

9. 5^{-3}

10. 10^{-4}

Evaluate each expression for the given value(s) of the variable(s).

11. b^{-4} for $b = 2$

12. $\left(\dfrac{2}{5}b\right)^{-4}$ for $b = 10$

13. $-2p^3 q^{-3}$ for $p = 3$ and $q = -2$

Simplify.

14. m^{-2}

15. bc^0

16. $-\dfrac{1}{2}x^{-2}y^{-4}$

17. $\dfrac{2b^6}{c^{-4}}$

18. $\dfrac{3a^2 c^{-2}}{4b^0}$

19. $\dfrac{q^{-1}r^{-2}}{s^{-3}}$

7-2 Powers of 10 and Scientific Notation (pp. 400–405)

 2.0

EXAMPLES

■ **Write 1,000,000 as a power of 10.**

1,000,000   *The decimal point is 6 places*
$1,000,000 = 10^6$ *to the right of 1.*

■ **Find the value of 386.21×10^5.**

$386.2\underbrace{1\,0\,0\,0}$ *Move the decimal point 5*
              places to the right.
$38,621,000$

■ **Write 0.000000041 in scientific notation.**

$0.0\underbrace{0\,0\,0\,0\,0\,0\,4}\,1$ *Move the decimal*
            point 8 places to the
4.1×10^{-8} *right to get a number*
                between 1 and 10.

EXERCISES

Find the value of each power of 10.

20. 10^7 **21.** 10^{-5}

Write each number as a power of 10.

22. 100 **23.** 0.00000000001

Find the value of each expression.

24. 3.25×10^5 **25.** 0.18×10^4

26. 17×10^{-2} **27.** 299×10^{-6}

28. Order the list of numbers from least to greatest.
$6.3 \times 10^{-3}, 1.2 \times 10^4, 5.8 \times 10^{-7}, 2.2 \times 10^2$

29. In 2003, the average daily value of shares traded on the New York Stock Exchange was about $\$3.85 \times 10^{10}$. Write this amount in standard form.

7-3 Multiplication Properties of Exponents (pp. 408–414)

 2.0

EXAMPLES

Simplify.

■ $5^3 \cdot 5^{-2}$
$5^3 \cdot 5^{-2}$ *The powers have the*
           same base.
$5^{3+(-2)}$ *Add the exponents.*
5^1
5

■ $a^4 \cdot b^{-3} \cdot b \cdot a^{-2}$
$a^4 \cdot b^{-3} \cdot b \cdot a^{-2}$ *Use properties to group*
$(a^4 \cdot a^{-2}) \cdot (b^{-3} \cdot b)$ *factors.*
$a^2 \cdot b^{-2}$ *Add the exponents of powers*
           with the same base.
$\dfrac{a^2}{b^2}$ *Write with a positive*
           exponent.

■ $(a^{-3}b^2)^{-2}$
$(a^{-3})^{-2} \cdot (b^2)^{-2}$ *Power of a Product Property*
$a^6 \cdot b^{-4}$ *Power of a Power Property*
$\dfrac{a^6}{b^4}$ *Write with a positive*
           exponent.

EXERCISES

Simplify.

30. $5^3 \cdot 5^6$ **31.** $2^6 \cdot 3 \cdot 2^{-3} \cdot 3^3$

32. $b^2 \cdot b^8$ **33.** $r^4 \cdot r$

34. $(x^3)^4$ **35.** $(s^3)^0$

36. $(2^3)^{-1}$ **37.** $(5^2)^{-2}$

38. $(4b^3)^{-2}$ **39.** $(g^3h^2)^4$

40. $(-x^2y)^2$ **41.** $-(x^2y)^2$

42. $(x^2y^3)(xy^3)^4$ **43.** $(j^2k^3)(j^4k^6)$

44. $(5^3 \cdot 5^{-2})^{-1}$ **45.** $(mn^3)^5(mn^5)^3$

46. $(4 \times 10^8)(2 \times 10^3)$ **47.** $(3 \times 10^2)(3 \times 10^5)$

48. $(5 \times 10^3)(2 \times 10^6)$ **49.** $(7 \times 10^5)(4 \times 10^9)$

50. $(3 \times 10^{-4})(2 \times 10^5)$ **51.** $(3 \times 10^{-8})(6 \times 10^{-1})$

52. In 2003, Wyoming's population was about 5.0×10^5. California's population was about 7.1×10 times as large as Wyoming's. What was the approximate population of California? Write your answer in scientific notation.

7-4 Division Properties of Exponents (pp. 415–421)

 2.0

EXAMPLE

■ Simplify $\dfrac{x^9}{x^2}$.

$\dfrac{x^9}{x^2} = x^{9-2} = x^7$ *Subtract the exponents.*

EXERCISES

Simplify.

53. $\dfrac{2^8}{2^2}$

54. $\dfrac{m^6}{m}$

55. $\dfrac{2^6 \cdot 4 \cdot 7^3}{2^5 \cdot 4^4 \cdot 7^2}$

56. $\dfrac{24b^6}{4b^5}$

57. $\dfrac{t^4v^5}{tv}$

58. $\left(\dfrac{1}{2}\right)^{-4}$

Simplify each quotient and write the answer in scientific notation.

59. $\left(2.5 \times 10^8\right) \div \left(0.5 \times 10^7\right)$

60. $\left(2 \times 10^{10}\right) \div \left(8 \times 10^2\right)$

7-5 Fractional Exponents (pp. 422–427)

 2.0

EXAMPLE

■ Simplify $\sqrt[3]{r^6s^{12}}$.

$\sqrt[3]{r^6s^{12}} = \left(r^6s^{12}\right)^{\frac{1}{3}}$ *Definition of $b^{\frac{1}{n}}$*

$= \left(r^6\right)^{\frac{1}{3}} \cdot \left(s^{12}\right)^{\frac{1}{3}}$ *Power of a Product Property*

$= \left(r^{6 \cdot \frac{1}{3}}\right) \cdot \left(s^{12 \cdot \frac{1}{3}}\right)$ *Power of a Power Property*

$= \left(r^2\right) \cdot \left(s^4\right)$ *Simplify exponents.*

$= r^2s^4$

EXERCISES

Simplify each expression.

61. $81^{\frac{1}{2}}$

62. $343^{\frac{1}{3}}$

63. $64^{\frac{2}{3}}$

64. $\left(2^6\right)^{\frac{1}{2}}$

Simplify each expression. All variables represent nonnegative numbers.

65. $\sqrt[5]{z^{10}}$

66. $\sqrt[3]{125x^6}$

67. $\sqrt{x^8y^6}$

68. $\sqrt[3]{m^6n^{12}}$

7-6 Polynomials (pp. 430–435)

 Prep for 10.0

EXAMPLES

■ Find the degree of the polynomial $3x^2 + 8x^5$.

$3x^2 + 8x^5$ *$8x^5$ has the highest degree.*

The degree is 5.

■ Classify the polynomial $y^3 - 2y$ according to its degree and number of terms.

Degree: 3
Terms: 2

The polynomial $y^3 - 2y$ is a **cubic** **binomial**.

EXERCISES

Find the degree of each monomial.

69. 5

70. $8st^3$

71. $3z^6$

72. $6h$

Write each polynomial in standard form. Then give the leading coefficient.

73. $2n - 4 + 3n^2$

74. $2a - a^4 - a^6 + 3a^3$

Classify each polynomial according to its degree and number of terms.

75. $2s - 6$

76. $-8p^5$

77. $-m^4 - m^2 - 1$

78. 2

7-7 Adding and Subtracting Polynomials (pp. 438–443)

 10.0

EXAMPLES

Add.

■ $\left(h^3 - 2h\right) + \left(3h^2 + 4h\right) - 2h^3$
$\left(h^3 - 2h\right) + \left(3h^2 + 4h\right) - 2h^3$
$\left(h^3 - 2h^3\right) + \left(3h^2\right) + \left(4h - 2h\right)$
$-h^3 + 3h^2 + 2h$

Subtract.

■ $\left(n^3 + 5 - 6n^2\right) - \left(3n^2 - 7\right)$
$\left(n^3 + 5 - 6n^2\right) + \left(-3n^2 + 7\right)$
$\left(n^3 + 5 - 6n^2\right) + \left(-3n^2 + 7\right)$
$n^3 + \left(-6n^2 - 3n^2\right) + (5 + 7)$
$n^3 - 9n^2 + 12$

EXERCISES

Add or subtract.

79. $3t + 5 - 7t - 2$

80. $4x^5 - 6x^6 + 2x^5 - 7x^5$

81. $-h^3 - 2h^2 + 4h^3 - h^2 + 5$

82. $\left(3m - 7\right) + \left(2m^2 - 8m + 6\right)$

83. $\left(12 + 6p\right) - \left(p - p^2 + 4\right)$

84. $\left(3z - 9z^2 + 2\right) + \left(2z^2 - 4z + 8\right)$

85. $\left(10g - g^2 + 3\right) - \left(-4g^2 + 8g - 1\right)$

86. $\left(-5x^3 + 2x^2 - x + 5\right) - \left(-5x^3 + 3x^2 - 5x - 3\right)$

7-8 Multiplying Polynomials (pp. 446–453)

 10.0

EXAMPLES

Multiply.

■ $(2x - 4)(3x + 5)$
$2x(3x) + 2x(5) - 4(3x) - 4(5)$
$6x^2 + 10x - 12x - 20$
$6x^2 - 2x - 20$

■ $(b - 2)\left(b^2 + 4b - 5\right)$
$b\left(b^2\right) + b(4b) - b(5) - 2\left(b^2\right) - 2(4b) - 2(-5)$
$b^3 + 4b^2 - 5b - 2b^2 + (-8b) + 10$
$b^3 + 2b^2 - 13b + 10$

EXERCISES

Multiply.

87. $(2r)(4r)$

88. $\left(3a^5\right)(2ab)$

89. $\left(-3xy\right)\left(-6x^2y\right)$

90. $\left(3s^3t^2\right)\left(2st^4\right)\left(\frac{1}{2}s^2t^8\right)$

91. $2\left(x^2 - 4x + 6\right)$

92. $-3ab\left(ab - 2a^2b + 5a\right)$

93. $(a + 3)(a - 6)$

94. $(b - 9)(b + 3)$

95. $(x - 10)(x - 2)$

96. $(t - 1)(t + 1)$

97. $\left(2q + 6\right)\left(4q + 5\right)$

98. $\left(5g - 8\right)\left(4g - 1\right)$

7-9 Special Products of Binomials (pp. 455–461)

 10.0

EXAMPLES

Multiply.

■ $\left(2h - 6\right)^2$
$\left(2h - 6\right)^2 = (2h)^2 + 2(2h)(-6) + (-6)^2$
$4h^2 - 24h + 36$

■ $\left(4x - 3\right)\left(4x + 3\right)$
$\left(4x - 3\right)\left(4x + 3\right) = (4x)^2 - 3^2$
$16x^2 - 9$

EXERCISES

Multiply.

99. $\left(p - 4\right)^2$

100. $\left(x + 12\right)^2$

101. $\left(m + 6\right)^2$

102. $\left(3c + 7\right)^2$

103. $\left(2r - 1\right)^2$

104. $\left(3a - b\right)^2$

105. $\left(2n - 5\right)^2$

106. $\left(h - 13\right)^2$

107. $(x - 1)(x + 1)$

108. $(z + 15)(z - 15)$

109. $\left(c^2 - d\right)\left(c^2 + d\right)$

110. $\left(3k^2 + 7\right)\left(3k^2 - 7\right)$

Evaluate each expression for the given value(s) of the variable(s).

1. $\left(\frac{1}{3}b\right)^{-2}$ for $b = 12$

2. $\left(14 - a^0 b^2\right)^{-3}$ for $a = -2$ and $b = 4$

Simplify.

3. $2r^{-3}$

4. $-3f^0 g^{-1}$

5. $m^2 n^{-3}$

6. $\frac{1}{2} s^{-5} t^3$

Write each number as a power of 10.

7. 0.0000001

8. $10{,}000{,}000{,}000{,}000$

9. 1

Find the value of each expression.

10. 1.25×10^{-5}

11. $10^8 \times 10^{-11}$

12. 325×10^{-2}

13. **Technology** In 2002, there were approximately 544,000,000 Internet users worldwide. Write this number in scientific notation.

Simplify.

14. $\left(f^4\right)^3$

15. $\left(4b^2\right)^0$

16. $\left(a^3 b^6\right)^6$

17. $-\left(x^3\right)^5 \cdot \left(x^2\right)^6$

Simplify each quotient and write the answer in scientific notation.

18. $\left(3.6 \times 10^9\right) \div \left(6 \times 10^4\right)$

19. $\left(3 \times 10^{12}\right) \div \left(9.6 \times 10^{16}\right)$

Simplify.

20. $\dfrac{y^4}{y}$

21. $\dfrac{d^2 f^5}{\left(d^3\right)^2 f^{-4}}$

22. $\dfrac{2^5 \cdot 3^3 \cdot 5^4}{2^8 \cdot 3^2 \cdot 5^4}$

23. $\left(\dfrac{4s}{3t}\right)^{-2} \cdot \left(\dfrac{2s}{6t}\right)^2$

24. **Geometry** The surface area of a cone is approximated by the polynomial $3.14r^2 + 3.14r\ell$, where r is the radius and ℓ is the slant height. Find the approximate surface area of a cone when $\ell = 5$ cm and $r = 3$ cm.

Simplify each expression. All variables represent nonnegative numbers.

25. $\left(\dfrac{27}{125}\right)^{\frac{1}{3}}$

26. $\sqrt[3]{43^3}$

27. $\sqrt{25y^8}$

28. $\sqrt[5]{3^5 t^{10}}$

Add or subtract.

29. $3a - 4b + 2a$

30. $\left(2b^2 - 4b^3\right) - \left(6b^3 + 8b^2\right)$

31. $-9g^2 + 3g - 4g^3 - 2g + 3g^2 - 4$

Multiply.

32. $-5\left(r^2 s - 6\right)$

33. $(2t - 7)(t + 4)$

34. $\left(4g - 1\right)\left(4g^2 - 5g - 3\right)$

35. $(m + 6)^2$

36. $(3t - 7)(3t + 7)$

37. $\left(3x^2 - 7\right)^2$

38. **Carpentry** Carpenters use a tool called a *speed square* to help them mark right angles. A speed square is a right triangle.

 a. Write a polynomial that represents the area of the speed square shown.

 b. Find the area when $x = 4.5$ in.

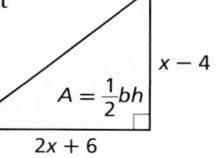

$x - 4$

$A = \frac{1}{2}bh$

$2x + 6$

COLLEGE ENTRANCE EXAM PRACTICE

CHAPTER 7

FOCUS ON SAT

When you receive your SAT scores, you will find a percentile for each score. The percentile tells you what percent of students scored lower than you on the same test. Your percentile at the national and state levels may differ because of the different groups being compared.

You may use some types of calculators on the math section of the SAT. For about 40% of the test items, a graphing calculator is recommended. Bring a calculator that you are comfortable using. You won't have time to figure out how a new calculator works.

You may want to time yourself as you take this practice test. It should take you about 7 minutes to complete.

---

1. If $(x + 1)(x + 4) - (x - 1)(x - 2) = 0$, what is the value of x?

   (A) -1

   (B) $-\dfrac{1}{4}$

   (C) 0

   (D) $\dfrac{1}{4}$

   (E) 1

---

2. Which of the following is equal to 4^5?

       I. $3^5 \times 1^5$

       II. 2^{10}

       III. $4^0 \times 4^5$

   (A) I only

   (B) II only

   (C) I and II only

   (D) II and III only

   (E) I, II, and III

---

3. If $x^{-4} = 81$, then $x =$

   (A) -3

   (B) $\dfrac{1}{4}$

   (C) $\dfrac{1}{3}$

   (D) 3

   (E) 9

---

4. What is the value of $2x^3 - 4x^2 + 3x + 1$ when $x = -2$?

   (A) -37

   (B) -25

   (C) -5

   (D) 7

   (E) 27

---

5. What is the area of a rectangle with a length of $x - a$ and a width of $x + b$?

   (A) $x^2 - a^2$

   (B) $x^2 + b^2$

   (C) $x^2 - abx + ab$

   (D) $x^2 - ax - bx - ab$

   (E) $x^2 + bx - ax - ab$

   $x - a$

   $x + b$

---

6. For integers greater than 0, define the following operations.

   $$a \,\square\, b = 2a^2 + 3b$$

   $$a \,\triangle\, b = 5a^2 - 2b$$

   What is $(a \,\square\, b) + (a \,\triangle\, b)$?

   (A) $7a^2 + b$

   (B) $-3a^2 + 5b$

   (C) $7a^2 - b$

   (D) $3a^2 - 5b$

   (E) $-3a^2 - b$

STRATEGIES FOR SUCCESS

Any Question Type: Use a Diagram

When a test item includes a diagram, use it to help solve the problem. Gather as much information from the drawing as possible. However, keep in mind that diagrams are not always drawn to scale and can be misleading.

EXAMPLE 1

Multiple Choice **What is the height of the triangle when $x = 4$ and $y = 1$?**

    Ⓐ 2   Ⓒ 8

    Ⓑ 4   Ⓓ 16

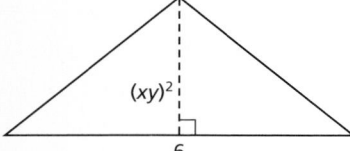

In the diagram, the height appears to be less than 6, so you might eliminate choices C and D. However, doing the math shows that the height is actually greater than 6. Do not rely solely on visual information. Always use the numbers given in the problem.

The height of the triangle is $(xy)^2$.

When $x = 4$ and $y = 1$, $(xy)^2 = (4 \cdot 1)^2 = (4)^2 = 16$.

Choice D is the correct answer.

If a test item does not have a diagram, draw a quick sketch of the problem situation. Label your diagram with the data given in the problem.

EXAMPLE 2

Short Response **A square placemat is lying in the middle of a rectangular table. The side length of the placemat is $\left(\frac{x}{2}\right)$. The length of the table is $12x$, and the width is $8x$. Write a polynomial to represent the area of the placemat. Then write a polynomial to represent the area of the table that surrounds the placemat.**

Use the information in the problem to draw and label a diagram. Then write the polynomials.

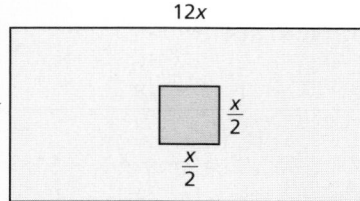

$\text{area of placemat} = s^2 = \left(\frac{x}{2}\right)^2 = \left(\frac{x}{2}\right)\left(\frac{x}{2}\right) = \frac{x^2}{4}$

$\text{area of table} = \ell w = (12x)(8x) = 96x^2$

$\text{area of table} - \text{area of placemat} = 96x^2 - \frac{x^2}{4} = \frac{384x^2 - x^2}{4} = \frac{383x^2}{4}$

The area of the placemat is $\frac{x^2}{4}$.

The area of the table that surrounds the placemat is $\frac{383x^2}{4}$.

If a given diagram does not reflect the problem, draw a sketch that is more accurate. If a test item does not have a diagram, use the given information to sketch your own. Try to make your sketch as accurate as possible.

Read each test item and answer the questions that follow.

Item A

Short Response The width of a rectangle is 1.5 feet more than 4 times its length. Write a polynomial expression for the area of the rectangle. What is the area when the length is 16.75 feet?

1. What is the unknown measure in this problem?

2. How will drawing a diagram help you solve the problem?

3. Draw and label a sketch of the situation.

Item B

Multiple Choice Rectangle *ABDC* is similar to rectangle *MNPO*. If the width of rectangle *ABDC* is 8, what is its length?

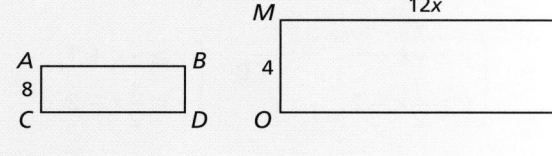

Ⓐ 2

Ⓑ $2x$

Ⓒ $24x$

Ⓓ 24

4. Look at the dimensions in the diagram. Do you think that the length of rectangle *ABDC* is greater or less than the length of rectangle *MNPO*?

5. Do you think the drawings reflect the information in the problem accurately? Why or why not?

6. Draw your own sketch to match the information in the problem.

Item C

Short Response Write a polynomial expression for the area of triangle *QRP*. Write a polynomial expression for the area of triangle *MNP*. Then use these expressions to write a polynomial expression for the area of *QRNM*.

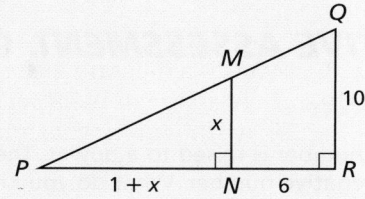

7. Describe how redrawing the figure can help you better understand the information in the problem.

8. After reading this test item, a student redrew the figure as shown below. Is this a correct interpretation of the original figure? Explain.

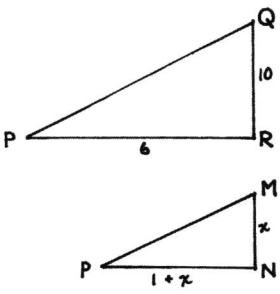

Item D

Multiple Choice The measure of angle *XYZ* is $(x^2 + 10x + 15)°$. What is the measure of angle *XYW*?

Ⓐ $(6x + 15)°$

Ⓑ $(2x^2 + 14x + 15)°$

Ⓒ $(14x + 15)°$

Ⓓ $(6x^2 + 15)°$

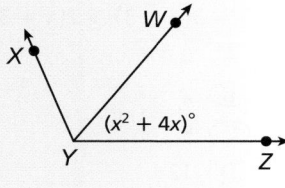

9. What information does the diagram provide that the problem does not?

10. Will the measure of angle *XYW* be less than or greater than the measure of angle *XYZ*? Explain.

go.hrw.com
Standards Practice Online
KEYWORD: MA8CA Practice

CUMULATIVE ASSESSMENT, CHAPTERS 1–7

Multiple Choice

1. A negative number is raised to a power. The result is a negative number. What do you know about the power?

    Ⓐ It is an even number.

    Ⓑ It is an odd number.

    Ⓒ It is zero.

    Ⓓ It is a whole number.

2. Which polynomial is the product of $2x + 3$ and $x - 4$?

    Ⓐ $2x^2 - 12$

    Ⓑ $2x^2 - 5x - 12$

    Ⓒ $2x^2 - 8x - 12$

    Ⓓ $2x^2 - 11x - 12$

3. Which ordered pair is a solution of this system of equations?
$$\begin{cases} \frac{1}{2}x + y = 4 \\ x - 2y = -12 \end{cases}$$

    Ⓐ $(4, 2)$ Ⓒ $(0, 4)$

    Ⓑ $(-6, 7)$ Ⓓ $(-2, 5)$

4. Which is a solution of the inequality $7 - 3(x - 3) > 2(x + 3)$?

    Ⓐ 0

    Ⓑ 2

    Ⓒ 5

    Ⓓ 12

5. One dose of Ted's medication contains 0.625 milligram, or $\frac{5}{8}$ milligram, of a drug. Which expression is equivalent to 0.625?

    Ⓐ $5(4)^{-2}$

    Ⓑ $5(2)^{-4}$

    Ⓒ $5(-2)^3$

    Ⓓ $5(2)^{-3}$

6. A restaurant claims to have served 352×10^6 hamburgers. What is this number in scientific notation?

    Ⓐ 3.52×10^6

    Ⓑ 3.52×10^8

    Ⓒ 3.52×10^4

    Ⓓ 352×10^6

7. The solutions of which system of inequalities can be represented by the shaded region?

    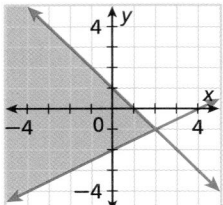

    Ⓐ $\begin{cases} y \le -x + 1 \\ y \le \frac{1}{2}x - 2 \end{cases}$ Ⓒ $\begin{cases} y \le -x + 1 \\ y \ge \frac{1}{2}x - 2 \end{cases}$

    Ⓑ $\begin{cases} y \ge -x + 1 \\ y \ge \frac{1}{2}x - 2 \end{cases}$ Ⓓ $\begin{cases} y \ge -x + 1 \\ y \le \frac{1}{2}x - 2 \end{cases}$

8. Which equation describes a line parallel to $y = 5 - 2x$?

    Ⓐ $y = -2x + 8$ Ⓒ $y = 5 + \frac{1}{2}x$

    Ⓑ $y = 2x - 5$ Ⓓ $y = 5 - \frac{1}{2}x$

9. A square has sides of length $x - 4$. A rectangle has a length of $x + 2$ and a width of $2x - 1$. What is the total combined area of the square and the rectangle?

    Ⓐ $10x - 14$

    Ⓑ $4x - 3$

    Ⓒ $3x^2 - 5x + 14$

    Ⓓ $3x^2 + 3x - 18$

10. Jennifer has a pocketful of change, all in nickels and quarters. There are 11 coins with a total value of $1.15. Which system of equations can you use to find the number of each type of coin?

Ⓐ $\begin{cases} n + q = 11 \\ n + q = 1.15 \end{cases}$

Ⓑ $\begin{cases} n + q = 11 \\ 5n + 25q = 1.15 \end{cases}$

Ⓒ $\begin{cases} 5n + 25q = 11 \\ n + q = 1.15 \end{cases}$

Ⓓ $\begin{cases} n + q = 11 \\ 0.05n + 0.25q = 1.15 \end{cases}$

11. Which of the following is a true statement?

Ⓐ $\left[(a^m)^n \right]^p = a^{m+n+p}$

Ⓑ $\left[(a^m)^n \right]^p = a^{mn+p}$

Ⓒ $\left[(a^m)^n \right]^p = a^{mnp}$

Ⓓ $\left[(a^m)^n \right]^p = (a^{m+n})^p$

12. In 1867, the United States purchased the Alaska Territory from Russia for 7.2×10^6. The total area was about 6×10^5 square miles. What was the price per square mile?

Ⓐ About $0.12 per square mile

Ⓑ About $1.20 per square mile

Ⓒ About $12.00 per square mile

Ⓓ About $120.00 per square mile

Gridded Response

13. Evaluate the expression $3b^{-2}c^0$ for $b = 2$ and $c = -3$.

14. What is the y-intercept of $5x + 6y - 4 = 0$?

15. The quotient $(5.6 \times 10^8) \div (8 \times 10^3)$ is written in scientific notation as (7×10^n). What is the value of n?

16. Jared multiplies the polynomials $2x - 1$ and $x^2 + 3x - 5$ and simplifies the product. What is the coefficient of the x^2-term?

Short Response

17. Line p is given by the equation $x + 2y = -6$. Point A has coordinates $(3, -2)$.

   a. Line q passes through point A and is perpendicular to line p. Write the equation of line q. Show your work.

   b. Find the intersection of lines p and q. Show your work.

18. A set of positive integers (a, b, c) is called a *Pythagorean triple* if $a^2 + b^2 = c^2$.

   a. Find a^2, b^2, and c^2 when $a = 2x$, $b = x^2 - 1$, and $c = x^2 + 1$. Show your work.

   b. Is $(2x, x^2 - 1, x^2 + 1)$ a Pythagorean triple? Explain your reasoning.

19. Ron is making an ice sculpture. The block of ice is in the shape of a rectangular prism with a length of $(x + 2)$ inches, a width of $(x - 2)$ inches, and a height of $2x$ inches.

   a. Write and simplify a polynomial expression for the volume of the block of ice. Show your work.

   b. The final volume of the ice sculpture is $(x^3 + 4x^2 - 10x + 1)$ cubic inches. Write an expression for the volume of ice that Ron carved away. Show your work.

20. Simplify the expression $(3 \cdot a^2 \cdot b^{-4} \cdot a \cdot b^{-3})^{-3}$ using two different methods. Show that the results are the same.

Extended Response

21. Look at the pentagon below.

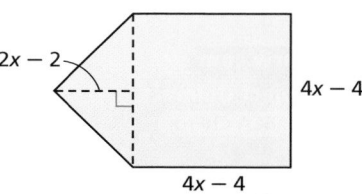

   a. Write and simplify an expression that represents the area of the pentagon. Show your work or explain your answer.

   b. Show one method of checking that your expression in part **a** is correct.

   c. The triangular part of the pentagon can be rearranged to form a square. Write the area of this square as the square of a binomial.

   d. Expand the product that you wrote in part **c**. What type of polynomial is this?

   e. Is the square of a binomial ever a binomial? Explain your reasoning.

CHAPTER 8

Factoring Polynomials

go.hrw.com
Chapter Project Online
KEYWORD: MA8CA ChProj

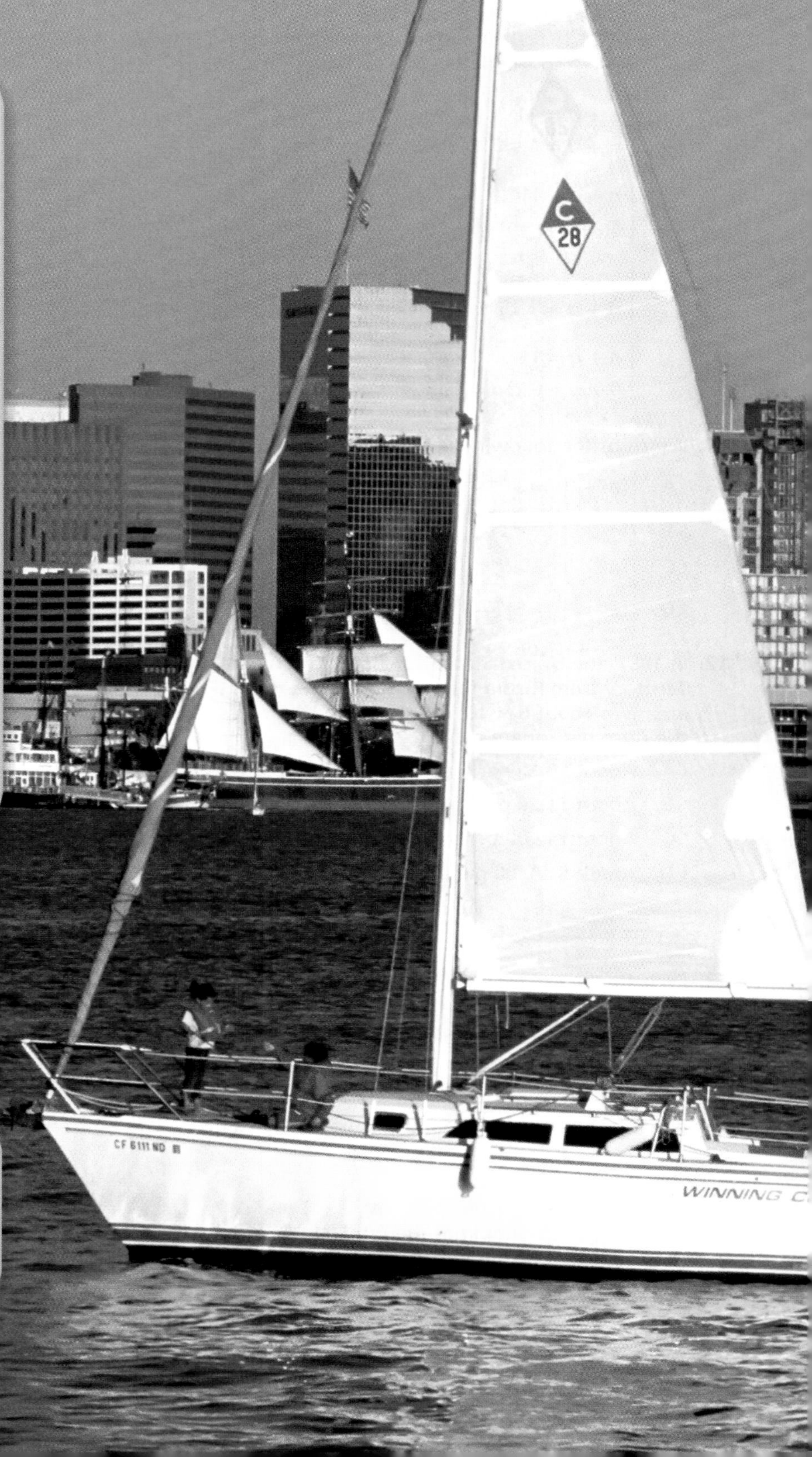

You can use polynomials to model area. When given the area of a sail as a polynomial, you can sometimes factor to find the sail's dimensions.

San Diego, CA

ARE YOU READY?

✓ Vocabulary

Match each term on the left with a definition on the right.

1. binomial
2. composite number
3. factor
4. multiple
5. prime number

A. a whole number greater than 1 that has more than two whole-number factors

B. a polynomial with two terms

C. the product of any number and a whole number

D. a number written as the product of its prime factors

E. a whole number greater than 1 that has exactly two positive factors, itself and 1

F. a number that is multiplied by another number to get a product

✓ Multiples

Write the first four multiples of each number.

6. 3   7. 4   8. 8   9. 15

✓ Factors

Tell whether the second number is a factor of the first number.

10. 20, 5   11. 50, 6   12. 120, 8   13. 245, 7

✓ Prime and Composite Numbers

Tell whether each number is prime or composite. If the number is composite, write it as the product of two numbers.

14. 2   15. 7   16. 10   17. 38

18. 115   19. 147   20. 151   21. 93

✓ Multiply Monomials and Polynomials

Simplify.

22. $2(x + 5)$ 23. $3h(h + 1)$ 24. $xy(x^2 - xy^3)$ 25. $6m(m^2 - 4m - 1)$

✓ Multiply Binomials

Find each product.

26. $(x + 3)(x + 8)$ 27. $(b - 7)(b + 1)$

28. $(2p - 5)(p - 1)$ 29. $(3n + 4)(2n + 3)$

Unpacking the Standards

The information below "unpacks" the standards. The Academic Vocabulary is highlighted and defined to help you understand the language of the standards. Refer to the lessons listed after each standard for help with the math terms and phrases. The Chapter Concept shows how the standard is applied in this chapter.

California Standard	Academic Vocabulary	Chapter Concept
11.0 Students apply basic factoring techniques to second- and simple third-degree polynomials. These techniques include finding a common factor for all terms in a polynomial, recognizing the difference of two squares, and recognizing perfect squares of binomials. (Lessons **8-2, 8-3, 8-5, 8-6**; Labs **8-2, 8-3**)	**apply** use **technique** a way of doing something **common** shared among all members of a group	You learn several ways to rewrite polynomials as products. **Example:** $x^2 + 3x$ Both terms in the polynomial contain the common term x, so the polynomial can be factored. $x^2 + 3x = x(x + 3)$
25.1 Students use properties of numbers to construct simple, valid arguments (direct and **indirect**) for, or formulate counterexamples to, **claimed assertions.** (pp. 484–485)	**construct** make or prepare **valid** true and correct **assertion** a statement that is made without proof	You learn a new method, indirect proof, for proving a mathematical statement.

 **Reading** and **Writing Math**

Reading Strategy: Read a Lesson for Understanding

To help you learn new concepts, you should read each lesson with a purpose. As you read a lesson, make notes. Include the main ideas of the lesson and any questions you have. In class, listen for explanations of the vocabulary, clarification of the examples, and answers to your questions.

Reading Tips

California Standards

➤ **2.0 Students understand and use such operations as** taking the opposite, finding the reciprocal, **taking a root,** and raising to a fractional

> The California Standards tell you the main standard covered in the lesson. The bold text indicates the specific part of the standard that the lesson focuses on.

If a power of 10 has a negative integer exponent, does that make the number negative?
How do I enter numbers written in scientific notation into my calculator?

> Write down questions you have as you read the lesson.

EXAMPLE 1 Evaluating Powers of 10

Find the value of each power of 10.

A 10^{-3}

Start with 1 and move the decimal point three places to the left.

0. 0 0 1

0.001

> Work through the examples and write down any questions you have.

CHECK IT OUT!

> Practice what you've learned in the Check It Out sections.

Try This

Read Lesson 8-1 prior to your next class. Then answer the questions below.

1. What vocabulary, formulas, and symbols are new?

2. Which examples, if any, are unclear?

3. What questions do you have about the lesson?

Factoring Polynomials **477**

8-1 Factors and Greatest Common Factors

California Standards

Preparation for 11.0 Students apply basic factoring techniques to second- and simple third-degree polynomials. These techniques include **finding a common factor** for all terms in a polynomial, recognizing the difference of two squares, and recognizing perfect squares of binomials.

Vocabulary
prime factorization
greatest common factor

Who uses this?
Web site designers who sell electronic greeting cards can use greatest common factors to design their Web sites. (See Example 4.)

The numbers that are multiplied to find a product are called *factors* of that product. A number is divisible by its factors.

Remember that a *prime number* is a whole number that has exactly two positive factors, itself and 1. The number 1 is not prime because it has only one factor.

You can use the factors of a number to write the number as a product. The number 12 can be factored several ways.

The order of the factors does not change the product, but there is only one example that cannot be factored further. The circled factorization is the **prime factorization** because all the factors are prime numbers. The prime factors can be written in any order, and, except for changes in the order, there is only one way to write the prime factorization of a number.

Factorizations of 12

$1 \cdot 12$

$2 \cdot 6$

$3 \cdot 4$

$1 \cdot 4 \cdot 3$

$\boxed{2 \cdot 2 \cdot 3}$

EXAMPLE 1 **Writing Prime Factorizations**

Write the prime factorization of 60.

Method 1 Factor tree
Choose any two factors of 60 to begin. Keep finding factors until each branch ends in a prime factor.

```
        60
       /  \
     ②  •  30
          /  \
        10 •  ③
       /  \
     ②  •  ⑤
```

$60 = 2 \cdot 2 \cdot 5 \cdot 3$

Method 2 Ladder diagram
Choose a prime factor of 60 to begin. Keep dividing by prime factors until the quotient is 1.

```
2 | 60
3 | 30
2 | 10
5 | 5
    1
```

$60 = 2 \cdot 3 \cdot 2 \cdot 5$

The prime factorization of 60 is $2 \cdot 2 \cdot 3 \cdot 5$ or $2^2 \cdot 3 \cdot 5$.

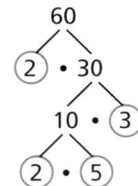 **CHECK IT OUT!** Write the prime factorization of each number.
    1a. 40   **1b.** 33   **1c.** 49   **1d.** 19

Factors that are shared by two or more whole numbers are called common factors. The greatest of these common factors is called the **greatest common factor**, or GCF.

Factors of 12: 1, 2, 3, 4, 6, 12

Factors of 32: 1, 2, 4, 8, 16, 32

Common factors: 1, 2,④

The greatest of the common factors is 4.

EXAMPLE 2 **Finding the GCF of Numbers**

Find the GCF of each pair of numbers.

A 24 and 60

Method 1 List the factors.

factors of 24: 1, 2, 3, 4, 6, 8, ⑫ 24   *List all the factors.*

factors of 60: 1, 2, 3, 4, 5, 6, 10, ⑫ 15, 20, 30, 60   *Circle the GCF.*

The GCF of 24 and 60 is 12.

B 18 and 27

Method 2 Use prime factorization.

$18 = 2 \cdot \boxed{3} \cdot \boxed{3}$ *Write the prime factorization of each number.*

$27 = \quad \boxed{3} \cdot \boxed{3} \cdot 3$ *Align the common factors.*

$3 \cdot 3 = 9$

The GCF of 18 and 27 is 9.

 **Find the GCF of each pair of numbers.**

2a. 12 and 16   **2b.** 15 and 25

You can also find the GCF of monomials that include variables. To find the GCF of monomials, write the prime factorization of each coefficient and write all powers of variables as products. Then find the product of the common factors.

EXAMPLE 3 **Finding the GCF of Monomials**

Find the GCF of each pair of monomials.

A $3x^3$ and $6x^2$

$3x^3 = \quad \boxed{3} \cdot \boxed{x} \cdot \boxed{x} \cdot x$ *Write the prime factorization of each*
$6x^2 = 2 \cdot \boxed{3} \cdot \boxed{x} \cdot \boxed{x}$ *coefficient and write powers as products.*
    Align the common factors.

$3 \cdot x \cdot x = 3x^2$ *Find the product of the common factors.*

The GCF of $3x^3$ and $6x^2$ is $3x^2$.

> **Helpful Hint**
>
> If two terms contain the same variable raised to different powers, the GCF will contain that variable raised to the lower power.

B $4x^2$ and $5y^3$

$4x^2 = 2 \cdot 2 \cdot \quad x \cdot x$ *Write the prime factorization of each*
$5y^3 = \quad 5 \cdot \quad y \cdot y \cdot y$ *coefficient and write powers as products.*
    Align the common factors.
    There are no common factors other than 1.

The GCF of $4x^2$ and $5y^3$ is 1.

 **Find the GCF of each pair of monomials.**

3a. $18g^2$ and $27g^3$ **3b.** $16a^6$ and $9b$ **3c.** $8x$ and $7v^2$

EXAMPLE 4   *Technology Application*

Garrison is creating a Web page that offers electronic greeting cards. He has 24 special occasion designs and 42 birthday designs. The cards will be displayed with the same number of designs in each row. Special occasion and birthday designs will not appear in the same row. How many rows will there be if Garrison puts the greatest possible number of designs in each row?

The 24 special occasion designs and 42 birthday designs must be divided into groups of equal size. The number of designs in each row must be a common factor of 24 and 42.

factors of 24: 1, 2, 3, 4, ⑥ 8, 12, 24   *Find the common factors of*
factors of 42: 1, 2, 3, ⑥ 7, 14, 21, 42   *24 and 42.*

The GCF of 24 and 42 is 6.

The greatest possible number of designs in each row is 6. Find the number of rows of each group of designs when there are 6 designs in each row.

$$\frac{24 \text{ special occasion designs}}{6 \text{ designs per row}} = 4 \text{ rows}$$

$$\frac{42 \text{ birthday designs}}{6 \text{ designs per row}} = 7 \text{ rows}$$

When the greatest possible number of designs is in each row, there are 11 rows in total.

4. Adrianne is shopping for a CD storage unit. She has 36 CDs by pop music artists and 48 CDs by country music artists. She wants to put the same number of CDs on each shelf without putting pop music and country music CDs on the same shelf. If Adrianne puts the greatest possible number of CDs on each shelf, how many shelves does her storage unit need?

THINK AND DISCUSS

1. Describe two ways you can find the prime factorization of a number.

2. GET ORGANIZED Copy and complete the graphic organizer. Show how to write the prime factorization of $100x^2$ by filling in each box.

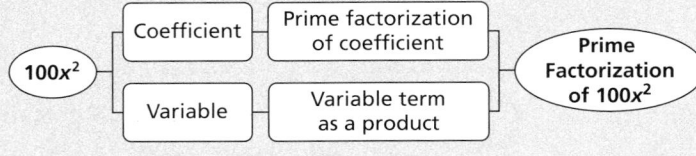

California Standards Practice

⬥ 10.0, Prep for 11.0, ⬥ 15.0, 25.1

go.hrw.com
Homework Help Online
KEYWORD: MA8CA 8-1
Parent Resources Online
KEYWORD: MA8CA Parent

GUIDED PRACTICE

1. **Vocabulary** Define the term *greatest common factor* in your own words.

SEE EXAMPLE 1
p. 478

Write the prime factorization of each number.

2. 20   3. 36   4. 27   5. 54

6. 96   7. 7   8. 100   9. 75

SEE EXAMPLE 2
p. 479

Find the GCF of each pair of numbers.

10. 12 and 60   11. 14 and 49   12. 55 and 121

13. 21 and 14   14. 13 and 40   15. 72 and 18

SEE EXAMPLE 3
p. 479

Find the GCF of each pair of monomials.

16. $15y^3$ and $-20y$ 17. $6x^2$ and $5x^2$ 18. $12r$ and $30r^2$

19. $2x^3$ and 6   20. $35a^2$ and $6a^3$ 21. $13q^4$ and $2p^2$

SEE EXAMPLE 4
p. 480

22. Samantha is making beaded necklaces using 54 glass beads and 18 clay beads. She wants each necklace to have the same number of beads, but each necklace will have only one type of bead. If she puts the greatest possible number of beads on each necklace, how many necklaces can she make?

PRACTICE AND PROBLEM SOLVING

Independent Practice

For Exercises	See Example
23–30	1
31–36	2
37–42	3
43	4

Extra Practice
Skills Practice p. EP16
Application Practice p. EP31

Write the prime factorization of each number.

23. 18   24. 64   25. 12   26. 150

27. 17   28. 226   29. 49   30. 63

Find the GCF of each pair of numbers.

31. 36 and 63   32. 14 and 15   33. 30 and 40

34. 15 and 75   35. 18 and 22   36. 16 and 99

Find the GCF of each pair of monomials.

37. $9s$ and $63s^3$ 38. $8a^2$ and 11   39. $-36w^3$ and $15w^2$

40. $5b^2$ and $3b$ 41. $3x^2$ and $9x$ 42. $-64n^4$ and $24n^2$

43. José is making fruit-filled tart shells for a party. He has 72 raspberries and 108 blueberries. The tarts will each have the same number of berries. Raspberries and blueberries will not be in the same tart. If he puts the greatest possible number of berries in each tart, how many tarts can he make?

Find the GCF of each pair of products.

44. $3 \cdot 5 \cdot t$ and $2 \cdot 2 \cdot 5 \cdot t \cdot t$ 45. $-1 \cdot 2 \cdot 2 \cdot x \cdot x$ and $2 \cdot 2 \cdot 7 \cdot x \cdot x \cdot x$

46. $2 \cdot 2 \cdot 2 \cdot 11 \cdot x \cdot x \cdot x$ and $3 \cdot 11$ 47. $2 \cdot 5 \cdot n \cdot n \cdot n$ and $-1 \cdot 2 \cdot 3 \cdot n$

48. **Write About It** Explain why the number 2 is the only even prime number.

49. **Reasoning** Show that the following statement is true or provide a counterexample to show it is false. If the GCF of two numbers is 1, then the two numbers are prime.

50. **Multi-Step** Angelo is making a rectangular floor for a clubhouse with an area of 84 square feet. The length of each side of the floor is a whole number of feet.

   a. What are the possible lengths and widths for Angelo's clubhouse floor?

   b. What is the minimum perimeter for the clubhouse floor?

   c. What is the maximum perimeter for the clubhouse floor?

51. **Music** The Cavaliers and the Blue Devils are two of the marching bands that are members of Drum Corps International (DCI). DCI bands are made up of percussionists, brass players, and color guard members who use flags and other props.

   In 2004, there were 35 color guard members in the Cavaliers and 40 in the Blue Devils. The two color guards will march in rows with the same number of people in each row without mixing the guards together. If the greatest possible number of people are in each row, how many rows will there be?

For each set of numbers, determine which two numbers have a GCF greater than 1, and find that GCF.

| 52. 11, 12, 14 | 53. 8, 20, 63 | 54. 16, 21, 27 |
| 55. 32, 63, 105 | 56. 25, 35, 54 | 57. 35, 54, 72 |

58. **Number Sense** The prime factorization of 24 is $2^3 \cdot 3$. Without performing any calculations or using a diagram, write the prime factorization of 48. Explain your reasoning.

Fill in each diagram. Then write the prime factorization of the number.

59.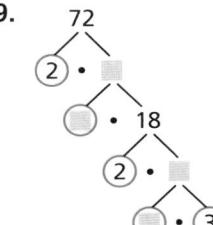

60.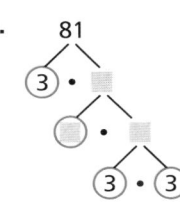

61.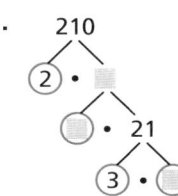

62.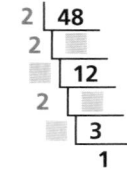

	56
2	28
2	
	7
	1

63.
	108
	54
3	
	9
3	3
	1

64.
2	136
	68
2	
	17
	1

65.
2	48
2	
	12
2	
	3
	1

66.
	140
2	
	35
7	7
	1

67.
2	40
	20
5	
	1

68. Kate has $12a^2$ raffle tickets and Henry has $18a$ raffle tickets. Kate makes equal piles using all of her tickets. Henry makes equal piles using all of his tickets. Henry and Kate have the same number of piles.

   a. Write an expression for the greatest number of piles that Kate and Henry can have.

   b. How many tickets will be in each of Kate's piles? in each of Henry's?

69. This problem will prepare you for the Concept Connection on page 512.

The equation for the motion of an object with constant acceleration is $d = vt + \frac{1}{2}at^2$ where d is distance traveled in feet, v is starting velocity in ft/s, a is acceleration in ft/s^2, and t is time in seconds.

   a. A toy car begins with a velocity of 2 ft/s and accelerates at 2 ft/s^2. Write an expression for the distance the toy car travels after t seconds.

   b. What is the GCF of the terms of your expression from part **a**?

Multiple Choice For Exercises 70 and 71, choose the best answer.

70. Which set of numbers has a GCF greater than 6?

   (A) 18, 24, 36   (B) 30, 35, 40   (C) 11, 29, 37   (D) 16, 24, 48

71. The slope of a line is the GCF of 48 and 12. The y-intercept is the GCF of the slope and 8. Which equation describes the line?

   (A) $y = 12x + 4$ (B) $y = 6x + 2$ (C) $y = 4x + 4$ (D) $y = 3x + 1$

72. Extended Response Patricia is making a dog pen in her back yard. The pen will be rectangular and have an area of 24 square feet. Draw and label a diagram that shows all possible whole-number dimensions for the pen. Find the perimeter of each rectangle you drew. Which dimensions should Patricia use in order to spend the least amount of money on fencing materials? Explain your reasoning.

CHALLENGE AND EXTEND

Find the GCF of each set.

73. $4n^3, 16n^2, 8n$

74. $27y^3, 18y^2, 81y$

75. $100, 25s^5, 50s$

76. $2p^4r, 8p^3r^2, 16p^2r^3$

77. $2x^3y, 8x^2y^2, 17xy^3$

78. $8a^4b^3, 4a^3b^3, 12a^2b^3$

 79. Geometry The area of a triangle is 10 in^2. What are the possible whole-number dimensions for the base and height of the triangle?

80. Number Sense The GCF of three different numbers is 7. The sum of the three numbers is 105. What are the three numbers?

81. Critical Thinking Find three different *composite* numbers whose GCF is 1. (*Hint:* A composite number has factors other than 1 and itself.)

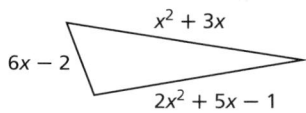

SPIRAL STANDARDS REVIEW   8.0, 🔑 10.0

Identify which lines are parallel. *(Lesson 5-7)*

82. $y = 2x + 6; y = 5x + 2; y = 2x; y = 2$

83. $y = 4x - 2; y = 9; y = 9x; y = 8$

84. At a local grocery store, grapes cost $2/lb and cherries cost $3/lb. How many pounds of each should be used to make a 10 lb mixture that costs $2.30/lb? *(Lesson 6-5)*

85. Write a simplified polynomial expression for the perimeter of the triangle. *(Lesson 7-7)*

$6x - 2$ $x^2 + 3x$ $2x^2 + 5x - 1$

LOGICAL REASONING

Indirect Proofs

In Chapter 1, you learned that some numbers are irrational. You now have enough knowledge to *prove* that some numbers are irrational by using deductive reasoning.

Use with Lesson 8-1

California Standards

25.1 Students use properties of numbers to construct simple, valid arguments (direct and **indirect**) **for,** or formulate counterexamples to, **claimed assertions.**

Example 1

Prove that if a prime number p is a factor of x^2, then p is also a factor of x.

Statements	Reasons
1. $x = p_1 p_2 p_3 \dots p_n$ where p_1, p_2, p_3,..., p_n are prime.	Every number can be written as the product of primes.
2. $x^2 = x \cdot x = (p_1 p_2 p_3 \dots p_n)(p_1 p_2 p_3 \dots p_n)$	Substitute $p_1 p_2 p_3 \dots p_n$ for x in Step 1.

The expression $(p_1 p_2 p_3 \dots p_n)(p_1 p_2 p_3 \dots p_n)$ contains only prime numbers, so it is the prime factorization of x^2. Since it contains only prime numbers that are factors of x, all prime numbers that are factors of x^2 are factors of x.

In other words, if a prime number is a factor of x^2, then it is also a factor of x.

Proving that some numbers are irrational often requires an *indirect proof*. In an **indirect proof,** first assume that the statement you want to prove is false—in other words, assume that the opposite of the statement is true.

Then use deductive reasoning to find a **contradiction**—two statements that cannot both be true at the same time.

An assumption that leads to a contradiction is false. Therefore, if you assume the opposite of a statement is true, and this leads to a contradiction, the assumption is false. This means the original statement must be true.

Try This

Write the opposite of each statement.

1. Susie is an only child.

2. All squares have four sides.

3. The sum of two even numbers is always even.

Find the two statements in each set that cannot both be true at the same time.

4. a and b are opposites.
   a and b are both negative.
   a and b are integers.

5. Angles A and B are both acute.
   Angles A and B are adjacent.
   Angles A and B are supplementary.

Example 2

Use an indirect proof to show that all prime numbers have irrational square roots.

Statements	Reasons
1. Suppose there were a number p that is prime and $\sqrt{p}$ is rational.	Assume the opposite of the statement you want to prove. In other words, assume the statement you want to prove is false.
2. $\sqrt{p} = \frac{a}{b}$ for integers a and b, $b \neq 0$. Assume a and b have no common factors besides 1; in other words, $\frac{a}{b}$ is in simplest form.	Definition of rational number; every rational number can be written in simplest form.
3. $p = \left(\frac{a}{b}\right)^2$	Definition of square root
4. $p = \frac{a^2}{b^2}$	Power of a Quotient Property
5. $pb^2 = a^2$	Multiplication Property of Equality (Multiply both sides by b^2.)
6. p is a factor of a^2.	Definition of factor
7. p is a factor of a.	Example 1
8. a can be written as the product of p and some number n: $a = pn$	Definition of factor
9. $pb^2 = (pn)^2$	Substitute pn for a in Statement 5.
10. $pb^2 = p^2n^2$	Product of a Power Property
12. $b^2 = pn^2$	Division Property of Equality (Divide both sides by p, $p \neq 0$.)
13. p is a factor of b^2.	Definition of factor
14. p is a factor of b.	Example 1
15. p is a factor of both a and b.	Statements 7 and 14

> Once you have proven a statement, you can use that statement in other proofs.

Statement 15 contradicts Statement 2. Therefore, the original statement, Statement 1, is false. There are no prime numbers that have rational square roots. In other words, all prime numbers have irrational square roots.

Try This

6. Complete the following indirect proof to show that there are infinitely many prime numbers.

Assume that there is a finite number of **a.** _____?_____ .

Then there is a prime number p that is the greatest prime number. Let n be the product of all prime numbers. In other words, $n = 2 \cdot 3 \cdot 5 \cdot \ldots \cdot p$. Then $n + 1 =$ **b.** _____?_____ . Since all numbers have a unique prime factorization, $n + 1$ must have a(n) **c.** _____?_____ .

However, 2 is not a factor of $n + 1$ because $n + 1$ is 1 greater than a multiple of **d.** _____?_____ . Also, 3 is not a factor of **e.** _____?_____ because $n + 1$ is **f.** _____?_____ . There is no prime number that is a factor of $n + 1$ because $n + 1$ is 1 greater than a multiple of **g.** _____?_____ . So, $n + 1$ does not have a prime factorization. This is a contradiction.

Therefore, the original assumption is false and **h.** _____?_____ .

8-2 Algebra LAB

Model Factorization by GCF

You can use algebra tiles to write a polynomial as the product of its factors. This process is called factoring. Factoring is the reverse of multiplying.

Use with Lesson 8-2

KEY

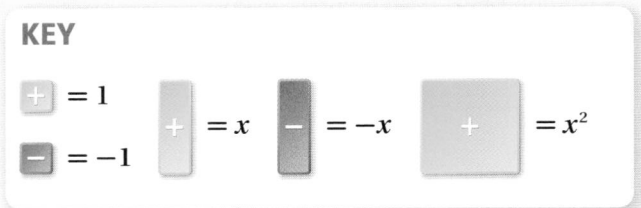

Activity

Use algebra tiles to factor $4x + 8$.

MODEL		ALGEBRA
	Model $4x + 8$.	$4x + 8$
x + 2 / 4	Arrange the tiles into a rectangle. The total area represents $4x + 8$. The length and width represent the factors. The rectangle has a width of $x + 2$ and a length of 4.	$4x + 8 = 4(x + 2)$

Use algebra tiles to factor $x^2 - 2x$.

MODEL		ALGEBRA
	Model $x^2 - 2x$.	$x^2 - 2x$
x − 2 / x	Arrange the tiles into a rectangle. The total area represents $x^2 - 2x$. The length and width represent the factors. The rectangle has a width of $x - 2$ and a length of x.	$x^2 - 2x = x(x - 2)$

Try This

Use algebra tiles to factor each polynomial.

1. $3x + 9$ **2.** $2x + 8$ **3.** $4x - 12$ **4.** $3x - 12$

5. $2x^2 + 2x$ **6.** $x^2 + 4x$ **7.** $x^2 - 3x$ **8.** $2x^2 - 4x$

8-2 Factoring by GCF

Why learn this?

You can determine the dimensions of a solar panel by factoring an expression representing the panel's area. (See Example 2.)

Recall the Distributive Property: $ab + ac = a(b + c)$. The Distributive Property allows you to "factor" out the GCF of the terms in a polynomial.

A polynomial is fully factored when it is written as a product of monomials and polynomials whose terms have no common factors other than 1.

Fully Factored	$2(3x - 4)$	Neither 2 nor $3x - 4$ can be factored.
Not Fully Factored	$2(3x - 4x)$	$3x - 4x$ can be factored. The terms have a common factor of x.

EXAMPLE **Factoring by Using the GCF**

Factor each polynomial. Check your answer.

Writing Math

Aligning common factors can help you find the greatest common factor of two or more terms.

A $4x^2 - 3x$

$$4x^2 = 2 \cdot 2 \cdot \boxed{x} \cdot x$$
$$3x = \qquad 3 \cdot \boxed{x}$$

Find the GCF.

$$\downarrow$$
$$x$$

The GCF of $4x^2$ and $3x$ is x.

$$4x(x) - 3(x)$$

Write terms as products using the GCF as a factor.

$$x(4x - 3)$$

Use the Distributive Property to factor out the GCF.

Check $x(4x - 3)$

Multiply to check your answer.

$$4x^2 - 3x \checkmark$$

The product is the original polynomial.

B $10y^3 + 20y^2 - 5y$

$$10y^3 = 2 \cdot \boxed{5} \cdot \boxed{y} \cdot y \cdot y$$
$$20y^2 = 2 \cdot 2 \cdot \boxed{5} \cdot \boxed{y} \cdot y$$
$$5y = \qquad\qquad \boxed{5} \cdot \boxed{y}$$

Find the GCF.

$$\downarrow \quad \downarrow$$
$$5 \cdot y = 5y$$

The GCF of $10y^3$, $20y^2$, and $5y$ is $5y$.

$$2y^2(5y) + 4y(5y) - 1(5y)$$

Write terms as products using the GCF as a factor.

$$5y(2y^2 + 4y - 1)$$

Use the Distributive Property to factor out the GCF.

Check $5y(2y^2 + 4y - 1)$

Multiply to check your answer.

$$10y^3 + 20y^2 - 5y \checkmark$$

The product is the original polynomial.

Factor each polynomial. Check your answer.

C $-12x - 8x^2$

$\qquad -1\left(12x + 8x^2\right)$ *Both coefficients are negative. Factor out -1.*

$\qquad\qquad 12x = \boxed{2} \cdot \boxed{2} \cdot 3 \cdot \boxed{x}$ *Find the GCF.*
$\qquad\qquad 8x^2 = \boxed{2} \cdot \boxed{2} \cdot 2 \cdot \boxed{x} \cdot x$

$\qquad\qquad\qquad\quad 2 \cdot 2 \cdot\qquad x = 4x$ *The GCF of $12x$ and $8x^2$ is $4x$.*

$\qquad -1\left[3(4x) + 2x(4x)\right]$ *Write each term as a product using the GCF.*
$\qquad -1\left[4x(3 + 2x)\right]$ *Use the Distributive Property to factor out*
$\qquad -1(4x)(3 + 2x)$ *the GCF.*
$\qquad -4x(3 + 2x)$

Check

$\qquad -4x(3 + 2x) = -12x - 8x^2 \checkmark$ *Multiply to check your answer.*

D $5x^2 + 7$

$\qquad\qquad 5x^2 = 5 \;\;\cdot x \cdot x$ *Find the GCF.*
$\qquad\qquad\quad 7 = \quad 7$

$\qquad\qquad 5x^2 + 7$ *There are no common factors other than 1.*

The polynomial cannot be factored further.

> **Caution!**
>
> When you factor out -1 as the first step, be sure to include it in all the other steps as well.

 **CHECK IT OUT!** Factor each polynomial. Check your answer.

1a. $5b + 9b^3$ **1b.** $9d^2 - 8^2$

1c. $-18y^3 - 7y^2$ **1d.** $8x^4 + 4x^3 - 2x^2$

To write expressions for the length and width of a rectangle with area expressed by a polynomial, you need to write the polynomial as a product. You can write a polynomial as a product by factoring it.

EXAMPLE 2   *Science Application*

Mandy's calculator is powered by solar energy. The area of the solar panel is $\left(7x^2 + x\right)$ cm². Factor this polynomial to find possible expressions for the dimensions of the solar panel.

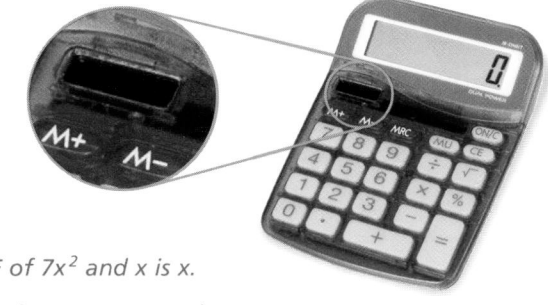

$\qquad A = 7x^2 + x$ *The GCF of $7x^2$ and x is x.*

$\qquad\quad = 7x(x) + 1(x)$ *Write each term as a product using the GCF as a factor.*

$\qquad\quad = x(7x + 1)$ *Use the Distributive Property to factor out the GCF.*

Possible expressions for the dimensions of the solar panel are x cm and $(7x + 1)$ cm.

CHECK IT OUT! **2. What if...?** The area of the solar panel on another calculator is $\left(2x^2 + 4x\right)$ cm². Factor this polynomial to find possible expressions for the dimensions of the solar panel.

Sometimes the GCF of terms is a binomial. This GCF is called a *common binomial factor*. You factor out a common binomial factor the same way you factor out a monomial factor.

EXAMPLE 3 **Factoring Out a Common Binomial Factor**

Factor each expression.

A $7(x - 3) - 2x(x - 3)$

$7(x - 3) - 2x(x - 3)$ *The terms have a common binomial factor of $(x - 3)$.*

$(x - 3)(7 - 2x)$ *Factor out $(x - 3)$.*

B $-t(t^2 + 4) + (t^2 + 4)$

$-t(t^2 + 4) + (t^2 + 4)$ *The terms have a common binomial factor of $(t^2 + 4)$.*

$-t(t^2 + 4) + 1(t^2 + 4)$ $(t^2 + 4) = 1(t^2 + 4)$

$(t^2 + 4)(-t + 1)$ *Factor out $(t^2 + 4)$.*

C $9x(x + 4) - 5(4 + x)$

$9x(x + 4) - 5(4 + x)$ $(x + 4) = (4 + x)$, *so the terms have a common binomial factor of $(x + 4)$.*

$9x(x + 4) - 5(x + 4)$

$(x + 4)(9x - 5)$ *Factor out $(x + 4)$.*

D $-3x^2(x + 2) + 4(x - 7)$

$-3x^2(x + 2) + 4(x - 7)$ *There are no common factors.*

The expression cannot be factored.

CHECK IT OUT! Factor each expression.

3a. $4s(s + 6) - 5(s + 6)$ **3b.** $7x(2x + 3) + (2x + 3)$

3c. $3x(y + 4) - 2y(x + 4)$ **3d.** $5x(5x - 2) - 2(5x - 2)$

You may be able to factor a polynomial by grouping. When a polynomial has four terms, you can sometimes make two groups and factor out the GCF from each group.

EXAMPLE 4 **Factoring by Grouping**

Factor each polynomial by grouping. Check your answer.

A $12a^3 - 9a^2 + 20a - 15$

$(12a^3 - 9a^2) + (20a - 15)$ *Group terms that have a common number or variable as a factor.*

$3a^2(4a - 3) + 5(4a - 3)$ *Factor out the GCF of each group.*

$3a^2(4a - 3) + 5(4a - 3)$ $(4a - 3)$ *is another common factor.*

$(4a - 3)(3a^2 + 5)$ *Factor out $(4a - 3)$.*

Check  *Multiply to check your solution.*

$4a(3a^2) + 4a(5) - 3(3a^2) - 3(5)$

$12a^3 + 20a - 9a^2 - 15$

$12a^3 - 9a^2 + 20a - 15$ ✓ *The product is the original polynomial.*

Factor each polynomial by grouping. Check your answer.

B $9x^3 + 18x^2 + x + 2$

$$\left(9x^3 + 18x^2\right) + (x + 2)$$ *Group terms.*

$$9x^2(x + 2) + 1(x + 2)$$ *Factor out the GCF of each group.*

$$9x^2(x + 2) + 1(x + 2)$$ *(x + 2) is a common factor.*

$$(x + 2)\left(9x^2 + 1\right)$$ *Factor out (x + 2).*

Check $(x + 2)\left(9x^2 + 1\right)$ *Multiply to check your solution.*

$$x\left(9x^2\right) + x(1) + 2\left(9x^2\right) + 2(1)$$

$$9x^3 + x + 18x^2 + 2$$

$$9x^3 + 18x^2 + x + 2 \checkmark$$ *The product is the original polynomial.*

 Factor each polynomial by grouping. Check your answer.

4a. $6b^3 + 8b^2 + 9b + 12$ **4b.** $4r^3 + 24r + r^2 + 6$

Helpful Hint

If two quantities are opposites, their sum is 0.

$$(5 - x) + (x - 5)$$
$$5 - x + x - 5$$
$$-x + x + 5 - 5$$
$$0 + 0$$
$$0$$

Recognizing opposite binomials can help you factor polynomials. The binomials $(5 - x)$ and $(x - 5)$ are opposites. Notice $(5 - x)$ can be written as $-1(x - 5)$.

$$-1(x - 5) = (-1)(x) + (-1)(-5)$$ *Distributive Property*

$$= -x + 5$$ *Simplify.*

$$= 5 - x$$ *Commutative Property of Addition*

So, $(5 - x) = -1(x - 5)$.

EXAMPLE 5   **Factoring with Opposites**

Factor $3x^3 - 15x^2 + 10 - 2x$.

$$\left(3x^3 - 15x^2\right) + (10 - 2x)$$ *Group terms.*

$$3x^2(x - 5) + 2(5 - x)$$ *Factor out the GCF of each group.*

$$3x^2(x - 5) + 2(-1)(x - 5)$$ *Write (5 − x) as −1(x − 5).*

$$3x^2(x - 5) - 2(x - 5)$$ *Simplify. (x − 5) is a common factor.*

$$(x - 5)\left(3x^2 - 2\right)$$ *Factor out (x − 5).*

 Factor each polynomial. Check your answer.

5a. $15x^2 - 10x^3 + 8x - 12$ **5b.** $8y - 8 - x + xy$

THINK AND DISCUSS

1. Explain how finding the GCF of monomials helps you factor a polynomial.

2. GET ORGANIZED Copy and complete the graphic organizer.

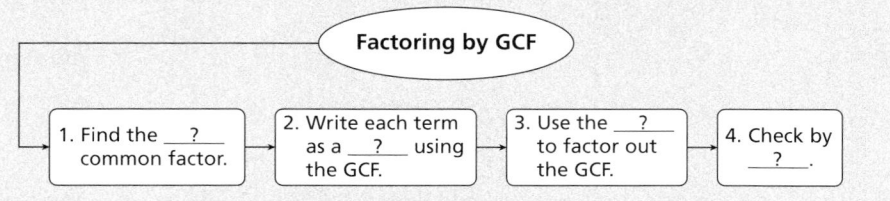

Factoring by GCF

1. Find the ___?___ common factor.

2. Write each term as a ___?___ using the GCF.

3. Use the ___?___ to factor out the GCF.

4. Check by ___?___.

GUIDED PRACTICE

SEE EXAMPLE 1
p. 487

Factor each polynomial. Check your answer.

1. $15a - 5a^2$
2. $10g^3 - 3g$
3. $-35x + 42$

4. $-4x^2 - 6x$
5. $12h^4 + 8h^2 - 6h$
6. $3x^2 - 9x + 3$

7. $9m^2 + m$
8. $14n^3 + 7n + 7n^2$
9. $36f + 18f^2 + 3$

SEE EXAMPLE 2
p. 488

10. Physical Science A model rocket is fired vertically into the air at 320 ft/s. The expression $-16t^2 + 320t$ gives the rocket's height after t seconds. Factor this expression.

SEE EXAMPLE 3
p. 489

Factor each expression.

11. $2b(b + 3) + 5(b + 3)$
12. $5(m - 2) - m(m - 2)$
13. $4(x - 3) - x(y + 2)$

SEE EXAMPLE 4
p. 489

Factor each polynomial by grouping. Check your answer.

14. $6x^3 + 4x^2 + 3x + 2$
15. $x^3 + 4x^2 + 2x + 8$
16. $10a^3 + 4a^2 + 5a + 2$

17. $7r^3 - 35r^2 + 6r - 30$
18. $2m^3 + 4m^2 + 6m + 12$
19. $4b^3 - 6b^2 + 10b - 15$

SEE EXAMPLE 5
p. 490

20. $6b^2 - 3b + 4 - 8b$
21. $2r^2 - 6r + 12 - 4r$
22. $6a^3 - 9a^2 - 12 + 8a$

23. $2m^3 - 6m^2 + 9 - 3m$
24. $3r - r^2 + 2r - 6$
25. $14q^2 - 21q + 6 - 4q$

PRACTICE AND PROBLEM SOLVING

Independent Practice

For Exercises	See Example
26–34	1
35	2
36–41	3
42–47	4
48–53	5

Extra Practice
Skills Practice p. EP16
Application Practice p. EP31

Factor each polynomial. Check your answer.

26. $36d^3 + 24$
27. $9y^2 + 45y$
28. $14x^3 + 63x^2 - 7x$

29. $-4d^4 + d^3 - 3d^2$
30. $-15f - 10f^2$
31. $-14x^4 + 5x^2$

32. $33d^3 + 22d + 11$
33. $21c^2 + 14c$
34. $-5g^3 - 15g^2$

35. Finance After t years, the amount of money in a savings account that earns simple interest is $P + Prt$, where P is the starting amount and r is the yearly interest rate. Factor this expression.

Factor each expression.

36. $-4x(x + 2) + 9(x + 2)$
37. $6a(a - 2) - 5b(b + 4)$
38. $5(3x - 2) + x(3x - 2)$

39. $-3(2 + b) + 4b(b + 2)$
40. $a(x - 3) + 2b(x - 3)$
41. $6y(y - 7) + (y - 7)$

Factor each polynomial by grouping. Check your answer.

42. $x^3 + 3x^2 + 5x + 15$
43. $2a^3 - 8a^2 + 3a - 12$
44. $10b^3 - 16b^2 + 25b - 40$

45. $n^3 - 2n^2 + 5n - 10$
46. $7x^3 + 2x^2 + 28x + 8$
47. $6x^3 + 18x^2 + x + 3$

48. $2d^3 - d^2 - 3 + 6d$
49. $2m^3 - 2m^2 + 3 - 3m$
50. $20 - 15x - 6x^2 + 8x$

51. $b^3 - 2b - 8 + 4b^2$
52. $5k^2 - k^3 + 3k - 15$
53. $6f^3 - 8f^2 + 20 - 15f$

54. Art Factor the expression for the area of the mural shown at right.

Area: $(12x^2 + x)$ ft²

Fill in the missing part of each factorization.

55. $16v + 12v^2 = 4v(4 + \blacksquare)$

56. $15x - 25x^2 = 5x(3 - \blacksquare)$

57. $-16k^3 - 24k^2 = -8k^2(\blacksquare + 3)$

58. $-x - 10 = -1(\blacksquare + 10)$

Copy and complete the table.

	Polynomial	Number of Terms	Name	Completely Factored Form
	$3y + 3x + 9$	3	trinomial	$3(y + x + 3)$
59.	$x^2 + 5x$	$\blacksquare$	$\blacksquare$	$\blacksquare$
60.	$28c^2 - 49c$	$\blacksquare$	$\blacksquare$	$\blacksquare$
61.	$a^4 + a^3 + a^2$	$\blacksquare$	$\blacksquare$	$\blacksquare$
62.	$36 + 99r - 40r^2 - 110r^3$	$\blacksquare$	$\blacksquare$	$\blacksquare$

63. **Personal Finance** The final amount of money in a certificate of deposit (CD) after n years can be represented by the expression Px^n, where P is the original amount contributed and x is the interest rate.

Year	Original Amount
2004	$100.00
2005	$200.00
2006	$400.00

Justin's aunt purchased CDs to help him pay for college. The table shows the amount of the CD she purchased each year. In 2007, she will pay $800.00 directly to the college.

   a. Each CD has the same interest rate x. Write expressions for the value of the CDs purchased in 2004, 2005, and 2006 when Justin starts college in 2007.

   b. Write a polynomial to represent the total value of the CDs purchased in 2004, 2005, and 2006 plus the amount paid to the college in 2007.

   c. Factor the polynomial in part **c** by grouping. Evaluate the factored form of the polynomial when the interest rate is 1.09.

64. **Write About It** Describe how to find the area of the figure shown. Show each step and write your answer in factored form.

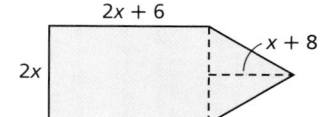

65. Critical Thinking Show two methods of factoring the expression $3a - 3b - 4a + 4b$.

66. **Geometry** The area of the triangle is represented by the expression $\frac{1}{2}(x^3 - 2x + 2x^2 - 4)$. The height of the triangle is $x + 2$. Write an expression for the base of the triangle. (*Hint:* The formula for the area of a triangle is $A = \frac{1}{2}bh$.)

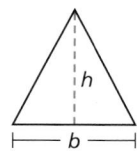

67. Write About It Explain how you know when two binomials are opposites.

CONCEPT CONNECTION

68. This problem will prepare you for the Concept Connection on page 512.

   a. What must be true about either a or b if $ab = 0$?

   b. A toy car's distance in feet from the starting point is given by the equation $d = t(3 - t)$. Explain why $t(3 - t) = 0$ means that either $t = 0$ or $3 - t = 0$.

   c. When $d = 0$, the car is at the starting point. Use the fact that $t = 0$ or $3 - t = 0$ when $d = 0$ to find the two times when the car is at the starting point.

69. Reasoning Fill in each blank with a property or definition that justifies the step.

$$7x^3 + 2x + 21x^2 + 6 = 7x^3 + 21x^2 + 2x + 6 \qquad \textbf{a.} \ \underline{\hspace{1.5cm} ? \hspace{1.5cm}}$$
$$= \left(7x^3 + 21x^2\right) + \left(2x + 6\right) \qquad \textbf{b.} \ \underline{\hspace{1.5cm} ? \hspace{1.5cm}}$$
$$= 7x^2(x + 3) + 2(x + 3) \qquad \textbf{c.} \ \underline{\hspace{1.5cm} ? \hspace{1.5cm}}$$
$$= (x + 3)\left(7x^2 + 2\right) \qquad \textbf{d.} \ \underline{\hspace{1.5cm} ? \hspace{1.5cm}}$$

70. ///**ERROR ANALYSIS**/// Which factorization of $3n^3 - n^2$ is incorrect? Explain.

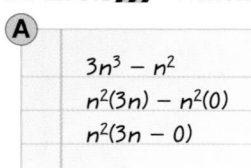
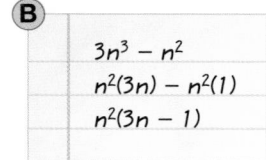

Multiple Choice For Exercises 71–73, choose the best answer.

71. Which is the complete factorization of $24x^3 - 12x^2$?

    Ⓐ $6\left(4x^3 - 2x^2\right)$ Ⓑ $12\left(2x^3 - x^2\right)$ Ⓒ $12x\left(2x^2 - x\right)$ Ⓓ $12x^2(2x - 1)$

72. Which is NOT a factor of $18x^2 + 36x$?

    Ⓐ 1   Ⓑ $4x$ Ⓒ $x + 2$ Ⓓ $18x$

73. The area of a rectangle is represented by the polynomial $x^2 + 3x - 6x - 18$. Which of the following could represent the length and width of the rectangle?

    Ⓐ Length: $x + 3$; width: $x + 6$ Ⓒ Length: $x + 3$; width: $x - 6$

    Ⓑ Length: $x - 3$; width: $x - 6$ Ⓓ Length: $x - 3$; width: $x + 6$

CHALLENGE AND EXTEND

Factor each polynomial. Check your answer.

74. $6ab^2 - 24a^2$ **75.** $-72a^2b^2 - 45ab$ **76.** $-18a^2b^2 + 21ab$

77. $ab + bc + ad + cd$ **78.** $4y^2 + 8ay - y - 2a$ **79.** $x^3 - 4x^2 + 3x - 12$

 80. Geometry The area between two concentric circles is called an *annulus*. The formula for area of an annulus is $A = \pi R^2 - \pi r^2$, where R is the radius of the larger circle and r is the radius of the smaller circle.

   a. Factor the formula for area of an annulus by using the GCF.

   b. Use the factored form to find the area of an annulus with $R = 12$ cm and $r = 5$ cm.

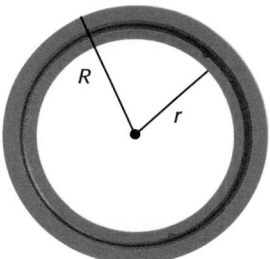

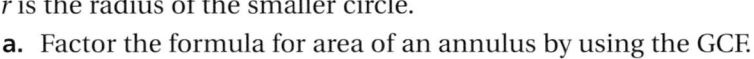 **SPIRAL STANDARDS REVIEW**   🐻 2.0, 8.0, 🐻 9.0, 25.1

81. The coordinates of the vertices of a quadrilateral are $A(-2, 5)$, $B(6, 5)$, $C(4, -3)$, and $D(-4, -3)$. Use slope to show that $ABCD$ is a parallelogram. *(Lesson 5-7)*

Solve each system by elimination. *(Lesson 6-3)*

82. $\begin{cases} x + 2y = 11 \\ 2x - y = 2 \end{cases}$ **83.** $\begin{cases} -2x + 2y = 14 \\ x - 3y = -19 \end{cases}$ **84.** $\begin{cases} 3x + 3y = 12 \\ x - 7y = -12 \end{cases}$

Simplify. *(Lesson 7-4)*

85. $\dfrac{5^6}{5^4}$ **86.** $\dfrac{4^5 \cdot 4^2}{4^6}$ **87.** $\dfrac{x^5 y^3 z}{y^3 z^4}$ **88.** $\dfrac{x^8 y^3 z^7}{x^2 y^4 z}$

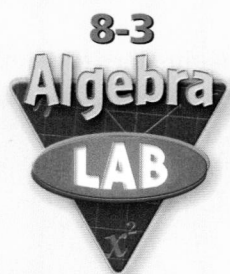

8-3

Algebra LAB

Model Factorization of $x^2 + bx + c$

You can use algebra tiles to express a trinomial as a product of two binomials. This is called factoring a trinomial.

Use with Lesson 8-3

California Standards

11.0 Students apply basic factoring techniques to second- and simple third-**degree polynomials.** These techniques include finding a common factor for all terms in a polynomial, recognizing the difference of two squares, and recognizing perfect squares of binomials.

KEY

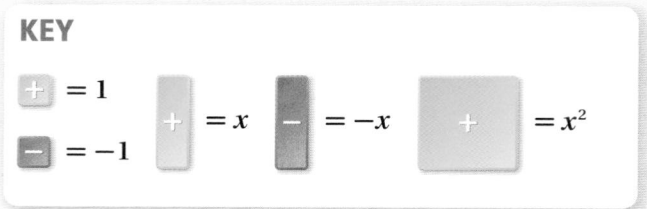

Activity 1

Use algebra tiles to factor $x^2 + 7x + 6$.

MODEL		ALGEBRA
	Model $x^2 + 7x + 6$.	$x^2 + 7x + 6$
	Try to arrange all of the tiles in a rectangle. Start by placing the x^2-tile in the upper left corner.	
	Arrange the unit tiles in a rectangle so that the top left corner of this rectangle touches the bottom right corner of the x^2-tile.	$x^2 + 7x + 6 \neq (x + 2)(x + 3)$
	Arrange the x-tiles so that all the tiles together make one large rectangle.	
	This arrangement does not work because two x-tiles are left over.	
	Rearrange the unit tiles to form another rectangle.	
	Fill in the empty spaces with x-tiles. All 7 x-tiles fit. This is the correct arrangement.	$x^2 + 7x + 6 = (x + 1)(x + 6)$
	The total area represents the trinomial. The length and width represent the factors.	

The rectangle has width $x + 1$ and length $x + 6$. So $x^2 + 7x + 6 = (x + 1)(x + 6)$.

Use algebra tiles to factor each trinomial.

1. $x^2 + 2x + 1$ **2.** $x^2 + 3x + 2$ **3.** $x^2 + 6x + 5$ **4.** $x^2 + 6x + 9$

5. $x^2 + 5x + 4$ **6.** $x^2 + 6x + 8$ **7.** $x^2 + 5x + 6$ **8.** $x^2 + 8x + 12$

Activity 2

Use algebra tiles to factor $x^2 + x - 2$.

MODEL		ALGEBRA
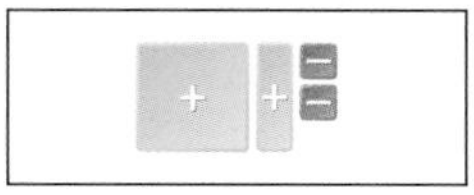	Model $x^2 + x - 2$.	$x^2 + x - 2$
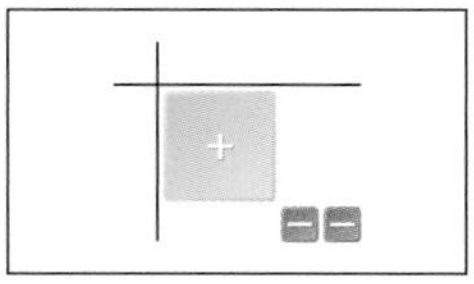 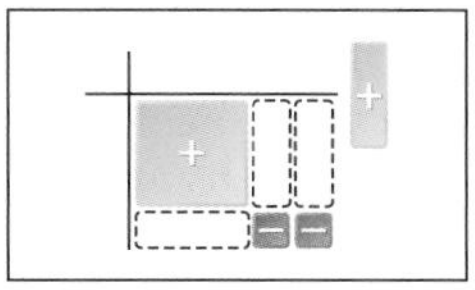	Start by placing the x^2-tile in the upper left corner. Arrange the unit tiles in a rectangle so that the top left corner of this rectangle touches the bottom right corner of the x^2-tile. To make a rectangle, you need to fill in the empty spaces, but there aren't enough x-tiles to fill in the empty spaces.	
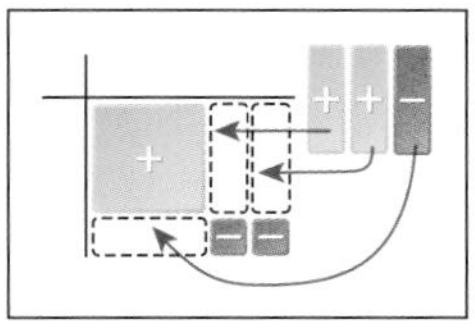	Add a zero pair. Arrange the x-tiles to complete the rectangle. The tiles in each row of the rectangle must be the same color.	
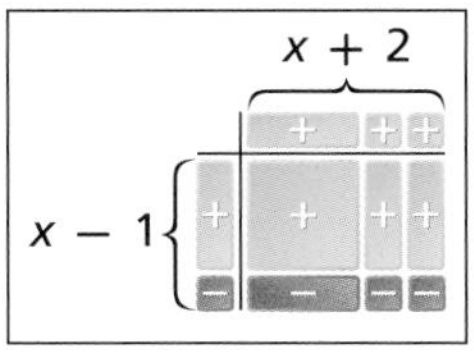	The total area represents the trinomial. The length and width represent the factors.	$x^2 + x - 2 = (x - 1)(x + 2)$

The rectangle has width $x - 1$ and length $x + 2$. So, $x^2 + x - 2 = (x - 1)(x + 2)$.

9. Why can you add one red $-x$-tile and one yellow x-tile?

Use algebra tiles to factor each polynomial.

10. $x^2 - x - 2$ **11.** $x^2 - 2x - 3$ **12.** $x^2 - 5x + 4$ **13.** $x^2 - 7x + 10$

14. $x^2 - 2x + 1$ **15.** $x^2 - 6x + 5$ **16.** $x^2 + 5x - 6$ **17.** $x^2 + 3x - 4$

18. $x^2 - x - 6$ **19.** $x^2 + 3x - 10$ **20.** $x^2 - 2x - 8$ **21.** $x^2 + x - 12$

8-3 Factoring $x^2 + bx + c$

California Standards

11.0 Students apply basic factoring techniques to **second-** and simple third-**degree polynomials.** These techniques include finding a common factor for all terms in a polynomial, recognizing the difference of two squares, and recognizing perfect squares of binomials.

Why learn this?

Factoring polynomials will help you find the dimensions of rectangular shapes, such as a fountain. (See Exercise 77.)

In Chapter 7, you learned how to multiply two binomials using the Distributive Property or the FOIL method. In this lesson, you will learn how to factor a trinomial into two binomials.

Notice that when you multiply $(x + 2)(x + 5)$, the constant term in the trinomial is the product of the constants in the binomials.

$$(x + 2)(x + 5) = x^2 + 7x + 10$$

Use this fact to factor some trinomials into binomial factors. Look for two integers (positive or negative) that are factors of the constant term in the trinomial. Write two binomials with those integers, and then multiply to check.

If no two factors of the constant term work, we say the trinomial is not factorable.

EXAMPLE 1 **Factoring Trinomials**

Factor $x^2 + 19x + 60$. Check your answer.

$(\blacksquare + \blacksquare)(\blacksquare + \blacksquare)$ *Write two sets of parentheses.*

$(x + \blacksquare)(x + \blacksquare)$ *The first term is x^2, so the variable terms have a coefficient of 1.*

The constant term in the trinomial is 60.

Try integer factors of 60 for the constant terms in the binomials.

$(x + 1)(x + 60) = x^2 + 61x + 60$ ✗

$(x + 2)(x + 30) = x^2 + 32x + 60$ ✗

$(x + 3)(x + 20) = x^2 + 23x + 60$ ✗

$(x + 4)(x + 15) = x^2 + 19x + 60$ ✓

The factors of $x^2 + 19x + 60$ are $(x + 4)$ and $(x + 15)$.

$x^2 + 19x + 60 = (x + 4)(x + 15)$

Check $(x + 4)(x + 15) = x^2 + 15x + 4x + 60$ *Use the FOIL method.*

$\qquad\qquad\qquad\quad = x^2 + 19x + 60$ ✓   *The product is the original trinomial.*

> **Remember!**
>
> When you multiply two binomials, multiply:
>
> **F**irst terms
> **O**uter terms
> **I**nner terms
> **L**ast terms

Factor each trinomial. Check your answer.

1a. $x^2 + 10x + 24$ **1b.** $x^2 + 7x + 12$

The method of factoring used in Example 1 can be made more efficient. Look at the product of $(x + a)$ and $(x + b)$.

$$\underbrace{(x + a)\ (x + b)}_{\substack{ax \\ bx}} \overset{\overbrace{x^2 \qquad ab}}{=} x^2 + ax + bx + ab$$
$$= x^2 + (a + b)x + ab$$

The coefficient of the middle term is the sum of a and b. The third term is the product of a and b.

Factoring $x^2 + bx + c$

WORDS	EXAMPLE
To factor a quadratic trinomial of the form $x^2 + bx + c$, find two integer factors of c whose sum is b.	To factor $x^2 + 9x + 18$, look for integer factors of 18 whose sum is 9.

Factors of 18	Sum	
1 and 18	19	✗
2 and 9	11	✗
3 and 6	9	✓

If no such integers exist, we say the trinomial is not factorable.

$x^2 + 9x + 18$
$(x + 3)(x + 6)$

When c is positive, its factors have the same sign. The sign of b tells you whether the factors are positive or negative. When b is positive, the factors are positive, and when b is negative, the factors are negative.

EXAMPLE 2   Factoring $x^2 + bx + c$ When c Is Positive

Factor each trinomial. Check your answer.

A $x^2 + 6x + 8$

$(x + \blacksquare)(x + \blacksquare)$ $b = 6$ and $c = 8$; look for factors of 8 whose sum is 6.

Factors of 8	Sum	
1 and 8	9	✗
2 and 4	6	✓

The factors needed are 2 and 4.

$(x + 2)(x + 4)$

Check $(x + 2)(x + 4) = x^2 + 4x + 2x + 8$ *Use the FOIL method.*
$\qquad\qquad\qquad\quad = x^2 + 6x + 8$ ✓   *The product is the original trinomial.*

B $x^2 + 5x + 6$

$(x + \blacksquare)(x + \blacksquare)$ $b = 5$ and $c = 6$; look for factors of 6 whose sum is 5.

Factors of 6	Sum	
1 and 6	7	✗
2 and 3	5	✓

The factors needed are 2 and 3.

$(x + 2)(x + 3)$

Check $(x + 2)(x + 3) = x^2 + 3x + 2x + 6$ *Use the FOIL method.*
$\qquad\qquad\qquad\quad = x^2 + 5x + 6$ ✓   *The product is the original trinomial.*

Factor each trinomial. Check your answer.

C $x^2 - 10x + 16$

$(x + \boxed{})(x + \boxed{})$ $b = -10$ and $c = 16$; look for factors of 16 whose sum is -10.

Factors of 16	Sum	
-1 and -16	-17	✗
-2 and -8	-10	✓
-4 and -4	-8	✗

The factors needed are -2 and -8.

$(x - 2)(x - 8)$

Check $(x - 2)(x - 8) = x^2 - 8x - 2x + 16$ Use the FOIL method.

$\qquad\qquad\qquad\quad = x^2 - 10x + 16$ ✓   The product is the original trinomial.

 Factor each trinomial. Check your answer.

2a. $x^2 + 8x + 12$ **2b.** $x^2 - 5x + 6$

2c. $x^2 + 13x + 42$ **2d.** $x^2 - 13x + 40$

When c is negative, its factors have opposite signs. The sign of b tells you which factor is positive and which is negative. The factor with the greater absolute value has the same sign as b.

EXAMPLE 3   **Factoring $x^2 + bx + c$ When c Is Negative**

Factor each trinomial.

A $x^2 + 7x - 18$

$(x + \boxed{})(x + \boxed{})$ $b = 7$ and $c = -18$; look for factors of -18 whose sum is 7. The factor with the greater absolute value is positive.

Factors of -18	Sum	
-1 and 18	17	✗
-2 and 9	7	✓
-3 and 6	3	✗

The factors needed are -2 and 9.

$(x - 2)(x + 9)$

B $x^2 - 5x - 24$

$(x + \boxed{})(x + \boxed{})$ $b = -5$ and $c = -24$; look for factors of -24 whose sum is -5. The factor with the greater absolute value is negative.

Factors of -24	Sum	
1 and -24	-23	✗
2 and -12	-10	✗
3 and -8	-5	✓
4 and -6	-2	✗

The factors needed are 3 and -8.

$(x + 3)(x - 8)$

Helpful Hint

If you have trouble remembering the rules for which factor is positive and which is negative, you can try all the factor pairs and check their sums.

 Factor each trinomial. Check your answer.

3a. $x^2 + 2x - 15$ **3b.** $x^2 - 6x + 8$ **3c.** $x^2 - 8x - 20$

A polynomial and the factored form of the polynomial are equivalent expressions. When you evaluate these two expressions for the same value of the variable, the results are the same.

EXAMPLE 4 **Evaluating Polynomials**

Factor $n^2 + 11n + 24$. Show that the original polynomial and the factored form have the same value for $n = 0, 1, 2, 3,$ and 4.

$n^2 + 11n + 24$

$(n + \boxed{})(n + \boxed{})$ *b = 11 and c = 24; look for factors of 24 whose sum is 11.*

Factors of 24	Sum	
1 and 24	25	✗
2 and 12	14	✗
3 and 8	11	✓
4 and 6	10	✗

The factors needed are 3 and 8.

$(n + 3)(n + 8)$

Evaluate the original polynomial and the factored form for $n = 0, 1, 2, 3,$ and 4.

n	$n^2 + 11n + 24$
0	$0^2 + 11(0) + 24 = 24$
1	$1^2 + 11(1) + 24 = 36$
2	$2^2 + 11(2) + 24 = 50$
3	$3^2 + 11(3) + 24 = 66$
4	$4^2 + 11(4) + 24 = 84$

n	$(n + 3)(n + 8)$
0	$(0 + 3)(0 + 8) = 24$
1	$(1 + 3)(1 + 8) = 36$
2	$(2 + 3)(2 + 8) = 50$
3	$(3 + 3)(3 + 8) = 66$
4	$(4 + 3)(4 + 8) = 84$

The original polynomial and the factored form have the same value for the given values of n.

CHECK IT OUT! 4. Factor $n^2 - 7n + 10$. Show that the original polynomial and the factored form have the same value for $n = 0, 1, 2, 3,$ and 4.

THINK AND DISCUSS

1. Explain in your own words how to factor $x^2 + 9x + 14$. Show how to check your answer.

2. Explain how you can determine the signs of the factors of c when factoring a trinomial of the form $x^2 + bx + c$.

3. GET ORGANIZED Copy and complete the graphic organizer. In each box, write an example of a trinomial with the given properties and factor it.

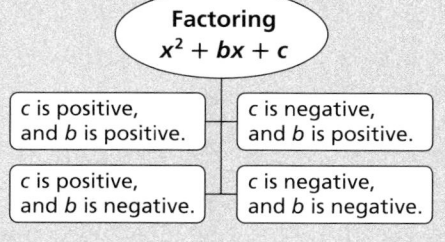

Factoring $x^2 + bx + c$

| c is positive, and b is positive. | c is negative, and b is positive. |
| c is positive, and b is negative. | c is negative, and b is negative. |

8-3 **Exercises**

California Standards Practice
🐻 10.0, 11.0, 🗝 15.0

go.hrw.com
Homework Help Online
KEYWORD: MA8CA 8-3
Parent Resources Online
KEYWORD: MA8CA Parent

GUIDED PRACTICE

SEE EXAMPLE **1**
p. 496

Factor each trinomial. Check your answer.

1. $x^2 + 13x + 36$

2. $x^2 + 11x + 24$

3. $x^2 + 14x + 40$

4. $x^2 + 5x + 4$

5. $x^2 + 6x + 5$

6. $x^2 + 8x + 15$

SEE EXAMPLE **2**
p. 497

7. $x^2 + 10x + 16$

8. $x^2 + 4x + 3$

9. $x^2 - 11x + 24$

10. $x^2 - 9x + 14$

11. $x^2 - 7x + 6$

12. $x^2 + 15x + 44$

SEE EXAMPLE **3**
p. 498

13. $x^2 + 6x - 27$

14. $x^2 - 6x - 7$

15. $x^2 - 4x - 45$

16. $x^2 - 3x - 18$

17. $x^2 - x - 2$

18. $x^2 + x - 30$

SEE EXAMPLE **4**
p. 499

19. Factor $n^2 + 6n - 7$. Show that the original polynomial and the factored form have the same value for $n = 0, 1, 2, 3,$ and 4.

PRACTICE AND PROBLEM SOLVING

Independent Practice

For Exercises	See Example
20–25	1
26–31	2
32–37	3
38	4

Extra Practice
Skills Practice p. EP16
Application Practice p. EP31

Factor each trinomial. Check your answer.

20. $x^2 + 11x + 28$

21. $x^2 + 13x + 30$

22. $x^2 + 11x + 18$

23. $x^2 + 13x + 40$

24. $x^2 + 12x + 20$

25. $x^2 + 16x + 48$

26. $x^2 + 12x + 11$

27. $x^2 + 16x + 28$

28. $x^2 + 15x + 36$

29. $x^2 - 6x + 5$

30. $x^2 - 9x + 18$

31. $x^2 - 12x + 32$

32. $x^2 + x - 12$

33. $x^2 + 4x - 21$

34. $x^2 + 9x - 36$

35. $x^2 - 12x - 13$

36. $x^2 - 10x - 24$

37. $x^2 - 2x - 35$

38. Factor $n^2 - 12n - 45$. Show that the original polynomial and the factored form have the same value for $n = 0, 1, 2, 3,$ and 4.

Match each trinomial with its correct factorization.

39. $x^2 + 3x - 10$

A. $(x - 2)(x - 5)$

40. $x^2 - 7x + 10$

B. $(x + 1)(x + 10)$

41. $x^2 - 9x - 10$

C. $(x - 2)(x + 5)$

42. $x^2 + 11x + 10$

D. $(x + 1)(x - 10)$

 43. Write About It Compare multiplying binomials with factoring polynomials into binomial factors.

Factor each trinomial, if possible. Check your answer.

44. $x^2 + x - 20$

45. $x^2 - 11x + 18$

46. $x^2 - 4x - 21$

47. $x^2 + 10x + 9$

48. $x^2 - 12x + 32$

49. $x^2 + 13x + 42$

50. $x^2 - 7x - 12$

51. $x^2 + 11x + 18$

52. $x^2 - 6x - 27$

53. $x^2 + 5x - 24$

54. $x^2 - 10x + 21$

55. $x^2 + 4x - 45$

56. Factor $n^2 + 11n + 28$. Show that the original polynomial and the factored form have the same value for $n = 0, 1, 2, 3,$ and 4.

57. Estimation The graph shows the areas of rectangles with dimensions $(x + 1)$ yards and $(x + 2)$ yards. Estimate the value of x for a rectangle with area 9 square yards.

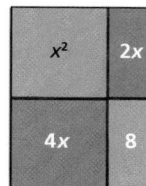

Area (yd²) graph with x-values axis

58. Geometry The area of a rectangle in square feet can be represented by $x^2 + 8x + 12$. The length is $(x + 6)$ ft. What is the width of the rectangle?

59. Remodeling A homeowner wants to enlarge a closet that has an area of $(x^2 + 3x + 2)$ ft². The length is $(x + 2)$ ft. After construction, the area will be $(x^2 + 8x + 15)$ ft² with a length of $(x + 3)$ ft.

  a. Find the dimensions of the closet before construction.

  b. Find the dimensions of the closet after construction.

  c. By how many feet will the length and width increase after construction?

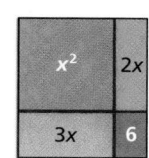
Art Write the polynomial modeled and then factor.

60.

x^2 $2x$
$3x$ 6

61.

x^2 $2x$
$4x$ 8

62.

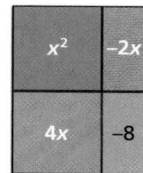

x^2 $-2x$
$4x$ -8

Copy and complete the table.

	$x^2 + bx + c$	Sign of c	Binomial Factors	Signs of Numbers in Binomials
	$x^2 + 4x + 3$	Positive	$(x + 1)(x + 3)$	Both positive
63.	$x^2 - 4x + 3$	▨	$(x \;▨\; 1)(x \;▨\; 3)$	▨
64.	$x^2 + 2x - 3$	▨	$(x \;▨\; 1)(x \;▨\; 3)$	▨
65.	$x^2 - 2x - 3$	▨	$(x \;▨\; 1)(x \;▨\; 3)$	▨

66. Geometry A rectangle has area $x^2 + 6x + 8$. The length is $x + 4$. Find the width of the rectangle. Could the rectangle be a square? Explain why or why not.

CONCEPT CONNECTION

67. This problem will prepare you for the Concept Connection on page 512.

The equation for the motion of an object with constant acceleration is $d = vt + \frac{1}{2}at^2$ where d is distance traveled in feet, v is starting velocity in feet per second, a is acceleration in feet per second squared, and t is time in seconds.

  a. Janna has two toy race cars on a track. One starts with a velocity of 0 ft/s and accelerates at 2 ft/s². Write an equation for the distance the car travels in time t.

  b. The second car travels at a constant speed of 4 ft/s. Write an equation for the distance the second car travels in time t. (*Hint:* When speed is constant, the acceleration is 0 ft/s².)

  c. By setting the equations equal to each other you can determine when the cars have traveled the same distance: $t^2 = 4t$. This can be written as $t^2 - 4t = 0$. Factor the left side of the equation.

68. Construction The length of a platform is $(x + 7)$ ft. The area of the platform is $(x^2 + 9x + 14)$ ft^2. Find the width of the platform. Check your answer.

(x + 7) ft

 Reasoning Tell whether each statement is true or false. If false, explain.

69. The third term in a factorable trinomial is equal to the product of the constants in its binomial factors.

70. The constants in the binomial factors of $x^2 + x - 2$ are both negative.

71. The correct factorization of $x^2 - 3x - 4$ is $(x + 4)(x - 1)$.

72. All trinomials of the form $x^2 + bx + c$ can be factored.

Fill in the missing part of each factorization.

73. $x^2 - 6x + 8 = (x - 2)(x - \blacksquare)$

74. $x^2 - 2x - 8 = (x + 2)(x - \blacksquare)$

75. $x^2 + 2x - 8 = (x - 2)(x + \blacksquare)$

76. $x^2 + 6x + 8 = (x + 2)(x + \blacksquare)$

77. Construction The area of a rectangular fountain is $(x^2 + 12x + 20)$ ft^2. The width is $(x + 2)$ ft.

   a. Find the length of the fountain.

   b. A 2-foot walkway is built around the fountain. Find the dimensions of the outside border of the walkway.

   c. Find the total area covered by the fountain and walkway.

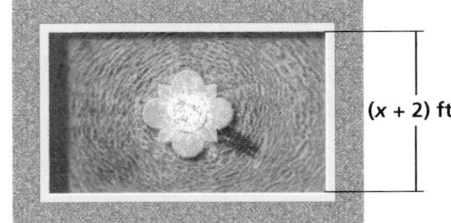

$(x + 2)$ ft

78. Critical Thinking Find all possible values of b so that $x^2 + bx + 6$ can be factored into binomial factors.

Multiple Choice For Exercises 79–81, choose the best answer.

79. Which is the correct factorization of $x^2 - 10x - 24$?

   Ⓐ $(x - 4)(x - 6)$ Ⓒ $(x - 2)(x + 12)$

   Ⓑ $(x + 4)(x - 6)$ Ⓓ $(x + 2)(x - 12)$

80. Which value of b would make $x^2 + bx - 20$ factorable?

   Ⓐ 9   Ⓑ 12   Ⓒ 19   Ⓓ 21

81. Which value of b would NOT make $x^2 + bx - 36$ factorable?

   Ⓐ 5   Ⓑ 9   Ⓒ 15   Ⓓ 16

82. Short Response What are the factors of $x^2 + 2x - 24$? Show and explain each step of factoring the polynomial.

CHALLENGE AND EXTEND

Factor each trinomial. Check your answer.

83. $x^4 + 18x^2 + 81$ **84.** $y^4 - 5y^2 - 24$ **85.** $d^4 + 22d^2 + 21$

86. $(u + v)^2 + 2(u + v) - 3$ **87.** $(de)^2 - (de) - 20$ **88.** $(m - n)^2 - 4(m - n) - 45$

89. Find all possible values of b such that, when $x^2 + bx + 28$ is factored, both constants in the binomials are positive.

90. Find all possible values of b such that, when $x^2 + bx + 32$ is factored, both constants in the binomials are negative.

91. Landscaping The area of Beth's rectangular garden is $(x^2 + 13x + 42)$ ft^2. The width is $(x + 6)$ ft.

Item	Cost
Fertilizer	$0.28/ft^2
Fencing	$2.00/ft

   a. What is the length of the garden?

   b. Find the perimeter in terms of x.

   c. Find the cost to fence the garden when x is 5.

   d. Find the cost of fertilizer when x is 5.

   e. Find the total cost to fence and fertilize Beth's garden when x is 5.

 SPIRAL STANDARDS REVIEW   🗝 2.0, 🗝 9.0, 11.0

Solve each system by substitution. *(Lesson 6-4)*

92. $\begin{cases} 3x + y = 13 \\ x - 3y = 1 \end{cases}$ **93.** $\begin{cases} 2x - y = 1 \\ x - y = -2 \end{cases}$ **94.** $\begin{cases} -x - y = -2 \\ x - 2y = 20 \end{cases}$

Simplify. *(Lesson 7-3)*

95. $x^3 x^2$ **96.** $m^8 n^3 m^{-12}$ **97.** $\left(t^4\right)^3$ **98.** $\left(-2xy^3\right)^5$

Factor each polynomial by grouping. *(Lesson 8-2)*

99. $x^3 + 2x^2 + 5x + 10$ **100.** $2n^3 - 8n^2 - 3n + 12$

101. $2p^4 - 4p^3 + 7p - 14$ **102.** $x^3 - 4x^2 + x - 4$

Career Path

go.hrw.com
Career Resources Online
KEYWORD: MA8CA Career

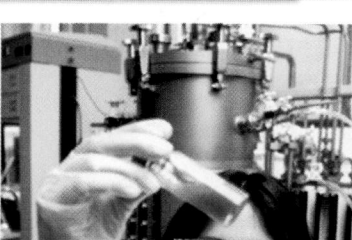

Jessica Rubino
Environmental Sciences major

Q: What math classes did you take in high school?

A: Algebra 1, Algebra 2, and Geometry

Q: What college math classes have you taken?

A: I took several computer modeling and programming classes as well as Statistics and Probability.

Q: How is math used in some of your projects?

A: Computer applications help me analyze data collected from a local waste disposal site. I used my mathematical knowledge to make recommendations on how to preserve surrounding water supplies.

Q: What plans do you have for the future?

A: I enjoy my studies in the area of water pollution. I would also like to research more efficient uses of natural energy resources.

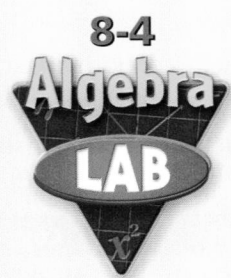

8-4

Algebra LAB

Model Factorization of $ax^2 + bx + c$

You can use algebra tiles to factor a trinomial whose lead coefficient is not 1.

Use with Lesson 8-4

California Standards

11.0 Students apply basic factoring techniques to second- and simple third-**degree polynomials.** These techniques include finding a common factor for all terms in a polynomial, recognizing the difference of two squares, and recognizing perfect squares of binomials.

KEY

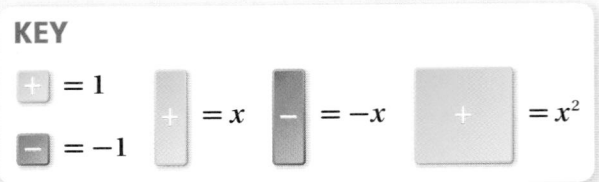

$\boxed{+} = 1$

$\boxed{-} = -1$

$= x$ $= -x$ $= x^2$

Activity 1

Use algebra tiles to factor $2x^2 + 5x + 2$.

MODEL		ALGEBRA
	Model $2x^2 + 5x + 2$.	$2x^2 + 5x + 2$
	Try to arrange all of the tiles in a rectangle. Place the x^2-tiles in the upper left corner. Arrange the unit tiles in a rectangle so that the top left corner of this rectangle touches the bottom right corner of the second x^2-tile. Arrange the x-tiles so that all the tiles together make one large rectangle. This does not work. One x-tile is left over.	$2x^2 + 5x + 2 \neq (x + 1)(2x + 2)$
	Rearrange the unit tiles to form another rectangle.	
$2x + 1$ $x + 2$	Fill in the empty spaces with x-tiles. All 5 x-tiles fit. This is the correct arrangement. The total area represents the trinomial $2x^2 + 5x + 2$. The length $2x + 1$ and width $x + 2$ represent the factors.	$2x^2 + 5x + 2 = (x + 2)(2x + 1)$

Try This

Use algebra tiles to factor each trinomial.

1. $3x^2 + 7x + 4$ **2.** $3x^2 + 4x - 4$ **3.** $2x^2 - x - 1$ **4.** $4x^2 - 8x + 3$

8-4 Factoring $ax^2 + bx + c$

California Standards

11.0 Students apply basic factoring techniques to second- and simple third-degree **polynomials.** These techniques include finding a common factor for all terms in a polynomial, recognizing the difference of two squares, and recognizing perfect squares of binomials.

Why learn this?

The height of a football that has been kicked can be modeled by a factored polynomial. (See Exercise 75.)

In the previous lesson you factored trinomials of the form $x^2 + bx + c$. Now you will factor trinomials of the form $ax^2 + bx + c$, where $a \neq 0$ or 1.

When you multiply $(3x + 2)(2x + 5)$, the coefficient of the x^2-term is the product of the coefficients of the x-terms. Also, the constant term in the trinomial is the product of the constants in the binomials.

$$(3x+2)(2x+5) = 6x^2 + 19x + 10$$

To factor a trinomial like $ax^2 + bx + c$ into its binomial factors, first write two sets of parentheses: $(\blacksquare x + \blacksquare)(\blacksquare x + \blacksquare)$.

Write two integers that are factors of a next to the x's and two integers that are factors of c in the other blanks. Then multiply to see if the product is the original trinomial. If there are not two such integers, the trinomial is not factorable.

EXAMPLE 1 **Factoring $ax^2 + bx + c$**

Factor $4x^2 + 16x + 15$. Check your answer.

$(\blacksquare x + \blacksquare)(\blacksquare x + \blacksquare)$ *The first term is $4x^2$, so at least one variable term has a coefficient other than 1.*

The coefficient of the x^2-term is **4**. The constant term in the trinomial is **15**.

$(1x + 15)(4x + 1) = 4x^2 + 61x + 15$ ✗   *Try integer factors of 4*
$(1x + 5)(4x + 3) = 4x^2 + 23x + 15$ ✗   *for the coefficients and*
$(1x + 3)(4x + 5) = 4x^2 + 17x + 15$ ✗   *integer factors of 15*
$(1x + 1)(4x + 15) = 4x^2 + 19x + 15$ ✗   *for the constant terms.*
$(2x + 15)(2x + 1) = 4x^2 + 32x + 15$ ✗
$(2x + 5)(2x + 3) = 4x^2 + 16x + 15$ ✓

Check $(2x + 5)(2x + 3) = 4x^2 + 6x + 10x + 15$ *Use the FOIL method.*
$= 4x^2 + 16x + 15$ ✓   *The product is the original trinomial.*

 Factor each trinomial. Check your answer.

1a. $6x^2 + 11x + 3$ **1b.** $3x^2 - 2x - 8$

So, to factor $ax^2 + bx + c$, check the factors of a and the factors of c in the binomials. The sum of the products of the outer and inner terms should be b.

Product = a $\overbrace{\hspace{2cm}}$ Product = c

$$(\blacksquare x + \blacksquare)(\blacksquare x + \blacksquare) = ax^2 + bx + c$$

Sum of outer and inner products = b

Since you need to check all the factors of a and all the factors of c, it may be helpful to make a table. Then check the products of the outer and inner terms to see if the sum is b. You can multiply the binomials to check your answer.

EXAMPLE 2   **Factoring $ax^2 + bx + c$ When c Is Positive**

Factor each trinomial. Check your answer.

A $2x^2 + 11x + 12$

$(\blacksquare x + \blacksquare)(\blacksquare x + \blacksquare)$ $a = 2$ and $c = 12$; Outer + Inner = 11

Factors of 2	Factors of 12	Outer + Inner
1 and 2	1 and 12	$1(12) + 2(1) = 14$ ✗
1 and 2	12 and 1	$1(1) + 2(12) = 25$ ✗
1 and 2	2 and 6	$1(6) + 2(2) = 10$ ✗
1 and 2	6 and 2	$1(2) + 2(6) = 14$ ✗
1 and 2	3 and 4	$1(4) + 2(3) = 10$ ✗
1 and 2	4 and 3	$1(3) + 2(4) = 11$ ✓

$(x + 4)(2x + 3)$

Check $(x + 4)(2x + 3) = 2x^2 + 3x + 8x + 12$ Use the FOIL method.
$= 2x^2 + 11x + 12$ ✓

B $5x^2 - 14x + 8$

$(\blacksquare x + \blacksquare)(\blacksquare x + \blacksquare)$ $a = 5$ and $c = 8$; Outer + Inner = -14

Factors of 5	Factors of 8	Outer + Inner
1 and 5	-1 and -8	$1(-8) + 5(-1) = -13$ ✗
1 and 5	-8 and -1	$1(-1) + 5(-8) = -41$ ✗
1 and 5	-2 and -4	$1(-4) + 5(-2) = -14$ ✓

$(x - 2)(5x - 4)$

Check $(x - 2)(5x - 4) = 5x^2 - 4x - 10x + 8$ Use the FOIL method.
$= 5x^2 - 14x + 8$ ✓

Remember!

When b is negative and c is positive, the factors of c are both negative.

 Factor each trinomial. Check your answer.

2a. $6x^2 + 17x + 5$ **2b.** $9x^2 - 15x + 4$ **2c.** $3x^2 + 13x + 12$

When c is negative, one factor of c will be positive and the other factor will be negative. Only some of the factors are shown in the examples, but you may need to check all of the possibilities.

EXAMPLE 3 **Factoring $ax^2 + bx + c$ When c Is Negative**

Factor each trinomial. Check your answer.

A $4y^2 + 7y - 2$

$(\boxed{}\,y + \boxed{})(\boxed{}\,y + \boxed{})$ *a = 4 and c = −2; Outer + Inner = 7*

Factors of 4	Factors of −2	Outer + Inner
1 and 4	1 and −2	$1(-2) + (4)1 = 2$ ✗
1 and 4	−1 and 2	$(1)2 + 4(-1) = -2$ ✗
1 and 4	2 and −1	$1(-1) + (4)2 = 7$ ✓

$(y + 2)(4y - 1)$

Check $(y + 2)(4y - 1) = 4y^2 - y + 8y - 2$ *Use the FOIL method.*

$= 4y^2 + 7y - 2$ ✓

B $4x^2 + 19x - 5$

$(\boxed{}\,x + \boxed{})(\boxed{}\,x + \boxed{})$ *a = 4 and c = −5; Outer + Inner = 19*

Factors of 4	Factors of −5	Outer + Inner
1 and 4	1 and −5	$1(-5) + (4)1 = -1$ ✗
1 and 4	−1 and 5	$(1)5 + 4(-1) = 1$ ✗
1 and 4	5 and −1	$1(-1) + (4)5 = 19$ ✓

$(x + 5)(4x - 1)$

Check $(x + 5)(4x - 1) = 4x^2 - x + 20x - 5$ *Use the FOIL method.*

$= 4x^2 + 19x - 5$ ✓

C $2x^2 - 7x - 15$

$(\boxed{}\,x + \boxed{})(\boxed{}\,x + \boxed{})$ *a = 2 and c = −15; Outer + Inner = −7*

Factors of 2	Factors of −15	Outer + Inner
1 and 2	1 and −15	$1(-15) + (2)1 = -13$ ✗
1 and 2	−1 and 15	$(1)15 + 2(-1) = 13$ ✗
1 and 2	3 and −5	$1(-5) + (2)3 = 1$ ✗
1 and 2	−3 and 5	$(1)5 + 2(-3) = -1$ ✗
1 and 2	5 and −3	$1(-3) + (2)5 = 7$ ✗
1 and 2	−5 and 3	$(1)3 + 2(-5) = -7$ ✓

$(x - 5)(2x + 3)$

Check $(x - 5)(2x + 3) = 2x^2 + 3x - 10x - 15$ *Use the FOIL method.*

$= 2x^2 - 7x - 15$ ✓

Factor each trinomial. Check your answer.

3a. $6x^2 + 7x - 3$ **3b.** $4n^2 - n - 3$

Factoring $ax^2 + bx + c$

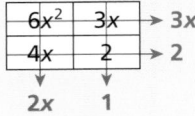

I like to use a box to help me factor trinomials. I look for factors of ac that add to b. Then I arrange the terms in a box and factor.

To factor $6x^2 + 7x + 2$, first I find the factors I need.

$ac = 2(6) = 12$ $b = 7$

Factors of 12	Sum
1 and 12	13
2 and 6	8
3 and 4	7

Then I rewrite the trinomial as
$6x^2 + 3x + 4x + 2$.

Now I arrange $6x^2 + 3x + 4x + 2$ in a box and factor out the common factors from each row and column.

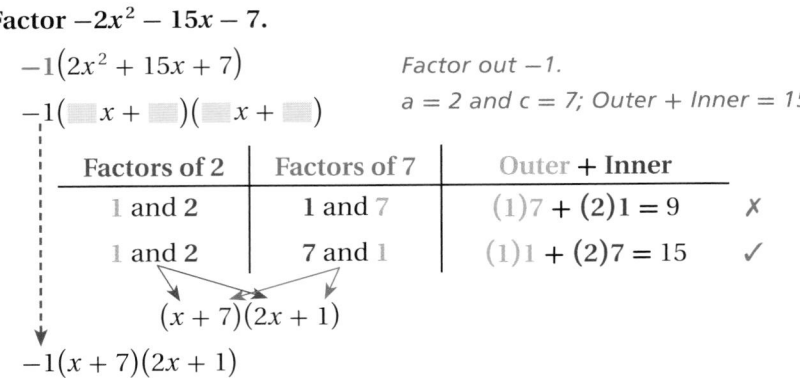

The factors are $(2x + 1)$ and $(3x + 2)$.

When the leading coefficient is negative, factor out -1 from each term before using other factoring methods.

EXAMPLE 4   **Factoring $ax^2 + bx + c$ When a Is Negative**

Factor $-2x^2 - 15x - 7$.

$-1(2x^2 + 15x + 7)$ *Factor out -1.*

$-1(\blacksquare x + \blacksquare)(\blacksquare x + \blacksquare)$ *$a = 2$ and $c = 7$; Outer + Inner = 15*

Factors of 2	Factors of 7	Outer + Inner	
1 and 2	1 and 7	$(1)7 + (2)1 = 9$	✗
1 and 2	7 and 1	$(1)1 + (2)7 = 15$	✓

$(x + 7)(2x + 1)$

$-1(x + 7)(2x + 1)$

Caution!

When you factor out -1 in an early step, you must carry it through the rest of the steps and into the answer.

Factor each trinomial. Check your answer.
4a. $-6x^2 - 17x - 12$ **4b.** $-3x^2 - 17x - 10$

THINK AND DISCUSS

1. Let a, b, and c be positive. If $ax^2 + bx + c$ is the product of two binomials, what do you know about the signs of the numbers in the binomials?

2. **GET ORGANIZED** Copy and complete the graphic organizer. Write each of the following trinomials in the appropriate box and factor each one.
$3x^2 + 10x - 8$ $3x^2 + 10x + 8$
$3x^2 - 10x + 8$ $3x^2 - 10x - 8$

Factoring $ax^2 + bx + c$	
c > 0	
b > 0	b < 0
c < 0	
b < 0	b > 0

8-4

Exercises

California Standards Practice

11.0, 🔑 15.0, 25.2

go.hrw.com
Homework Help Online
KEYWORD: MA8CA 8-4
Parent Resources Online
KEYWORD: MA8CA Parent

GUIDED PRACTICE

Factor each trinomial. Check your answer.

SEE EXAMPLE **1**
p. 505

1. $2x^2 + 9x + 10$
2. $5x^2 + 31x + 6$
3. $5x^2 + 7x - 6$
4. $6x^2 + 37x + 6$
5. $3x^2 - 14x - 24$
6. $6x^2 + x - 2$

SEE EXAMPLE **2**
p. 506

7. $5x^2 + 11x + 2$
8. $2x^2 + 11x + 5$
9. $4x^2 - 9x + 5$
10. $2y^2 - 11y + 14$
11. $5x^2 + 9x + 4$
12. $3x^2 + 7x + 2$

SEE EXAMPLE **3**
p. 507

13. $4a^2 + 8a - 5$
14. $15x^2 + 4x - 3$
15. $2x^2 + x - 6$
16. $6n^2 - 11n - 10$
17. $10x^2 - 9x - 1$
18. $7x^2 - 3x - 10$

SEE EXAMPLE **4**
p. 508

19. $-2x^2 + 5x + 12$
20. $-4n^2 - 16n + 9$
21. $-5x^2 + 7x + 6$
22. $-6x^2 + 13x - 2$
23. $-4x^2 - 8x + 5$
24. $-5x^2 + x + 18$

PRACTICE AND PROBLEM SOLVING

Independent Practice

For Exercises	See Example
25–33	1
34–42	2
43–48	3
49–51	4

Extra Practice

Skills Practice p. EP17
Application Practice p. EP31

Factor each trinomial. Check your answer.

25. $9x^2 + 9x + 2$
26. $2x^2 + 7x + 5$
27. $3n^2 + 8n + 4$
28. $10d^2 + 17d + 7$
29. $4c^2 - 17c + 15$
30. $6x^2 + 14x + 4$
31. $8x^2 + 22x + 5$
32. $6x^2 - 13x + 6$
33. $5x^2 + 9x - 18$
34. $6x^2 + 23x + 7$
35. $10n^2 - 17n + 7$
36. $3x^2 + 11x + 6$
37. $7x^2 + 15x + 2$
38. $3n^2 + 4n + 1$
39. $3x^2 - 19x + 20$
40. $6x^2 + 11x + 4$
41. $4x^2 - 31x + 21$
42. $10x^2 + 31x + 15$
43. $12y^2 + 17y - 5$
44. $3x^2 + 10x - 8$
45. $4x^2 + 4x - 3$
46. $2n^2 - 7n - 4$
47. $3x^2 - 4x - 15$
48. $3n^2 - n - 4$
49. $-4x^2 - 4x + 15$
50. $-3x^2 + 16x - 16$
51. $-3x^2 - x + 2$

📐 **Geometry** For Exercises 52–54, write the polynomial modeled and then factor.

52.

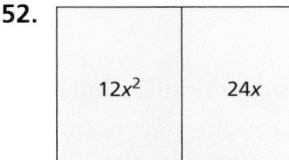

53.

$2x^2$	$-x$
$-4x$	2

54.

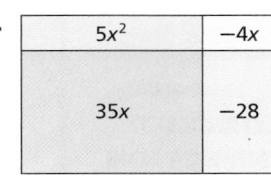

Factor each trinomial, if possible. Check your answer.

55. $9n^2 + 17n + 8$
56. $2x^2 - 7x - 4$
57. $4x^2 - 12x + 5$
58. $5x^2 - 4x + 12$
59. $3x^2 + 14x + 16$
60. $-3x^2 - 11x + 4$
61. $6x^2 - x - 12$
62. $10a^2 + 11a + 3$
63. $4x^2 - 12x + 9$
64. $-6x^2 - 11x + 2$
65. $12x^2 - 8x + 1$
66. $-8x^2 - 7x + 1$
67. $15x^2 + 23x + 8$
68. $8x^2 - 4x - 4$
69. $9x^2 - x + 2$

70. **Geometry** The area of a rectangle is $6x^2 + 11x + 5$ cm². The width is $(x + 1)$ cm. What is the length of the rectangle?

71. **Write About It** Write a paragraph describing how to factor $6x^2 + 13x + 6$. Show each step you would take and explain your steps.

Complete each factorization.

72. $$8x^2 + 18x - 5$$
$$8x^2 + 20x - 2x - 5$$
$$(8x^2 + 20x) - (2x + 5)$$
$$\blacksquare(\blacksquare + \blacksquare) - \blacksquare(2x + 5)$$
$$(\blacksquare - \blacksquare)(2x + 5)$$

73. $$4x^2 + 9x + 2$$
$$4x^2 + 8x + x + 2$$
$$(4x^2 + 8x) + (x + 2)$$
$$\blacksquare(\blacksquare + \blacksquare) + \blacksquare(x + 2)$$
$$(\blacksquare + \blacksquare)(x + 2)$$

74. **Gardening** The length of Rebecca's rectangular garden was two times the width w. Rebecca increased the length and width of the garden so that the area of the new garden is $(2w^2 + 7w + 6)$ square yards. By how much did Rebecca increase the length and the width of the garden?

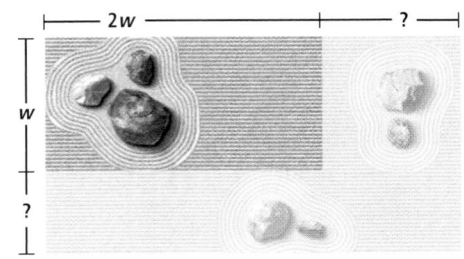

75. **Physical Science** The height of a football that has been thrown or kicked can be described by the expression $-16t^2 + vt + h$ where t is the time in seconds, v is the initial upward velocity, and h is the initial height in feet.

   a. Write an expression for the height of a football at time t when the initial upward velocity is 20 feet per second and the initial height is 6 feet.

   b. Factor your expression from part **a**. Check your answer.

   c. Find the height of the football after 1 second.

76. **/// ERROR ANALYSIS ///** A student attempted to factor $2x^2 + 11x + 12$ as shown. Find and explain the error.

$2x^2 + 11x + 12$		
Factors of 12	Sum	
1 and 12	13	✔
2 and 6	8	✗
3 and 4	7	✗
$(2x + 1)(x + 12)$		

CONCEPT CONNECTION

77. This problem will prepare you for the Concept Connection on page 512.

   The equation $d = 2t^2$ gives the distance from the start point of a toy boat that starts at rest and accelerates at 4 cm/s². The equation $d = 10t - 8$ gives the distance from the start point of a second boat that starts at rest 8 cm behind the first boat and travels at a constant rate of 10 cm/s.

   a. By setting the equations equal to each other, you can determine when the cars are the same distance from the start point: $2t^2 = 10t - 8$. Use properties of algebra to collect all terms on the left side of the equation, leaving 0 on the right side.

   b. Factor the expression on the left side of the equation.

   c. The boats are the same distance from the start point at $t = 1$ and $t = 4$. Explain how the factors you found in part **b** are related to these two times.

Match each trinomial with its correct factorization.

78. $6x^2 - 29x - 5$ **A.** $(x + 5)(6x + 1)$

79. $6x^2 - 31x + 5$ **B.** $(x - 5)(6x - 1)$

80. $6x^2 + 31x + 5$ **C.** $(x + 5)(6x - 1)$

81. $6x^2 + 29x - 5$ **D.** $(x - 5)(6x + 1)$

82. Reasoning A quadratic trinomial $ax^2 + bx + c$ has $a > 0$ and can be factored into the product of two binomials.

   a. Explain what you know about the signs of the constants in the factors if $c > 0$.

   b. Explain what you know about the signs of the constants in the factors if $c < 0$.

Multiple Choice For Exercises 83–86, choose the best answer.

83. What value of b would make $3x^2 + bx - 8$ factorable?

   Ⓐ 3   Ⓑ 10   Ⓒ 11   Ⓓ 25

84. Which product of binomials is represented by the model?

   Ⓐ $(x + 4)(3x + 5)$ Ⓒ $(x + 3)(5x + 4)$

   Ⓑ $(x + 4)(5x + 3)$ Ⓓ $(x + 5)(3x + 4)$

$5x^2$	$4x$
$15x$	12

85. Which binomial is a factor of $24x^2 - 49x + 2$?

   Ⓐ $x - 2$ Ⓑ $x - 1$ Ⓒ $x + 1$ Ⓓ $x + 2$

86. Which value of c would make $2x^2 + x + c$ NOT factorable?

   Ⓐ -15 Ⓑ -9 Ⓒ -6 Ⓓ -1

CHALLENGE AND EXTEND

Factor each trinomial. Check your answer.

87. $1 + 4x + 4x^2$ **88.** $1 - 14x + 49x^2$ **89.** $1 + 18x + 81x^2$

90. $25 + 30x + 9x^2$ **91.** $4 + 20x + 25x^2$ **92.** $4 - 12x + 9x^2$

93. Find all possible values of b such that $3x^2 + bx + 2$ can be factored.

94. Find all possible values of b such that $3x^2 + bx - 2$ can be factored.

95. Find all possible values of b such that $5x^2 + bx + 1$ can be factored.

 SPIRAL STANDARDS REVIEW   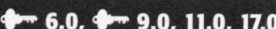 6.0, 9.0, 11.0, 17.0

96. Archie makes $12 per hour and is paid for whole numbers of hours. The function $f(x) = 12x$ gives the amount of money that Archie makes in x hours. Graph this function and give its domain and range. *(Lesson 5-1)*

Graph each system of linear inequalities. Give two ordered pairs that are solutions and two that are not solutions. *(Lesson 6-6)*

97. $\begin{cases} y < -2x + 1 \\ y > 3x - 5 \end{cases}$ **98.** $\begin{cases} y \geq -x + 2 \\ y \leq x - 3 \end{cases}$ **99.** $\begin{cases} y \leq -4x \\ y > 2x - 6 \end{cases}$

Factor each trinomial. Check your answer. *(Lesson 8-3)*

100. $x^2 + 6x + 8$ **101.** $x^2 - 8x - 9$ **102.** $x^2 - 8x + 12$

CONCEPT CONNECTION

Factoring

Red Light, Green Light The equation for the motion of an object with constant acceleration is $d = vt + \frac{1}{2}at^2$ where d is distance traveled in meters, v is starting velocity in m/s, a is acceleration in m/s², and t is time in seconds.

1. A car is stopped at a traffic light. The light changes to green and the driver starts to drive, accelerating at a rate of 4 m/s². Write an equation for the distance the car travels in time t.

2. A bus is traveling at a speed of 15 m/s. The driver approaches the same traffic light in another traffic lane. He does not brake, and continues at the same speed. Write an equation for the distance the bus travels in time t. (*Hint:* At a constant speed, the acceleration is 0 m/s².)

Speed = 15 m/s

Acceleration = 4 m/s²

3. Set the equations equal to each other so you can determine when the car and bus are the same distance from the intersection. Collect all the terms on the left side of this new equation, leaving 0 on the right side. Factor the expression on the left side of the equation. Check your answer.

4. Let $t = 0$ be the point at which the car is just starting to drive and the bus is even with the car. Find the other time when the vehicles will be the same distance from the intersection.

5. What distance will the two vehicles have traveled when they are again at the same distance from the intersection?

6. A truck traveling at 16 m/s is 24 meters behind the bus at $t = 0$. The equation $d = -24 + 16t$ gives the position of the truck. At what time will the truck be the same distance from the intersection as the bus? What will that distance be?

READY TO GO ON?

Quiz for Lessons 8-1 Through 8-4

8-1 Factors and Greatest Common Factors

Write the prime factorization of each number.

1. 54   **2.** 42   **3.** 50   **4.** 120   **5.** 44   **6.** 78

Find the GCF of each pair of monomials.

7. $6p^3$ and $2p$ **8.** $12x^3$ and $18x^4$ **9.** -15 and $20s^4$ **10.** $3a$ and $4b^2$

11. Brent is making a wooden display case for his baseball collection. He has 24 balls from American League games and 30 balls from National League games. He wants to display the same number of baseballs in each row and does not want to put American League baseballs in the same row as National League baseballs. How many rows will Brent need in the display case to put the greatest number of baseballs possible in each row?

8-2 Factoring by GCF

Factor each polynomial. Check your answer.

12. $2d^3 + 4d$

13. $m^2 - 8m^5$

14. $12x^4 - 8x^3 - 4x^2$

15. $3k^2 + 6k - 3$

16. The surface area of a cone can be found using the expression $s\pi r + \pi r^2$, where s represents the slant height and r represents the radius of the base. Factor this expression.

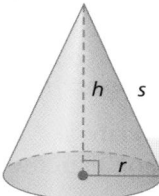

Factor each polynomial by grouping. Check your answer.

17. $w^3 - 4w^2 + w - 4$

18. $3x^3 + 6x^2 - 4x - 8$

19. $2p^3 - 6p^2 + 15 - 5p$

20. $n^3 - 6n^2 + 5n - 30$

8-3 Factoring $x^2 + bx + c$

Factor each trinomial. Check your answer.

21. $n^2 + 9n + 20$ **22.** $d^2 - 6d - 7$ **23.** $x^2 - 6x + 8$

24. $y^2 + 7y - 30$ **25.** $k^2 - 6k + 5$ **26.** $c^2 - 10c + 24$

27. Simplify and factor the polynomial $n(n + 3) - 4$. Show that the original polynomial and the factored form have the same value for $n = 0, 1, 2, 3,$ and 4.

8-4 Factoring $ax^2 + bx + c$

Factor each trinomial. Check your answer.

28. $2x^2 + 11x + 5$ **29.** $3n^2 + 16n + 21$ **30.** $5y^2 - 7y - 6$

31. $4g^2 - 10g + 6$ **32.** $6p^2 - 18p - 24$ **33.** $12d^2 + 7d - 12$

34. The area of a rectangle is $\left(8x^2 + 8x + 2\right)$ cm^2. The width is $(2x + 1)$ cm. What is the length of the rectangle?

8-5 Factoring Special Products

California Standards

11.0 Students apply basic factoring techniques to second- and simple third-**degree polynomials. These techniques include** finding a common factor for all terms in a polynomial, **recognizing the difference of two squares, and recognizing perfect squares of binomials.**

Who uses this?

Urban planners can use the area of a square park to find its length and width. (See Example 2.)

You studied the patterns of some special products of binomials in Chapter 7. You can use those patterns to factor certain polynomials.

A trinomial is a perfect square if:
- The **first** and **last** terms are perfect squares.
- The **middle** term is two times one factor from the first term and one factor from the last term.

$$9x^2 + 12x + 4$$
$$3x \cdot 3x \quad 2(3x \cdot 2) \quad 2 \cdot 2$$

Factoring Perfect-Square Trinomials

PERFECT-SQUARE TRINOMIAL	EXAMPLES
$a^2 + 2ab + b^2 = (a + b)(a + b) = (a + b)^2$	$x^2 + 6x + 9 = (x + 3)(x + 3) = (x + 3)^2$
$a^2 - 2ab + b^2 = (a - b)(a - b) = (a - b)^2$	$x^2 - 2x + 1 = (x - 1)(x - 1) = (x - 1)^2$

EXAMPLE 1 **Recognizing and Factoring Perfect-Square Trinomials**

Determine whether each trinomial is a perfect square. If so, factor. If not, explain.

A $x^2 + 12x + 36$

$$x^2 + 12x + 36$$
$$x \cdot x \quad 2(x \cdot 6) \quad 6 \cdot 6$$

The trinomial is a perfect square. Factor.

Method 1 Factor.
$x^2 + 12x + 36$

Factors of 36	Sum	
1 and 36	37	✗
2 and 18	20	✗
3 and 12	15	✗
4 and 9	13	✗
6 and 6	12	✓

$(x + 6)(x + 6)$

Method 2 Use the rule.

$x^2 + 12x + 36$	*$a = x, b = 6$*
$x^2 + 2(x)(6) + 6^2$	*Write the trinomial as $a^2 + 2ab + b^2$.*
$(x + 6)^2$	*Write the trinomial as $(a + b)^2$.*

Determine whether each trinomial is a perfect square. If so, factor. If not, explain.

B $4x^2 - 12x + 9$

$$4x^2 - 12x + 9$$

$$2x \cdot 2x \qquad 2(2x \cdot 3) \qquad 3 \cdot 3$$

The trinomial is a perfect square. Factor.

$$4x^2 - 12x + 9$$
$$(2x)^2 - 2(2x)(3) + 3^2$$
$$(2x - 3)^2$$

$a = 2x,\ b = 3$
$a^2 - 2ab + b^2$
$(a - b)^2$

C $x^2 + 9x + 16$

$$x^2 + 9x + 16$$

$$x \cdot x \qquad 2(x \cdot 4) \qquad 4 \cdot 4 \qquad\qquad 2(x \cdot 4) \neq 9x$$

$x^2 + 9x + 16$ is not a perfect-square trinomial because $9x \neq 2(x \cdot 4)$.

CHECK IT OUT! Determine whether each trinomial is a perfect square. If so, factor. If not, explain.

1a. $x^2 + 4x + 4$ **1b.** $x^2 - 14x + 49$ **1c.** $9x^2 - 6x + 4$

EXAMPLE 2   *Problem-Solving Application*

The park in the center of the Place des Vosges in Paris, France, is in the shape of a square. The area of the park is $(25x^2 + 70x + 49)$ ft². The side length of the park is in the form $cx + d$, where c and d are whole numbers. Find an expression in terms of x for the perimeter of the park. Find the perimeter when $x = 8$ ft.

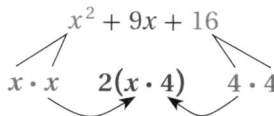

1 Understand the Problem

The **answer** will be an expression for the perimeter of the park and the value of the expression when $x = 8$.

List the **important information:**
- The park is a square with area $(25x^2 + 70x + 49)$ ft².
- The side length of the park is in the form $cx + d$, where c and d are whole numbers.

2 Make a Plan

The formula for the area of a square is area = $(\text{side})^2$.

Factor $25x^2 + 70x + 49$ to find the side length of the park. Write a formula for the perimeter of the park, and evaluate the expression for $x = 8$.

3 Solve

$$25x^2 + 70x + 49 \qquad a = 5x,\ b = 7$$
$$(5x)^2 + 2(5x)(7) + 7^2 \qquad \text{Write the trinomial as } a^2 + 2ab + b^2.$$
$$(5x + 7)^2 \qquad \text{Write the trinomial as } (a + b)^2.$$

$$25x^2 + 70x + 49 = (5x + 7)(5x + 7)$$

Each side length of the park is $(5x + 7)$ ft.

Write a formula for the perimeter of the park.

$$P = 4s \qquad \text{Write the formula for the perimeter of a square.}$$
$$= 4(5x + 7) \qquad \text{Substitute the side length for } s.$$
$$= 20x + 28 \qquad \text{Distribute 4.}$$

An expression for the perimeter of the park in feet is $20x + 28$.

Evaluate the expression when $x = 8$.

$$P = 20x + 28$$
$$= 20(8) + 28 \qquad \text{Substitute 8 for } x.$$
$$= 188$$

When $x = 8$ ft, the perimeter of the park is 188 ft.

4 Look Back

For a square with a perimeter of 188 ft, the side length is $\frac{188}{4} = 47$ ft and the area is $47^2 = 2209$ ft^2.

Evaluate $25x^2 + 70x + 49$ for $x = 8$:

$$25(8)^2 + 70(8) + 49$$
$$1600 + 560 + 49$$
$$2209 \checkmark$$

 **2. What if...?** A company produces square sheets of aluminum, each of which has an area of $(9x^2 + 6x + 1)$ m^2. The side length of each sheet is in the form $cx + d$, where c and d are whole numbers. Find an expression in terms of x for the perimeter of a sheet. Find the perimeter when $x = 3$ m.

In Chapter 7 you learned that the difference of two squares has the form $a^2 - b^2$. The difference of two squares can be written as the product $(a + b)(a - b)$. You can use this pattern to factor some polynomials.

A polynomial is a difference of two squares if:
- There are two terms, one subtracted from the other.
- Both terms are perfect squares.

$$4x^2 - 9$$
$$2x \cdot 2x \quad 3 \cdot 3$$

Factoring a Difference of Two Squares

DIFFERENCE OF TWO SQUARES	EXAMPLE
$a^2 - b^2 = (a + b)(a - b)$	$x^2 - 9 = (x + 3)(x - 3)$

EXAMPLE 3

Recognizing and Factoring the Difference of Two Squares

Determine whether each binomial is a difference of two squares.
If so, factor. If not, explain.

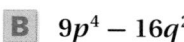
Reading Math

Recognize a difference of two squares: the coefficients of variable terms are perfect squares, powers on variable terms are even, and constants are perfect squares.

A $x^2 - 81$

$$x^2 - 81$$
$$x \cdot x \quad 9 \cdot 9$$

The polynomial is a difference of two squares.

$$x^2 - 9^2 \qquad a = x, b = 9$$
$$(x + 9)(x - 9) \qquad \text{Write the polynomial as } (a + b)(a - b).$$
$$x^2 - 81 = (x + 9)(x - 9)$$

B $9p^4 - 16q^2$

$$9p^4 - 16q^2$$
$$3p^2 \cdot 3p^2 \quad 4q \cdot 4q$$

The polynomial is a difference of two squares.

$$\left(3p^2\right)^2 - \left(4q\right)^2 \qquad a = 3p^2, b = 4q$$
$$\left(3p^2 + 4q\right)\left(3p^2 - 4q\right) \qquad \text{Write the polynomial as } (a + b)(a - b).$$
$$9p^4 - 16q^2 = \left(3p^2 + 4q\right)\left(3p^2 - 4q\right)$$

C $x^6 - 7y^2$

$$x^6 - 7y^2$$
$$x^3 \cdot x^3$$

$7y^2$ is not a perfect square.

$x^6 - 7y^2$ is not the difference of two squares because $7y^2$ is not a perfect square.

CHECK IT OUT! Determine whether the binomial is a difference of two squares. If so, factor. If not, explain.

3a. $1 - 4x^2$ **3b.** $p^8 - 49q^6$ **3c.** $16x^2 - 4y^5$

THINK AND DISCUSS

1. The binomial $1 - x^4$ is a difference of two squares. Use the rule to identify a and b in $1 - x^4$.

2. The polynomial $x^2 + 8x + 16$ is a perfect-square trinomial. Use the rule to identify a and b in $x^2 + 8x + 16$.

3. GET ORGANIZED Copy and complete the graphic organizer. Write an example of each type of special product and factor it.

Special Product	Factored Form
Perfect-square trinomial with positive coefficient of middle term	
Perfect-square trinomial with negative coefficient of middle term	
Difference of two squares	

8-5

Exercises

California
Standards Practice
🔑 **10.0, 11.0, 25.2**

go.hrw.com
Homework Help Online
KEYWORD: MA8CA 8-5
Parent Resources Online
KEYWORD: MA8CA Parent

GUIDED PRACTICE

SEE EXAMPLE **1**
p. 514

Determine whether each trinomial is a perfect square. If so, factor. If not, explain.

1. $x^2 - 4x + 4$ **2.** $x^2 - 4x - 4$ **3.** $9x^2 - 12x + 4$

4. $x^2 + 2x + 1$ **5.** $x^2 - 6x + 9$ **6.** $x^2 - 6x - 9$

SEE EXAMPLE **2**
p. 515

7. City Planning A city purchases a rectangular plot of land with an area of $(x^2 + 24x + 144)$ yd² for a park. The dimensions of the plot are of the form $ax + b$, where a and b are whole numbers. Find an expression for the perimeter of the park. Find the perimeter when $x = 10$ yd.

SEE EXAMPLE **3**
p. 517

Determine whether each binomial is a difference of two squares. If so, factor. If not, explain.

8. $1 - 4x^2$ **9.** $s^2 - 4^2$ **10.** $81x^2 - 1$

11. $4x^4 - 9y^2$ **12.** $x^8 - 50$ **13.** $x^6 - 9$

PRACTICE AND PROBLEM SOLVING

Independent Practice

For Exercises	See Example
14–19	1
20	2
21–26	3

Extra Practice
Skills Practice p. EP17
Application Practice p. EP31

Determine whether the trinomial is a perfect square. If so, factor. If not, explain.

14. $4x^2 - 4x + 1$ **15.** $4x^2 - 4x - 1$ **16.** $36x^2 - 12x + 1$

17. $25x^2 + 10x + 4$ **18.** $9x^2 + 18x + 9$ **19.** $16x^2 - 40x + 25$

20. Measurement You are given a sheet of paper and told to cut out a rectangular piece with an area of $(4x^2 - 44x + 121)$ mm². The dimensions of the rectangle have the form $ax - b$, where a and b are whole numbers. Find an expression for the perimeter of the rectangle you cut out. Find the perimeter when $x = 41$ mm.

Determine whether each binomial is a difference of two squares. If so, factor. If not, explain.

21. $1^2 - 4x^2$ **22.** $25m^2 - 16n^2$ **23.** $4x - 9y$

24. $49p^{12} - 9q^6$ **25.** $9^2 - 100x^4$ **26.** $x^3 - y^3$

Find the missing term in each perfect-square trinomial.

27. $x^2 + 14x + \blacksquare$ **28.** $9x^2 + \blacksquare + 25$ **29.** $\blacksquare - 36y + 81$

Factor each polynomial using the rule for perfect-square trinomials or the rule for a difference of two squares. Tell which rule you used and check your answer.

30. $x^2 - 8x + 16$ **31.** $100x^2 - 81y^2$ **32.** $36x^2 + 24x + 4$

33. $4r^6 - 25s^6$ **34.** $49x^2 - 70x + 25$ **35.** $x^{14} - 144$

 36. Write About It What is similar about a perfect-square trinomial and a difference of two squares? What is different?

37. Critical Thinking Describe two ways to create a perfect-square trinomial.

38. For what value of b would $(x + b)(x + b)$ be the factored form of $x^2 - 22x + 121$?

39. For what value of c are the factors of $x^2 + cx + 256$ the same?

40. This problem will prepare you for the Concept Connection on page 528.

Juanita designed a vegetable garden in the shape of a square and purchased fencing for that design. Then she decided to change the design to a rectangle.

a. The square garden had an area of x^2 ft^2. The area of the rectangular garden is $(x^2 - 25)$ ft^2. Factor the expression for the area of the rectangular garden.

b. The rectangular garden must have the same perimeter as the square garden, so Juanita added a number of feet to the length and subtracted the same number of feet from the width. Use your factors from part **a** to determine how many feet were added to the length and subtracted from the width.

c. If the original length of the square garden was 8 feet, what are the length and width of the new garden?

41. Multi-Step The area of a square is represented by $25z^2 - 40z + 16$.

   a. What expression represents the length of a side of the square?

   b. What expression represents the perimeter of the square?

   c. What are the length of a side, the perimeter, and the area of the square when $z = 3$?

42. Multi-Step A small rectangle is drawn inside a larger rectangle as shown.

   a. What is the area of each rectangle?

   b. What is the area of the green region?

   c. Factor the expression for the area of the green region. (*Hint:* First factor out the common factor of 3 and then factor the binomial.)

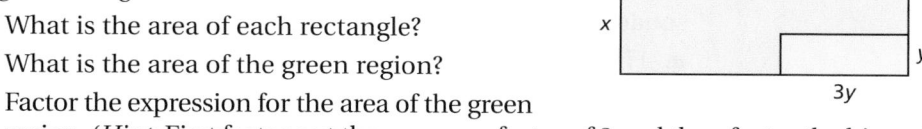

43. Evaluate each expression for the values of x.

	x	$x^2 + 10x + 25$	$(x + 5)^2$	$(x - 5)^2$	$x^2 - 10x + 25$	$x^2 - 25$
a.	−5					
b.	−1					
c.	0					
d.	1					
e.	5					

44. In the table above, which columns have equivalent values? Explain why.

45. Geometry A model for the difference of two squares is shown below. Copy and complete the second figure by writing the missing labels.

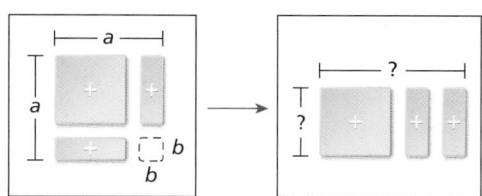

46. ///**ERROR ANALYSIS**/// Two students factored $25x^4 - 9y^2$. Which is incorrect? Explain the error.

Ⓐ
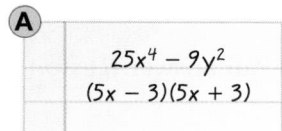

$25x^4 - 9y^2$

$(5x - 3)(5x + 3)$

Ⓑ
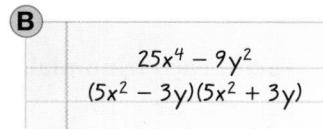

$25x^4 - 9y^2$

$(5x^2 - 3y)(5x^2 + 3y)$

Multiple Choice For Exercises 47 and 48, choose the best answer.

47. A polynomial expression is evaluated for the x- and y-values shown in the table. Which expression was evaluated to give the values shown in the third column?

x	y	Value of Expression
0	0	0
-1	-1	0
1	1	0
1	-1	4

   Ⓐ $x^2 - y^2$

   Ⓑ $x^2 + 2xy + y^2$

   Ⓒ $x^2 - 2xy + y^2$

   Ⓓ None of the above

48. The area of a square is $4x^2 + 20x + 25$. Which expression can also be used to model the area of the square?

   Ⓐ $(2x - 5)(5 - 2x)$ Ⓒ $(2x - 5)^2$

   Ⓑ $(2x + 5)(2x - 5)$ Ⓓ $(2x + 5)^2$

49. **Gridded Response** Evaluate the polynomial expression $x^2 - 18x + 81$ for $x = 10$.

CHALLENGE AND EXTEND

50. The binomial $81x^4 - 16$ can be factored using the rule for a difference of two squares.

   a. Fill in the factorization: $81x^4 - 16$

$$\left(9x^2 + \blacksquare\right)\left(\blacksquare - \blacksquare\right)$$

   b. One binomial from part **a** can be further factored. Identify the binomial and factor it. What is the complete factorization of $81x^4 - 16$?

   c. Write your own binomial that can be factored twice as the difference of two squares.

51. The expression $4 - (v + 2)^2$ is the difference of two squares, because it fits the rule $a^2 - b^2$.

   a. Identify a and b in the expression.

   b. Factor and simplify $4 - (v + 2)^2$.

The *difference of cubes* is an expression of the form $a^3 - b^3$. It can be factored according to the rule $a^3 - b^3 = (a - b)\left(a^2 + ab + b^2\right)$. For each binomial, identify a and b, and factor using the rule. Check your answer.

52. $x^3 - 1$ 53. $27y^3 - 64$ 54. $n^6 - 8$

SPIRAL STANDARDS REVIEW   🔑 10.0, 11.0, 16.0, 17.0, 18.0

Find the domain and range for each relation and tell whether the relation is a function. *(Lesson 4-2)*

55. $\{(5, 2), (4, 1), (3, 0), (2, -1)\}$ 56. $\{(-3, 6), (-1, 6), (1, 6), (3, 6)\}$

57. $\{(2, -8), (2, -2), (2, 4), (2, 10)\}$ 58. $\{(-2, 4), (-1, 1), (0, 0), (1, 1)\}$

Multiply. *(Lesson 7-7)*

59. $2a\left(3a^2 + 7a - 5\right)$ 60. $(x + 3)(x - 8)$ 61. $(t - 4)^2$

Factor each trinomial. Check your answer. *(Lesson 8-3)*

62. $x^2 + 3x - 10$ 63. $x^2 - x - 12$ 64. $x^2 + 7x + 8$

Connecting
Algebra to

Number Theory

Mental Math

Recognizing patterns of special products can help you perform calculations mentally.

Remember these special products that you studied in Chapter 7 and in Lesson 8-5.

Patterns of Special Products	
Difference of Two Squares	$(a + b)(a - b) = a^2 - b^2$
Perfect-Square Trinomial	$(a + b)^2 = a^2 + 2ab + b^2$ $(a - b)^2 = a^2 - 2ab + b^2$

Example 1

Simplify $17^2 - 7^2$.

This expression is a difference of two squares with $a = 17$ and $b = 7$.

$$a^2 - b^2 = (a + b)(a - b) \qquad \textit{Write the rule for a difference of two squares.}$$
$$17^2 - 7^2 = (17 + 7)(17 - 7) \qquad \textit{Substitute 17 for a and 7 for b.}$$
$$= (24)(10) \qquad \textit{Simplify each group.}$$
$$= 240$$

Example 2

Simplify $14^2 + 2(14)(6) + 6^2$.

This expression is a perfect-square trinomial with $a = 14$ and $b = 6$.

$$a^2 + 2ab + b^2 = (a + b)^2 \qquad \textit{Write the rule for a perfect-square trinomial.}$$
$$14^2 + 2(14)(6) + 6^2 = (14 + 6)^2 \qquad \textit{Substitute 14 for a and 6 for b.}$$
$$= (20)^2 \qquad \textit{Simplify.}$$
$$= 400$$

Try This

Simplify each expression using the rules for special products.

1. $18^2 - 12^2$

2. $11^2 + 2(11)(14) + 14^2$

3. $22^2 - 18^2$

4. $38^2 - 2(38)(27) + 27^2$

5. $29^2 - 2(29)(17) + 17^2$

6. $55^2 + 2(55)(45) + 45^2$

7. $14^2 - 9^2$

8. $13^2 - 12^2$

9. $14^2 + 2(14)(16) + 16^2$

Choosing a Factoring Method

California Standards

11.0 Students apply basic factoring techniques to second- and simple third-degree polynomials. These techniques include finding a common factor for all terms in a polynomial, recognizing the difference of two squares, and recognizing perfect squares of binomials.

Why learn this?

You can factor polynomials to model the height of a leaping person or animal. (See Exercise 42.)

The height of a leaping frog can be modeled by a quadratic polynomial. Solving an equation that involves the polynomial may require factoring the polynomial.

Recall that a polynomial is fully or completely factored when it is written as a product of monomials and polynomials whose terms have no common factors other than 1.

EXAMPLE 1 **Determining Whether an Expression Is Completely Factored**

Tell whether each expression is completely factored. If not, factor it.

A $2x(x^2 + 4)$

$2x(x^2 + 4)$ *Neither 2x nor $x^2 + 4$ can be factored further.*

$2x(x^2 + 4)$ is completely factored.

> **Caution!**
>
> $x^2 + 4$ is a *sum* of squares, and cannot be factored.

B $(2x + 6)(x + 5)$

$(2x + 6)(x + 5)$ *2x + 6 can be factored further.*

$2(x + 3)(x + 5)$ *Factor out 2, the GCF of 2x and 6.*

$2(x + 3)(x + 5)$ is completely factored.

C $2n(n^2 + 4n - 21)$

$2n(n^2 + 4n - 21)$ *$n^2 + 4n - 21$ can be factored further.*

$2n(n + 7)(n - 3)$ *Factor $n^2 + 4n - 21$.*

$2n(n + 7)(n - 3)$ is completely factored.

Tell whether each expression is completely factored. If not, factor it.

1a. $5x^2(x - 1)$ **1b.** $(4x + 4)(x + 1)$

To factor a polynomial completely, you may need to use more than one factoring method. Use the steps below to factor a polynomial completely.

Factoring Polynomials
Step 1 Check for a greatest common factor.
Step 2 Check for a pattern that fits the difference of two squares or a perfect-square trinomial.
Step 3 To factor $x^2 + bx + c$, look for two integers whose sum is b and whose product is c. To factor $ax^2 + bx + c$, check integer factors of a and c in the binomial factors. The sum of the products of the outer and inner terms should be b.
Step 4 Check for common factors.

EXAMPLE 2 **Factoring by GCF and Recognizing Patterns**

Factor $-2xy^2 + 16xy - 32x$ completely. Check your answer.

$$-2xy^2 + 16xy - 32x$$
$$-2x(y^2 - 8y + 16)$$ *Factor out the GCF. $y^2 - 8y + 16$ is a perfect-square trinomial of the form $a^2 - 2ab + b^2$.*
$$-2x(y - 4)^2$$ *$a = y$, $b = 4$*

Check $\quad -2x(y - 4)^2 = -2x(y^2 - 8y + 16)$
$$= -2xy^2 + 16xy - 32x \checkmark$$

CHECK IT OUT! Factor each polynomial completely. Check your answer.

2a. $4x^3 + 16x^2 + 16x$ **2b.** $2x^2y - 2y^3$

EXAMPLE 3 **Factoring by Multiple Methods**

Factor each polynomial completely.

A $2x^2 + 5x + 4$

$$2x^2 + 5x + 4$$ *The GCF is 1 and there is no pattern.*
$$(\blacksquare x + \blacksquare)(\blacksquare x + \blacksquare)$$ *$a = 2$ and $c = 4$; Outer + Inner = 5*

Factors of 2	Factors of 4	Outer + Inner	
1 and 2	1 and 4	$(1)4 + (2)1 = 6$	✗
1 and 2	4 and 1	$(1)1 + (2)4 = 9$	✗
1 and 2	2 and 2	$(1)2 + (2)2 = 6$	✗

$2x^2 + 5x + 4$ cannot be factored any further. It is factored completely.

Remember!

For a polynomial of the form $ax^2 + bx + c$, if there are no integers whose sum is b and whose product is ac, then the polynomial is said to be unfactorable.

B $3n^4 - 15n^3 + 12n^2$

$$3n^2(n^2 - 5n + 4)$$ *Factor out the GCF. There is no pattern.*
$$(n + \blacksquare)(n + \blacksquare)$$ *$b = -5$ and $c = 4$; look for integer factors of 4 whose sum is -5.*

Factors of 4	Sum	
-1 and -4	-5	✓
-2 and -2	-4	✗

The factors needed are -1 and -4.

$$3n^2(n - 1)(n - 4)$$

C $4x^3 + 18x^2 + 20x$

$$2x(2x^2 + 9x + 10)$$ *Factor out the GCF. There is no pattern.*
$$(\blacksquare x + \blacksquare)(\blacksquare x + \blacksquare)$$ *$a = 2$ and $c = 10$; Outer + Inner = 9*

Factors of 2	Factors of 10	Outer + Inner	
1 and 2	1 and 10	$(1)10 + (2)1 = 12$	✗
1 and 2	10 and 1	$(1)1 + (2)10 = 21$	✗
1 and 2	2 and 5	$(1)5 + (2)2 = 9$	✓

$$(x + 2)(2x + 5)$$
$$2x(x + 2)(2x + 5)$$

D $p^5 - p$

$\quad p(p^4 - 1)$ *Factor out the GCF.*

$\quad p(p^2 + 1)(p^2 - 1)$ *$p^4 - 1$ is a difference of two squares.*

$\quad p(p^2 + 1)(p + 1)(p - 1)$ *$p^2 - 1$ is a difference of two squares.*

 **Factor each polynomial completely. Check your answer.**

3a. $3x^2 + 7x + 4$ **3b.** $2p^5 + 10p^4 - 12p^3$

3c. $9q^6 + 30q^5 + 24q^4$ **3d.** $2x^4 + 18$

Methods to Factor Polynomials

Any Polynomial—Look for the greatest common factor.

$ab - ac = a(b - c)$	$6x^2y + 10xy^2 = 2xy(3x + 5y)$

Binomials—Look for a difference of two squares.

$a^2 - b^2 = (a + b)(a - b)$	$x^2 - 9y^2 = (x + 3y)(x - 3y)$

Trinomials—Look for perfect-square trinomials and other factorable trinomials.

$a^2 + 2ab + b^2 = (a + b)^2$	$x^2 + 4x + 4 = (x + 2)^2$
$a^2 - 2ab + b^2 = (a - b)^2$	$x^2 - 2x + 1 = (x - 1)^2$
$x^2 + bx + c = (x + \boxed{})(x + \boxed{})$	$x^2 + 3x + 2 = (x + 1)(x + 2)$
$ax^2 + bx + c = (\boxed{}x + \boxed{})(\boxed{}x + \boxed{})$	$6x^2 + 7x + 2 = (2x + 1)(3x + 2)$

Polynomials of Four or More Terms—Factor by grouping.

$ax + bx + ay + by = x(a + b) + y(a + b)$	$2x^3 + 4x^2 + x + 2 = (2x^3 + 4x^2) + (x + 2)$
$\qquad\qquad\qquad\quad = (x + y)(a + b)$	$\qquad\qquad\qquad = 2x^2(x + 2) + 1(x + 2)$
	$\qquad\qquad\qquad = (x + 2)(2x^2 + 1)$

THINK AND DISCUSS

1. Give an expression that includes a polynomial that is not completely factored.

2. Give an example of an unfactorable binomial and an unfactorable trinomial.

 **3. GET ORGANIZED** Copy the graphic organizer. Draw an arrow from each expression to the method you would use to factor it.

Factoring Methods	
Polynomial	**Method**
1. $16x^4 - 25y^8$	**A.** Factoring out the GCF
2. $x^2 + 10x + 25$	**B.** Factoring by grouping
3. $9t^2 + 27t + 18t^4$	**C.** Unfactorable
4. $a^2 + 3a - 7a - 21$	**D.** Difference of two squares
5. $100b^2 + 81$	**E.** Perfect-square trinomial

8-6 Exercises

California Standards Practice
11.0, 25.2

go.hrw.com
Homework Help Online
KEYWORD: MA8CA 8-6
Parent Resources Online
KEYWORD: MA8CA Parent

GUIDED PRACTICE

SEE EXAMPLE **1**
p. 522

Tell whether each expression is completely factored. If not, factor it.

1. $3x(9x^2 + 1)$ **2.** $2(4x^3 - 3x^2 - 8x)$ **3.** $2k^2(4 - k^3)$

4. $(2x + 3)(3x - 5)$ **5.** $4(4p^4 - 1)$ **6.** $a(a^3 + 2ab + b^2)$

SEE EXAMPLE **2**
p. 523

Factor each polynomial completely. Check your answer.

7. $3x^5 - 12x^3$ **8.** $4x^3 + 8x^2 + 4x$ **9.** $8pq^2 + 8pq + 2p$

10. $18rs^2 - 2r$ **11.** $mn^5 - m^3n$ **12.** $2x^2y - 20xy + 50y$

SEE EXAMPLE **3**
p. 523

13. $6x^4 - 3x^3 - 9x^2$ **14.** $3y^2 + 14y + 4$ **15.** $p^5 + 3p^3 + p^2 + 3$

16. $7x^5 + 21x^4 - 28x^3$ **17.** $2z^2 + 11z + 6$ **18.** $9p^2 - q^2 + 3p$

PRACTICE AND PROBLEM SOLVING

Independent Practice	
For Exercises	See Example
19–24	1
25–30	2
31–36	3

Extra Practice
Skills Practice p. EP17
Application Practice p. EP31

Tell whether each expression is completely factored. If not, factor it.

19. $2x(y^3 - 4y^2 + 5y)$ **20.** $2r(25r^6 - 36)$ **21.** $3n^2(n^2 - 25)$

22. $2m(m + 1)(m + 4)$ **23.** $2y^2(4x^2 + 9)$ **24.** $4(7g + 9h^2)$

Factor each polynomial completely. Check your answer.

25. $-4x^3 + 24x^2 - 36x$ **26.** $24r^2 - 6r^4$ **27.** $5d^2 - 60d + 135$

28. $4y^8 + 36y^7 + 81y^6$ **29.** $98x^3 - 50xy^2$ **30.** $4x^3y - 4x^2y - 8xy$

31. $5x^2 - 10x + 14$ **32.** $121x^2 + 36y^2$ **33.** $p^4 - 16$

34. $4m^6 - 30m^5 + 36m^4$ **35.** $2k^3 + 3k^2 + 6k + 9$ **36.** $ab^4 - 16a$

Write an expression for each situation. Factor your expression.

37. the square of Ella's age plus 12 times Ella's age plus 36

38. the square of the distance from point A to point B minus 81

39. the square of the number of seconds Bob can hold his breath minus 16 times the number of seconds plus 28

40. three times the square of apples on a tree minus 22 times the number of apples plus 35

41. the square of Beth's score minus 49

42. Physical Science The height in meters of a ballet dancer's center of mass when she leaps can be modeled by the polynomial $-5t^2 + 30t + 1$, where t is time in seconds after the jump. Tell whether the polynomial is fully factored when written as $-1(5t^2 - 30t - 1)$. Explain.

 43. Write About It When asked to factor a polynomial completely, you first determine that the terms in the polynomial do not share any common factors. What would be your next step?

Factor and simplify each expression. Check your answer.

44. $12(x + 1)^2 + 60(x + 1) + 75$ **45.** $(2x + 3)^2 - (x - 4)^2$

46. $45x(x - 2)^2 + 60x(x - 2) + 20x$ **47.** $(3x - 5)^2 - (y + 2)^2$

48. This problem will prepare you for the Concept Connection on page 528.

   a. The area of a Marci's rectangular flower garden is $(x^2 + 2x - 15)$ ft². Factor this expression for area. Check your answer.

   b. Draw a diagram of the garden and label the length and width with your factors from part **a.**

   c. Find the length and width of the flower garden if $x = 7$ ft.

49. Critical Thinking Show two methods of factoring $4x^2 - 100$.

50. Estimation Estimate the value of $2x^2 + 5xy + 3y^2$ when $x = -10.1$ and $y = 10.05$. (*Hint:* Factor the expression first.)

51. ///**ERROR ANALYSIS**/// Examine the factorization shown. Explain why the factorization is incorrect.

$12x^2 - 12x - 3$
$3(4x^2 - 4x - 1)$
$3(2x - 1)(2x - 1)$

Blaise Pascal was a French mathematician who lived in the 1600s.

Math History Use the following information for Exercises 52–54.

The triangle at right is called *Pascal's Triangle*. The triangle starts with 1 and each of the other numbers in the triangle is the sum of the two numbers in the row above it.

0					1					
1				1		1				
2			1		2		1			
3		1		3		3		1		
4	1		4		6		4		1	
5	1	5		10		10		5		1

Pascal's Triangle can be used to write the product of a binomial raised to an integer power. The numbers in each row give you the coefficients of each term in the product.

$$(a + b)^3 = a^3 + 3a^2b + 3ab^2 + b^3$$

The numbers in row **3** are 1, 3, 3, 1. These are the coefficients of the terms in the product $(a + b)^3$. The power of a decreases in each term and the power of b increases in each term.

Use the patterns you see in Pascal's Triangle to write the power of the binomial $a + b$ given by each product.

52. $a^6 + 6a^5b + 15a^4b^2 + 20a^3b^3 + 15a^2b^4 + 6ab^5 + b^6 = (a + b)^{\square}$

53. $a^8 + 8a^7b + 28a^6b^2 + 56a^5b^3 + 70a^4b^4 + 56a^3b^5 + 28a^2b^6 + 8ab^7 + b^8 = (a + b)^{\square}$

54. $a^7 + 7a^6b + 21a^5b^2 + 35a^4b^3 + 35a^3b^4 + 21a^2b^5 + 7ab^6 + b^7 = (a + b)^{\square}$

Multiple Choice For Exercises 55–57, choose the best answer.

55. Which expression equals $6x^2 + 7x - 10$?

   (A) $(6x + 2)(x - 5)$ (C) $(x + 2)(6x - 5)$

   (B) $(2x + 5)(3x - 2)$ (D) $(3x + 2)(2x - 5)$

56. What is the complete factorization of $16x^{12} - 256$?

   (A) $16(x^6 + 4)(x^6 - 4)$ (C) $16(x^6 + 4)(x^3 + 2)(x^3 - 2)$

   (B) $(4x^6 + 16)(4x^6 - 16)$ (D) $(4x^6 + 16)(2x^3 + 4)(2x^3 - 4)$

57. Which of the expressions below represents the fifth step of the factorization?

Step 1: $40a^3 - 60a^2 - 10a + 15$

Step 2: $5(8a^3 - 12a^2 - 2a + 3)$

Step 3: $5[(8a^3 - 12a^2) - (2a - 3)]$

Step 4: $5[4a^2(2a - 3) - 1(2a - 3)]$

Step 5: ▨▨▨▨▨▨▨▨▨▨

Step 6: $5(2a - 3)(2a + 1)(2a - 1)$

(A) $5(2a - 3)(2a + 3)(4a^2 - 1)$

(B) $5(2a - 3)(4a^2 + 1)$

(C) $5(2a - 3)(4a^2 - 1)$

(D) $5(2a - 3)(2a - 3)(4a^2 - 1)$

58. Short Response Use the polynomial $8x^3 + 24x^2 + 18x$ for the following.

a. Factor the polynomial. Explain each step and tell whether you used any rules for special products.

b. Explain another set of steps that could be used to factor the polynomial.

CHALLENGE AND EXTEND

59. Geometry The volume of the cylinder shown is represented by the expression $72\pi p^3 + 48\pi p^2 + 8\pi p$. The height of the cylinder is $8p$.

a. Factor the expression for volume.

b. What expression represents the radius of the cylinder?

c. If the radius is 4 cm, what are the height and volume of the cylinder?

$V = \pi r^2 h$

Factor. Check your answer.

60. $g^7 + g^3 + g^5 + g^4$

61. $h^2 + h^8 + h^6 + h^4$

62. $x^{n+2} + x^{n+1} + x^n$

63. $x^{n+5} + x^{n+4} + x^{n+3}$

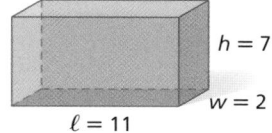

64. Geometry The rectangular prism has the dimensions shown.

a. Write expressions for the height and length of the prism using w.

b. Write a polynomial that represents the volume of the prism using w.

$h = 7$

$w = 2$

$\ell = 11$

SPIRAL STANDARDS REVIEW

8.0, 11.0, 16.0, 17.0, 18.0

Give the domain and range of the relation. Tell whether the relation is a function.
(Lesson 4-2)

65.

x	−1	0	1	2
y	−2	1	4	7

66.

x	1	2	3	1
y	−2	−1	0	−2

Identify which lines are perpendicular. *(Lesson 5-7)*

67. $y = -5x + 4; y = \frac{1}{5}x + 2; y = 5; y = 0$

68. $y = -x + 3; y = 8x; y = -\frac{1}{8}x + 5; y = x$

Factor each trinomial. Check your answer. *(Lesson 8-4)*

69. $2x^2 + 13x + 15$

70. $4x^2 + 4x - 3$

71. $6x^2 - 11x - 10$

CONCEPT CONNECTION

Factoring

Shaping the Environment The Environmental Awareness Club is going to plant a garden on the front lawn of the school. Henry suggests a garden in the shape of a square. Theona suggests a rectangular shape.

1. Henry's plans include a square garden with an area of $(x^2 + 12x + 36)$ m². Write expressions for the length and width of the square garden.

2. A drawing of the square garden shows a length of 12 m. What is the width of the square garden? What is the value of x? What is the total area of the square garden?

3. Theona's plans include a rectangular garden with an area of $(x^2 + 14x + 24)$ m². Write expressions for the length and width of the rectangular garden.

4. A drawing of the rectangular garden shows that the length is 6 m longer than the length of the square garden. What is the width of the rectangular garden? How much shorter is the width of the rectangular garden than the square garden?

5. Find the perimeter of each garden in terms of x.

6. Which plan should the club choose if they want the garden that covers the most area? Which plan should the club choose if they want the garden that requires the least fencing around it? Explain your reasoning.

Width = ?

Length = 12 m

Width = ?

Length = (12 + 6) m

READY TO GO ON?

Quiz for Lessons 8-5 Through 8-6

☑ 8-5 Factoring Special Products

Determine whether each trinomial is a perfect square. If so, factor. If not, explain.

1. $x^2 + 8x + 16$　　　**2.** $4x^2 - 20x + 25$　　　**3.** $x^2 + 3x + 9$

4. $2x^2 - 4x + 4$　　　**5.** $9x^2 - 12x + 4$　　　**6.** $x^2 - 12x - 36$

7. An architect is designing rectangular windows with an area of $(x^2 + 20x + 100)$ ft^2. The dimensions of the windows are of the form $ax + b$, where a and b are whole numbers. Find an expression for the perimeter of the windows. Find the perimeter of a window when $x = 4$ ft.

Determine whether each binomial is a difference of two squares. If so, factor. If not, explain.

8. $x^2 - 121$　　　**9.** $4t^2 - 20$　　　**10.** $1 - 9y^4$

11. $25m^2 - 4m^6$　　　**12.** $16x^2 + 49$　　　**13.** $r^4 - t^2$

14. The area of a square is $(36d^2 - 36d + 9)$ in^2.

    a. What expression represents the length of a side of the square?

    b. What expression represents the perimeter of the square?

    c. What are the length of a side, the perimeter, and the area of the square when $d = 2$ in.?

☑ 8-6 Choosing a Factoring Method

Tell whether each expression is completely factored. If not, factor it.

15. $5(x^2 + 3x + 1)$　　　　　　**16.** $6x(5x^2 - x)$

17. $3t(t^4 - 9)$　　　　　　**18.** $2(m^2 - 10m + 25)$

19. $3(2y^2 - 5)(y + 1)$　　　　　　**20.** $(2n + 6)(n - 4)$

Factor each polynomial completely. Check your answer.

21. $3x^3 - 12x^2 + 12x$　　　**22.** $16m^3 - 4m$　　　**23.** $5x^3y - 45xy$

24. $3t^2 + 5t - 1$　　　**25.** $3c^2 + 12c - 63$　　　**26.** $x^5 - 81x$

Write an expression for each situation. Then factor your expression.

27. the difference of the square of a board's length and 36

28. the square of Michael's age minus 8 times Michael's age plus 16

29. two times the square of a car's speed plus 2 times the car's speed minus 12

30. three times the cube of Jessie's height plus 3 times the square of Jessie's height minus 6 times Jessie's height

31. Write an expression for the area of the shaded region. Then factor the expression.

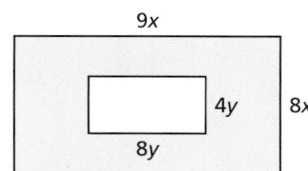

Study Guide: Review

Vocabulary

Complete the sentences below with vocabulary words from the list above.

1. A number written as a product so that each of its factors has no factors other than 1 and itself is the ___?___ .

2. The ___?___ of two monomials is the greatest of the factors that the monomials share.

8-1 Factors and Greatest Common Factors (pp. 478–483)

 Prep for **11.0**

EXAMPLES

■ Write the prime factorization of 84.

84
4 · 21
(2) · (2) · (3) · (7)

Write as a product. Continue until all factors are prime.

■ Write the prime factorization of 75.

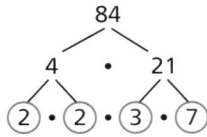

Keep dividing by prime factors until the quotient is 1.

$75 = 3 \cdot 5 \cdot 5 = 3 \cdot 5^2$

■ Find the GCF of 36 and 90.

$36 = 2 \cdot \boxed{2} \cdot \boxed{3} \cdot \boxed{3}$
$90 = \quad \boxed{2} \cdot \boxed{3} \cdot \boxed{3} \cdot 5$

$2 \cdot 3 \cdot 3 = 18$

The GCF of 36 and 90 is 18.

Write the prime factorization of each number. Find the product of the common factors.

■ Find the GCF of $10x^5$ and $4x^2$.

$10x^5 = \boxed{2} \cdot 5 \cdot \boxed{x} \cdot \boxed{x} \cdot x \cdot x \cdot x$
$4x^2 = \boxed{2} \cdot 2 \cdot \boxed{x} \cdot \boxed{x}$

$2 \cdot \quad x \cdot x = 2x^2$

Write the prime factorization of each coefficient. Write powers as products. Find the product of the common factors.

The GCF of $10x^5$ and $4x^2$ is $2x^2$.

EXERCISES

Write the prime factorization of each number.

3. 12
4. 20
5. 32
6. 23
7. 40
8. 64
9. 66
10. 114

Find the GCF of each pair of numbers.

11. 15 and 50
12. 36 and 132
13. 29 and 30
14. 54 and 81
15. 20 and 48

Find the GCF of each pair of monomials.

16. $9m$ and 3
17. $4x$ and $2x^2$
18. $-18b^4$ and $27b^2$
19. $100r$ and $25r^5$

20. A hardware store carries 42 types of boxed nails and 36 types of boxed screws. The store manager wants to build a rack so that he can display the hardware in rows. He wants to put the same number of boxes in each row, but he wants no row to contain both nails and screws. What is the greatest number of boxes that he can display in one row? How many rows will there be if the manager puts the greatest number of boxes in each row?

8-2 Factoring by GCF (pp. 487–493)

EXAMPLES

■ Factor $3t^3 - 9t^2$. Check your answer.

$3t^3 = 3 \cdot t \cdot t \cdot t$
$9t^2 = 3 \cdot 3 \cdot t \cdot t$ *Find the GCF.*

GCF: $3 \cdot t \cdot t = 3t^2$

$3t^3 - 9t^2 = 3t^2(t) - 3t^2(3)$
         $= 3t^2(t - 3)$ *Factor out the GCF.*

Check $3t^2(t - 3) = 3t^3 - 9t^2$ ✓

■ Factor $-12s - 6s^3$. Check your answer.

$-1(12s + 6s^3)$ *Factor out −1.*

$12s = 2 \cdot 2 \cdot 3 \cdot s$
$6s^3 = 2 \cdot 3 \cdot s \cdot s \cdot s$ *Find the GCF.*

GCF: $2 \cdot 3 \cdot s = 6s$

$-1(12s + 6s^3)$

$1[(6s)(2) + (6s)(s^2)]$

$-1[(6s)(2 + s^2)]$

$-6s(2 + s^2)$ *Factor out the GCF.*

Check $-6s(2 + s^2) = -12s - 6s^3$ ✓

■ Factor $5(x - 7) + 3x(x - 7)$.

$5(x - 7) + 3x(x - 7)$ *The terms have a common factor of $(x - 7)$.*

$(x - 7)(5 + 3x)$ *Factor out $(x - 7)$.*

■ Factor $6b^3 + 8b + 15b^2 + 20$ by grouping.

$(6b^3 + 8b) + (15b^2 + 20)$ *Group terms that have a common factor.*

$2b(3b^2 + 4) + 5(3b^2 + 4)$ *Factor each group.*

$(3b^2 + 4)(2b + 5)$ *Factor out $(3b^2 + 4)$.*

■ Factor $2m^3 - 6m^2 + 15 - 5m$. Check your answer.

$(2m^3 - 6m^2) + (15 - 5m)$ *Group terms.*
$2m^2(m - 3) + 5(3 - m)$ *Factor each group.*

$2m^2(m - 3) + 5(-1)(m - 3)$ *Rewrite $(3 - m)$ as $(-1)(m - 3)$.*

$2m^2(m - 3) - 5(m - 3)$ *Simplify.*
$(m - 3)(2m^2 - 5)$ *Factor out $(m - 3)$.*

Check $(m - 3)(2m^2 - 5)$

$ 2m^3 - 5m - 6m^2 + 15$
$ 2m^3 - 6m^2 + 15 - 5m$ ✓

EXERCISES

Factor each polynomial. Check your answer.

21. $5x - 15x^3$ **22.** $-16b + 32$

23. $-14v - 21$ **24.** $4a^2 - 12a - 8$

25. $5g^5 - 10g^3 - 15g$ **26.** $40p^2 - 10p + 30$

27. A civil engineer needs the area of a rectangular lot to be $(6x^2 + 5x)$ ft^2. Factor this polynomial to find expressions for the dimensions of the lot.

Factor each expression.

28. $2x(x - 4) + 9(x - 4)$

29. $t(3t + 5) - 6(3t + 5)$

30. $5(6 - n) - 3n(6 - n)$

31. $b(b + 4) + 2(b + 4)$

32. $x^2(x - 3) + 7(x - 3)$

Factor each polynomial by grouping. Check your answer.

33. $n^3 + n - 4n^2 - 4$

34. $6b^2 - 8b + 15b - 20$

35. $2h^3 - 7h + 14h^2 - 49$

36. $3t^2 + 18t + t + 6$

37. $10m^3 + 15m^2 - 2m - 3$

38. $8p^3 + 4p - 6p^2 - 3$

39. $5r - 10 + 2r - r^2$

40. $b^3 - 5b + 15 - 3b^2$

41. $6t - t^3 - 4t^2 + 24$

42. $12h - 3h^2 + h - 4$

43. $d - d^2 + d - 1$

44. $6b - 5b^2 + 10b - 12$

45. $5t - t^2 - t + 5$

46. $8b^2 - 2b^3 - 5b + 20$

47. $3r - 3r^2 - 1 + r$

48. Write an expression for the area of each of the two rectangles shown. Then write and factor an expression for the combined area.

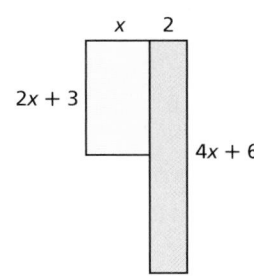

8-3 Factoring $x^2 + bx + c$ (pp. 496–503)

EXAMPLES

Factor each trinomial. Check your answer.

■ $x^2 + 14x + 45$

$(x + \boxed{})(x + \boxed{})$ *Look for factors of 45*

$(x + 9)(x + 5)$ *whose sum is 14.*

  Check $(x + 9)(x + 5) = x^2 + 5x + 9x + 45$

                 $= x^2 + 14x + 45 \checkmark$

■ $x^2 + 6x - 27$

$(x + \boxed{})(x - \boxed{})$ *Look for factors of −27*

$(x + 9)(x - 3)$ *whose sum is 6.*

  Check $(x + 9)(x - 3) = x^2 - 3x + 9x - 27$

                 $= x^2 + 6x - 27 \checkmark$

EXERCISES

Factor each trinomial. Check your answer.

49. $x^2 + 6x + 5$ 50. $x^2 + 6x + 8$

51. $x^2 + 8x + 15$ 52. $x^2 - 8x + 12$

53. $x^2 + 10x + 25$ 54. $x^2 - 13x + 22$

55. $x^2 + 24x + 80$ 56. $x^2 - 26x + 120$

57. $x^2 + 5x - 84$ 58. $x^2 - 5x - 24$

59. $x^2 - 3x - 28$ 60. $x^2 + 4x - 5$

61. $x^2 + x - 6$ 62. $x^2 + x - 20$

63. $x^2 - 2x - 48$ 64. $x^2 - 5x - 36$

65. $x^2 - 6x - 72$ 66. $x^2 - 3x - 70$

67. $x^2 + 14x - 120$ 68. $x^2 + 6x - 7$

69. The rectangle shown has an area of $(y^2 + 8y + 15)$ m^2. What is the width of the rectangle?

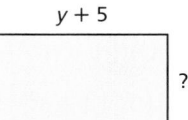

8-4 Factoring $ax^2 + bx + c$ (pp. 505–511)

EXAMPLES

Factor each trinomial.

■ $6x^2 + 17x + 5$

$(\boxed{} x + \boxed{})(\boxed{} x + \boxed{})$ *a = 6 and c = 5;*

                    Outer + Inner = 17

Factors of 6	Factors of 5	Outer + Inner
1 and 6	5 and 1	$(1)1 + (6)5 = 31$
2 and 3	1 and 5	$(2)5 + (3)1 = 13$
2 and 3	5 and 1	$(2)1 + (3)5 = 17$

$(2x + 5)(3x + 1)$

■ $2n^2 - n - 10$

$(\boxed{} n + \boxed{})(\boxed{} n + \boxed{})$ *a = 2 and c = −10;*

                    Outer + Inner = −1

Factors of 2	Factors of −10	Outer + Inner
1 and 2	1 and −10	$1(-10) + 2(1) = -8$
1 and 2	−1 and 10	$1(10) + 2(-1) = 8$
1 and 2	2 and −5	$1(-5) + 2(2) = -1$

$(1n + 2)(2n - 5) = (n + 2)(2n - 5)$

EXERCISES

Factor each trinomial. Check your answer.

70. $2x^2 + 11x + 5$ 71. $3x^2 + 10x + 7$

72. $2x^2 - 3x + 1$ 73. $3x^2 + 8x + 4$

74. $5x^2 + 28x + 15$ 75. $6x^2 - 19x + 15$

76. $4x^2 + 13x + 10$ 77. $3x^2 + 10x + 8$

78. $7x^2 - 37x + 10$ 79. $9x^2 + 18x + 8$

80. $2x^2 - x - 1$ 81. $3x^2 - 11x - 4$

82. $2x^2 - 11x + 5$ 83. $7x^2 - 19x - 6$

84. $5x^2 - 9x - 2$ 85. $-6x^2 - x + 2$

86. $6x^2 - x - 5$ 87. $6x^2 + 17x - 14$

88. $-4x^2 + 8x + 5$ 89. $-10x^2 + 11x + 6$

90. Write the polynomial modeled and then factor.

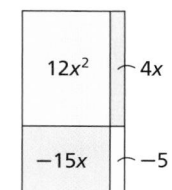

8-5 Factoring Special Products (pp. 514–520)

 11.0

EXAMPLES

■ Determine whether $x^2 + 18x + 81$ is a perfect square. If so, factor. If not, explain.

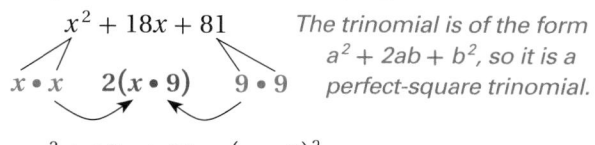

The trinomial is of the form $a^2 + 2ab + b^2$, so it is a perfect-square trinomial.

$$x^2 + 18x + 81 = (x + 9)^2$$

■ Determine whether $49x^4 - 25y^6$ is a difference of two squares. If so, factor. If not, explain.

$$49x^4 - 25y^6$$
$$7x^2 \cdot 7x^2 \quad 5y^3 \cdot 5y^3$$

The binomial is a difference of two squares.

$$\left(7x^2\right)^2 - \left(5y^3\right)^2 \qquad a = 7x^2,\ b = 5x^3$$

$$\left(7x^2 + 5y^3\right)\left(7x^2 - 5y^3\right) \qquad \text{Write the binomial as } (a + b)(a - b).$$

$$49x^4 - 25y^6 = \left(7x^2 + 5y^3\right)\left(7x^2 - 5y^3\right)$$

EXERCISES

Determine whether each trinomial is a perfect square. If so, factor. If not, explain.

91. $x^2 + 12x + 36$ **92.** $x^2 + 5x + 25$

93. $4x^2 - 2x + 1$ **94.** $9x^2 + 12x + 4$

95. $16x^2 + 8x + 4$ **96.** $x^2 + 14x + 49$

Determine whether each binomial is a difference of two squares. If so, factor. If not, explain.

97. $100x^2 - 81$ **98.** $x^2 - 2$

99. $5x^4 - 10y^6$ **100.** $(-12)^2 - \left(x^3\right)^2$

101. $121b^2 + 9c^8$ **102.** $100p^2 - 25q^2$

Factor each polynomial using the pattern of perfect-square trinomials or the difference of two squares. Tell which pattern you used and check your answer.

103. $x^2 - 25$ **104.** $x^2 + 20x + 100$

105. $j^2 - k^4$ **106.** $9x^2 - 42x + 49$

107. $81x^2 + 144x + 64$ **108.** $16b^4 - 121c^6$

8-6 Choosing a Factoring Method (pp. 522–527)

11.0

EXAMPLES

■ Tell whether $(3x - 9)(x + 4)$ is completely factored. If not, factor it.

$(3x - 9)(x + 4)$ $3x - 9$ can be factored.

$3(x - 3)(x + 4)$ Factor out 3, the GCF of $3x$ and 9.

■ $3ab^2 - 48a$

$3a(b^2 - 16)$ Factor out the GCF.

$3a(b + 4)(b - 4)$ Factor the difference of two squares.

Check $3a(b + 4)(b - 4) = 3a(b^2 - 16)$
$$= 3ab^2 - 48a \checkmark$$

■ $2m^3 + 4m^2 - 48m$

$2m(m^2 + 2m - 24)$ Factor out the GCF.

$2m(m - 4)(m + 6)$ Factor the trinomial.

Check $2m(m - 4)(m + 6)$
$$2m(m^2 + 2m - 24)$$
$$2m^3 + 4m^2 - 48m \checkmark$$

EXERCISES

Tell whether each polynomial is completely factored. If not, factor it.

109. $4x^2 + 10x + 6 = (4x + 6)(x + 1)$

110. $3y^2 + 75 = 3(y^2 + 25)$

111. $b^4 - 81 = (b^2 + 9)(b^2 - 9)$

112. $x^2 - 6x + 9 = (x - 3)^2$

Factor each polynomial completely. Check your answer.

113. $4x^2 - 64$ **114.** $3b^5 - 6b^4 - 24b^3$

115. $a^4b^3 - a^2b^5$ **116.** $t^{20} - t^4$

117. $5x^2 + 20x + 15$ **118.** $2x^4 - 50x^2$

119. $8t + 32 + 2st + 8s$

120. $25m^3 - 90m^2 - 40m$

121. $32x^4 - 48x^3 + 8x^2 - 12x$

122. $6s^4t + 12s^3t^2 + 6s^2t^3$

123. $10m^3 + 4m^2 - 90m - 36$

CHAPTER TEST

Find the GCF of each pair of monomials.

1. $3t^4$ and $8t^2$

2. $2y^3$ and $-12y$

3. $15n^5$ and $9n^4$

4. Write the prime factorization of 360.

5. A coin collector is arranging a display of three types of nickels. The types of nickels and number of each type are shown in the table. The collector wants to arrange them in rows with the same number in each row without having different types in the same row. How many rows will she need if she puts the greatest possible number of nickels in each row?

Type of Nickel	Number of Nickels
Liberty	16
Buffalo	24
Jefferson	40

Factor each expression.

6. $24m^2 + 4m^3$

7. $9x^5 - 12x$

8. $-2r^4 - 6$

9. $3(c - 5) + 4c(c - 5)$

10. $10x^3 + 4x - 25x^2 - 10$

11. $4y^3 - 4y^2 - 3 + 3y$

12. A model rocket is shot vertically from a deck into the air at a speed of 50 m/s. The expression $-5t^2 + 50t + 5$ gives the approximate height of the rocket after t seconds. Factor this expression.

Factor each trinomial.

13. $x^2 + 6x + 5$

14. $x^2 - 4x - 21$

15. $x^2 - 8x + 15$

16. $2x^2 + 9x + 7$

17. $2x^2 + 9x - 18$

18. $-3x^2 - 2x + 8$

Determine whether each trinomial is a perfect square. If so, factor. If not, explain.

19. $a^2 + 14a + 49$

20. $2x^2 + 10x + 25$

21. $9t^2 - 6t + 1$

Determine whether each binomial is a difference of two squares. If so, factor. If not, explain.

22. $b^2 - 16$

23. $25y^2 - 10$

24. $9a^2 - b^{10}$

25. A company is producing rectangular sheets of plastic. Each has an area of $(9x^2 + 30x + 25)$ ft². The dimensions of each sheet are of the form $ax + b$, where a and b are whole numbers. Find an expression for the perimeter of a sheet. Find the perimeter when $x = 4$ ft.

Tell whether each expression is completely factored. If not, factor it.

26. $(6x - 3)(x + 5)$

27. $(v^5 + 10)(v^5 - 10)$

28. $(2b + 3)(3b - 2)$

Factor each polynomial completely.

29. $8x^3 + 72x^2 + 160x$

30. $3x^5 - 27x^3$

31. $8x^3 + 64x^2 - 20x - 160$

32. $cd^4 - c^7d^6$

33. $100x^2 - 80x + 16$

34. $7m^8 - 7$

FOCUS ON ACT

The ACT Mathematics test booklet usually has writing space for scratch work. If not, the administrator of the test should have blank paper for you to use. The scratch work is for your use only. Be sure to transfer your final answer to the answer sheet.

If you are unsure how to solve a problem, look through the answer choices. They may provide you with a clue to the solution method. It may take longer to work backward from the answer choices, so make sure you monitor your time.

You may want to time yourself as you take this practice test. It should take you about 6 minutes to complete.

---

1. What is the value of $c^2 - d^2$ if $c + d = 7$ and $c - d = -2$?

(A) -14

(B) -5

(C) 5

(D) 14

(E) 45

---

2. Which of the following is the complete factorization of $6a^3b + 3a^2b^3$?

(F) $6a^3b^3$

(G) $9a^5b^4$

(H) $3ab(2a^2 + ab^2)$

(J) $3a^2b(2a + b^2)$

(K) $(6a^3b)(3a^2b^3)$

---

3. Which of the following is a factor of $x^2 + 3x - 18$?

(A) $x + 2$

(B) $x + 3$

(C) $x + 6$

(D) $x + 9$

(E) $x + 18$

---

4. The binomial $x - 3$ is NOT a factor of which of the following trinomials?

(F) $2x^2 - x - 3$

(G) $2x^2 - 5x - 3$

(H) $2x^2 - 8x + 6$

(J) $3x^2 - 6x - 9$

(K) $3x^2 - 10x + 3$

---

5. For what value of n is $4x^2 + 20x + n^2 = (2x + n)^2$ true for any real number x?

(A) 4

(B) 5

(C) 8

(D) 10

(E) 25

---

6. What is the factored form of $x^2 + \dfrac{2x}{3} + \dfrac{x}{2} + \dfrac{2}{6}$?

(F) $\left(x + \dfrac{1}{3}\right)\left(x + \dfrac{1}{2}\right)$

(G) $\left(x + \dfrac{1}{2}\right)\left(x + \dfrac{2}{3}\right)$

(H) $\left(x + \dfrac{2}{3}\right)\left(x + \dfrac{1}{6}\right)$

(J) $(x + 2)\left(x + \dfrac{1}{3}\right)$

(K) $\left(x + \dfrac{1}{3}\right)\left(x + \dfrac{2}{3}\right)$

STRATEGIES FOR SUCCESS

Any Question Type: Translate Words to Math

When reading a word problem, look for actions and context clues to help you translate the words into a mathematical equation or expression.

Some actions, such as those shown in this table, imply certain mathematical operations.

Action	Math Operation
Combining, increasing	Addition
Decreasing, reducing	Subtraction
Increasing or decreasing by a factor	Multiplication
Separating	Division

EXAMPLE 1

Short Response The polynomial $x^2 + 7x + 12$ represents the area of a rectangle in square meters. The width is $(x + 3)$ meters. Find the combined measure of the length and the width.

Use actions and context clues to translate the words into equations.

$x^2 + 7x + 12$ **represents** the **area of a rectangle** in square meters.
$$x^2 + 7x + 12 \quad = \quad A$$
The **width** is $(x + 3)$ meters.
$$w = (x + 3)$$
Find the **combined measure** of the **length** and the **width**.
$$m \quad = \quad \ell \quad + \quad w$$

Now use the equations to solve the problem.

$A = \ell w$	*Write the formula for area of a rectangle.*
$x^2 + 7x + 12 = \ell(x + 3)$	*Substitute $x^2 + 7x + 12$ for A and $(x + 3)$ for w.*
$(x + \boxed{?})(x + 3)$	*Factor $x^2 + 7x + 12$ to find an expression for the length.*
$(x + 4)(x + 3)$	*$3(4) = 12$; $3 + 4 = 7$*

The length is $(x + 4)$.

$m = \ell + w$	*Write the equation for the combined measure of the length and width.*
$m = (x + 4) + (x + 3)$	*Substitute $(x + 4)$ for ℓ and $(x + 3)$ for w.*
$m = 2x + 7$	*Combine like terms.*

The combined measure of the length and width is $(2x + 7)$ meters.

HOT TIP! Sometimes you cannot write an expression or equation in the order that the actions appear. For example, the expression "4 years younger than Maria" is written mathematically as $m - 4$.

Read each test item and answer the questions that follow.

Item A
Short Response The width of Alvin's rectangular mural is 6 times the length x. Alvin plans to make a new mural with an area of $(6x^2 - 24x + 24)$ square meters. By how much did Alvin decrease the area of the mural? Show your work.

1. What important words or context clues are in the first sentence of the test item? Use these clues to write an expression that represents the width of the rectangle.

2. Write an equation to represent the area of Alvin's first mural.

3. What math operation does the action *decrease* represent?

Item B
Multiple Choice Which factored expression represents the phrase shown below?

the square of the number of hours it takes to empty a cistern minus 20 times the number of hours plus 64

(A) $(h - 16)(h - 4)$ (C) $(h - 8)(h - 8)$
(B) $(h^2 - 20)(h - 64)$ (D) $(h - 16)(h + 4)$

4. Which word in the phrase tells you to use an exponent in your expression?

5. What is the unknown value in the expression? Define a variable to represent this value.

6. Identify other action words and the mathematical operation phrase each one represents.

Item C
Multiple Choice A company owns two packaging plants. The polynomial $0.05x^2 + 16x - 9400$ models one plant's profit, where x is the number of units packaged. The polynomial $-0.01x^2 + 17x - 5400$ models the other plant's profit. If x is 25,000, what is the total profit of both plants?

(A) $-\$5,830,300$
(B) $\$25,810,200$
(C) $\$31,640,500$
(D) $\$37,471,000$

7. What mathematical symbol does the action *models* represent?

8. Write an equation for each plant that can be used to determine its profit P.

9. What mathematical operation does the term "total profit" represent?

Item D
Gridded Response One of the bases of a trapezoid is 12 meters greater than its height. The other base is 4 meters less than its height. Find the area of the trapezoid when the height is 6 meters.

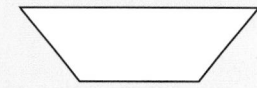

10. Identify the unknown dimension, and assign it a variable.

11. A student is unsure how many bases a trapezoid has. Identify the context clues that can help this student.

12. Make a list of the actions in the problem, and link each word to its mathematical meaning.

13. Write an expression for each base of the trapezoid.

MASTERING THE STANDARDS

CUMULATIVE ASSESSMENT, CHAPTERS 1–8

Multiple Choice

1. A rectangle has an area of $(x^2 + 5x - 24)$ square units. Which of the following are possible expressions for the length and the width of the rectangle?

- **A** Length: $(x - 24)$ units; width: $(x + 1)$ units
- **B** Length: $(x - 4)$ units; width: $(x + 6)$ units
- **C** Length: $(x - 3)$ units; width: $(x + 8)$ units
- **D** Length: $(x + 12)$ units; width: $(x - 2)$ units

2. Which property of real numbers is used to transform the equation in Step 1 into the equation in Step 2?

Step 1: $4(x - 5) + 8 = 88$
Step 2: $4x - 20 + 8 = 88$
Step 3: $\qquad 4x - 12 = 88$
Step 4: $\qquad\qquad 4x = 100$
Step 5: $\qquad\qquad 4x = 25$

- **A** Commutative Property of Multiplication
- **B** Associative Property of Multiplication
- **C** Multiplication Property
- **D** Distributive Property

3. If $\frac{2}{3}x - 9 = 3$, what is the value of the expression $8x - 3$?

- **A** -75
- **C** 61
- **B** -35
- **D** 141

4. Carlos and Bonita were just hired at a manufacturing plant. Carlos will earn $12.50 per hour. He will receive a hiring bonus of $300. Bonita will not get a hiring bonus, but she will earn $14.50 per hour. Which equation can you use to determine the number of hours h when both employees will have earned the same total amount?

- **A** $300 + 14.50h = 12.50h$
- **B** $14.50h + 300 = 12.50h$
- **C** $14.50h + 12.50h = 300$
- **D** $300 + 12.50h = 14.50h$

5. Which of the following expressions is equivalent to $x^2 - 8x + 16$?

- **A** $(x + 4)^2$
- **C** $(x + 8)(x + 2)$
- **B** $(x + 4)(x - 4)$
- **D** $(x - 4)^2$

6. Michael claims that the whole numbers are closed under subtraction. Stephanie disagrees. Which equation can Stephanie use as a counterexample to show that Michael's claim is false?

- **A** $6 - 4 = 2$
- **B** $-3 - 8 = -11$
- **C** $4 - 5 = -1$
- **D** $7 - (-2) = 9$

7. What is the value of y if the line through $(1, -1)$ and $(2, 2)$ is parallel to the line through $(-2, 1)$ and $(-1, y)$?

- **A** -8
- **C** 3
- **B** -2
- **D** 4

8. Which of the following shows the complete factorization of $2x^3 + 4x^2 - 6x$?

- **A** $(2x^2 - 2x)(x + 3)$
- **B** $2x(x^2 + 2x - 3)$
- **C** $2x(x - 1)(x + 3)$
- **D** $2(x^3 + 2x^2 - 3x)$

9. Which graph shows the solution set of the compound inequality $-9 \le 5 - 2x \le 13$?

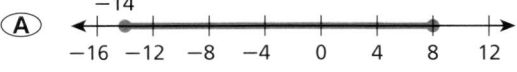

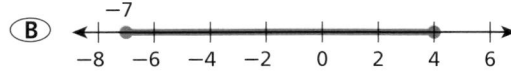

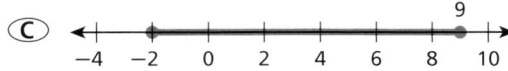

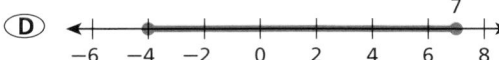

10. Which point lies on the graph of both functions?

$$f(x) = 2x - 10$$
$$g(x) = 10 - 2x$$

(A) $(5, 0)$ (C) $(0, 0)$

(B) $(1, -8)$ (D) $(2, 6)$

11. Hayley plans to solve the system of equations below.

$$\begin{cases} x + 3y = 8 \\ 5x - y = 8 \end{cases}$$

Which of the following does NOT show an equation Hayley can use to solve the system of equations?

(A) $x + 3(5x - 8) = 8$

(B) $5(8 - 3y) - y = 8$

(C) $x = 8 - 3y$

(D) $5x - (-x + 8) = 8$

12. Which value of b would make $x^2 + bx - 2$ factorable?

(A) -2 (C) 0

(B) -1 (D) 3

13. Which expression is equivalent to $xy \cdot \left(x^3 y^{\frac{1}{2}}\right)^4$?

(A) $x^4 y^{\frac{3}{2}}$ (C) $x^{13} y^3$

(B) $x^{16} y^6$ (D) $x^8 y^{\frac{11}{2}}$

Gridded Response

14. The complete factorization of $-12x^3 + 14x^2 + 6x$ is $-2x(ax + 1)(2x - 3)$. What is the value of a?

15. The expression $x^2 + x + b$ is a perfect-square trinomial. What is the value of b?

16. What is the slope of a line that is perpendicular to the line described by $2y + 5x = 6$?

17. The point $(3, k)$ lies on the line $3x - 4y = 7$. What is the value of k?

Short Response

18. The area of a certain circle is $\pi(9x^2 + 6x + 1)$ square centimeters. Find an expression for the length of the circle's radius. Explain how you found your answer.

19. A rectangle has an area of $(x^2 - 25)$ square feet.

   a. Use factoring to write possible expressions for the length and width of the rectangle.

   b. Use your expressions from part **a** to write an expression for the perimeter of the rectangle. Simplify the expression.

   c. Use your expressions from parts **a** and **b** to find the perimeter and the area of the rectangle when $x = 10$ feet. Show your work.

20. Write the numbers 57,000,000,000 and 19,000 in scientific notation. Then show how to divide 57,000,000,000 by 19,000 using properties of exponents.

21. Show that you can factor the expression $x^2 y - 12 + 3y - 4x^2$ by grouping in two different ways.

Extended Response

22. The diagram below can be used to show that the expression $(a + b)^2$ is equivalent to the expression $a^2 + 2ab + b^2$.

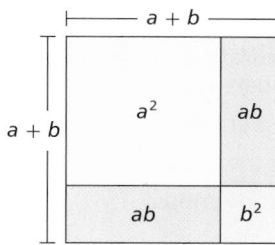

   a. Make a diagram similar to the one above to model the expression $(a + b + c)^2$. Label each distinct area.

   b. Use the labels from your diagram to write an expression equivalent to $(a + b + c)^2$.

   c. Show that your expression in part **b** is equivalent to $(a + b + c)^2$ by evaluating each expression for $a = 4$, $b = 2$, and $c = 1$.

   d. Factor $x^2 + y^2 + 9 + 2xy + 6x + 6y$. Show or explain how you found your answer.

CHAPTER 9

Quadratic Functions and Equations

go.hrw.com
Chapter Project Online
KEYWORD: MA8CA ChProj

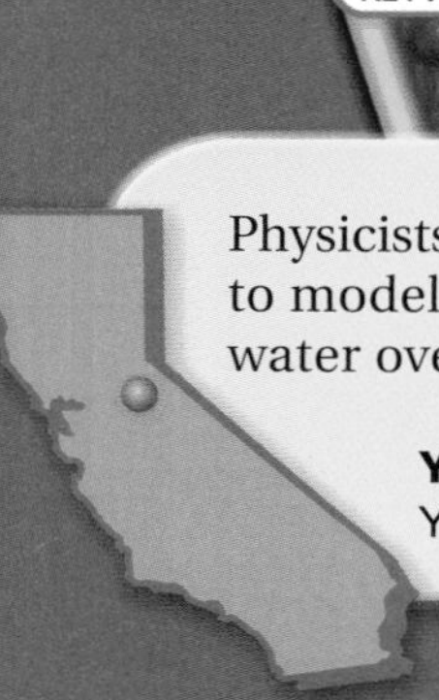

Physicists use quadratic equations to model falling objects such as water over a waterfall.

Yosemite Falls
Yosemite National Park, CA

ARE YOU READY?

✓ Vocabulary

Match each term on the left with a definition on the right.

1. factoring

2. quadratic

3. trinomial

4. x-intercept

A. the process of writing a number or an algebraic expression as a product

B. the x-coordinate of a point where a graph intersects the x-axis

C. a polynomial with three terms

D. a polynomial with degree 2

E. the first number of an ordered pair of numbers that describes the location of a point on the coordinate plane

✓ Graph Functions

Graph each function.

5. $y = -2x + 8$

6. $y = (x + 1)^2$

7. $y = x^2 + 3$

8. $y = 2x^2$

✓ Multiply Binomials

Find each product.

9. $(m + 2)(m + 5)$

10. $(y - 7)(y + 2)$

11. $(2a + 4)(5a + 6)$

12. $(x + 1)(x + 1)$

13. $(t + 5)(t + 5)$

14. $(3n - 8)(3n - 8)$

✓ Factor Trinomials

Factor each polynomial completely.

15. $x^2 - 2x + 1$

16. $x^2 + x - 2$

17. $x^2 - 6x + 5$

18. $x^2 - x - 12$

19. $x^2 - 9x + 18$

20. $x^2 - 7x - 18$

✓ Squares and Square Roots

Evaluate each expression.

21. $\sqrt{36}$

22. $\sqrt{121}$

23. $-\sqrt{64}$

24. $\sqrt{16}\,\sqrt{81}$

25. $\sqrt{\dfrac{9}{25}}$

26. $-\sqrt{6(24)}$

✓ Solve Multi-Step Equations

Solve each equation. Check your answer.

27. $3m + 5 = 11$

28. $3t + 4 = 10$

29. $5n + 13 = 28$

30. $2(k - 4) + k = 7$

31. $10 = \dfrac{r}{3} + 8$

32. $2(y - 6) = 8.6$

Unpacking the Standards

The information below "unpacks" the standards. The Academic Vocabulary is highlighted and defined to help you understand the language of the standards. Refer to the lessons listed after each standard for help with the math terms and phrases. The Chapter Concept shows how the standard is applied in this chapter.

California Standard	Academic Vocabulary	Chapter Concept
14.0 Students solve a quadratic equation by factoring or completing the square. (Lessons **9-5, 9-7**)	**quadratic equation** an equation that has a variable term raised to the second power **_Example:_** $3x^2 - x + 5 = 0$	You use factoring to solve quadratic equations, and you learn a solution method called completing the square.
19.0 Students know the quadratic formula and are familiar with its proof by completing the square. (Lesson **9-8**)	**quadratic formula** a formula that can be used to solve any quadratic equation	You learn another solution method called the quadratic formula, and you understand why the formula works.
20.0 Students use the quadratic formula to find the roots of a second-degree polynomial and to solve quadratic equations. (Lesson **9-8**)	**roots of a polynomial** values of the variable for which the polynomial is equal to 0	You apply what you have learned about solving quadratic equations to quadratic polynomials.
21.0 Students graph quadratic functions and know that their roots are the _x_-intercepts. (Lessons **9-1, 9-2, 9-3, 9-4, Lab 9-4**)	**quadratic function** a function that is described by a quadratic equation **_Example:_** $y = 3x^2 - x + 5$	You extend your knowledge of functions to include quadratic functions and their properties.
22.0 Students use the quadratic formula or factoring techniques or both to determine whether the graph of a quadratic function will intersect the _x_-axis in zero, one, or two points. (Lesson **9-9**)	**technique** a way of doing something **determine** find out	You make connections between the solutions of a quadratic equation and the graph of a quadratic function.
23.0 Students apply quadratic equations to physical problems, such as the motion of an object under the force of gravity. (Lessons **9-2, 9-3, 9-4, 9-5, 9-6, 9-7**)	**apply** use **physical** having to do with scientific rules or ideas **motion** movement	You use quadratic equations to model situations involving gravity and other scientific theories.

Standards 2.0, 7.0, 17.0, 24.1, and 25.3 are also covered in this chapter. To see these standards unpacked, go to Chapter 1, p. 4; Chapter 2, p. 70; Chapter 4, p. 198; Chapter 5, p. 254.

Study Strategy: Learn Vocabulary

California Standards

English-Language Arts Reading 8.1.3

Mathematics has a vocabulary all its own. Many new terms appear on the pages of your textbook. Learn these new terms as they are introduced. They will give you the necessary tools to understand new concepts.

Some tips to learning new vocabulary include:

• Look at the **context** in which a new word appears.

• Use **prefixes** or **suffixes** to figure out the word's meaning.

• Relate the new term to familiar **everyday words.** Keep in mind that a word's mathematical meaning may not exactly match its everyday meaning.

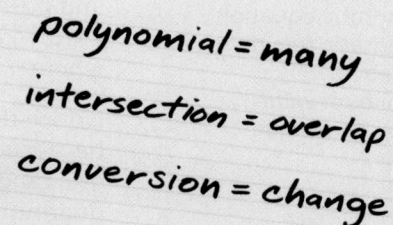

polynomial = many
intersection = overlap
conversion = change

Vocabulary Word	Study Tip	Definition
Polynomial	The prefix "poly-" means many.	One monomial or the sum or the difference of monomials
Intersection	Relate it to the meaning of the "intersection of two roads".	The overlapping region that shows the solution to a system of equations
Conversion Factor	Relate it to the word "convert", which means change or alter.	Used to convert a measurement to different units

Complete the chart.

	Vocabulary Word	Study Tips	Definition
1.	Trinomial		
2.	Independent system		
3.	Variable		

Use the context of each sentence to define the underlined word. Then relate the word to everyday words.

4. If two linear equations in a system have the same graph, the graphs are called <u>coincident</u> lines, or simply the same line.

5. In the formula $d = rt$, d is <u>isolated</u>.

9-1 Quadratic Equations and Functions

California Standards

🗝 **21.0 Students graph quadratic functions** and know that their roots are the *x*-intercepts.

Also covered: **17.0**

Vocabulary
quadratic equation
quadratic function
parabola
minimum value
maximum value
vertex

Why learn this?
The height of a soccer ball after it is kicked into the air can be described by a quadratic function. (See Exercise 60.)

Solutions of the equation $y = x^2$ are shown in the graph. Notice that the graph is not linear. The equation $y = x^2$ is a *quadratic equation*. A **quadratic equation** in two variables can be written in the form $y = ax^2 + bx + c$, where *a*, *b*, and *c* are real numbers and $a \neq 0$. The equation $y = x^2$ can be written as $y = 1x^2 + 0x + 0$, where $a = 1$, $b = 0$, and $c = 0$.

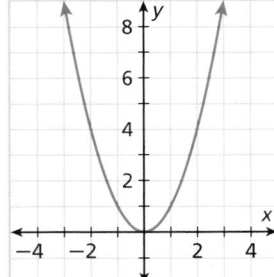

Notice that the graph of $y = x^2$ represents a function because each domain value is paired with exactly one range value. A function represented by a quadratic equation is a **quadratic function** .

Quadratic Equations and Their Graphs

For any quadratic equation in two variables
- all points on its graph are solutions to the equation.
- all solutions to the equation appear on its graph.

EXAMPLE 1 **Determining Whether a Point Is on a Graph**

Without graphing, tell whether each point is on the graph of $y = -3x^2 - 4$.

A $(2, 1)$

Substitute $(2, 1)$ into $y = -3x^2 - 4$.

$$y = -3x^2 - 4$$
$$1 \overset{?}{=} -3(2)^2 - 4$$
$$1 \overset{?}{=} -3 \cdot 4 - 4$$
$$1 \overset{?}{=} -12 - 4$$
$$1 \neq -16 \; ✗$$

Since $(2, 1)$ is not a solution of $y = -3x^2 - 4$, $(2, 1)$ is not on the graph.

B $(-1, -7)$

Substitute $(-1, -7)$ into $y = -3x^2 - 4$.

$$y = -3x^2 - 4$$
$$-7 \overset{?}{=} -3(-1)^2 - 4$$
$$-7 \overset{?}{=} -3 \cdot 1 - 4$$
$$-7 \overset{?}{=} -3 - 4$$
$$-7 = -7 \; ✓$$

Since $(-1, -7)$ is a solution of $y = -3x^2 - 4$, $(-1, -7)$ is on the graph.

 Without graphing, tell whether each point is on the graph of $x^2 + y = 2$.

1a. $(1, 1)$ **1b.** $\left(\dfrac{1}{2}, \dfrac{3}{2}\right)$ **1c.** $(-3.5, 10.5)$

The graph of a quadratic function is a curve called a **parabola**. To graph a quadratic function, generate enough ordered pairs to see the shape of the parabola. Then connect the points with a smooth curve.

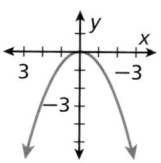

EXAMPLE 2 **Graphing Quadratic Functions**

Graph each quadratic function.

A $y = 2x^2$

x	$y = 2x^2$
−2	8
−1	2
0	0
1	2
2	8

Make a table of values. Choose values of x and use them to find values of y.

Graph the points. Then connect the points with a smooth curve.

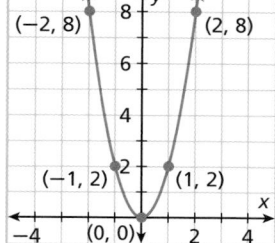

Helpful Hint

When choosing values of *x*, be sure to choose positive values, negative values, and 0.

B $y = -2x^2$

x	$y = -2x^2$
−2	−8
−1	−2
0	0
1	−2
2	−8

Make a table of values. Choose values of x and use them to find values of y.

Graph the points. Then connect the points with a smooth curve.

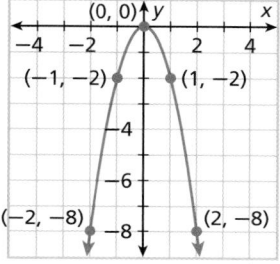

 Graph each quadratic function.

2a. $y = x^2 + 2$ **2b.** $y = -3x^2 + 1$

As shown in the graphs in Examples 2A and 2B, some parabolas open upward and some open downward. Notice that the only difference between the two equations is the value of *a*. When a quadratic function is written in the form $y = ax^2 + bx + c$, the value of *a* determines the direction the parabola opens.

• A parabola opens upward when $a > 0$.
• A parabola opens downward when $a < 0$.

EXAMPLE 3 **Identifying the Direction of a Parabola**

Tell whether the graph of each quadratic function opens upward or downward. Explain.

A $y = 4x^2$

$y = 4x^2$
$a = 4$ *Identify the value of a.*

Since $a > 0$, the parabola opens upward.

Tell whether the graph of each quadratic function opens upward or downward. Explain.

 **B** $2x^2 + y = 5$

$$2x^2 + y = 5$$
$$\underline{-2x^2 \qquad -2x^2}$$ *Write the function in the form $y = ax^2 + bx + c$*
$$\qquad y = -2x^2 + 5$$ *by solving for y. Subtract $2x^2$ from both sides.*
$$\qquad a = -2$$ *Identify the value of a.*

Since $a < 0$, the parabola opens **downward**.

CHECK IT OUT! Tell whether the graph of each quadratic function opens upward or downward. Explain.

3a. $f(x) = -4x^2 - x + 1$ **3b.** $y - 5x^2 = 2x - 6$

The **minimum value** of a function is the least possible y-value for that function. The **maximum value** of a function is the greatest possible y-value for that function.

The highest or lowest point on a parabola is the **vertex**. Therefore, the minimum or maximum value of a quadratic function occurs at the vertex.

Know it! Note

 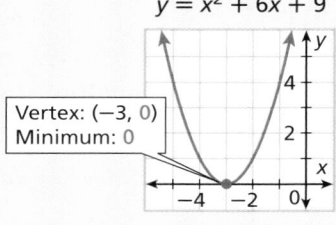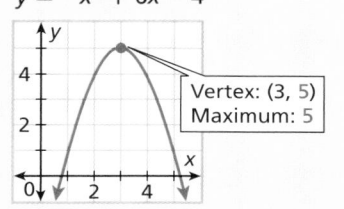
EXAMPLE 4   **Identifying the Vertex and the Minimum or Maximum**

Identify the vertex of each parabola. Then give the minimum or maximum value of the function.

A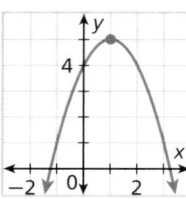

The vertex is $(1, 5)$, and the maximum is 5.

B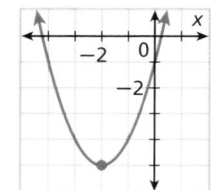

The vertex is $(-2, -5)$, and the minimum is -5.

 Identify the vertex of each parabola. Then give the minimum or maximum value of the function.

4a. 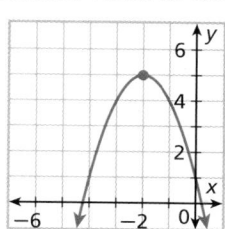 4b.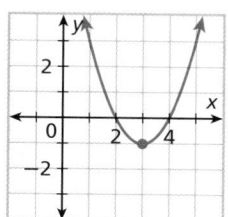

Caution!

You may not be able to see the entire graph, but that does not mean the graph stops. Remember that the arrows indicate that the graph continues.

Unless a specific domain is given, the domain of a quadratic function is all real numbers. One way to find the range of a quadratic function is by looking at its graph.

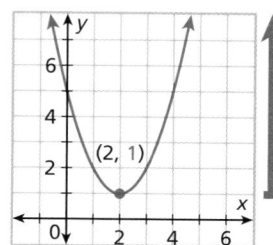

For the graph of $y = x^2 - 4x + 5$, the **range** begins at the minimum value of the function, where $y = 1$. All y-values greater than or equal to 1 appear somewhere on the graph. So the range is $y \geq 1$.

EXAMPLE 5 **Finding Domain and Range**

Find the domain and range.

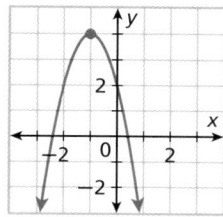

Step 1 The graph opens downward, so identify the maximum.
The vertex is $(-1, 4)$, so the maximum is 4.

Step 2 Find the domain and range.
D: all real numbers
R: $y \leq 4$

 Find the domain and range.

5a. 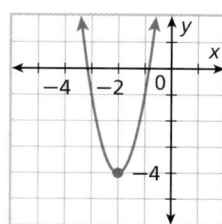 5b.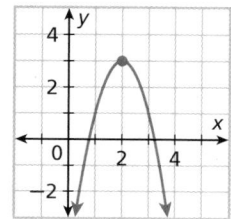

THINK AND DISCUSS

1. How can you identify a quadratic function?

2. GET ORGANIZED Copy and complete the graphic organizer. In each box, sketch and describe the graph and tell whether the function has a maximum value or a minimum value.

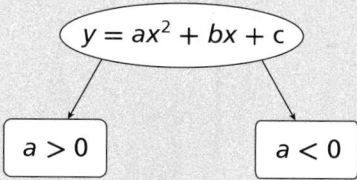

9-1 Quadratic Equations and Functions **547**

9-1 **Exercises**

California Standards Practice
15.0, 17.0, 21.0, 23.0

go.hrw.com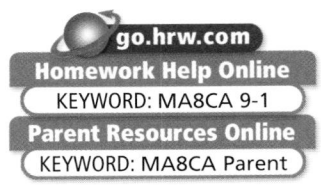
Homework Help Online
KEYWORD: MA8CA 9-1
Parent Resources Online
KEYWORD: MA8CA Parent

GUIDED PRACTICE

1. **Vocabulary** The y-value of the vertex of a parabola that opens upward is the ____?____ value of the function. (*maximum* or *minimum*)

SEE EXAMPLE **1**
p. 544

Without graphing, tell whether each point is on the graph of the given equation.

2. $y = x^2 + 9$; $(2, 11)$

3. $5x^2 + y = -40$; $(20, 20)$

4. $x^2 - 49 = y$; $(7, 0)$

5. $y + 3 = 2x^2$; $(1.5, 1.5)$

6. $y = x^2 - 10x + 25$; $(1, 15)$

7. $y = x^2 + 4x$; $(0, 0)$

SEE EXAMPLE **2**
p. 545

Graph each quadratic function.

8. $y = 4x^2$

9. $y = \frac{1}{2}x^2$

10. $y = -x^2 + 1$

11. $y = -5x^2$

12. $y = -x^2 - 3$

13. $y = 3 - 2x^2$

14. $y = x^2 + 4$

15. $y = -3x^2 - x$

SEE EXAMPLE **3**
p. 545

Tell whether the graph of each quadratic function opens upward or downward. Explain.

16. $y = -3x^2 + 4x$

17. $y = 1 - 2x + 6x^2$

18. $y + x^2 = -x - 2$

19. $y + 2 = x^2$

20. $y - 2x^2 = -3$

21. $y + 2 + 3x^2 = 1$

SEE EXAMPLE **4**
p. 546

Identify the vertex of each parabola. Then give the minimum or maximum value of the function.

22.

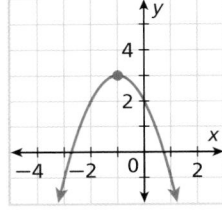

23.

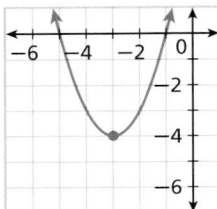

SEE EXAMPLE **5**
p. 547

Find the domain and range.

24.

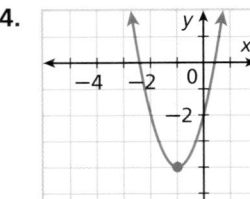

25.

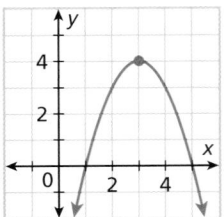

26.

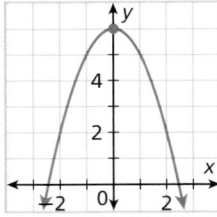

27.

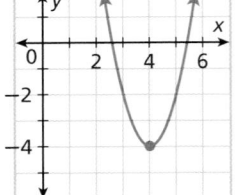

Independent Practice

For Exercises	See Example
28–33	1
34–37	2
38–40	3
41–42	4
43–46	5

Extra Practice

Skills Practice p. EP18

Application Practice p. EP32

Without graphing, tell whether each point is on the graph of the given equation.

28. $y = x^2 + 14$; $(-2, 10)$

29. $8x^2 - y = 8$; $(-1, 0)$

30. $y = x^2 - 10x$; $(6, 8)$

31. $y = 2x^2 - 14$; $(5, 86)$

32. $y = 16x^2 + 1$; $\left(\frac{1}{2}, 5\right)$

33. $y = -\frac{1}{3}x^2$; $(6, 12)$

Graph each quadratic function.

34. $y = x^2 - 5$

35. $y = -\frac{1}{2}x^2$

36. $y = -2x^2 + 2$

37. $y = 3x^2 - 2$

Tell whether the graph of each quadratic function opens upward or downward. Explain.

38. $y = 7x^2 - 4x$

39. $x - 3x^2 + y = 5$

40. $y = -\frac{2}{3}x^2$

Identify the vertex of each parabola. Then give the minimum or maximum value of the function.

41.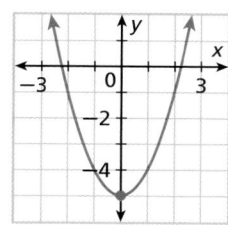

42.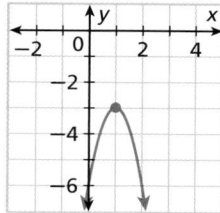

Find the domain and range.

43.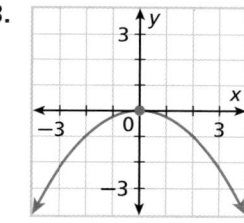

44.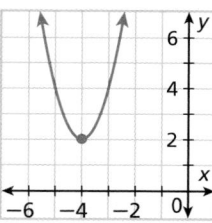

45.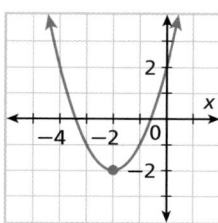

46.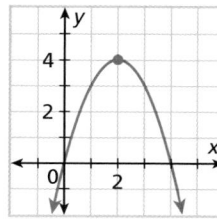

 Reasoning Tell whether each statement is sometimes, always, or never true. Explain.

47. The graph of a quadratic function is a straight line.

48. The range of a quadratic function is the set of all real numbers.

49. The highest power of any variable term in a quadratic function is 2.

50. The graph of a quadratic function contains the point $(0, 0)$.

51. The vertex of a parabola occurs at the minimum value of the function.

52. The graph of a quadratic function that has a minimum opens upward.

Tell whether each function is quadratic. If it is, write the function in the form $y = ax^2 + bx + c$. If not, explain why not.

53. $y = 3x - 1$

54. $y = 2x^2 - 5 + 3x$

55. $y = (x + 1)^2$

56. $y = 5 - (x - 1)^2$

57. $y = 3x^2 - 9$

58. $y = (x + 1)^3 - x^2$

59. Estimation The graph shows the approximate height y in meters of a volleyball x seconds after it is served.

   a. Estimate the time it takes for the volleyball to reach its greatest height.

   b. Estimate the greatest height that the volleyball reaches.

   c. Critical Thinking If the domain of a quadratic function is all real numbers, why is the domain of this function limited to nonnegative numbers?

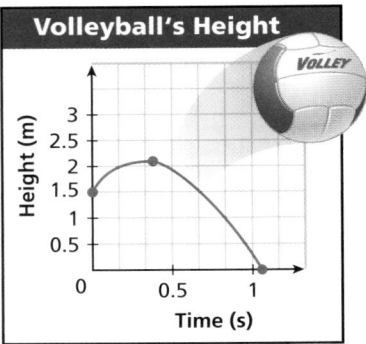

60. Sports The height in feet of a soccer ball x seconds after it is kicked into the air is modeled by the function $y = 48x - 16x^2$.

   a. Graph the function.

   b. In this situation, what values make sense for the domain?

   c. Does the soccer ball ever reach a height of 50 ft? How do you know?

Tell whether each function is linear, quadratic, or neither.

61. $y = \frac{1}{2}x - x^2$

62. $y = \frac{1}{2}x - 3$

63. $y + 3 = -x^2$

64. $y = (x + 2)^2$

65. $y = \frac{1}{2}x(x^2)$

66. $y = \frac{3}{x^2}$

67. $y = \frac{3}{2}x$

68. $x^2 + 2x + 1 = y$

69. Marine Biology A scientist records the motion of a dolphin as it jumps from the water. The function $h(t) = -16t^2 + 32t$ models the dolphin's height in feet above the water after t seconds.

   a. Graph the function.

   b. What domain makes sense for this situation?

   c. What is the dolphin's maximum height above the water?

   d. How long is the dolphin out of the water?

70. Write About It Explain how to tell the difference between a linear function and a quadratic function when given each of the following:

   a. the equation

   b. the graph

CONCEPT CONNECTION

71. This problem will prepare you for the Concept Connection on page 566.

A rocket team is using simulation software to create and study water bottle rockets. The team begins by simulating the launch of a rocket without a parachute. The table gives data for one rocket design.

   a. Graph the data and connect the points.

   b. Does this function have a maximum or a minimum? What does this value represent?

Time (s)	Height (m)
0	0
1	34.3
2	58.8
3	73.5
4	78.4
5	73.5
6	58.8
7	34.3
8	0

72. Critical Thinking Given the function $-3 - y = x^2 + x$, why is it incorrect to state that the parabola opens upward and has a minimum?

Multiple Choice For Exercises 73 and 74, choose the best answer.

73. Which of the following could be the graph of a quadratic function?

(A)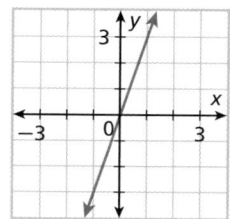

(C)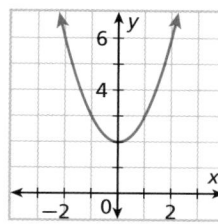

(B)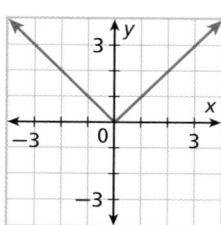

(D)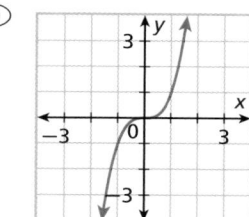

74. Which of the following quadratic functions has a maximum?

Ⓐ $2x^2 - y = 3x - 2$

Ⓑ $y = x^2 + 4x + 16$

Ⓒ $y - x^2 + 6 = 9x$

Ⓓ $y + 3x^2 = 9$

75. Short Response Is the function $f(x) = 5 - 2x^2 + 3x$ quadratic? Explain your answer by using two different methods of identification.

CHALLENGE AND EXTEND

76. Multi-Step A rectangular picture measuring 6 in. by 10 in. is surrounded by a frame with uniform width x. Write a quadratic function to show the combined area of the picture and frame.

77. Graphing Calculator Use a graphing calculator to find the domain and range of the quadratic functions $y = x^2 - 4$ and $y = -(x + 2)^2$.

SPIRAL STANDARDS REVIEW   🔑 2.0, 16.0

Write each number as a power of the given base. *(Lesson 1-4)*

78. 10,000; base 10   **79.** 16; base -2 **80.** $\frac{8}{27}$; base $\frac{2}{3}$

81. A map shows a scale of 1 inch:3 miles. On the map, the distance from Lin's home to the park is $14\frac{1}{4}$ inches. What is the actual distance? *(Lesson 2-5)*

Identify the independent and dependent variables. Write a rule in function notation for each situation. *(Lesson 4-3)*

82. Camp Wildwood has collected $400 in registration fees. It can enroll another 3 campers for $25 each.

83. Sal works between 30 and 35 hours per week. He earns $9 per hour.

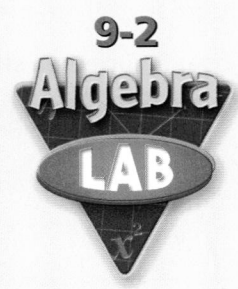

9-2 Algebra LAB

Use with Lesson 9-2

Explore the Axis of Symmetry

Every graph of a quadratic function is a parabola that is symmetric about a vertical line through its vertex called the *axis of symmetry*.

There is a relationship between a and b in the quadratic function and the equation of the axis of symmetry. In this activity, you will look at examples of quadratic functions and use inductive reasoning to make a conjecture about this relationship.

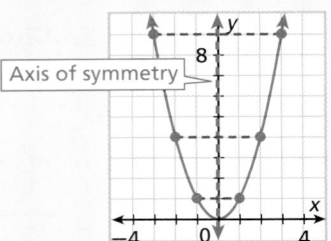

California Standards

24.1 Students explain the difference between inductive and deductive reasoning and identify and **provide examples** of each.

Activity

1 Complete the table.

Function	$y = 1x^2 - 2x - 3$	$y = -2x^2 - 8x - 6$	$y = -1x^2 + 4x$
Graph			
a	1	▨	▨
b	-2	▨	▨
$\dfrac{b}{a}$	▨	▨	▨
Axis of Symmetry (from graph)	$x = 1$	▨	▨

2 Compare the axis of symmetry with $\frac{b}{a}$ in your chart. What can you multiply $\frac{b}{a}$ by to get the number in the equation of the axis of symmetry? (*Hint:* Write and solve an equation to find the value.) Check your answer for each function.

3 Use your answer from Problem 2 to make a conjecture about the equation of the axis of symmetry of a quadratic function. $x = $ _____?_____

Try This

For the graph of each quadratic function, find the equation of the axis of symmetry.

1. $y = 2x^2 + 12x - 7$

2. $y = 4x^2 + 8x - 12$

3. $y = 5x^2 - 20x + 10$

4. $y = -3x^2 + 9x + 1$

5. $y = x^2 - 7$

6. $y = 3x^2 + x + 4$

9-2 Characteristics of Quadratic Functions

California Standards

🔑 **21.0** Students graph quadratic functions and **know that their roots are the** *x***-intercepts.**
Also covered: 🔑 **23.0**

Vocabulary
zero of a function
axis of symmetry

Who uses this?
Engineers can use characteristics of quadratic functions to find the height of the arch supports of bridges. (See Example 5.)

Recall that an *x*-intercept of a function is a value of *x* when *y* = 0. A **zero of a function** is an *x*-value that makes the function equal to 0. So a zero of a function is the same as an *x*-intercept. Since a graph intersects the *x*-axis at the point or points containing an *x*-intercept, these intersections are also at the zeros of the function. A quadratic function may have one, two, or no zeros.

E X A M P L E 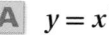 **Finding Zeros of Quadratic Functions From Graphs**

Find the zeros of each quadratic function from its graph. Check your answer.

A $y = x^2 - x - 2$

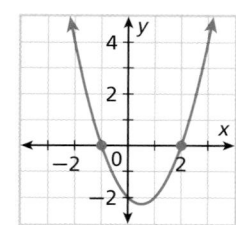

The zeros appear to be −1 and 2.
Check
$y = x^2 - x - 2$
$y = (-1)^2 - (-1) - 2$
$= 1 + 1 - 2 = 0$ ✓
$y = 2^2 - 2 - 2$
$= 4 - 2 - 2 = 0$ ✓

B $y = -2x^2 + 4x - 2$

The only zero appears to be 1.
Check
$y = -2x^2 + 4x - 2$
$y = -2(1)^2 + 4(1) - 2$
$= -2(1) + 4 - 2$
$= -2 + 4 - 2$
$= 0$ ✓

C $y = \frac{1}{4}x^2 + 1$

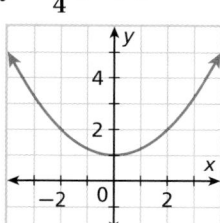

The graph does not cross the *x*-axis, so this function has no zeros.

Helpful Hint

Notice that if a function has only one zero, the zero is the *x*-coordinate of the vertex.

 Find the zeros of each quadratic function from its graph. Check your answer.

1a. $y = -4x^2 - 2$

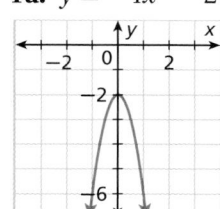

1b. $y = x^2 - 6x + 9$

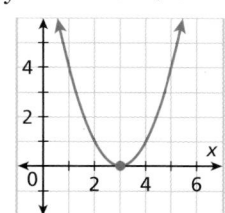

The vertical line that divides a parabola into two symmetrical halves is the **axis of symmetry** . The axis of symmetry always passes through the vertex of the parabola. You can use the zeros to find the axis of symmetry.

Finding the Axis of Symmetry by Using Zeros

WORDS	NUMBERS	GRAPH
One Zero If a function has one zero, use the x-coordinate of the vertex to find the axis of symmetry.	Vertex: $(3, 0)$ Axis of symmetry: $x = 3$	
Two Zeros If a function has two zeros, use the average of the two zeros to find the axis of symmetry.	Zeros: -4 and 0 $\dfrac{-4 + 0}{2} = \dfrac{-4}{2} = -2$ Axis of symmetry: $x = -2$	

E X A M P L E   2   **Finding the Axis of Symmetry by Using Zeros**

Find the axis of symmetry of each parabola.

A

$(2, 0)$ *Identify the x-coordinate of the vertex.*

The axis of symmetry is $x = 2$.

B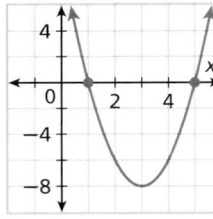

$\dfrac{1 + 5}{2} = \dfrac{6}{2} = 3$ *Find the average of the zeros.*

The axis of symmetry is $x = 3$.

CHECK IT OUT!   Find the axis of symmetry of each parabola.

2a. 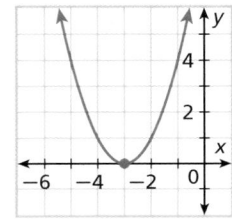   **2b.**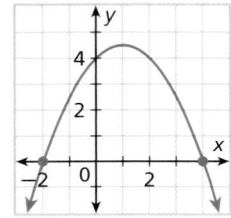

If a function has no zeros or they are difficult to identify from a graph, you can use a formula to find the axis of symmetry. The formula works for all quadratic functions.

 **Know it! Note**

Finding the Axis of Symmetry by Using the Formula

FORMULA	EXAMPLE
For a quadratic function $y = ax^2 + bx + c$, the axis of symmetry is the vertical line $$x = -\frac{b}{2a}.$$	$y = 2x^2 + 4x + 5$ $$x = -\frac{b}{2a}$$ $$= -\frac{4}{2(2)} = -1$$ The axis of symmetry is $x = -1$.

EXAMPLE **3** **Finding the Axis of Symmetry by Using the Formula**

Find the axis of symmetry of the graph of $y = x^2 + 3x + 4$.

Step 1 Find the values of a and b.
$y = 1x^2 + 3x + 4$
$a = 1, b = 3$

Step 2 Use the formula $x = -\dfrac{b}{2a}$.

$$x = -\frac{3}{2(1)} = -\frac{3}{2} = -1.5$$

The axis of symmetry is $x = -1.5$.

 **3.** Find the axis of symmetry of the graph of $y = 2x^2 + x + 3$.

Once you have found the axis of symmetry, you can use it to identify the vertex.

 **Know it! Note**

Finding the Vertex of a Parabola

Step 1 To find the x-coordinate of the vertex, find the axis of symmetry by using zeros or the formula.

Step 2 To find the corresponding y-coordinate, substitute the x-coordinate of the vertex into the function.

Step 3 Write the vertex as an ordered pair.

EXAMPLE **4** **Finding the Vertex of a Parabola**

Find the vertex.

A $y = -x^2 - 2x$

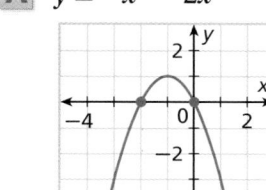

Step 1 Find the x-coordinate of the vertex.
The zeros are -2 and 0.
$$x = \frac{-2 + 0}{2} = \frac{-2}{2} = -1$$

Step 2 Find the y-coordinate of the vertex.
$y = -x^2 - 2x$ *Use the function rule.*
$= -(-1)^2 - 2(-1) = 1$ *Substitute -1 for x.*

Step 3 Write the ordered pair.
$(-1, 1)$

The vertex is $(-1, 1)$.

 **Helpful Hint**

In Example 4A Step 2, use the order of operations to simplify the function.
$-(-1)^2 = -(1) = -1$

Find the vertex.

B $y = 5x^2 - 10x + 3$

    Step 1 Find the x-coordinate of the vertex.

      $a = 5, b = -10$ *Identify a and b.*

      $x = -\dfrac{b}{2a}$

      $= -\dfrac{-10}{2(5)} = -\dfrac{-10}{10} = 1$ *Substitute 5 for a and −10 for b.*

    Step 2 Find the y-coordinate of the vertex.

      $y = 5x^2 - 10x + 3$

      $= 5(1)^2 - 10(1) + 3$ *Use the function rule.*

      $= 5 - 10 + 3$ *Substitute 1 for x.*

      $= -2$

    Step 3 Write the ordered pair.

  The vertex is $(1, -2)$.

 **4.** Find the vertex of the graph of $y = x^2 - 4x - 10$.

EXAMPLE 5   *Architecture Application*

The height above water level of a curved arch support for a bridge can be modeled by $f(x) = -0.007x^2 + 0.84x + 0.8$, where x is the distance in feet from where the arch support enters the water. Can a sailboat that is 24 feet tall pass under the bridge? Explain.

The vertex represents the highest point of the arch support.

Step 1 Find the x-coordinate of the vertex.

    $a = -0.007, b = 0.84$ *Identify a and b.*

    $x = -\dfrac{b}{2a}$

    $= -\dfrac{0.84}{2(-0.007)} = 60$ *Substitute −0.007 for a and 0.84 for b.*

Step 2 Find the y-coordinate of the vertex.

    $f(x) = -0.007x^2 + 0.84x + 0.8$ *Use the function rule.*

    $= -0.007(60)^2 + 0.84(60) + 0.8$ *Substitute 60 for x.*

    $= 26$

Since the height of the arch support is 26 feet, the sailboat can pass under the bridge.

 **5.** The height of a small rise in a roller coaster track is modeled by $f(x) = -0.07x^2 + 0.42x + 6.37$, where x is the distance in feet from a support pole at ground level. Find the height of the rise.

THINK AND DISCUSS

1. How do you find the zeros of a function from its graph?

2. Describe how to find the axis of symmetry of a quadratic function if its graph does not cross the *x*-axis

3. GET ORGANIZED Copy and complete the graphic organizer. In each box, sketch a graph that fits the given description.

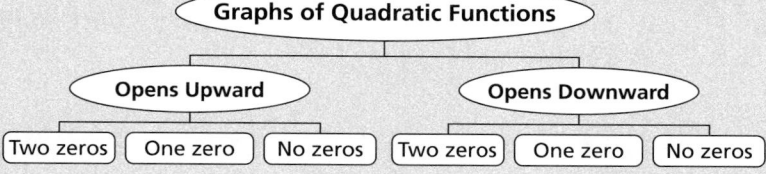

Graphs of Quadratic Functions

Opens Upward | Opens Downward

Two zeros | One zero | No zeros | Two zeros | One zero | No zeros

---

9-2 Exercises

California Standards Practice
◆━ 21.0, ◆━ 23.0, 24.1

go.hrw.com
Homework Help Online
KEYWORD: MA8CA 9-2
Parent Resources Online
KEYWORD: MA8CA Parent

GUIDED PRACTICE

Vocabulary Apply the vocabulary from this lesson to answer each question.

1. Why is the *zero of a function* the same as an *x*-intercept of a function?

2. Where is the *axis of symmetry* of a parabola located?

SEE EXAMPLE 1
p. 553

Find the zeros of each quadratic function from its graph. Check your answer.

3. $y = x^2 + 2x + 1$

4. $y = 9 - x^2$

5. $y = -x^2 - x - 4$

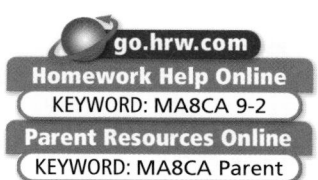

SEE EXAMPLE 2
p. 554

Find the axis of symmetry of each parabola.

6.

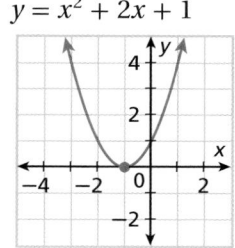

7.

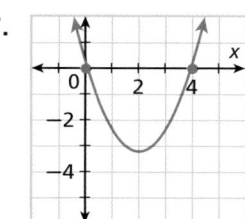

8.

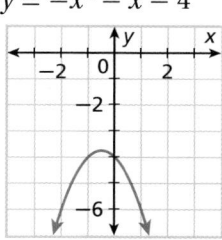

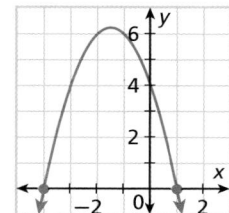
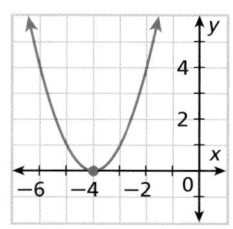

SEE EXAMPLE 3
p. 555

For each quadratic function, find the axis of symmetry of its graph.

9. $y = x^2 + 4x - 7$

10. $y = 3x^2 - 18x + 1$

11. $y = 2x^2 + 3x - 4$

12. $y = -3x^2 + x + 5$

SEE EXAMPLE 4
p. 555

Find the vertex.

13. $y = -5x^2 + 10x + 3$

15. $y = x^2 + 4x - 7$

16. $y = \frac{1}{2}x^2 + 2x$

17. $y = -x^2 + 6x + 1$

14.

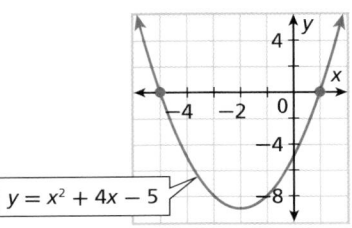

$y = x^2 + 4x - 5$

SEE EXAMPLE 5
p. 556

18. Archery The height in feet above the ground of an arrow t seconds after it is shot can be modeled by $y = -16t^2 + 63t + 4$. Can the arrow pass over a tree that is 68 feet tall? Explain.

PRACTICE AND PROBLEM SOLVING

Independent Practice

For Exercises	See Example
19–21	1
22–24	2
25–28	3
29–33	4
34	5

Extra Practice

Skills Practice p. EP18

Application Practice p. EP32

Find the zeros of each quadratic function from its graph. Check your answer.

19. $y = \frac{1}{4}x^2 - x + 3$

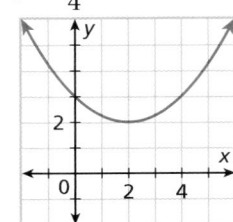

20. $y = -\frac{1}{3}x^2$

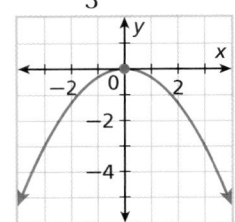

21. $y = x^2 + 10x + 16$

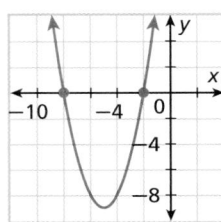

Find the axis of symmetry of each parabola.

22.

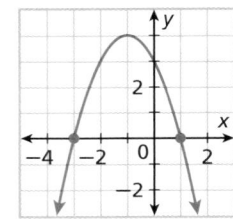

23.

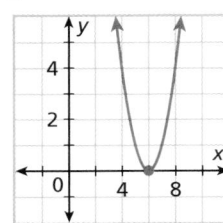

24.

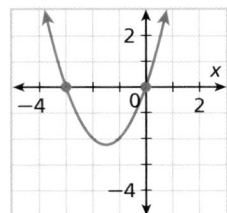

California LINK

Engineering

The Bixby Bridge in Big Sur, California, is a single span concrete arch bridge. It is over 700 feet long and over 260 feet high. Arch bridges are strong because the curve carries the weight of the bridge outward to the supports at the end.

For each quadratic function, find the axis of symmetry of its graph.

25. $y = x^2 + x + 2$

26. $y = (3x + 3)(x - 6)$

27. $y = \frac{1}{2}x^2 - 5x + 4$

28. $y + 2x^2 = \frac{1}{3}x - \frac{3}{4}$

Find the vertex.

29. $y = x(x + 7)$

31. $y - 8x = 16 - x^2$

32. $y = -2x^2 - 8x - 3$

33. $y = -x^2 + \frac{1}{2}x + 2$

30.

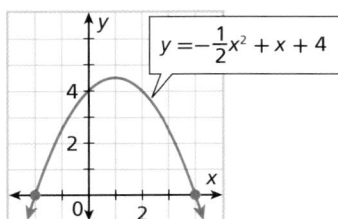

$y = -\frac{1}{2}x^2 + x + 4$

34. Engineering The height in feet of the curved arch support for a pedestrian bridge over a creek can be modeled by $f(x) = -0.628x^2 + 4.5x$, where x is the distance in feet from where the arch support enters the water. If there is a flood that raises the level of the creek by 5.5 feet, will the top of the arch support be above the water? Explain.

35. Reasoning For quadratic functions $y = ax^2 + bx + c$ in which $b = 0$, use deductive reasoning to show that the axis of symmetry is the y-axis.

CONCEPT CONNECTION

36. This problem will prepare you for the Concept Connection on page 566.

a. Use the graph of the height of a water bottle rocket to estimate the coordinates of the parabola's vertex.

b. What does the vertex represent?

c. Find the zeros of the function. What do they represent?

d. Find the axis of symmetry. How is it related to the vertex and the zeros?

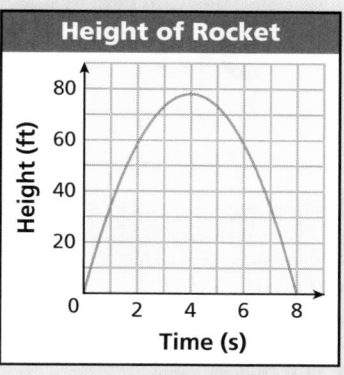

Height of Rocket

 Graphing Calculator Tell how many zeros each quadratic function has.

37. $y = 8x^2 - 4x + 2$　　　**38.** $0 = y + 16x^2$　　　**39.** $\frac{1}{4}x^2 - 7x - 12 = y - 4$

 40. Write About It If you are given the axis of symmetry of a parabola and know that the function has two zeros, how would you describe the location of the two zeros?

Multiple Choice For Exercises 41 and 42, choose the best answer.

41. Which function has the zeros shown in the graph?

Ⓐ $y = x^2 + 2x + 8$　　Ⓒ $y = x^2 + 2x - 8$

Ⓑ $y = x^2 - 2x - 8$　　Ⓓ $y = 2x^2 - 2x + 8$

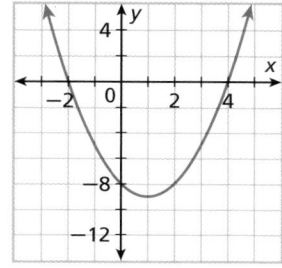

42. Which of the following functions has a graph with an axis of symmetry of $x = -\frac{1}{2}$?

Ⓐ $y = 2x^2 - 2x + 5$　　Ⓒ $2x^2 + y = 2x + 5$

Ⓑ $2x + 5 = 2x^2 - y$　　Ⓓ $2x - y = 5 - 2x^2$

43. Gridded Response For the graph of $f(x) = -3 + 20x - 5x^2$, what is the x-coordinate of its vertex?

CHALLENGE AND EXTEND

44. Describe the domain and range of a quadratic function that has exactly one zero and whose graph opens downward.

 45. Graphing Calculator The height in feet of a parabolic bridge support is modeled by $f(x) = -0.01x^2 + 20$, where $y = -5$ represents ground level and the x-axis represents the middle of the bridge. Find the height and the width of the bridge support.

 SPIRAL STANDARDS REVIEW　　　🔑 7.0, 🔑 10.0

Without graphing, tell whether each point lies on the graph of $2x + y = 8$. *(Lesson 5-1)*

46. $(1, 5)$　　　　**47.** $(3, 2)$　　　　**48.** $(6, -4)$

49. The length of a rug is 6 inches longer than its width. Write a polynomial that represents the area of the rug. *(Lesson 7-8)*

Without graphing, tell whether each point is on the graph of the given equation. *(Lesson 9-1)*

50. $y = 5x^2 - 7x$; $(2, 7)$　　　**51.** $x^2 - 5x = 2 + y$; $(1, -6)$　　**52.** $y = -x^2 - 6x + 1$; $(-5, 6)$

9-3 Graphing Quadratic Functions

California Standards

⟜ **21.0** Students graph quadratic functions and know that their roots are the *x*-intercepts.

⟜ **23.0** Students apply quadratic equations to physical problems, such as the motion of an object under the force of gravity.

Why use this?

Graphs of quadratic functions can help you determine how high an object is tossed or kicked. (See Exercise 14.)

Recall that a *y*-intercept is the *y*-coordinate of the point where a graph intersects the *y*-axis. The *x*-coordinate of this point is always 0. For a quadratic function written in the form $y = ax^2 + bx + c$, when $x = 0$, $y = c$. So the *y*-intercept of a quadratic function is *c*.

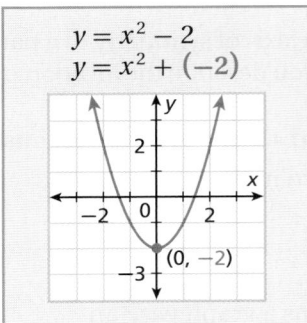

$y = x^2 - 2$
$y = x^2 + (-2)$

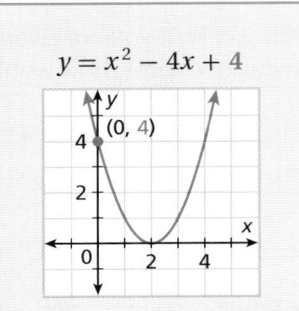

$y = x^2 - 4x + 4$

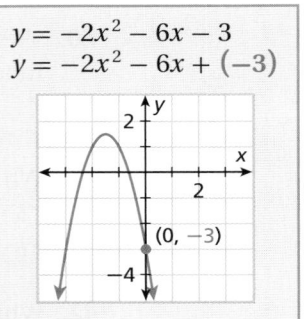

$y = -2x^2 - 6x - 3$
$y = -2x^2 - 6x + (-3)$

In the previous lesson, you found the axis of symmetry and vertex of a parabola. You can use these characteristics, the *y*-intercept, and symmetry to graph a quadratic function.

EXAMPLE 1 | **Graphing a Quadratic Function**

Graph $y = x^2 - 4x - 5$.

Step 1 Find the axis of symmetry.

$$x = -\frac{-4}{2(1)}$$ *Use $x = -\frac{b}{2a}$. Substitute 1 for a and −4 for b.*

$$= 2$$ *Simplify.*

The axis of symmetry is $x = 2$.

Step 2 Find the vertex.

$y = x^2 - 4x - 5$

    The x-coordinate of the vertex is 2. Substitute 2 for x.

$= 2^2 - 4(2) - 5$

$= 4 - 8 - 5$ *Simplify.*

$= -9$ *The y-coordinate of the vertex is −9.*

The vertex is $(2, -9)$.

Step 3 Find the *y*-intercept.

$y = x^2 - 4x - 5$

$y = x^2 - 4x + (-5)$ *Identify c.*

The *y*-intercept is −5; the graph passes through $(0, -5)$.

Step 4 Find two more points on the same side of the axis of symmetry as the point containing the y-intercept.

Since the axis of symmetry is $x = 2$, choose x-values less than 2.

Let $x = 1$.

$y = 1^2 - 4(1) - 5$ *Substitute x-coordinates.*   Let $x = -1$.

$= 1 - 4 - 5$ *Simplify.* $y = (-1)^2 - 4(-1) - 5$

$= -8$ $= 1 + 4 - 5$

$= 0$

Two other points are $(1, -8)$ and $(-1, 0)$.

Step 5 Graph the **axis of symmetry**, the **vertex**, the point containing the y-intercept, and **two other points**.

Step 6 **Reflect** the points across the axis of symmetry. Connect the points with a smooth curve.

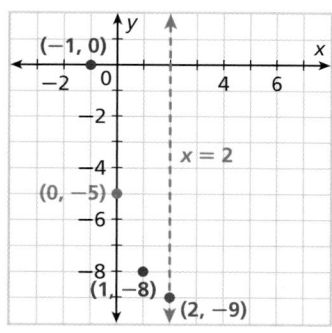
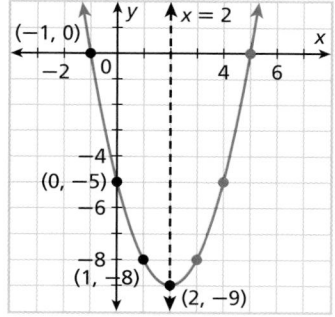

 **Graph each quadratic function.**

1a. $y = 2x^2 + 6x + 2$ **1b.** $y + 6x = x^2 + 9$

Helpful Hint

Because a parabola is symmetrical, each point is the same number of units away from the axis of symmetry as its reflected point.

EXAMPLE 2   ***Problem-Solving Application***

PROBLEM SOLVING

The height in feet of a football that is kicked can be modeled by the function $f(x) = -16x^2 + 64x$, where x is the time in seconds after it is kicked. Find the football's maximum height and the time it takes the football to reach this height. Then find how long the football is in the air.

1 **Understand the Problem**

The **answer** includes three parts: the maximum height, the time to reach the maximum height, and the time to reach the ground.

List the important information:
- The function $f(x) = -16x^2 + 64x$ models the height of the football after x seconds.

2 **Make a Plan**

Find the vertex of the graph because the maximum height of the football and the time it takes to reach it are the coordinates of the vertex. The football will hit the ground when its height is 0, so find the zeros of the function. You can do this by graphing.

Remember!

The vertex is the highest or lowest point on a parabola. Therefore, in the example, it gives the maximum height of the football.

Step 1 Find the axis of symmetry.

$$x = -\frac{64}{2(-16)}$$ *Use $x = -\frac{b}{2a}$. Substitute -16 for a and 64 for b.*

$$= -\frac{64}{-32} = 2$$ *Simplify.*

The axis of symmetry is $x = 2$.

Step 2 Find the vertex.

$$y = -16x^2 + 64x$$

$$= -16(2)^2 + 64(2)$$ *The x-coordinate of the vertex is 2. Substitute 2 for x.*

$$= -16(4) + 128$$ *Simplify.*

$$= -64 + 128$$

$$= 64$$ *The y-coordinate of the vertex is 64.*

The vertex is $(2, 64)$.

Step 3 Find the *y*-intercept.

$$y = -16x^2 + 64x + 0$$ *Identify c.*

The *y*-intercept is **0**; the graph passes through $(0, 0)$.

Step 4 Find another point on the same side of the axis of symmetry as the point containing the *y*-intercept.

Since the axis of symmetry is $x = 2$, choose an *x*-value that is less than 2. Let $x = 1$.

$$y = -16(1)^2 + 64(1)$$ *Substitute 1 for x.*

$$= -16 + 64$$ *Simplify.*

$$= 48$$

Another point is $(1, 48)$.

Step 5 Graph the **axis of symmetry**, the **vertex**, the point containing the **y-intercept**, and the **other point**. Then **reflect** the points across the axis of symmetry. Connect the points with a smooth curve.

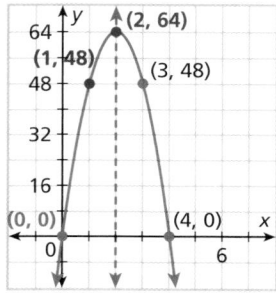

The vertex is $(2, 64)$. So at 2 seconds, the football has reached its maximum height of 64 feet. The graph shows the zeros of the function are 0 and 4. At 0 seconds the football has not yet been kicked, and at 4 seconds it reaches the ground. The football is in the air for 4 seconds.

4 Look Back

Check by substituting $(2, 64)$ and $(4, 0)$ into the function.

$64 = -16(2)^2 + 64(2)$		$0 = -16(4)^2 + 64(4)$	
64	$-64 + 128$	0	$-256 + 256$
64	$64\ \checkmark$	0	$0\ \checkmark$

 **2.** As Molly dives into her pool, her height in feet above the water can be modeled by the function $f(x) = -16x^2 + 24x$, where x is the time in seconds after she begins diving. Find the maximum height of her dive and the time it takes Molly to reach this height. Then find how long it takes her to reach the pool.

THINK AND DISCUSS

1. Explain how to find the y-intercept of a quadratic function that is written in the form $ax^2 - y = bx + c$.

2. Explain how to graph a quadratic function.

3. What do you think the vertex and zeros of the function will tell you for the situation in the Check It Out for Example 2?

4. GET ORGANIZED Copy and complete the graphic organizer using your own quadratic function.

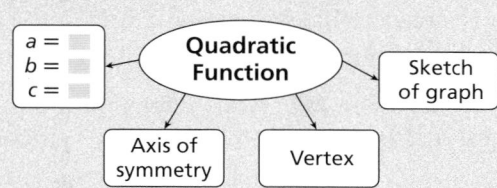

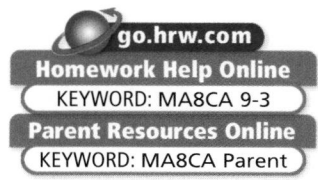
GUIDED PRACTICE

SEE EXAMPLE **1**
p. 560

Graph each quadratic function.

1. $y = x^2 - 2x - 3$

2. $-y - 3x^2 = -3$

3. $y = 2x^2 + 2x - 4$

4. $y = x^2 + 4x - 8$

5. $y + x^2 + 5x + 2 = 0$

6. $y = 4x^2 + 2$

SEE EXAMPLE **2**
p. 561

7. Multi-Step The height in feet of a golf ball that is hit from the ground can be modeled by the function $f(x) = -16x^2 + 96x$, where x is the time in seconds after the ball is hit. Find the ball's maximum height and the time it takes the ball to reach this height. Then find how long the ball is in the air.

PRACTICE AND PROBLEM SOLVING

Independent Practice

For Exercises	See Example
8–13	1
14	2

Extra Practice
Skills Practice p. EP18
Application Practice p. EP32

Graph each quadratic function.

8. $y = -4x^2 + 12x - 5$

9. $y = 3x^2 + 12x + 9$

10. $y - 7x^2 - 14x = 3$

11. $y = -x^2 + 2x$

12. $y - 1 = 4x^2 + 8x$

13. $y = -2x^2 - 3x + 4$

14. Multi-Step A juggler tosses a ring into the air. The height of the ring in feet above the juggler's hands can be modeled by the function $f(x) = -16x^2 + 16x$, where x is the time in seconds after the ring is tossed. Find the ring's maximum height above the juggler's hands and the time it takes the ring to reach this height. Then find how long the ring is in the air.

For each quadratic function, find the axis of symmetry and the vertex of its graph.

15. $y = x^2 - 8x$

16. $y = -x^2 + 6x - 4$

17. $y = 4 - 3x^2$

18. $y = -2x^2 - 4$

19. $y = -x^2 - x - 4$

20. $y = x^2 + 8x + 16$

Graph each quadratic function. On your graph, label the coordinates of the vertex. Draw and label the axis of symmetry.

21. $y = -x^2$

22. $y = -x^2 + 4x$

23. $y = x^2 - 6x + 4$

24. $x + y = x^2$

25. $y + 4 = 3x^2$

26. $y + 2x^2 + 25 = -16x$

27. Travel While on a vacation in Italy, Rudy visited the Leaning Tower of Pisa. When he leaned over the railing to look down from the tower, his sunglasses fell off. The height in meters of the sunglasses as they fell can be approximated by the function $y = -5x^2 + 50$, where x is the time in seconds.

  a. Graph the function.

  b. What is a reasonable domain and range?

  c. How long did it take for the glasses to reach the ground?

28. /// ERROR ANALYSIS /// Two students found the equation of the axis of symmetry for the graph of $f(x) = -x^2 - 2x + 1$. Who is incorrect? Explain the error.

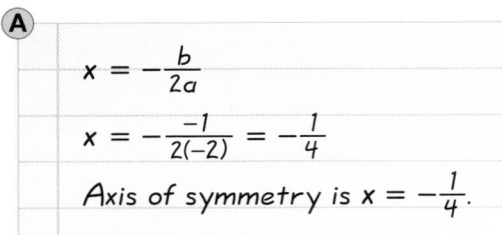

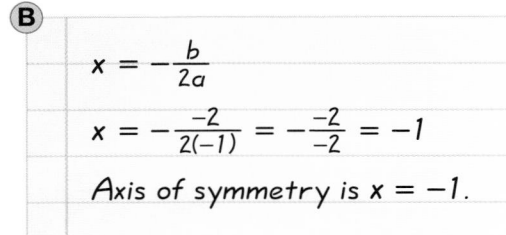

29. Critical Thinking The point $(5, 4)$ lies on the graph of a quadratic function whose axis of symmetry is $x = 2$. Find another point on the graph. Explain how you found the point.

Engineering Use the graph for Exercises 30–32. The velocity v in centimeters per second of a fluid flowing in a pipe varies according to the radius r of the pipe.

30. Find the radius of the pipe when the velocity is 7 cm/s.

31. Find the velocity of the fluid when the radius is 2 cm.

32. What is a reasonable domain for this function? Explain.

33. Critical Thinking The graph of a quadratic function has the vertex $(0, 5)$. One point on the graph is $(1, 6)$. Find another point on the graph. Explain how you found the point.

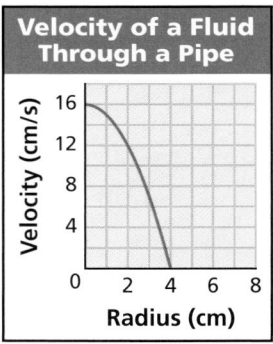

34. Write About It Explain how the vertex and the range can help you graph a quadratic function.

CONCEPT CONNECTION

35. This problem will prepare you for the Concept Connection on page 566.

A water bottle rocket is shot upward with an initial velocity of $v_i = 45$ ft/s from the roof of a school, which is at h_i, 50 ft above the ground. The equation $h = -\frac{1}{2}at^2 + v_i t + h_i$ models the rocket's height as a function of time. The acceleration due to gravity a is 32 ft/s².

  a. Write the equation for height as a function of time for this situation.

  b. Find the vertex of this parabola.

  c. Sketch the graph of this parabola and label the vertex.

  d. What do the coordinates of the vertex represent in terms of time and height?

36. Copy and complete the table for each function.

Function	Graph Opens	Axis of Symmetry	Vertex	Zeros	Domain and Range
$y = x^2 + 4$	▩	$x =$ ▩	(▩ , ▩)	▩	D: ▩ R: ▩
$y = -x^2 + 4$	▩	$x =$ ▩	(▩ , ▩)	▩	D: ▩ R: ▩
$y + 8 - x^2 = -2x$	▩	$x =$ ▩	(▩ , ▩)	▩	D: ▩ R: ▩

Multiple Choice For Exercises 37–39, choose the best answer.

37. Which is the axis of symmetry for the graph of $f(x) = 6 - 5x + \frac{1}{2}x^2$?

(A) $x = 5$ (B) $x = \frac{1}{20}$ (C) $x = -5$ (D) $x = -\frac{1}{20}$

38. What are the coordinates of the vertex for the graph of $f(x) = x^2 - 5x + 6$?

(A) $\left(-\frac{5}{2}, -\frac{1}{4}\right)$ (B) $\left(-\frac{5}{2}, \frac{1}{4}\right)$ (C) $\left(\frac{5}{2}, \frac{1}{4}\right)$ (D) $\left(\frac{5}{2}, -\frac{1}{4}\right)$

39. Which function's graph has an axis of symmetry of $x = 1$ and a vertex of $(1, 8)$?

(A) $y = -x^2 + x + 8$ (C) $y = 2x^2 - 4x - 8$

(B) $y = x^2 + 8x + 1$ (D) $y = -3x^2 + 6x + 5$

40. **Short Response** Graph $y = x^2 + 3x + 2$. What are the zeros, the axis of symmetry, and the coordinates of the vertex? Show your work.

CHALLENGE AND EXTEND

41. The graph of a quadratic function has its vertex at $(1, -4)$ and one zero of the function is 3. Find the other zero. Explain how you found the other zero.

42. The x-intercepts of a quadratic function are 3 and -3. The y-intercept is 6. What are the coordinates of the vertex? Does the function have a maximum or a minimum? Explain.

Find the x- and y-intercepts. *(Lesson 5-2)*

43. 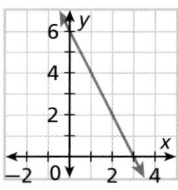   **44.** 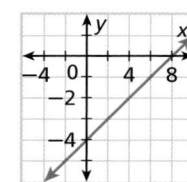   **45.**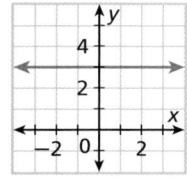

Solve each system by using any method. Check your answer. *(Lessons 6-1, 6-2, and 6-3)*

46. $\begin{cases} 3x - y = 2 \\ x + 4y = 18 \end{cases}$ **47.** $\begin{cases} 2x + 3y = 3 \\ 4x - y = 13 \end{cases}$ **48.** $\begin{cases} -2x + 3y = 12 \\ 6x + y = 4 \end{cases}$

49. Shelly kicks her ball into the air. The height in feet above the ground of the ball can be modeled by $y = -5x^2 + 10x$. Will Shelly's ball go over a fence that is 6 feet tall? Explain. *(Lesson 9-2)*

CONCEPT CONNECTION

Quadratic Functions

The Sky's the Limit The Physics Club is using computer simulation software to design a water bottle rocket that doesn't have a parachute. The data for their current design are shown in the table.

1. Graph the data and connect the points.

2. Find and label the zeros, axis of symmetry, and vertex.

3. Explain what the x- and y-coordinates of the vertex represent in the context of the problem.

Time (s)	Height (ft)
0	0
1	80
2	128
3	144
4	128
5	80

4. Estimate how many seconds it will take the rocket to reach 110 feet. Explain.

READY TO GO ON?

Quiz for Lessons 9-1 Through 9-3

9-1 Quadratic Equations and Functions

Without graphing, tell whether each point is on the graph of the given equation.

1. $y + 2x^2 = 3x$; $(2, 2)$ **2.** $x^2 + y = 4$; $(3, -3)$ **3.** $y = -3x^2 - 12$; $(2.5, -6.75)$

4. $y - 3 = 3x^2$; $(2, 14)$ **5.** $y = x^2 - x + 5$; $(-3, 17)$ **6.** $y + 5x^2 = 4 + x$; $(1, 1)$

Tell whether the graph of each quadratic function opens upward or downward and whether the parabola has a maximum or a minimum.

7. $y = -x^2 - 7x + 18$ **8.** $y - 2x^2 = 4x + 3$ **9.** $f(x) = 5x - 0.5x^2$

10. Graph the function $y = \frac{1}{2}x^2 - 2$ and give the domain and range.

9-2 Characteristics of Quadratic Functions

Find the zeros of each function from its graph. Then find its the axis of symmetry.

11. 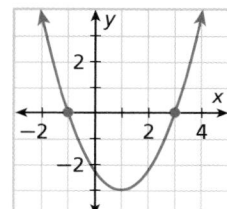   **12.** 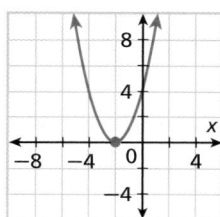   **13.**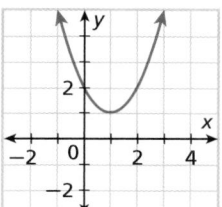

Find the vertex.

14. $y = x^2 + 6x + 2$ **15.** $y = 3 + 4x - 2x^2$ **16.** $y = 3x^2 + 12x - 12$

17. $f(x) = x^2 + 2x - 8$ **18.** $y = x^2 + 8x - 20$ **19.** $f(x) = -x^2 - 12 + 8x$

20. The height in feet of the curved roof of an aircraft hangar can be modeled by $y = -0.02x^2 + 1.6x$, where x is the distance in feet from one wall at ground level. How tall is the hangar?

9-3 Graphing Quadratic Functions

Graph each quadratic function.

21. $y = x^2 + 3x + 9$ **22.** $y = x^2 - 2x - 15$ **23.** $y = x^2 - 2x - 8$

24. $y = 2x^2 - 6$ **25.** $y = 4x^2 + 8x - 2$ **26.** $y = 2x^2 + 10x + 1$

27. The height in feet of a baseball after it is hit can be modeled by the function $f(x) = -16x^2 + 100x$, where x is the time in seconds after the ball is hit. Find the ball's maximum height and the time it takes the ball to reach this height. Then find how long the ball is in the air.

28. Trent is a kicker for his football team. The height in feet of a football after one of Trent's kicks can be modeled by the function $f(x) = -16x^2 + 55x$, where x is the time in seconds after the kick. Find the football's maximum height and the time it takes the ball to reach this height. Then find how long the ball is in the air.

9-4 Solving Quadratic Equations by Graphing

California Standards

⚬━ **21.0** Students graph quadratic functions and know that their roots are the *x*-intercepts.

Also covered: ⚬━ **23.0**

Who uses this?

Dolphin trainers can use solutions of quadratic equations to plan the choreography for their shows. (See Example 3.)

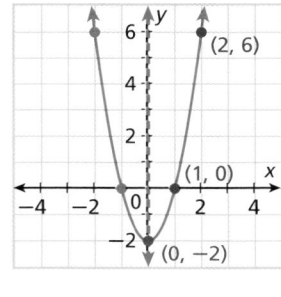

Every quadratic function has a related quadratic equation. The standard form of a quadratic equation is $ax^2 + bx + c = 0$, where a, b, and c are real numbers and $a \neq 0$.

When writing a quadratic function as its related quadratic equation, you replace y with 0.

$$y = ax^2 + bx + c$$
$$0 = ax^2 + bx + c$$

One way to solve a quadratic equation in standard form is to graph the related function and find the *x*-values where $y = 0$. In other words, find the zeros of the related function. Recall that a quadratic function may have two, one, or no zeros.

Solving Quadratic Equations by Graphing
Step 1 Write the related function.
Step 2 Graph the related function.
Step 3 Find the zeros of the related function.

EXAMPLE 1 Solving Quadratic Equations by Graphing

Solve each equation by graphing the related function.

A $2x^2 - 2 = 0$

Step 1 Write the related function.
$2x^2 - 2 = y$, or $y = 2x^2 + 0x - 2$

Step 2 Graph the function.

- The axis of symmetry is $x = 0$.
- The vertex is $(0, -2)$.
- Two other points are $(1, 0)$ and $(2, 6)$.
- Graph the points and **reflect** them across the axis of symmetry.

Step 3 Find the zeros.
The zeros appear to be -1 and 1.
The solutions of $2x^2 - 2 = 0$ are -1 and 1.

Check

$2x^2 - 2 = 0$	
$2(-1)^2 - 2$	0
$2(1) - 2$	0
$2 - 2$	0
0	0 ✓

Substitute −1 and 1 for x in the original equation.

$2x^2 - 2 = 0$	
$2(1)^2 - 2$	0
$2(1) - 2$	0
$2 - 2$	0
0	0 ✓

Solve each equation by graphing the related function.

B $x^2 + 5 = 4x$

Step 1 Write the equation in standard form. Then write the related function.

$x^2 - 4x + 5 = 0$

$y = x^2 - 4x + 5$

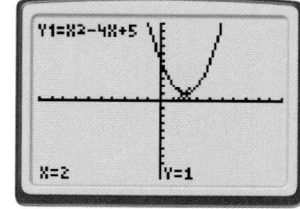

Step 2 Graph the function. Use a graphing calculator.

Step 3 Find the zeros. The function appears to have no zeros.

The equation has no real-number solutions.

CHECK IT OUT! **Solve each equation by graphing the related function.**

1a. $x^2 - 8x - 16 = 2x^2$

1b. $6x + 10 = -x^2$

1c. $-x^2 + 4 = 0$

Recall from Chapter 7 that a root of a polynomial is a value of the variable that makes the polynomial equal to 0. So, finding the roots of a quadratic polynomial is the same as solving the related quadratic equation.

EXAMPLE 2 **Finding Roots of Quadratic Polynomials**

Find the roots of $-x^2 - 4x - 4$.

Step 1 Write the related equation.

$0 = -x^2 - 4x - 4$

Step 2 Write the related function.

$y = -x^2 - 4x - 4$

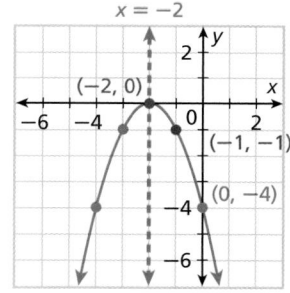

Step 3 Graph the function.

• The axis of symmetry is $x = -2$.

• The vertex is $(-2, 0)$.

• The y-intercept is -4.

• Another point is $(-1, -1)$.

• Graph the points and **reflect** them across the axis of symmetry.

Step 4 Find the zeros.

The only zero appears to be -2. This means -2 is the only root of $-x^2 - 4x - 4$.

Check $-x^2 - 4x - 4$

$-(-2)^2 - 4(-2) - 4$

$-(4) + 8 - 4$

$-4 + 4$

$0 ✓$

CHECK IT OUT! **Find the roots of each quadratic polynomial.**

2a. $x^2 + x - 2$

2b. $9x^2 - 6x + 1$

2c. $3x^2 - 2x + 5$

EXAMPLE 3 *Aquatics Application*

A dolphin jumps out of the water. The quadratic function $y = -16x^2 + 20x$ models the dolphin's height above the water after x seconds. About how long is the dolphin out of the water? Check your answer.

When the dolphin leaves the water, its height is 0, and when the dolphin reenters the water, its height is 0. So solve $0 = -16x^2 + 20x$ to find the times when the dolphin leaves and reenters the water.

Step 1 Write the related function.

$$0 = -16x^2 + 20x$$
$$y = -16x^2 + 20x$$

Step 2 Graph the function.

Use a graphing calculator.

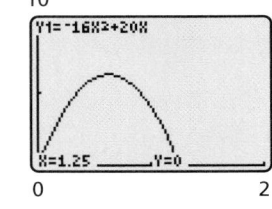

Step 3 Use TRACE to estimate the zeros.

The zeros appear to be 0 and 1.25.
The dolphin leaves the water at 0 seconds and reenters the water at 1.25 seconds.

The dolphin is out of the water for about 1.25 seconds.

Check $0 = -16x^2 + 20x$

0	$-16(1.25)^2 + 20(1.25)$	*Substitute 1.25 for x in the*
0	$-16(1.5625) + 25$	*original equation.*
0	$-25 + 25$	
0	0 ✓	

 3. **What if…?** Another dolphin jumps out of the water. The quadratic function $y = -16x^2 + 32x$ models the dolphin's height above the water after x seconds. About how long is the dolphin out of the water? Check your answer.

THINK AND DISCUSS

1. Describe the graph of a quadratic function whose related quadratic equation has only one solution.

2. Describe the graph of a quadratic function whose related quadratic equation has no real solutions.

3. Describe the graph of a quadratic function whose related quadratic equation has two solutions.

 4. **GET ORGANIZED** Copy and complete the graphic organizer. In each of the boxes, write the steps for solving quadratic equations by graphing.

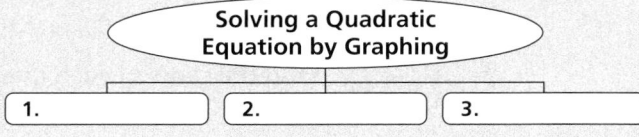

9-4

Exercises

California
Standards Practice
← 21.0, ← 23.0, 25.3

go.hrw.com
Homework Help Online
KEYWORD: MA8CA 9-4
Parent Resources Online
KEYWORD: MA8CA Parent

GUIDED PRACTICE

SEE EXAMPLE 1
p. 568

Solve each equation by graphing the related function. Check your answer.

1. $x^2 - 4 = 0$ **2.** $x^2 = 16$ **3.** $-2x^2 - 6 = 0$

4. $-x^2 + 12x - 36 = 0$ **5.** $-x^2 = -9$ **6.** $2x^2 = 3x^2 - 2x - 8$

SEE EXAMPLE 2
p. 569

Find the roots of each quadratic polynomial.

7. $x^2 - 6x + 9$ **8.** $-4x^2 - 8x - 4$ **9.** $x^2 + 5x + 4$

10. $x^2 + 2$ **11.** $x^2 - 6x - 7$ **12.** $x^2 + 5x + 8$

SEE EXAMPLE 3
p. 570

13. Sports A baseball coach uses a pitching machine to simulate pop flies during practice. A baseball is shot out of the pitching machine with an initial velocity of 80 feet per second. The quadratic function $y = -16x^2 + 80x$ gives the height y of the baseball x seconds after being shot from the machine. How long is the baseball in the air?

PRACTICE AND PROBLEM SOLVING

Independent Practice

For Exercises	See Example
14–19	1
20–22	2
23	3

Extra Practice

Skills Practice p. EP19

Application Practice p. EP32

Solve each equation by graphing the related function. Check your answer.

14. $-x^2 + 16 = 0$ **15.** $3x^2 = -7$ **16.** $5x^2 - 12x + 10 = x^2 + 10x$

17. $x^2 + 10x + 25 = 0$ **18.** $-4x^2 - 24x = 36$ **19.** $-9x^2 + 10x - 9 = -8x$

Find the roots of each quadratic polynomial.

20. $-x^2 - 1$ **21.** $3x^2 - 27$ **22.** $2x^2 - 4x + 5$

23. Geography Yosemite Falls in California is made of three smaller waterfalls. The upper fall drops 1450 feet. The height h in feet of a water droplet falling from the upper fall to the next fall is modeled by the quadratic function $h = -16t^2 + 1450$, where t is the time in seconds after the initial fall. Estimate the time it takes for the droplet to reach the next fall.

 Reasoning Tell whether each statement is always, sometimes, or never true. Explain.

24. If the graph of a quadratic function has its vertex at the origin, then the related quadratic equation has exactly one solution.

25. If the graph of a quadratic function opens upward, then the related quadratic equation has two solutions.

26. If the graph of a quadratic function has its vertex on the x-axis, then the related quadratic equation has exactly one solution.

27. If the graph of a quadratic function has its vertex in the first quadrant, then the related quadratic equation has two solutions.

28. A quadratic equation in the form $ax^2 - c = 0$, where $a < 0$ and $c > 0$, has two solutions.

 29. Graphing Calculator A fireworks shell is fired from a mortar. Its height is modeled by the quadratic function $h = -16(t - 7)^2 + 784$, where t is the time in seconds after the shell is fired and h is the height in feet. Graph the function. If the shell is supposed to explode at its maximum height, at what height should it explode? If the shell does not explode, how long will it take to return to the ground?

30. Athletics The graph shows the height y in feet of a gymnast jumping off a vault after x seconds.

   a. How long does the gymnast stay in the air?

   b. What is the maximum height that the gymnast reaches?

   c. Explain why the function $y = -5x^2 + 10x$ cannot accurately model the gymnast's motion.

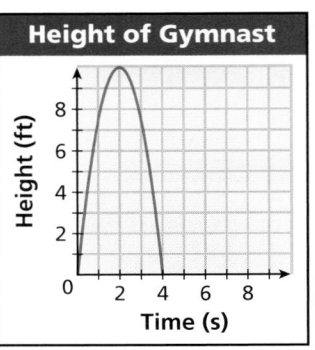

Height of Gymnast

31. Solve the equation $x^2 = x + 12$ by graphing $y = x^2$ and $y = x + 12$ on the same coordinate plane and finding the x-coordinates of the points of intersection. Check your answer.

32. Biology The quadratic function $y = -5x^2 + 7x$ approximates the height y of a kangaroo x seconds after it has jumped. About how long does it take the kangaroo to return to the ground?

For Exercises 33–35, use the table to determine the solutions of the related quadratic equation.

33.

x	y
−2	−1
−1	0
0	−1
1	−4
2	−9

34.

x	y
−2	−6
−1	0
0	2
1	0
2	−6

35.

x	y
−2	6
−1	3
0	2
1	3
2	6

 36. Geometry The hypotenuse of a right triangle is 4 cm longer than one leg and 8 cm longer than the other leg. Let x represent the length of the hypotenuse.

   a. Write an expression for the length of each leg in terms of x.

   b. Use the Pythagorean Theorem to write an equation that can be solved for x.

   c. Find the solutions of your equation from part **b**.

   d. Critical Thinking What do the solutions of your equation represent? Are both solutions reasonable? Explain.

 **37. Write About It** Explain how to find solutions of a quadratic equation by analyzing a table of values.

38. Critical Thinking Explain why a quadratic equation in the form $ax^2 - c = 0$, where $a > 0$ and $c > 0$, will always have two solutions. Then explain why a quadratic equation in the form $ax^2 + c = 0$, where $a > 0$ and $c > 0$, will never have any real-number solutions.

CONCEPT CONNECTION

39. This problem will prepare you for the Concept Connection on page 610.

The quadratic equation $0 = -16t^2 + 80t$ gives the time t in seconds when a golf ball is at height 0 feet.

   a. How long is the golf ball in the air?

   b. What is the maximum height of the golf ball?

   c. After how many seconds is the ball at its maximum height?

   d. What is the height of the ball after 3.5 seconds? Is there another time when the ball reaches that height? Explain.

Multiple Choice For Exercises 40 and 41, choose the best answer.

40. Use the graph to find the number of solutions of $-2x^2 + 2 = 0$.

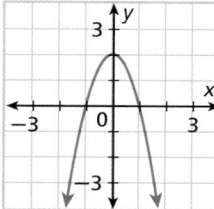

Ⓐ 0   Ⓒ 2

Ⓑ 1   Ⓓ 3

41. Which graph could be used to find the roots of $x^2 + 4x - 12$?

Ⓐ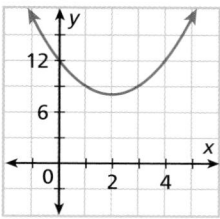

Ⓒ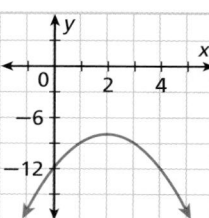

Ⓑ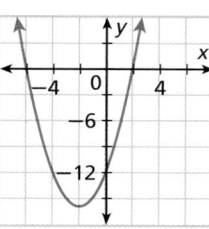

Ⓓ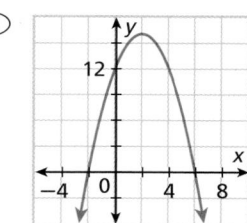

42. Short Response Find the solutions of $2x^2 + x - 1 = 0$ by graphing. Explain how the graph of the related function shows the solutions of the equation.

CHALLENGE AND EXTEND

 Graphing Calculator Use a graphing calculator to estimate the solutions of each quadratic equation.

43. $\dfrac{5}{16}x + \dfrac{1}{4}x^2 = \dfrac{3}{5}$

44. $1200x^2 - 650x - 100 = -200x - 175$

45. $\dfrac{1}{5}x + \dfrac{3}{4}x^2 = \dfrac{7}{12}$

46. $400x^2 - 100 = -300x + 456$

 SPIRAL STANDARDS REVIEW

Write an equation in point-slope form for the line with the given slope that contains the given point. *(Lesson 5-6)*

47. slope $= \dfrac{1}{2}$; $(2, 3)$ **48.** slope $= -3$; $(-2, 4)$ **49.** slope $= 0$; $(2, 1)$

Simplify. *(Lesson 7-4)*

50. $\dfrac{3^4}{3}$ **51.** $\dfrac{5^2 \cdot 2^4}{5 \cdot 2^2}$ **52.** $\dfrac{\left(x^4\right)^5}{\left(x^3\right)^3}$ **53.** $\left(\dfrac{x^3}{y^2}\right)^{-3}$

54. $\left(\dfrac{a^2 b^3}{ab^2}\right)^3$ **55.** $\left(\dfrac{4s}{3t}\right)^{-2}$ **56.** $\left(\dfrac{2}{3}\right)^{-3} \cdot \left(\dfrac{a^3}{b}\right)^{-2}$ **57.** $\left(\dfrac{-k^2}{5k^3}\right)^{-3}$

58. A baton is tossed into the air by a dancer. The height of the baton in feet above the dancer's hand can be modeled by $y = -10x^2 + 20x$ where x is the time in seconds after the toss. Find the baton's maximum height and the time it takes the baton to reach this height. Then find how long the baton is in the air. *(Lesson 9-3)*

Technology LAB

Use with Lesson 9-4

Explore Roots, Zeros, and *x*-Intercepts

The roots of a quadratic polynomial, the solutions of the related equation, and the *x*-intercepts, or zeros, of the related function are very closely connected. You can use tables or graphs to understand these connections.

California Standards

21.0 Students graph quadratic functions and know that their roots are the *x*-intercepts.

go.hrw.com
Lab Resources Online
KEYWORD: MA8CA Lab9

Activity 1

Find the roots of $5x^2 + 8x - 4$ by using a table. Check your answer.

1 To find the roots, solve $5x^2 + 8x - 4 = 0$

2 Enter the related function in Y_1.

3 Press **2nd** **GRAPH** to use the **TABLE** function.

4 Scroll through the values by using ▲ and ▼. Look for values of 0 in the Y_1 column. The corresponding *x*-value is a zero of the function. There appears to be one zero at −2.

The signs of the *y*-values change.

Also look for places where the signs of nonzero *y*-values change. There is a zero between the corresponding *x*-values. So there is another zero somewhere between 0 and 1.

5 To get a better estimate of the zero, change the table settings. Press **2nd** **WINDOW** to view the **TABLE SETUP** screen. Set **TblStart = 0** and the step value △**Tbl = .1**. Press **2nd** **GRAPH** to see the table again.

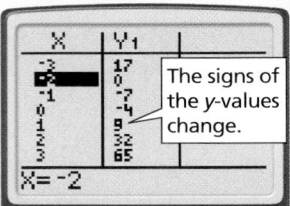

6 Scroll through the values by using ▲ and ▼. The second zero appears to be at 0.4.

The zeros of the function, −2 and 0.4, are the solutions of $5x^2 + 8x - 4 = 0$ and the roots of $5x^2 + 8x - 4$.

Check	$5x^2 + 8x - 4 = 0$		$5x^2 + 8x - 4 = 0$	
	$5(-2)^2 + 8(-2) - 4$	0	$5(0.4)^2 + 8(0.4) - 4$	0
	$5(4) - 16 - 4$	0	$5(0.16) + 3.2 - 4$	0
	$20 - 16 - 4$	0	$0.8 + 3.2 - 4$	0
	0	0 ✓	0	0 ✓

Try This

Find the roots of each polynomial by using a table. Check your answer.

1. $x^2 - 4x - 5$ **2.** $x^2 - x - 6$ **3.** $2x^2 + x - 1$ **4.** $5x^2 - 6x - 8$

5. Critical Thinking How would you find the zero of a function that showed a sign change in the *y*-values between the *x*-values 1.2 and 1.3?

6. Make a Conjecture If you scrolled up and down the list and found only positive values, what might you conclude?

Activity 2

Solve $5x^2 + x - 8.4 = 0$ by using a table and a graph. Check your answer.

1 Enter the related function in **Y₁**.

2 To view both the table and the graph at the same time, set your calculator to the Graph-Table mode. Press **MODE** and select **G-T**.

3 Press **GRAPH**. You should see the graph and the table. Notice that the function appears to have one negative zero and one positive zero near the *y*-axis.

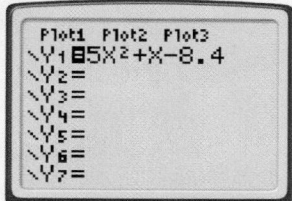

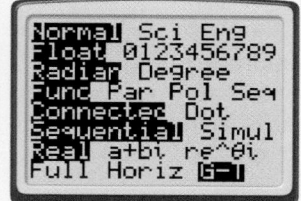

4 To get a closer view of the graph, press **ZOOM** and select **4:ZDecimal**.

5 Press **TRACE**. Use ◄ to scroll to find the negative zero. The graph and the table show that the zero appears to be −1.4.

6 Use ► to scroll and find the positive zero. The graph and the table show that the zero appears to be 1.2.

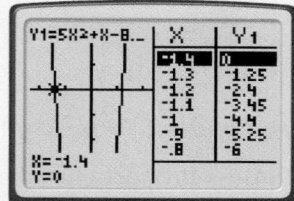

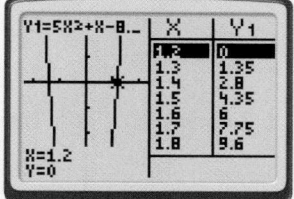

The solutions are −1.4 and 1.2.

Check

$5x^2 + x - 8.4 = 0$	
$5(-1.4)^2 + (-1.4) - 8.4$	0
$5(1.96) - 1.4 - 8.4$	0
$9.8 - 1.4 - 8.4$	0
0	0 ✓

$5x^2 + x - 8.4 = 0$	
$5(1.2)^2 + (1.2) - 8.4$	0
$5(1.44) + 1.2 - 8.4$	0
$7.2 + 1.2 - 8.4$	0
0	0 ✓

Try This

Solve each equation by using a table and a graph. Check your answer.

7. $2x^2 - x - 3 = 0$ **8.** $5x^2 + 13x + 6 = 0$ **9.** $10x^2 - 3x - 4$ **10.** $x^2 - 2x - 0.96 = 0$

11. Critical Thinking Suppose that when you graphed a quadratic function, you could see only one side of the graph and one zero. What methods would you use to try to find the other zero?

9-5 Solving Quadratic Equations by Factoring

California Standards

🔑 **14.0** Students solve a quadratic equation by factoring or completing the square.

🔑 **23.0** Students apply quadratic equations to physical problems, such as the motion of an object under the force of gravity.

Who uses this?

In order to determine how many seconds she will be in the air, a high diver can use a quadratic equation. (See Example 3.)

You have solved quadratic equations by graphing. Another method used to solve quadratic equations is to factor and use the Zero Product Property.

Know it! Note

Zero Product Property

WORDS	NUMBERS	ALGEBRA
If the product of two quantities equals zero, at least one of the quantities equals zero.	$3(0) = 0$ $0(4) = 0$	For all real numbers a and b, if $ab = 0$, then $a = 0$ or $b = 0$.

EXAMPLE 1 **Using the Zero Product Property**

Use the Zero Product Property to solve each equation. Check your answer.

A $(x - 3)(x + 7) = 0$

$x - 3 = 0$ or $x + 7 = 0$ *Use the Zero Product Property.*

$x = 3$ or $x = -7$ *Solve each equation.*

Check

$(x - 3)(x + 7) = 0$	
$(3 - 3)(3 + 7)$	0
$(0)(10)$	0
0	0 ✓

Substitute each solution for x in the original equation.

$(x - 3)(x + 7) = 0$	
$(-7 - 3)(-7 + 7)$	0
$(-10)(0)$	0
0	0 ✓

B $(x)(x - 5) = 0$

$x = 0$ or $x - 5 = 0$ *Use the Zero Product Property.*

$x = 0$ or $x = 5$ *Solve the second equation.*

Check

$(x)(x - 5) = 0$	
$(0)(0 - 5)$	0
$(0)(-5)$	0
0	0 ✓

Substitute each solution for x in the original equation.

$(x)(x - 5) = 0$	
$(5)(5 - 5)$	0
$(5)(0)$	0
0	0 ✓

 **CHECK IT OUT!** Use the Zero Product Property to solve each equation. Check your answer.

1a. $(x)(x + 4) = 0$ **1b.** $(x + 4)(x - 3) = 0$

You may need to factor before using the Zero Product Property. You can check your answers by substituting into the original equation or by graphing. If the factored form of the equation has two different factors, the graph of the related function will cross the x-axis in two places. If the factored form has two identical factors, the graph will cross the x-axis in one place.

EXAMPLE 2 Solving Quadratic Equations by Factoring

Solve each quadratic equation by factoring. Check your answer.

A $x^2 + 7x + 10 = 0$

$$(x + 5)(x + 2) = 0 \qquad \text{Factor the trinomial.}$$
$$x + 5 = 0 \quad \text{or } x + 2 = 0 \qquad \text{Use the Zero Product Property.}$$
$$x = -5 \text{ or } \qquad x = -2 \qquad \text{Solve each equation.}$$

Check

$x^2 + 7x + 10 = 0$		$x^2 + 7x + 10 = 0$	
$(-5)^2 + 7(-5) + 10$	0	$(-2)^2 + 7(-2) + 10$	0
$25 - 35 + 10$	0	$4 - 14 + 10$	0
0	$0 \checkmark$	0	$0 \checkmark$

Helpful Hint

To review factoring techniques, see Lessons 8-3 through 8-5.

B $x^2 + 2x = 8$

$$
\begin{aligned}
x^2 + 2x &= 8 \\
\underline{-8 \quad -8} & \\
x^2 + 2x - 8 &= 0 \\
(x + 4)(x - 2) &= 0 \\
x + 4 = 0 \quad \text{or } x - 2 &= 0 \\
x = -4 \text{ or } \qquad x &= 2
\end{aligned}
$$

The equation must be written in standard form. Subtract 8 from both sides.

Factor the trinomial.

Use the Zero Product Property.

Solve each equation.

Check Graph the related quadratic function. Because there are two solutions found by factoring, the graph should cross the x-axis in two places.

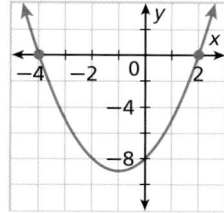

The graph of $y = x^2 + 2x - 8$ intersects the x-axis at $x = -4$ and $x = 2$, the same as the solutions found by factoring. $\checkmark$

Caution!

In some cases, it may be difficult to read the zeros from the graph. You can always check by substituting into the original equation.

C $x^2 + 2x + 1 = 0$

$$(x + 1)(x + 1) = 0 \qquad \text{Factor the trinomial.}$$
$$x + 1 = 0 \quad \text{or } x + 1 = 0 \qquad \text{Use the Zero Product Property.}$$
$$x = -1 \text{ or } \qquad x = -1 \qquad \text{Solve each equation.}$$

Both factors result in the same solution, so there is one solution, -1.

Check Graph the related quadratic function.

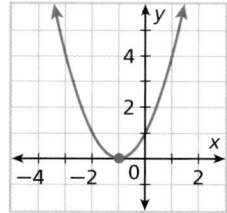

The graph of $y = x^2 + 2x + 1$ shows one zero at -1, the same as the solution found by factoring. $\checkmark$

Solve each quadratic equation by factoring. Check your answer.

 $-2x^2 = 18 - 12x$

$$-2x^2 + 12x - 18 = 0 \quad \textit{Write the equation in standard form.}$$
$$-2(x^2 - 6x + 9) = 0 \quad \textit{Factor out the GCF, } -2.$$
$$-2(x - 3)(x - 3) = 0 \quad \textit{Factor the trinomial.}$$
$$-2 \neq 0 \quad \text{or} \quad x - 3 = 0 \quad \textit{Use the Zero Product Property.} -2 \textit{ cannot equal 0.}$$
$$x = 3 \quad \textit{Solve the remaining equation.}$$

The only solution is 3.

Helpful Hint

$(x - 3)(x - 3)$ is a perfect square. Since both factors are the same, you solve only one equation.

Check
$$\begin{array}{c|c}
\multicolumn{2}{c}{-2x^2 = 18 - 12x} \\
\hline
-2(3)^2 & 18 - 12(3) \\
-18 & 18 - 36 \\
-18 & -18 \checkmark
\end{array}$$
Substitute 3 into the original equation.

CHECK IT OUT! Solve each quadratic equation by factoring. Check your answer.

2a. $x^2 - 6x + 9 = 0$ **2b.** $x^2 + 4x = 5$

2c. $30x = -9x^2 - 25$ **2d.** $3x^2 - 4x + 1 = 0$

EXAMPLE 3 **Sports Application**

The height of a diver above the water during a dive can be modeled by $h = -16t^2 + 8t + 48$, where h is height in feet and t is time in seconds. Find the time it takes for the diver to reach the water.

48 ft

$$h = -16t^2 + 8t + 48$$
$$0 = -16t^2 + 8t + 48 \qquad \textit{The diver reaches the water when } h = 0.$$
$$0 = -8(2t^2 - t - 6) \qquad \textit{Factor out the GCF, } -8.$$
$$0 = -8(2t + 3)(t - 2) \qquad \textit{Factor the trinomial.}$$
$$-8 \neq 0, \; 2t + 3 = 0 \quad \text{or} \; t - 2 = 0 \qquad \textit{Use the Zero Product Property.}$$
$$2t = -3 \; \text{or} \qquad t = 2 \qquad \textit{Solve each equation.}$$
$$t = -\frac{3}{2} \; \text{✗} \qquad \textit{Since time cannot be negative, } -\frac{3}{2} \textit{ does not make sense in this situation.}$$

It takes the diver 2 seconds to reach the water.

Check
$$\begin{array}{c|c}
\multicolumn{2}{c}{0 = -16t^2 + 8t + 48} \\
\hline
0 & -16(2)^2 + 8(2) + 48 \\
0 & -64 + 16 + 48 \\
0 & 0 \checkmark
\end{array}$$
Substitute 2 into the original equation.

CHECK IT OUT! **3. What if...?** The equation for the height above the water for another diver can be modeled by $h = -16t^2 + 8t + 24$. Find the time it takes this diver to reach the water.

THINK AND DISCUSS

1. Explain two ways to solve $x^2 + x - 6 = 0$. How are these two methods similar?

2. For the quadratic equation $0 = (x + 2)(x - 6)$, what are the *x*-intercepts of the related function?

3. **GET ORGANIZED** Copy and complete the graphic organizer. In each box, write a step used to solve a quadratic equation by factoring.

Solving Quadratic Equations by Factoring

| 1. Write in standard form | → | 2. | → | 3. | → | 4. |

9-5 Exercises

California Standards Practice
14.0, 23.0, 25.2

go.hrw.com
Homework Help Online
KEYWORD: MA8CA 9-5
Parent Resources Online
KEYWORD: MA8CA Parent

GUIDED PRACTICE

SEE EXAMPLE 1
p. 576

Use the Zero Product Property to solve each equation. Check your answer.

1. $(x + 2)(x - 8) = 0$
2. $(x - 6)(x - 5) = 0$
3. $(x + 7)(x + 9) = 0$
4. $(x)(x - 1) = 0$
5. $(x)(x + 11) = 0$
6. $(3x + 2)(4x - 1) = 0$

SEE EXAMPLE 2
p. 577

Solve each quadratic equation by factoring. Check your answer.

7. $x^2 + 4x - 12 = 0$
8. $x^2 - 8x - 9 = 0$
9. $x^2 - 5x + 6 = 0$
10. $x^2 - 3x = 10$
11. $x^2 + 10x = -16$
12. $x^2 + 2x = 15$
13. $x^2 - 8x + 16 = 0$
14. $-3x^2 = 18x + 27$
15. $x^2 + 36 = 12x$
16. $x^2 + 14x + 49 = 0$
17. $x^2 - 16x + 64 = 0$
18. $2x^2 + 6x = -18$

SEE EXAMPLE 3
p. 578

19. **Games** A group of friends tries to keep a beanbag from touching the ground without using their hands. Once the beanbag has been kicked, its height can be modeled by $h = -16t^2 + 14t + 2$, where *h* is the height in feet above the ground and *t* is the time in seconds. Find the time it takes the beanbag to reach the ground.

PRACTICE AND PROBLEM SOLVING

Independent Practice

For Exercises	See Example
20–25	1
26–31	2
32	3

Extra Practice

Skills Practice p. EP19

Application Practice p. EP32

Use the Zero Product Property to solve each equation. Check your answer.

20. $(x - 8)(x + 6) = 0$
21. $(x + 4)(x + 7) = 0$
22. $(x - 2)(x - 5) = 0$
23. $(x - 9)(x) = 0$
24. $(x)(x + 25) = 0$
25. $(2x + 1)(3x - 1) = 0$

Solve each quadratic equation by factoring. Check your answer.

26. $x^2 + 8x + 15 = 0$
27. $x^2 - 2x - 8 = 0$
28. $x^2 - 4x + 3 = 0$
29. $x^2 + 10x + 25 = 0$
30. $x^2 - x = 12$
31. $-x^2 = 4x + 4$

32. Multi-Step The height of a flare can be approximated by the function $h = -16t^2 + 95t + 6$, where h is the height in feet and t is the time in seconds. Find the time it takes the flare to hit the ground.

Determine the number of x-intercepts of each function.

33. $y = (x + 8)(x + 8)$ **34.** $(x - 3)(x + 3) = y$ **35.** $y = (x + 7)^2$

36. $3x^2 + 12x + 9 = y$ **37.** $y = x^2 + 12x + 36$ **38.** $(x - 2)^2 - 9 = y$

39. /// ERROR ANALYSIS /// Which solution is incorrect? Explain the error.

A

$x^2 + x - 2 = 0$
$(x - 1)(x + 2) = 0$
$x = 1$ or $x = -2$

B

$x^2 + x - 2 = 0$
$(x - 1)(x + 2) = 0$
$x = -1$ or $x = 2$

40. Number Theory Write an equation that could be used to find two consecutive even integers whose product is 24. Let x represent the first integer. Solve the equation and give the two integers.

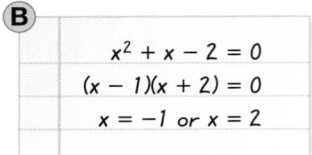

41. Geometry The photo shows a traditional thatched house as found in Santana, Madeira in Portugal. The front of the house is in the shape of a triangle. Suppose the base of the triangle is 1 m less than its height and the area of the triangle is 15 m². Find the height of the triangle. (*Hint:* Use $A = \frac{1}{2}bh$.)

42. Multi-Step The length of a rectangle is 1 ft less than 3 times the width. The area is 310 ft². Find the dimensions of the rectangle.

43. Physical Science The height of a fireworks rocket in meters can be approximated by $h = -5t^2 + 30t$, where h is the height in meters and t is time in seconds. Find the time it takes the rocket to reach the ground after it has been launched.

44. Geometry One base of a trapezoid is the same length as the height of the trapezoid. The other base is 4 cm more than the height. The area of the trapezoid is 48 cm². Find the length of the shorter base. (*Hint:* Use $A = \frac{1}{2}h(b_1 + b_2)$.)

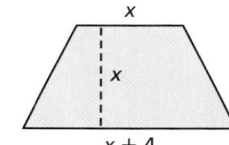

45. Critical Thinking Can you solve $(x - 2)(x + 3) = 5$ by solving $x - 2 = 5$ and $x + 3 = 5$? Why or why not?

46. Write About It Explain why you set each factor equal to zero when solving a quadratic equation by factoring.

CONCEPT CONNECTION

47. This problem will prepare you for the Concept Connection on page 610.

A tee box is 48 feet above its fairway. Starting with an initial elevation of 48 ft at the tee box and an initial velocity of 32 ft/s, the quadratic equation $0 = -16t^2 + 32t + 48$ gives the time t in seconds when a golf ball is at height 0 feet on the fairway.

a. Solve the quadratic equation by factoring to see how long the ball is in the air.

b. What is the height of the ball at 1 second?

c. Is the ball at its maximum height at 1 second? Explain.

Multiple Choice For Exercises 48 and 49, choose the best answer.

48. What are the solutions to $(x - 1)(2x + 5) = 0$?

    Ⓐ -1 and $\dfrac{5}{2}$ Ⓒ 1 and $-\dfrac{5}{2}$

    Ⓑ -1 and $\dfrac{2}{5}$ Ⓓ 1 and $-\dfrac{2}{5}$

49. Which graph could be used to help solve the equation $x^2 - 5x + 6 = 0$?

Ⓐ 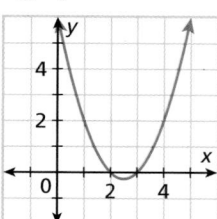   Ⓒ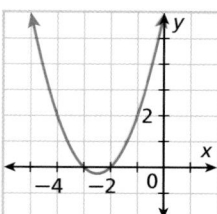

Ⓑ 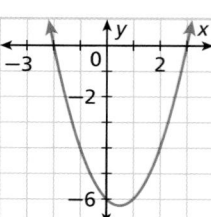   Ⓓ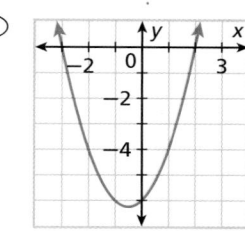

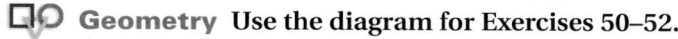

CHALLENGE AND EXTEND

Geometry Use the diagram for Exercises 50–52.

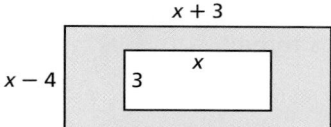

50. Write a polynomial to represent the area of the larger rectangle.

51. Write a polynomial to represent the area of the smaller rectangle.

52. Write a polynomial to represent the area of the shaded region. Then solve for x given that the area of the shaded region is 48 square units.

 53. Reasoning Suppose m and n are the roots of a quadratic polynomial. Name two points that must be on the graph of the related quadratic function.

SPIRAL STANDARDS REVIEW    2.0,   21.0

Find each square root. *(Lesson 1-5)*

54. $\sqrt{121}$ **55.** $-\sqrt{64}$ **56.** $-\sqrt{100}$ **57.** $\sqrt{225}$

58. Veronica is 63 inches tall, and she is 4 inches shorter than her friend. Write and solve an equation to find the height of her friend. *(Lesson 2-1)*

59. A tire manufacturer has 325 tires. Write and solve an equation to find the number of minivans m that can be built using this number of tires. Each minivan has 4 tires and 1 spare tire. *(Lesson 2-1)*

Solve each equation by graphing the related function. Check your answer. *(Lesson 9-4)*

60. $x^2 - 49 = 0$ **61.** $x^2 = x + 12$ **62.** $-x^2 + 8x = 15$

9-6 Solving Quadratic Equations by Using Square Roots

California Standards

🔑 **2.0 Students understand and use such operations as** taking the opposite, finding the reciprocal, **taking a root,** and raising to a fractional power. They understand and use the rules of exponents.

🔑 **23.0 Students apply quadratic equations to physical problems,** such as the motion of an object under the force of gravity.

Why learn this?

Square roots can be used to find how much fencing is needed for a pen at a zoo. (See Example 4.)

Some quadratic equations cannot be easily solved by factoring. Square roots can be used to solve some of these quadratic equations. Recall from Lesson 1–5 that every positive real number has two square roots, one positive and one negative. (Remember also that the symbol $\sqrt{}$ indicates a nonnegative square root.)

$$3(3) = 3^2 = 9 \longrightarrow \sqrt{9} = 3 \longleftarrow \text{Positive square root of 9}$$

$$(-3)(-3) = (-3)^2 = 9 \longrightarrow -\sqrt{9} = -3 \longleftarrow \text{Negative square root of 9}$$

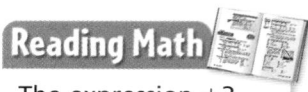

Reading Math

The expression ± 3 means "3 or -3" and is read "plus or minus three."

When you take a square root to solve an equation, you must find both the positive and negative square root. This is indicated by the symbol $\pm\sqrt{}$.

$$\pm\sqrt{9} = \pm 3 \longleftarrow \text{Positive and negative square roots of 9}$$

Square-Root Property

WORDS	NUMBERS	ALGEBRA
To solve a quadratic equation in the form $x^2 = a$, take the square root of both sides.	$x^2 = 15$ $x = \pm\sqrt{15}$	If $x^2 = a$ and a is a positive real number, then $x = \pm\sqrt{a}$.

EXAMPLE 1 Using Square Roots to Solve $x^2 = a$

Solve using square roots. Check your answer.

A $x^2 = 16$

$\quad x = \pm\sqrt{16}$ *Solve for x by taking the square root of both*

$\quad x = \pm 4$ *sides. Use $\pm$ to show both square roots.*

The solutions are 4 and -4.

Check
$$\begin{array}{c|c} x^2 = 16 & \\ \hline (4)^2 & 16 \\ 16 & 16 \checkmark \end{array}$$
Substitute 4 into the original equation.

$$\begin{array}{c|c} x^2 = 16 & \\ \hline (-4)^2 & 16 \\ 16 & 16 \checkmark \end{array}$$
Substitute -4 into the original equation.

Solve using square roots.

B $x^2 = -4$

$x = \pm\sqrt{-4}$ *There is no real number whose square is negative.*

There is no real solution. The solution set is the empty set, $\varnothing$.

 Solve using square roots. Check your answer.

1a. $x^2 = 121$ **1b.** $x^2 = 0$ **1c.** $x^2 = -16$

If a quadratic equation is not written in the form $x^2 = a$, use inverse operations to isolate x^2 before taking the square root of both sides.

EXAMPLE 2 **Using Square Roots to Solve Quadratic Equations**

Solve using square roots.

A $x^2 + 5 = 5$

$$x^2 + 5 = 5$$
$$\underline{-5 \quad -5}$$
$$x^2 = 0$$ *Subtract 5 from both sides.*

$$x = \pm\sqrt{0} = 0$$ *Take the square root of both sides.*

Helpful Hint

The square root of 0 is neither positive nor negative. It is only 0.

B $4x^2 - 25 = 0$

$$4x^2 - 25 = 0$$
$$\underline{+25 \quad +25}$$ *Add 25 to both sides.*
$$\frac{4x^2}{4} = \frac{25}{4}$$ *Divide by 4 on both sides.*
$$x^2 = \frac{25}{4}$$

$$x = \pm\sqrt{\frac{25}{4}} = \pm\frac{5}{2}$$ *Take the square root of both sides. Use $\pm$ to show both square roots.*

Check

$4x^2 - 25 = 0$		$4x^2 - 25 = 0$	
$4\left(\frac{5}{2}\right)^2 - 25$	0	$4\left(-\frac{5}{2}\right)^2 - 25$	0
$4\left(\frac{25}{4}\right) - 25$	0	$4\left(\frac{25}{4}\right) - 25$	0
$25 - 25$	$0 \checkmark$	$25 - 25$	$0 \checkmark$

 Solve by using square roots. Check your answer.

2a. $100x^2 + 49 = 0$ **2b.** $36x^2 = 1$

When solving quadratic equations by using square roots, the solutions may be irrational. In this case, you can give the exact solutions by leaving the square root in your answer, or you can approximate the solutions.

EXAMPLE 3 **Approximating Solutions**

Solve. Round to the nearest hundredth.

A $x^2 = 10$

$x = \pm\sqrt{10}$ *Take the square root of both sides.*

$x \approx \pm 3.16$ *Estimate $\sqrt{10}$.*

The exact solutions are $\sqrt{10}$ and $-\sqrt{10}$.
The approximate solutions are 3.16 and −3.16.

Solve. Round to the nearest hundredth.

B $0 = -2x^2 + 80$

$$0 = -2x^2 + 80$$
$$\underline{-80 \qquad\qquad -80} \qquad \textit{Subtract 80 from both sides.}$$
$$-80 = -2x^2$$
$$\frac{-80}{-2} = \frac{-2x^2}{-2} \qquad \textit{Divide both sides by } -2.$$
$$40 = x^2$$
$$\pm\sqrt{40} = x \qquad \textit{Take the square root of both sides.}$$
$$x \approx \pm 6.32 \qquad \textit{Estimate } \sqrt{40}.$$

The exact solutions are $\sqrt{40}$ and $-\sqrt{40}$.
The approximate solutions are 6.32 and −6.32.

Check Use a graphing calculator to support your answer.

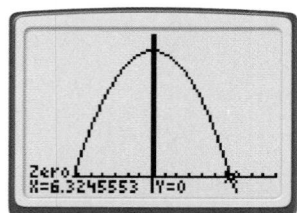

Use the zero function.
The approximate solutions
are 6.32 and −6.32. ✓

 Solve. Round to the nearest hundredth.

3a. $0 = 90 - x^2$ **3b.** $2x^2 - 64 = 0$ **3c.** $x^2 + 45 = 0$

EXAMPLE **4** *Consumer Application*

A zookeeper is buying fencing to enclose a pen at the zoo. The pen is an isosceles right triangle. There is already a fence on the side that borders a path. The area of the pen will be 4500 square feet. The zookeeper can buy the fencing in whole feet only. How many feet of fencing should he buy?

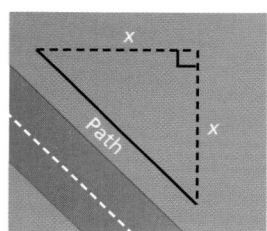

Let x represent the length of one of the sides.

$$\frac{1}{2}bh = A \qquad \textit{Use the formula for area of a triangle.}$$
$$\frac{1}{2}x(x) = 4500 \qquad \textit{Substitute x for both b and h and 4500 for A.}$$
$$(2)\frac{1}{2}x^2 = 4500(2) \qquad \textit{Simplify. Multiply both sides by 2.}$$
$$x = \pm\sqrt{9000} \qquad \textit{Take the square root of both sides.}$$
$$x \approx \pm 94.9 \qquad \textit{Estimate } \sqrt{9000}.$$

Lengths are not negative, so $x \approx 94.9$ is the only solution that makes sense. The zookeeper needs 95 + 95, or 190, feet of fencing.

 **4.** A lot is shaped like a trapezoid with bases x and $2x$. Its area is 6000 ft². Find x. Round to the nearest foot. (*Hint:* Use $A = \frac{1}{2}h(b_1 + b_2)$.)

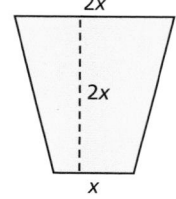

Remember!

To review estimating square roots, see Lesson 1-5.

Remember!

An isosceles triangle has at least two sides of the same length.

See Skills Bank p. SB18.

THINK AND DISCUSS

1. Explain why there are no solutions to the quadratic equation $x^2 = -9$.

2. Describe how to estimate the solutions of $4 = x^2 - 16$. What are the approximate solutions?

3. GET ORGANIZED Copy and complete the graphic organizer. In each box, write an example of a quadratic equation with the given number of solutions. Solve each equation.

> Solving Quadratic Equations by Using Square Roots When the Equation Has...
>
> | No real solutions | One solution | Two solutions |

9-6

Exercises

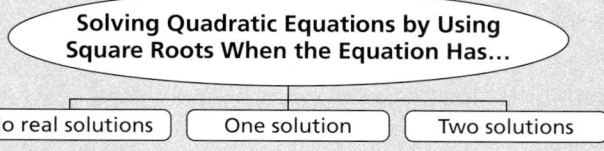

California Standards Practice

◆ 2.0, ◆ 23.0, 25.1, 25.2, 25.3

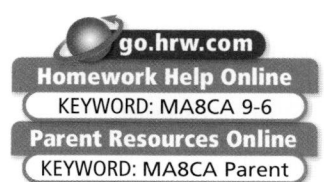

go.hrw.com
Homework Help Online
KEYWORD: MA8CA 9-6
Parent Resources Online
KEYWORD: MA8CA Parent

GUIDED PRACTICE

SEE EXAMPLE 1
p. 582

Solve using square roots. Check your answer.

1. $x^2 = 225$ **2.** $x^2 = 49$ **3.** $x^2 = -100$

4. $x^2 = 400$ **5.** $-25 = x^2$ **6.** $36 = x^2$

SEE EXAMPLE 2
p. 583

7. $3x^2 - 75 = 0$ **8.** $0 = 81x^2 - 25$ **9.** $49x^2 + 64 = 0$

10. $16x^2 + 10 = 131$ **11.** $0 = 4x^2 - 16$ **12.** $100x^2 + 26 = 10$

SEE EXAMPLE 3
p. 583

Solve. Round to the nearest hundredth.

13. $3x^2 = 81$ **14.** $0 = x^2 - 60$ **15.** $100 - 5x^2 = 0$

SEE EXAMPLE 4
p. 584

16. Geometry The length of a rectangle is 3 times its width. The area of the rectangle is 170 square meters. Find the width. Round to the nearest tenth of a meter. (*Hint:* Use $A = bh$.)

PRACTICE AND PROBLEM SOLVING

Independent Practice	
For Exercises	See Example
17–22	1
23–28	2
29–34	3
35	4

Extra Practice

Skills Practice p. EP19

Application Practice p. EP32

Solve using square roots. Check your answer.

17. $x^2 = 169$ **18.** $x^2 = 25$ **19.** $x^2 = -36$

20. $x^2 = 10{,}000$ **21.** $-121 = x^2$ **22.** $625 = x^2$

23. $4 - 81x^2 = 0$ **24.** $-4x^2 - 49 = 0$ **25.** $64x^2 - 5 = 20$

26. $9x^2 + 9 = 25$ **27.** $49x^2 + 1 = 170$ **28.** $81x^2 + 17 = 81$

Solve. Round to the nearest hundredth.

29. $4x^2 = 88$ **30.** $x^2 - 29 = 0$ **31.** $x^2 + 40 = 144$

32. $3x^2 - 84 = 0$ **33.** $50 - x^2 = 0$ **34.** $2x^2 - 10 = 64$

35. Entertainment For a scene in a movie, a sack of money is dropped from the roof of a 600 ft skyscraper. The height of the sack above the ground is given by $h = -16t^2 + 600$, where t is the time in seconds. How long will it take the sack to reach the ground? Round to the nearest tenth of a second.

36. Geometry The area of a square is 196 m². Find the dimensions of the square.

37. Number Theory If $a = 2b$ and $2ab = 36$, find all possible solutions for a and b.

38. Estimation The area y of any rectangle with side length x and one side twice as long as the other is represented by $y = 2x^2$. Use the graph to estimate the dimensions of such a rectangle whose area is 35 square feet.

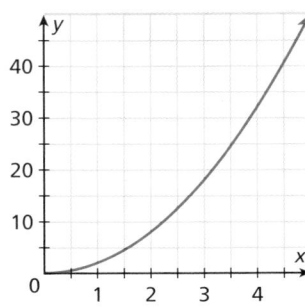

39. Physical Science The period of a pendulum is the amount of time it takes to swing back and forth one time. The relationship between the length of the pendulum L in inches and the length of the period t in seconds can be approximated by $L = 9.78t^2$. Find the period of a pendulum whose length is 60 inches. Round to the nearest tenth of a second.

40. ///ERROR ANALYSIS/// Which solution is incorrect? Explain the error.

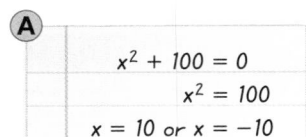

A
$x^2 + 100 = 0$
$x^2 = 100$
$x = 10 \text{ or } x = -10$

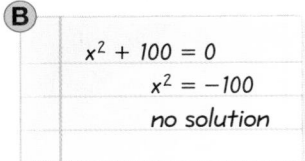

B
$x^2 + 100 = 0$
$x^2 = -100$
no solution

Reasoning Determine whether each statement is always, sometimes, or never true. Explain.

41. There are two solutions to $x^2 = n$ when n is positive.

42. If n is a rational number, then the solutions to $x^2 = n$ are rational numbers.

43. Multi-Step The height in feet of a soccer ball kicked upward from the ground with initial velocity 60 feet per second is modeled by $h = -16t^2 + 60t$, where t is the time in seconds. Find the time it takes for the ball to return to the ground. Round to the nearest hundredth of a second.

44. Geometry The geometric mean of two positive numbers a and b is the positive number x such that $\frac{a}{x} = \frac{x}{b}$. Find the geometric mean of 2 and 18.

45. Critical Thinking For the equation $x^2 = a$, describe the values of a that will result in each of the following.
   a. two solutions
   b. one solution
   c. no solution

CONCEPT CONNECTION

46. This problem will prepare you for the Concept Connection on page 610.
   The equation $d = 16t^2$ describes the distance d in feet that a golf ball falls in relation to the number of seconds t that it falls.
   a. How many seconds will it take a golf ball to drop to the ground from a height of 4 feet?
   b. Make a table and graph the related function.
   c. How far will the golf ball drop in 1 second?
   d. How many seconds will it take the golf ball to drop 64 feet?

For the quadratic equation $x^2 + a = 0$, determine whether each value of a will result in two rational solutions. Explain.

47. $-\dfrac{1}{2}$ **48.** $\dfrac{1}{2}$ **49.** $-\dfrac{1}{4}$ **50.** $\dfrac{1}{4}$

 51. Write About It Explain why the quadratic equation $x^2 + 4 = 0$ has no solutions but the quadratic equation $x^2 - 4 = 0$ has two solutions.

Multiple Choice For Exercises 52–54, choose the best answer.

52. The height of a cylinder is 100 cm, and the approximate volume is 1256 cm³. Find the radius of the cylinder. Use 3.14 for π.

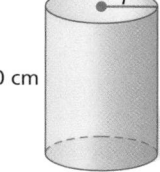

   Ⓐ 400 cm   Ⓒ 4 cm

   Ⓑ 20 cm   Ⓓ 2 cm

53. Which best describes the positive solution of $\frac{1}{2}x^2 = 20$?

   Ⓐ Between 4 and 5   Ⓒ Between 6 and 7

   Ⓑ Between 5 and 6   Ⓓ Between 7 and 8

54. Which best describes the solutions of $81x^2 - 169 = 0$?

   Ⓐ Two rational solutions   Ⓒ No solution

   Ⓑ Two irrational solutions   Ⓓ One solution

CHALLENGE AND EXTEND

Find the solutions of each equation. Check your answer.

55. $288x^2 - 19 = -1$ **56.** $-75x^2 = -48$ **57.** $x^2 = \dfrac{128}{242}$

 58. Geometry The Pythagorean Theorem states that $a^2 + b^2 = c^2$ if a and b represent the lengths of the legs of a right triangle and c represents the length of the hypotenuse.

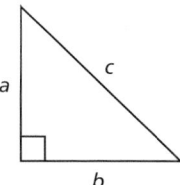

   a. Find the length of the hypotenuse if the lengths of the legs are 9 cm and 12 cm.

   b. Find the length of each leg of an isosceles right triangle whose hypotenuse is 10 cm. Round to the nearest tenth of a centimeter.

 **SPIRAL STANDARDS REVIEW**   🔑 4.0, 8.0, 🔑 14.0

59. The figures shown have the same perimeter. What is the value of x? *(Lesson 2-4)*

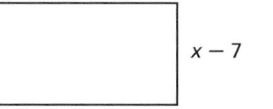
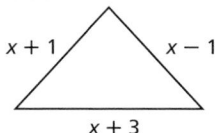

Identify which of the following lines are parallel. *(Lesson 5-7)*

60. $y = -2x + 3$, $2x - y = 8$, $6x - 2y = 10$, and $y + 4 = 2(3 - x)$

61. $y = 4x - 7$; $-\dfrac{1}{4}x - y = -2$; $-y = 4(2 - x)$; and $x = 1 + 3y$

Solve each quadratic equation by factoring. Check your answer. *(Lesson 9-5)*

62. $x^2 - 6x + 8 = 0$ **63.** $x^2 + 5x - 6 = 0$ **64.** $x^2 - 5x = 14$

65. $x^2 + x - 12 = 0$ **66.** $x^2 - 3x = 40$ **67.** $x^2 + 8x - 9 = 0$

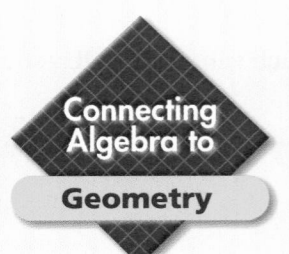

The Distance Formula

You can find the length of a vertical or horizontal line segment in the coordinate plane by subtracting coordinates.

California Standards

Reinforcement of **7MG3.2** Understand and use coordinate graphs to plot simple figures, **determine lengths** and areas related to them, and determine their image under translations and reflections.

WORDS	NUMBERS	ALGEBRA
The length of a vertical line segment is the absolute value of the difference between the y-coordinates of the endpoints.	$AB = \lvert 2 - (-4) \rvert = \lvert 6 \rvert = 6$	The distance between $P(x_1, y_1)$ and $Q(x_1, y_2)$ is $\lvert y_2 - y_1 \rvert$.
The length of a horizontal line segment is the absolute value of the difference between the x-coordinates of the endpoints.	$CD = \lvert -2 - 3 \rvert = \lvert -5 \rvert = 5$	The distance between $P(x_1, y_1)$ and $Q(x_2, y_1)$ is $\lvert x_2 - x_1 \rvert$.

Example 1

Find the length of the line segment that connects $S(-4.5, 7.1)$ and $T(-4.5, 0.3)$.

The x-coordinates are the same, so this is a vertical line segment. Subtract the y-coordinates and find the absolute value of the difference.

$\lvert y_2 - y_1 \rvert$ *Formula for the length of a vertical line segment*

$\lvert 0.3 - 7.1 \rvert$ *Substitute.*

$\lvert -6.8 \rvert = 6.8$ *Subtract and find the absolute value.*

Try This

Find the length of the line segment that connects each pair of points.

1. $X(-1, 3)$ and $Y(4, 3)$ **2.** $M(5, -2)$ and $N(5, -8)$ **3.** $C(3, -1)$ and $D(3, 5)$

4. $P(14, -5)$ and $Q(25, -5)$ **5.** $A(-6, 0.5)$ and $B(-6, -4.3)$ **6.** $E(1.4, -0.7)$ and $F(3.8, -0.7)$

Find the length of each segment.

7. the altitude of $\triangle PQR$

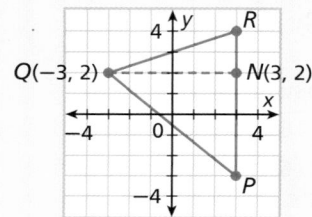

8. the height of parallelogram $EFGH$

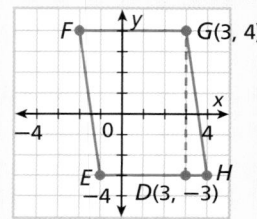

9. the height of trapezoid $ACDF$

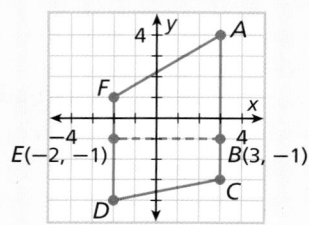

To find the length of a line segment that is not vertical or horizontal, such as PQ, think of it as the hypotenuse of a right triangle. Then you can use the Pythagorean Theorem.

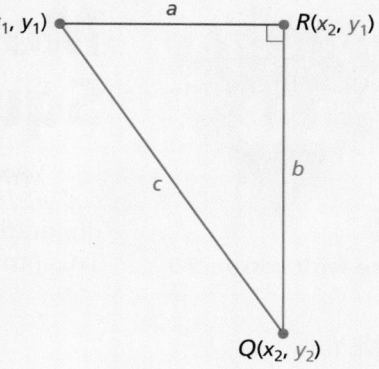

$$c^2 = a^2 + b^2 \qquad \text{Pythagorean Theorem}$$

$$(PQ)^2 = (PR)^2 + (QR)^2 \qquad \text{Substitute.}$$

$$PQ = \sqrt{(PR)^2 + (QR)^2} \qquad \begin{array}{l}\text{Solve for PQ. Use the positive} \\ \text{square root to represent} \\ \text{distance.}\end{array}$$

$$= \sqrt{\underbrace{(x_2 - x_1)^2}_{\substack{\text{Horizontal} \\ \text{segment}}} + \underbrace{(y_2 - y_1)^2}_{\substack{\text{Vertical} \\ \text{segment}}}} \qquad \begin{array}{l}\text{Use the Formula to find the} \\ \text{length of each segment.}\end{array}$$

This is the Distance Formula.

The Distance Formula

The distance between points P and Q with coordinates $P(x_1, y_1)$ and $Q(x_2, y_2)$ is given by

$$D = \sqrt{(x_2 - x_1)^2 + (y_2 - y_1)^2}.$$

Example 2

Find the length of the line segment that connects $H(20, -11)$ and $K(-4, 18)$.

Use the Distance Formula. Let $(20, -11)$ be (x_1, y_1) and $(-4, 18)$ be (x_2, y_2).

$$D = \sqrt{(x_2 - x_1)^2 + (y_2 - y_1)^2} \qquad \text{Write the formula.}$$

$$= \sqrt{(-4 - 20)^2 + [18 - (-11)]^2} \qquad \text{Substitute.}$$

$$= \sqrt{(-24)^2 + (29)^2} \qquad \text{Find the differences.}$$

$$= \sqrt{576 + 841} \qquad \text{Square the differences.}$$

$$= \sqrt{1417} \approx 37.64 \qquad \text{Estimate the square root.}$$

Try This

Find the length of the line segment that connects each pair of points. Round to the nearest hundredth.

10. $F(-8, 3)$ and $G(-11, -4)$ **11.** $S(30, -15)$ and $T(-55, 40)$ **12.** $W(0.5, 1.2)$ and $X(0.6, 2.5)$

Find the length of each dashed line segment. Round to the nearest hundredth.

13. the altitude of $\triangle WYZ$

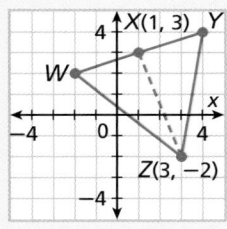

14. the height of parallelogram $ABCD$

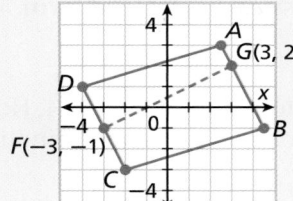

15. the height of trapezoid $LMNO$

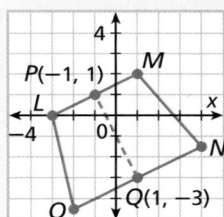

9-7

Algebra LAB

Use with Lesson 9-7

Model Completing the Square

One way to solve a quadratic equation is by using a procedure called *completing the square*. In this procedure, you add something to a quadratic expression to make it a perfect-square trinomial. This procedure can be modeled with algebra tiles.

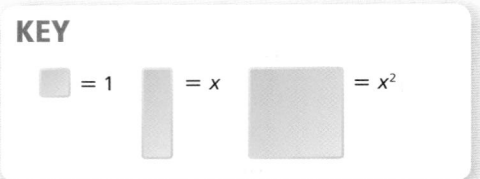

KEY

$\square$ = 1   = x = x^2

California Standards

Preparation for ⬦ **14.0** Students solve a quadratic equation by factoring or **completing the square.**

Activity

Use algebra tiles to model $x^2 + 6x$. Add unit tiles to complete a perfect-square trinomial. Then write the new expression in factored form.

MODEL		ALGEBRA
	Arrange the tiles to form part of a large square. *Part of the square is missing. How many unit tiles do you need to complete it?*	$x^2 + 6x$
	Complete the square by placing 9 unit tiles on the mat. $x^2 + 6x + 9$ *is a perfect-square trinomial.*	$x^2 + 6x + 9$
x + 3 ⎧ *x + 3*	*Use the length and the width of the square to rewrite the area expression in factored form.*	$(x + 3)^2$

Try This

Use algebra tiles to model each expression. Add unit tiles to complete a perfect-square trinomial. Then write the new expression in factored form.

1. $x^2 + 4x$ **2.** $x^2 + 2x$ **3.** $x^2 + 10x$ **4.** $x^2 + 8x$

5. Make a Conjecture Examine the pattern in Problems 1–4. How many unit tiles would you have to add to make $x^2 + 12x$ a perfect-square trinomial?

Completing the Square

California Standards

14.0 Students solve a quadratic equation **by factoring** or **completing the square.**

23.0 Students apply quadratic equations to physical problems, such as the motion of an object under the force of gravity.

Also covered: **2.0**

Vocabulary
completing the square

Who uses this?
Landscapers can solve quadratic equations to find dimensions of patios. (See Example 4.)

In the previous lesson, you solved quadratic equations by isolating x^2 and then using square roots. This method also works if the quadratic equation, when written in standard form, is a perfect square.

When a trinomial is a perfect square, there is a relationship between the **coefficient of the x-term** and the **constant term**.

$$(x + n)^2$$
$$= x^2 + 2nx + n^2$$
$$\left(\frac{2n}{2}\right)^2 = n^2$$

Divide the coefficient of the x-term by 2. Then square the result to get the constant term.

$$(x - n)^2$$
$$= x^2 - 2nx + n^2$$
$$\left(\frac{-2n}{2}\right)^2 = n^2$$

An expression in the form $x^2 + bx$ is not a perfect square. However, you can use the relationship shown above to add a term to $x^2 + bx$ to form a trinomial that is a perfect square. This is called **completing the square**.

Completing the Square

WORDS	NUMBERS	ALGEBRA
To complete the square of $x^2 + bx$, add $\left(\frac{b}{2}\right)^2$ to the expression. This will form a perfect-square trinomial.	$x^2 + 6x + \blacksquare$ $x^2 + 6x + \left(\frac{6}{2}\right)^2$ $x^2 + 6x + 9$ $(x + 3)^2$	$x^2 + bx + \blacksquare$ $x^2 + bx + \left(\frac{b}{2}\right)^2$ $\left(x + \frac{b}{2}\right)^2$

EXAMPLE 1 **Completing the Square**

Complete the square to form a perfect-square trinomial.

A $x^2 + 10x + \blacksquare$
$x^2 + 10x$ *Identify b.*
$\left(\frac{10}{2}\right)^2 = 5^2 = 25$ *Find $\left(\frac{b}{2}\right)^2$.*
$x^2 + 10x + 25$ *Add $\left(\frac{b}{2}\right)^2$ to the expression.*

B $x^2 - 9x + \blacksquare$
$x^2 + -9x$
$\left(\frac{-9}{2}\right)^2 = \frac{81}{4}$
$x^2 - 9x + \frac{81}{4}$

 Complete the square to form a perfect-square trinomial.
     1a. $x^2 + 12x + \blacksquare$ **1b.** $x^2 - 5x + \blacksquare$ **1c.** $8x + x^2 + \blacksquare$

To solve a quadratic equation in the form $x^2 + bx = c$, first complete the square of $x^2 + bx$. Then you can solve using square roots.

Solving a Quadratic Equation by Completing the Square
Step 1 Write the equation in the form $x^2 + bx = c$.
Step 2 Find $\left(\frac{b}{2}\right)^2$.
Step 3 Complete the square by adding $\left(\frac{b}{2}\right)^2$. Because this is an equation, you must add $\left(\frac{b}{2}\right)^2$ to both sides.
Step 4 Factor the perfect-square trinomial.
Step 5 Take the square root of both sides.
Step 6 Write two equations, using both the positive and negative square root, and solve each equation.

EXAMPLE **2** **Solving $x^2 + bx = c$ by Completing the Square**

Solve by completing the square. Check your answer.

A $x^2 + 14x = 15$

Step 1 $x^2 + 14x = 15$ *The equation is in the form $x^2 + bx = c$.*

Step 2 $\left(\frac{14}{2}\right)^2 = 7^2 = 49$ *Find $\left(\frac{b}{2}\right)^2$.*

Step 3 $x^2 + 14x + 49 = 15 + 49$ *Complete the square.*

Step 4 $(x + 7)^2 = 64$ *Factor and simplify.*

Step 5 $x + 7 = \pm 8$ *Take the square root of both sides.*

Step 6 $x + 7 = 8$ or $x + 7 = -8$ *Write and solve two equations.*
        $x = 1$ or $x = -15$

Check

$x^2 + 14x = 15$	
$(1)^2 + 14\,(1)$	15
$1 + 14$	15
15	15 ✓

$x^2 + 14x = 15$	
$(-15)^2 + 14\,(-15)$	15
$225 - 210$	15
15	15 ✓

B $x^2 - 2x - 2 = 0$

Step 1 $x^2 + (-2x) = 2$ *Write in the form $x^2 + bx = c$.*

Step 2 $\left(\frac{-2}{2}\right)^2 = (-1)^2 = 1$ *Find $\left(\frac{b}{2}\right)^2$.*

Step 3 $x^2 - 2x + 1 = 2 + 1$ *Complete the square.*

Step 4 $(x - 1)^2 = 3$ *Factor and simplify.*

Step 5 $x - 1 = \pm\sqrt{3}$ *Take the square root of both sides.*

Step 6 $x - 1 = \sqrt{3}$ or $x - 1 = -\sqrt{3}$ *Write and solve*
       $x = 1 + \sqrt{3}$ or $x = 1 - \sqrt{3}$ *two equations.*

The exact solutions are $1 + \sqrt{3}$ and $1 - \sqrt{3}$.

Check Use a graphing calculator to check your answer.

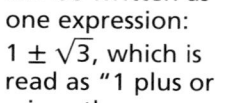

Writing Math

The expressions $1 + \sqrt{3}$ and $1 - \sqrt{3}$ can be written as one expression: $1 \pm \sqrt{3}$, which is read as "1 plus or minus the square root of 3."

Solve by completing the square. Check your answer.

2a. $x^2 + 10x = -9$ **2b.** $t^2 - 8t - 5 = 0$

EXAMPLE **3** **Solving $ax^2 + bx = c$ by Completing the Square**

Solve by completing the square.

A $3x^2 - 10x = -3$

Step 1 $\dfrac{3x^2}{3} - \dfrac{10x}{3} = \dfrac{-3}{3}$ *Divide both sides of the equation by 3 so that a = 1.*

$x^2 - \dfrac{10}{3}x = -1$

$x^2 + \left(-\dfrac{10}{3}x\right) = -1$ *Write in the form $x^2 + bx = c$.*

Step 2 $\left(-\dfrac{10}{3} \cdot \dfrac{1}{2}\right)^2 = \left(-\dfrac{10}{6}\right)^2 = \dfrac{100}{36} = \dfrac{25}{9}$ *Find $\left(\dfrac{b}{2}\right)^2$.*

Step 3 $x^2 - \dfrac{10}{3}x + \dfrac{25}{9} = -1 + \dfrac{25}{9}$ *Complete the square.*

$x^2 - \dfrac{10}{3}x + \dfrac{25}{9} = -\dfrac{9}{9} + \dfrac{25}{9}$ *Rewrite using like denominators.*

Step 4 $\left(x - \dfrac{5}{3}\right)^2 = \dfrac{16}{9}$ *Factor and simplify.*

Step 5 $x - \dfrac{5}{3} = \pm\dfrac{4}{3}$ *Take the square root of both sides.*

Step 6 $x - \dfrac{5}{3} = \dfrac{4}{3}$ or $x - \dfrac{5}{3} = -\dfrac{4}{3}$ *Write and solve two equations.*

$x = 3$ or $x = \dfrac{1}{3}$

> **Remember!**
>
> Multiplying by $\frac{1}{2}$ is the same as dividing by 2.

B $-2x^2 + 12x - 20 = 0$

Step 1 $\dfrac{-2x^2}{-2} + \dfrac{12x}{-2} - \dfrac{20}{-2} = \dfrac{0}{-2}$ *Divide both sides of the equation by -2 so that $a = 1$.*

$x^2 - 6x + 10 = 0$

$x^2 - 6x = -10$ *Write in the form $x^2 + bx = c$.*

$x^2 + (-6x) = -10$

Step 2 $\left(\dfrac{-6}{2}\right)^2 = (-3)^2 = 9$ *Find $\left(\dfrac{b}{2}\right)^2$.*

Step 3 $x^2 - 6x + 9 = -10 + 9$ *Complete the square.*

Step 4 $(x - 3)^2 = -1$ *Factor and simplify.*

There is no real number whose square is negative, so there are no real solutions.

 Solve by completing the square. Check your answer.

    3a. $3x^2 - 5x - 2 = 0$ **3b.** $4t^2 - 4t + 9 = 0$

EXAMPLE **4**   *Problem-Solving Application*

A landscaper is designing a rectangular brick patio. She has enough bricks to cover 144 square feet. She wants the length of the patio to be 10 feet greater than the width. What dimensions should she use for the patio? Round to the nearest hundredth of a foot.

1   **Understand the Problem**

The **answer** will be the length and width of the patio.

 **Geometry**

List the important information:
- There are enough bricks to cover 144 square feet.
- One edge of the patio is to be 10 feet longer than the other edge.

 Make a Plan

Set the formula for the area of a rectangle equal to 144, the area of the patio. Solve the equation.

 Solve

Let x be the width. Then $x + 10$ is the length. Use the formula for area of a rectangle.

$$\ell \quad \cdot \quad w \quad = \quad A$$

length	times	width	=	area of patio

$$x + 10 \quad \cdot \quad x \quad = \quad 144$$

The equation is $(x + 10)x = 144$.

Step 1 $x^2 + 10x = 144$		*Simplify.*
Step 2 $\left(\dfrac{10}{2}\right)^2 = 5^2 = 25$		*Find $\left(\dfrac{b}{2}\right)^2$.*
Step 3 $x^2 + 10x + 25 = 144 + 25$		*Complete the square.*
Step 4 $(x + 5)^2 = 169$		*Factor the perfect-square trinomial.*
Step 5 $x + 5 = \pm 13$		*Take the square root of both sides.*
Step 6 $x + 5 = 13$ or $x + 5 = -13$		*Write and solve two equations.*
$\quad\quad x = 8$ or $\quad x = -18$		

Negative numbers are not reasonable for length, so $x = 8$ is the only solution that makes sense.

The width is 8 feet, and the length is $8 + 10$, or 18, feet.

 Look Back

The length of the patio is 10 feet greater than the width. Also, $8(18) = 144$.

 **4.** A rectangular room has an area of 400 ft². The length is 8 ft longer than the width. Find the dimensions of the room. Round to the nearest tenth of a foot.

THINK AND DISCUSS

1. Tell how to solve a quadratic equation in the form $x^2 + bx + c = 0$ by completing the square.

 **2. GET ORGANIZED** Copy and complete the graphic organizer. In each box, write and solve an example of the given type of quadratic equation.

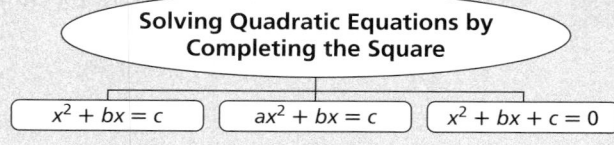

Solving Quadratic Equations by Completing the Square

$x^2 + bx = c$	$ax^2 + bx = c$	$x^2 + bx + c = 0$

9-7

Exercises

California
Standards Practice
🐻 2.0, 🔑 14.0, 🔑 21.0,
🔑 23.0, 25.2

go.hrw.com
Homework Help Online
KEYWORD: MA8CA 9-7
Parent Resources Online
KEYWORD: MA8CA Parent

GUIDED PRACTICE

1. **Vocabulary** Describe in your own words how to *complete the square* for the equation $1 = x^2 + 4x$.

SEE EXAMPLE **1**
p. 591

Complete the square to form a perfect-square trinomial.

2. $x^2 + 14x + $ ▨

3. $x^2 - 4x + $ ▨

4. $x^2 - 3x + $ ▨

SEE EXAMPLE **2**
p. 592

Solve by completing the square. Check your answer.

5. $x^2 + 6x = -5$

6. $x^2 - 8x = 9$

7. $x^2 + x = 30$

8. $x^2 + 2x = 21$

9. $x^2 - 10x = -9$

10. $x^2 + 16x = 92$

SEE EXAMPLE **3**
p. 593

11. $-x^2 - 5x = -5$

12. $-x^2 - 3x + 2 = 0$

13. $-6x = 3x^2 + 9$

14. $2x^2 - 6x = -10$

15. $-x^2 + 8x - 6 = 0$

16. $4x^2 + 16 = -24x$

SEE EXAMPLE **4**
p. 593

17. Multi-Step The length of a rectangle is 4 meters longer than the width. The area of the rectangle is 80 square meters. Find the length and width. Round your answers to the nearest tenth of a meter.

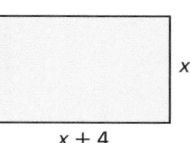

x

$x + 4$

PRACTICE AND PROBLEM SOLVING

Independent Practice	
For Exercises	See Example
18–20	1
21–26	2
27–32	3
33	4

Extra Practice
Skills Practice p. EP19
Application Practice p. EP32

Complete the square to form a perfect-square trinomial.

18. $x^2 - 16x + $ ▨

19. $x^2 - 2x + $ ▨

20. $x^2 + 11x + $ ▨

Solve by completing the square. Check your answer.

21. $x^2 - 10x = 24$

22. $x^2 - 6x = -9$

23. $x^2 + 15x = -26$

24. $x^2 + 6x = 16$

25. $x^2 - 2x = 48$

26. $x^2 + 12x = -36$

27. $-x^2 + x + 6 = 0$

28. $2x^2 = -7x - 29$

29. $-x^2 - x + 1 = 0$

30. $3x^2 - 6x - 9 = 0$

31. $-x^2 = 15x + 30$

32. $2x^2 + 20x - 10 = 0$

⌐◯ **33. Geometry** The base of a parallelogram is 8 inches longer than twice the height. The area is 64 square inches. What is the height?

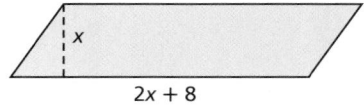

x

$2x + 8$

Solve each equation by completing the square. Check your answer.

34. $3x^2 + x = 10$

35. $x^2 = 2x + 6$

36. $2a^2 = 5a + 12$

37. $2x^2 + 5x = 3$

38. $4x = 7 - x^2$

39. $8x = -x^2 + 20$

40. Hobbies The height in feet h of a water bottle rocket launched from a rooftop is given by the equation $h = -16t^2 + 320t + 32$, where t is the time in seconds. After the rocket is fired, how long will it take to return to the ground? Solve by completing the square. Round your answer to the nearest tenth of a second.

Complete each trinomial so that it is a perfect square.

41. $x^2 + 18x + $ ▨

42. $x^2 - 100x + $ ▨

43. $x^2 - 7x + $ ▨

44. $x^2 + $ ▨ $x + 4$

45. $x^2 - $ ▨ $x + \dfrac{81}{4}$

46. $x^2 + $ ▨ $x + \dfrac{1}{36}$

47. Multi-Step A roped-off area of width x is created around a 34-by-10-foot rectangular museum display of Egyptian artifacts, as shown. The combined area of the display and the roped-off area is 640 square feet.

   a. Write an equation for the combined area.

   b. Find the width of the roped-off area.

48. Graphing Calculator Compare solving a quadratic equation by completing the square with finding the solutions on a graphing calculator.

   a. Complete the square to solve $2x^2 - 3x - 2 = 0$.

   b. Use your graphing calculator to graph $y = 2x^2 - 3x - 2$.

   c. Explain how to use this graph to find the solutions of $2x^2 - 3x - 2 = 0$.

   d. Compare the two methods of solving the equation. What are the advantages and disadvantages of each?

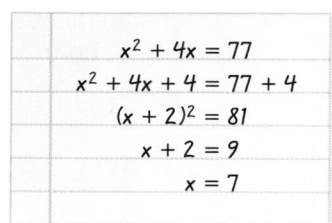

49. /// ERROR ANALYSIS /// Explain the error below. What is the correct answer?

$$x^2 + 4x = 77$$
$$x^2 + 4x + 4 = 77 + 4$$
$$(x + 2)^2 = 81$$
$$x + 2 = 9$$
$$x = 7$$

Find the roots of each quadratic polynomial. Check your answer.

50. $5x^2 - 50x - 55$ **51.** $3x^2 + 36x + 27$ **52.** $28x - 2x^2 - 26$

53. $36x + 3x^2 + 108$ **54.** $4x^2 + 32x + 44$ **55.** $16x + 40 + 2x^2$

56. $x^2 - 5x + 6$ **57.** $x^2 + 6x + 18$ **58.** $x^2 + x + 1$

59. Write About It Jamal prefers to solve $x^2 + 20x - 21 = 0$ by completing the square. Heather prefers to solve $x^2 + 11x + 18 = 0$ by factoring. Explain their reasoning.

60. Critical Thinking What should be done to the binomial $x^2 + y^2$ to make it a perfect-square trinomial? Explain.

CONCEPT CONNECTION

61. This problem will prepare you for the Concept Connection on page 610.

The function $h(t) = -16t^2 + vt + c$ models the height in feet of a golf ball after t seconds when it is hit with initial velocity v from initial height c feet. A golfer stands on a tee box that is 32 feet above the fairway. He hits the golf ball from the tee at an initial velocity of 64 feet per second.

   a. Write an equation that gives the time t when the golf ball lands on the fairway at height 0.

   b. What number would be added to both sides of the equation in part **a** to complete the square while solving for t?

   c. Solve the equation from part **a** by completing the square to find the time it takes the ball to reach the fairway. Round to the nearest tenth of a second.

62. Write About It Compare solving an equation of the form $x^2 + bx + c = 0$ by completing the square and solving an equation of the form $ax^2 + bx + c = 0$ by completing the square.

Multiple Choice For Exercises 63–65, choose the best answer.

63. What value of c will make $x^2 + 16x + c$ a perfect-square trinomial?

    Ⓐ 32   Ⓑ 64   Ⓒ 128   Ⓓ 256

64. What value of b will make $x^2 + b + 25$ a perfect-square trinomial?

    Ⓐ 5   Ⓑ $5x$ Ⓒ 10   Ⓓ $10x$

65. Which of the following is closest to a solution of $3x^2 + 2x - 4 = 0$?

    Ⓐ 0   Ⓑ 1   Ⓒ 2   Ⓓ 3

66. Short Response Solve $x^2 - 8x - 20 = 0$ by completing the square. Explain each step in your solution.

CHALLENGE AND EXTEND

Solve each equation by completing the square. Check your answer.

67. $6x^2 + 5x = 6$ **68.** $7x + 3 = 6x^2$ **69.** $4x = 1 - 3x^2$

70. What should be done to the binomial $ax^2 + bx$ to obtain a perfect-square trinomial?

71. Solve $ax^2 + bx = 0$ for x.

 72. Geometry The hypotenuse of a right triangle is 20 cm. One of the legs is 4 cm longer than the other leg. Find the area of the triangle. (*Hint:* Use the Pythagorean Theorem.)

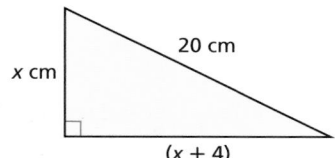

SPIRAL STANDARDS REVIEW
🔑 2.0, 🔑 6.0, 🔑 10.0

Graph the line with the given slope and y-intercept. *(Lesson 5-5)*

73. slope $= 4$, y-intercept $= -3$ **74.** slope $= -\frac{2}{3}$, y-intercept $= 4$

75. slope $= -2$, y-intercept $= -2$ **76.** slope $= -\frac{4}{3}$, y-intercept $= 0$

Multiply. *(Lesson 7-8)*

77. $(x - 4)^2$ **78.** $(x - 4)(x + 4)$ **79.** $(4 - t)^2$

80. $(2z + 3)^2$ **81.** $(8b^2 - 2)(8b^2 + 2)$ **82.** $(2x - 6)(2x + 6)$

Solve using square roots. Check your answer. *(Lesson 9-6)*

83. $5x^2 = 5$ **84.** $x^2 + 3 = 12$ **85.** $5x^2 = 80$

86. $9x^2 = 64$ **87.** $25 + x^2 = 250$ **88.** $64x^2 + 3 = 147$

Solve. Round to the nearest hundredth. *(Lesson 9-6)*

89. $12 = 5x^2$ **90.** $3x^2 - 4 = 15$ **91.** $x^2 - 7 = 19$

92. $6 + x^2 = 72$ **93.** $10x^2 - 10 = 12$ **94.** $2x^2 + 2 = 33$

9-8 The Quadratic Formula

California Standards

🔑 **19.0** Students know the quadratic formula and are familiar with its proof by completing the square.

🔑 **20.0** Students use the quadratic formula to find the roots of a second-degree polynomial and **to solve quadratic equations.**

Why learn this?

You can use the Quadratic Formula to model the motion of objects, such as skipping stones. (See Exercise 62.)

In the previous lesson, you completed the square to solve quadratic equations. If you complete the square of $ax^2 + bx + c = 0$, you can derive the *Quadratic Formula*.

Numbers		Algebra
$2x^2 + 6x + 1 = 0$		$ax^2 + bx + c = 0,\ a \neq 0$
$\frac{2}{2}x^2 + \frac{6}{2}x + \frac{1}{2} = \frac{0}{2}$	Divide both sides by a.	$\frac{a}{a}x^2 + \frac{b}{a}x + \frac{c}{a} = \frac{0}{a}$
$x^2 + 3x + \frac{1}{2} = 0$		$x^2 + \frac{b}{a}x + \frac{c}{a} = 0$
$x^2 + 3x = -\frac{1}{2}$	Subtract $\frac{c}{a}$ from both sides.	$x^2 + \frac{b}{a}x = -\frac{c}{a}$
$x^2 + 3x + \left(\frac{3}{2}\right)^2 = -\frac{1}{2} + \left(\frac{3}{2}\right)^2$	Complete the square.	$x^2 + \frac{b}{a}x + \left(\frac{b}{2a}\right)^2 = -\frac{c}{a} + \left(\frac{b}{2a}\right)^2$
$\left(x + \frac{3}{2}\right)^2 = \frac{9}{4} - \frac{1}{2}$	Factor and simplify.	$\left(x + \frac{b}{2a}\right)^2 = \frac{b^2}{4a^2} - \frac{c}{a}$
$\left(x + \frac{3}{2}\right)^2 = \frac{9}{4} - \frac{2}{4}$	Use common denominators.	$\left(x + \frac{b}{2a}\right)^2 = \frac{b^2}{4a^2} - \frac{4ac}{4a^2}$
$\left(x + \frac{3}{2}\right)^2 = \frac{7}{4}$	Simplify.	$\left(x + \frac{b}{2a}\right)^2 = \frac{b^2 - 4ac}{4a^2}$
$x + \frac{3}{2} = \pm\frac{\sqrt{7}}{2}$	Take square roots.	$x + \frac{b}{2a} = \pm\frac{\sqrt{b^2 - 4ac}}{2a}$
$x = -\frac{3}{2} \pm \frac{\sqrt{7}}{2}$	Subtract $\frac{b}{2a}$ from both sides.	$x = -\frac{b}{2a} \pm \frac{\sqrt{b^2 - 4ac}}{2a}$
$x = \frac{-3 \pm \sqrt{7}}{2}$	Simplify.	$x = \frac{-b \pm \sqrt{b^2 - 4ac}}{2a}$

Remember!

To add or subtract fractions, you need a common denominator.

$$\frac{b^2}{4a^2} - \frac{c}{a} = \frac{b^2}{4a^2} - \frac{c}{a}\left(\frac{4a}{4a}\right)$$

$$= \frac{b^2}{4a^2} - \frac{4ac}{4a^2}$$

$$= \frac{b^2 - 4ac}{4a^2}$$

See Skills Bank p. SB8.

Know it!
Note

The Quadratic Formula

The solutions of $ax^2 + bx + c = 0$, where $a \neq 0$, are $x = \dfrac{-b \pm \sqrt{b^2 - 4ac}}{2a}$.

EXAMPLE 1 **Using the Quadratic Formula**

Solve using the Quadratic Formula.

A $2x^2 + 3x - 5 = 0$

$$2x^2 + 3x + (-5) = 0$$ *Identify a, b, and c.*

$$x = \frac{-b \pm \sqrt{b^2 - 4ac}}{2a}$$ *Use the Quadratic Formula.*

$$x = \frac{-3 \pm \sqrt{3^2 - 4(2)(-5)}}{2(2)}$$ *Substitute 2 for a, 3 for b, and −5 for c.*

$$x = \frac{-3 \pm \sqrt{9 - (-40)}}{4}$$ *Simplify.*

$$x = \frac{-3 \pm \sqrt{49}}{4} = \frac{-3 \pm 7}{4}$$ *Simplify.*

$$x = \frac{-3 + 7}{4} \text{ or } x = \frac{-3 - 7}{4}$$ *Write as two equations.*

$$x = 1 \quad \text{ or } \quad x = -\frac{5}{2}$$ *Solve each equation.*

B $2x = x^2 - 3$

$$1x^2 + (-2x) + (-3) = 0$$ *Write in standard form.*

$$x = \frac{-(-2) \pm \sqrt{(-2)^2 - 4(1)(-3)}}{2(1)}$$ *Substitute 1 for a, −2 for b, and −3 for c.*

$$x = \frac{2 \pm \sqrt{4 - (-12)}}{2}$$ *Simplify.*

$$x = \frac{2 \pm \sqrt{16}}{2} = \frac{2 \pm 4}{2}$$ *Simplify.*

$$x = \frac{2 + 4}{2} \text{ or } x = \frac{2 - 4}{2}$$ *Write as two equations.*

$$x = 3 \quad \text{ or } \quad x = -1$$ *Solve each equation.*

> **Helpful Hint**
>
> You can graph the related quadratic function to see if your solutions are reasonable.

 **Solve using the Quadratic Formula. Check your answer.**

1a. $-3x^2 + 5x + 2 = 0$ **1b.** $2 - 5x^2 = -9x$

Because the Quadratic Formula contains a square root, the solutions may be irrational. You can give the exact solutions by leaving the square root in your answer, or you can approximate the solutions.

EXAMPLE 2 **Using the Quadratic Formula to Estimate Solutions**

Solve $x^2 - 2x - 4 = 0$ using the Quadratic Formula.

$$x = \frac{-(-2) \pm \sqrt{(-2)^2 - 4(1)(-4)}}{2(1)}$$

$$x = \frac{2 \pm \sqrt{4 - (-16)}}{2} = \frac{2 \pm \sqrt{20}}{2}$$

$$x = \frac{2 + \sqrt{20}}{2} \quad \text{ or } \quad x = \frac{2 - \sqrt{20}}{2}$$

Estimate $\sqrt{20}$: $x \approx 3.24$ or $x \approx -1.24$.

Check reasonableness

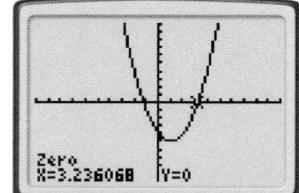

 **2.** Solve $2x^2 - 8x + 1 = 0$ using the Quadratic Formula.

There is no one correct way to solve a quadratic equation. Many quadratic equations can be solved using several different methods: graphing, factoring, completing the square, using square roots, and using the Quadratic Formula.

EXAMPLE 3 **Solving Using Different Methods**

Solve $x^2 + 7x + 6 = 0$. Show your work.

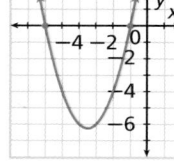

Method 1 Solve by graphing.

$y = x^2 + 7x + 6$ *Write the related quadratic function and graph it.*

The solutions are the *x*-intercepts, -6 and -1.

Method 2 Solve by factoring.

$$x^2 + 7x + 6 = 0$$

$$(x + 6)(x + 1) = 0 \qquad \textit{Factor.}$$

$$x + 6 = 0 \text{ or } x - 1 = 0 \qquad \textit{Use the Zero Product Property.}$$

$$x = -6 \quad \text{or} \quad x = -1 \qquad \textit{Solve each equation.}$$

Method 3 Solve by completing the square.

$$x^2 + 7x + 6 = 0$$

$$x^2 + 7x = -6$$

$$x^2 + 7x + \frac{49}{4} = -6 + \frac{49}{4} \qquad \textit{Add } \left(\frac{b}{2}\right)^2 \textit{ to both sides.}$$

$$\left(x + \frac{7}{2}\right)^2 = \frac{25}{4} \qquad \textit{Factor and simplify.}$$

$$x + \frac{7}{2} = \pm\frac{5}{2} \qquad \textit{Take the square root of both sides.}$$

$$x + \frac{7}{2} = \frac{5}{2} \text{ or } x + \frac{7}{2} = -\frac{5}{2} \qquad \textit{Solve each equation.}$$

$$x = -1 \quad \text{or} \quad x = -6$$

Method 4 Solve using the Quadratic Formula.

$$1x^2 + 7x + 6 = 0 \qquad \textit{Identify a, b, and c.}$$

$$x = \frac{-7 \pm \sqrt{7^2 - 4(1)(6)}}{2(1)} \qquad \textit{Substitute 1 for a, 7 for b, and 6 for c.}$$

$$x = \frac{-7 \pm \sqrt{49 - 24}}{2} \qquad \textit{Simplify.}$$

$$\frac{-7 \pm \sqrt{25}}{2}$$

$$\frac{-7 \pm 5}{2}$$

$$x = \frac{-7 + 5}{2} \text{ or } x = \frac{-7 - 5}{2} \qquad \textit{Write as two equations.}$$

$$x = -1 \quad \text{or} \quad x = -6 \qquad \textit{Solve each equation.}$$

 **Solve using at least two different methods. Check your answer.**

3a. $x^2 + 7x + 10 = 0$ **3b.** $-14 + x^2 = 5x$ **3c.** $2x^2 + 4x - 21 = 0$

Notice that all of the methods in Example 3 produce the same solutions, -1 and -6. The only method you cannot use to solve $x^2 + 7x + 6 = 0$ is using square roots. Sometimes one method is better for solving certain types of equations. The table below gives some advantages and disadvantages of the different methods.

Methods of Solving Quadratic Equations

METHOD	ADVANTAGES	DISADVANTAGES
Graphing	• Always works to give approximate solutions • Can quickly see the number of solutions	• Cannot always get an exact solution
Factoring	• Good method to try first • Straightforward if the equation is factorable	• Complicated if the equation is not easily factorable • Not all quadratic equations are factorable.
Using square roots	• Quick when the equation has no x-term	• Cannot easily use when there is an x-term
Completing the square	• Always works	• Sometimes involves difficult calculations
Using the Quadratic Formula	• Always works • Can always find exact solutions	• Other methods may be easier or less time consuming.

Student to Student

Binh Pham
Johnson High School

Solving Quadratic Equations

No matter what method I use, I like to check my answers for reasonableness by graphing.

I used the Quadratic Formula to solve $2x^2 - 7x - 10 = 0$. I found that $x \approx -1.09$ and $x \approx 4.59$. Then I graphed $y = 2x^2 - 7x - 10$. The x-intercepts appeared to be close to -1 and 4.5, so I knew my solutions were reasonable.

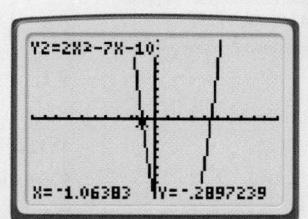

THINK AND DISCUSS

1. Choose a method to solve $x^2 + 5x + 4 = 0$ and explain why you chose that method.

2. GET ORGANIZED Copy and complete the graphic organizer. In each box, write the method you would use to solve each equation and explain why.

Equation	$x^2 + 5 = 20$	$x^2 + 6x + 9 = 0$	$3x^2 - 7 + 11 = 0$
Method			

9-8 Exercises

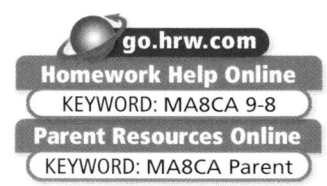

California Standards Practice
🔑 19.0, 🔑 20.0, 🔑 23.0

go.hrw.com
Homework Help Online
KEYWORD: MA8CA 9-8
Parent Resources Online
KEYWORD: MA8CA Parent

GUIDED PRACTICE

SEE EXAMPLE 1
p. 599

Solve using the Quadratic Formula. Check your answer.

1. $x^2 - 5x + 4 = 0$ **2.** $2x^2 = 7x - 3$

3. $x^2 - 6x - 7 = 0$ **4.** $x^2 = -14x - 40$

5. $3x^2 - 2x = 8$ **6.** $4x^2 - 4x - 3 = 0$

SEE EXAMPLE 2
p. 599

7. $2x^2 - 6 = 0$ **8.** $x^2 + 6x + 3 = 0$

9. $x^2 - 7x + 2 = 0$ **10.** $3x^2 = -x + 5$

11. $x^2 - 4x - 7 = 0$ **12.** $2x^2 + x - 5 = 0$

SEE EXAMPLE 3
p. 600

Solve using at least two different methods. Check your answer.

13. $x^2 + x - 12 = 0$ **14.** $x^2 + 6x + 9 = 0$

15. $2x^2 - x - 1 = 0$ **16.** $4x^2 + 4x + 1 = 0$

17. $2x^2 + 5x - 7 = 0$ **18.** $9x = 2x^2 - 3x$

PRACTICE AND PROBLEM SOLVING

Independent Practice

For Exercises	See Example
19–21	1
22–24	2
25–33	3

Extra Practice

Skills Practice p. EP19
Application Practice p. EP32

Solve using the Quadratic Formula. Check your answer.

19. $3x^2 = 13x - 4$ **20.** $x^2 - 10x + 9 = 0$ **21.** $1 = 3x^2 + 2x$

22. $x^2 - 2x + 1 = 0$ **23.** $3x^2 - 5 = 0$ **24.** $2x^2 + 6x = -4$

Solve using at least two different methods. Check your answer.

25. $x^2 + 4x + 3 = 0$ **26.** $x^2 + 2x = 15$ **27.** $x^2 - 12 = -x$

28. $x^2 - 6x = -9$ **29.** $x^2 + 12 = -7x$ **30.** $-x^2 + 81 = 0$

31. $2x^2 + 7x + 6 = 0$ **32.** $3x^2 = 7 - 4x$ **33.** $-7x = 12 + x^2$

Write each equation in standard form. Solve by using the Quadratic Formula. Check your answer.

34. $-7 = x^2$ **35.** $-12x = -9x^2 - 4$ **36.** $x^2 - 16 = 0$

37. $2x = -4 + 2x^2$ **38.** $x^2 = 2x + 8$ **39.** $2 = 7x + 4x^2$

40. $12 + 6x = -4x^2$ **41.** $7.2x^2 = -3.6x$ **42.** $6x = 14x^2 + 6$

Use the Quadratic Formula to find the x-intercepts. Check your answer.

43. $y + 21 = 2x^2 - x$ **44.** $y = 5x^2 + 12x + 8$

45. $y = x^2 - 10x + 25$ **46.** $y = 3x^2 - 4x - 20$

47. $y + 2x^2 = 9x + 18$ **48.** $y = 5x^2 - 8x - 4$

 49. Write About It Explain how you would decide which method to try first when solving a quadratic equation.

 50. Reasoning Explain why the Quadratic Formula will not work for a function in the form $y = mx + b$.

51. This problem will prepare you for the Concept Connection on page 610.
   The equation $0 = -14t^2 + 65t + 25$ gives the time t when a golf ball is at height 0.
   a. Can you solve the equation by graphing?
   b. Can you solve the equation by using square roots?
   c. Solve the quadratic equation using the Quadratic Formula.
   d. Explain why the Quadratic Formula is the best method to use for this equation.

52. **Physical Science** The distance in feet d traveled by an object with acceleration a in t seconds is given by the equation $d = \frac{1}{2}at^2$. If an object travels 64 ft with an acceleration of 32 ft/s^2, for how much time did it travel?

For each quadratic equation, identify the values of a, b, and c.

53. $x^2 + x = -7$

54. $-5x^2 - 17 = 0$

55. $10x^2 + 2 - 17x = 0$

56. $16x^2 = 3x$

57. $1.5x + 3.7 = -0.5x^2$

58. $x^2 = 8 - 3x$

59. $\frac{1}{2}x^2 + 1 = -\frac{3}{4}x$

60. $-4x^2 = -9$

61. $-24x^2 + 13 = 29x$

62. **Multi-Step** Burke skips 3 stones over water. The height in centimeters h of each stone during its first skip can be modeled by a different quadratic function, as shown in the table, where s represents the number of milliseconds after the stone first hits the water. Use the table to find the length of time each stone was in the air during its first skip. Which stone was in the air the longest?

Stone	Quadratic Function
1	$-0.4s^2 + 0.5s = h$
2	$-0.3s^2 + 0.3s = h$
3	$-0.5s^2 + 0.6s = h$

63. **Critical Thinking** When using the Quadratic Formula to solve a quadratic equation in the form $ax^2 + bx + c$, explain what will happen when b^2 is less than $4ac$ and $4ac$ is positive.

California LINK

Sports

The Galaxy is Los Angeles's Major League Soccer (MLS) team. The team was formed in 1995 and played in the MLS opening season in 1996. The team trains and plays in Carson, California.

Choose a method to solve each equation. Explain why you chose the method you did.

64. $-2 = x^2 + 3x$

65. $x^2 + 2x = 6 - 3x^2$

66. $2x^2 - 3x = 8$

67. $-3x^2 - 8x + 1 = -10x$

68. $4x - 3x^2 + x = -8$

69. $2x^2 + 9 = 15$

70. **Sports** A soccer player kicks a ball off the ground. The height of the ball can be modeled by the quadratic function $-0.5s^2 + 3s = h$, where s is the time in seconds after the kick and h is the height of the ball in feet.
   a. Find the maximum height of the ball.
   b. How long is the ball in the air?
   c. Find the height of the ball after 2 seconds.
   d. How long would the ball be in the air if the ball was kicked from a platform 0.5 ft above the ground? Round your answer to the nearest tenth of a second. (*Hint:* In this situation, the function $-0.5s^2 + 3s + 0.5 = h$ models the height.)

71. **Business** The total profit p made by a manufacturing company is given by the equation $p = x^2 - x - 56$, where x is the number of items produced. Find the number of items the company needs to make to break even.

72. On page 598, the equation $2x^2 + 6x + 1 = 0$ is solved by completing the square in order to show a specific example of the Quadratic Formula. Solve the equation $x^2 + 3x - 1 = 0$ in a similar manner.

Multiple Choice For Exercises 73–75, choose the best answer.

73. Which are the best approximations for the solutions of $x^2 + 6x - 14 = 0$?

    (A) $\approx 7.1, \approx -1.4$ (C) $\approx 1.8, \approx -7.8$

    (B) $\approx 6.2, \approx 2.3$ (D) $\approx 2.4, \approx -6.7$

74. Which quadratic equation has the solutions $x = \dfrac{-5 \pm \sqrt{25 - 56}}{4}$?

    (A) $2x^2 + 5x + 6 = 0$ (C) $7x^2 + 2x + 5 = 0$

    (B) $5x^2 + 2x + 7 = 0$ (D) $2x^2 + 5x + 7 = 0$

75. For which two consecutive integers is the following statement true?
    3 times the square of the first integer is equal to 7 more than 5 and the product of the second integer.

    (A) 3, 4   (B) 5, 6   (C) 11, 12   (D) 8, 9

CHALLENGE AND EXTEND

76. **Agriculture** A rancher has 80 yards of fencing material to build a rectangular pen. Let w represent the width of the pen and write an equation giving the area of the pen. Find the dimensions of the pen when the area is 400 square yards.

77. **Agriculture** A farmer wants to make a four-sided grazing area using an existing fence for one side. His proposed grazing area is shown in the diagram. He has 1000 feet of fencing material available and he wants the western boundary of the grazing area to be twice as long as the northern boundary. Can he enclose a grazing area of 125,000 square feet? Explain why or why not. (*Hint:* Use the formula for the area of a trapezoid.)

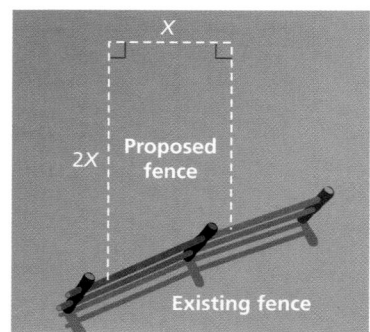

SPIRAL STANDARDS REVIEW

⬥⟶ 4.0, ⬥⟶ 5.0, 11.0, ⬥⟶ 14.0

Solve each inequality. Check your answer. (*Lesson 3-5*)

78. $3(3 - x) \geq 9$ 79. $2(x + 4) \geq 3x$ 80. $3(x + 5) > 4(x + 4)$

Factor each polynomial by grouping. (*Lesson 8-2*)

81. $s^2r^3 + 5r^3 + 5t + s^2t$ 82. $b^3 - 4b^2 + 2b - 8$ 83. $n^5 - 6n^4 - 2n + 12$

Solve by completing the square. Check your answer. (*Lesson 9-7*)

84. $x^2 - 2x - 24 = 0$ 85. $x^2 + 6x = 40$

86. $-3x^2 + 12x = 15$ 87. $2x^2 + 10x = 12$

88. $3x^2 - 18x + 15 = 0$ 89. $4x^2 - 16x = 20$

9-9 The Discriminant

Vocabulary
discriminant

Why learn this?
You can use the discriminant to determine whether the weight in a carnival strength test will reach a certain height. (See Example 3.)

Recall that quadratic equations can have two, one, or no real solutions. You can determine the number of solutions by evaluating the *discriminant*. If a quadratic equation is in standard form, its **discriminant** is $b^2 - 4ac$. Notice that this is the expression under the square root in the Quadratic Formula.

Equation	$x^2 - 4x + 3 = 0$	$x^2 + 2x + 1 = 0$	$x^2 - 2x + 2 = 0$
Graph of Related Function	The related function has **two** x-intercepts.	The related function has **one** x-intercept.	The related function has **no** x-intercepts.
Discriminant	$a = 1, b = -4, c = 3$ $b^2 - 4ac =$ $(-4)^2 - 4(1)(3) = 4$ $b^2 - 4ac > 0$	$a = 1, b = 2, c = 1$ $b^2 - 4ac =$ $2^2 - 4(1)(1) = 0$ $b^2 - 4ac = 0$	$a = 1, b = -2, c = 2$ $b^2 - 4ac =$ $(-2)^2 - 4(1)(2) = -4$ $b^2 - 4ac < 0$
Number of Solutions	When $b^2 - 4ac$ is **positive**, it has two square roots. The Quadratic Formula gives **two solutions**.	When $b^2 - 4ac$ is **0**, it has one square root. The Quadratic Formula gives **one solution**.	When $b^2 - 4ac$ is **negative**, it has no real square roots. The Quadratic Formula gives **no real solutions**.

Know it! Note

The Discriminant of $ax^2 + bx + c = 0$

If $b^2 - 4ac > 0$, the equation has **two** real solutions.

If $b^2 - 4ac = 0$, the equation has **one** real solution.

If $b^2 - 4ac < 0$, the equation has **no** real solutions.

EXAMPLE 1 Using the Discriminant

Find the number of solutions of $3x^2 + 10x + 2 = 0$.

$a = 3, b = 10, c = 2$ *Identify the values of a, b, and c.*

$b^2 - 4ac = 10^2 - 4(3)(2)$ *Substitute 3, 10, and 2 for a, b, and c.*

$= 100 - 24 = 76$ *Simplify.*

$b^2 - 4ac$ is positive. There are two solutions.

Find the number of solutions of each equation.

1a. $2x^2 - 2x + 3 = 0$ **1b.** $x^2 + 4x + 4 = 0$

Recall that the solutions to a quadratic equation are the same as the x-intercepts of the related function. The discriminant can be used to find the number of x-intercepts.

E X A M P L E **2**   **Using the Discriminant to Find the Number of x-Intercepts**

Find the number of x-intercepts of $y = 2x^2 + x + 1$ by using the discriminant.

$a = 2, b = 1, c = 1$ *Identify the values of a, b, and c.*

$b^2 - 4ac = 1^2 - 4(2)(1)$ *Substitute 2, 1, and 1 for a, b, and c.*

$= 1 - 8$ *Simplify.*

$= -7$

$b^2 - 4ac$ is negative.

There are no real solutions.

Therefore, the function $y = x^2 + x + 1$ has no x-intercepts. You can check by graphing. Notice that the graph does not intersect the x-axis.

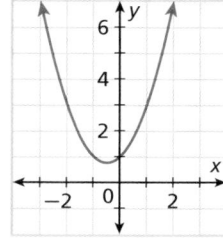

Find the number of x-intercepts of each function by using the discriminant.

2a. $y = 5x^2 + 3x + 1$ **2b.** $y = x^2 - 9x + 4$

E X A M P L E **3**   *Physical Science Application*

The height h in feet of an object shot straight up with initial velocity v in feet per second is given by $h = -16t^2 + vt + c$, where c is the beginning height of the object above the ground.

A weight 1 foot above the ground on a carnival strength test is shot straight up with an initial velocity of 35 feet per second. Will it reach a height of 20 feet? Use the discriminant to explain your answer.

> **Helpful Hint**
>
> If the object is shot straight up from the ground, the initial height of the object above the ground equals 0.

$h = -16t^2 + vt + 1$

$20 = -16t^2 + 35t + 1$ *Substitute 20 for h, 35 for v, and 1 for c.*

$0 = -16t^2 + 35t + (-19)$ *Write the equation in standard form by subtracting 20 from both sides.*

$b^2 - 4ac$ *Evaluate the discriminant.*

$35^2 - 4(-16)(-19) = 9$ *Substitute −16 for a, 35 for b, and −19 for c.*

The discriminant is positive, so the equation has two solutions. In other words, there are two times t when the height h is 20. The weight will reach a height of 20 feet twice, once on the way up and once on the way down.

3. What if...? Suppose the weight is shot straight up from the ground with an initial velocity of 20 feet per second. Will it reach a height of 45 feet? Use the discriminant to explain your answer.

THINK AND DISCUSS

1. Describe how to use the discriminant to find the number of solutions to a quadratic equation.

2. Describe how the discriminant can be used to determine if an object will reach a given height.

3. GET ORGANIZED Copy and complete the graphic organizer. In each box, write the number of real solutions.

> The number of real solutions of $ax^2 + bx + c = 0$ when...
>
> | $b^2 - 4ac > 0$ | $b^2 - 4ac < 0$ | $b^2 - 4ac = 0$ |

9-9 Exercises

California Standards Practice
🔑 19.0, 🔑 20.0, 22.0,
🔑 23.0, 25.1

go.hrw.com
Homework Help Online
KEYWORD: MA8CA 9-9
Parent Resources Online
KEYWORD: MA8CA Parent

GUIDED PRACTICE

1. Vocabulary If the *discriminant* is negative, the quadratic equation has _____?_____ solution(s). (*no*, *one*, or *two*)

SEE EXAMPLE **1**
p. 605

Find the number of solutions of each equation.

2. $2x^2 + 4x + 3 = 0$

3. $x^2 + 4x + 4 = 0$

4. $2x^2 - 11x + 6 = 0$

5. $x^2 + x + 1 = 0$

6. $3x^2 = 5x - 1$

7. $-2x + 3 = 2x^2$

SEE EXAMPLE **2**
p. 606

Find the number of *x*-intercepts of each function by using the discriminant.

8. $y = 2x^2 + 12x + 18$

9. $y = 5x^2 + 3x + 4$

10. $y = -8x + 1 - x^2$

11. $y = x^2 + 2x + 3$

12. $y = -3x^2 + 5x - 1$

13. $y = 2x^2 - 2x + 3$

SEE EXAMPLE **3**
p. 606

14. Hobbies The height above the ground in meters of a model rocket on a particular launch can be modeled by the equation $h = -4.9t^2 + 102t + 100$, where t is the time in seconds after its engine burns out 100 m above the ground. Will the rocket reach a height of 600 m? Use the discriminant to explain your answer.

PRACTICE AND PROBLEM SOLVING

Independent Practice

For Exercises	See Example
15–23	1
24–32	2
33	3

Extra Practice

Skills Practice p. EP19

Application Practice p. EP32

Find the number of solutions of each equation.

15. $2x = 3 + 2x^2$

16. $x^2 = 2x + 1$

17. $2 = 7x + 4x^2$

18. $-7 = x^2$

19. $-12x = -9x^2 - 4$

20. $x^2 - 14 = 0$

21. $y = 7.1x^2 - 1.8x + 4$

22. $y = -4x^2 - 6x + 2$

23. $y = 3x^2 + 6x + 3$

Find the number of *x*-intercepts of each function.

24. $y = x^2 + 4 + x$

25. $y = -17 + 2x^2$

26. $y = -6x - x^2 + 5$

27. $y = 5x^2 - 10x + 5$

28. $y = 14x^2 + 8x - 1$

29. $y = x^2 - 1.6x + 1.2$

30. $y = 4x^2 - 8x + 4$

31. $y = x^2 + 5x + 3$

32. $y = 3x^2 + 2x - 15$

33. Multi-Step A gymnast who can stretch her arms up to reach 6 feet jumps straight up on a trampoline. The height of her feet above the trampoline can be modeled by the equation $h = -16x^2 + 12x$, where x is the time in seconds after her jump. Do the gymnast's hands reach a height of 10 feet above the trampoline? Use the discriminant to explain. (*Hint:* Let $h = 10 - 6$, or 4.)

10 ft

Solve.

34. $x^2 + 4x + 3 = 0$ **35.** $x^2 + 2x = 15$ **36.** $x^2 - 12 = -x$

37. $x^2 + 10x = 0$ **38.** $x^2 - 144 = 0$ **39.** $x^2 - x - 30 = 0$

Use the discriminant to determine the number of solutions of each equation. Then solve.

40. $3x^2 - 6x + 3 = 0$ **41.** $x^2 - 7x - 8 = 0$ **42.** $7x^2 + 6x + 2 = 0$

Use the discriminant to determine the number of x-intercepts. Then find them.

43. $x^2 - 5x - 36 = y$ **44.** $2x^2 - x + 6 = y$ **45.** $y = 9x^2 + 12x + 4$

46. Copy and complete the table.

Quadratic Equation	Discriminant	Number of Solutions
$x^2 + 12x - 20 = 0$		
$8x + x^2 = -16$		
$0.5x^2 + x - 3 = 0$		
$-3x^2 - 2x = 1$		

47. Sports A diver begins on a platform 10 meters above the surface of the water. The diver's height is given by the equation $h(t) = -4.9t^2 + 3.5t + 10$, where t is the time in seconds after the diver jumps.

   a. How long does it take the diver to reach a point 1 meter above the water?

   b. How many solutions does your equation from part **a** have?

   c. Do all of the solutions to the equation make sense in the situation? Explain.

 48. Reasoning How many solutions does the equation $x^2 = k$ have when $k > 0$, when $k < 0$, and when $k = 0$? Use the discriminant to explain.

CONCEPT CONNECTION

49. This problem will prepare you for the Concept Connection on page 610.

The equation $0 = -16t^2 + 80t + 20$ gives the time t when a golf ball is at height 0 after being hit.

   a. Will the height of the golf ball reach 130 feet? Explain.

   b. Will the golf ball reach a height of 116 feet? If so, when?

   c. Solve the quadratic equation by using the Quadratic Formula.

50. Write About It How can you use the discriminant to save time when solving quadratic equations?

Multiple Choice For Exercises 51 and 52, choose the best answer.

51. How many solutions does $4x^2 - 3x + 1 = 0$ have?

    Ⓐ 0   Ⓑ 1   Ⓒ 2   Ⓓ 4

52. For which of the following conditions does $ax^2 + bx + c = 0$ have two solutions?

    I. $b^2 = 4ac$

    II. $b^2 > 4ac$

    III. $a = b, c = b$

    Ⓐ I only   Ⓑ II only   Ⓒ III only   Ⓓ II and III

CHALLENGE AND EXTEND

53. Reasoning Graph $y = x^2 + 6x + 1$ and use the discriminant to find the number of x-intercepts. Graph $y = x^2 + 6x + 1 + 20$ and use the discriminant to find the number of x-intercepts. Construct an argument about the change in c in the two equations and the effect on the discriminant and the number of solutions.

Write each equation in standard form. Use the discriminant to determine the number of solutions. Then solve.

54. $2x^2 - 4x + 2x^2 - 13 = 3x - 11$ **55.** $41 - 5x^2 - 7 = -19x + 3x^2$

56. $8x^2 - 22 + 8x = 21x - 34$ **57.** $-5 + 32x^2 - 24x^2 + 44 = 6x$

58. $0.8x - 0.9 + 3.9x^2 = 1.9x^2 + 11.7x$ **59.** $7x - 3x + 2 = 2x^2 - 2 - 4x^2$

60. Reasoning The graph of $y = ax^2 - 6x + 1$ crosses the x-axis at two points. What are the possible values of a?

61. Thom recorded the ages of his neighbors for a school project. Write and solve an equation to find the average age of the families. *(Lesson 2-1)*

Family	Average Age
Davenports	31.5
Keenans	28.7
Simpsons	19.2
Nguyens	21.3
Williams	36.5

Write an equation in point-slope form for the line with the given slope that contains the given point. *(Lesson 5-6)*

62. slope $= 6$; $(2, 9)$ **63.** slope $= \dfrac{1}{2}$; $(6, 11)$ **64.** slope $= -2$; $(3, -11)$

65. slope $= 3$; $(5, 12)$ **66.** slope $= 1$; $(4, 1)$ **67.** slope $= \dfrac{3}{4}$; $(12, 4)$

Factor each polynomial by grouping. *(Lesson 8-2)*

68. $3v + 3w^4 + vw^4 + v^2$ **69.** $-20 + 5y^2 + 4z - y^2z$ **70.** $7k - 14 - 2k^2 + k^3$

Solve using the Quadratic Formula. Check your answer. *(Lesson 9-8)*

71. $2x^2 - 4x - 15 = 0$ **72.** $-x^2 = 10x + 21$ **73.** $4x^2 - 52x + 160 = 0$

CONCEPT CONNECTION

Solving Quadratic Equations

Seeing Green A golf player hits a golf ball from a tee with an initial velocity of 80 feet per second. The height of the golf ball t seconds after it is hit is given by $h = -16t^2 + 80t$.

1. How long is the golf ball in the air?

2. What is the maximum height of the golf ball?

3. How long after the golf ball is hit does it reach its maximum height?

4. What is the height of the golf ball after 3.5 seconds?

5. At what times is the golf ball 64 feet in the air? Explain.

READY TO GO ON?

Quiz for Lessons 9-4 Through 9-9

9-4 Solving Quadratic Equations by Graphing

Solve each equation by graphing the related function.

1. $x^2 - 9 = 0$

2. $x^2 + 3x - 4 = 0$

3. $4x^2 + 8x = 32$

4. The height of a fireworks rocket launched from a platform 35 feet above the ground can be approximated by $h = -5t^2 + 30t + 35$, where h is the height in meters and t is the time in seconds. Find the time it takes the rocket to reach the ground after it is launched.

9-5 Solving Quadratic Equations by Factoring

Use the Zero Product Property to solve each equation. Check your answer.

5. $(x + 1)(x + 3) = 0$
6. $(x - 6)(x - 3) = 0$
7. $x(x + 3) = 18$
8. $(x + 2)(x - 5) = 60$

Solve each quadratic equation by factoring. Check your answer.

9. $x^2 - 4x - 32 = 0$
10. $x^2 - 8x + 15 = 0$
11. $x^2 + x = 6$
12. $-8x - 33 = -x^2$

13. The height of a soccer ball kicked from the ground can be approximated by the function $h = -16t^2 + 64t$, where h is the height in feet and t is the time in seconds. Find the time it takes for the ball to return to the ground.

9-6 Solving Quadratic Equations by Using Square Roots

Solve using square roots. Check your answer.

14. $3x^2 = 48$

15. $36x^2 - 49 = 0$

16. $-12 = x^2 - 21$

17. Solve $3x^2 + 5 = 21$. Round to the nearest hundredth.

9-7 Completing the Square

Complete the square to form a perfect-square trinomial.

18. $x^2 - 12x +$ ▨

19. $x^2 + 4x +$ ▨

20. $x^2 + 9x +$ ▨

Solve by completing the square. Check your answer.

21. $x^2 + 2x = 3$

22. $x^2 - 5 = 2x$

23. $x^2 + 7x = 8$

9-8 The Quadratic Formula

Solve using the Quadratic Formula. Round your answer to the nearest hundredth, if necessary.

24. $x^2 + 5x + 1 = 0$

25. $3x^2 + 1 = 2x$

26. $5x + 8 = 3x^2$

9-9 The Discriminant

Find the number of solutions of each equation.

27. $2x^2 - 3x + 4 = 0$

28. $x^2 + 1 + 2x = 0$

29. $x^2 - 5 + 4x = 0$

Study Guide: Review

Vocabulary

Complete the sentences below with vocabulary words from the list above.

1. The ___?___ is the highest or lowest point on a parabola.

2. A quadratic function has a ___?___ if its graph opens upward and a ___?___ if its graph opens downward.

3. A ___?___ can also be called an *x*-intercept of the function.

4. Finding the ___?___ can tell you how many real-number solutions a quadratic equation has.

5. ___?___ is a process that results in a perfect-square trinomial.

9-1 Quadratic Equations and Functions (pp. 544–551)

 21.0

EXAMPLE

■ Graph $y = -5x^2 + 40x$.

Step 1 Make a table of values.

Choose values of *x* and use them to find values of *y*.

x	0	1	3	4	6	7	8
y	0	35	75	80	60	35	0

Step 2 Plot the points and connect them with a smooth curve.

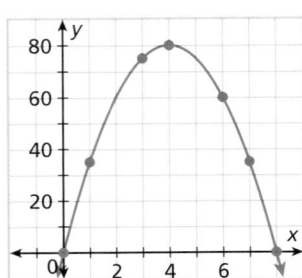

EXERCISES

Without graphing, tell whether each point is on the graph of the given equation.

6. $y = 2x^2 + 9x - 5$; $(1, 6)$ **7.** $y = -4x + 3 - 2x$; $(3, 15)$

8. $y - 2 = \frac{1}{2}x^2 + x$; $(4, 14)$ **9.** $y = 5x^2 + 8 + 7x$; $(-2, 16)$

Graph each quadratic function.

10. $y = 6x^2$ **11.** $y = -4x^2$

12. $y = \frac{1}{4}x^2$ **13.** $y = -3x^2$

Tell whether the graph of each function opens upward or downward. Explain.

14. $y = 5x^2 - 12$ **15.** $y = -x^2 + 3x - 7$

16. Identify the vertex of the parabola. Then give the minimum or maximum value of the function.

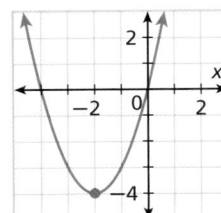

9-2 Characteristics of Quadratic Functions (pp. 553–559)

21.0

EXAMPLE

■ Find the zeros of
$y = 2x^2 - 4x - 6$ from
its graph. Then find
the axis of symmetry
and the vertex.

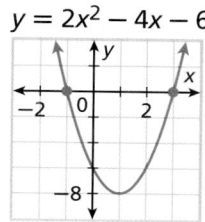

$y = 2x^2 - 4x - 6$

Step 1 Use the graph to find the zeros.
The zeros are -1 and 3.

Step 2 Find the axis of symmetry.

$x = \dfrac{-1 + 3}{2} = \dfrac{2}{2} = 1$ *Find the average of the zeros.*

The axis of symmetry is the vertical line $x = 1$.

Step 3 Find the vertex.

$y = 2x^2 - 4x - 6$
$y = 2(1)^2 - 4(1) - 6$ *Substitute 1 into the*
$y = -8$ *function to find the*
    y-value of the vertex.
The vertex is $(1, -8)$.

EXERCISES

Find the zeros of each quadratic function from its
graph. Check your answer.

17. $y = x^2 + 3x - 10$

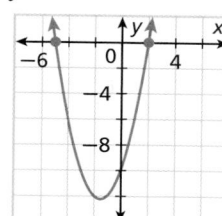

18. $y = x^2 - x - 2$

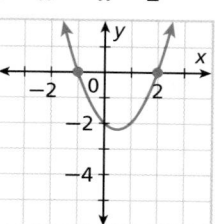

Find the axis of symmetry and vertex of each
parabola.

19. $y = -x^2 + 12x - 32$

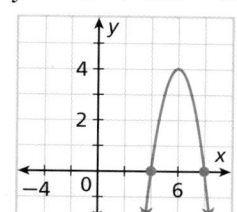

20. $y = 2x^2 + 4x - 16$

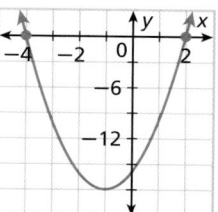

9-3 Graphing Quadratic Functions (pp. 560–565)

21.0, 23.0

EXAMPLE

■ Graph $y = 2x^2 - 8x - 10$.

Step 1 Find the axis of
symmetry.

$x = \dfrac{-b}{2a} = \dfrac{-(-8)}{2(2)} = \dfrac{8}{4} = 2$

The axis of symmetry
is $x = 2$.

Step 2 Find the
vertex.

$y = 2x^2 - 8x - 10$
$y = 2(2)^2 - 8(2) - 10$
$y = -18$

The vertex is $(2, -18)$.

Step 3 Find the y-intercept.
$c = -10$

Step 4 Find one more point on the graph.

$y = 2(-1)^2 - 8(-1) - 10 = 0$
Use $(-1, 0)$.

Step 5 Graph the axis of
symmetry and the
points. **Reflect** the
points and connect with
a smooth curve.

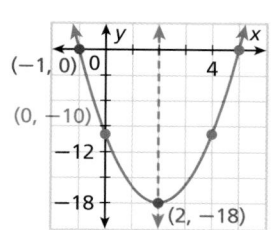

EXERCISES

Graph each quadratic function.

21. $y = x^2 + 6x + 6$

22. $y = x^2 - 4x - 12$

23. $y = x^2 - 8x + 7$

24. $y = 2x^2 - 6x - 8$

25. $3x^2 + 6x = y - 3$

26. $2 - 4x^2 + y = 8x - 10$

27. Water that is sprayed upward from a
sprinkler with an initial velocity of
20 m/s can be approximated by the
function $y = -5x^2 + 20x$, where y is
the height of a drop of water x seconds
after it is released. Graph this function.
Find the time it takes a drop of water
to reach its maximum height, the
water's maximum height, and the time
it takes the water to reach the ground.

9-4 Solving Quadratic Equations by Graphing (pp. 568–573)

 21.0

EXAMPLE

■ Solve $-4 = 4x^2 - 8x$ by graphing the related function.

Step 1 Write the equation in standard form.

$$0 = 4x^2 - 8x + 4$$

Step 2 Graph the related function, $y = 4x^2 - 8x + 4$.

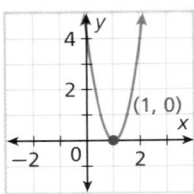

Step 3 Find the zeros. The only zero is 1. The solution is $x = 1$.

EXERCISES

Solve each equation by graphing the related function. Check your answer.

28. $0 = x^2 + 4x + 3$

29. $0 = x^2 + 6x + 9$

30. $-4x^2 = 3$

31. $x^2 + 5 = 6x$

32. $-4x^2 = 64 - 32x$

33. $9 = 9x^2$

34. $-3x^2 + 2x = 5$

9-5 Solving Quadratic Equations by Factoring (pp. 576–581)

 14.0, 23.0

EXAMPLE

■ Solve $3x^2 - 6x = 24$ by factoring.

$$
\begin{array}{ll}
3x^2 - 6x = 24 & \textit{Write the equation in} \\
3x^2 - 6x - 24 = 0 & \textit{standard form.} \\
3(x^2 - 2x - 8) = 0 & \textit{Factor out 3.} \\
3(x + 2)(x - 4) = 0 & \textit{Factor the trinomial.} \\
\\
3 \neq 0, x + 2 = 0 \text{ or } x - 4 = 0 & \textit{Zero Product} \\
& \textit{Property} \\
x = -2 \text{ or } x = 4 & \textit{Solve.}
\end{array}
$$

EXERCISES

Solve each quadratic equation by factoring. Check your answer.

35. $x^2 + 6x + 5 = 0$ **36.** $x^2 + 9x + 14 = 0$

37. $x^2 - 2x - 15 = 0$ **38.** $2x^2 - 2x - 4 = 0$

39. $x^2 + 10x + 25 = 0$ **40.** $4x^2 - 36x = -81$

41. A rectangle is 2 feet longer than it is wide. The area of the rectangle is 48 square feet. Write and solve an equation to find the width.

9-6 Solving Quadratic Equations by Using Square Roots (pp. 582–587)

EXAMPLE

EXERCISES

 2.0, 23.0

■ Solve $2x^2 = 98$ using square roots.

$$
\begin{array}{ll}
\dfrac{2x^2}{2} = \dfrac{98}{2} & \textit{Divide both sides of the equation} \\
& \textit{by 2 to isolate } x^2. \\
x^2 = 49 & \\
x = \pm\sqrt{49} & \textit{Take the square root of both sides.} \\
x = \pm 7 & \textit{Use } \pm \textit{ to show both roots.}
\end{array}
$$

Solve using square roots. Check your answer.

42. $5x^2 = 320$ **43.** $-x^2 + 144 = 0$

44. $x^2 = -16$ **45.** $x^2 + 7 = 7$

46. $2x^2 = 50$ **47.** $4x^2 = 25$

48. A rectangle is twice as long as it is wide. The area of the rectangle is 32 square feet. Find the rectangle's width.

9-7 Completing the Square (pp. 591–597)

 14.0, 23.0

EXAMPLE

■ Solve $x^2 - 6x = -5$ by completing the square.

$\left(\dfrac{-6}{2}\right)^2 = 9$ *Find $\left(\dfrac{b}{2}\right)^2$.*

$x^2 - 6x + 9 = -5 + 9$ *Complete the square.*

$x^2 - 6x + 9 = 4$

$(x - 3)^2 = 4$ *Factor the trinomial.*

$x - 3 = \pm\sqrt{4}$ *Take the square root of both sides.*

$x - 3 = 2$ or $x - 3 = -2$ *Solve each*
$x = 5$ or $x = 1$ *equation.*

EXERCISES

Solve by completing the square. Check your answer.

49. $x^2 + 2x = 48$

50. $x^2 + 4x = 21$

51. $2x^2 - 12x + 10 = 0$

52. $x^2 - 10x = -20$

53. A homeowner is planning an addition to her house. The new family room will have an area of 192 square feet and its length will be 4 more feet than the width. What will the dimensions of the new room be? Round to the nearest hundredth.

9-8 The Quadratic Formula (pp. 598–604)

 19.0, 20.0

EXAMPLE

■ Solve $x^2 + 4x + 4 = 0$ using the Quadratic Formula.

The equation $x^2 + 4x + 4 = 0$ is in standard form with $a = 1$, $b = 4$, and $c = 4$.

$x = \dfrac{-b \pm \sqrt{b^2 - 4ac}}{2a}$ *Write the Quadratic Formula.*

$= \dfrac{-4 \pm \sqrt{4^2 - 4\,(1)(4)}}{2(1)}$ *Substitute for a, b, and c.*

$= \dfrac{-4 \pm \sqrt{16 - 16}}{2}$ *Simplify.*

$= \dfrac{-4 \pm \sqrt{0}}{2} = \dfrac{-4}{2} = -2$

EXERCISES

Solve using the Quadratic Formula. Check your answer.

54. $x^2 - 5x - 6 = 0$

55. $2x^2 - 9x - 5 = 0$

56. $4x^2 - 8x + 4 = 0$

57. $x^2 - 6x = -7$

Solve using at least two different methods. Check your answer.

58. $0 = x^2 + 7.3x + 13.02$

59. $6 = 2x^2 + 4x$

60. $5x^2 + x + 3 = 0$

61. $-14x = 6x^2 + 4$

9-9 The Discriminant (pp. 605–609)

 22.0, 23.0

EXAMPLE

■ Find the number of solutions of
$7x^2 + 8x + 1 = 0$.

$a = 7$, $b = 8$, $c = 1$ *Identify the values of a, b, and c.*

$b^2 - 4ac = 8^2 - 4(7)(1)$ *Find the discriminant.*

$= 64 - 28$ *Simplify.*

$= 36$

$b^2 - 4ac$ is positive. There are two solutions.

EXERCISES

Find the number of solutions of each equation.

62. $x^2 - 12x + 36 = 0$ **63.** $3x^2 + 5 = 0$

64. $2x^2 - 13x = -20$ **65.** $6x^2 - 20 = 15x + 1$

Find the number of x-intercepts of each function by using the discriminant.

66. $6x + y = 7x^2 + 1$ **67.** $y = 3x^2 - x + 3$

68. $y = x^2 + 4x + 4$ **69.** $4x + y = x^2 + 5$

CHAPTER TEST

Without graphing, tell whether each point is on the graph of the given equation.

1. $6 - 16x^2 = 2y;\ (-1, -5)$

2. $3x^2 + y = 4 + 3x;\ (2, 2)$

3. Tell whether the graph of $y = -2x^2 + 7x - 5$ opens upward or downward and whether the parabola has a maximum or a minimum.

4. Find the zeros of the quadratic function from its graph.

5. Find the axis of symmetry of the parabola.

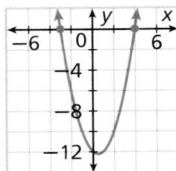

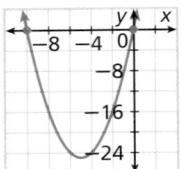

6. Find the vertex of the graph of $y = x^2 + 6x + 8$.

7. Graph $y = x^2 - 4x + 2$.

8. A rocket is launched with an initial velocity of 110 meters per second. The height h of the rocket in meters is approximated by the quadratic equation $h = -5t^2 + 110t$, where t is the time after launch in seconds. About how long after the launch does the rocket return to the ground?

Solve each quadratic equation by factoring.

9. $x^2 + 6x + 5 = 0$

10. $x^2 - 12x = -36$

11. $x^2 - 81 = 0$

Solve by using square roots.

12. $-2x^2 = -72$

13. $9x^2 - 49 = 0$

14. $3x^2 + 12 = 0$

Solve by completing the square.

15. $x^2 + 10x = -21$

16. $x^2 - 6x + 4 = 0$

17. $2x^2 + 16x = 0$

18. A landscaper has enough cement to make a patio with an area of 150 square feet. The homeowner wants the length of the patio to be 6 feet longer than the width. What dimensions should be used for the patio? Round your answer to the nearest tenth of a foot.

Solve using the Quadratic Formula. Round to the nearest hundredth if necessary.

19. $x^2 + 3x - 40 = 0$

20. $2x^2 + 7x = -5$

21. $8x^2 + 3x - 1 = 0$

Find the number of x-intercepts of each function by using the discriminant.

22. $4x^2 - 4x + 1 = y$

23. $y = 2x^2 + 5x - 25$

24. $y = \frac{1}{2}x^2 + 8$

COLLEGE ENTRANCE EXAM PRACTICE

FOCUS ON SAT SUBJECT TESTS

In addition to the SAT, some colleges require the SAT Subject Tests for admission. Colleges that don't require the SAT Subject Tests may still use the scores to learn about your academic background and to place you in the appropriate college math class.

Take the SAT Subject Test in mathematics while the material is still fresh in your mind. You are not expected to be familiar with all of the test content, but you should have completed at least three years of college-prep math.

You may want to time yourself as you take this practice test. It should take you about 6 minutes to complete.

---

1. The graph below corresponds to which of the following quadratic functions?

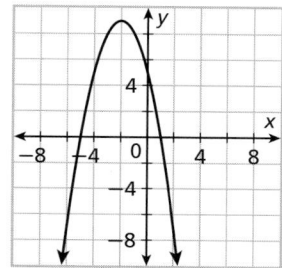

   (A) $f(x) = x^2 + 4x - 5$

   (B) $f(x) = -x^2 - 4x + 3$

   (C) $f(x) = -x^2 + 5x - 4$

   (D) $f(x) = -x^2 - 4x + 5$

   (E) $f(x) = -x^2 - 3x + 5$

---

2. What is the sum of the solutions to the equation $9x^2 - 6x = 8$?

   (A) $\dfrac{4}{3}$

   (B) $\dfrac{2}{3}$

   (C) $\dfrac{1}{3}$

   (D) $-\dfrac{2}{3}$

   (E) $-\dfrac{8}{3}$

---

3. If $h(x) = ax^2 + bx + c$, where $b^2 - 4ac < 0$ and $a < 0$, which of the following statements must be true?

   I. The graph of $h(x)$ has no points in the first or second quadrants.
   II. The graph of $h(x)$ has no points in the third or fourth quadrants.
   III. The graph of $h(x)$ has points in all quadrants.

   (A) I only

   (B) II only

   (C) III only

   (D) I and II only

   (E) None of the statements are true.

---

4. What is the axis of symmetry for the graph of a quadratic function whose zeros are -2 and 4?

   (A) $x = -2$

   (B) $x = 0$

   (C) $x = 1$

   (D) $x = 2$

   (E) $x = 6$

---

5. How many real-number solutions does $0 = x^2 - 7x + 1$ have?

   (A) None

   (B) One

   (C) Two

   (D) All real numbers

   (E) It is impossible to determine.

STRATEGIES FOR SUCCESS

Extended Response: Explain Your Reasoning

Extended response test items often include multipart questions that evaluate your understanding of a math concept. To receive full credit, you must answer the problem correctly, show all of your work, and explain your reasoning. Use complete sentences and show your problem-solving method clearly.

EXAMPLE 1

Extended Response Given $\frac{1}{2}x^2 + y = 4x - 3$ and $y = 2x - 12x$, identify which is a quadratic function. Provide an explanation for your decision. For the quadratic function, tell whether the graph of the function opens upward or downward and whether the parabola has a maximum or a minimum. Explain your reasoning.

Read the solutions provided by two different students.

Student A

> The quadratic function is $\frac{1}{2}x^2 + y = 4x - 3$ because it can be written in standard form,
>
> $y = -\frac{1}{2}x^2 + 4x - 3$, where $a, b,$ and c are real numbers and $a \neq 0$. The other function,
>
> $y = 2x - 12x$, is not quadratic because there is no x^2-term.
>
> The graph of this function will open downward because a, which is equal to $-\frac{1}{2}$, is less than 0. Because the parabola opens downward, the graph will have a maximum.

Excellent Explanation

The response includes the correct answers along with a detailed explanation for each part of the problem. The explanation is written using complete sentences and is presented in an order that is easy to follow and to understand. It is obvious that this student knows how to determine and interpret a quadratic function.

Student B

> $\frac{1}{2}x^2 + y = 4x - 3$ There is an x^2.
>
> When I graphed the function on my calculator, I saw a parabola that opened downward.
>
> It had a maximum.

Poor Explanation

The response includes the correct answers, but the explanation does not include details. The student shows a lack of understanding of how to write and interpret a quadratic function in standard form.

Include as many details as possible to support your reasoning. This increases the chance of getting full credit for your response.

Read each test item and answer the questions that follow.

Item A
The height h in feet of a tennis ball x seconds after it is ejected from a serving machine is modeled by the function $h = -2t^2 - t + 10$, where t is the time in seconds after the ball is ejected. When does the ball first hit the ground? Explain your answers.

1. What should a student include in the explanation to receive full credit?

2. Read the two explanations below. Which explanation is better? Why?

Student A

$0 = -2t^2 - t + 10$

$t = 2$ or $t = -2.5$

2 seconds

Student B

When the ball hits the ground, the height will be 0.

$0 = -2t^2 - t + 10$

Solve by factoring: $0 = (-t + 2)(2t + 5)$

$-t + 2 = 0$ or $2t + 5 = 0$

$t = 2$ or $t = -\dfrac{5}{2}$

Time can't be negative, so the only solution is $t = 2$.
The ball hits the ground after 2 seconds.

Item B
The height of a golf ball can be modeled by the function $y = -5x^2 + 20x + 8$, where y is the height in meters above the ground and x is the time in seconds after the ball is hit. What is the ball's maximum height? How long does it take for the ball to reach this height? Explain.

3. A student correctly found the following answers. Use this information to write a clear and concise explanation.

Axis of symmetry is the vertical line at $x = 2$.
Vertex is at $(2, 28)$.
28 meters; 2 seconds
2 seconds versus 4 seconds

Item C
The function $h = -16t^2 + 96t$ represents the height in feet of a model rocket with an initial vertical velocity of 96 feet per second. Find the time that the rocket is in the air. Explain how you found your answer.

4. Read the two responses below.

   a. Which student provided the better explanation? Why?

   b. What advice would you give the other student to improve his or her explanation?

Student C

Graph the function $h = -16t^2 + 96t$, and then find the zeros. The first zero is when $t = 0$, when the rocket is launched. The second zero is when the rocket hits the ground: $t = 6$. The difference between 6 and 0 is the time that the rocket is in the air: 6 seconds.

Student D

6 seconds.

Graph the function to find how long the rocket is in the air, and find the values where it crosses the x-axis.

Item D
The base of a parallelogram is 12 centimeters more than its height. The area of the parallelogram is 13 square centimeters. Explain how to determine the height and base of the figure. What is the height? What is the base?

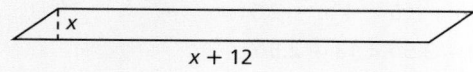

5. Read the following response. Identify any areas that need improvement. Rewrite the response so that it will receive full credit.

$x^2 + 12x + 36 = 49$ Complete the square.

$(x + 6)^2 = 49$

$x + 6 = \sqrt{49}$

$x + 6 = \pm 7; x = 1$ or -13

base $= 13$, height $= 1$

MASTERING THE STANDARDS

CUMULATIVE ASSESSMENT, CHAPTERS 1–9

Multiple Choice

1. Which expression is NOT equal to the other three?

(A) 0^1

(C) 1^0

(B) 1^1

(D) $(-1)^0$

2. Which of the following shows the complete factorization of $3x^3 - 3x^2 - 6x$?

(A) $3(x^2 + x)(x - 2)$

(B) $3(x^2 - x)(x + 2)$

(C) $3x(x + 1)(x - 2)$

(D) $3x(x - 1)(x + 2)$

3. The area of a circle is $\pi(9x^2 + 42x + 49)$. What is the circumference of the circle?

(A) $\pi(3x + 7)$

(B) $2\pi(3x + 7)$

(C) $2\pi(3x + 7)^2$

(D) $6x + 14$

4. Mike's Bikes charges $10.00 plus $3.50 per hour to rent a bike. The Pedal Palace charges $13.00 plus $2.50 per hour to rent a bike. Which inequality can you use to find the number of hours h for which renting a bike at the Pedal Palace is cheaper?

(A) $10h + 3.5 > 13h + 2.5$

(B) $10 + 3.5h > 13 + 2.5h$

(C) $10h + 3.5 < 13h + 2.5$

(D) $10 + 3.5h < 13 + 2.5h$

5. What is the numerical solution to the equation *five less than three times a number equals four more than eight times the number?*

(A) $-\dfrac{9}{5}$

(C) $-\dfrac{1}{5}$

(B) $\dfrac{1}{11}$

(D) $\dfrac{1}{5}$

6. Which function is graphed below?

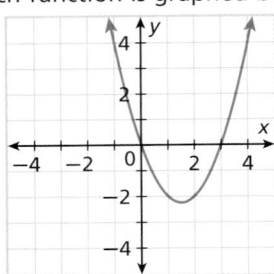

(A) $y = -x^2 - 3x$

(B) $y = -x^2 + 3x$

(C) $y = x^2 + 3x$

(D) $y = x^2 - 3x$

7. Which of the following is the graph of $f(x) = -x^2 + 2$?

(A)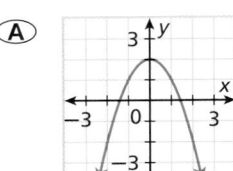

(C)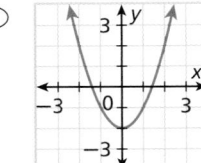

(B)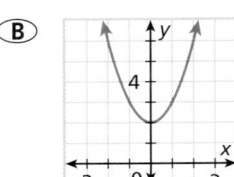

(D)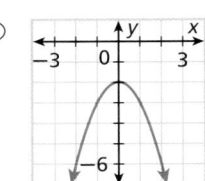

8. At how many points does the graph of $y = x^2 - 2x + 1$ intersect the x-axis?

(A) none

(C) two

(B) one

(D) three

9. What is the slope of the line that passes through the points $(4, 7)$ and $(5, 3)$?

(A) 4

(C) -4

(B) $\dfrac{1}{4}$

(D) $-\dfrac{1}{4}$

10. Putting Green Mini Golf charges a $4 golf club rental fee plus $1.25 per game. Good Times Golf charges a $1.25 golf club rental fee plus $3.75 per game. Which system of equations could be solved to determine for how many games the cost is the same at both places?

Ⓐ $\begin{cases} y = 4x + 1.25 \\ y = 3.75 + 1.25x \end{cases}$

Ⓑ $\begin{cases} y = 4 - 1.25x \\ y = -3.75 + 1.25x \end{cases}$

Ⓒ $\begin{cases} y = 1.25x + 4 \\ y = 3.75x + 1.25 \end{cases}$

Ⓓ $\begin{cases} y = 1.25x - 4 \\ y = 1.25x + 3.75 \end{cases}$

11. The graph of which function has an axis of symmetry of $x = -2$?

Ⓐ $y = 2x^2 - x + 3$

Ⓑ $y = 4x^2 + 2x + 3$

Ⓒ $y = x^2 - 2x + 3$

Ⓓ $y = x^2 + 4x + 3$

12. Which polynomial is the product of $x - 4$ and $x^2 - 4x + 1$?

Ⓐ $-4x^2 + 17x - 4$

Ⓑ $x^3 - 8x^2 + 17x - 4$

Ⓒ $x^3 + 17x - 4$

Ⓓ $x^3 - 15x + 4$

Gridded Response

13. The equation $2x^2 - 6x - 20 = 0$ has two solutions. One solution is -2. What is the other solution?

14. What is the slope of a line that is parallel to the line described by $6x - 9y = 2$?

15. Use the Quadratic Formula to find the positive solution of $4x^2 = 10x + 2$. Round your answer to the nearest hundredth.

Short Response

16. Use the system $\begin{cases} y \le \frac{1}{3}x + 1 \\ y \le -2x + 2 \end{cases}$ for the following.

a. Sketch the region defined by the system.

b. Is $(1, -2)$ a solution of the system? Explain how you can use your graph to decide.

17. Consider the relation shown in the graph.

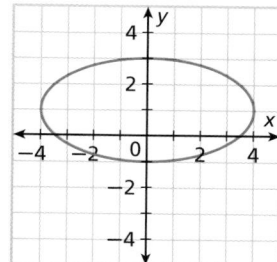

a. Is the relation a function? Explain.

b. What are the domain and range of the relation?

18. a. Show how to solve $x^2 - 2x - 8 = 0$ by graphing the related function. Show all your work.

b. Show another way to solve the equation in part a. Show all your work.

19. What can you say about the value of a if the equation $y = ax^2 - 8$ has no solutions? Explain.

Extended Response

20. The graph shows the quadratic function $f(x) = ax^2 + bx + c$.

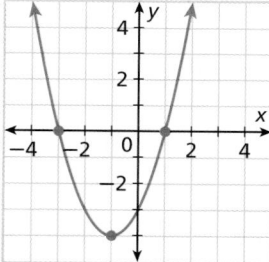

a. What are the solutions of the equation $0 = ax^2 + bx + c$? Explain how you know.

b. If the point $(-5, 12)$ lies on the graph of $f(x)$, the point $(a, 12)$ also lies on the graph. Find the value of a.

c. What do you know about the relationship between the values of a and b? Use the coordinates of the vertex in your explanation.

d. Use what you know about solving quadratic equations by factoring to make a conjecture about the values of a, b, and c in the function $f(x) = ax^2 + bx + c$.

CHAPTER 10

Rational Functions and Equations

go.hrw.com
Chapter Project Online
KEYWORD: MA8CA ChProj

Ratios and rational expressions can be used to explore perspective.

Golden Gate Bridge
San Francisco, CA

ARE YOU READY?

✓ Vocabulary

Match each term on the left with a definition on the right.

1. perfect-square trinomial
2. greatest common factor
3. monomial
4. polynomial
5. reciprocals

A. the greatest factor that is shared by two or more terms

B. a number, a variable, or a product of numbers and variables with whole-number exponents

C. two numbers whose product is 1

D. a polynomial with three terms

E. the sum or difference of monomials

F. a trinomial that is the result of squaring a binomial

✓ Simplify Fractions

Simplify.

6. $\dfrac{12}{4}$

7. $\dfrac{100}{36}$

8. $\dfrac{240}{18}$

9. $\dfrac{121}{66}$

✓ Add and Subtract Fractions

Add or subtract.

10. $\dfrac{1}{3} + \dfrac{1}{2}$

11. $\dfrac{7}{8} - \dfrac{1}{6}$

12. $\dfrac{3}{4} + \dfrac{2}{3} + \dfrac{1}{2}$

13. $\dfrac{5}{9} + \dfrac{1}{12} - \dfrac{1}{3}$

✓ Factor GCF from Polynomials

Factor each polynomial.

14. $x^2 + 2x$

15. $x^2 + x$

16. $2x^2 + x$

17. $x^2 - x$

18. $3x^2 + 2x$

19. $4x^2 - 4$

20. $3x^2 - 6x$

21. $x^3 - x^2$

✓ Properties of Exponents

Simplify each expression.

22. $4x \cdot 3x^2$

23. $-5 \cdot 2jk$

24. $-2a^3 \cdot 3a^4$

25. $3ab \cdot 4a^2b$

26. $2x \cdot 3y \cdot xy$

27. $a^2b \cdot 3ab^3$

28. $3rs \cdot 3rs^3$

29. $5m^2n^2 \cdot 4mn^2$

✓ Simplify Polynomial Expressions

Simplify each expression.

30. $4x - 2y - 8y$

31. $2r - 4s + 3s - 8r$

32. $ab^2 - ab + 4ab^2 + 2a^2b + a^2b^2$

33. $3g(g - 4) + g^2 + g$

Unpacking the Standards

The information below "unpacks" the standards. The Academic Vocabulary is highlighted and defined to help you understand the language of the standards. Refer to the lessons listed after each standard for help with the math terms and phrases. The Chapter Concept shows how the standard is applied in this chapter.

California Standard	Academic Vocabulary	Chapter Concept
10.0 Students add, subtract, multiply, and **divide monomials and polynomials. Students solve multistep problems, including word problems, by using these techniques.** (Lab **10-6**) (Lesson **10-6**)	**technique** a way of doing something	You use long division to divide a polynomial by a binomial.
12.0 Students simplify fractions with polynomials in the numerator and denominator by factoring both and reducing them to the lowest terms. (Lesson **10-3, 10-6**)	**factoring** expressing a quantity as a product of two or more quantities **reduce to lowest terms** simplify	You use division to write a rational expression in simpler form.
13.0 Students add, subtract, multiply, and divide rational expressions and functions. Students solve both computationally and conceptually challenging problems by using these techniques. (Lessons 10-1, 10-2, 10-3, **10-4, 10-5**)	**computational** having to do with numbers and operations **conceptual** having to do with general ideas	You add and subtract rational expressions with like and unlike denominators. You also use the rules you learned to multiply and divide fractions to multiply and divide rational expressions.
15.0 Students apply algebraic techniques to solve rate problems, work problems, and percent mixture problems. (Lesson **10-5, 10-7, 10-8**)	**percent mixture** a combination of parts that are expressed as percents of the whole	You learn how to solve rational equations so that you can solve real-world problems that involve rational expressions.

Standard 17.0 is also covered in this chapter. To see this standard unpacked, go to Chapter 4, p. 198.

Reading *and* Writing Math

Study Strategy: Remember Formulas

In math, there are many formulas, properties, and rules that you should commit to memory.

To memorize a formula, create flash cards. Write the name of the formula on one side of a card. Write the formula on the other side of the card. You might also include a diagram or an example if helpful. Study your flash cards on a regular basis.

Sample Flash Card

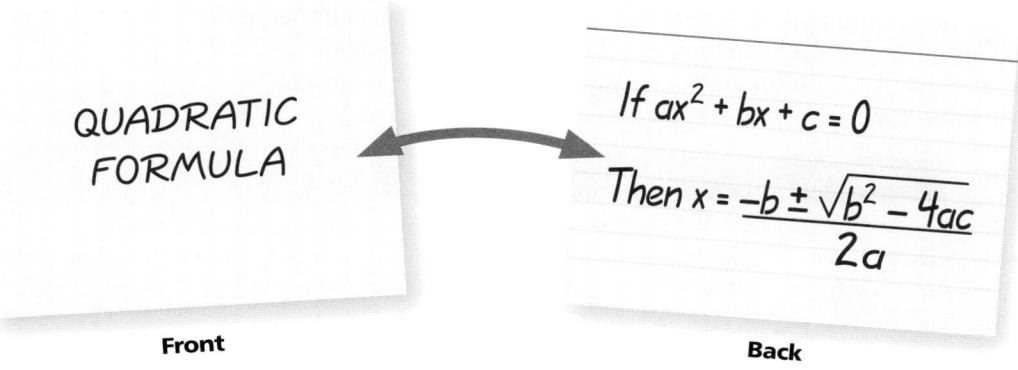

QUADRATIC
FORMULA

If $ax^2 + bx + c = 0$

Then $x = \dfrac{-b \pm \sqrt{b^2 - 4ac}}{2a}$

Front   **Back**

Knowing when and how to apply a mathematical formula is as important as memorizing the formula itself.

To know what formula to apply, read the problem carefully.

> **Solve each quadratic equation.**
>
> **1.** $x^2 - 7x + 10 = 0$ **2.** $3x^2 - 4x - 1 = 0$ **3.** $x^2 - 10x + 25 = 0$

You can use the Quadratic Formula to solve all of these equations. But other solution methods may be simpler. The first problem can be easily solved by factoring. In the third problem, the left side of the equation is a perfect-square trinomial. This equation can be solved by factoring or by using square roots.

Try This

Read each problem. Then write the formula(s) needed to solve it. What helped you identify the formula?

1. Find the equation of the line with slope $\frac{2}{3}$ that passes through the point (1, 1).

2. The area of a rectangular pool is 120 square feet. The length is 1 foot less than twice the width. What is the perimeter of the pool?

10-1 Algebra LAB

Model Inverse Variation

The relationship between the width and the length of a rectangle with a constant area is an inverse variation. In this activity, you will study this relationship by modeling rectangles with square tiles or grid paper.

Use with Lesson 10-1

California Standards

Preparation for ◆━ **13.0** Students add, subtract, multiply, and divide **rational** expressions and **functions.** Students solve both computationally and conceptually challenging problems by using these techniques.

Activity

Use 12 square tiles to form a rectangle with an area of 12 square units, or draw the rectangle on grid paper. Use a width of 1 unit and a length of 12 units.

Your rectangle should look like the one shown.

Using the same 12 square tiles, continue forming rectangles by changing the width and length until you have formed all the different rectangles you can that have an area of 12 square units. Copy and complete the table as you form each rectangle.

Width (x)	Length (y)	Area (xy)
1	12	12
		12
		12
		12
		12
		12

Plot the ordered pairs from the table on a graph. Draw a smooth curve through the points.

Try This

1. Look at the table and graph above. What happens to the length as the width increases? Why?

2. This relationship between length and width is an example of an *inverse variation.* Why do you think it is called that?

3. For each point, what does xy equal? Complete the equation $xy = \underline{}$. Solve this equation for y.

4. Form all the different rectangles that have an area of 24 square units. Record their widths and lengths in a table. Graph your results. Write an equation relating the width x and length y.

5. **Make a Conjecture** Using the equations you wrote in 3 and 4, what do you think the equation of any inverse variation might look like when solved for y?

10-1 Inverse Variation

California Standards

Preparation for ⟶ 13.0
Students add, subtract, multiply, and divide **rational** expressions and **functions.** Students solve both computationally and conceptually challenging problems by using these techniques.
Also covered: **17.0**

Vocabulary
inverse variation

Why learn this?

Inverse variation can be used to find the frequency at which a guitar string vibrates. (See Example 3.)

A relationship that can be written in the form $y = \frac{k}{x}$, where k is a nonzero constant and $x \neq 0$, is an **inverse variation**. The constant k is the constant of variation.

Multiplying both sides of $y = \frac{k}{x}$ by x gives $xy = k$. So, for any inverse variation, the product of x and y is a nonzero constant.

Inverse Variations

WORDS	NUMBERS	ALGEBRA
y varies inversely as x.	$y = \frac{3}{x}$	$y = \frac{k}{x}$
y is inversely proportional to x.	$xy = 3$	$xy = k \ (k \neq 0)$

There are two methods to determine whether a relationship between data is an inverse variation. You can write a function rule in $y = \frac{k}{x}$ form, or you can check whether xy is constant for each ordered pair.

EXAMPLE **1** **Identifying an Inverse Variation**

Tell whether each relationship is an inverse variation. Explain.

A

x	y
1	20
2	10
4	5

B

x	y
2	6
3	9
6	18

Method 1 Write a function rule.

$y = \dfrac{20}{x}$ *Can write in $y = \frac{k}{x}$ form.*

The relationship is an inverse variation.

Method 2 Find xy for each ordered pair.

$1(20) = 20, 2(10) = 20, 4(5) = 20$

The product xy is constant, so the relationship is an inverse variation.

Method 1 Write a function rule.

$y = 3x$ *Cannot write in $y = \frac{k}{x}$ form.*

The relationship is not an inverse variation.

Method 2 Find xy for each ordered pair.

$2(6) = 12, 3(9) = 27, 6(18) = 108$

The product xy is not constant, so the relationship is not an inverse variation.

Tell whether each relationship is an inverse variation. Explain.

 $5xy = -21$

$$\frac{5xy}{5} = \frac{-21}{5}$$ *Find xy. Since xy is multiplied by 5, divide both sides by 5 to undo the multiplication.*

$$xy = \frac{-21}{5}$$ *Simplify.*

xy equals the constant $\frac{-21}{5}$, so the relationship is an inverse variation.

CHECK IT OUT! **Tell whether each relationship is an inverse variation. Explain.**

1a.

x	y
−12	24
1	−2
8	−16

1b.

x	y
3	3
9	1
18	0.5

1c. $2x + y = 10$

An inverse variation can also be identified by its graph. Some inverse variation graphs are shown. Notice that each graph has two parts that are not connected.

Also notice that none of the graphs contain $(0, 0)$. In other words, $(0, 0)$ can never be a solution of an inverse variation equation.

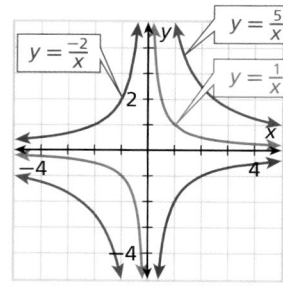

EXAMPLE 2 **Graphing an Inverse Variation**

Write and graph the inverse variation in which $y = 2$ when $x = 4$.

Step 1 Find *k*.

$k = xy$ *Write the rule for constant of variation.*

$\quad = 4(2)$ *Substitute 4 for x and 2 for y.*

$\quad = 8$

Step 2 Use the value of *k* to write an inverse variation equation.

$y = \dfrac{k}{x}$ *Write the rule for inverse variation.*

$y = \dfrac{8}{x}$ *Substitute 8 for k.*

Step 3 Use the equation to make a table of values.

x	−4	−2	−1	1	2	4
y	−2	−4	−8	8	4	2

Step 4 Plot the points and connect them with smooth curves.

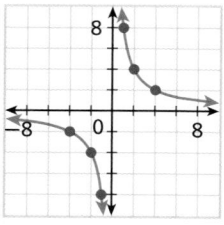

CHECK IT OUT! **2.** Write and graph the inverse variation in which $y = \frac{1}{2}$ when $x = 10$.

EXAMPLE 3   *Music Application*

The inverse variation $xy = 2400$ relates the vibration frequency y in hertz (Hz) to the length x in centimeters of a guitar string. Determine a reasonable domain and range, and then graph this inverse variation.

Step 1 Solve the function for y.

$$xy = 2400$$
$$y = \frac{2400}{x}$$ *Divide both sides by x.*

Step 2 Decide on a reasonable domain and range.

$x > 0$ *Length is never negative and $x \neq 0$.*

$y > 0$ *Because x and xy are both positive, y is also positive.*

Remember!

Recall that sometimes domain and range are restricted in real-world situations.

Step 3 Use values of the domain to generate reasonable ordered pairs.

x	20	40	60	120
y	120	60	40	20

Step 4 Plot the points. Connect them with a smooth curve.

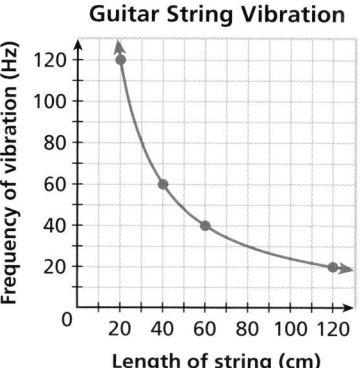

Guitar String Vibration

 **CHECK IT OUT!**

3. The inverse variation $xy = 100$ represents the relationship between the pressure x in atmospheres (atm) and the volume y in mm^3 of a certain gas. Determine a reasonable domain and range, and then graph this inverse variation.

The fact that $xy = k$ is the same for every ordered pair in any inverse variation can help you find missing values in the relationship.

Know it! Note

Product Rule for Inverse Variation

If (x_1, y_1) and (x_2, y_2) are solutions of an inverse variation, then $x_1y_1 = x_2y_2$.

EXAMPLE 4   Using the Product Rule

Let $x_1 = 3$, $y_1 = 2$, and $y_2 = 6$. Let y vary inversely as x. Find x_2.

$x_1y_1 = x_2y_2$ *Write the Product Rule for Inverse Variation.*

$(3)(2) = x_2(6)$ *Substitute 3 for x_1, 2 for y_1, and 6 for y_2.*

$6 = 6x_2$ *Simplify.*

$\frac{6}{6} = \frac{6x_2}{6}$ *Solve for x_2 by dividing both sides by 6.*

$1 = x_2$ *Simplify.*

 **CHECK IT OUT!**

4. Let $x_1 = 2$, $y_1 = -6$, and $x_2 = -4$. Let y vary inversely as x. Find y_2.

EXAMPLE 5 **Physical Science Application**

Boyle's law states that the pressure of a quantity of gas *x* varies inversely as the volume of the gas *y*. The volume of air inside a bicycle pump is 5.2 in³, and the pressure is 15.5 pounds per square inch (psi). Assuming no air escapes, what is the pressure of the air inside the pump after the handle is pushed in and the air is compressed to a volume of 2.6 in³?

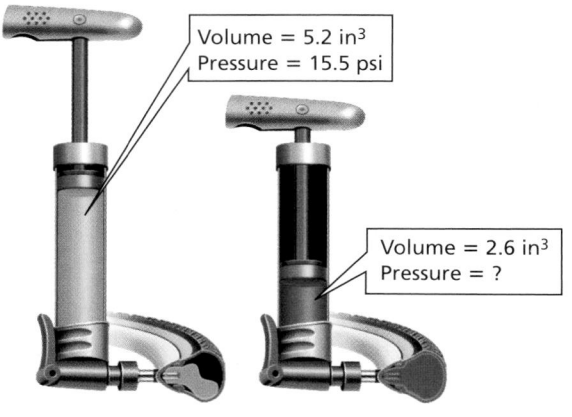

Volume = 5.2 in³
Pressure = 15.5 psi

Volume = 2.6 in³
Pressure = ?

Reading Math

In Example 5, x_1 and y_1 represent volume and pressure **before** the handle is pushed in, and x_2 and y_2 represent volume and pressure **after** the handle is pushed in.

$$x_1 y_1 = x_2 y_2$$ Use the Product Rule for Inverse Variation.

$$(5.2)(15.5) = (2.6)y_2$$ Substitute 5.2 for x_1, 15.5 for y_1, and 2.6 for x_2.

$$80.6 = 2.6y_2$$ Simplify.

$$\frac{80.6}{2.6} = \frac{2.6y_2}{2.6}$$ Solve for y_2 by dividing both sides by 2.6.

$$31 = y_2$$ Simplify.

The pressure after the handle is pushed in is 31 psi.

CHECK IT OUT!

5. On a balanced lever, weight varies inversely as the distance from the fulcrum to the weight. The diagram shows a balanced lever. How much does the child weigh?

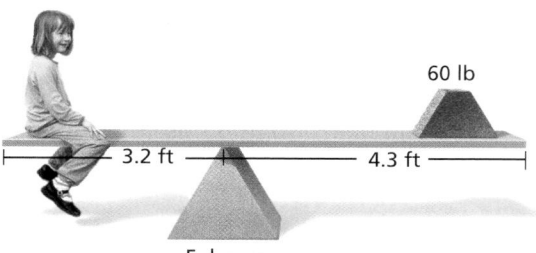

60 lb

3.2 ft   4.3 ft

Fulcrum

THINK AND DISCUSS

1. Name two ways you can identify an inverse variation.

2. GET ORGANIZED Copy and complete the graphic organizer. In each box, write an example of the parts of the given inverse variation.

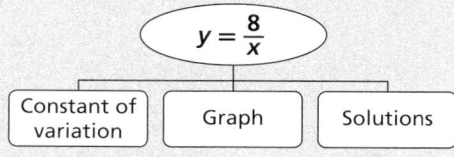

$$y = \frac{8}{x}$$

Constant of variation   Graph   Solutions

Know it!
Note

10-1 **Exercises**

California Standards Practice
Preparation for ⚬ 13.0; 17.0

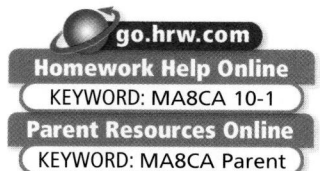
go.hrw.com
Homework Help Online
KEYWORD: MA8CA 10-1
Parent Resources Online
KEYWORD: MA8CA Parent

GUIDED PRACTICE

1. **Vocabulary** Describe the graph of an *inverse variation*.

SEE EXAMPLE **1**
p. 627

Tell whether each relationship is an inverse variation. Explain.

2.

x	y
1	8
4	2
2	4

3.

x	y
$\frac{1}{6}$	1
$\frac{1}{3}$	2
2	12

4. $x + y = 8$

5. $4xy = 3$

SEE EXAMPLE **2**
p. 628

6. Write and graph the inverse variation in which $y = 2$ when $x = 2$.

7. Write and graph the inverse variation in which $y = 6$ when $x = -1$.

SEE EXAMPLE **3**
p. 629

8. **Travel** The inverse variation $xy = 30$ relates the constant speed x in mi/h to the time y in hours that it takes to travel 30 miles. Determine a reasonable domain and range, and then graph this inverse variation.

SEE EXAMPLE **4**
p. 629

9. Let $x_1 = 3$, $y_1 = 12$, and $x_2 = 9$. Let y vary inversely as x. Find y_2.

10. Let $x_1 = 1$, $y_1 = 4$, and $y_2 = 16$. Let y vary inversely as x. Find x_2.

SEE EXAMPLE **5**
p. 630

11. **Mechanics** The rotational speed of a gear varies inversely as the number of teeth on the gear. A gear with 12 teeth has a rotational speed of 60 rpm. How many teeth are on a gear that has a rotational speed of 45 rpm?

PRACTICE AND PROBLEM SOLVING

Independent Practice

For Exercises	See Example
12–15	1
16–17	2
18	3
19–20	4
21	5

Extra Practice
Skills Practice p. EP20
Application Practice p. EP33

Tell whether each relationship is an inverse variation. Explain.

12.

x	y
3	−3
−5	5
7	−7

13.

x	y
2	5
0.5	20
8	1.25

14. $x = \dfrac{13}{y}$

15. $y = 5x$

16. Write and graph the inverse variation in which $y = -2$ when $x = 5$.

17. Write and graph the inverse variation in which $y = -6$ when $x = -\frac{1}{3}$.

18. **Engineering** The inverse variation $xy = 12$ relates the current x in amps to the resistance y in ohms of a circuit attached to a 12-volt battery. Determine a reasonable domain and range, and then graph this inverse variation.

19. Let $x_1 = -3$, $y_1 = -4$, and $y_2 = 6$. Let y vary inversely as x. Find x_2.

20. Let $x_1 = 7$, $y_1 = 9$, and $x_2 = 6$. Let y vary inversely as x. Find y_2.

21. Home Economics The length of fabric that June can afford varies inversely as the price per yard of the fabric. June can afford exactly 5 yards of fabric that costs $10.50 per yard. How many yards of fabric that costs $4.25 per yard can June buy? (Assume that she can only buy whole yards.)

22. Winter Sports When a person is snowshoeing, the pressure on the top of the snow in psi varies inversely as the area of the bottom of the snowshoe in square inches. The constant of variation is the weight of the person wearing the snowshoes in pounds.

   a. Helen weighs 120 pounds. About how much pressure does she put on top of the snow if she wears snowshoes that cover 360 in²?

   b. Max weighs 207 pounds. If he exerts 0.4 psi of pressure on top of the snow, what is the area of the bottom of his snowshoes in square inches?

Determine if each equation represents a direct variation, an inverse variation, or neither. Find the constant of variation when one exists.

23. $y = 8x$

24. $y = \dfrac{14}{x}$

25. $y = \dfrac{1}{3}x - 2$

26. $y = \dfrac{1}{5}x$

27. $y = 4\dfrac{3}{x}$

28. $y = \dfrac{x}{2} + 7$

29. $y = \dfrac{15}{x}$

30. $y = 5x$

31. Multi-Step A track team is competing in a 10 km race. The distance will be evenly divided among the team members. Write an equation that represents the distance d each runner will run if there are n runners. Does this represent a direct variation, inverse variation, or neither?

Determine whether each data set represents a direct variation, an inverse variation, or neither.

32.

x	2	4	8
y	5	10	20

33.

x	6	12	15
y	6	8	9

34.

x	1	2	3
y	12	6	4

35. Multi-Step Your club awards one student a $2000 scholarship each year, and each member contributes an equal amount. Your contribution y depends on the number of members x. Write and graph an inverse variation equation that represents this situation. What are a reasonable domain and range?

36. Estimation Estimate the value of y if y is inversely proportional to x, $x = 4$, and the constant of variation is 6π.

37. Why will the point $(0, 0)$ never be a solution to an inverse variation?

 38. Write About It Explain how to write an inverse variation equation of the form $y = \dfrac{k}{x}$ when values of x and y are known.

 39. Write About It List all the mathematical terms you know that contain the word *inverse*. How are these terms all similar? How is *inverse variation* similar to these terms?

CONCEPT CONNECTION

40. This problem will prepare you for the Concept Connection on page 650. The total number of workdays it takes to build the frame of a house varies inversely as the number of people working in a crew. Let x be the number of people in the crew, and let y be the number of workdays.

   a. Find the constant of variation when $y = 75$ and $x = 2$.

   b. Write the rule for the inverse of variation equation.

   c. Graph the equation of this inverse variation.

41. Which equation best represents the graph?

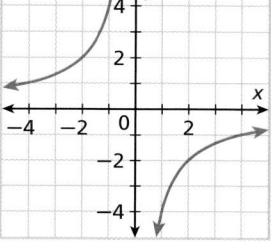

Ⓐ $y = -\frac{1}{4}x$ Ⓒ $y = -\frac{4}{x}$

Ⓑ $y = \frac{1}{4}x$ Ⓓ $y = \frac{4}{x}$

42. Determine the constant of variation if y varies inversely as x and $y = 2$ when $x = 7$.

Ⓐ $\frac{2}{7}$ Ⓑ $\frac{7}{2}$ Ⓒ 3.5   Ⓓ 14

43. Which of the following relationships does NOT represent an inverse variation?

Ⓐ

x	2	4	5
y	10	5	4

Ⓒ

x	2	4	5
y	8	16	20

Ⓑ $y = \frac{17.5}{x}$

Ⓓ $\frac{11}{2} = xy$

44. Gridded Response At a carnival, the number of tickets Brad can buy is inversely proportional to the price of the tickets. He can afford 12 tickets that cost $2.50 each. How many tickets can Brad buy if each costs $3.00?

CHALLENGE AND EXTEND

45. The definition of inverse variation says that k is a nonzero constant. What function would $y = \frac{k}{x}$ represent if $k = 0$?

46. Mechanics A part of a car's braking system uses a lever to multiply the force applied to the brake pedal. The force at the end of a lever varies inversely with the distance from the fulcrum. Point P is the end of the lever. A force of 2 lb is applied to the brake pedal. What is the force created at the point P?

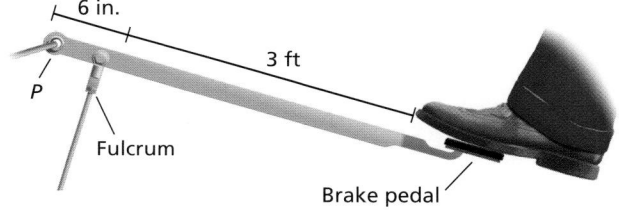

47. Communication The strength of a radio signal varies inversely with the square of the distance from the transmitter. A signal has a strength of 2000 watts when it is 4 kilometers from the transmitter. What is the strength of the signal 6 kilometers from the transmitter?

 SPIRAL STANDARDS REVIEW    14.0, 16.0, 17.0, 18.0

Find the domain and range for each relation. Tell whether the relation is a function. *(Lesson 4-2)*

48. $\{(-2, -4), (-2, -2), (-2, 0), (-2, 2)\}$ **49.** $\{(-4, 5), (-2, 3), (0, 1), (2, 3), (4, 5)\}$

Solve by completing the square. *(Lesson 9-7)*

50. $x^2 + 12x = 45$ **51.** $d^2 - 6d - 7 = 0$ **52.** $2y^2 + 6y = -\frac{5}{2}$

53. Find the number of solutions of $4x^2 + 3x - 6 = 0$ using the discriminant. *(Lesson 9-9)*

10-2 Rational Functions

California Standards

13.0 Students add, subtract, multiply, and divide **rational** expressions and **functions.** Students solve both computationally and conceptually challenging problems by using these techniques.

Also covered: **17.0**

Who uses this?

Gemologists can use rational functions to maximize reflected light. (See Example 4.)

A **rational function** is a function whose rule is a quotient of polynomials. The inverse variations you studied in the previous lesson are a special type of rational function.

Rational functions: $y = \dfrac{2}{x}$, $y = \dfrac{3}{4 - 2x}$, $y = \dfrac{1}{x^2}$

For any function involving x and y, an **excluded value** is any x-value that makes the function value y undefined. For a rational function, an excluded value is any value that makes the denominator equal 0.

EXAMPLE 1 **Identifying Excluded Values**

Identify any excluded values for each rational function.

Vocabulary
rational function
excluded value
discontinuous function
asymptote

A $y = \dfrac{8}{x}$

$x = 0$ *Set the denominator equal to 0.*

The excluded value is 0.

B $y = \dfrac{3}{x + 3}$

$x + 3 = 0$ *Set the denominator equal to 0.*

$x = -3$ *Solve for x.*

The excluded value is -3.

C $y = \dfrac{4}{x^2 + 1}$

$x^2 + 1 = 0$ *Set the denominator equal to 0.*

$x^2 = -1$

This equation has no real solutions, so the function has no excluded values.

 Identify any excluded values for each rational function.

1a. $y = \dfrac{10}{x}$ **1b.** $y = \dfrac{4}{x - 1}$ **1c.** $y = -\dfrac{5}{x + 4}$

Many rational functions are **discontinuous functions**, meaning their graphs contain one or more jumps, breaks, or holes. This occurs at an excluded value.

One place that a graph of a rational function may be discontinuous is at an *asymptote*. An **asymptote** is a line that a graph gets closer to as the absolute value of a variable increases. In the graph shown, both the x- and y-axes are asymptotes. A graph will get closer and closer to but never touch its asymptotes.

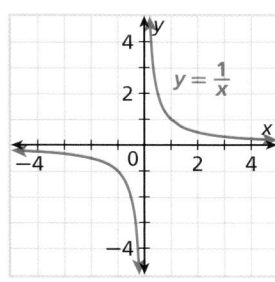

Vertical lines are written in the form $x = b$, and horizontal lines are written in the form $y = c$.

Look at the graph of $y = \frac{1}{x}$. The denominator is 0 when $x = 0$, so **0** is an excluded value. This means there is a vertical asymptote at $x = 0$. Notice the horizontal asymptote at $y = 0$. This is because there is no value of x for which $y = 0$.

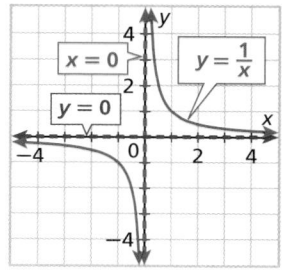

Look at the graph of $y = \frac{1}{x-3} + 2$. Notice that there is a vertical asymptote at $x = 3$ and there is a horizontal asymptote at $y = 2$. This is because there is no value of x for which $\frac{1}{x-3} = 0$. If $\frac{1}{x-3}$ is never 0, then $y = \frac{1}{x-3} + 2$ can never be equal to 2.

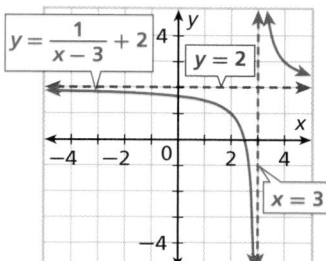

Know it!
Note

Identifying Asymptotes

WORDS	EXAMPLES	
A rational function in the form $$y = \frac{a}{x-b} + c$$ has a vertical asymptote at the excluded value $(x = b)$ and a horizontal asymptote at $y = c$.	$y = \frac{2}{x}$ $= \frac{2}{x-0} + 0$ Vertical asymptote: $x = 0$ Horizontal asymptote: $y = 0$	$y = \frac{1}{x+2} + 4$ $= \frac{1}{x-(-2)} + 4$ Vertical asymptote: $x = -2$ Horizontal asymptote: $y = 4$

EXAMPLE 2   Identifying Asymptotes

Identify the asymptotes.

A $y = \dfrac{1}{x-6}$

 Step 1 Write in $y = \dfrac{1}{x-b} + c$ form.

 $y = \dfrac{1}{x-6} + 0$

 Step 2 Identify the asymptotes.
  vertical: $x = 6$
  horizontal: $y = 0$

B $y = \dfrac{2}{3x-10} - 7$

 Step 1 Identify the vertical asymptote.

 $\begin{aligned} 3x - 10 &= 0 \\ +10 \quad\; &+10 \\ \hline 3x &= 10 \\ x &= \frac{10}{3} \end{aligned}$

 Find the excluded value. Set the denominator equal to 0.

 Add 10 to both sides.

 Solve for x. $\frac{10}{3}$ is an excluded value.

Step 2 Identify the horizontal asymptote.

$$c = -7 \qquad \text{\textit{-7 can be written as} } + (-7)$$
$$y = -7 \qquad \text{\textit{y} } = c$$

vertical asymptote: $x = \frac{10}{3}$; horizontal asymptote: $y = -7$

 **Identify the asymptotes.**

2a. $y = \dfrac{2}{x - 5}$ **2b.** $y = \dfrac{1}{4x + 16} + 5$ **2c.** $y = \dfrac{3}{x + 77} - 15$

To graph a rational function in the form $y = \dfrac{a}{x - b} + c$, you can use the asymptotes and a table of values.

EXAMPLE 3   **Graphing Rational Functions Using Asymptotes**

Graph each function.

A $y = \dfrac{2}{x + 1}$

Step 1 Identify the asymptotes.

vertical: $x = -1$ *Use $x = b$. $x + 1 = x - (-1)$, so $b = -1$.*

horizontal : $y = 0$ *Use $y = c$. $c = 0$*

Step 2 Graph the asymptotes using dashed lines.

Step 3 Make a table of values. Choose x-values on both sides of the vertical asymptote.

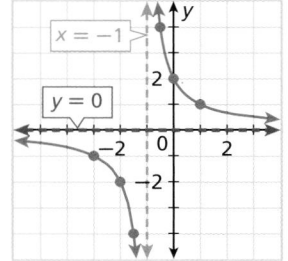

x	-3	-2	$-\frac{3}{2}$	$-\frac{1}{2}$	0	1
y	-1	-2	-4	4	2	1

Step 4 Plot the points and connect them with smooth curves. The curves should not touch the asymptotes.

B $y = \dfrac{1}{x - 2} - 4$

Step 1 Identify the asymptotes.

vertical: $x = 2$ *Use $x = b$. $b = 2$*

horizontal: $y = -4$ *Use $y = c$. $c = -4$*

Step 2 Graph the asymptotes using dashed lines.

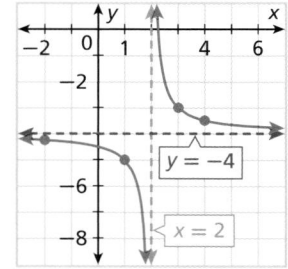

Step 3 Make a table of values. Choose x-values on both sides of the vertical asymptote.

x	-2	0	1	3	4
y	-4.25	-4.5	-5	-3	-3.5

Step 4 Plot the points and connect them with smooth curves. The curves should not touch the asymptotes.

 **Graph each function.**

3a. $y = \dfrac{1}{x + 7} + 3$ **3b.** $y = \dfrac{2}{x - 3} + 2$

EXAMPLE 4 *Gemology Application*

Some diamonds are cut using ratios calculated by the mathematician Marcel Tolkowsky in 1919. The amount of light reflected up through the top of a diamond (brilliancy) can be maximized using the ratio between the width of the diamond and the depth of the diamond. A gemologist has a diamond with a width of 9 millimeters. If x represents the depth of the diamond, then $y = \frac{9}{x}$ represents the brilliancy ratio y.

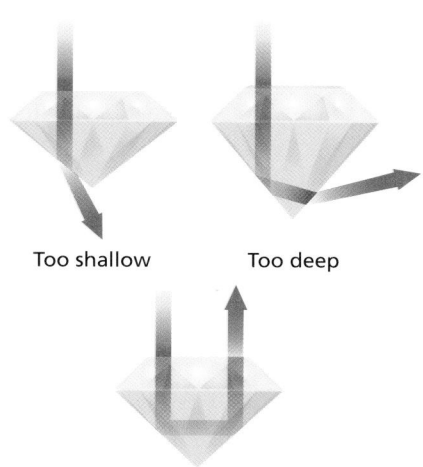

Too shallow   Too deep

Ideal

a. Describe a reasonable domain and range.

Both the depth of the diamond and the brilliancy ratio will be nonnegative, so nonnegative values are reasonable for the domain and range.

b. Graph the function.

Step 1 Identify the vertical and horizontal asymptotes.

vertical: $x = 0$ *Use x = b. b = 0*
horizontal: $y = 0$ *Use y = c. c = 0*

Step 2 Graph the asymptotes using dashed lines. The asymptotes will be the x- and y-axes.

Step 3 Since the domain is restricted to nonnegative values, only choose x-values on the right side of the vertical asymptote.

Depth of Diamond (mm)	2	3	4.5	9
Brilliancy Ratio	4.5	3	2	1

Step 4 Plot the points and connect them with smooth curves.

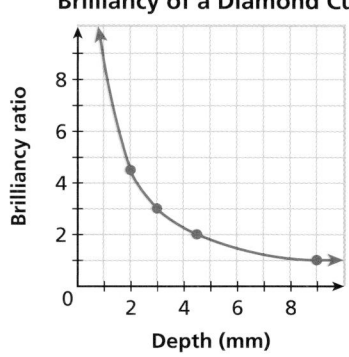

Brilliancy of a Diamond Cut

4. A librarian has a budget of $500 to buy copies of a software program. She will receive 10 free copies when she sets up an account with the supplier. The number of copies y of the program that she can buy is given by $y = \frac{500}{x} + 10$, where x is the price per copy.

a. Describe a reasonable domain and range.

b. Graph the function.

The table shows some of the properties of the three types of functions you have studied and their graphs.

Types of Functions

LINEAR FUNCTIONS

$$y = mx + b$$

- Graph is a straight line.
- m is the slope. When $m = 0$, the graph is a horizontal line.
- When $m < 0$, the graph slopes down from left to right.
- When $m > 0$, the graph slopes up from left to right.
- b is the y-intercept.

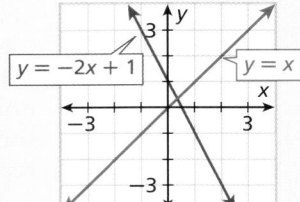

QUADRATIC FUNCTIONS

$$y = ax^2 + bx + c, a \neq 0$$

- Graph is a parabola.
- When $a > 0$, the parabola opens up.
- When $a < 0$, the parabola opens down.
- The axis of symmetry is the vertical line $x = -\frac{b}{2a}$.
- The function has a maximum or minimum value at the vertex.

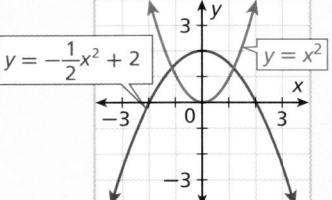

RATIONAL FUNCTIONS OF THE FORM $y = \dfrac{a}{x - b} + c$

$$y = \frac{1}{x - b} + c$$

- Graph is discontinuous.
- b is an excluded value; $x = b$ is the vertical asymptote.
- $y = c$ is the horizontal asymptote.

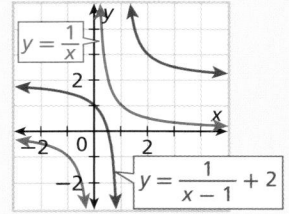

THINK AND DISCUSS

1. Does $y = \frac{1}{x-5}$ have any excluded values? Explain.
2. Tell how to find the vertical and horizontal asymptotes of $y = \frac{1}{x+9} - 5$.

3. **GET ORGANIZED** Copy and complete the graphic organizer. In each box, find the asymptotes for the given rational function.

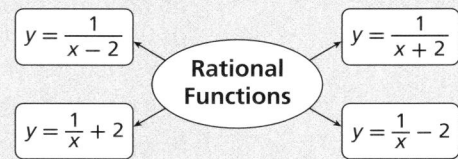

10-2 Exercises

California Standards Practice

🔑 **13.0**, 🔑 **15.0, 17.0, 24.1, 25.2**

go.hrw.com
Homework Help Online
KEYWORD: MA8CA 10-2
Parent Resources Online
KEYWORD: MA8CA Parent

GUIDED PRACTICE

1. **Vocabulary** An x-value that makes a function undefined is a(n) ____?____ . (*asymptote* or *excluded value*)

SEE EXAMPLE 1
p. 634

Identify any excluded values for each rational function.

2. $y = \dfrac{4}{x}$

3. $y = \dfrac{2}{x^2 + 3}$

4. $y = -\dfrac{2}{x}$

5. $y = \dfrac{16}{x - 4}$

SEE EXAMPLE 2
p. 635

Identify the asymptotes.

6. $y = \dfrac{1}{x - 3}$

7. $y = \dfrac{4}{3x + 15}$

8. $y = \dfrac{2}{3x - 5} + 2$

9. $y = \dfrac{1}{x + 9} - 10$

SEE EXAMPLE 3
p. 636

Graph each function.

10. $y = \dfrac{2}{x + 6}$

11. $y = \dfrac{1}{x - 2} - 6$

12. $y = \dfrac{1}{x} + 2$

13. $y = \dfrac{1}{x - 3} - 2$

SEE EXAMPLE 4
p. 637

14. **Catering** A caterer has $100 in her budget for fruit. Slicing and delivery of each pound of fruit costs $5. If x represents the cost per pound of the fruit itself, then $y = \dfrac{100}{x + 5}$ represents the number of pounds y she can buy.
   a. Describe a reasonable domain and range.
   b. Graph the function.

PRACTICE AND PROBLEM SOLVING

Identify any excluded values for each rational function.

15. $y = \dfrac{7}{x}$

16. $y = \dfrac{1}{x - 4}$

17. $y = -\dfrac{15}{x}$

18. $y = \dfrac{12}{x - 5}$

Identify the asymptotes.

19. $y = \dfrac{9}{x - 4}$

20. $y = \dfrac{2}{x + 4}$

21. $y = \dfrac{7}{4x - 12} + 4$

22. $y = \dfrac{7}{3x + 5} - 9$

Graph each function.

23. $y = \dfrac{5}{x - 5}$

24. $y = \dfrac{1}{x + 5} - 6$

25. $y = \dfrac{1}{x + 4}$

26. $y = \dfrac{1}{x - 4} + 2$

27. **Business** A wholesaler is buying auto parts. He has $200 to spend. He receives 5 parts free with the order. The number of parts y he can buy, if the average price of the parts is x dollars, is $y = \dfrac{200}{x} + 5$.
   a. Describe a reasonable domain and range.
   b. Graph the function.

Find the excluded value for each rational function.

28. $y = \dfrac{4}{x}$

29. $y = \dfrac{1}{x - 7}$

30. $y = \dfrac{2}{x + 4}$

31. $y = \dfrac{3}{2x + 1}$

Graph each rational function. Show the asymptotes.

32. $y = \dfrac{1}{x - 2}$

33. $y = \dfrac{2}{x} + 3$

34. $y = \dfrac{3}{x + 1} + 2$

35. $y = \dfrac{1}{x - 4} - 1$

36. The function $y = \dfrac{60}{x^2}$ relates the luminescence in lumens y of a 60-watt lightbulb viewed from a distance of x ft. Graph this function.

Identify the asymptotes of each rational function.

37. $y = \dfrac{7}{x+1}$ **38.** $y = \dfrac{1}{x} - 5$ **39.** $y = \dfrac{12}{x-2} + 5$ **40.** $y = \dfrac{18}{x+3} - 9$

Match each graph with one of the following functions.

A. $y = \dfrac{1}{x+1} + 2$ **B.** $y = \dfrac{1}{x+2} - 1$ **C.** $y = \dfrac{1}{x-2} + 1$

41.
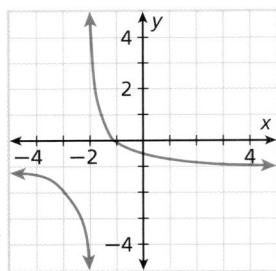

42.
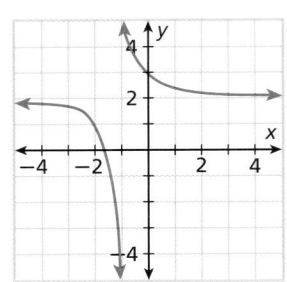

43.
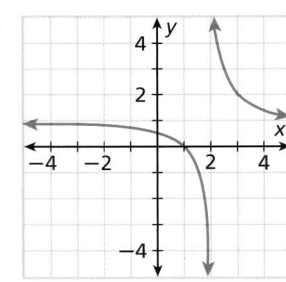

44. ///**ERROR ANALYSIS**/// In finding the horizontal asymptote of $y = \frac{1}{x+2} - 3$, student A said the asymptote is at $y = -3$, and student B said it is at $y = -2$. Who is incorrect? Explain the error.

45. Finance The time in months y that it will take to pay off a bill of $1200, when x dollars are paid each month and the finance charge is $15 per month, is $y = \frac{1200}{x-15}$. Describe a reasonable domain and range, and graph the function.

46. The table shows how long it takes different size landscaping teams to complete a project.

a. Graph the data.

b. Write a rational function to represent the data.

c. How many hours would it take 12 landscapers to complete the project?

Landscapers	Time (h)
2	30
4	15
5	12
10	6

Graph each function. Compare its graph to the graph of $y = \frac{1}{x}$.

47. $y = \dfrac{1}{x-6}$ **48.** $y = \dfrac{1}{x+7}$ **49.** $y = \dfrac{1}{x} + 4$ **50.** $y = \dfrac{1}{x-2} - 9$

Find the domain that makes the range positive.

51. $y = \dfrac{10}{x-2}$ **52.** $y = \dfrac{10}{x+2}$ **53.** $y = \dfrac{5}{5x+1}$ **54.** $y = \dfrac{4}{3x-7}$

55. Critical Thinking In which quadrants would you find the graph of $y = \frac{a}{x}$ when a is positive? when a is negative?

CONCEPT CONNECTION

56. This problem will prepare you for the Concept Connection on page 650.

It takes a total of 250 workdays to build a house for charity. For example, if 2 workers build the house, it takes them 125 actual construction days. If 10 workers are present, it takes 25 construction days to build the house.

a. Write a function that represents the number of construction days to build as a function of the number of workers.

b. What is the domain of this function?

c. Sketch a graph of the function.

57. Reasoning Graph each pair of functions. Then use inductive reasoning to make a conjecture about the relationship between the graphs of the rational functions $y = \frac{k}{x}$ and $y = \frac{-k}{x}$.

For help with inductive reasoning, see p. 233 and pp. 280–281.

a. $y = \frac{1}{x}$; $y = \frac{-1}{x}$
b. $y = \frac{3}{x}$; $y = \frac{-3}{x}$
c. $y = \frac{5}{x}$; $y = \frac{-5}{x}$

Multiple Choice For Exercises 58 and 59, choose the best answer.

58. Which function is graphed?

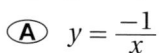

Ⓐ $y = \frac{2}{x + 3} - 4$ Ⓒ $y = \frac{2}{x - 3} + 4$

Ⓑ $y = \frac{2}{x + 4} - 3$ Ⓓ $y = \frac{2}{x - 4} + 3$

59. Which rational function has a graph with the horizontal asymptote $y = -1$?

Ⓐ $y = \frac{-1}{x}$ Ⓒ $y = \frac{1}{x + 1}$

Ⓑ $y = \frac{1}{x - 1}$ Ⓓ $y = \frac{1}{x} - 1$

60. Short Response Write a rational function whose graph is the same shape as the graph of $f(x) = \frac{1}{x}$, but has a vertical asymptote at $x = -2$ and a horizontal asymptote at $y = -3$. Graph the function.

CHALLENGE AND EXTEND

61. Graph the equation $y = \frac{1}{x^2 + 1}$.
   a. Does this equation represent a rational function? Explain.
   b. What is the domain of the function?
   c. What is the range of the function?
   d. Is the graph discontinuous?

62. Graphing Calculator Are the graphs of $f(x) = \frac{(x - 3)(x - 1)}{(x - 3)}$ and $g(x) = x - 1$ identical? Explain. (*Hint:* Are there any excluded values?)

63. Critical Thinking Write the equation of a rational function that has a horizontal asymptote at $y = 3$ and a vertical asymptote at $x = -2$ and contains the point $(1, 4)$.

SPIRAL STANDARDS REVIEW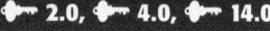

Solve each inequality. *(Lesson 3-5)*

64. $4t + 5 < 3(t + 1)$ **65.** $2(r + 1) \geq r - 6$ **66.** $j + 10 < 4j - 29$

67. $5(g + 2) \leq 2g - 5$ **68.** $c - 5 > 2c + 7$ **69.** $6(m - 2) < 2(6 - m)$

Solve each quadratic equation by factoring. *(Lesson 9-5)*

70. $4 - x^2 = 0$ **71.** $3x^2 = x^2 + 2x + 12$ **72.** $-x^2 = -6x + 9$

73. Marie has a square piece of cloth. She needs another piece with a length 2 inches shorter than the side of the square piece and a width 2 inches longer. The area for the new piece of cloth is 780 in². What will be the dimensions of the new piece of cloth? *(Lesson 9-6)*

10-3 Simplifying Rational Expressions

California Standards

 12.0 Students simplify fractions with polynomials in the numerator and denominator by factoring both and reducing them to the lowest terms.

Vocabulary
rational expression

Why learn this?

The shapes and sizes of plants and animals are partly determined by the ratio of surface area to volume.

If an animal's body is small and its surface area is large, the rate of heat loss will be high. Hummingbirds must maintain a high metabolism to compensate for the loss of body heat due to having a high surface-area-to-volume ratio. Formulas for surface-area-to-volume ratios are *rational expressions*.

A **rational expression** is an algebraic expression whose numerator and denominator are polynomials. The value of the polynomial expression in the denominator cannot be zero since division by zero is undefined. This means that rational expressions, like rational functions, may have excluded values.

EXAMPLE 1 Identifying Excluded Values

Find any excluded values of each rational expression.

A $\dfrac{5}{8r}$

$8r = 0$ *Set the denominator equal to 0.*

$r = \dfrac{0}{8} = 0$ *Solve for r by dividing both sides by 8.*

The excluded value is 0.

B $\dfrac{9d + 1}{d^2 - 2d}$

$d^2 - 2d = 0$ *Set the denominator equal to 0.*

$d(d - 2) = 0$ *Factor.*

$d = 0$ or $d - 2 = 0$ *Use the Zero Product Property.*

$d = 0$ or $d = 2$ *Solve for d.*

The excluded values are 0 and 2.

C $\dfrac{x + 4}{x^2 + 5x + 6}$

$x^2 + 5x + 6 = 0$ *Set the denominator equal to 0.*

$(x + 3)(x + 2) = 0$ *Factor.*

$x + 3 = 0$ or $x + 2 = 0$ *Use the Zero Product Property.*

$x = -3$ or $x = -2$ *Solve each equation for x.*

The excluded values are -3 and -2.

Remember!

To review the Zero Product Property, see Lesson 9-5.

To review factoring trinomials, see Chapter 8.

 Find any excluded values of each rational expression.

1a. $\dfrac{12}{t^2 + 5}$ **1b.** $\dfrac{3b}{b^2 + 5b}$ **1c.** $\dfrac{3k^2}{k^2 + 7k + 12}$

A rational expression is in its simplest form when the numerator and denominator have no common factors except 1. Remember that to simplify fractions you can divide out common factors that appear in both the numerator and the denominator. You can do the same to simplify rational expressions.

EXAMPLE 2 **Simplifying Rational Expressions**

Simplify each rational expression, if possible. Identify any excluded values.

A $\dfrac{3t^3}{12t}$

$\dfrac{3t^3}{3 \cdot 4t}$ *Factor 12.*

$\dfrac{3t^{3}t^2}{3 \cdot 4t}$ *Divide out common factors. Note that if t = 0, the expression is undefined.*

$\dfrac{t^2}{4}; t \neq 0$ *Simplify. The excluded value is 0.*

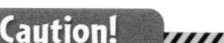
Caution!

Be sure to use the original denominator when finding excluded values. The excluded values may not be "seen" in the simplified denominator.

B $\dfrac{3x^2 - 9x}{x - 3}$

$\dfrac{3x(x - 3)}{x - 3}$ *Factor the numerator.*

$\dfrac{3x(x - 3)}{x - 3}$ *Divide out common factors. Note that if x = 3, the expression is undefined.*

$3x; x \neq 3$ *Simplify. The excluded value is 3.*

C $\dfrac{c}{c + 5}$

$\dfrac{c}{c + 5}; c \neq -5$ *The numerator and denominator have no common factors. The excluded value is −5.*

CHECK IT OUT! Simplify each rational expression, if possible. Identify any excluded values.

2a. $\dfrac{5m^2}{15m}$ **2b.** $\dfrac{6p^3 + 12p}{p^2 + 2}$ **2c.** $\dfrac{3n}{n - 2}$

From this point forward, you do not need to include excluded values in your answers unless they are asked for.

EXAMPLE 3 **Simplifying Rational Expressions with Trinomials**

Simplify each rational expression, if possible.

A $\dfrac{k + 1}{k^2 - 4k - 5}$

$\dfrac{k + 1}{(k + 1)(k - 5)}$ *Factor the numerator and the denominator when possible.*

$\dfrac{k + 1^{1}}{(k + 1)(k - 5)}$ *Divide out common factors.*

$\dfrac{1}{k - 5}$ *Simplify.*

B $\dfrac{y^2 - 16}{y^2 - 8y + 16}$

$\dfrac{(y + 4)(y - 4)}{(y - 4)(y - 4)}$

$\dfrac{(y + 4)(y - 4)}{(y - 4)(y - 4)}$

$\dfrac{y + 4}{y - 4}$

 Simplify each rational expression, if possible.

3a. $\dfrac{r + 2}{r^2 + 7r + 10}$

3b. $\dfrac{b^2 - 25}{b^2 + 10b + 25}$

Recall from Chapter 8 that opposite binomials can help you factor polynomials. Recognizing opposite binomials can also help you simplify rational expressions.

Consider $\dfrac{x - 3}{3 - x}$. The numerator and denominator are opposite binomials. Therefore,

$$\frac{x - 3}{3 - x} = \frac{x - 3}{-x + 3} = \frac{x - 3^1}{-1(x - 3)} = \frac{1}{-1} = -1.$$

E X A M P L E **4** **Simplifying Rational Expressions Using Opposite Binomials**

Simplify each rational expression, if possible.

A $\dfrac{2x - 10}{25 - x^2}$

$\dfrac{2(x - 5)}{(5 - x)(5 + x)}$ *Factor.*

$\dfrac{2(x - 5)}{(5 - x)(5 + x)}$ *Identify opposite binomials.*

$\dfrac{2(x - 5)}{-1(x - 5)(5 + x)}$ *Rewrite one opposite binomial.*

$\dfrac{2(x - 5)}{-1(x - 5)(5 + x)}$ *Divide out common factors.*

$-\dfrac{2}{5 + x}$ *Simplify.*

B $\dfrac{2 - 2m}{2m^2 + 2m - 4}$

$\dfrac{2(1 - m)}{2(m + 2)(m - 1)}$

$\dfrac{2(1 - m)}{2(m + 2)(m - 1)}$

$\dfrac{2(1 - m)}{2(m + 2)(-1)(1 - m)}$

$\dfrac{2(1 - m)^1}{2(m + 2)(-1)(1 - m)}$

$-\dfrac{1}{m + 2}$

 Simplify each rational expression, if possible.

4a. $\dfrac{3x - 12}{16 - x^2}$

4b. $\dfrac{6 - 2x}{2x^2 - 4x - 6}$

4c. $\dfrac{3x - 33}{x^2 - 121}$

Student to Student   *Opposite Binomials*

Tanika Brown,
Washington High School

I didn't understand why the quotient of opposite binomials simplified to –1. My teacher showed me an example on a number line:

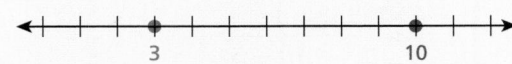

The distance between 3 and 10 is always the same (7 units). But depending on the order of the subtraction, the difference could be positive or negative.

$$10 - 3 = 7 \qquad 3 - 10 = -7$$

So whenever you divide something in the form $\dfrac{a - b}{b - a}$, you get a number divided by its opposite, which is always –1.

EXAMPLE 5 *Biology Application*

Water evaporates from a plant's surface. In two plants with different surface areas, the same volume of water will evaporate at a faster rate from the plant with the greater surface area. In the desert, plants must conserve water in order to survive. This means that the greater a plant's surface-area-to-volume ratio, the less likely the plant is to survive in the desert.

a. What is the surface-area-to-volume ratio of a spherical barrel cactus? (*Hint:* For a sphere, $S = 4\pi r^2$ and $V = \frac{4}{3}\pi r^3$.)

$\dfrac{4\pi r^2}{\frac{4}{3}\pi r^3}$ *Write the ratio of surface area to volume.*

$\dfrac{4\cancel{\pi}r^2}{\frac{4}{3}\cancel{\pi}r^3}$ *Divide out common factors.*

$\dfrac{4\cancel{r^2}}{\frac{4}{3}\cancel{r^3}r}$ *Use properties of exponents.*

$\dfrac{4}{r} \cdot \dfrac{3}{4}$ *To divide by $\frac{4}{3}$, multiply by its reciprocal, $\frac{3}{4}$.*

$\dfrac{\cancel{4}}{r} \cdot \dfrac{3}{\cancel{4}}$ *Divide out common factors.*

$\dfrac{3}{r}$ *Simplify.*

b. Which barrel cactus has a greater chance of survival in the desert, one with a radius of 4 inches or one with a radius of 7 inches? Explain.

$\dfrac{3}{r} = \dfrac{3}{4}$ $\dfrac{3}{r} = \dfrac{3}{7}$ *Write the ratio of surface area to volume twice. Substitute 4 and 7 for r.*

$\dfrac{3}{4} > \dfrac{3}{7}$ *Compare the ratios.*

The cactus with a radius of 7 inches has a greater chance of survival because its surface-area-to-volume ratio is lesser.

Remember!

For two fractions with the same numerator, the value of the fraction with a greater denominator is less than the value of the other fraction.

$9 > 3$

$\dfrac{2}{9} < \dfrac{2}{3}$

CHECK IT OUT! 5. Which barrel cactus has less of a chance to survive in the desert, one with a radius of 6 inches or one with a radius of 3 inches? Explain.

THINK AND DISCUSS

1. Write a rational expression that has an excluded value that cannot be identified when the expression is in its simplified form.

Know it! Note

2. GET ORGANIZED Copy and complete the graphic organizer. In each box, write and simplify one of the given rational expressions using the most appropriate method. $\frac{x-3}{x^2-6x+9}$, $\frac{5x^4}{x^2}$, $\frac{4-x}{x-4}$, $\frac{4x^2-4x}{8x}$

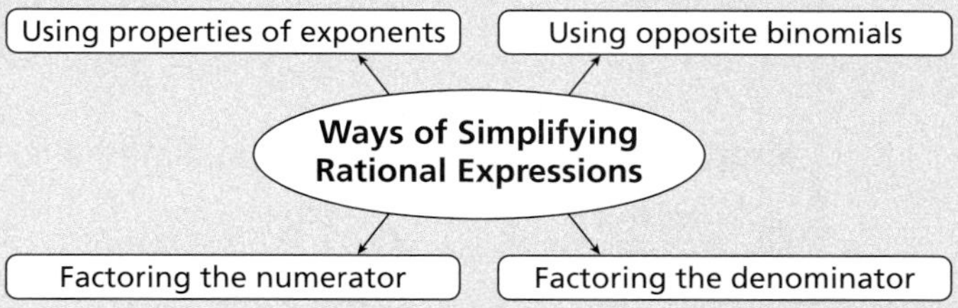

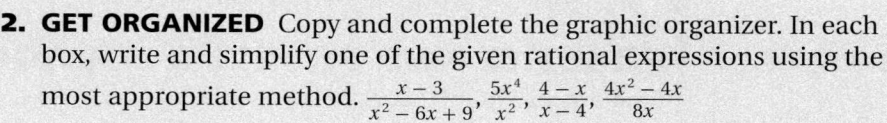

California Standards Practice
Preparation for ◆— 13.0;
◆— 12.0, ◆— 15.0

go.hrw.com
Homework Help Online
KEYWORD: MA8CA 10-3
Parent Resources Online
KEYWORD: MA8CA Parent

GUIDED PRACTICE

1. **Vocabulary** What is true about both the numerator and denominator of rational expressions?

SEE EXAMPLE 1
p. 642

Find any excluded values of each rational expression.

2. $\dfrac{5}{m}$

3. $\dfrac{x+2}{x^2-8x}$

4. $\dfrac{p^2}{p^2-2p-15}$

SEE EXAMPLE 2
p. 643

Simplify each rational expression, if possible. Identify any excluded values.

5. $\dfrac{4a^2}{8a}$

6. $\dfrac{2d^2+12d}{d+6}$

7. $\dfrac{2}{y+3}$

8. $\dfrac{10}{5-y}$

9. $\dfrac{2h}{2h+4}$

10. $\dfrac{3(x+4)}{6x}$

SEE EXAMPLE 3
p. 643

Simplify each rational expression, if possible.

11. $\dfrac{b+4}{b^2+5b+4}$

12. $\dfrac{s^2-4}{s^2+4s+4}$

13. $\dfrac{c^2+5c+6}{(c+3)(c-4)}$

14. $\dfrac{(x-2)(x+1)}{x^2+4x+3}$

15. $\dfrac{j^2-25}{j^2+2j-15}$

16. $\dfrac{p+1}{p^2-4p-5}$

SEE EXAMPLE 4
p. 644

17. $\dfrac{2n-16}{64-n^2}$

18. $\dfrac{8-4x}{2x^2-12x+16}$

19. $\dfrac{10-5r}{r^2+4r-12}$

20. $\dfrac{2x-14}{49-x^2}$

21. $\dfrac{5q-50}{100-q^2}$

22. $\dfrac{36-12a}{a^2+2a-15}$

SEE EXAMPLE 5
p. 645

23. **Construction** The side of a triangular roof is to have the same height h and base b_2 as the side of a trapezoidal roof.

   a. What is the ratio of the area of the triangular roof to the area of the trapezoidal roof?

   (*Hint:* For a triangle, $A=\frac{1}{2}b_2h$.

   For a trapezoid, $A=\dfrac{b_1+b_2}{2}h$.)

   b. Compare the ratio from part **a** to what the ratio will be if b_1 is doubled for the trapezoidal roof and b_2 is doubled for both roofs.

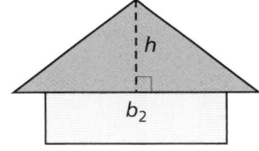

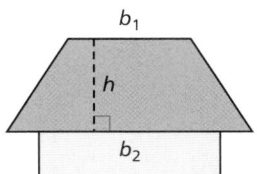

PRACTICE AND PROBLEM SOLVING

Find any excluded values of each rational expression.

24. $\dfrac{c}{c^2+c}$

25. $\dfrac{2}{-3x}$

26. $\dfrac{4}{x^2-3x-10}$

27. $\dfrac{n^2-1}{2n^2-7n-4}$

Simplify each rational expression, if possible. Identify any excluded values.

28. $\dfrac{4d^3+4d^2}{d+1}$

29. $\dfrac{3m^2}{m-4}$

30. $\dfrac{10y^4}{2y}$

31. $\dfrac{2t^2}{16t}$

For Exercises	See Example
24–27	1
28–31	2
32–37	3
38–40	4
41	5

Independent Practice

Extra Practice

Skills Practice p. EP20

Application Practice p. EP33

Simplify each rational expression, if possible.

32. $\dfrac{q - 6}{q^2 - 9q + 18}$

33. $\dfrac{z^2 - 2z + 1}{z^2 - 1}$

34. $\dfrac{t - 3}{t^2 - 5t + 6}$

35. $\dfrac{p^2 - 6p - 7}{p^2 - 4p - 5}$

36. $\dfrac{x^2 - 1}{x^2 + 4x + 3}$

37. $\dfrac{2x - 4}{x^2 - 6x + 8}$

38. $\dfrac{20 - 4x}{x^2 - 25}$

39. $\dfrac{3 - 3b}{3b^2 + 18b - 21}$

40. $\dfrac{3v - 36}{144 - v^2}$

41. Geometry When choosing package sizes, a company wants a package that uses the least amount of material to hold the greatest volume of product.

Box A   Box B

a. What is the surface-area-to-volume ratio for a rectangular prism? (*Hint:* For a rectangular prism, $S = 2\ell w + 2\ell h + 2wh$ and $V = \ell wh$.)

b. Which box should the company choose? Explain.

Biology

As a result of a nation-wide policy of protection and reintroduction, the population of bald eagles in the lower 48 states grew from 417 nesting pairs in 1963 to more than 6400 nesting pairs in 2000.

Source: U.S. Fish and Wildlife Service

 42. Biology The table gives information on two populations of animals that were released into the wild. Suppose 16 more predators and 20 more prey are released into the area. Write and simplify a rational expression to show the ratio of predator to prey.

	Predator	Prey
Original Population	x	x
Population 5 Years Later	4x	5x

Simplify each rational expression, if possible.

43. $\dfrac{p^2 + 12p + 36}{12p + 72}$

44. $\dfrac{3n^3 + 33n^2 + 15n}{3n^3 + 15n}$

45. $\dfrac{a}{2a + a}$

46. $\dfrac{j - 5}{j^2 - 25}$

47. $\dfrac{6w^2 + 11w - 7}{6w - 3}$

48. $\dfrac{n^2 - n - 56}{n^2 - 16n + 64}$

49. $\dfrac{(x + 1)^2}{x^2 + 2x + 1}$

50. $\dfrac{5}{(x + 5)^2}$

51. $\dfrac{25 - x^2}{x^2 - 3x - 10}$

CONCEPT CONNECTION

52. This problem will prepare you for the Concept Connection on page 650.

It takes 250 workdays to build a house. The number of construction days is determined by the size of the crew. The crew includes one manager who supervises workers and checks for problems, but does not do any building.

a. The table shows the number of construction days as a function of the number of workers. Copy and complete the table.

b. Use the table to write a function that represents the number of construction days.

c. Identify the excluded values of the function.

Crew Size (x)	$\dfrac{\text{Workdays}}{\text{Workers}}$	Construction Days (y)
2	$\dfrac{250}{2 - 1}$	250
3	$\dfrac{250}{3 - 1}$	
6		
11		25

53. Geometry Let s represent the length of an edge of a cube.

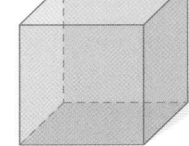

a. Write the ratio of a cube's surface area to volume in simplified form. (*Hint:* For a cube, $S = 6s^2$.)

b. What is the ratio of the cube's surface area to volume when $s = 2$?

c. What is the ratio of the cube's surface area to volume when $s = 6$?

54. Write About It Explain how to find excluded values for a rational expression.

55. Critical Thinking Give an example of a rational expression that has x in both the numerator and denominator, but cannot be simplified.

Multiple Choice For Exercises 56 and 57, choose the best answer.

56. Which expression is undefined for $x = 4$ and $x = -1$?

(A) $\dfrac{x-1}{x+4}$ (B) $\dfrac{x-4}{x+4}$ (C) $\dfrac{x}{x^2+3x-4}$ (D) $\dfrac{x}{x^2-3x-4}$

57. Which expression is the ratio of the area of a triangle to the area of a rectangle that has the same base and height?

(A) $\dfrac{1}{2}$ (B) $\dfrac{bh}{2}$ (C) $\dfrac{(bh)^2}{2}$ (D) 2

58. Gridded Response What is the excluded value for $\dfrac{x-4}{x^2-8x+16}$?

CHALLENGE AND EXTEND

 Reasoning Tell whether each statement is sometimes, always, or never true. Explain.

59. A rational expression has an excluded value.

60. A rational expression has a variable inside a square root in the numerator.

61. The graph of a rational function has at least one asymptote.

Simplify each rational expression.

62. $\dfrac{9v - 6v^2}{4v^2 - 4v - 3}$ **63.** $\dfrac{2a^2 - 7a + 3}{2a^2 + 9a - 5}$ **64.** $\dfrac{0.25y - 0.10}{0.25y^2 - 0.04}$

Identify any excluded values of each rational expression.

65. $\dfrac{\frac{1}{4}x^2 - 7x + 49}{\frac{1}{4}x^2 - 49}$ **66.** $\dfrac{-80x + 40x^2 + 40}{-30 - 30x^2 + 60x}$ **67.** $\dfrac{6x + 12}{12x + 6x^2}$

 **SPIRAL STANDARDS REVIEW**   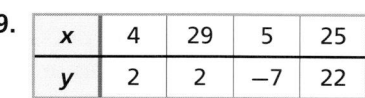 2.0, 6.0, 17.0

Give the domain and range of each relation. (*Lesson 4-2*)

68.

x	3	1	2	9
y	4	2	6	5

69.

x	4	29	5	25
y	2	2	-7	22

Use intercepts to graph the line described by each equation. (*Lesson 5-2*)

70. $5x - 3y = -15$ **71.** $y = 8x - 8$ **72.** $\frac{1}{2}x + y = 2$

Simplify. (*Lesson 7-1*)

73. $5h^{-3}$ **74.** $s^{-2}t^6$ **75.** $\dfrac{12}{b^4}$ **76.** $\dfrac{v^{-3}}{w^{-4}}$

10-3 Technology LAB

Graph Rational Functions

You can use a graphing calculator to graph rational functions and to compare graphs of rational functions before and after they are simplified.

Use with Lesson 10-3

California Standards

13.0 Students add, subtract, multiply, and divide **rational** expressions and **functions**. Students solve both computationally and conceptually challenging problems by using these techniques.

Activity

Simplify $y = \frac{x-1}{x^2 - 5x + 4}$ and give any excluded values. Then graph both the original function and the simplified function, and compare the graphs.

go.hrw.com
Lab Resources Online
KEYWORD: MA8CA Lab10

1 Simplify the function and find the excluded values.

$$\frac{x-1}{x^2 - 5x + 4} = \frac{x-1}{(x-1)(x-4)} = \frac{1}{x-4}; \text{ excluded values: } 4, 1$$

2 Enter $y = \frac{x-1}{x^2 - 5x + 4}$ and $y = \frac{1}{x-4}$ into your calculator as shown and press **GRAPH**.

3 To compare the graphs, press **TRACE**. At the top of the screen, you can see which graph the cursor is on. To change between graphs, press ▲ and ▼.

4 The graphs appear to be the same, but check the excluded values, 4 and 1. While on **Y1,** press 4 **ENTER**. Notice that there is no *y*-value at $x = 4$. The function is undefined.

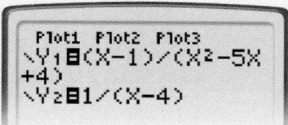

5 Press ▼ to switch to **Y2** and press 4 **ENTER**. This function is also undefined at $x = 4$. The graphs are the same at this excluded value.

6 Return to **Y1** and press 1 **ENTER**. This function is undefined at $x = 1$. However, this is not a vertical asymptote. Instead, this graph has a "hole" at $x = 1$.

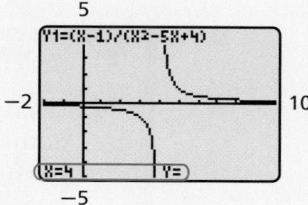

7 Switch to **Y2** and press 1 **ENTER**. This function is defined at $x = 1$. So the two graphs are the same except at $x = 1$.

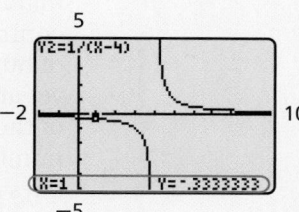

Try This

1. Why is $x = 1$ an excluded value for one function but not for the other?

2. Are the functions $y = \frac{x-1}{x^2 - 5x + 4}$ and $y = \frac{1}{x-4}$ truly equivalent for all values of *x*? Explain.

3. **Make a Conjecture** Complete each statement.

   a. If a value of *x* is excluded from a function and its simplified form, it appears on the graph as a(n) ___?___.

   b. If a value of *x* is excluded from a function but not its simplified form, it appears on the graph as a(n) ___?___.

CONCEPT CONNECTION

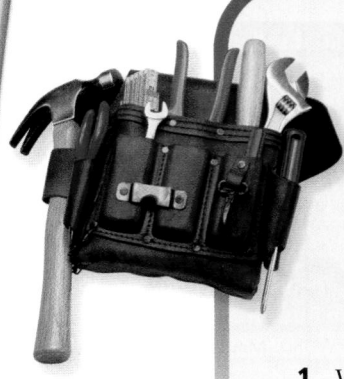

Rational Functions and Expressions

Construction Daze

Robert is part of a volunteer crew constructing houses for low-income families. The table shows how many construction days it takes to complete a house for work crews of various sizes.

Crew Size	Construction Days	Workdays
2	100	200
4	50	200
8	25	200
10	20	200
20	10	200

1. Working at the same rate, how many construction days should it take a crew of 40 people to build the house?

2. Express the number of construction days as a function of the crew size. Define the variables. What type of relationship is formed in the situation?

3. Explain how the crew size affects the number of construction days.

4. About how many construction days would it take a crew of 32 to complete a house?

5. If a crew can complete a house in 12.5 days, how many people are in the crew?

6. What are a reasonable domain and range of the function?

7. Suppose there are two managers that do not contribute to the work of building the house, yet are counted as part of the crew. Express the number of construction days as a function of the crew size. What are the asymptotes of this function? Graph the function.

READY TO GO ON?

Quiz for Lessons 10-1 Through 10-3

✓ 10-1 Inverse Variation

Tell whether each relationship represents an inverse variation. Explain.

1.

x	−5	−4	−3
y	10	−8	6

2.

x	18	9	6
y	2	4	6

3. $y = \dfrac{3}{x}$ **4.** $y + x = \dfrac{3}{4}$ **5.** $xy = -2$ **6.** $y = \dfrac{x}{5}$

7. Write and graph the inverse variation in which $y = 3$ when $x = 2$.

8. Write and graph the inverse variation in which $y = 4$ when $x = -1$.

9. The number of calculators Mrs. Hopkins can buy for the classroom varies inversely as the cost of each calculator. She can buy 24 calculators that cost $60 each. How many calculators can she buy if they cost $80 each?

✓ 10-2 Rational Functions

Identify any excluded values and the asymptotes for each rational function. Then graph each function.

10. $y = \dfrac{12}{x}$ **11.** $y = \dfrac{6}{x + 2}$ **12.** $y = \dfrac{4}{x - 1}$ **13.** $y = \dfrac{2}{x + 1} - 3$

14. Jeff builds model train layouts. He has $75 to spend on packages of miniature landscape items. He receives 6 free packages with each order. The number of packages y that Jeff can buy is given by $y = \dfrac{75}{x} + 6$, where x represents the cost of each package in dollars. Describe the reasonable domain and range values and graph the function.

✓ 10-3 Simplifying Rational Expressions

Find any excluded values of each rational expression.

15. $\dfrac{15}{n}$ **16.** $\dfrac{p}{p - 8}$ **17.** $\dfrac{x + 2}{x^2 + 6x + 8}$ **18.** $\dfrac{t - 1}{t^2 + t}$

Simplify each rational expression, if possible. Identify any excluded values.

19. $\dfrac{3x^2}{6x^3}$ **20.** $\dfrac{2n}{n^2 - 3n}$ **21.** $\dfrac{s + 1}{s^2 - 4s - 5}$ **22.** $\dfrac{12 - 3x}{x^2 - 8x + 16}$

23. Suppose a cone and a cylinder have the same radius and that the slant height ℓ of the cone is the same as the height h of the cylinder. Find the ratio of the cone's surface area to the cylinder's surface area.

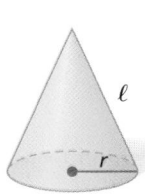

$S = \pi r \ell + \pi r^2$

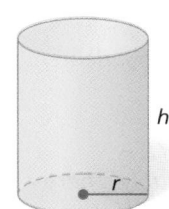

$S = 2\pi r h + 2\pi r^2$

10-4 Multiplying and Dividing Rational Expressions

California Standards

← **13.0** Students add, subtract, **multiply, and divide rational expressions** and functions. **Students solve both computationally and conceptually challenging problems by using these techniques.**

Why learn this?

You can multiply rational expressions to determine the probabilities of winning prizes at carnivals. (See Example 5.)

The rules for multiplying rational expressions are the same as the rules for multiplying fractions. You multiply the numerators, and you multiply the denominators.

Multiplying Rational Expressions

If a, b, c, and d are nonzero polynomials, then $\dfrac{a}{b} \cdot \dfrac{c}{d} = \dfrac{ac}{bd}$.

EXAMPLE 1 **Multiplying Rational Expressions**

Multiply. Simplify your answer.

A $\dfrac{a+3}{2} \cdot \dfrac{6}{3a+9}$

$\dfrac{6(a+3)}{2(3a+9)}$ *Multiply the numerators and denominators.*

$\dfrac{6(a+3)}{2 \cdot 3(a+3)}$ *Factor.*

$\dfrac{\cancel{6}(a+3)^1}{\cancel{6}(a+3)}$ *Divide out the common factors.*

1 *Simplify.*

B $\dfrac{12b^3c^2}{5ac} \cdot \dfrac{15a^2b}{3b^2c}$

$\dfrac{(12)(15)a^2(b^3 \cdot b)c^2}{(5)(3)ab^2(c \cdot c)}$ *Multiply the numerators and the denominators. Arrange the expression so like variables are together.*

$\dfrac{180a^2b^4c^2}{15ab^2c^2}$ *Simplify.*

$12a^1b^2c^0$ *Divide out common factors. Use properties of exponents.*

$12ab^2$ *Simplify. Remember that $c^0 = 1$.*

C $\dfrac{5x^2}{2y^3} \cdot \dfrac{3x}{2y^2}$

$\dfrac{15x^3}{4y^5}$ *Multiply. There are no common factors, so the product cannot be simplified.*

Remember!

Review the Quotient of Powers Property in Lesson 7-4.

$\dfrac{a^m}{a^n} = a^{m-n}$

**CHECK IT OUT!** **Multiply. Simplify your answer.**

1a. $\dfrac{(c-4)}{5} \cdot \dfrac{45}{(-4c+16)}$

1b. $\dfrac{5y^5z}{3xy^2z} \cdot \dfrac{2x^4y^2}{4xy}$

EXAMPLE 2 Multiplying a Rational Expression by a Polynomial

Multiply $(x^2 + 8x + 15)\dfrac{4}{2x+6}$. Simplify your answer.

Remember!

Just as you can write an integer as a fraction, you can write any expression as a rational expression by writing it with a denominator of 1.

$\dfrac{x^2 + 8x + 15}{1} \cdot \dfrac{4}{2x+6}$ *Write the polynomial over 1.*

$\dfrac{(x+3)(x+5)}{1} \cdot \dfrac{4}{2(x+3)}$ *Factor the numerator and denominator.*

$\dfrac{(\cancel{x+3})(x+5)\cancel{4}^2}{\cancel{2}\cancel{(x+3)}}$ *Divide out common factors.*

$2x + 10$ *Multiply remaining factors.*

**CHECK IT OUT!** **2.** Multiply $\dfrac{m-5}{m^2 - 4m - 12} \cdot 3m + 6$. Simplify your answer.

There are two methods for simplifying rational expressions. You can **simplify first** by dividing out common factors and **then multiply** the remaining factors. You can also **multiply first** and **then simplify**. Using either method will result in the same answer.

EXAMPLE 3 Multiplying Rational Expressions Containing Polynomials

Multiply $\dfrac{4d^3 + 4d}{16f} \cdot \dfrac{2f}{7d^2f + 7f}$. Simplify your answer.

Method 1 Simplify first.

$\dfrac{4d^3 + 4d}{16f} \cdot \dfrac{2f}{7d^2f + 7f}$

$\dfrac{4d(d^2 + 1)}{16f} \cdot \dfrac{2f}{7f(d^2 + 1)}$ *Factor.*

$\dfrac{\cancel{4}d\cancel{(d^2+1)}}{\cancel{16}^2 f} \cdot \dfrac{\cancel{2}f}{7f\cancel{(d^2+1)}}$ *Divide out common factors.*

Then multiply.

$\dfrac{d}{14f}$ *Simplify.*

Method 2 Multiply first.

$\dfrac{4d^3 + 4d}{16f} \cdot \dfrac{2f}{7d^2f + 7f}$

$\dfrac{(4d^3 + 4d)2f}{16f(7d^2f + 7f)}$ *Multiply.*

$\dfrac{8d^3f + 8df}{112d^2f^2 + 112f^2}$ *Distribute.*

Then simplify.

$\dfrac{8df(d^2 + 1)}{112f^2(d^2 + 1)}$ *Factor.*

$\dfrac{\cancel{8}df\cancel{(d^2+1)}}{\cancel{112}^{14} f^{\cancel{2}f}\cancel{(d^2+1)}}$ *Divide out common factors.*

$\dfrac{d}{14f}$ *Simplify.*

**CHECK IT OUT!** **Multiply. Simplify your answer.**

3a. $\dfrac{n-5}{n^2 + 4n} \cdot \dfrac{n^2 + 8n + 16}{n^2 - 3n - 10}$

3b. $\dfrac{p+4}{p^2 + 2p} \cdot \dfrac{p^2 - 3p - 10}{p^2 + 16}$

The rules for dividing rational expressions are the same as the rules for dividing fractions. To divide by a rational expression, multiply by its reciprocal.

Dividing Rational Expressions

If a, b, c, and d are nonzero polynomials, then $\dfrac{a}{b} \div \dfrac{c}{d} = \dfrac{a}{b} \cdot \dfrac{d}{c} = \dfrac{ad}{bc}$.

E X A M P L E 4 Dividing by Rational Expressions and Polynomials

Divide. Simplify your answer.

A $\dfrac{1}{x} \div \dfrac{x-2}{2x}$

$\dfrac{1}{x} \cdot \dfrac{2x}{x-2}$ *Write as multiplication by the reciprocal.*

$\dfrac{1(2x)}{x(x-2)}$ *Multiply the numerators and the denominators.*

$\dfrac{2\cancel{x}}{\cancel{x}(x-2)}$ *Divide out common factors.*

$\dfrac{2}{x-2}$ *Simplify.*

B $\dfrac{x^2-2x}{x} \div \dfrac{2-x}{x^2+2x+1}$

$\dfrac{x^2-2x}{x} \cdot \dfrac{x^2+2x+1}{2-x}$ *Write as multiplication by the reciprocal.*

$\dfrac{x(x-2)}{x} \cdot \dfrac{(x+1)(x+1)}{2-x}$ *Factor.*

$\dfrac{x(x-2)}{x} \cdot \dfrac{(x+1)(x+1)}{-1(x-2)}$ *Rewrite one opposite binomial.*

$\dfrac{\cancel{x}\cancel{(x-2)}^1}{\cancel{x}} \cdot \dfrac{(x+1)(x+1)}{-1\cancel{(x-2)}}$ *Divide out common factors.*

$-(x+1)^2$ *Multiply.*

C $\dfrac{3a^2b}{b} \div (3a^2+6a)$

$\dfrac{3a^2b}{b} \div \dfrac{3a^2+6a}{1}$ *Write the binomial over 1.*

$\dfrac{3a^2b}{b} \cdot \dfrac{1}{3a^2+6a}$ *Write as multiplication by the reciprocal.*

$\dfrac{3a^2b}{b(3a^2+6a)}$ *Multiply the numerators and the denominators.*

$\dfrac{\cancel{3}\cancel{a^2}^a\cancel{b}}{\cancel{b}[\cancel{3}\cancel{a}(a+2)]}$ *Factor. Divide out common factors.*

$\dfrac{a}{(a+2)}$ *Simplify.*

 **Divide. Simplify your answer.**

4a. $\dfrac{3}{x^2} \div \dfrac{x^3}{(x-5)}$ **4b.** $\dfrac{18vw^2}{6v} \div \dfrac{3v^2x^4}{2w^4x}$

4c. $\dfrac{x^2-x}{x+2} \div (x^2+2x-3)$

EXAMPLE 5 **Probability Application**

Marty is playing a carnival game. He needs to pick two items out of a bag without looking. The bag has red and blue items. There are three more red items than blue items.

a. Write and simplify an expression that represents the probability that Marty will pick two blue items without replacing the first item.

Let x = the number of blue items.

Blue	+	Red	=	Total
x	+	$x+3$	=	$2x+3$

Write expressions for the number of each color item and for the total number of items.

The probability of picking a blue item and then another blue item is the product of the probabilities of the individual events.

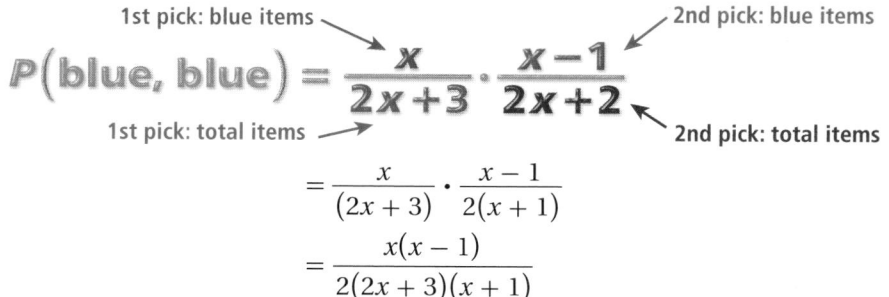

1st pick: blue items   2nd pick: blue items

$$P(\text{blue, blue}) = \frac{x}{2x+3} \cdot \frac{x-1}{2x+2}$$

1st pick: total items   2nd pick: total items

$$= \frac{x}{(2x+3)} \cdot \frac{x-1}{2(x+1)}$$

$$= \frac{x(x-1)}{2(2x+3)(x+1)}$$

b. What is the probability that Marty picks two blue items if there are 10 blue items in the bag before his first pick? Round your answer to the nearest hundredth.

Since x represents the number of blue items, substitute 10 for x.

$$P(\text{blue, blue}) = \frac{10(10-1)}{2(2 \cdot 10 + 3)(10+1)}$$ *Substitute.*

$$= \frac{10(9)}{2(23)(11)} = \frac{90}{506} \approx 0.18$$ *Use the order of operations to simplify.*

The probability is approximately 0.18.

5. What if...? There are 50 blue items in the bag before Marty's first pick. What is the probability that Marty picks two blue items? Round your answer to the nearest hundredth.

THINK AND DISCUSS

1. Explain how to divide by a polynomial.

2. GET ORGANIZED Copy and complete the graphic organizer. In each box, describe how to perform the operation with rational expressions.

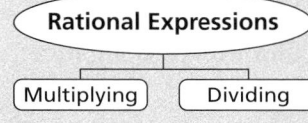

Rational Expressions

Multiplying   Dividing

10-4 **Exercises**

California Standards Practice

🔑 **13.0, 25.2**

go.hrw.com
Homework Help Online
KEYWORD: MA8CA 10-4
Parent Resources Online
KEYWORD: MA8CA Parent

GUIDED PRACTICE

SEE EXAMPLE **1**
p. 652

Multiply. Simplify your answer.

1. $\dfrac{4hj^2}{10j^3} \cdot \dfrac{3h^3k}{h^3k^3}$

2. $\dfrac{4y}{x^5} \cdot \dfrac{2yz^2}{9x^2}$

3. $\dfrac{x-2}{x+3} \cdot \dfrac{4x+12}{6}$

4. $\dfrac{ab}{c} \cdot \dfrac{2a^2}{3c}$

5. $\dfrac{7c^4d}{10c} \cdot \dfrac{5a}{21c^3d}$

6. $\dfrac{12p^2q}{5p} \cdot \dfrac{15p^4q^3}{12q}$

SEE EXAMPLE **2**
p. 653

7. $\dfrac{12}{4y+8}(y^2-4)$

8. $\dfrac{x+2}{6x^2}(5x+10)$

9. $\dfrac{3m}{6m+18}(m^2-7m-30)$

10. $\dfrac{4p}{8p+16}(p^2-5p-14)$

11. $\dfrac{a^2}{a}(a^2+10a+25)$

12. $\dfrac{-c}{4c+4}(c^2-c-2)$

SEE EXAMPLE **3**
p. 653

13. $\dfrac{a^2+6ab}{b} \cdot \dfrac{5+3a}{3a^2b+5ab}$

14. $\dfrac{x^2+5x+4}{x-4} \cdot \dfrac{x^2-2x-8}{x^2+6x+8}$

15. $\dfrac{j-1}{j^2-4j+3} \cdot \dfrac{j^2-5j+6}{2j-4}$

16. $\dfrac{p^3+4pq}{p} \cdot \dfrac{6q^3-8}{2q}$

17. $\dfrac{r^2+15r+14}{r^2-16} \cdot \dfrac{2r+8}{r+1}$

18. $\dfrac{y-8}{y^2-1} \cdot \dfrac{y+2}{y^2-49}$

SEE EXAMPLE **4**
p. 654

Divide. Simplify your answer.

19. $\dfrac{3a^4b}{2a^2c^3} \div \dfrac{12a^2c}{8c^4}$

20. $\dfrac{2m^3+2m}{m^2-2m} \div \dfrac{4m^2+4}{m-1}$

21. $\dfrac{x^2+4x-5}{3x-3} \div (x^2-25)$

SEE EXAMPLE **5**
p. 655

22. **Probability** While playing a game, Rachel pulls two tiles out of a bag without looking and without replacing the first tile. The bag has two colors of tiles—black and white. There are 10 more white tiles than black tiles.

   a. Write and simplify an expression that represents the probability that Rachel will pick a black tile, then a white tile.

   b. What is the probability that Rachel pulls a black tile and then a white tile if there are 5 black tiles in the bag before her first pick? Round your answer to the nearest hundredth.

PRACTICE AND PROBLEM SOLVING

Independent Practice

For Exercises	See Example
23–25	1
26–28	2
29–31	3
32–34	4
35	5

Extra Practice
Skills Practice p. EP21
Application Practice p. EP33

Multiply. Simplify your answer.

23. $\dfrac{p^6q^2}{7r^3} \cdot \dfrac{-3p^2}{r}$

24. $\dfrac{3r^2t}{6st^3} \cdot \dfrac{2r^2s^3t^2}{8r^4s^2}$

25. $\dfrac{10}{y+5} \cdot \dfrac{y+2}{3}$

26. $\dfrac{3}{2a+6}(a^2+4a+3)$

27. $\dfrac{4m^2-8m}{m^2+6m-16}(m^2+7m-8)$

28. $\dfrac{x}{2x^2-12x+18}(2x^2-4x-6)$

29. $\dfrac{6n^2+18n}{n^2+9n+8} \cdot \dfrac{n^2-1}{2n+6}$

30. $\dfrac{3a^2b}{5a^3+10a^2b} \cdot \dfrac{2a+4b}{6a^3b+6a^2b^2}$

31. $\dfrac{t^2-100}{5t+50} \cdot \dfrac{5}{t-10}$

Divide. Simplify your answer.

32. $\dfrac{6j^2k^5}{5j} \div \dfrac{4j^3k^3}{3j}$

33. $\dfrac{a-4}{a^2} \div (8a-2a^2)$

34. $\dfrac{x^2-9}{x^2+6x+9} \div \dfrac{4x^2-12x}{16x}$

35. Entertainment A carnival game board is covered completely in small balloons. You throw darts at the board and try to pop the balloons.

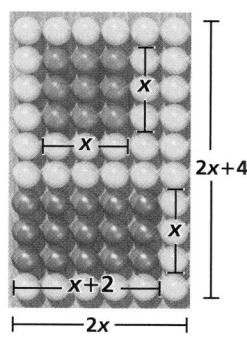

   a. Write and simplify an expression describing the probability that the next two balloons popped are red and then blue. (*Hint:* Write the probabilities as ratios of the areas of rectangles.)

   b. What is the probability that the next two balloons popped are red and then blue if $x = 3$?

36. ///ERROR ANALYSIS/// Which is incorrect? Explain the error.

A

$$\frac{4a^2 - b^2}{a^2} \cdot \frac{a}{2a - b}$$

$$\frac{\overset{2}{\cancel{4}}a^2 - b^2}{\cancel{a}^2} \cdot \frac{\cancel{a}}{\cancel{2}\cancel{a} - b} = -\frac{2 - b^2}{b}$$

B

$$\frac{4a^2 - b^2}{a^2} \cdot \frac{a}{2a - b}$$

$$\frac{(2a - b)(2a + b)}{\cancel{a}a^2} \cdot \frac{\cancel{a}}{2a - b} = \frac{2a + b}{a}$$

37. Critical Thinking Which of the following expressions is NOT equivalent to the other three? Explain why.

   a. $\dfrac{4x^2}{x^2 - 3x} \cdot \dfrac{2x - 6}{8y^2}$

   b. $\dfrac{6xy^2}{x^2} \div \dfrac{3y^4}{2x^2}$

   c. $\dfrac{10x^4y}{5xy^2} \div 2x^2y$

   d. $\dfrac{4x}{xy^2 + 2y^2} \cdot \dfrac{x^2 - 4}{4x - 8}$

Multiply or divide. Simplify your answer.

38. $\dfrac{5p^3}{p^2q} \cdot \dfrac{2q^3}{p^2}$

39. $\dfrac{6m^2 - 18m}{12m^3 + 12m^2} \div \dfrac{m^2 - 9}{m^2 + 4m + 3}$

40. $\dfrac{2x^2}{4x - 8} \cdot \dfrac{x^2 - 5x + 6}{x^5}$

41. $\dfrac{x^2 - 9}{4x} \div \left(4x^2 - 36\right)$

42. $\dfrac{33m - 3m^2}{-2m - 4} \div \dfrac{6m - 66}{m^2 - 4m}$

43. $\dfrac{12w^4x^7}{3w^3} \cdot \dfrac{w^{-1}x^{-7}}{4}$

44. Write About It Explain how to divide $\frac{1}{m} \div \frac{3}{4m}$.

45. This problem will prepare you for the Concept Connection on page 684.

The size of an image projected on a screen depends on how far the object is from the lens, the magnification of the lens, and the distance between the image and the lens. Magnification of a lens is $M = \frac{I}{O} = \frac{y}{x}$ where I is the height of the image, O is the height of the object, x is the distance of the object from the lens, and y is the distance of the image from the lens.

   a. If an object 16 cm high is placed 15 cm from the lens, it forms an image 60 cm from the lens. What is the height of the image?

   b. Marie moves the same object to a distance of 20 cm from the lens. If the image is the same size as part **a**, what is the distance between the image and the lens?

   c. What is the magnification of the lens?

CONCEPT CONNECTION

Multiple Choice For Exercises 46–48, choose the best answer.

46. Which expression is equivalent to $\dfrac{t+4}{9} \cdot \dfrac{t+4}{3}$?

(A) $\dfrac{(t+4)^2}{27}$ (B) $\dfrac{t^2+16}{27}$ (C) $\dfrac{1}{3}$ (D) $\dfrac{1}{27}$

47. Identify the product $-\dfrac{20b^2}{a^2} \cdot \dfrac{3ab}{15b}$.

(A) $-\dfrac{a}{4b^2}$ (B) $-4b^2$ (C) $-\dfrac{4b^2}{a}$ (D) $-\dfrac{b^2}{4a}$

48. Which of the following is equivalent to $\dfrac{2x}{x+5}$?

(A) $\dfrac{x-2}{8x} \cdot \dfrac{4}{x^2+3x-10}$ (C) $\dfrac{x-2}{4} \div \dfrac{x^2+3x-10}{8x}$

(B) $\dfrac{x^2-3x-10}{8x} \cdot \dfrac{4}{x-2}$ (D) $\dfrac{x^2-3x-10}{4} \div \dfrac{x-2}{8x}$

49. Short Response Simplify $\dfrac{x^2-10x+24}{3x^2-12x} \div (x^2-3x-18)$. Show your work.

CHALLENGE AND EXTEND

Simplify.

50. $\dfrac{x-3}{3x-6} \cdot \dfrac{3x+12}{x+1} \cdot \dfrac{2x-4}{x^2+x-12}$ **51.** $\dfrac{x^2-1}{x+2} \div \dfrac{3x+3}{x+2} \div (x-1)$

A *complex fraction* is a fraction that contains one or more fractions in the numerator or the denominator. Simplify each complex fraction.

$\left(\textit{Hint: }\text{Use the rule } \dfrac{\frac{a}{b}}{\frac{c}{d}} = \dfrac{a}{b} \div \dfrac{c}{d}.\right)$

52. $\dfrac{\frac{c+5}{c^2-4}}{\frac{c^2+6c+5}{c+2}}$ **53.** $\dfrac{\frac{x^2y}{xz^3}}{\frac{x^2y}{x^2z}}$ **54.** $\dfrac{\frac{x^2}{2} \cdot \frac{x}{3}}{\frac{x}{6}}$ **55.** $\dfrac{\frac{a+1}{a^2+6a+5}}{\frac{2a+2}{a+5}}$

 SPIRAL STANDARDS REVIEW  4.0, 8.0, 12.0

56. Danny runs laps around the track each week. This week, he wants to run at least 12 laps. He ran 3 laps earlier in the week, and today he ran 2 laps. Write and solve an inequality to determine how many more laps Danny has to run to meet his goal. *(Lesson 3-4)*

57. Pierce has $30 to spend on a night out. He already spent $12 on dinner and $9 on a movie ticket. He will spend some money m on movie-theatre snacks. Write and solve an inequality that will show all the values of m that Pierce can spend on snacks. *(Lesson 3-4)*

Identify which lines are parallel. *(Lesson 5-7)*

58. $y = 3x + 4;\ y = 7;\ y = -3x + 4,\ y = 2$

59. $y = 5x - 7;\ y = -x + 5;\ y = -x - 7,\ y = 5x + 5$

60. $y = -7x;\ y = 12;\ y = -x + 4,\ y = -7x + 5$

Simplify each rational expression, if possible. Identify any excluded values. *(Lesson 10-3)*

61. $\dfrac{x+2}{x^2-4}$ **62.** $\dfrac{2(x-3)}{3(x+4)}$ **63.** $\dfrac{4x-10}{2x^2-8}$

10-5 Adding and Subtracting Rational Expressions

Who uses this?

Kayakers can use rational expressions to figure out travel time for different river trips. (See Example 5.)

The rules for adding rational expressions are the same as the rules for adding fractions. If the denominators are the same, you add the numerators and keep the common denominator.

$$\frac{3}{8} + \frac{2}{8} = \frac{3+2}{8} = \frac{5}{8}$$

Know it! Note

> **Adding Rational Expressions with Like Denominators**
>
> If a, b, and c represent polynomials and $c \neq 0$, then $\frac{a}{c} + \frac{b}{c} = \frac{a+b}{c}$.

EXAMPLE 1 **Adding Rational Expressions with Like Denominators**

Add. Simplify your answer.

A $\dfrac{3b}{b^2} + \dfrac{5b}{b^2}$

$\dfrac{3b + 5b}{b^2} = \dfrac{8\cancel{b}}{\cancel{b}^{2\,b}}$ *Combine like terms in the numerator. Divide out common factors.*

$= \dfrac{8}{b}$ *Simplify.*

B $\dfrac{x^2 - 8x}{x - 4} + \dfrac{2x + 8}{x - 4}$

$\dfrac{x^2 - 8x + 2x + 8}{x - 4} = \dfrac{x^2 - 6x + 8}{x - 4}$ *Combine like terms in the numerator.*

$= \dfrac{(x - 2)(x - 4)}{x - 4}$ *Factor. Divide out common factors.*

$= x - 2$ *Simplify.*

C $\dfrac{2m + 4}{m^2 - 9} + \dfrac{2}{m^2 - 9}$

$\dfrac{2m + 4 + 2}{m^2 - 9} = \dfrac{2m + 6}{m^2 - 9}$ *Combine like terms in the numerator.*

$= \dfrac{2(m + 3)}{(m - 3)(m + 3)}$ *Factor. Divide out common factors.*

$= \dfrac{2}{m - 3}$ *Simplify.*

CHECK IT OUT!   Add. Simplify your answer.

1a. $\dfrac{n}{2n} + \dfrac{3n}{2n}$ **1b.** $\dfrac{3y^2}{y + 1} + \dfrac{3y}{y + 1}$

EXAMPLE 2 Subtracting Rational Expressions with Like Denominators

Subtract. Simplify your answer.

$$\frac{3m-6}{m^2+m-6} - \frac{-m+2}{m^2+m-6}$$

$$\frac{3m-6-(-m+2)}{m^2+m-6} = \frac{3m-6+m-2}{m^2+m-6} \qquad \textit{Subtract numerators.}$$

$$= \frac{4m-8}{m^2+m-6} \qquad \textit{Combine like terms.}$$

$$= \frac{4(m-2)}{(m+3)(m-2)} \qquad \textit{Factor. Divide out common factors.}$$

$$= \frac{4}{m+3} \qquad \textit{Simplify.}$$

 **Caution!**

Make sure you add the opposite of each term in the numerator of the second expression when subtracting rational expressions.

 **CHECK IT OUT!** Subtract. Simplify your answer.

2a. $\dfrac{5a+2}{a^2-4} - \dfrac{2a-4}{a^2-4}$
 2b. $\dfrac{2b+14}{b^2+3b-4} - \dfrac{-2b+2}{b^2+3b-4}$

As with fractions, rational expressions must have a common denominator before they can be added or subtracted. If they do not have a common denominator, you can use any common multiple of the denominators to find one. You can also use the least common multiple (LCM) of the denominators.

To find the LCM of two expressions, write the prime factorization of both expressions. Line up the factors as shown. To find the LCM, multiply one number from each column.

$$6x^2 = 2 \quad\ \cdot 3 \cdot x \cdot x \qquad\qquad 5x+15 = 5(x+3)$$
$$8x = 2 \cdot 2 \cdot 2 \cdot\ \ \cdot x \qquad\qquad x^2-9 = \ \ (x+3)(x-3)$$
$$\text{LCM} = 2 \cdot 2 \cdot 2 \cdot 3 \cdot x \cdot x = 24x^2 \qquad \text{LCM} = 5(x+3)(x-3)$$

EXAMPLE 3 Identifying the Least Common Multiple

Find the LCM of the given expressions.

A $24a^3, 4a$

$$24a^3 = 2 \cdot 2 \cdot 2 \cdot 3 \cdot a \cdot a \cdot a \qquad \textit{Write the prime factorization of each}$$
$$4a = 2 \cdot 2 \cdot \qquad\qquad\ a \qquad\qquad\quad \textit{expression. Align common factors.}$$
$$\text{LCM} = 2 \cdot 2 \cdot 2 \cdot 3 \cdot a \cdot a \cdot a = 24a^3$$

B $2d^2 + 10d + 12, d^2 + 7d + 12$

$$2d^2 + 10d + 12 = 2(d^2 + 5d + 6) \qquad \textit{Factor each expression.}$$
$$= 2(d+3)(d+2) \qquad \textit{Align common factors.}$$
$$d^2 + 7d + 12 = \ \ (d+3) \qquad\quad (d+4)$$
$$\text{LCM} = 2(d+3)(d+2)(d+4)$$

 **CHECK IT OUT!** Find the LCM of the given expressions.

3a. $5f^2h, 15fh^2$
 3b. $x^2 - 4x - 12, (x-6)(x+5)$

The LCM of the denominators of rational expressions is also called the least common denominator, or LCD, of the rational expressions. You can use the LCD to add or subtract rational expressions.

Adding or Subtracting Rational Expressions
Step 1 Identify a common denominator.
Step 2 Multiply each expression by an appropriate form of 1 so that each term has the common denominator as its denominator.
Step 3 Write each expression using the common denominator.
Step 4 Add or subtract the numerators, combining like terms as needed.
Step 5 Factor as needed.
Step 6 Simplify as needed.

EXAMPLE 4 **Adding and Subtracting with Unlike Denominators**

Add or subtract. Simplify your answer.

A $\dfrac{3x}{6x^2} + \dfrac{2x}{4x}$

$$6x^2 = 2 \quad \cdot 3 \cdot x \cdot x$$

Step 1 $\quad 4x = 2 \cdot 2 \quad \cdot x \qquad$ *Identify the LCD.*

$$\text{LCD} = 2 \cdot 2 \cdot 3 \cdot x \cdot x = 12x^2$$

Step 2 $\dfrac{3x}{6x^2}\left(\dfrac{2}{2}\right) + \dfrac{2x}{4x}\left(\dfrac{3x}{3x}\right) \qquad$ *Multiply each expression by an appropriate form of 1.*

Step 3 $\quad \dfrac{6x}{12x^2} + \dfrac{6x^2}{12x^2} \qquad$ *Write each expression using the LCD.*

Step 4 $\quad \dfrac{6x + 6x^2}{12x^2} \qquad$ *Add the numerators.*

Step 5 $\quad \dfrac{\cancel{6}x(1 + x)}{\cancel{6} \cdot 2x^{\cancel{2}x}} \qquad$ *Factor and divide out common factors.*

Step 6 $\quad \dfrac{1 + x}{2x} \qquad$ *Simplify.*

> **Remember!**
>
> Expressions like $m - 3$ and $3 - m$ are opposite binomials.
> $3 - m = -1(m - 3)$
> and
> $m - 3 = -1(3 - m)$

B $\dfrac{1}{m - 3} - \dfrac{5}{3 - m}$

Step 1 The denominators are **opposite binomials**.
The LCD can be either $m - 3$ or $3 - m$. *Identify the LCD.*

Step 2 $\dfrac{1}{m - 3} - \dfrac{5}{3 - m}\left(\dfrac{-1}{-1}\right) \qquad$ *Multiply the second expression by $\frac{-1}{-1}$ to get an LCD of $m - 3$.*

Step 3 $\quad \dfrac{1}{m - 3} - \dfrac{-5}{m - 3} \qquad$ *Write each expression using the LCD.*

Step 4 $\quad \dfrac{1 - (-5)}{m - 3} \qquad$ *Subtract the numerators.*

Steps 5, 6 $\quad \dfrac{6}{m - 3} \qquad$ *No factoring is needed, so just simplify.*

 Add or subtract. Simplify your answer.

4a. $\dfrac{4}{3d} - \dfrac{2d}{2d^3}$ **4b.** $\dfrac{a^2 + 4a}{a^2 + 2a - 8} + \dfrac{8}{a - 2}$

EXAMPLE 5 *Recreation Application*

Katy wants to find out how long it will take to kayak 1 mile up a river and return to her starting point. Katy's average paddling rate is 4 times the speed of the river's current.

a. **Write and simplify an expression for the time it will take Katy to kayak the round-trip in terms of the rate of the river's current.**

> **Step 1** Write expressions for the distances and rates in the problem. The **distance** in both directions is **1 mile.**
>
> Let x represent the rate of the current, and let $4x$ represent Katy's paddling rate.
>
> Katy's **rate against the current** is $4x - x$, or $3x$.
>
> Katy's **rate with the current** is $4x + x$, or $5x$.
>
> **Step 2** Use a table to write expressions for time.

Helpful Hint

To write expressions for time in terms of distance and rate, solve $d = rt$ for t.

$$t = \frac{d}{r}$$

Direction	Distance (mi)	Rate (mi/h)	Time (h) $= \frac{\text{distance}}{\text{rate}}$
Upstream (against current)	1	$3x$	$\frac{1}{3x}$
Downstream (with current)	1	$5x$	$\frac{1}{5x}$

> **Step 3** Write and simplify an expression for the total time.
>
> total time = time upstream + time downstream

$$\text{total time} = \frac{1}{3x} + \frac{1}{5x} \qquad \textit{Substitute known values.}$$

$$= \frac{1}{3x}\left(\frac{5}{5}\right) + \frac{1}{5x}\left(\frac{3}{3}\right) \qquad \textit{Multiply each fraction by an appropriate form of 1.}$$

$$= \frac{5}{15x} + \frac{3}{15x} \qquad \textit{Write each expression using the LCD, 15x.}$$

$$= \frac{8}{15x} \qquad \textit{Add the numerators.}$$

b. **The rate of the river is 2 miles per hour. How long will it take Katy to kayak round trip?**

$$\frac{8}{15(2)} = \frac{4}{15} \qquad \textit{Substitute 2 for x. Simplify.}$$

It will take Katy $\frac{4}{15}$ of an hour, or 16 minutes, to kayak the round-trip.

 **CHECK IT OUT!** **5. What if?...** Katy's average paddling rate increases to 5 times the speed of the current. Now how long will it take Katy to kayak the round trip?

THINK AND DISCUSS

1. Explain how to find the least common denominator of rational expressions.

2. GET ORGANIZED Copy and complete the graphic organizer. In each box, compare and contrast operations with fractions and rational expressions.

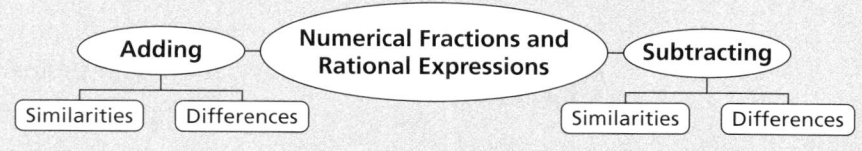

10-5
Exercises

California Standards Practice
🔑 13.0, 🔑 15.0, 25.2

go.hrw.com
Homework Help Online
KEYWORD: MA8CA 10-5
Parent Resources Online
KEYWORD: MA8CA Parent

GUIDED PRACTICE

SEE EXAMPLE 1
p. 659

Add. Simplify your answer.

1. $\dfrac{y}{3y^2} + \dfrac{5y}{3y^2}$

2. $\dfrac{4m+30}{m+5} + \dfrac{m^2+8m+5}{m+5}$

3. $\dfrac{x}{x^2-16} + \dfrac{4}{x^2-16}$

SEE EXAMPLE 2
p. 660

Subtract. Simplify your answer.

4. $\dfrac{7}{2x^3} - \dfrac{3}{2x^3}$

5. $\dfrac{7a-2}{a^2+3a+2} - \dfrac{5a-6}{a^2+3a+2}$

6. $\dfrac{3x^2+1}{2x+2} - \dfrac{2x^2-2x}{2x+2}$

SEE EXAMPLE 3
p. 660

Find the LCM of the given expressions.

7. $3xy^2,\ 6x^3yz$

8. $x^2+9x+20,\ (x+5)(x-4)$

9. $y^2-16,\ (y+9)(y-4)$

SEE EXAMPLE 4
p. 661

Add or subtract. Simplify your answer.

10. $\dfrac{3}{c} - \dfrac{4}{3c}$

11. $\dfrac{x^2+x}{x^2+3x+2} + \dfrac{3}{x+2}$

12. $\dfrac{2x}{x-5} + \dfrac{x}{5-x}$

SEE EXAMPLE 5
p. 662

13. **Travel** The Escobar family went on a car trip. They drove 100 miles on country roads and 240 miles on the highway. They drove 50% faster on the highway than on the country roads. Let r represent their rate on country roads in miles per hour.

   a. Write and simplify an expression that represents the number of hours it took the Escobar family to complete their trip in terms of r. (*Hint:* 50% faster means 150% of the original rate.)

   b. Find their total travel time if they drove the posted speed limit.

PRACTICE AND PROBLEM SOLVING

Independent Practice	
For Exercises	See Example
14–16	1
17–19	2
20–25	3
26–31	4
32	5

Extra Practice
Skills Practice p. EP21
Application Practice p. EP33

Add. Simplify your answer.

14. $\dfrac{4y}{y^3} + \dfrac{4y}{y^3}$

15. $\dfrac{a^2-3}{a+3} + \dfrac{2a}{a+3}$

16. $\dfrac{4x-13}{x^2-5x+6} + \dfrac{1}{x^2-5x+6}$

Subtract. Simplify your answer.

17. $\dfrac{m^2}{m-6} - \dfrac{6m}{m-6}$

18. $\dfrac{c+3}{4c^2-25} - \dfrac{-c+8}{4c^2-25}$

19. $\dfrac{-2a^2-9a}{a-2} - \dfrac{-5a^2-4a+2}{a-2}$

Find the LCM of the given expressions.

20. $4jk^4m,\ 25jm$

21. $12a^2+4a,\ 27a+9$

22. $p^2-3p,\ pqr^2$

23. $5xy^2z,\ 10y^3$

24. $5x^2,\ 7x-14$

25. $y^2+7y+10,\ y^2+9y+20$

Add or subtract. Simplify your answer.

26. $\dfrac{2x}{5x} + \dfrac{10x}{3x^2}$

27. $\dfrac{y^2-y}{y^2-4y+3} - \dfrac{2y-2}{3y-9}$

28. $\dfrac{-3t}{t-4} - \dfrac{2t+4}{4-t}$

29. $\dfrac{z}{3z^2} + \dfrac{4}{7z}$

30. $\dfrac{5x}{2x-6} + \dfrac{x+2}{3-x}$

31. $\dfrac{3m}{4m-8} - \dfrac{m^2}{m^2-4m+4}$

32. Fitness Ira walks one mile from his house to the recreation center. After playing basketball, he walks home at only 85% of his normal walking speed. Let w be Ira's normal rate of walking.

   a. Write an expression to represent Ira's round-trip walking time.

   b. If Ira's normal rate of walking is 3 miles per hour, how long did it take for him to complete his walking?

33. Travel A train travels 500 miles across the Midwest—50 miles through cities and 450 miles through open country. As it passes through cities, it slows to one-fifth the speed it travels through open territory. Let r represent the rate in open territory in miles per hour.

   a. Write and simplify an expression that represents the number of hours it takes the train to travel 500 miles in terms of r.

   b. Find the total travel time if the train's rate through open territory is 50 miles per hour.

   c. Critical Thinking If you knew the time it took the train to make the round-trip, how could you find its average rate?

Add or subtract. Simplify your answer.

34. $\dfrac{10}{5+y} + \dfrac{2y}{5+y}$

35. $\dfrac{7}{49 - c^2} - \dfrac{c}{49 - c^2}$

36. $\dfrac{6a}{a - 12} + \dfrac{4}{12 - a}$

37. $\dfrac{b}{2b^3} + \dfrac{3}{3b^2}$

38. $\dfrac{r^2 + 2r}{r + 3} - \dfrac{2r + 9}{r + 3}$

39. $\dfrac{x^2 - 2x}{3x - 15} - \dfrac{8x - 25}{3x - 15}$

40. $\dfrac{2y}{8y^2} + \dfrac{9}{4y^3}$

41. $\dfrac{2}{x + 2} + \dfrac{6}{x + 4}$

42. $\dfrac{2y}{3y - 9} - \dfrac{y + 1}{y^2 - 9}$

43. ///**ERROR ANALYSIS**/// Two students were asked to find the excluded values of the expression $\dfrac{p}{p^2 - p - 12} - \dfrac{4}{p^2 - p - 12}$. Student A identified the excluded value as $p = -3$. Student B identified the excluded values as $p = -3$ and $p = 4$. Who is incorrect? What is the error?

44. Multi-Step At the spring fair there is a square Velcro target as shown. A player tosses a ball, which will stick to the target in some random spot. If the ball sticks to a spot in either the small square or the circle, the player wins a prize. What is the probability that a player will win a prize, assuming the ball sticks somewhere on the target? Round your answer to the nearest hundredth.

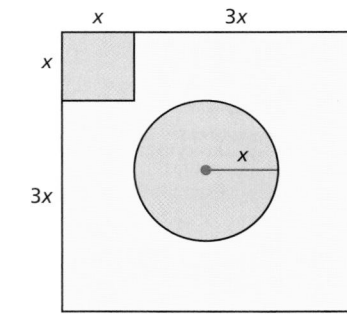

45. Critical Thinking Write two expressions whose sum is $\dfrac{x}{x + 1}$.

46. This problem will prepare you for the Concept Connection on page 684.

   Jonathan is studying light in his science class. He finds that a magnifying glass can be used to project upside-down images on a piece of paper. The equation $\dfrac{1}{f} = \dfrac{1}{x} + \dfrac{1}{y}$ relates the focal length of the lens f, the distance of the object from the lens x, and the distance of the image from the lens y. The focal length of Jonathan's lens is 12 cm.

   a. Jonathan wants to write y, the distance of the image from the lens, as a function of x, the distance of the object from the lens. To begin, he rewrote the equation as $\dfrac{1}{y} = \dfrac{1}{12} - \dfrac{1}{x}$. Explain how he did this.

   b. Explain how Jonathan simplified the equation in part **a** to $\dfrac{1}{y} = \dfrac{x - 12}{12x}$.

47. Critical Thinking Identify three common denominators that could be used to add $\frac{3}{2x^2}$ to $\frac{3}{4x}$.

48. Write About It Explain how to find the least common denominator of two rational expressions when the denominators are opposite binomials.

Multiple Choice For Exercises 49–51, choose the best answer.

49. What is the LCD of $\frac{6}{3p+3}$ and $\frac{4}{p+1}$?

    (A) $p+1$ (B) 12 (C) $3p+1$ (D) $3p+3$

50. Simplify $\frac{4}{2x} - \frac{1}{x}$.

    (A) $\frac{1}{x}$ (B) $\frac{3}{x}$ (C) $\frac{5}{x}$ (D) $\frac{3}{2x}$

51. Which of the following is equivalent to $\frac{2x}{x-2}$?

    (A) $\frac{x}{x+2} + \frac{x}{x-2}$ (C) $\frac{x^2+4x}{x^2-4} + \frac{x}{x+2}$

    (B) $\frac{2x}{x^2-4} + \frac{4}{x-2}$ (D) $\frac{x}{x+2} + \frac{x^2+6x}{x^2-4}$

52. Extended Response Andrea biked 3 miles to the post office and 5 miles to the library. The rate at which she biked to the library was three times faster than her rate to the post office r.

    a. Write an expression that represents Andrea's total biking time in hours. Explain what each part of your expression means in the situation.

    b. Simplify the expression.

    c. How long did it take Andrea to bike the 8 miles if her biking rate to the post office was 3 miles per hour?

CHALLENGE AND EXTEND

Add or subtract and simplify. Find the excluded values.

53. $\frac{3}{x+y} - \frac{2x+y}{x^2-y^2}$ **54.** $\frac{3}{2m} + \frac{4}{m^2} + \frac{2}{5m}$ **55.** $\frac{a}{xy} + \frac{b}{xz} + \frac{c}{yz}$

56. Simplify the complex fraction $\dfrac{\frac{1}{x} - \frac{1}{y}}{\frac{x}{xy} - \frac{1}{x}}$. (*Hint:* Simplify the numerator and denominator of the complex fraction first.)

Factor each polynomial. Check your answer. *(Lesson 8-2)*

57. $2x^2 - 5 - 13x + 4x^2$ **58.** $6a + 2a^3 - 2 - 10a^2$ **59.** $15h + 5h^2 - 20h - 60$

60. $12s^3 + 8s^2$ **61.** $56t^3 - 14t^2 - 42t$ **62.** $-10 + 2m^2 + m^3 - 5m$

Solve each quadratic equation by factoring. Check your answer. *(Lesson 9-5)*

63. $d^2 - 4d - 12 = 0$ **64.** $2g^2 - 9g = -4$ **65.** $9x^2 + 6x + 1 = 0$

Simplify each rational expression, if possible. Identify any excluded values. *(Lesson 10-3)*

66. $\frac{2t^2-8}{t^2-4}$ **67.** $\frac{n^2+5n}{n^2+3n-10}$ **68.** $\frac{4-x}{x^2-16}$

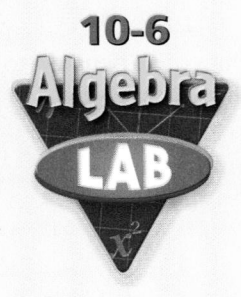

10-6
Algebra LAB

Use with Lesson 10-6

Model Polynomial Division

Some polynomial divisions can be modeled by algebra tiles. If a polynomial can be modeled by a rectangle, then its factors are represented by the length and width of the rectangle. If one factor is a divisor, then the other factor is a quotient.

California Standards

10.0 Students add, subtract, multiply, and **divide** monomials and **polynomials.** Students solve multistep problems, including word problems, by using these techniques.

KEY

$\boxed{+} = 1$

$\boxed{-} = -1$

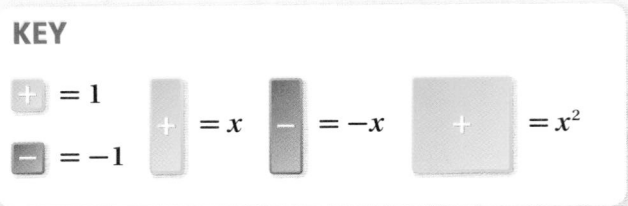

Activity 1

Use algebra tiles to find the quotient $(x^2 + 5x + 6) \div (x + 2)$.

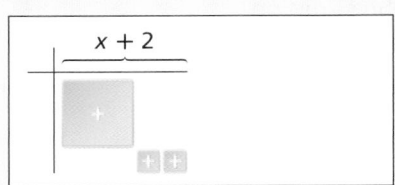

Model $x^2 + 5x + 6$.

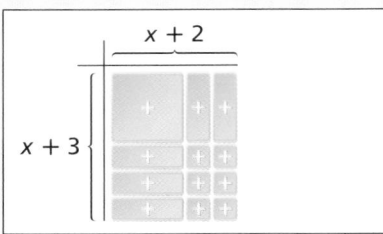

Try to form a rectangle with a length of $x + 2$.
Place the x^2-tile in the upper-left corner. Then place two unit tiles in a row at the lower-right corner.

Try to use all the remaining tiles to complete a rectangle.
If you can complete a rectangle, then the width of the rectangle is the quotient.

The rectangle has length $x + 2$ and width $x + 3$. So, $(x^2 + 5x + 6) \div (x + 2) = x + 3$.

You can check your answer by multiplying.

$(x + 3)(x + 2)$
$x^2 + 2x + 3x + 6$ *Use the FOIL method.*
$x^2 + 5x + 6$ ✓

Try This

Use algebra tiles to find each quotient.

1. $(x^2 + 5x + 4) \div (x + 1)$ **2.** $(x^2 + 7x + 10) \div (x + 5)$ **3.** $(x^2 + 4x - 5) \div (x - 1)$

4. $(2x^2 + 5x + 2) \div (x + 2)$ **5.** $(x^2 - 6x + 8) \div (x - 2)$ **6.** $(2x^2 - x - 3) \div (x + 1)$

7. Describe what happens when you try to model $(x^2 - 4x + 3) \div (x + 1)$.

10-6 Dividing Polynomials

California Standards

→ **10.0 Students** add, subtract, multiply, and **divide** monomials and **polynomials.** Students solve multistep problems, including word problems, by using these techniques.

→ **12.0 Students simplify fractions with polynomials in the numerator and denominator by factoring both and reducing them to the lowest terms.**

Why learn this?
Division of polynomials can be used to compare the energy produced by solar panels.

The electrical power (in watts) produced by a solar panel is directly proportional to the surface area of the solar panel. Division of polynomials can be used to compare energy production by solar panels of different sizes.

To divide a polynomial by a monomial, you can first write the division as a rational expression. Then divide each term in the polynomial by the monomial.

EXAMPLE **1** **Dividing a Polynomial by a Monomial**

Divide $(6x^3 + 8x^2 - 4x) \div 2x$.

$\dfrac{6x^3 + 8x^2 - 4x}{2x}$ *Write as a rational expression.*

$\dfrac{6x^3}{2x} + \dfrac{8x^2}{2x} - \dfrac{4x}{2x}$ *Divide each term in the polynomial by the monomial 2x.*

$\dfrac{\cancel{6}^{3}\cancel{x^3}^{x^2}}{\cancel{2}\cancel{x}} + \dfrac{\cancel{8}^{4}\cancel{x^2}^{x}}{\cancel{2}\cancel{x}} - \dfrac{\cancel{4}^{2}\cancel{x}}{\cancel{2}\cancel{x}}$ *Divide out common factors in each term.*

$3x^2 + 4x - 2$ *Simplify.*

CHECK IT OUT! **Divide. Check your answer.**

1a. $(8p^3 - 4p^2 + 12p) \div (-4p^2)$

1b. $(6x^3 + 2x - 15) \div 6x$

Division of a polynomial by a binomial is similar to division of whole numbers.

Know it!
note

Dividing Polynomials

		WORDS	NUMBERS	POLYNOMIALS
Step 1		Factor the numerator and/or denominator if possible.	$\dfrac{168}{3} = \dfrac{56 \cdot 3}{3}$	$\dfrac{r^2 + 3r + 2}{r + 2} = \dfrac{(r + 2)(r + 1)}{(r + 2)}$
Step 2		Divide out any common factors.	$\dfrac{56 \cdot \cancel{3}}{\cancel{3}}$	$\dfrac{\cancel{(r + 2)}(r + 1)}{\cancel{(r + 2)}}$
Step 3		Simplify.	56	$r + 1$

EXAMPLE 2 **Dividing a Polynomial by a Binomial**

Divide.

A $\dfrac{c^2 + 4c - 5}{c - 1}$

$\dfrac{(c + 5)(c - 1)}{c - 1}$ *Factor the numerator.*

$\dfrac{(c + 5)\cancel{(c - 1)}}{\cancel{(c - 1)}}$ *Divide out common factors.*

$c + 5$ *Simplify.*

B $\dfrac{3x^2 - 10x - 8}{4 - x}$

$\dfrac{(3x + 2)(x - 4)}{4 - x}$ *Factor the numerator.*

$\dfrac{(3x + 2)(x - 4)}{-1(x - 4)}$ *Factor one opposite binomial.*

$\dfrac{(3x + 2)\cancel{(x - 4)}}{-1\cancel{(x - 4)}}$ *Divide out common factors.*

$-3x - 2$ *Simplify.*

Helpful Hint

Put each term of the numerator over the denominator only when the denominator is a monomial. If the denominator is a polynomial, try to factor first.

Divide. Check your answer.

2a. $\dfrac{10 + 7k + k^2}{k + 2}$ **2b.** $\dfrac{b^2 - 49}{b + 7}$ **2c.** $\dfrac{s^2 + 12s + 36}{s + 6}$

Recall how you used long division to divide whole numbers as shown at right. You can also use long division to divide polynomials. An example is shown below.

$$\left(x^2 + 3x + 2\right) \div \left(x + 2\right)$$

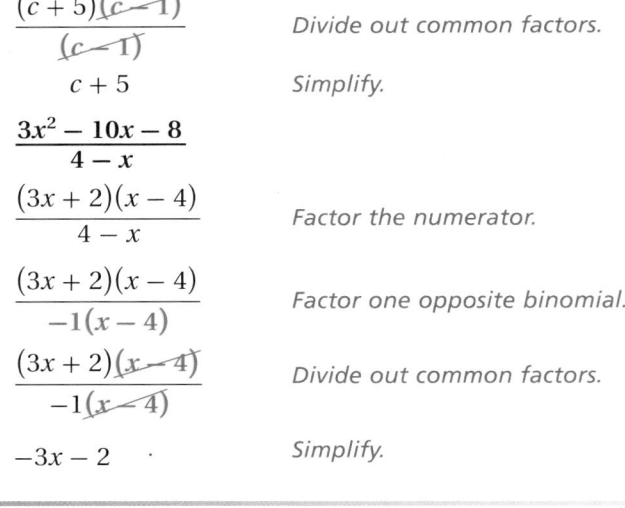

$$\begin{array}{r} 15 \\ 23\overline{)345} \\ -23 \\ \hline 115 \\ -115 \\ \hline 0 \end{array}$$

Using Long Division to Divide a Polynomial by a Binomial
Step 1 Write the binomial and polynomial in standard form.
Step 2 Divide the first term of the dividend by the first term of the divisor. This is the first term of the quotient.
Step 3 Multiply this first term of the quotient by the binomial divisor and place the product under the dividend, aligning like terms.
Step 4 Subtract the product from the dividend.
Step 5 Bring down the next term in the dividend.
Step 6 Repeat Steps 2–5 as necessary until you get 0 or until the degree of the remainder is less than the degree of the binomial.

EXAMPLE **3** **Polynomial Long Division**

Divide using long division. Check your answer.

A $(x^2 + 2 + 3x) \div (x + 2)$

Step 1 $x + 2 \overline{)x^2 + 3x + 2}$

Write in long division form with expressions in standard form.

Step 2 $x + 2 \overline{)\begin{matrix} x \\ x^2 + 3x + 2 \end{matrix}}$

*Divide the first term of the dividend by the first term of the divisor to get the **first term of the quotient**.*

Step 3 $x + 2 \overline{)\begin{matrix} x \\ x^2 + 3x + 2 \\ \underline{x^2 + 2x} \end{matrix}}$

*Multiply the **first term of the quotient** by the binomial divisor. Place the product under the dividend, aligning like terms.*

Step 4 $x + 2 \overline{)\begin{matrix} x \\ x^2 + 3x + 2 \\ \underline{-(x^2 + 2x)} \\ 0 + x \end{matrix}}$

Subtract the product from the dividend.

Step 5 $x + 2 \overline{)\begin{matrix} x \\ x^2 + 3x + 2 \\ \underline{-(x^2 + 2x)} \downarrow \\ x + 2 \end{matrix}}$

Bring down the next term in the dividend.

Step 6 $x + 2 \overline{)\begin{matrix} x + 1 \\ x^2 + 3x + 2 \\ \underline{-(x^2 + 2x)} \\ x + 2 \\ \underline{-(x + 2)} \\ 0 \end{matrix}}$

Repeat Steps 2–5 as necessary.
The remainder is 0.

Helpful Hint

When the remainder is 0, you can check your simplified answer by multiplying it by the divisor. You should get the numerator.

Check Multiply the answer and the divisor.

$(x + 2)(x + 1)$
$x^2 + x + 2x + 2$
$x^2 + 3x + 2 \checkmark$

B $\dfrac{x^2 + 4x + 3}{x + 1}$

$x + 1 \overline{)x^2 + 4x + 3}$

Write in long division form.

$x + 1 \overline{)\begin{matrix} x + 3 \\ x^2 + 4x + 3 \\ \underline{-(x^2 + x)} \downarrow \\ 3x + 3 \\ \underline{-(3x + 3)} \\ 0 \end{matrix}}$

$x^2 \div x = x$
Multiply $x \cdot (x + 1)$. Subtract.
Bring down the 3. $3x \div x = 3$
Multiply $3(x + 1)$. Subtract.
The remainder is 0.

Check Multiply the answer and the divisor.

$(x + 1)(x + 3)$
$x^2 + 3x + 1x + 3$
$x^2 + 4x + 3 \checkmark$

 Divide using long division. Check your answer.

3a. $(2y^2 - 5y - 3) \div (y - 3)$ **3b.** $(a^2 - 8a + 12) \div (a - 6)$

Sometimes the divisor is not a factor of the dividend, so the remainder is not 0. Then the remainder can be written as a rational expression.

EXAMPLE **4** **Long Division with a Remainder**

Divide $(2x^2 + 3x - 6) \div (x - 2)$.

$$x - 2\overline{)2x^2 + 3x - 6}$$ *Write in long division form.*

$$\begin{array}{r} 2x + 7 \\ x - 2\overline{)2x^2 + 3x - 6} \\ -(2x^2 - 4x) \end{array}$$ $2x^2 \div x = 2x$

    Multiply $2x(x - 2)$. Subtract.

$$7x - 6$$ *Bring down the -6. $7x \div x = 7$*

$$-(7x - 14)$$ *Multiply $7(x - 2)$. Subtract.*

$$8$$ *The remainder is 8.*

$$\frac{8}{x - 2}$$ *Write the remainder as a rational expression using the divisor as the denominator.*

$$2x + 7 + \frac{8}{x - 2}$$ *Write the quotient with the remainder.*

 **Divide.**

4a. $(3m^2 + 4m - 2) \div (m + 3)$ **4b.** $(y^2 + 3y + 2) \div (y - 3)$

Sometimes you need to write a placeholder for a term using a zero coefficient. This is best seen if you write the polynomials in standard form.

EXAMPLE **5** **Dividing Polynomials That Have a Zero Coefficient**

Divide $(3x - 4x^3 - 15) \div (2x + 3)$.

$$(-4x^3 + 3x - 15) \div (2x + 3)$$ *Write the polynomials in standard form.*

$$2x + 3\overline{)-4x^3 + 0x^2 + 3x - 15}$$ *Write in long division form. Use $0x^2$ as a placeholder for the x^2 term.*

> **Remember!**
>
> Recall from Chapter 7 that a polynomial in one variable is written in standard form when the degrees of the terms go from greatest to least.

$$\begin{array}{r} -2x^2 + 3x - 3 \\ 2x + 3\overline{)-4x^3 + 0x^2 + 3x - 15} \\ -(-4x^3 - 6x^2) \end{array}$$ $-4x^3 \div 2x = -2x^2$

    Multiply $-2x^2(2x + 3)$. Subtract.

$$6x^2 + 3x$$ *Bring down $3x$. $6x^2 \div 2x = 3x$*

$$-(6x^2 + 9x)$$ *Multiply $3x(2x + 3)$. Subtract.*

$$-6x - 15$$ *Bring down -15. $-6x \div 2x = -3$*

$$-(-6x - 9)$$ *Multiply $-3(2x + 3)$. Subtract.*

$$-6$$ *The remainder is -6.*

$$(3x - 4x^3 - 15) \div (2x + 3) = -2x^2 + 3x - 3 + \frac{-6}{2x + 3}.$$

 **Divide.**

5a. $(1 - 4x^2 + x^3) \div (x - 2)$

5b. $(4p - 1 + 2p^3) \div (p + 1)$

THINK AND DISCUSS

1. When dividing a polynomial by a binomial, what does it mean when the remainder is 0?

2. Suppose that the final answer to a polynomial division problem is $x - 5 + \frac{3}{x+2}$. Find an excluded value. Justify your answer.

3. GET ORGANIZED Copy and complete the graphic organizer. In each box, show an example.

Long Division
- Polynomials
- Whole numbers

10-6 Exercises

California Standards Practice
🔑 10.0, 🔑 12.0, 25.2

go.hrw.com
Homework Help Online
KEYWORD: MA8CA 10-6
Parent Resources Online
KEYWORD: MA8CA Parent

GUIDED PRACTICE

SEE EXAMPLE 1
p. 667

Divide. Check your answer.

1. $(4x^2 - x) \div 2x$

2. $(16a^4 - 4a^3) \div 4a$

3. $(21b^2 - 14b + 24) \div 3b$

4. $(18r^2 - 12r + 6) \div -6r$

5. $(6x^3 + 12x^2 + 9x) \div 3x^2$

6. $(5m^4 + 15m^2 - 10) \div 5m^3$

SEE EXAMPLE 2
p. 668

7. $\dfrac{2x^2 - x - 3}{x + 1}$

8. $\dfrac{a^2 - a - 12}{a - 4}$

9. $\dfrac{6y^2 + 11y - 10}{3y - 2}$

10. $\dfrac{t^2 - 6t + 8}{t - 4}$

11. $\dfrac{x^2 + 16x + 15}{x + 15}$

12. $\dfrac{p^2 - p - 20}{p + 4}$

SEE EXAMPLE 3
p. 669

Divide using long division. Check your answer.

13. $(c^2 + 7c + 12) \div (c + 4)$

14. $(3s^2 - 12s - 15) \div (s - 5)$

15. $\dfrac{x^2 + 5x - 14}{x + 7}$

16. $\dfrac{x^2 + 4x - 12}{x - 2}$

SEE EXAMPLE 4
p. 670

17. $(a^2 + 4a + 3) \div (a + 2)$

18. $(2r^2 + 11r + 5) \div (r - 3)$

19. $(n^2 + 8n + 15) \div (n + 4)$

20. $(2t^2 - t + 4) \div (t - 1)$

21. $(8n^2 - 6n - 7) \div (2n + 1)$

22. $(b^2 - b + 1) \div (b + 2)$

SEE EXAMPLE 5
p. 670

23. $(3x - 2x^3 - 10) \div (3 + x)$

24. $(3p^3 - 2p^2 - 4) \div (p - 2)$

25. $(m^2 + 2) \div (m - 1)$

26. $(3x^2 + 4x^3 - 5) \div (5 + x)$

27. $(4k^3 - 2k - 8) \div (k + 1)$

28. $(j^3 + 6j + 2) \div (j + 4)$

PRACTICE AND PROBLEM SOLVING

Divide. Check your answer.

29. $(9t^3 + 12t^2 - 6t) \div 3t^2$

30. $(5n^3 - 10n + 15) \div (-5n)$

31. $(-16p^4 + 4p^3 + 8) \div 4p^3$

32. $\dfrac{4r^2 - 9r + 2}{r - 2}$

33. $\dfrac{8t^2 + 2t - 3}{2t - 1}$

34. $\dfrac{3g^2 + 7g - 6}{g + 3}$

Independent Practice

For Exercises	See Example
29–31	1
32–34	2
35–38	3
39–41	4
42–44	5

Extra Practice

Skills Practice p. EP21

Application Practice p. EP33

Divide using long division. Check your answer.

35. $(x^2 - 5x + 6) \div (x - 2)$

36. $(2m^2 + 8m + 8) \div (m + 2)$

37. $(6a^2 + 7a - 3) \div (2a + 3)$

38. $(3x^2 - 10x - 8) \div (x - 4)$

39. $(3x^2 - 2x + 6) \div (x - 2)$

40. $(2m^2 + 5m + 8) \div (m + 1)$

41. $(6x^2 - x - 3) \div (2x - 1)$

42. $(2m^3 - 4m - 30) \div (2m - 10)$

43. $(6t^3 + 21t + 9) \div (3t + 9)$

44. $(p^4 - 7p^2 + p + 1) \div (p - 3)$

45. Multi-Step Find the value of n so that $x - 4$ is a factor of $x^2 + x + n$.

Geometry The area of each of three rectangles is $(2x^2 - 3x - 2)$ cm². Below are the different widths of the rectangles. Find each corresponding length.

46. $x - 2$

47. $x + 1$

48. $2x + 1$

49. Graphing Calculator Use the table of values for $f(x) = \dfrac{(x^2 + 3x + 4)}{x - 5}$ to answer the following.

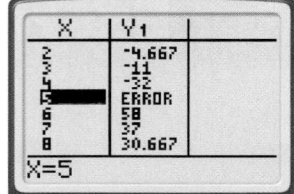

   a. Describe what is happening to the values of y as x increases from 2 to 4.

   b. Describe what is happening to the values of y as x increases from 6 to 8.

   c. Explain why there is no value in the y column when x is 5.

50. Estimation Estimate the value of $\dfrac{x^2 + 10x + 25}{x^2 - 25} \div \dfrac{x^4 - 4x^3 - 45x^2}{x^2 - 14x + 45}$ for $x = 2.88$.

 51. Solar Energy The greater the area of a solar panel, the greater the number of watts of energy produced. The area of two solar panels A and B, in square meters, can be represented by $A = m^2 + 3m + 2$ and $B = 2m + 2$. Divide the polynomials to find an expression that represents the ratio of the area of A to the area of B.

52. /// ERROR ANALYSIS /// Two students attempted to divide $\dfrac{4x^2 - 6x + 12}{-2x}$. Which is incorrect? Explain the error.

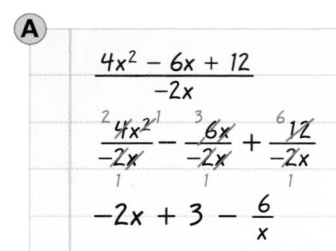

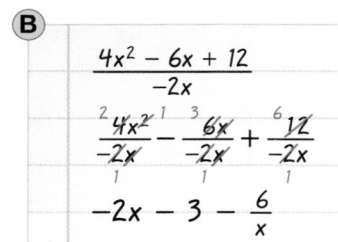

CONCEPT CONNECTION

53. This problem will prepare you for the Concept Connection on page 684.

Jonathan continues to study lenses and uses the equation $\frac{1}{y} = \frac{x - 12}{12x}$.

   a. Jonathan wants to write y, the distance of the image from the lens, as a function of x, the distance of the object from the lens. What is the equation solved for y?

   b. Use a graphing calculator to create a table of values for the function $y(x)$. For which value of x is the function undefined?

54. Write About It When dividing a polynomial by a binomial, what does it mean when there is a remainder?

55. Critical Thinking Divide $2x + 3\overline{)2x^2 + 7x + 6}$. Find a value for each expression by substituting 10 for x in the original problem. Repeat the division. Compare the results of each division.

56. Write About It Is $3x + 2$ a factor of $3x^2 + 14x + 8$? Explain.

Multiple Choice For Exercises 57–60, choose the best answer.

57. Which expression has an excluded value of $-\dfrac{1}{2}$?

Ⓐ $\dfrac{4x^2 - 2x - 2}{4x - 2}$ Ⓑ $\dfrac{4x^2 - 2x - 2}{2x - 4}$ Ⓒ $\dfrac{4x^2 - 2x - 2}{4x + 2}$ Ⓓ $\dfrac{4x^2 - 2x - 2}{2x + 4}$

58. Find $(x^2 - 1) \div (x + 2)$.

Ⓐ $x - 2 + \dfrac{-5}{x + 2}$ Ⓑ $x - 2 + \dfrac{3}{x + 2}$ Ⓒ $x + 2 + \dfrac{-5}{x - 2}$ Ⓓ $x + 2 + \dfrac{3}{x - 2}$

59. Which expression is a factor of $x^2 - 4x - 5$?

Ⓐ $x - 1$ Ⓑ $x + 1$ Ⓒ $x - 4$ Ⓓ $x + 5$

60. Which of the following expressions is equivalent to $(x^3 + 2x^2 + 3x + 1) \div (x - 1)$?

Ⓐ $x^2 + 3x + 6 + \dfrac{7}{x - 1}$ Ⓒ $x^2 + 3x + 6 + \dfrac{-5}{x - 1}$

Ⓑ $x^2 + x + 2 + \dfrac{-1}{x - 1}$ Ⓓ $x^2 + x + 2 + \dfrac{3}{x - 1}$

CHALLENGE AND EXTEND

Divide. Simplify your answer.

61. $(6x^3y - x^2 + 4xy^2) \div (2x^2y)$ **62.** $(x^3 - 1) \div (x - 1)$

63. $(x^3 + 2x^2 - x - 2) \div (x^2 - 1)$ **64.** $(x^3 + 8) \div (x + 2)$

65. Geometry The base of a triangle is $(2x + 4)$ m and the area is $(2x^2 + 5x + 2)$ m². How much longer is the base than the height?

66. Geometry The formula for finding the volume of a cylinder is $V = BH$, where B is the area of the base of the cylinder and H is the height.

  a. Find the height of the cylinder given that $V = \pi(x^3 + 4x^2 + 5x + 2)$ and $B = \pi(x^2 + 2x + 1)$.

  b. Find an expression for the radius of the base.

SPIRAL STANDARDS REVIEW

3.0, ⟜ 5.0, ⟜ 13.0

67. Billy and James are collecting guitar picks. James has 38 picks and adds 2 to his collection every week. Billy starts with 2 picks and collects 14 picks a week. Write and solve an equation to find the number of weeks it will take Billy to accumulate the same number of picks as James. *(Lesson 2-4)*

68. Jane is shopping for a new phone. She wants to spend $130 on the phone, but she is willing to pay within $25 of her ideal price. Write and solve an absolute-value equation to find the maximum and minimum prices Jane is willing to pay. *(Lesson 2-7)*

Multiply. Simplify your answer. *(Lesson 10-4)*

69. $(x^2 + 4x + 3) \cdot \dfrac{8}{2(x + 3)}$ **70.** $\dfrac{9xy^2}{2x^3} \cdot \dfrac{8y}{3x^4}$ **71.** $\dfrac{2k^2 + 4k^3}{k + 1} \cdot \dfrac{k^2 + 3k + 2}{2k^2}$

10-7 Solving Rational Equations

California Standards

Preparation for ◆ 15.0
Students apply algebraic techniques to solve rate problems, work problems, and percent mixture problems.

Who uses this?
Athletes can use rational equations to determine how to improve their statistics. (See Exercise 44.)

A **rational equation** is an equation that contains one or more rational expressions. If a rational equation is a proportion, it can be solved using the Cross Product Property.

EXAMPLE 1 Solving Rational Equations by Using Cross Products

Solve $\dfrac{3}{t-3} = \dfrac{2}{t}$. Check your answer.

Vocabulary
rational equation
extraneous solution

$\dfrac{3}{t-3} = \dfrac{2}{t}$ *Use cross products.*

$3t = (t-3)(2)$

$3t = 2t - 6$ *Distribute 2 on the right side.*

$t = -6$ *Subtract 2t from both sides.*

Check $\dfrac{3}{t-3} = \dfrac{2}{t}$ *Substitute −6 for t in the original equation.*

$$\dfrac{3}{-6-3} \;\Big|\; \dfrac{2}{-6}$$

$$\dfrac{3}{-9} \;\Big|\; \dfrac{2}{-6}$$

$$-\dfrac{1}{3} \;\Big|\; -\dfrac{1}{3} \checkmark$$

 Solve. Check your answer.

1a. $\dfrac{1}{n} = \dfrac{3}{n+4}$ **1b.** $\dfrac{4}{h+1} = \dfrac{2}{h}$ **1c.** $\dfrac{21}{x-7} = \dfrac{3}{x}$

Some rational equations contain sums or differences of rational expressions. To solve these, you must find a common denominator for all the rational expressions in the equation.

EXAMPLE 2 Solving Rational Equations by Using the LCD

Solve $\dfrac{1}{c} + \dfrac{3}{2c} = \dfrac{2}{c+1}$. Check your answer.

Step 1 Find the LCD.

$2c(c+1)$ *Include every factor of the denominators.*

Step 2 Multiply both sides by the LCD.

$$2c(c+1)\left(\dfrac{1}{c} + \dfrac{3}{2c}\right) = 2c(c+1)\left(\dfrac{2}{c+1}\right)$$

$$2c(c+1)\left(\dfrac{1}{c}\right) + 2c(c+1)\left(\dfrac{3}{2c}\right) = 2c(c+1)\left(\dfrac{2}{c+1}\right)$$ *Distribute on the left side.*

Step 3 Simplify and solve.

$$2\ell(c+1)\left(\frac{1}{\ell}\right) + 2c(c+1)\left(\frac{3}{2c}\right) = 2c(c+1)\left(\frac{2}{c+1}\right) \qquad \textit{Divide out common factors in each term.}$$

$$2(c+1) + (c+1)3 = (2c)2 \qquad \textit{Simplify.}$$

$$2c + 2 + 3c + 3 = 4c \qquad \textit{Distribute and multiply.}$$

$$5c + 5 = 4c \qquad \textit{Combine like terms.}$$

$$c + 5 = 0 \qquad \textit{Subtract 4c from both sides.}$$

$$c = -5 \qquad \textit{Subtract 5 from both sides.}$$

Check

$$\frac{1}{c} + \frac{3}{2c} = \frac{2}{c+1}$$

$\dfrac{1}{-5} + \dfrac{3}{2(-5)}$	$\dfrac{2}{-5+1}$
$\dfrac{2}{-10} + \dfrac{3}{-10}$	$\dfrac{2}{-4}$
$-\dfrac{5}{10}$ or $-\dfrac{1}{2}$	$-\dfrac{1}{2}$ ✓

Solve each equation. Check your answer.

2a. $\dfrac{2}{a+1} + \dfrac{1}{a+1} = \dfrac{4}{a}$

2b. $\dfrac{6}{j+2} - \dfrac{10}{j} = \dfrac{4}{2j}$

When you multiply each side of an equation by the LCD, you may get an *extraneous solution*. An **extraneous solution** is a solution to a resulting equation that is not a solution to the original equation. Because of extraneous solutions, it is especially important to check your answers.

EXAMPLE 3 **Extraneous Solutions**

Solve $\dfrac{x-9}{x^2-9} = \dfrac{-3}{x-3}$. **Check your answer.**

$$(x-9)(x-3) = -3(x^2-9) \qquad \textit{Use cross products.}$$

$$x^2 - 12x + 27 = -3x^2 + 27 \qquad \textit{Multiply the left side. Distribute } -3 \textit{ on the right side.}$$

$$4x^2 - 12x + 27 = 27 \qquad \textit{Add } 3x^2 \textit{ to both sides.}$$

$$4x^2 - 12x = 0 \qquad \textit{Subtract 27 from both sides.}$$

$$4x(x-3) = 0 \qquad \textit{Factor the quadratic expression.}$$

$$4x = 0 \text{ or } x - 3 = 0 \qquad \textit{Use the Zero Product Property.}$$

$$x = 0 \text{ or } x = 3 \qquad \textit{Solve for x.}$$

Check

$$\frac{x-9}{x^2-9} = \frac{-3}{x-3}$$

$\dfrac{0-9}{0^2-9}$	$\dfrac{-3}{0-3}$
$\dfrac{-9}{-9}$	$\dfrac{-3}{-3}$
1	1 ✓

$$\frac{x-9}{x^2-9} = \frac{-3}{x-3}$$

$\dfrac{3-9}{3^2-9}$	$\dfrac{-3}{3-3}$
$\dfrac{-6}{0}$	$\dfrac{-3}{0}$

Because both $\frac{-6}{0}$ and $\frac{-3}{0}$ are undefined, 3 is not a solution.

3 is an extraneous solution. The only solution is 0.

Solve. Check your answer.

3a. $\dfrac{3}{x-7} = \dfrac{x-2}{x-7}$

3b. $\dfrac{x+1}{x-2} = \dfrac{4}{x-3}$

3c. $\dfrac{9}{x^2+2x} = \dfrac{6}{x^2}$

THINK AND DISCUSS

1. Why is it important to check your answers to rational equations?
2. For what values of x are the rational expressions in the equation $\frac{x}{x-3} = \frac{2}{x+3}$ undefined?
3. Explain why some rational equations, such as $\frac{x}{x-4} = \frac{4}{x-4}$, have no solutions.

4. **GET ORGANIZED** Copy and complete the graphic organizer. In each box, write the solution and check.

> **Solving Rational Equations**
>
> | Solve by using cross products. | Solve by using the LCD. |
> |---|---|
> | $\frac{3}{x} = \frac{2}{x+1}$ | $\frac{7}{x-1} - \frac{4}{x-1} = \frac{6}{x}$ |

10-7 Exercises

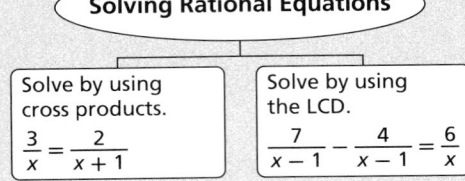

California Standards Practice
Preparation for 🔑 15.0; 25.1

go.hrw.com
Homework Help Online
KEYWORD: MA8CA 10-7
Parent Resources Online
KEYWORD: MA8CA Parent

GUIDED PRACTICE

Vocabulary Apply the vocabulary from this lesson to answer each question.

1. A(n) ____?____ contains one or more rational expressions. (*extraneous solution* or *rational equation*)

2. A(n) ____?____ is a solution to a resulting equation that is not a solution to the original equation. (*extraneous solution* or *rational equation*)

Solve. Check your answer.

SEE EXAMPLE **1**
p. 674

3. $\frac{3}{x+4} = \frac{2}{x}$

4. $\frac{5}{s-6} = \frac{4}{s}$

5. $\frac{20}{p+100} = \frac{-10}{2p}$

6. $\frac{4}{j} = \frac{1}{j+2}$

7. $\frac{3}{x-4} = \frac{9}{x-2}$

8. $\frac{6}{2x-1} = 3$

SEE EXAMPLE **2**
p. 674

9. $\frac{6}{x} - \frac{5}{x} = \frac{1}{3}$

10. $\frac{a}{9} + \frac{1}{3} = \frac{2}{5}$

11. $\frac{3}{x+1} = \frac{2}{x} + \frac{3}{x}$

12. $\frac{8}{d} = \frac{1}{d+2} - \frac{3}{d}$

13. $\frac{3}{s-6} = \frac{4}{s} + \frac{1}{2s}$

14. $\frac{7}{r} + \frac{2}{r-1} = \frac{-1}{2r}$

15. $\frac{3}{a-4} = \frac{a}{a-2}$

16. $\frac{r}{2} - \frac{2}{r} = \frac{5}{6}$

17. $\frac{6}{n} = \frac{7}{n^2} - 1$

18. $\frac{4}{x+1} = x - 2$

19. $\frac{5}{a^2} = \frac{-4}{a} + 1$

20. $\frac{1}{p} = \frac{-3}{p^2} + 2$

SEE EXAMPLE **3**
p. 675

Solve. Check your answer.

21. $\frac{3}{c-4} = \frac{c-1}{c-4}$

22. $\frac{w+3}{w^2-1} - \frac{2w}{w-1} = 1$

23. $\frac{3x-7}{x-5} + \frac{x}{2} = \frac{8}{x-5}$

PRACTICE AND PROBLEM SOLVING

Independent Practice

For Exercises	See Example
24–27	1
28–35	2
36–43	3

Extra Practice

Skills Practice p. EP21

Application Practice p. EP33

Solve. Check your answer.

24. $\dfrac{8}{x-2} = \dfrac{2}{x+1}$

25. $\dfrac{12}{3n-1} = \dfrac{3}{n}$

26. $\dfrac{x}{x+4} = \dfrac{x}{x-1}$

27. $\dfrac{9}{x+5} = \dfrac{4}{x}$

28. $\dfrac{6}{s} - \dfrac{2}{s} = 5$

29. $\dfrac{1}{2x} + \dfrac{1}{4x} = \dfrac{7}{8x}$

30. $\dfrac{7}{c} - \dfrac{2}{c} = \dfrac{4}{c-1}$

31. $\dfrac{9}{m} - \dfrac{3}{2m} = \dfrac{15}{m}$

32. $\dfrac{3}{x^2} = \dfrac{2}{x}$

33. $\dfrac{r}{3} - 3 = -\dfrac{6}{r}$

34. $\dfrac{6}{x^2} = \dfrac{1}{2} + \dfrac{1}{2x}$

35. $\dfrac{8}{3x^2} = \dfrac{2}{x} - \dfrac{1}{3}$

Solve. Check your answer.

36. $\dfrac{x+4}{x+1} = \dfrac{3}{x-3}$

37. $\dfrac{x+1}{x-4} = \dfrac{3(x+1)}{x-4}$

38. $\dfrac{5x}{x-3} = 8 + \dfrac{15}{x-3}$

39. $\dfrac{3t}{t-3} = \dfrac{t+4}{t-3}$

40. $\dfrac{2}{x} = \dfrac{x+1}{x^2-1}$

41. $\dfrac{1}{x} = \dfrac{x-4}{x^2-16}$

42. $\dfrac{x+2}{3} = \dfrac{x+7}{x+3}$

43. $\dfrac{x+4}{2x-2} = \dfrac{x+3}{x-1}$

44. Multi-Step Clancy has been keeping his free throw statistics. Use his data to write the ratio of the number of free throws Clancy has made to the number of attempts.

Clancy's Free Throws	
Attempts	Made
45	39

  a. What percentage has he made?

  b. Write and solve an equation to find how many free throws f Clancy would have to make in a row to improve his free-throw percentage to 90%. (*Hint:* Clancy needs to make f more free throws in f more attempts.)

45. Karla and Andrew are sorting their book collections. Karla has 12 books and divides them evenly into stacks. Andrew has 18 books and evenly divides his books into 2 fewer stacks than Karla. He also has 6 more books in each stack than Karla. Copy and complete the table. Then find the number of stacks of books Karla has.

	Karla	Andrew
Books		18
Stacks	x	
Books per Stack		$\dfrac{18}{x-2}$

CONCEPT CONNECTION

46. This problem will prepare you for the Concept Connection on page 684.

Blanca sets up a lens with a focal length f of 15 cm and places a candle 24 cm from the lens. She knows that $\dfrac{1}{f} = \dfrac{1}{x} + \dfrac{1}{y}$ where x is the distance of the object from the lens and y is the distance of the image from the lens.

  a. Write the equation using the given values.

  b. For the values of f and x given above, how far will the image appear from the lens?

  c. How will distance between the image and the lens be affected if Blanca uses a lens with a focal length of 18 cm?

47. Critical Thinking Can you cross multiply to solve all rational equations? If so, explain. If not, how do you identify which ones can be solved using cross products?

 48. Write About It Solve $\frac{1}{x} + \frac{3}{x} = \frac{3}{x-1}$. Explain each step and why you chose the method you used.

Multiple Choice For Exercises 49–51, choose the best answer.

49. Which value is an extraneous solution to $\dfrac{x}{x+4} - \dfrac{4}{x-4} = \dfrac{x^2+16}{x^2-16}$?

    Ⓐ -16 Ⓑ -4 Ⓒ 4 Ⓓ 16

50. Which is a solution to $\dfrac{x+2}{x-3} - \dfrac{1}{x} = \dfrac{3}{x^2-3x}$?

    Ⓐ -1 Ⓑ 0 Ⓒ 1 Ⓓ 3

51. What are the solutions of $\dfrac{5}{x^2} = \dfrac{1}{3} + \dfrac{2}{3x}$?

    Ⓐ -3 and 5 Ⓑ -3 and 2 Ⓒ 2 and 3 Ⓓ 3 and -5

CHALLENGE AND EXTEND

 52. Reasoning Below is a solution to the rational equation $\dfrac{3}{x} = \dfrac{6}{x+4}$. Use an algebraic property to justify each step.

Statements	Reasons
a. $3(x+4) = 6x$	
b. $3x + 12 = 6x$	
c. $12 = 3x$	
d. $4 = x$	

53. For what value of a will the equation $\dfrac{x+4}{x-a} = \dfrac{7}{x-a}$ have no solution?

54. Jill has a 10-year-old sister and a sister who will be 12 next year. The equation $\dfrac{10}{j} + \dfrac{12}{j+1} = 4$, where j is Jill's age, describes the relationship between the ages of Jill and her sisters. Angela has one sister who is 16 this year and a sister who will be 18 next year. The equation $\dfrac{16}{a} + \dfrac{18}{a+1} = 4$, where a is Angela's age, describes the relationship between the ages of Angela and her sisters. What is the difference between Jill's and Angela's ages?

 SPIRAL STANDARDS REVIEW   8.0, ⚷ 9.0

Identify which lines are parallel and which lines are perpendicular. *(Lesson 5-8)*

55. $y = \frac{1}{3}x; \; y = 3x + 1; \; y = 3x - 1$ **56.** $y = -2x; \; y = 2x - 2; \; y = \frac{1}{2}x + 4$

57. $y = -x - 3; \; y = x - 2; \; y = x + 3$ **58.** $y = -\frac{2}{3}x + 2; \; y = \frac{3}{2}x + 3; \; y = -\frac{3}{2}x - 1$

Solve each system by elimination. *(Lesson 6-3)*

59. $\begin{cases} x - y = -3 \\ 2x + 2y = 22 \end{cases}$ **60.** $\begin{cases} x - 2y = 18 \\ 2x + 3y = 15 \end{cases}$ **61.** $\begin{cases} -3x - 2y = 27 \\ 4x - 3y = -2 \end{cases}$

62. Find the number of solutions of $7x^2 + 5x - 13 = 0$ using the discriminant. *(Lesson 9-9)*

Applying Rational Equations

California Standards

◆━ **15.0** Students apply algebraic techniques to solve rate problems, work problems, and percent mixture problems.

Why learn this?

You can use rational equations to find out how long it takes two people working together to complete a job.

When two people team up to complete a job, each person completes a fraction of the whole job. You can use this idea to write and solve a rational equation to find how long it will take to complete a job.

EXAMPLE 1 *Gardening Application*

Danielle can weed a garden in 2 hours. It takes Omar 3 hours to weed the same garden. How long will it take them to weed the garden if they work together?

Let h be the number of hours Danielle and Omar need to weed the garden. Danielle weeds the garden in 2 hours, so she weeds $\frac{1}{2}$ of the garden per hour. Omar weeds the garden in 3 hours, so he weeds $\frac{1}{3}$ of the garden per hour. The table shows the part of the garden that each person weeds in h hours.

Danielle's Part	+	Omar's Part	=	Whole Garden
$\frac{1}{2}h$	+	$\frac{1}{3}h$	=	1

$\frac{1}{2}h + \frac{1}{3}h = 1$ *Solve this equation for h.*

$6\left(\frac{1}{2}h + \frac{1}{3}h\right) = 6(1)$ *Multiply both sides by the LCD, 6.*

$3h + 2h = 6$ *Distribute 6 on the left side.*

$5h = 6$ *Combine like terms.*

$h = \frac{6}{5} = 1\frac{1}{5}$ *Divide by 5 on both sides.*

Working together, Danielle and Omar can weed the garden in $1\frac{1}{5}$ hours, or 1 hour 12 minutes.

Check Danielle weeds $\frac{1}{2}$ of the garden per hour, so in $1\frac{1}{5}$ hours, she weeds $\frac{1}{2} \cdot \frac{6}{5} = \frac{3}{5}$ of the garden. Omar weeds $\frac{1}{3}$ of the garden per hour, so in $1\frac{1}{5}$ hours, he weeds $\frac{1}{3} \cdot \frac{6}{5} = \frac{2}{5}$ of the garden. Together, they weed $\frac{3}{5} + \frac{2}{5} = 1$ garden.

1. Cindy mows a lawn in 50 minutes. It takes Sara 40 minutes to mow the same lawn. How long will it take them to mow the lawn if they work together?

EXAMPLE 2 *Chemistry Application*

A chemist has 500 milliliters of a solution that is half alcohol. He needs a solution that is 60% alcohol. How many milliliters of alcohol should he add?

Let a be the number of milliliters of alcohol that the chemist should add.

The table shows the amount of alcohol and the total amount of the solution.

	Alcohol (mL)	Total (mL)
Original	250	500
New	$250 + a$	$500 + a$

The new solution is 60% alcohol, so $\frac{250 + a}{500 + a} = 0.6$. Solve for a.

$250 + a = 0.6(500 + a)$ *Multiply both sides by 500 + a.*

$250 + a = 300 + 0.6a$ *Distribute 0.6 on the right side.*

$0.4a = 50$ *Subtract 250 from both sides and 0.6a from both sides.*

$a = 125$ *Divide both sides by 0.4.*

The chemist should add 125 mL of alcohol to the solution.

 **2.** Suppose the chemist wants a solution that is 80% alcohol. How many milliliters of alcohol should he add?

EXAMPLE 3 *Transportation Application*

A passenger train travels 20 mi/h faster than a freight train, and it takes the passenger train 2 hours less time to travel 240 miles. How long does the freight train take to make the trip?

Let t be the time it takes the freight train to travel 240 miles.

	Distance (mi)	Time (h)	Rate (mi/h)
Freight Train	240	t	$\frac{240}{t}$
Passenger Train	240	$t - 2$	$\frac{240}{t - 2}$

> **Remember!**
> distance = rate · time, so rate = $\frac{distance}{time}$.

The passenger train is 20 mi/h faster, so $\dfrac{240}{t - 2} = \dfrac{240}{t} + 20$.

$t(t - 2)\dfrac{240}{t - 2} = t(t - 2)\left(\dfrac{240}{t} + 20\right)$ *Multiply both sides by the LCD.*

$240t = (t - 2)240 + (t^2 - 2t)(20)$ *Distribute t(t − 2) on the right side. Simplify.*

$240t = 240t - 480 + 20t^2 - 40t$ *Distribute and multiply.*

$0 = 20t^2 - 40t - 480$ *Subtract 240t from both sides.*

$0 = t^2 - 2t - 24$ *Divide both sides by 20.*

$0 = (t - 6)(t + 4)$, so $t = -4, 6$ *Factor and solve. Time is nonnegative, so −4 is extraneous.*

The freight train makes the trip in 6 hours.

 **3.** Ryan drives 10 mi/h slower than Maya, and it takes Ryan 1 hour longer to travel 300 miles. How long does it take Maya to make the trip?

THINK AND DISCUSS

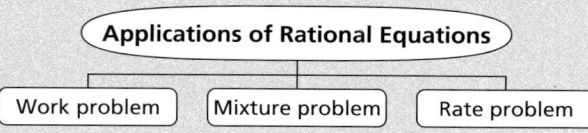

1. Explain why it makes sense that the answer to Example 1 is less than the time it takes Danielle or Omar to weed the garden when working alone.

2. GET ORGANIZED Copy and complete the graphic organizer. In each box, write an example of each type of application and its solution.

Applications of Rational Equations

| Work problem | Mixture problem | Rate problem |

10-8 Exercises

California Standards Practice
🔑 15.0, 25.2

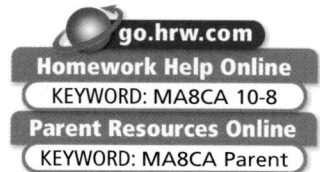

go.hrw.com
Homework Help Online
KEYWORD: MA8CA 10-8
Parent Resources Online
KEYWORD: MA8CA Parent

GUIDED PRACTICE

SEE EXAMPLE 1 p. 679

1. Summer can paint a room in 3 hours. Louise can paint the room in 5 hours. How many hours will it take them to paint the room if they work together?

SEE EXAMPLE 2 p. 680

2. Cooking A chef has 4 quarts of a soup that consists of equal parts chicken stock and vegetable stock. She wants to make a soup that is 75% chicken stock. How many quarts of chicken stock should she add to the mixture?

SEE EXAMPLE 3 p. 680

3. Fitness Connor and Matt walk a 12-mile course as part of a fitness program. Matt walks 1 mi/h faster than Connor, and it takes him 1 hour less than Connor to complete the course. How long does it take Connor to complete the course?

PRACTICE AND PROBLEM SOLVING

Independent Practice

For Exercises	See Example
4–5	1
6	2
7	3

Extra Practice

Skills Practice p. EP21

Application Practice p. EP33

4. Technology Lawrence's old robotic vacuum can clean his apartment in $1\frac{1}{2}$ hours. His new robotic vacuum can clean his apartment in 45 minutes. How long will it take both vacuums working together to clean his apartment?

5. The table shows the time it takes for pipes of different sizes to fill a reservoir with water. How long would it take for both pipes working at the same time to fill the reservoir?

Pipe Output	
Diameter (ft)	Time to Fill Reservoir (h)
2	12
3	6

6. Maria has 8 cups of a fruit punch that consists of 25% orange juice and 75% apple juice. She wants to make a drink that is 40% orange juice. How many cups of orange juice should Maria add to the mixture?

7. Transportation The average speed of an express train is 15 mi/h faster than the average speed of a local train. It takes the local train 2 hours longer than the express train to cover 360 miles. What is the average speed of the express train?

8. **Sports** A race consists of a 20-mile bike ride and a 12-mile run. Jen's rate while biking is 4 mi/h faster than while running. She completes the race in 4 hours.

   a. Let r be Jen's rate while biking. Copy and complete the table.

   b. Use the information in the Time column to write a rational equation.

   c. Solve the equation to find Jen's rate while biking.

	Distance (mi)	Rate (mi/h)	Time (h)
Biking		r	$\frac{20}{r}$
Running	12		

9. **Geometry** Both rectangle A and rectangle B have areas of 96 m². The length of B is twice the length of A. The width of A is 4 m greater than the width of B.

   a. Let ℓ be the length of rectangle A. Copy and complete the table.

	Area (m²)	Length (m)	Width (m)
Rectangle A	96	ℓ	$\frac{96}{\ell}$
Rectangle B			

   b. Use the information in the Width column to write a rational equation.

   c. Solve the equation to find the length and width of rectangle A.

10. **Multi-Step** The manager of a copy center can use two of the machines in the graph to make 1000 photocopies of a leaflet. Will the job be completed more quickly with machines A and D or with machines B and C? Explain.

11. A number plus the reciprocal of the number is $\frac{5}{4}$ of the number. What is the number?

12. **/// ERROR ANALYSIS ///** Jordan can wash the windows in his house in 4 hours. His brother can do the job in 6 hours. They want to know how long it will take if they work together. Which solution to the problem is incorrect? Explain the error.

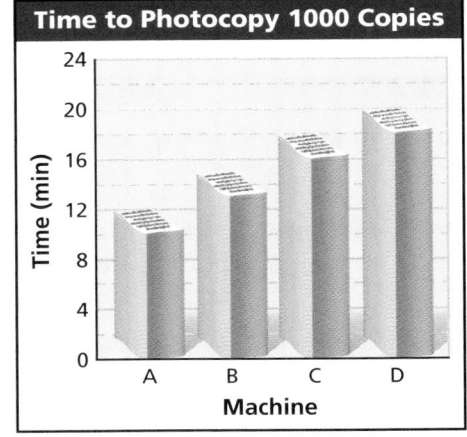

Time to Photocopy 1000 Copies

(bar graph: Time (min) vs Machine A, B, C, D)

A

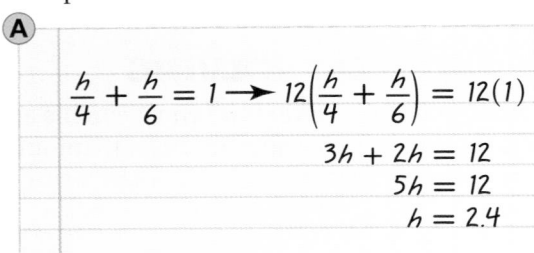

$$\frac{h}{4} + \frac{h}{6} = 1 \rightarrow 12\left(\frac{h}{4} + \frac{h}{6}\right) = 12(1)$$
$$3h + 2h = 12$$
$$5h = 12$$
$$h = 2.4$$

B

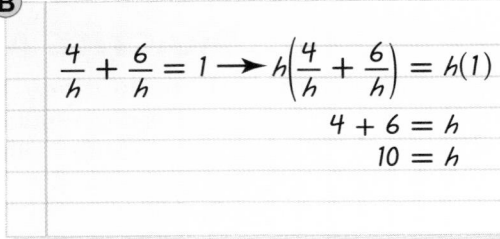

$$\frac{4}{h} + \frac{6}{h} = 1 \rightarrow h\left(\frac{4}{h} + \frac{6}{h}\right) = h(1)$$
$$4 + 6 = h$$
$$10 = h$$

CONCEPT CONNECTION

13. This problem will prepare you for the Concept Connection on page 684.

    Melinda has a lens with a focal length f of 12 cm. She wants to place a candle so that the distance from the candle to the lens is 10 cm more than the distance from the candle's image to the lens. She knows that $\frac{1}{f} = \frac{1}{x} + \frac{1}{y}$, where x is the distance from the object to the lens and y is the distance from the image to the lens.

    a. Write and solve a rational equation to find the distance from the candle to the lens.

    b. How far will the candle's image be from the lens?

14. Critical Thinking Working individually, Tyrone and Cheryl can each mow the lawn in 48 minutes. How long will it take them to mow the lawn if they work together? What do you notice about your answer? Explain why this makes sense.

15. Write About It Write an original problem that can be solved using a rational equation. Include the solution to the problem.

Multiple Choice For Exercises 16 and 17, choose the best answer.

16. A chemist has 80 milliliters of a solution that consists of equal amounts of water and ethanol. The chemist wants to make a solution that is 70% water. Which equation can be used to find the additional amount of water w that should be added to the solution?

(A) $\dfrac{40 + w}{80 + w} = 0.7$ (B) $\dfrac{w}{80} + \dfrac{w}{40} = 0.7$ (C) $\dfrac{80 + w}{40 + w} = 0.7$ (D) $\dfrac{80}{w} + \dfrac{40}{w} = 0.7$

17. Ms. Yamashiro can grade her students' homework in 30 minutes. Her teaching assistant can grade the same papers in 45 minutes. If they work together, how long will it take them to grade the papers?

(A) 9 minutes   (B) 18 minutes   (C) 37.5 minutes   (D) 75 minutes

CHALLENGE AND EXTEND

18. A water tank contains three drains. The table shows the time it takes for each drain to empty the tank. How long does it take to empty the tank when all three drains are used?

Time Needed to Empty Tank	
Drain A	3 hours
Drain B	6 hours
Drain C	4 hours

19. Luke, Eddie, and Ryan can complete a job in 1 hour and 20 minutes if they work together. Working alone, it takes Ryan 1 hour more to complete the job than it takes Luke, and Luke works twice as fast as Eddie. How much time would it take each to complete the job working alone?

20. A bowl contains fruit punch that is $\frac{1}{2}$ cranberry juice. When 6 cups of cranberry juice are added to the bowl, the resulting punch is $\frac{2}{3}$ cranberry juice. How many cups of punch were in the bowl to start with?

 SPIRAL STANDARDS REVIEW    7.0, 11.0, 12.0

Without graphing, tell whether each point is on the graph of $4x + 2y = 14$. *(Lesson 5-1)*

21. $(1, 5)$ **22.** $(0, 8)$ **23.** $(-2, 11)$

24. $(5, -2)$ **25.** $(9, -11)$ **26.** $(4, -2)$

Determine whether each trinomial is a perfect square. If so, factor. If not, explain. *(Lesson 8-5)*

27. $4x^2 + 12x + 9$ **28.** $9x^2 - 6x + 1$ **29.** $16x^2 - 24x - 9$

30. $49x^2 - 4x + 4$ **31.** $25x^2 + 8x - 16$ **32.** $36x^2 + 8x + 16$

Divide. Check your answer. *(Lesson 10-6)*

33. $\dfrac{x^2 + 3x + 2}{x + 2}$ **34.** $\dfrac{x^2 - 6x - 16}{x - 8}$ **35.** $\dfrac{x^2 + 7x + 12}{x + 3}$

36. $\dfrac{x^2 - 4x + 21}{x - 7}$ **37.** $\dfrac{x^2 - 9x + 18}{x - 3}$ **38.** $\dfrac{x^2 - 3x - 40}{x + 5}$

CONCEPT CONNECTION

Operations with Rational Expressions and Equations

An Upside-Down World Jamal is studying lenses and their images for a science project. He finds in a science book that a magnifying glass can be used to project upside-down images on a screen. The equation $\frac{1}{f} = \frac{1}{x} + \frac{1}{y}$ relates the focal length of the lens f, the distance of the object from the lens x, and the distance of the image from the lens y. The focal length of Jamal's lens is 10 cm.

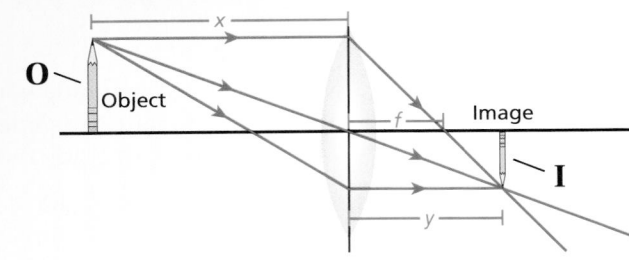

1. Solve the given equation for y using the given value of f.

2. Jamal experiments with a candle, the lens, and a screen. Given that the focal length remains constant, use a table for the x-values 0, 2, 4, 6, 8, 10, 12, 14, and 16 cm. For which x-values are the y-values positive?

3. Graph the function $y(x)$. Label the axes.

Magnification for images is the ratio of the height of the image to the height of the object. This is also equal to the ratio of the distance between the image and the lens and the distance between the object and the lens: $M = \frac{I}{O} = \frac{y}{x}$. I is the height of the image, O is the height of the object, y is the distance of the image from the lens, and x is the distance of the object from the lens.

4. If the height of a candle is 15 cm and the projected image of that candle is 37.5 cm, what is the magnification of the lens?

5. As Jamal moves the candle further from the lens (increases x), and the distance between the lens and the screen decreases (y decreases), does the magnification M stay the same, increase, or decrease?

READY TO GO ON?

Quiz for Lessons 10-4 Through 10-8

10-4 Multiplying and Dividing Rational Expressions

Multiply. Simplify your answer.

1. $\dfrac{n+3}{n-5} \cdot (n^2 - 5n)$

2. $\dfrac{6xy^2}{2x^2y^6} \cdot \dfrac{6x^4y^4}{9x^3}$

3. $\dfrac{3h^3 - 6h}{10g^2} \cdot \dfrac{4g}{gh^2 - 2g}$

4. $\dfrac{m^2 + m - 2}{m^2 - 2m - 8} \cdot \dfrac{m^2 - 8m + 16}{3m - 3}$

Divide. Simplify your answer.

5. $\dfrac{2}{n^3} \div \dfrac{n-6}{n^5}$

6. $\dfrac{2x^2 + 8x + 6}{x} \div \dfrac{2x^2 + 2x}{x^3 - x^2}$

7. $\dfrac{8b^3c}{b^2c} \div (4b^2 + 4b)$

10-5 Adding and Subtracting Rational Expressions

Add or subtract. Simplify your answer.

8. $\dfrac{15}{2p} - \dfrac{13}{2p}$

9. $\dfrac{3m^2}{4m^5} + \dfrac{5m^2}{4m^5}$

10. $\dfrac{x^2 + 8x}{x-2} - \dfrac{3x + 14}{x-2}$

11. $\dfrac{2t}{4t^2} + \dfrac{2}{t}$

12. $\dfrac{m^2 - m - 2}{m^2 + 6m + 5} - \dfrac{2}{m+5}$

13. $\dfrac{4x}{x-2} + \dfrac{3x}{2-x}$

10-6 Dividing Polynomials

Divide. Check your answer.

14. $(6d^2 + 4d) \div 2d$

15. $(15x^4 + 3x^3 - x) \div (-3x^2)$

16. $(2x^2 - 7x - 4) \div (2x + 1)$

Divide using long division. Check your answer.

17. $(a^2 + 3a - 10) \div (a - 2)$

18. $(4y^2 - 9) \div (2y - 3)$

19. $(2x^2 + 5x - 8) \div (x + 2)$

10-7 Solving Rational Equations

Solve. Check your answer.

20. $\dfrac{3}{x} = \dfrac{4}{x-1}$

21. $\dfrac{1}{x} = \dfrac{2}{x^2}$

22. $\dfrac{2}{t} + \dfrac{4}{3t} = \dfrac{4}{t+2}$

23. $\dfrac{4}{n^2} = \dfrac{7}{n} + 2$

24. $\dfrac{d+2}{d+8} = \dfrac{-6}{d+8}$

25. $\dfrac{x-6}{x^2-6} = \dfrac{-4}{x-4}$

10-8 Applying Rational Equations

26. It takes Dustin 2 hours to shovel the snow from his driveway and sidewalk. It takes his sister 3 hours to shovel the same area. How long will it take them to shovel the walk if they work together?

27. A chemistry student needs to make a solution that is 70% water and 30% hydrochloric acid. The student's current mixture of 300 mL is 60% water and 40% hydrochloric acid. How much water must the student add to achieve his desired solution?

Study Guide: Review

Vocabulary

Complete the sentences below with vocabulary words from the list above.

1. A(n) ___?___ is an algebraic expression whose numerator and denominator are polynomials.

2. A function whose rule is a quotient of polynomials in which the denominator has a degree of at least 1 is a(n) ___?___ .

3. A(n) ___?___ is an equation that contains one or more rational expressions.

4. A(n) ___?___ is a relationship that can be written in the form $y = \frac{k}{x}$, where k is a nonzero constant.

5. A function is a(n) ___?___ if its graph contains one or more jumps, breaks, or holes.

10-1 Inverse Variation (pp. 627–633)

 Prep for ☞ 13.0

EXAMPLE

■ Write and graph the inverse variation in which $y = 2$ when $x = 3$.

$y = \frac{k}{x}$ Use the form $y = \frac{k}{x}$.

$2 = \frac{k}{3}$ Substitute known values.

$6 = k$ Multiply by 3 to find the value of k.

$y = \frac{6}{x}$ Substitute 6 for k in $y = \frac{k}{x}$.

x	−6	−3	−2	−1	0	1	2	3	6
y	−1	−2	−3	−6	und.	6	3	2	1

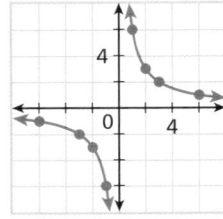

Make a table of values and plot the points.

EXERCISES

Tell whether each relationship represents an inverse variation. Explain.

6.

x	y
4	−3
−12	1
6	−2

7.

x	y
2	4
6	8
10	12

8. Write and graph the inverse variation in which $y = 4$ when $x = -1$.

9. Write and graph the inverse variation in which $y = \frac{1}{2}$ when $x = 2$.

10. Let $x_1 = 5$, $y_1 = -6$, and $x_2 = 2$. Let y vary inversely as x. Find y_2.

11. The number of fleet vehicles a town can afford to buy varies inversely as the price of each car. If the town can afford 3 cars priced at \$22,000 each, what must the price of a car be in order for the town to purchase 5 of them?

10-2 Rational Functions (pp. 634–641)

Prep for ⬦ 13.0

EXAMPLE

■ Graph the function $y = \dfrac{1}{x+1} + 3$.

Find the asymptotes.

$x = -1 \qquad b = -1$
$y = 3 \qquad c = 3$

Graph the asymptotes using dashed lines.

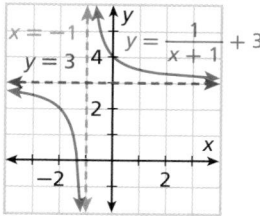

Make a table of values. Choose x-values on both sides of the vertical asymptote.

x	-3	-2	0	1
y	$\frac{5}{2}$	2	4	$\frac{7}{2}$

Plot the points and connect them with smooth curves.

EXERCISES

Identify any excluded values and the asymptotes for each rational function.

12. $y = \dfrac{1}{x+4}$

13. $y = \dfrac{1}{x+1} + 3$

14. $y = \dfrac{-5}{2x+6} - 4$

15. $y = \dfrac{2}{4x-7} + 5$

Graph each function.

16. $y = \dfrac{3}{x}$

17. $y = \dfrac{4}{x+5}$

18. $y = \dfrac{1}{x+4} - 2$

19. $y = \dfrac{1}{x-6} + 2$

20. A rectangle has an area of 24 cm². If x represents the width, then $y = \frac{24}{x}$ represents the length y. Describe the reasonable domain and range values and graph the function.

10-3 Simplifying Rational Expressions (pp. 642–648)

⬦ 12.0

EXAMPLE

Simplify the rational expression, if possible. Identify any excluded values.

■ $\dfrac{x-1}{x^2 + 2x - 3}$

$\dfrac{x-1}{(x+3)(x-1)}$ *Factor the denominator.*

$\dfrac{x-1^{\,1}}{(x+3)(x-1)}$ *Divide out common factors.*

$\dfrac{1}{x+3}$ *Simplify.*

Identify the excluded values.

$x^2 + 2x - 3 = 0$ *Set the denominator equal to 0.*

$(x+3)(x-1) = 0$ *Factor.*

$x + 3 = 0$ or $x - 1 = 0$ *Use the Zero Product Property.*

$x = -3$ or $x = 1$ *Solve each equation.*

The excluded values are -3 and 1.

EXERCISES

Identify any excluded values of each rational expression.

21. $\dfrac{3}{5p}$

22. $\dfrac{-2}{r-7}$

23. $\dfrac{t}{t^2 - t}$

24. $\dfrac{-4}{x^2 - 4x - 5}$

25. $\dfrac{x-1}{x^2 - 25}$

26. $\dfrac{x+4}{x^2 - 11x + 28}$

Simplify each rational expression, if possible. Identify any excluded values.

27. $\dfrac{7r^2}{21r^3}$

28. $\dfrac{3k^2}{6k^3 - 9k^2}$

29. $\dfrac{x+6}{x^2 + 4x - 12}$

30. $\dfrac{2x-6}{9 - x^2}$

31. $\dfrac{3x+15}{x^2 + 4x - 5}$

32. $\dfrac{x^2 + 9x + 18}{x^2 + x - 30}$

33. What is the ratio of the area of the square to the area of the circle?

10-4 Multiplying and Dividing Rational Expressions (pp. 652–658)

 13.0

EXAMPLE

■ **Divide. Simplify your answer.**

$$\frac{32x^2y^2}{7z} \div \frac{2xy^2}{28xz^3}$$

$$\frac{32x^2y^2}{7z} \cdot \frac{28xz^3}{2xy^2}$$ *Multiply by the reciprocal.*

$$\frac{\cancel{32}^{16}\,x^2\,\cancel{y^2}}{7\cancel{z}} \cdot \frac{\cancel{28}^4\,\cancel{x}\,z^{3\,z^2}}{\cancel{2}\,\cancel{x}\cancel{y^2}}$$ *Divide out common factors.*

$$64x^2z^2$$ *Simplify.*

EXERCISES

Multiply or divide. Simplify your answer.

34. $\dfrac{2b}{3b-6} \cdot (b^2 - b - 2)$

35. $\dfrac{4x}{3x+9} \cdot (x^2 - 9)$

36. $\dfrac{5ab^2}{2ab} \cdot \dfrac{3a^2b^2}{a^2b}$

37. $16n^3 \div \dfrac{4m^2n}{3mn}$

38. $\dfrac{b+2}{2b^2+12b} \cdot \dfrac{b^2+2b-24}{b^2-16}$

39. $\dfrac{x^2+2x-3}{4x} \div \dfrac{x^2-4}{x}$

10-5 Adding and Subtracting Rational Expressions (pp. 659–665)

 13.0

EXAMPLES

Add or subtract. Simplify your answer.

■ $\dfrac{7x}{3xy} - \dfrac{x^2-3x}{3xy}$

$\dfrac{7x-(x^2-3x)}{3xy}$ *Subtract numerators.*

$\dfrac{7x-x^2+3x}{3xy}$ *Distribute.*

$\dfrac{10x-x^2}{3xy}$ *Simplify.*

■ $\dfrac{3w}{w-5} + \dfrac{4}{w^2-2w-15}$

$\dfrac{3w}{w-5} + \dfrac{4}{(w-5)(w+3)}$ *Factor to find the LCD.*

$\dfrac{3w(w+3)}{(w-5)(w+3)} + \dfrac{4}{(w-5)(w+3)}$ *Write each expression using the LCD.*

$\dfrac{3w^2+9w}{(w-5)(w+3)} + \dfrac{4}{(w-5)(w+3)}$

$\dfrac{3w^2+9w+4}{(w-5)(w+3)}$ *Add and simplify.*

EXERCISES

Find the LCM of the given expressions.

40. $5a^2b,\ 10ab^2$ 41. $2x^2 - 6x,\ 5x - 15$

Add or subtract. Simplify your answer.

42. $\dfrac{b^2}{2b} + \dfrac{8}{2b}$ 43. $\dfrac{3x^2-4}{x^2-2} + \dfrac{2x}{x^2-2}$

44. $\dfrac{8p}{p^2-4p+2} - \dfrac{2}{p^2-4p+2}$

45. $\dfrac{3b+4}{7-b} - \dfrac{5-2b}{7-b}$ 46. $\dfrac{n-5}{n^2-1} - \dfrac{n+5}{n^2-1}$

47. $\dfrac{3}{5m} + \dfrac{m+2}{10m^2}$ 48. $\dfrac{h^2+2h}{h-5} - \dfrac{3h-1}{5-h}$

49. A scout troop hikes 10 miles to the top of a mountain. Because the return trip is downhill, the scouts are able to hike 3 times faster on their way down. Let r represent the troop's rate to the mountaintop. Write and simplify an expression for the round-trip hiking time in terms of r.

10-6 Dividing Polynomials (pp. 667–673)

 10.0, 12.0

EXAMPLE

■ Divide $(4x^3 - 2x^2 + 5x - 1) \div (x - 2)$.

$$
\begin{array}{r}
4x^2 + 6x + 17 \\
x - 2 \overline{)4x^3 - 2x^2 + 5x - 1} \\
\underline{-\left(4x^3 - 8x^2\right)} \\
6x^2 + 5x \\
\underline{-\left(6x^2 - 12x\right)} \\
17x - 1 \\
\underline{-\left(17x - 34\right)} \\
33
\end{array}
$$

$$4x^2 + 6x + 17 + \frac{33}{x - 2}$$

EXERCISES

Divide. Check your answer.

50. $\left(-5x^3 + 10x - 25\right) \div \left(-5x^2\right)$

51. $\dfrac{x^2 - 8x - 20}{x - 10}$

52. $\dfrac{6n^2 - 13n - 5}{2n - 5}$

Divide using long division. Check your answer.

53. $\left(x^2 + 5x + 6\right) \div (x + 3)$

54. $\left(x^2 + x - 30\right) \div (x - 5)$

55. $\left(3b^3 - 4b + 2\right) \div (b - 2)$

10-7 Solving Rational Equations (pp. 674–678)

Prep for 15.0

EXAMPLE

■ Solve $\dfrac{3}{x + 3} = \dfrac{2}{x}$. Check your answer.

$$
\begin{aligned}
3x &= 2(x + 3) && \textit{Use cross products.} \\
3x &= 2x + 6 && \textit{Distribute.} \\
\underline{-2x} &\ \underline{-2x} && \textit{Subtract 2x from both sides.} \\
x &= 6
\end{aligned}
$$

Check

$$
\begin{array}{c|c}
\dfrac{3}{x + 3} & \dfrac{2}{x} \\[2mm]
\dfrac{3}{6 + 3} & \dfrac{2}{6} \\[2mm]
\dfrac{3}{9} & \dfrac{1}{3} \\[2mm]
\dfrac{1}{3} & \dfrac{1}{3} \quad \checkmark
\end{array}
$$

EXERCISES

Solve. Check your answer.

56. $-4 = \dfrac{3}{r}$

57. $\dfrac{6}{7} = \dfrac{x}{2}$

58. $\dfrac{6}{b} = \dfrac{-5}{3 + b}$

59. $\dfrac{7}{3y^2} = \dfrac{-2}{y}$

60. $\dfrac{2}{x - 1} = \dfrac{3x}{1 - x}$

61. $\dfrac{2x}{x^2} + \dfrac{1}{x^2} = 3$

62. $\dfrac{2}{3} + \dfrac{4}{x} = \dfrac{6}{3x}$

63. $-\dfrac{1}{3x} + \dfrac{x}{4} = -\dfrac{1}{12x}$

64. $\dfrac{2}{3b} + 4 = \dfrac{1}{3b}$

65. $\dfrac{4}{x - 4} = \dfrac{8}{x^2 - 16}$

66. $\dfrac{5x - 10}{x + 1} = \dfrac{x}{2}$

67. $\dfrac{2x}{x + 3} + \dfrac{x}{4} = \dfrac{3}{x + 3}$

68. $\dfrac{9m}{m - 5} = 7 - \dfrac{3}{m - 5}$

69. $\dfrac{x - 4}{x^2 - 4} = \dfrac{-2}{x - 2}$

10-8 Applying Rational Equations (pp. 679–683)

 15.0

EXAMPLE

■ Armin can clean a house in 5 hours. It takes Greg 7 hours to clean the same house. How long will it take them if they work together?

$$35\left(\dfrac{1}{5}h + \dfrac{1}{7}h\right) = 35(1) \quad \begin{array}{l}\textit{Multiply both sides by}\\ \textit{the LCD, 35}\end{array}$$

$$7h + 5h = 35 \quad \textit{Distribute 35 on the left side.}$$

$$12h = 35 \quad \textit{Combine like terms.}$$

$$h = \dfrac{35}{12} = 2\dfrac{11}{12} \quad \textit{Divide both sides by 12.}$$

Together they can clean the house in $2\frac{11}{12}$ h, or 2 h 55 min.

EXERCISES

70. A liquid poured into pipe A fills a storage tank in 12 hours. The same liquid poured into pipe B fills the tank in 18 hours. How long would it take to fill the tank if the liquid is poured into both pipes at the same time?

71. A chemist has 400 milliliters of a solution that is 40% water and 60% chlorine. She wants a solution that is 50% water and 50% chlorine. How many milliliters of water should she add to the solution?

CHAPTER TEST

1. Write and graph the inverse variation in which $y = -4$ when $x = 2$.

2. The number of posters the Spanish Club can buy varies inversely as the cost of each poster. The club can buy 15 posters that cost \$2.60 each. How many posters can the club buy if they cost \$3.25 each?

Identify any excluded values and the asymptotes for each rational function.

3. $y = \dfrac{3}{x + 1}$

4. $y = \dfrac{1}{2x - 1} + 5$

5. $y = \dfrac{1}{x + 3} - 3$

Simplify each rational expression, if possible. Identify any excluded values.

6. $\dfrac{2b}{4b^2}$

7. $\dfrac{x^2 - 16}{x^2 + 3x - 4}$

8. $\dfrac{b^2 - 2b - 15}{5 - b}$

9. $\dfrac{x^2 + 4x - 5}{x^2 - 25}$

Multiply. Simplify your answer.

10. $\dfrac{-4}{x^2 - 9} \cdot (x - 3)$

11. $\dfrac{2a^2b^2}{5b^3} \cdot \dfrac{15a^2b}{8a^4}$

12. $\dfrac{x^2 - x - 12}{x^2 - 16} \cdot \dfrac{x^2 + x - 12}{x^2 + 3x + 2}$

Divide. Simplify your answer.

13. $\dfrac{4x^2y^4}{3xy^2} \div \dfrac{12xy}{15x^3y^2}$

14. $\dfrac{3b^2 - 6b}{2b^3 + 3b^2} \div \dfrac{2b - 4}{8b + 12}$

15. $\dfrac{x^2 + 2x - 15}{x^2 - 9} \div \dfrac{x^2 - 25}{x^2 + 3x + 2}$

Add or subtract. Simplify your answer.

16. $\dfrac{b^2 + 3}{5b} + \dfrac{4}{5b}$

17. $\dfrac{5x - 2}{x^2 + 2} - \dfrac{2x}{x^2 + 2}$

18. $\dfrac{2}{3x^2} - \dfrac{5 - 2x}{3x^2}$

19. $\dfrac{3m}{2m^2} + \dfrac{1}{2m}$

20. $\dfrac{3x}{2x + 4} - \dfrac{1}{x + 2}$

21. $\dfrac{y^2 + 4}{y - 3} + \dfrac{y^2}{3 - y}$

Divide.

22. $(8t^2 - 2t) \div 2t$

23. $\dfrac{3x^2 + 2x - 8}{x + 2}$

24. $\dfrac{k^2 - 2k - 35}{k + 5}$

Divide using long division.

25. $(2w^2 + 5w - 12) \div (w + 4)$

26. $(x^2 - 4x + 9) \div (x + 2)$

27. The area of a rectangle can be modeled by $A(x) = x^3 - 1$. The length is $x - 1$.

   a. Find a polynomial to represent the width of the rectangle.

   b. Find the width when x is 6 cm.

Solve. Check your answer.

28. $\dfrac{2}{x - 1} = \dfrac{9}{2x - 3}$

29. $\dfrac{3}{n - 1} = \dfrac{n}{n + 4}$

30. $\dfrac{2}{n + 2} = \dfrac{n - 4}{n^2 - 4}$

31. Julio can wash and wax the family car in 2 hours. It takes Leo 3 hours to wash and wax the same car. How long will it take them to wash and wax the car if they work together?

COLLEGE ENTRANCE EXAM PRACTICE

FOCUS ON SAT MATHEMATICS SUBJECT TESTS

The topics covered on each SAT Mathematics Subject Test vary only slightly each time the test is given. Find out the general distribution of test items across topics, and then identify the areas you need to concentrate on while studying.

To prepare for the SAT Math Subject Tests, start reviewing material several months before your test date. Take sample tests to find the areas you need to focus on. You are not expected to have studied all topics on the test.

You may want to time yourself as you take this practice test. It should take you about 6 minutes to complete.

---

1. Which set of ordered pairs satisfies an inverse variation?

   (A) $(6, 3)$ and $(8, 4)$

   (B) $(2, -3)$ and $(4, 5)$

   (C) $(4, -2)$ and $(-5, 10)$

   (D) $(2, 6)$ and $(-3, -4)$

   (E) $\left(4, \dfrac{1}{4}\right)$ and $\left(-4, \dfrac{1}{4}\right)$

---

2. If $\dfrac{3}{x + 3} = \dfrac{7x}{x^2 - 9}$, what is x?

   (A) -12

   (B) -3

   (C) $-\dfrac{9}{4}$

   (D) $\dfrac{9}{4}$

   (E) 3

---

3. What is h if $\left(x^3 + 2x^2 - 4x + h\right) \div (x + 1)$ has a remainder of 15?

   (A) -10

   (B) -5

   (C) 5

   (D) 10

   (E) 20

---

4. The graph of which function is shown?

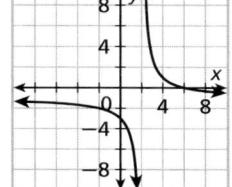

   (A) $f(x) = \dfrac{2}{x + 4} + 1$

   (B) $f(x) = \dfrac{4}{x + 2} - 1$

   (C) $f(x) = \dfrac{4}{x - 2} + 1$

   (D) $f(x) = \dfrac{4}{x - 2} - 1$

   (E) $f(x) = \dfrac{2}{x - 4} + 1$

---

5. Which function has the same graph as $f(x) = \dfrac{x^2 - 4x - 5}{x^2 - 3x - 10}$ except at $x = 5$?

   (A) $g(x) = \dfrac{x - 1}{x - 2}$

   (B) $g(x) = \dfrac{x + 1}{x + 2}$

   (C) $g(x) = \dfrac{x + 1}{(x - 5)(x + 2)}$

   (D) $g(x) = \dfrac{(x + 5)(x - 1)}{x + 2}$

   (E) $g(x) = \dfrac{(x - 5)(x + 1)}{x - 2}$

STRATEGIES FOR SUCCESS

Multiple Choice: Choose Combinations of Answers

Some multiple-choice test items require selecting a combination of correct answers. The correct response is the most complete option available. To solve this type of test item, determine if each statement is true or false. Then choose the option that includes each correct statement.

EXAMPLE 1

Which of the following has an excluded value of −5?

I. $\dfrac{5}{x-5}$

III. $\dfrac{x^2-10}{5x+25} \cdot \dfrac{5}{x+10}$

II. $\dfrac{8x^2+36x-20}{2(x+5)}$

IV. $\dfrac{2(x+2)}{2x^2+12x+10}$

(A) I only

(C) II, III, and IV

(B) II and III

(D) III and IV

Look at each statement separately and determine whether it is true. You can keep track of which statements are true in a table.

Statement I
The denominator, $x-5$, equals 0 when $x=5$.

Statement I does not answer the question, so it is false.

Statement	True/False
I	False
II	True
III	True
IV	True

Statement II
The denominator, $2(x+5)$, equals 0 when $x=-5$.

Statement II does answer the question, so it is true.

Statement III
The denominator, $(5x+25)(x+10)$, equals 0 when $x=-5$ or $x=-10$.

Statement III does answer the question, so it is true.

Statement IV
The denominator, $2x^2+12x+10$, can be factored as $2(x+5)(x+1)$. This expression equals 0 when $x=-5$ or $x=-1$.

Statement IV does answer the question, so it is true.

Statements II, III, and IV are all true. Option C is the correct response because it includes all the true statements.

Options B and D contain some of the true statements, but option C is the **most complete** answer.

Evaluate all of the statements before deciding on an answer choice. Make a table to keep track of whether each statement is true or false.

Read each test item and answer the questions that follow.

Item A

Which dimensions represent a rectangle that has an area equivalent to the expression $2x^2 + 18x + 16$?

I. $\ell = x + 8$

$w = 2(x + 1)$

II. $\ell = 2x + 2$

$w = \dfrac{x^2 + 3x - 40}{x - 5}$

III. $\ell = x + 2$

$w = \dfrac{(2x + 2)(x + 4)}{1} \cdot \dfrac{(3x - 1)}{(3x^2 - 11x - 4)}$

Ⓐ I only   Ⓒ I and II

Ⓑ III only   Ⓓ I, II, and III

1. How do you determine the area of a rectangle?

2. Daisy realized that the area of the rectangle described in I was equivalent to the given area and selected option A as her response. Do you agree? Explain your reasoning.

3. Write a simplified expression for the width of the rectangle described in II.

4. Explain each step for determining the area of the rectangle described in III.

5. If the rectangle described in II has an area equivalent to the given expression, then which options can you eliminate?

Item B

Which expression is undefined for $x = 3$ or $x = -2$?

I. $2x + 12 \cdot \dfrac{4}{2(x - 3)(x + 6)}$ III. $\dfrac{(x - 2)}{(x + 2)(x - 1)}$

II. $\dfrac{9x - 1}{x^2 + 3}$ IV. $\dfrac{14}{x^2 - x - 6}$

Ⓐ I, III, and IV   Ⓒ III and IV

Ⓑ I and II   Ⓓ I and IV

6. When is an expression undefined?

7. Henry determined that expression I is undefined when $x = 3$. He decides it is an incorrect answer because the expression is defined when $x = -2$. Should he select option C by process of elimination? Explain your reasoning.

8. Make a table to determine the correct response.

Item C

Which rational function has a graph with a horizontal asymptote of $y = 4$?

I. $y = \dfrac{-4}{x}$ III. $y = \dfrac{1}{x - 4}$

II. $y = \dfrac{1}{x} + 4$ IV. $y = -\dfrac{1}{x} + 4$

Ⓐ I and III   Ⓒ I and II

Ⓑ II only   Ⓓ II and IV

9. Where does the horizontal asymptote of the function in statement I occur?

10. Using your answer from Problem 9, which option(s) can you eliminate? Explain your reasoning.

11. Look at the options remaining. Which statement would be best to check next? Explain your reasoning.

CUMULATIVE ASSESSMENT, CHAPTERS 1–10

Multiple Choice

1. At how many points does the graph of $y = (x - 6)^2$ intersect the x-axis?

  Ⓐ none   Ⓒ two

  Ⓑ one   Ⓓ three

2. Which point lies on the line described by $2x - 3y - 9 = 0$?

  Ⓐ $(-2, 2)$ Ⓒ $(0, 3)$

  Ⓑ $(4, -5)$ Ⓓ $(3, -1)$

3. Which function is shown in the graph?

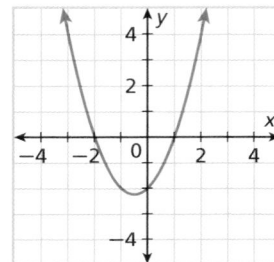

  Ⓐ $y = x^2 + x - 2$

  Ⓑ $y = x^2 - x - 2$

  Ⓒ $y = -x^2 - x + 2$

  Ⓓ $y = x^2 - 2$

4. A city map is laid out on a coordinate plane. Elm Street is described by the line $x + 2y = -6$. Oak Street intersects Elm Street at a right angle. Which of the following could be the equation for Oak Street?

  Ⓐ $2x + y = 5$

  Ⓑ $-2x + y = 3$

  Ⓒ $x + 2y = 4$

  Ⓓ $-x - 2y = 8$

5. Which expression is NOT equivalent to $\dfrac{3}{x - 1}$?

  Ⓐ $\dfrac{3x + 6}{x^2 + x - 2}$ Ⓒ $\dfrac{3x + 3}{x^2 - 1}$

  Ⓑ $\dfrac{3x - 3}{x^2 - 2x + 1}$ Ⓓ $\dfrac{3x - 3}{x - 1}$

6. What are the x- and y-intercepts of the line described by $6x - 2y = 4$?

  Ⓐ x-intercept: $\dfrac{2}{3}$

     y-intercept: 2

  Ⓑ x-intercept: $-\dfrac{2}{3}$

     y-intercept: 2

  Ⓒ x-intercept: $\dfrac{2}{3}$

     y-intercept: -2

  Ⓓ x-intercept: -2

     y-intercept: $\dfrac{2}{3}$

7. Which expression is equivalent to $\dfrac{3m^2 n}{5m} \cdot \dfrac{20mn}{n^6}$?

  Ⓐ $\dfrac{12m^2}{n^4}$ Ⓒ $12m^2 n^3$

  Ⓑ $\dfrac{12m^3}{n^3}$ Ⓓ $\dfrac{12m}{n}$

8. Simplify $\dfrac{3}{x} + \dfrac{3}{5x}$.

  Ⓐ $\dfrac{1}{x}$ Ⓒ $\dfrac{18}{5x}$

  Ⓑ $\dfrac{18}{10x}$ Ⓓ $\dfrac{1}{2x}$

9. Which of these is the graph of $y = x^2 - 4x + 4$?

  Ⓐ 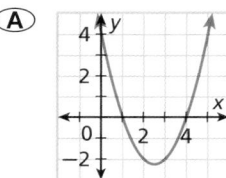   Ⓒ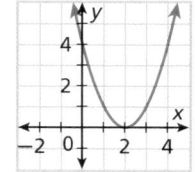

  Ⓑ 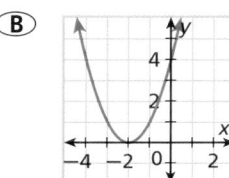   Ⓓ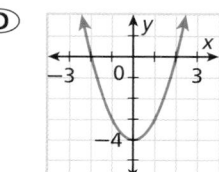

10. What is $(-12x^6 + x) \div (-4x^2)$?

Ⓐ $3x^3 - \dfrac{1}{4x}$ Ⓒ $3x^5$

Ⓑ $3x^4 - \dfrac{1}{4x}$ Ⓓ $3x^4 + x$

11. What is the greatest common factor of the terms of the polynomial $6x^3 - 18x^2 + 12x + 3$?

Ⓐ 3 Ⓒ $6x$

Ⓑ $3x$ Ⓓ $6x^2$

12. Which is a solution to $\dfrac{n}{n+2} = \dfrac{-8}{n}$?

Ⓐ -4 Ⓒ 2

Ⓑ -2 Ⓓ 4

13. Which of the following is equivalent to $\left(\dfrac{2x^5y^2}{8x}\right)^{-2}$?

Ⓐ $\dfrac{16}{x^8y^4}$ Ⓒ $\dfrac{4}{x^4y^2}$

Ⓑ $\dfrac{x^8}{16y^4}$ Ⓓ $\dfrac{x^5}{16}$

14. Which of the following is a true statement about the function $y = \dfrac{1}{x}$?

Ⓐ The domain is all real numbers.

Ⓑ The range is all real numbers.

Ⓒ The domain is all real numbers except 0.

Ⓓ The range is all real numbers except 1.

 **If you are allowed to write in your test booklet, you may want to add additional information to a given diagram. Be sure to mark your answer on the answer sheet because you will not receive any credit for marks in the test booklet.**

Gridded Response

15. What is the excluded value for the rational expression $\dfrac{x^2 - 4}{3x - 6}$?

16. The trinomial $x^2 - 6x + c$ is a perfect square trinomial. What is the value of c?

17. Find the positive solution of the equation $x^2 + 5x - 4 = 0$. Round your answer to the nearest tenth.

18. What is the value of $4^0 - (2^{-3})$?

19. Identify the excluded value for $y = \dfrac{x-4}{x-2}$.

Short Response

20. Mr. Lui wrote $\dfrac{15 - 5x}{x^2 - 9x + 18}$ on the board.

   a. Explain what kind of expression it is.

   b. Simplify the expression. Show your work.

   c. Identify any excluded values.

21. Lynne can paint a wall in 40 minutes. Jeff can paint the same wall in 60 minutes. How long will it take Lynne and Jeff to paint the wall if they work together? Show your work.

22. What are 2 values of b that will make $2x^2 - bx - 20$ factorable? Explain your answer.

23. The sum of the digits of a two-digit number is 11. If 45 is added to the number, the digits will be reversed.

   a. Write a system of equations that you can use to find the digits of the number. Tell what each variable represents.

   b. Solve the system of equations to find the two-digit number. Show your work.

Extended Response

24. Principal Farley has $200 to pay for some teachers to attend a technology conference. The company hosting the conference is allowing 2 teachers to attend for free. The number of teachers y that can be sent to the conference is given by the function $y = \dfrac{200}{x} + 2$, where x is the cost per teacher.

   a. Describe the reasonable domain and range values for this function.

   b. Identify the vertical and horizontal asymptotes.

   c. Graph the function.

   d. Give two points on the graph whose coordinates are whole numbers and describe what they mean in the context of this situation.

CHAPTER 11

Preview of Algebra II

Radical and Exponential Functions

go.hrw.com
Chapter Project Online
KEYWORD: MA8CA ChProj

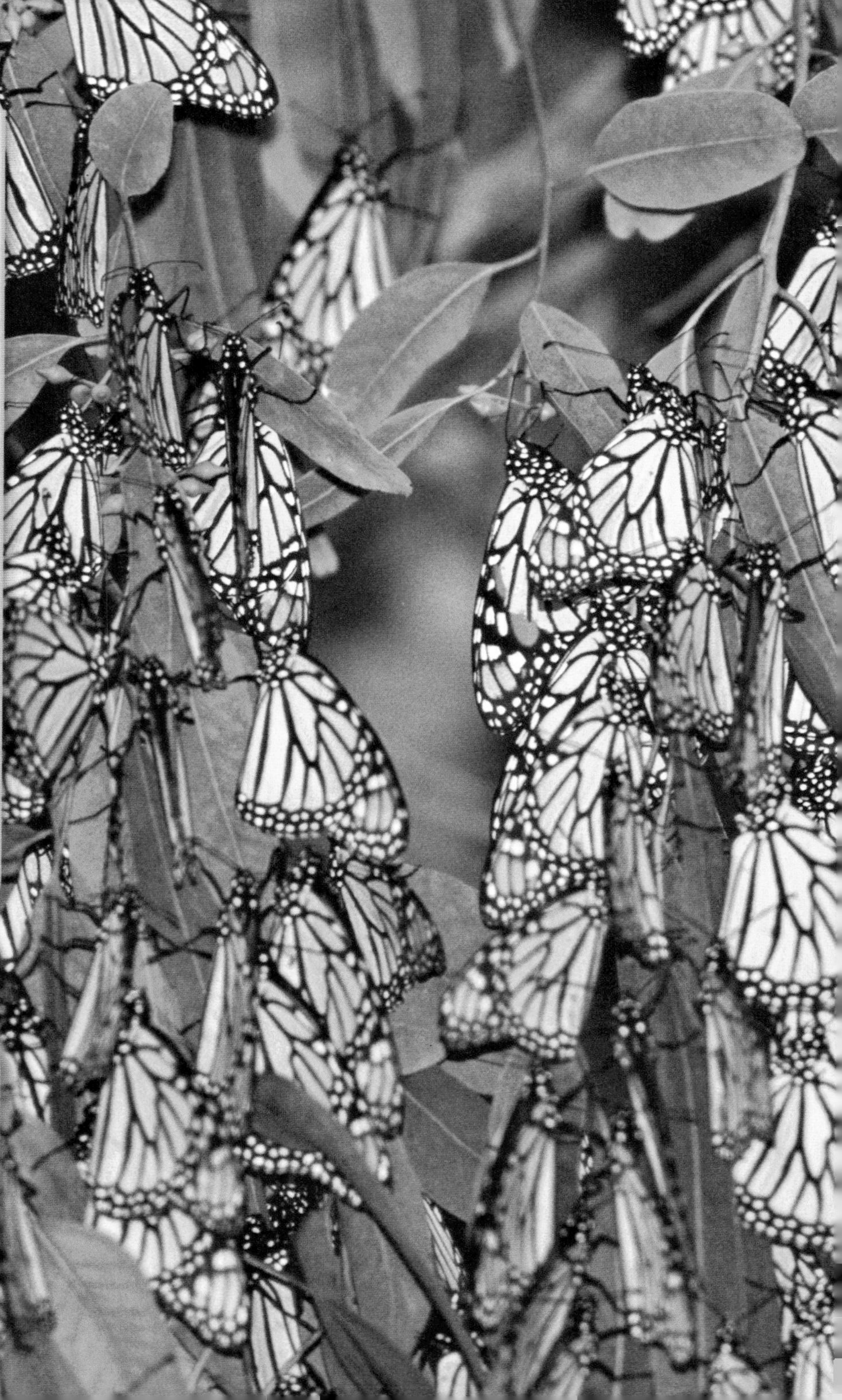

The concepts in this chapter are used to model many real-world phenomena, such as changes in wildlife populations.

Natural Bridges State Park
Santa Cruz, CA

ARE YOU READY?

✓ Vocabulary

Match each term on the left with a definition on the right.

1. like terms
2. square root
3. domain
4. perfect square
5. exponent

A. the set of second elements of a relation

B. terms that contain the same variable raised to the same power

C. the set of first elements of a relation

D. a number that tells how many times a base is used as a factor

E. a number whose positive square root is a whole number

F. one of two equal factors of a number

✓ Squares and Square Roots

Find each square root.

6. $\sqrt{36}$
7. $\sqrt{81}$
8. $\sqrt{25}$
9. $\sqrt{64}$

✓ Pythagorean Theorem

Find the length of the hypotenuse in each right triangle.

10.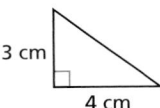
3 cm
4 cm

11.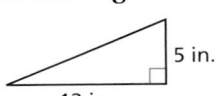
5 in.
12 in.

12.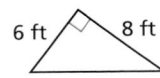
6 ft
8 ft

✓ Multiply Monomials and Polynomials

Multiply.

13. $5(2m - 3)$
14. $3x(8x + 9)$
15. $2t(3t - 1)$
16. $4r(4r - 5)$

✓ Evaluate Powers

Find the value of each expression.

17. 2^4
18. 5^0
19. $7 \cdot 3^2$
20. $3 \cdot 5^3$

21. 3^5
22. $-6^2 + 8^1$
23. $40 \cdot 2^3$
24. $7^2 \cdot 3^1$

✓ Graph Functions

Graph each function.

25. $y = 8$
26. $y = x + 3$
27. $y = x^2 - 4$
28. $y = x^2 + 2$

✓ Fractions, Decimals, and Percents

Write each percent as a decimal.

29. 50%
30. 25%
31. 15.2%
32. 200%

33. 1.9%
34. 0.3%
35. 0.1%
36. 1.04%

CHAPTER 11

Unpacking the Standards

The information below "unpacks" the standards. The Academic Vocabulary is highlighted and defined to help you understand the language of the standards. Refer to the lessons listed after each standard for help with the math terms and phrases. The Chapter Concept shows how the standard is applied in this chapter.

California Standard	Academic Vocabulary	Chapter Concept
Extension of 🔑 1A2.0 Students understand and use such **operations** as taking the opposite, finding the reciprocal, **taking a root**, and raising to a fractional power. **They understand and use the rules of exponents.** (Lessons **11-1, 11-2, 11-3, 11-4, 11-5**)	**operations** calculations you use when you work out a problem	You learn to calculate and graph square-root functions. ***Example:*** $y = \sqrt{2x + 1}$ You also learn how to add, subtract, multiply, and divide expressions that have radicals.
1A17.0 Students determine the domain of **independent variables** and the range of dependent variables defined **by** a graph, a set of ordered pairs, or **a symbolic expression.** (Lesson **11-1**)	**independent** not determined by anything else	You find the *x*-values that make the value under the radical sign greater than or equal to zero.
Preview of Algebra II 12.0 Students know the laws of fractional exponents, **understand exponential functions, and use these functions in problems involving exponential growth and decay.** (Lessons **11-7, 11-8**)	**growth** an increase **decay** a decrease	You find the value of exponential functions by substituting numbers for the variable that appears as the exponent. You also learn to identify, write, and graph functions that contain exponents.
Preview of Algebra II Preparation for 2A22.0 Students **find the general term** and the sums of arithmetic series and **of both finite and infinite geometric series.** (Lesson **11-6**)	**general** applying to every member of a group	You find an expression that describes every term in a geometric sequence.

Study Strategy: Prepare for Your Final Exam

Math is a cumulative subject, so your final exam will probably cover all of the material you have learned since the beginning of the course. Preparation is essential for you to be successful on your final exam. It may help you to make a study timeline like the one below.

2 weeks before the final:

- Look at previous exams and homework to determine areas I need to focus on; rework problems that were incorrect or incomplete.
- Make a list of all formulas and properties I need to know for the final.
- Create a practice exam using problems from the book that are similar to problems from each exam.

1 week before the final:

- Take the practice exam and check it. For each problem I miss, find 2 or 3 similar ones and work those.
- Work with a friend in the class to quiz each other on formulas and properties from my list.

1 day before the final:

- Make sure I have pencils, calculator (check batteries!), ruler, compass, and protractor.

FINAL

Try This

1. Create a timeline that you will use to study for your final exam.

11-1 Square-Root Functions

California Standards

Extension of ⟢ **2.0** Students understand and use such **operations as** taking the opposite, finding the reciprocal, **taking a root**, and raising to a fractional power. They understand and use the rules of exponents.

Also covered: **17.0**

Vocabulary
square-root function

Who uses this?
Astronauts can use square-root functions to calculate their speed in free fall.

Astronauts at NASA practice living in the weightlessness of space by training in the KC-135, also known as the "Vomit Comet." This aircraft flies to a certain altitude and then free falls for a period of time, simulating a zero-gravity environment.

The function $y = 8\sqrt{x}$ gives the speed in feet per second of an object in free fall after falling x feet. This function is different from others you have seen so far. It contains a variable under the square-root sign, $\sqrt{}$.

Square-Root Function

WORDS	EXAMPLES	NONEXAMPLES
A **square-root function** is a function whose rule contains a variable under a square-root sign.	$y = \sqrt{x}$ $y = \sqrt{2x + 1}$ $y = 3\sqrt{\dfrac{x}{2}} - 6$	$y = x^2$ $y = \dfrac{2}{x + 1}$ $y = \sqrt{3}x$

EXAMPLE 1   Evaluating Square-Root Functions

A Find the speed of an object in free fall after it has fallen 4 feet.

$y = 8\sqrt{x}$ *Write the speed function.*
$ = 8\sqrt{4}$ *Substitute 4 for x.*
$ = 8(2)$ *Simplify.*
$ = 16$

After an object has fallen 4 feet, its speed is 16 ft/s.

Helpful Hint

Check that your answer is reasonable. In Example 1B, $8\sqrt{49} = 8(7) = 56$, so $8\sqrt{50} \approx 56.6$ is reasonable.

B Find the speed of an object in free fall after it has fallen 50 feet. Round your answer to the nearest tenth.

$y = 8\sqrt{x}$ *Write the speed function.*
$ = 8\sqrt{50}$ *Substitute 50 for x.*
$ \approx 56.6$ *Use a calculator.*

After an object has fallen 50 feet, its speed is about 56.6 ft/s.

1a. Find the speed of an object in free fall after it has fallen 25 feet.
1b. Find the speed of an object in free fall after it has fallen 15 feet. Round your answer to the nearest hundredth.

Recall that the square root of a negative number is not a real number. The domain (x-values) of a square-root function is restricted to numbers that make the value under the radical sign greater than or equal to 0.

EXAMPLE 2 **Finding the Domain of Square-Root Functions**

Find the domain of each square-root function.

A $y = \sqrt{x + 4} - 3$

$x + 4 \geq 0$ *The expression under the radical sign must be greater than or equal to 0.*

$x \geq -4$ *Solve the inequality. Subtract 4 from both sides.*

B $y = \sqrt{3(x - 2)}$

$3(x - 2) \geq 0$ *The expression under the radical sign must be greater than or equal to 0.*

$3x - 6 \geq 0$ *Solve the inequality. Distribute 3 on the left side.*

$3x \geq 6$ *Add 6 to both sides.*

$x \geq 2$ *Divide both sides by 3.*

Helpful Hint

Another way to solve the inequality in Example 2B is to first divide both sides by 3 and then add 2 to both sides.

CHECK IT OUT! **2.** Find the domain of $y = \sqrt{2x - 1}$

The function $y = \sqrt{x}$ is graphed at right. Notice there are no x-values to the left of 0 because the domain is $x \geq 0$.

Remember that the symbol $\sqrt{}$ indicates the positive square root only. For this reason, the range of $y = \sqrt{x}$ is $y \geq 0$.

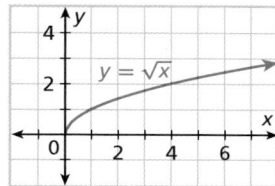

EXAMPLE 3 **Graphing Square-Root Functions**

Graph $y = \sqrt{2x} + 3$.

Step 1 Find the domain of the function.

$2x \geq 0$ *The expression under the radical sign must be greater than or equal to 0.*

$x \geq 0$ *Solve the inequality by dividing both sides by 2.*

Step 2 Choose x-values greater than or equal to 0 and generate ordered pairs.

Step 3 Plot the points. Then connect them with a smooth curve.

x	$y = \sqrt{2x} + 3$
0	3
2	5
8	7
18	9
32	11

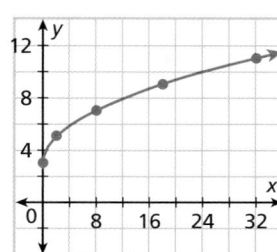

Helpful Hint

In Example 3, when generating ordered pairs, choose x-values that make the expression under the radical sign a perfect square.

CHECK IT OUT! **3.** Graph $y = \sqrt{x - 4}$

THINK AND DISCUSS

1. How do you find the domain of a square-root function?

2. GET ORGANIZED Copy and complete the graphic organizer. In each box, graph the function and give its domain.

Square-Root Functions

| $y = \sqrt{x}$ | $y = \sqrt{x} + 5$ | $y = \sqrt{x+5}$ | $y = \sqrt{5x}$ |

11-1 Exercises

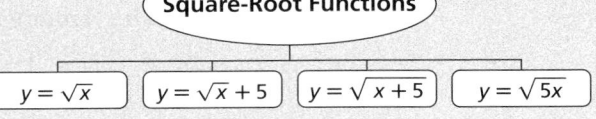

California Standards Practice
Extension of 🔑 2.0;
17.0, 24.1

go.hrw.com
Homework Help Online
KEYWORD: MA8CA 11-1
Parent Resources Online
KEYWORD: MA8CA Parent

GUIDED PRACTICE

1. Vocabulary Explain why $y = x + \sqrt{3}$ is not a *square-root function*.

SEE EXAMPLE 1
p. 700

2. Geometry In a right triangle, $c = \sqrt{a^2 + b^2}$, where c is the length of the hypotenuse (the longest side) and a and b are the lengths of the legs (the other two sides). What is the length of the hypotenuse of a right triangle if its legs measure 14 cm and 8 cm? Round your answer to the nearest hundredth.

SEE EXAMPLE 2
p. 701

Find the domain of each square-root function.

3. $y = \sqrt{x+6}$　　　**4.** $y = 4 - \sqrt{3-x}$　　　**5.** $y = \sqrt{2x} - 5$

6. $y = \sqrt{x+2}$　　　**7.** $y = \sqrt{3x+9}$　　　**8.** $y = x + \sqrt{x-5}$

SEE EXAMPLE 3
p. 701

Graph each square-root function.

9. $y = \sqrt{x-1}$　　　**10.** $y = -\sqrt{2x}$　　　**11.** $y = \sqrt{x} + 1$

12. $y = \sqrt{x} - 12$　　　**13.** $y = \sqrt{4-x}$　　　**14.** $y = \sqrt{x+4}$

PRACTICE AND PROBLEM SOLVING

Independent Practice

For Exercises	See Example
15	1
16–21	2
22–27	3

15. Law Enforcement At the scene of a car accident, police measure the length of the skid marks to estimate the speed that the car was traveling. On dry concrete, $f(x) = \sqrt{24x}$ gives the speed in mi/h when the length of the skid mark is x feet. Find the speed that a car was traveling if it left a skid mark that was 104 ft long. Round your answer to the nearest hundredth.

Extra Practice
Skills Practice p. EP22
Application Practice p. EP34

Find the domain of each square-root function.

16. $y = \sqrt{-2x+3}$　　　**17.** $y = 2\sqrt{x+1} - 2$　　　**18.** $y = \sqrt{3(x+2) - 1}$

19. $y = \sqrt{2(x+4)} - 3$　　　**20.** $y = 7\sqrt{\dfrac{x}{5} - 8}$　　　**21.** $y = \sqrt{2(3x-6)}$

Graph each square-root function.

22. $y = \sqrt{x-5}$　　　**23.** $y = \sqrt{2x} - 4$　　　**24.** $y = -1 - \sqrt{x}$

25. $y = \sqrt{x} - 4$　　　**26.** $y = 3\sqrt{x-6}$　　　**27.** $y = \dfrac{1}{2}\sqrt{x+4}$

28. Geometry If you know a circle's area, you can use the formula $r = \sqrt{\frac{A}{\pi}}$ to find the radius. What is the radius of a circle whose area is 60 cm²? Use 3.14 for π. Round your answer to the nearest hundredth of a centimeter.

 29. Graphing Calculator Use a graphing calculator for the following.
   a. Graph $y = \sqrt{x}$, $y = \frac{1}{2}\sqrt{x}$, $y = 2\sqrt{x}$, $y = 3\sqrt{x}$, and $y = 4\sqrt{x}$ on the same screen.
   b. What is the domain of each function?
   c. What is the range of each function?
    d. Reasoning Use inductive reasoning to make a conjecture about the characteristics of the graph of $y = a\sqrt{x}$ for $a > 0$.

 30. Graphing Calculator Use a graphing calculator for the following.
   a. Graph $y = -\sqrt{x}$, $y = -\frac{1}{2}\sqrt{x}$, $y = -2\sqrt{x}$, $y = -3\sqrt{x}$, and $y = -4\sqrt{x}$ on the same screen.
   b. What is the domain of each function?
   c. What is the range of each function?
    d. Reasoning Use inductive reasoning to make a conjecture about the characteristics of $y = a\sqrt{x}$ for $a < 0$.

31. Geology Tsunamis are large waves that move across deep oceans at high speeds. When tsunamis hit shallow water, their energy moves them upward into a destructive force. The speed of a tsunami in meters per second can be found using the function $y = \sqrt{9.8x}$, where x is the depth of the water in meters. Graph this function. Then find the speed of a tsunami when the water depth is 500 meters.

Geology

In December 2004, devastating tsunamis struck south and southeast Asia and eastern Africa. A worldwide relief effort ensued. Aid from the United States, both public and private, totaled over $2 billion in the year following the disaster.

32. Astronomy A planet's *escape velocity* is the initial velocity that an object must have to escape the planet's gravity. Escape velocity v in meters per second can be found by using the formula $v = \sqrt{2gr}$, where g is the planet's surface gravity and r is the planet's radius. Find the escape velocity for each planet in the table to the nearest whole number.

Planet	g (m/s²)	r (m)
Mercury	3.7	2.4×10^6
Venus	8.8	6.1×10^6
Earth	9.8	6.4×10^6
Mars	3.7	3.4×10^6

33. Critical Thinking Can the range of a square-root function be all real numbers? Explain.

34. Multi-Step For the function $y = \sqrt{3(x - 5)}$, find the value of y that corresponds to the least possible value for x.

35. Write About It Explain how to find the domain of a square-root function. Why is the domain not all real numbers?

CONCEPT CONNECTION

36. This problem will prepare you for the Concept Connection on page 730.

   a. The Ocean Motion ride at Ohio's Cedar Point amusement park is a giant ship that swings like a pendulum. If a pendulum is under the influence of gravity only, then the time in seconds that it takes for one complete swing back and forth (called the pendulum's period) is $T = 2\pi\sqrt{\frac{\ell}{32}}$, where ℓ is the length of the pendulum in feet. What is the domain of this function?

   b. What is the period of a pendulum whose length is 80 feet? Use 3.14 for π and round your answer to the nearest hundredth.

   c. The length of the Ocean Motion pendulum is about 80 feet. Do you think your answer to part **b** is its period? Explain why or why not.

Multiple Choice For Exercises 37–39, choose the best answer.

37. Which function is graphed at right?

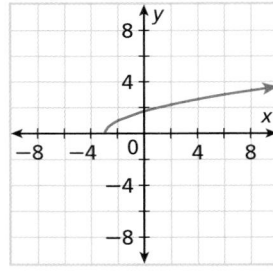

   (A) $y = \sqrt{x + 3}$ (C) $y = \sqrt{x - 3}$

   (B) $y = \sqrt{x} + 3$ (D) $y = \sqrt{x} - 3$

38. Which function has domain $x \geq 2$?

   (A) $y = \sqrt{2x}$ (C) $y = \sqrt{\dfrac{x}{2}}$

   (B) $y = \sqrt{x + 2}$ (D) $y = \sqrt{x - 2}$

39. The function $y = \sqrt{\frac{1}{5}x}$ gives the approximate time y in seconds that it takes an object to fall to the ground from a height of x meters. About how long will it take an object 25 meters above the ground to fall to the ground?

   (A) 11.2 seconds   (C) 2.2 seconds

   (B) 5 seconds   (D) 0.4 seconds

40. **Gridded Response** If $g(x) = \sqrt{4x} - 1$, what is $g(9)$?

CHALLENGE AND EXTEND

Find the domain of each function.

41. $y = \sqrt{x^2 - 25}$ 42. $y = \sqrt{x^2 + 5x + 6}$ 43. $y = \sqrt{2x^2 + 5x - 12}$

Find the domain and range of each function.

44. $y = 2 - \sqrt{x + 3}$ 45. $y = 4 - \sqrt{3 - x}$ 46. $y = 6 - \sqrt{\dfrac{x}{2}}$

47. Give an example of a square-root function whose graph is above the x-axis.

48. Give an example of a square-root function whose graph is in Quadrant IV.

49. **Multi-Step** Justin is given the function $y = 3 - \sqrt{2(x - 5)}$ and $x = 2, 4, 5,$ and 7. He notices that two of these values are not in the function's domain.

   a. Which two values are not in the domain? How do you know?

   b. What are the values of y for the two given x-values that are in the domain?

 SPIRAL STANDARDS REVIEW  ✦ 6.0, ✦ 10.0

Write each equation in slope-intercept form, and then graph. *(Lesson 5-5)*

50. $2y = 4x - 8$ 51. $3x + 6y = 12$ 52. $2x = -y - 9$

Find each product. *(Lesson 7-9)*

53. $(3x - 1)^2$ 54. $(2x - 5)(2x + 5)$ 55. $(a - b^2c)^2$

56. $(x^2 + 2y)^2$ 57. $(3r - 2s)(3r + 2s)$ 58. $(a^3b^2 - c^4)(a^3b^2 + c^4)$

Divide by using long division. Check your answer. *(Lesson 10-6)*

59. $(x^2 - 12x - 28) \div (x + 2)$ 60. $(y^2 - 2y - 15) \div (y + 3)$

61. $(2r^2 - 9r - 5) \div (r - 5)$ 62. $(t^2 + 4t - 21) \div (t + 7)$

63. $\dfrac{(3s^2 - 14s - 24)}{s - 6}$ 64. $\dfrac{(h^2 + 11h + 24)}{(h + 3)}$

11-2 Radical Expressions

California Standards

Extension of ⚷ 2.0
Students understand and use such operations as taking the opposite, finding the reciprocal, **taking a root,** and raising to a fractional power. **They understand and use the rules of exponents.**

Vocabulary
radical expression
radicand

Why learn this?
You can use a radical expression to find the length of a throw in baseball. (See Example 5.)

An expression that contains a radical sign $(\sqrt{\ })$ is a **radical expression**. There are many types of radical expressions (such as square roots, cube roots, fourth roots, and so on), but in this chapter, you will study radical expressions that contain only square roots.

Examples of radical expressions: $\sqrt{14}$ $\sqrt{\ell^2 + w^2}$ $\sqrt{2gd}$ $\dfrac{\sqrt{d}}{4}$ $5\sqrt{2}$

The expression under a radical sign is the **radicand**. A radicand may contain numbers, variables, or both. It may contain one term or more than one term.

Know it! Note

Simplest Form of a Square-Root Expression

An expression containing square roots is in simplest form when
- the radicand has no perfect square factors other than 1.
- the radicand has no fractions.
- there are no square roots in any denominator.

Helpful Hint
- $\sqrt{x^2} = |x|$
- $\sqrt{x^4} = x^2$
- $\sqrt{x^6} = |x^3|$

Remember that $\sqrt{\ }$ indicates a nonnegative square root. When you simplify a square-root expression containing variables, you must be sure that your answer is not negative. For example, you might think that $\sqrt{x^2} = x$. But this is incorrect because you do not know if x is positive or negative.

If $x = 3$, then $\sqrt{x^2} = \sqrt{3^2} = \sqrt{9} = 3$. In this case, $\sqrt{x^2} = x$.

If $x = -3$, then $\sqrt{x^2} = \sqrt{(-3)^2} = \sqrt{9} = 3$. In this case, $\sqrt{x^2} \neq x$.

In both cases $\sqrt{x^2} = |x|$. This is the correct simplification of $\sqrt{x^2}$.

EXAMPLE 1 Simplifying Square-Root Expressions

Simplify each expression.

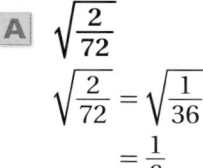

A $\sqrt{\dfrac{2}{72}}$

$\sqrt{\dfrac{2}{72}} = \sqrt{\dfrac{1}{36}}$

$= \dfrac{1}{6}$

B $\sqrt{3^2 + 4^2}$

$\sqrt{3^2 + 4^2} = \sqrt{9 + 16}$

$= \sqrt{25}$

$= 5$

C $\sqrt{x^2 + 8x + 16}$

$\sqrt{x^2 + 8x + 16} = \sqrt{(x+4)^2}$

$= |x + 4|$

Simplify each expression.

1a. $\sqrt{\dfrac{256}{4}}$ **1b.** $\sqrt{40 + 9}$ **1c.** $\sqrt{5^2 + 12^2}$ **1d.** $\sqrt{(3-x)^2}$

11-2 Radical Expressions **705**

Product Property of Square Roots

WORDS	NUMBERS	ALGEBRA
For any nonnegative real numbers a and b, the square root of ab is equal to the square root of a times the square root of b.	$\sqrt{4(25)} = \sqrt{100} = 10$ $\sqrt{4(25)} = \sqrt{4}\sqrt{25} = 2(5) = 10$	$\sqrt{ab} = \sqrt{a}\sqrt{b}$, where $a \geq 0$ and $b \geq 0$

EXAMPLE 2   **Using the Product Property of Square Roots**

Simplify. All variables represent nonnegative numbers.

A $\sqrt{18}$

$$\sqrt{18} = \sqrt{9(2)} \qquad \textit{Factor the radicand using perfect squares.}$$
$$= \sqrt{9}\sqrt{2} \qquad \textit{Product Property of Square Roots}$$
$$= 3\sqrt{2} \qquad \textit{Simplify.}$$

Helpful Hint

When factoring the radicand, use factors that are perfect squares. In Example 2A, you could have factored 18 as 6 · 3, but this contains no perfect squares.

B $\sqrt{x^4 y^3}$

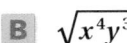

$$\sqrt{x^4 y^3} = \sqrt{x^4}\sqrt{y^3} \qquad \textit{Product Property of Square Roots}$$
$$= \sqrt{x^4}\sqrt{y^2}\sqrt{y} \qquad \textit{Product Property of Square Roots}$$
$$= x^2 y\sqrt{y} \qquad \textit{Since y is nonnegative, } \sqrt{y^2} = y.$$

 Simplify. All variables represent nonnegative numbers.

2a. $\sqrt{128}$ **2b.** $\sqrt{x^3 y^2}$ **2c.** $\sqrt{48a^2 b}$

Quotient Property of Square Roots

WORDS	NUMBERS	ALGEBRA
For any real numbers a and b ($a \geq 0$ and $b > 0$), the square root of $\frac{a}{b}$ is equal to the square root of a divided by the square root of b.	$\sqrt{\dfrac{36}{4}} = \sqrt{9} = 3$ $\sqrt{\dfrac{36}{4}} = \dfrac{\sqrt{36}}{\sqrt{4}} = \dfrac{6}{2} = 3$	$\sqrt{\dfrac{a}{b}} = \dfrac{\sqrt{a}}{\sqrt{b}}$, where $a \geq 0$ and $b > 0$

EXAMPLE 3   **Using the Quotient Property of Square Roots**

Simplify. All variables represent nonnegative numbers.

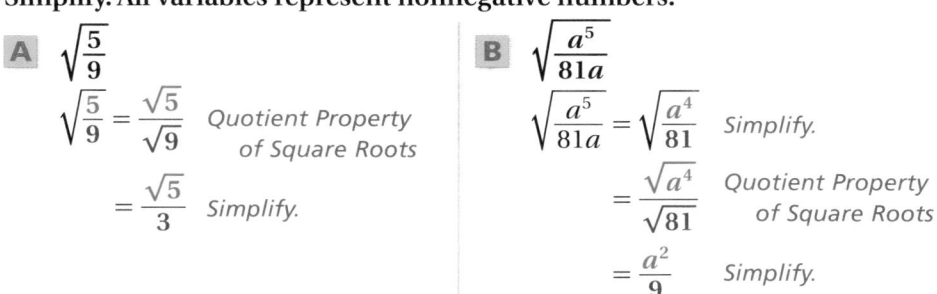

A $\sqrt{\dfrac{5}{9}}$

$$\sqrt{\dfrac{5}{9}} = \dfrac{\sqrt{5}}{\sqrt{9}} \qquad \textit{Quotient Property of Square Roots}$$
$$= \dfrac{\sqrt{5}}{3} \qquad \textit{Simplify.}$$

B $\sqrt{\dfrac{a^5}{81a}}$

$$\sqrt{\dfrac{a^5}{81a}} = \sqrt{\dfrac{a^4}{81}} \qquad \textit{Simplify.}$$
$$= \dfrac{\sqrt{a^4}}{\sqrt{81}} \qquad \textit{Quotient Property of Square Roots}$$
$$= \dfrac{a^2}{9} \qquad \textit{Simplify.}$$

 **Simplify. All variables represent nonnegative numbers.**

3a. $\sqrt{\dfrac{12}{27}}$ **3b.** $\sqrt{\dfrac{36}{x^4}}$ **3c.** $\sqrt{\dfrac{y^6}{4}}$

EXAMPLE 4 **Using the Product and Quotient Properties Together**

Simplify. All variables represent nonnegative numbers.

A $\sqrt{\dfrac{80}{25}}$

$\dfrac{\sqrt{80}}{\sqrt{25}}$ *Quotient Property*

$\dfrac{\sqrt{16(5)}}{\sqrt{25}}$ *Write 80 as 16(5).*

$\dfrac{\sqrt{16}\,\sqrt{5}}{\sqrt{25}}$ *Product Property*

$\dfrac{4\sqrt{5}}{5}$ *Simplify.*

> **Caution!** ⚠️
>
> In the expression $\frac{4\sqrt{5}}{5}$, $\sqrt{5}$ and 5 are not common factors. $\frac{4\sqrt{5}}{5}$ is completely simplified.

B $\sqrt{\dfrac{4x^5}{9}}$

$\dfrac{\sqrt{4x^5}}{\sqrt{9}}$ *Quotient Property*

$\dfrac{\sqrt{4}\,\sqrt{x^5}}{\sqrt{9}}$ *Product Property*

$\dfrac{\sqrt{4}\,\sqrt{x^4}\,\sqrt{x}}{\sqrt{9}}$

$\dfrac{2x^2\sqrt{x}}{3}$ *Simplify.*

 **Simplify. All variables represent nonnegative numbers.**

4a. $\sqrt{\dfrac{20}{49}}$ **4b.** $\sqrt{\dfrac{z^5}{25y^2}}$ **4c.** $\sqrt{\dfrac{p^6}{q^{10}}}$

EXAMPLE 5 **Sports Application**

A baseball diamond is a square with sides of 90 feet. How far is a throw from third base to first base? Give the answer as a radical expression in simplest form. Then estimate the length to the nearest tenth of a foot.

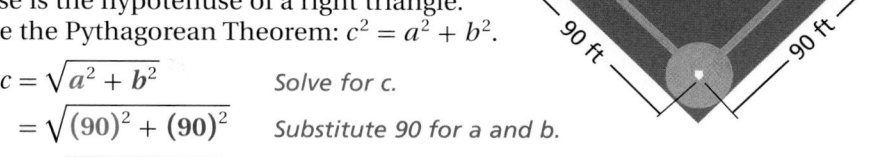

3rd base   1st base

90 ft   90 ft

The distance from third base to first base is the hypotenuse of a right triangle. Use the Pythagorean Theorem: $c^2 = a^2 + b^2$.

$c = \sqrt{a^2 + b^2}$ *Solve for c.*

$= \sqrt{(90)^2 + (90)^2}$ *Substitute 90 for a and b.*

$= \sqrt{8100 + 8100}$ *Simplify.*

$= \sqrt{16{,}200}$

$= \sqrt{100(81)(2)}$ *Factor 16,200 using perfect squares.*

$= \sqrt{100}\,\sqrt{81}\,\sqrt{2}$ *Use the Product Property of Square Roots.*

$= 10(9)\sqrt{2}$

$= 90\sqrt{2}$ *Simplify.*

≈ 127.3 *Use a calculator and round to the nearest tenth.*

The distance is $90\sqrt{2}$, or about 127.3, feet.

 **5.** A softball diamond is a square with sides of 60 feet. How long is a throw from third base to first base in softball? Give the answer as a radical expression in simplest form. Then estimate the length to the nearest tenth of a foot.

THINK AND DISCUSS

1. Show two ways to evaluate each of the following expressions: $\sqrt{16(9)}$, $\sqrt{\dfrac{100}{4}}$

2. In the Product and Quotient Properties of Square Roots, why can't a or b be negative?

3. **GET ORGANIZED** Copy and complete the graphic organizer. In each box, write the property and give an example.

	Product Property of Square Roots	Quotient Property of Square Roots
Words		
Example		

11-2 Exercises

California Standards Practice
Extension of ⬚ 2.0; 24.1

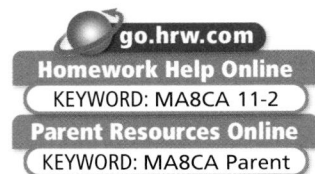
go.hrw.com
Homework Help Online
KEYWORD: MA8CA 11-2
Parent Resources Online
KEYWORD: MA8CA Parent

GUIDED PRACTICE

1. **Vocabulary** In the expression $\sqrt{3x - 6} + 7$, what is the *radicand*?

SEE EXAMPLE **1**
p. 705

Simplify each expression.

2. $\sqrt{81}$

3. $\sqrt{\dfrac{98}{2}}$

4. $\sqrt{(a + 7)^2}$

SEE EXAMPLE **2**
p. 706

Simplify. All variables represent nonnegative numbers.

5. $\sqrt{180}$

6. $\sqrt{40}$

7. $\sqrt{648}$

8. $\sqrt{m^5 n^3}$

9. $\sqrt{32x^4 y^3}$

10. $\sqrt{200a^2 b}$

SEE EXAMPLE **3**
p. 706

11. $\sqrt{\dfrac{17}{25}}$

12. $\sqrt{\dfrac{7}{16}}$

13. $\sqrt{\dfrac{6}{49}}$

14. $\sqrt{\dfrac{b}{c^2}}$

15. $\sqrt{\dfrac{4x^2}{36x}}$

16. $\sqrt{\dfrac{7a^4}{9a^3}}$

SEE EXAMPLE **4**
p. 707

17. $\sqrt{\dfrac{108}{49}}$

18. $\sqrt{\dfrac{204}{25}}$

19. $\sqrt{\dfrac{512}{81}}$

20. $\sqrt{\dfrac{1}{36x^2}}$

21. $\sqrt{\dfrac{50x^2}{169}}$

22. $\sqrt{\dfrac{72x^7}{4x^4}}$

SEE EXAMPLE **5**
p. 707

23. **Recreation** Your boat is traveling due north from a dock. Your friend's boat left at the same time from the same dock and is headed due east. After an hour, your friend calls and tells you that he has just stopped because of engine trouble. How far must you travel to meet your friend? Give your answer as a radical expression in simplest form. Then estimate the distance to the nearest mile.

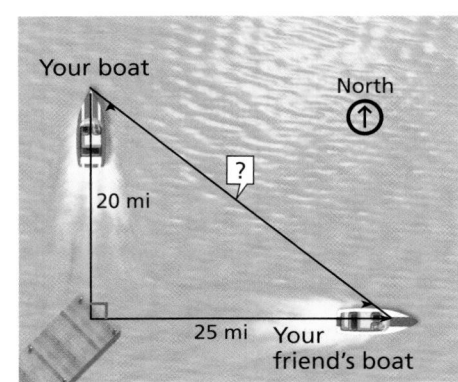

Your boat
North ↑
?
20 mi
25 mi Your friend's boat

PRACTICE AND PROBLEM SOLVING

Simplify.

Independent Practice

For Exercises	See Example
24–31	1
32–35	2
36–39	3
40–43	4
44	5

Extra Practice

Skills Practice p. EP22

Application Practice p. EP34

24. $\sqrt{100}$

25. $\sqrt{\dfrac{800}{2}}$

26. $\sqrt{3^2 + 4^2}$

27. $\sqrt{3 \cdot 27}$

28. $\sqrt{a^4}$

29. $\sqrt{(x+1)^2}$

30. $\sqrt{(5-x)^2}$

31. $\sqrt{(x-3)^2}$

Simplify. All variables represent nonnegative numbers.

32. $\sqrt{125}$

33. $\sqrt{4000}$

34. $\sqrt{216a^2b^2}$

35. $\sqrt{320r^2s^2}$

36. $\sqrt{\dfrac{15}{64}}$

37. $\sqrt{\dfrac{45}{4}}$

38. $\sqrt{\dfrac{64a^4}{4a^6}}$

39. $\sqrt{\dfrac{14z^3}{9z^3}}$

40. $\sqrt{\dfrac{128}{81}}$

41. $\sqrt{\dfrac{x^3}{y^6}}$

42. $\sqrt{\dfrac{150}{196x^2}}$

43. $\sqrt{\dfrac{192s^3}{49s}}$

44. Amusement Parks A thrill ride at an amusement park carries riders 160 feet straight up and then releases them for a free fall. The time t in seconds that it takes an object in free fall to reach the ground is $t = \sqrt{\dfrac{d}{16}}$, where d is the distance in feet that it falls. How long does it take the riders to reach the ground? Give your answer as a radical expression in simplest form. Then estimate the answer to the nearest tenth of a second.

Simplify. All variables represent nonnegative numbers.

45. $-4\sqrt{75}$

46. $-\sqrt{80}$

47. $5x\sqrt{63}$

48. $3\sqrt{48x}$

49. $2\sqrt{\dfrac{x^2}{4}}$

50. $\dfrac{1}{2}\sqrt{\dfrac{1}{25}}$

51. $3x\sqrt{\dfrac{x^5}{81}}$

52. $\dfrac{12}{x}\sqrt{\dfrac{x^2y}{36}}$

Use the Product Property or the Quotient Property of Square Roots to write each expression as a single square root. Then simplify if possible.

53. $\sqrt{12}\,\sqrt{3}$

54. $\sqrt{18}\,\sqrt{8}$

55. $\sqrt{10}\,\sqrt{5}$

56. $\sqrt{8}\,\sqrt{14}$

57. $\dfrac{\sqrt{33}}{\sqrt{11}}$

58. $\dfrac{\sqrt{24}}{\sqrt{2}}$

59. $\dfrac{\sqrt{60}}{\sqrt{3}}$

60. $\dfrac{\sqrt{72}}{\sqrt{9}}$

61. Multi-Step How many whole feet of fencing would be needed to enclose the triangular garden that is sketched at right? Explain your answer.

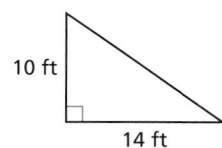

10 ft

14 ft

62. Write About It Write a series of steps that you could use to simplify $\sqrt{\dfrac{28}{49}}$.

CONCEPT CONNECTION

63. This problem will prepare you for the Concept Connection on page 730.

  a. The vertical component of a roller coaster's speed in feet per second at the bottom of a hill is $v = \sqrt{64h}$, where h is the hill's height in feet. Simplify this expression. Then estimate the velocity at the bottom of a 137-foot hill.

  b. The distance along the track of a hill is $d = \sqrt{x^2 + h^2}$, where x is the horizontal distance along the ground and h is the hill's height. Where does this equation come from?

  c. For the hill in part **a**, the horizontal distance along the ground is 103 feet. What is the distance along the track? Round your answer to the nearest tenth.

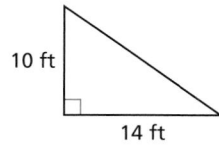

h

x

64. Critical Thinking The Product Property of Square Roots states that $\sqrt{ab} = \sqrt{a}\sqrt{b}$, where $a \geq 0$ and $b \geq 0$. Why must a and b be greater than or equal to zero?

65. Architecture The formula $d = \frac{\sqrt{6h}}{3}$ estimates the distance d in miles that a person can see to the horizon from h feet above the ground. Find the distance you could see to the horizon from the top of each building in the graph. Give your answers as radical expressions in simplest form and as estimates to the nearest tenth of a mile.

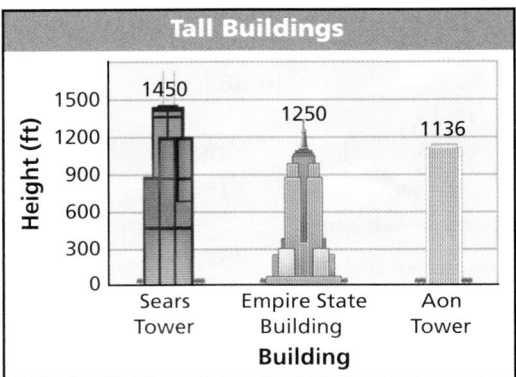

66. Math History Heron's formula for the area A of a triangle is $A = \sqrt{s(s-a)(s-b)(s-c)}$, where a, b, and c are the side lengths and $s = \frac{1}{2}(a + b + c)$. Find the area of a triangle with side lengths of 7 m, 9 m, and 12 m. Give your answer as a radical expression in simplest form and as an estimate to the nearest tenth.

Multiple Choice For Exercises 67–69, choose the best answer.

67. Which expression is in simplest form?

    (A) $\sqrt{49}$ (B) $\sqrt{48}$ (C) $\sqrt{35}$ (D) $\sqrt{36}$

68. Which expression is equal to $\sqrt{60}$?

    (A) $2\sqrt{15}$ (B) $6\sqrt{10}$ (C) $15\sqrt{2}$ (D) $10\sqrt{60}$

69. How long is the diagonal of a square whose area is 100 square feet?

    (A) $2\sqrt{10}$ feet   (B) 10 feet   (C) $10\sqrt{2}$ feet   (D) 20 feet

CHALLENGE AND EXTEND

Simplify. All radicands represent nonnegative numbers.

70. $\sqrt{4x + 16}$ **71.** $\sqrt{x^3 + x^2}$ **72.** $\sqrt{9x^3 - 18x^2}$

73. Let x represent any real number (including negative numbers). Simplify each of the following expressions, using absolute-value symbols when necessary.

    a. $\sqrt{x^2}$ **b.** $\sqrt{x^4}$ **c.** $\sqrt{x^6}$ **d.** $\sqrt{x^8}$ **e.** $\sqrt{x^{10}}$

    f. Reasoning Use your results in parts **a–e** and inductive reasoning to make a conjecture about the following statement: For any nonnegative integer n, $\sqrt{x^{2n}} = \blacksquare$ if n is even, and $\sqrt{x^{2n}} = \blacksquare$ if n is odd. Explain why you think your conjecture is true.

SPIRAL STANDARDS REVIEW   ⚷ 7.0, 17.0

Without graphing, tell whether each point is on the graph of the given line. *(Lesson 5-1)*

74. $-5x + 4y = 12; (1, 2)$ **75.** $6x + 3y = 9; (2, -1)$

76. $12x - 2y = 18; (2, 3)$ **77.** $-4x - 4y = 14; (-5, 1)$

Find the domain of each square-root function. *(Lesson 11-1)*

78. $y = \sqrt{x + 5}$ **79.** $y = \sqrt{2x - 4}$ **80.** $y = 3\sqrt{-x - 3} + 5$

81. $y = 7 - \sqrt{x - 1}$ **82.** $y = 9\sqrt{x} + 3$ **83.** $y = \sqrt{-x + 6}$

11-3 Adding and Subtracting Radical Expressions

Vocabulary
like radicals

Why learn this?
You can add or subtract radical expressions to find perimeter. (See Example 3.)

Square-root expressions with the same radicand are examples of **like radicals** .

Like Radicals	$2\sqrt{5}$ and $4\sqrt{5}$	$6\sqrt{x}$ and $-2\sqrt{x}$	$3\sqrt{4t}$ and $\sqrt{4t}$
Unlike Radicals	2 and $\sqrt{15}$	$6\sqrt{x}$ and $\sqrt{6x}$	$3\sqrt{2}$ and $2\sqrt{3}$

Like radicals can be combined by adding or subtracting. You can use the Distributive Property to show how this is done:

$$2\sqrt{5} + 4\sqrt{5} = (2 + 4)\sqrt{5} = 6\sqrt{5}$$

$$6\sqrt{x} - 2\sqrt{x} = (6 - 2)\sqrt{x} = 4\sqrt{x}$$

Notice that you can combine like radicals by adding or subtracting the numbers multiplied by the radical and keeping the radical the same.

EXAMPLE 1 Adding and Subtracting Square-Root Expressions

Add or subtract.

Helpful Hint

Combining like radicals is similar to combining like terms.
$2\sqrt{5} + 4\sqrt{5} = 6\sqrt{5}$
$2x + 4x = 6x$

A $3\sqrt{7} + 8\sqrt{7}$
$\quad 3\sqrt{7} + 8\sqrt{7}$ *The terms are like radicals.*
$\quad\quad 11\sqrt{7}$

B $9\sqrt{y} - \sqrt{y}$
$\quad 9\sqrt{y} - 1\sqrt{y}$ $\sqrt{y} = 1\sqrt{y}$; *the terms are like radicals.*
$\quad\quad 8\sqrt{y}$

C $12\sqrt{2} - 4\sqrt{11}$
$\quad 12\sqrt{2} - 4\sqrt{11}$ *The terms are unlike radicals. Do not combine.*

D $-8\sqrt{3d} + 6\sqrt{2d} + 10\sqrt{3d}$
$\quad -8\sqrt{3d} + 6\sqrt{2d} + 10\sqrt{3d}$ *Identify like radicals.*
$\quad\quad 2\sqrt{3d} + 6\sqrt{2d}$ *Combine like radicals.*

 Add or subtract.
1a. $5\sqrt{7} - 6\sqrt{7}$ **1b.** $8\sqrt{3} - 5\sqrt{3}$
1c. $4\sqrt{n} + 4\sqrt{n}$ **1d.** $\sqrt{2s} - \sqrt{5s} + 9\sqrt{5s}$

Sometimes radicals do not appear to be like until they are simplified. Simplify all radicals in an expression before trying to identify like radicals.

EXAMPLE 2 **Simplifying Before Adding or Subtracting**

Simplify each expression. All variables represent nonnegative numbers.

A $\sqrt{12} + \sqrt{27}$

$\sqrt{4(3)} + \sqrt{9(3)}$ *Factor the radicands using perfect squares.*

$\sqrt{4}\sqrt{3} + \sqrt{9}\sqrt{3}$ *Product Property of Square Roots*

$2\sqrt{3} + 3\sqrt{3}$ *Simplify.*

$5\sqrt{3}$ *Combine like radicals.*

B $3\sqrt{8} + \sqrt{45}$

$3\sqrt{4(2)} + \sqrt{9(5)}$ *Factor the radicands using perfect squares.*

$3\sqrt{4}\,\sqrt{2} + \sqrt{9}\,\sqrt{5}$ *Product Property of Square Roots*

$3(2)\sqrt{2} + 3\sqrt{5}$ *Simplify.*

$6\sqrt{2} + 3\sqrt{5}$ *The terms are unlike radicals. Do not combine.*

> **Remember!**
>
> When you write a radicand as a product, make at least one factor a perfect square.

C $5\sqrt{28x} - 8\sqrt{7x}$

$5\sqrt{4(7x)} - 8\sqrt{7x}$ *Factor 28x using a perfect square.*

$5\sqrt{4}\,\sqrt{7x} - 8\sqrt{7x}$ *Product Property of Square Roots*

$5(2)\sqrt{7x} - 8\sqrt{7x}$ *Simplify.*

$10\sqrt{7x} - 8\sqrt{7x}$

$2\sqrt{7x}$ *Combine like radicals.*

D $\sqrt{125b} + 3\sqrt{20b} - \sqrt{45b}$

$\sqrt{25(5b)} + 3\sqrt{4(5b)} - \sqrt{9(5b)}$ *Factor the radicands using perfect squares.*

$\sqrt{25}\,\sqrt{5b} + 3\sqrt{4}\,\sqrt{5b} - \sqrt{9}\,\sqrt{5b}$ *Product Property of Square Roots*

$5\sqrt{5b} + 3(2)\sqrt{5b} - 3\sqrt{5b}$ *Simplify.*

$5\sqrt{5b} + 6\sqrt{5b} - 3\sqrt{5b}$

$8\sqrt{5b}$ *Combine like radicals.*

 Simplify each expression. All variables represent nonnegative numbers.

2a. $\sqrt{54} + \sqrt{24}$ **2b.** $4\sqrt{27} - \sqrt{18}$ **2c.** $\sqrt{12y} + \sqrt{27y}$

EXAMPLE 3 *Geometry Application*

Find the perimeter of the triangle. Give your answer as a radical expression in simplest form.

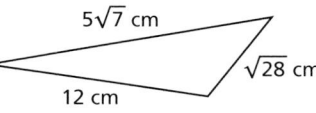

$12 + 5\sqrt{7} + \sqrt{28}$ *Write an expression for perimeter.*

$12 + 5\sqrt{7} + \sqrt{4(7)}$ *Factor 28 using a perfect square.*

$12 + 5\sqrt{7} + \sqrt{4}\sqrt{7}$ *Product Property of Square Roots*

$12 + 5\sqrt{7} + 2\sqrt{7}$ *Simplify.*

$12 + 7\sqrt{7}$ *Combine like radicals.*

The perimeter is $\left(12 + 7\sqrt{7}\right)$ cm.

 **3.** Find the perimeter of a rectangle whose length is $2\sqrt{b}$ inches and whose width is $3\sqrt{b}$ inches. Give your answer as a radical expression in simplest form.

THINK AND DISCUSS

1. Rearrange the following into two groups of like radicals: $2\sqrt{6}$, $6\sqrt{5}$, $\sqrt{600}$, $\sqrt{150}$, $-\sqrt{20}$, $\sqrt{5}$.

2. Tell why you should simplify radicals before adding and subtracting expressions with radicals.

3. **GET ORGANIZED** Copy and complete the graphic organizer.

Like Radicals
↓
Definition
┌─────────┴─────────┐
Examples   Nonexamples

11-3 **Exercises**

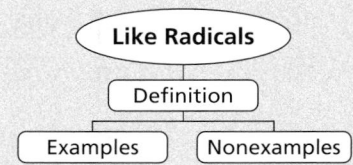

California Standards Practice
Extension of 🔑 2.0; 25.2

go.hrw.com
Homework Help Online
KEYWORD: MA8CA 11-3
Parent Resources Online
KEYWORD: MA8CA Parent

GUIDED PRACTICE

1. **Vocabulary** Give an example of *like radicals*.

SEE EXAMPLE 1 p. 711

Add or subtract.

2. $14\sqrt{3} - 6\sqrt{3}$

3. $9\sqrt{5} + \sqrt{5}$

4. $6\sqrt{2} + 5\sqrt{2} - 15\sqrt{2}$

5. $3\sqrt{7} + 5\sqrt{2}$

6. $5\sqrt{a} - 9\sqrt{a}$

7. $9\sqrt{6a} + 6\sqrt{5a} - 4\sqrt{6a}$

SEE EXAMPLE 2 p. 712

Simplify each expression. All variables represent nonnegative numbers.

8. $\sqrt{32} - \sqrt{8}$

9. $4\sqrt{12} + \sqrt{75}$

10. $2\sqrt{3} + 5\sqrt{12} - \sqrt{27}$

11. $\sqrt{20x} - \sqrt{45x}$

12. $\sqrt{28c} + 9\sqrt{24c}$

13. $\sqrt{50t} - 2\sqrt{12t} + 3\sqrt{2t}$

SEE EXAMPLE 3 p. 712

14. **Geometry** Find the perimeter of the trapezoid shown. Give your answer as a radical expression in simplest form.

PRACTICE AND PROBLEM SOLVING

Independent Practice

For Exercises	See Example
15–20	1
21–29	2
30	3

Extra Practice
Skills Practice p. EP22
Application Practice p. EP34

Add or subtract.

15. $4\sqrt{3} + 2\sqrt{3}$

16. $\frac{1}{2}\sqrt{72} - 12$

17. $2\sqrt{11} + \sqrt{11} - 6\sqrt{11}$

18. $6\sqrt{7} + 7\sqrt{6}$

19. $-3\sqrt{n} - \sqrt{n}$

20. $2\sqrt{2y} + 3\sqrt{2y} - 2\sqrt{3y}$

Simplify each expression. All variables represent nonnegative numbers.

21. $\sqrt{175} + \sqrt{28}$

22. $2\sqrt{80} - \sqrt{20}$

23. $5\sqrt{8} - \sqrt{32} + 2\sqrt{18}$

24. $\sqrt{150r} + \sqrt{54r}$

25. $\sqrt{63x} - 4\sqrt{27x}$

26. $\sqrt{48p} + 3\sqrt{18p} - 2\sqrt{27p}$

27. $\sqrt{180j} - \sqrt{45j}$

28. $3\sqrt{90c} - \sqrt{40c}$

29. $2\sqrt{75m} - \sqrt{12m} - \sqrt{108m}$

30. Fitness What is the total length of the jogging path? Give your answer as a radical expression in simplest form.

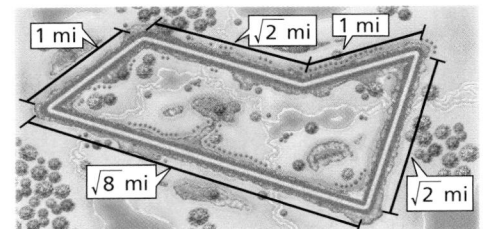

Simplify each expression. All variables represent nonnegative numbers.

31. $5\sqrt{7} + 7\sqrt{7}$

32. $18\sqrt{ab} - 10\sqrt{ab}$

33. $-3\sqrt{3} + 3\sqrt{3}$

34. $\sqrt{98} + \sqrt{128}$

35. $\sqrt{300} - \sqrt{27}$

36. $\sqrt{45x} + \sqrt{500x}$

37. $\frac{5}{2}\sqrt{8} + \frac{\sqrt{32}}{2}$

38. $\frac{1}{6}\sqrt{18} - \frac{\sqrt{2}}{2}$

 39. Geometry Use the diagram to answer the following:

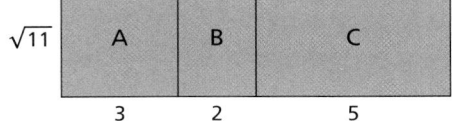

a. What is the area of section A? section B? section C?

b. What is the combined area of the three sections?

c. Explain how this model relates to adding like radicals.

Simplify each expression. All variables represent nonnegative numbers.

40. $\sqrt{450ab} - \sqrt{50ab}$

41. $\sqrt{12} + \sqrt{125} + \sqrt{25}$

42. $\sqrt{338} - \sqrt{18}$

43. $\sqrt{700x} - \sqrt{28x} - \sqrt{70x}$

44. $-3\sqrt{90} - 3\sqrt{160}$

45. $7\sqrt{80k} + 2\sqrt{20k} + \sqrt{45k}$

46. $\sqrt{24abc} + \sqrt{600abc}$

47. $\sqrt{12} + \sqrt{20} + \sqrt{27} + \sqrt{45}$

48. **///ERROR ANALYSIS///** Which expressions are simplified incorrectly? Explain the error in each incorrect simplification.

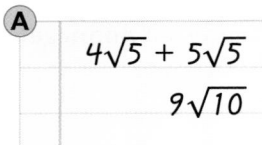

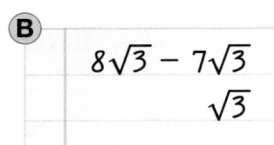

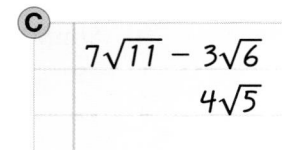

49. Write About It Tell how to identify like radicals. Give examples and nonexamples of like radicals in your answer.

Complete each box to make a true statement.

50. $5\sqrt{ab} + 2\sqrt{} - 3\sqrt{a} = 7\sqrt{ab} - 3\sqrt{a}$

51. $4\sqrt{x} - \sqrt{}\,x = \sqrt{x}$

52. $5\sqrt{2} - \sqrt{} + \sqrt{2} = 4\sqrt{2}$

53. $\sqrt{} + 8\sqrt{2} = 11\sqrt{2}$

54. $3\sqrt{3} + 2\sqrt{3} + \sqrt{} = 9\sqrt{3}$

55. $2x - \sqrt{} = -4x$

CONCEPT CONNECTION

56. This problem will prepare you for the Concept Connection on page 730.

a. The first Ferris wheel was designed by George W. Ferris and introduced at the 1893 Chicago World's Fair. Its diameter was 250 feet. What was its radius?

b. For a rider halfway up on the ride, the distance from the boarding point can be found by using the equation $d = \sqrt{2r^2}$, where r is the radius of the wheel. Explain where this equation comes from. (*Hint:* Draw a picture.)

57. Multi-Step A square has an area of 48 in^2. Another square has an area of 12 in^2. Write a simplified radical expression for the perimeter of each square. Then write a simplified radical expression for the combined perimeters of the two squares.

58. Critical Thinking How are like radicals similar to like terms?

Multiple Choice For Exercises 59–61, choose the best answer.

59. Which of the following expressions CANNOT be simplified?

(A) $3\sqrt{5} + 4\sqrt{5}$ (C) $2\sqrt{8} + 3\sqrt{2}$

(B) $5\sqrt{6} + 6\sqrt{5}$ (D) $3\sqrt{12} + \sqrt{27}$

60. What is $-5\sqrt{7x} + 6\sqrt{7x}$?

(A) $\sqrt{7x}$ (B) $\sqrt{14x^2}$ (C) $\sqrt{14x}$ (D) $7x$

61. What is $\sqrt{18} - \sqrt{2}$?

(A) $2\sqrt{2}$ (B) 4 (C) $4\sqrt{2}$ (D) $8\sqrt{2}$

CHALLENGE AND EXTEND

Simplify. All radicands represent nonnegative numbers.

62. $5\sqrt{x-5} + 2\sqrt{x-5}$

63. $x\sqrt{x} + 2\sqrt{x}$

64. $4\sqrt{x-3} + \sqrt{25x-75}$

65. $2\sqrt{x+7} - \sqrt{4x+28}$

66. $\sqrt{4x^3 + 24x^2} + \sqrt{x^3 + 6x^2}$

67. $\sqrt{x^3 - x^2} + \sqrt{4x-4}$

68. $\sqrt{x^3 + 2x^2} - \sqrt{x+2}$

69. $\sqrt{9x+9} - \sqrt{x^3 + 2x^2}$

 70. Geometry Find the area of the trapezoid. Use the formula $A = \frac{1}{2}h(b_1 + b_2)$.

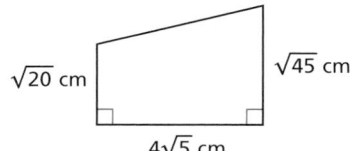
$\sqrt{20}$ cm $\sqrt{45}$ cm $4\sqrt{5}$ cm

SPIRAL STANDARDS REVIEW   8.0, 14.0, 17.0, 25.1

71. Use slope to show that *ABCD* is a parallelogram. *(Lesson 5-7)*

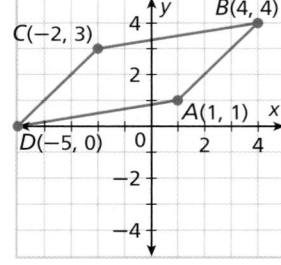

72. Use slope to show that *XYZ* is a right triangle. *(Lesson 5-7)*

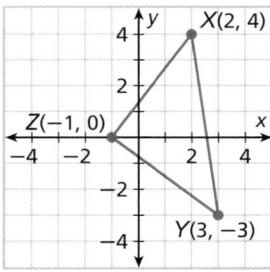

Solve each quadratic equation by factoring. Check your answer. *(Lesson 9-5)*

73. $x^2 + 2x - 3 = 0$ **74.** $x^2 + 5x + 4 = 0$ **75.** $x^2 - 7x - 18 = 0$

Find the domain of each square-root function. *(Lesson 11-1)*

76. $y = \sqrt{4x-2}$ **77.** $y = -2\sqrt{x+3}$ **78.** $y = 1 + \sqrt{x+6}$

Multiplying and Dividing Radical Expressions

California Standards

Extension of ⚷ 2.0
Students understand and use such operations as taking the opposite, finding the reciprocal, **taking a root,** and raising to a fractional power. **They understand and use the rules of exponents.**

Who uses this?
Electricians can divide radical expressions to find how much current runs through an appliance. (See Exercise 68.)

DON'T GO IN THERE!

Off the Mark. Cartoon copyrighted by Mark Parisi, printed with permission.

You can use the Product and Quotient Properties of square roots you have already learned to multiply and divide expressions containing square roots.

EXAMPLE 1 **Multiplying Square Roots**

Multiply. Write each product in simplest form. All variables represent nonnegative numbers.

A $\sqrt{3}\sqrt{6}$

$\sqrt{3(6)}$ *Product Property of Square Roots*

$\sqrt{18}$ *Multiply the factors in the radicand.*

$\sqrt{9(2)}$ *Factor 18 using a perfect-square factor.*

$\sqrt{9}\sqrt{2}$ *Product Property of Square Roots*

$3\sqrt{2}$ *Simplify.*

B $\left(5\sqrt{3}\right)^2$

$5\sqrt{3}\cdot 5\sqrt{3}$ *Expand the expression.*

$5(5)\sqrt{3}\sqrt{3}$ *Commutative Property of Multiplication*

$25\sqrt{3(3)}$ *Product Property of Square Roots*

$25\sqrt{9}$ *Simplify the radicand.*

$25(3)$ *Simplify the square root.*

75 *Multiply.*

C $2\sqrt{8x}\sqrt{4x}$

$2\sqrt{8x(4x)}$ *Product Property of Square Roots*

$2\sqrt{32x^2}$ *Multiply the factors in the radicand.*

$2\sqrt{16(2)x^2}$ *Factor 32 using a perfect-square factor.*

$2\sqrt{16}\sqrt{2}\sqrt{x^2}$ *Product Property of Square Roots*

$2(4)\sqrt{2}(x)$ *Simplify.*

$8x\sqrt{2}$

Helpful Hint

For all nonnegative real numbers a, $\sqrt{a}\sqrt{a} = a$. So, in Example 1B, you can reduce the number of steps by immediately writing $\sqrt{3}\sqrt{3}$ as 3.

 **Multiply. Write each product in simplest form. All variables represent nonnegative numbers.**

1a. $\sqrt{5}\sqrt{10}$ **1b.** $\left(3\sqrt{7}\right)^2$ **1c.** $\sqrt{2m}\sqrt{14m}$

EXAMPLE 2 **Using the Distributive Property**

Multiply. Write each product in simplest form.

A $\sqrt{2}\left(5 + \sqrt{12}\right)$

$\sqrt{2}\left(5 + \sqrt{12}\right)$

$\sqrt{2}(5) + \sqrt{2}\sqrt{12}$ *Distribute $\sqrt{2}$.*

$5\sqrt{2} + \sqrt{2(12)}$ *Product Property of Square Roots*

$5\sqrt{2} + \sqrt{24}$ *Multiply the factors in the second radicand.*

$5\sqrt{2} + \sqrt{4(6)}$ *Factor 24 using a perfect-square factor.*

$5\sqrt{2} + \sqrt{4}\sqrt{6}$ *Product Property of Square Roots*

$5\sqrt{2} + 2\sqrt{6}$ *Simplify.*

B $\sqrt{3}\left(\sqrt{3} - \sqrt{5}\right)$

$\sqrt{3}\left(\sqrt{3} - \sqrt{5}\right)$

$\sqrt{3}\sqrt{3} - \sqrt{3}\sqrt{5}$ *Distribute $\sqrt{3}$.*

$3 - \sqrt{3(5)}$ *Product Property of Square Roots*

$3 - \sqrt{15}$ *Multiply the factors in the second radicand.*

 **Multiply. Write each product in simplest form.**

2a. $\sqrt{6}\left(\sqrt{8} - 3\right)$ **2b.** $\sqrt{5}\left(\sqrt{10} + 4\sqrt{3}\right)$

Remember!

First terms
Outer terms
Inner terms
Last terms

See Lesson 7-8.

In Chapter 7, you multiplied binomials by using the FOIL method. The same method can be used to multiply square-root expressions that contain two terms.

$$\left(4 + \sqrt{3}\right)\left(5 + \sqrt{3}\right) = 4(5) + \underbrace{4\sqrt{3} + 5\sqrt{3}} + \sqrt{3}\sqrt{3}$$

$$= 20 \qquad + 9\sqrt{3} \qquad + 3 \quad = \quad 23 + 9\sqrt{3}$$

EXAMPLE 3 **Multiplying Sums and Differences of Radicals**

Multiply. Write each product in simplest form.

A $\left(4 + \sqrt{5}\right)\left(3 - \sqrt{5}\right)$

$12 - 4\sqrt{5} + 3\sqrt{5} - 5$ *Use the FOIL method.*

$7 - \sqrt{5}$ *Simplify by combining like terms.*

B $\left(\sqrt{7} - 5\right)^2$

$\left(\sqrt{7} - 5\right)\left(\sqrt{7} - 5\right)$ *Expand the expression.*

$7 - 5\sqrt{7} - 5\sqrt{7} + 25$ *Use the FOIL method.*

$32 - 10\sqrt{7}$ *Simplify by combining like terms.*

 **Multiply. Write each product in simplest form.**

3a. $\left(9 + \sqrt{2}\right)^2$ **3b.** $\left(4 - \sqrt{3}\right)\left(\sqrt{3} + 5\right)$

A quotient with a square root in the denominator is **not** simplified. To simplify these expressions, multiply by a form of 1 to get a perfect-square radicand in the denominator. This is called *rationalizing the denominator*.

E X A M P L E | 4 | **Rationalizing the Denominator**

Simplify each quotient. All variables represent nonnegative numbers.

A $\dfrac{\sqrt{7}}{\sqrt{2}}$

$\dfrac{\sqrt{7}}{\sqrt{2}}\left(\dfrac{\sqrt{2}}{\sqrt{2}}\right)$ *Multiply by a form of 1 to get a perfect-square radicand in the denominator.*

$\dfrac{\sqrt{14}}{2}$ *Product Property of Square Roots*

B $\dfrac{\sqrt{7}}{\sqrt{8n}}$

$\dfrac{\sqrt{7}}{\sqrt{4(2n)}}$ *Write 8n using a perfect-square factor.*

$\dfrac{\sqrt{7}}{2\sqrt{2n}}$ *Simplify the denominator.*

$\dfrac{\sqrt{7}}{2\sqrt{2n}}\left(\dfrac{\sqrt{2n}}{\sqrt{2n}}\right)$ *Multiply by a form of 1 to get a perfect-square radicand in the denominator.*

$\dfrac{\sqrt{14n}}{2\sqrt{4n^2}}$ *Product Property of Square Roots*

$\dfrac{\sqrt{14n}}{2(2n)}$ *Simplify the square root in the denominator.*

$\dfrac{\sqrt{14n}}{4n}$ *Simplify the denominator.*

CHECK IT OUT! Simplify each quotient. All variables represent nonnegative numbers.

4a. $\dfrac{\sqrt{13}}{\sqrt{5}}$ **4b.** $\dfrac{\sqrt{7a}}{\sqrt{12}}$ **4c.** $\dfrac{2\sqrt{80}}{\sqrt{7}}$

THINK AND DISCUSS

1. Explain why multiplying $\dfrac{\sqrt{6}}{\sqrt{5}}$ by $\dfrac{\sqrt{5}}{\sqrt{5}}$ does not change the value of $\dfrac{\sqrt{6}}{\sqrt{5}}$.

Know it! Note

2. GET ORGANIZED Copy and complete the graphic organizer. In each box, give an example and show how to simplify it.

```
                Multiplying Radical Expressions
            ┌──────────────┬──────────────┬──────────┐
        Multiplying      Using the       Using
        two square       Distributive     FOIL
          roots           Property
```

Exercises

California Standards Practice

Extension of 🔑 2.0

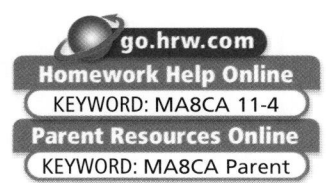

go.hrw.com
Homework Help Online
KEYWORD: MA8CA 11-4
Parent Resources Online
KEYWORD: MA8CA Parent

GUIDED PRACTICE

SEE EXAMPLE 1
p. 716

Multiply. Write each product in simplest form. All variables represent nonnegative numbers.

1. $\sqrt{2}\sqrt{3}$

2. $\sqrt{3}\sqrt{8}$

3. $\left(5\sqrt{5}\right)^2$

4. $\left(4\sqrt{2}\right)^2$

5. $3\sqrt{3a}\sqrt{10}$

6. $2\sqrt{15p}\sqrt{3p}$

SEE EXAMPLE 2
p. 717

7. $\sqrt{6}\left(2+\sqrt{7}\right)$

8. $\sqrt{3}\left(5-\sqrt{3}\right)$

9. $\sqrt{7}\left(\sqrt{5}-\sqrt{3}\right)$

10. $\sqrt{2}\left(\sqrt{10}+8\sqrt{2}\right)$

11. $\sqrt{5}\left(\sqrt{15}+4\right)$

12. $\sqrt{2}\left(\sqrt{6}-\sqrt{2}\right)$

SEE EXAMPLE 3
p. 717

13. $\left(2+\sqrt{2}\right)\left(5+\sqrt{2}\right)$

14. $\left(4+\sqrt{6}\right)\left(3-\sqrt{6}\right)$

15. $\left(\sqrt{3}-4\right)\left(\sqrt{3}+2\right)$

16. $\left(5+\sqrt{3}\right)^2$

17. $\left(\sqrt{6}-5\sqrt{3}\right)^2$

18. $\left(6+3\sqrt{2}\right)^2$

SEE EXAMPLE 4
p. 718

Simplify each quotient. All variables represent nonnegative numbers.

19. $\dfrac{\sqrt{13}}{\sqrt{2}}$

20. $\dfrac{\sqrt{20}}{\sqrt{8}}$

21. $\dfrac{\sqrt{11}}{6\sqrt{3}}$

22. $\dfrac{\sqrt{28}}{\sqrt{3s}}$

23. $\dfrac{2}{\sqrt{7}}$

24. $\dfrac{3}{\sqrt{6}}$

25. $\dfrac{1}{\sqrt{5x}}$

26. $\dfrac{\sqrt{3}}{\sqrt{x}}$

PRACTICE AND PROBLEM SOLVING

Independent Practice

For Exercises	See Example
27–32	1
33–38	2
39–44	3
45–52	4

Extra Practice

Skills Practice p. EP22

Application Practice p. EP34

Multiply. Write each product in simplest form. All variables represent nonnegative numbers.

27. $\sqrt{3}\sqrt{5}\sqrt{6}$

28. $3\sqrt{6}\left(5\sqrt{6}\right)$

29. $\left(2\sqrt{2}\right)^2$

30. $\left(3\sqrt{6}\right)^2$

31. $\sqrt{21d}\left(2\sqrt{3d}\right)$

32. $4\sqrt{5n}\left(2\sqrt{5n}\right)\left(3\sqrt{3n}\right)$

33. $\sqrt{5}\left(4-\sqrt{10}\right)$

34. $\sqrt{2}\left(\sqrt{6}+2\right)$

35. $\sqrt{2}\left(\sqrt{6}-\sqrt{10}\right)$

36. $3\sqrt{3}\left(\sqrt{8}-2\sqrt{6}\right)$

37. $\sqrt{3}\left(\sqrt{3}+12\right)$

38. $\sqrt{8}\left(\sqrt{10}+\sqrt{2}\right)$

39. $\left(15+\sqrt{15}\right)\left(4+\sqrt{15}\right)$

40. $\left(\sqrt{6}+4\right)\left(\sqrt{2}-7\right)$

41. $\left(3-\sqrt{2}\right)\left(4+\sqrt{2}\right)$

42. $\left(\sqrt{5}-5\right)^2$

43. $\left(\sqrt{3}+8\right)^2$

44. $\left(2\sqrt{3}+4\sqrt{5}\right)^2$

Simplify each quotient. All variables represent nonnegative numbers.

45. $\dfrac{\sqrt{75}}{\sqrt{2}}$

46. $\dfrac{\sqrt{5}}{4\sqrt{8}}$

47. $\dfrac{\sqrt{27}}{3\sqrt{x}}$

48. $\dfrac{\sqrt{48k}}{\sqrt{5}}$

49. $\dfrac{\sqrt{49x}}{\sqrt{2}}$

50. $\dfrac{3\sqrt{27}}{\sqrt{b}}$

51. $\dfrac{\sqrt{12y}}{\sqrt{3}}$

52. $\dfrac{\sqrt{12t}}{\sqrt{6}}$

Geometry Find the area of each figure. Give your answer as a radical expression in simplest form.

53.

$6\sqrt{5}$ in.

$6\sqrt{5}$ in.

54.

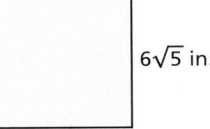

$\sqrt{6}$ m

$2\sqrt{3}$ m

55.

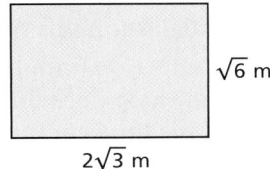

$\left(6\sqrt{2}-2\right)$ cm

$\sqrt{5}$ cm

Simplify. All variables represent nonnegative numbers.

56. $\sqrt{3}\left(\dfrac{\sqrt{2}}{\sqrt{7}}\right)$

57. $\dfrac{15\sqrt{10}}{5\sqrt{3}}$

58. $\dfrac{6+\sqrt{18}}{3}$

59. $(\sqrt{3}-4)(\sqrt{3}+2)$

60. $\sqrt{2}\left(6+\sqrt{12}\right)$

61. $\dfrac{\sqrt{1}+\sqrt{25}}{\sqrt{2}}$

62. $\dfrac{\sqrt{15}+\sqrt{10}}{\sqrt{5}}$

63. $\sqrt{12}\left(\sqrt{3}+8\right)^2$

64. $\sqrt{3}\left(4-2\sqrt{5}\right)$

65. $\left(\sqrt{x}-\sqrt{y}\right)^2$

66. $\left(\sqrt{x}-5\right)(3\sqrt{x}+7)$

67. $\left(\sqrt{3}+\sqrt{x}\right)^2$

Electricity

People began using wind to generate electricity in the early twentieth century. A modern wind turbine is 120–180 feet tall and, depending on its construction, can generate up to 1 megawatt of power.

68. Electricity Electrical current in amps can be represented by $\dfrac{\sqrt{W}}{\sqrt{R}}$, where W is power in watts and R is resistance in ohms. How much electrical current is running through a microwave oven that has 850 watts of power and 5 ohms of resistance? Give the answer as a radical expression in simplest form. Then estimate the amount of current to the nearest tenth.

69. Physical Science The *period* of a pendulum is the amount of time it takes the pendulum to make one complete swing and return to its starting point. The period of a pendulum in seconds can be represented by $2\pi\sqrt{\dfrac{\ell}{32}}$, where ℓ is the length of the pendulum in feet. What is the period of a pendulum whose length is 3 feet? Give the answer as a radical expression in simplest form. Then estimate the period to the nearest tenth.

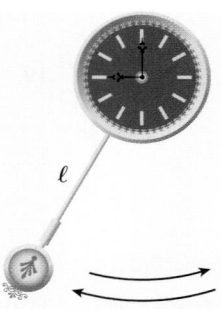

ℓ

Geometry Find the area of each triangle. Give the exact answer in simplest form. (*Hint:* The formula for the area of a triangle is $A=\frac{1}{2}bh$.)

70.

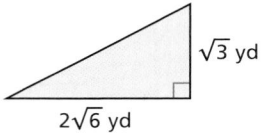

$\sqrt{3}$ yd

$2\sqrt{6}$ yd

71.

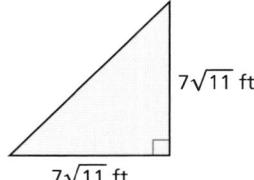

$7\sqrt{11}$ ft

$7\sqrt{11}$ ft

72.

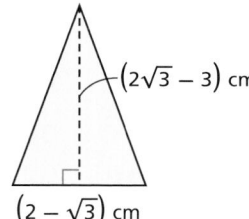

$(2\sqrt{3}-3)$ cm

$(2-\sqrt{3})$ cm

73. Write About It Describe an expression for which you would have to rationalize the denominator. How would you do it? Include an explanation of how you would choose what to multiply the original expression by.

CONCEPT CONNECTION

74. This problem will prepare you for the Concept Connection on page 730.

a. Many amusement parks have free-fall rides in which cars travel straight up a tower and then are allowed to fall back to the ground. The time in seconds for any object in free fall is $t=\sqrt{\dfrac{d}{16}}$, where d is the distance that the object falls in feet. On a particular free-fall ride, the cars are in free fall for 100 feet. How long does free fall last on this ride?

b. The cars in the ride from part **a** travel up the tower at a speed of 18 feet per second. How long does this trip take? Round your answer to the nearest tenth. How does this time compare with the time spent in free fall?

Multiple Choice For Exercises 75–77, choose the best answer.

75. What is the product of $3\sqrt{5}$ and $\sqrt{15}$?

(A) $5\sqrt{3}$ (B) $15\sqrt{3}$ (C) $15\sqrt{15}$ (D) $45\sqrt{5}$

76. Which of the following is the result of rationalizing the denominator in the expression $\frac{4}{3\sqrt{2}}$?

(A) $\frac{\sqrt{2}}{3}$ (B) $2\sqrt{2}$ (C) $\frac{2\sqrt{2}}{3}$ (D) $\frac{3\sqrt{2}}{2}$

77. Which of the following is equivalent to $\left(5\sqrt{10}\right)^2$?

(A) 50 (B) 100 (C) 125 (D) 250

CHALLENGE AND EXTEND

The expressions $\sqrt{a} + \sqrt{b}$ and $\sqrt{a} - \sqrt{b}$ are called *conjugates*. When a and b are nonnegative, you can use the FOIL to multiply conjugates as follows:

$$\left(\sqrt{a} - \sqrt{b}\right)\left(\sqrt{a} + \sqrt{b}\right) = a + \sqrt{ab} - \sqrt{ab} - b = a - b$$
$$\left(\sqrt{3} - \sqrt{5}\right)\left(\sqrt{3} + \sqrt{5}\right) = 3 + \sqrt{15} - \sqrt{15} - 5 = 3 - 5 = -2$$

Notice that the product does not contain any square roots. This means that you can use conjugates to rationalize denominators that contain sums or differences of square roots:

$$\frac{\sqrt{2}}{\sqrt{7} + \sqrt{2}}\left(\frac{\sqrt{7} - \sqrt{2}}{\sqrt{7} - \sqrt{2}}\right) = \frac{\sqrt{2}\left(\sqrt{7} - \sqrt{2}\right)}{\left(\sqrt{7} + \sqrt{2}\right)\left(\sqrt{7} - \sqrt{2}\right)} = \frac{\sqrt{14} - \sqrt{4}}{7 - 2} = \frac{\sqrt{14} - 2}{5}$$

Simplify.

78. $\dfrac{4}{\sqrt{3} - \sqrt{2}}$

79. $\dfrac{8}{\sqrt{3} + \sqrt{5}}$

80. $\dfrac{\sqrt{5}}{\sqrt{10} + \sqrt{3}}$

81. $\dfrac{\sqrt{2} + \sqrt{3}}{\sqrt{2} - \sqrt{3}}$

82. $\dfrac{\sqrt{3}}{\sqrt{2} + \sqrt{3}}$

83. $\dfrac{\sqrt{2}}{\sqrt{8} + \sqrt{6}}$

84. $\dfrac{6}{\sqrt{2} + \sqrt{3}}$

85. $\dfrac{2}{\sqrt{6} - \sqrt{5}}$

 86. Geometry One rectangle is $4\sqrt{6}$ feet long and $\sqrt{2}$ feet wide. Another rectangle is $8\sqrt{2}$ feet long and $2\sqrt{6}$ feet wide. How much more area does the larger rectangle cover than the smaller rectangle? (*Hint:* The formula for the area of a rectangle is $A = \ell w$.)

SPIRAL STANDARDS REVIEW

Solve each inequality. *(Lesson 3-5)*

87. $2(x + 5) > 3x + 2$ **88.** $x + 1 \geq 5(x - 3)$ **89.** $x(3 + 2) \geq 14 - 2x$

Factor each polynomial completely. Check your answer. *(Lesson 8-6)*

90. $x^2 + 7x - 30$ **91.** $6x^2 + 11x + 3$ **92.** $x^2 - 16$

93. $3x^2 + 30x + 75$ **94.** $2x^4 - 18$ **95.** $8x^3 - 20x^2 - 12x$

Simplify. All variables represent nonnegative numbers. *(Lesson 11-2)*

96. $\sqrt{360}$ **97.** $\sqrt{\dfrac{72}{16}}$ **98.** $\sqrt{\dfrac{49x^2}{64y^4}}$ **99.** $\sqrt{\dfrac{50a^7}{9a^3}}$

11-5 Solving Radical Equations

California Standards

Extension of ☞ 2.0
Students understand and use such operations as taking the opposite, finding the reciprocal, **taking a root,** and raising to a fractional power. **They understand and use the rules of exponents.**

Vocabulary
radical equation

Who uses this?
Meteorologists can use radical equations to estimate the size of a storm. (See Exercise 76.)

A **radical equation** is an equation that contains a variable within a radical. In this chapter, you will study radical equations that contain only square roots.

Recall that you use inverse operations to solve equations. For nonnegative numbers, squaring and taking the square root are inverse operations. When an equation contains a variable within a square root, you can solve by squaring both sides of the equation.

Power Property of Equality		
WORDS	**NUMBERS**	**ALGEBRA**
You can square both sides of an equation, and the resulting equation is still true.	$3 = 1 + 2$ $(3)^2 = (1 + 2)^2$ $9 = 9$	If a and b are real numbers and $a = b$, then $a^2 = b^2$.

EXAMPLE 1 **Solving Simple Radical Equations**

Solve each equation. Check your answer.

A $\sqrt{x} = 8$
$(\sqrt{x})^2 = (8)^2$ *Square both sides.*
$x = 64$

Check $\dfrac{\sqrt{x} = 8}{\sqrt{64} \mid 8}$
$\phantom{\sqrt{64}}8 \mid 8 \checkmark$
Substitute 64 for x in the original equation.
Simplify.

B $6 = \sqrt{4x}$
$(6)^2 = (\sqrt{4x})^2$ *Square both sides.*
$36 = 4x$
$9 = x$ *Divide both sides by 4.*

Check $\dfrac{6 = \sqrt{4x}}{6 \mid \sqrt{4(9)}}$
$6 \mid \sqrt{36}$
$6 \mid 6 \checkmark$
Substitute 9 for x in the original equation.
Simplify.

Solve each equation. Check your answer.
1a. $\sqrt{x} = 6$ **1b.** $9 = \sqrt{27x}$ **1c.** $\sqrt{3x} = 1$ **1d.** $\sqrt{\dfrac{x}{3}} = 2$

Some square-root equations do not have the square root isolated. To solve these equations, you may have to isolate the square root before squaring both sides. You can do this by using one or more inverse operations.

EXAMPLE 2 **Solving Radical Equations by Adding or Subtracting**

Solve each equation. Check your answer.

A $\sqrt{x} + 3 = 10$

$\sqrt{x} = 7$ — Subtract 3 from both sides.

$(\sqrt{x})^2 = (7)^2$ — Square both sides.

$x = 49$

Check $\sqrt{x} + 3 = 10$

$\sqrt{49} + 3$	10
$7 + 3$	10
10	10 ✓

B $\sqrt{x - 5} = 4$

$(\sqrt{x - 5})^2 = (4)^2$ — Square both sides.

$x - 5 = 16$

$x = 21$ — Add 5 to both sides.

Check $\sqrt{x - 5} = 4$

$\sqrt{21 - 5}$	4
$\sqrt{16}$	4
4	4 ✓

C $\sqrt{2x - 1} + 4 = 7$

$\sqrt{2x - 1} = 3$ — Subtract 4 from both sides.

$(\sqrt{2x - 1})^2 = (3)^2$ — Square both sides.

$2x - 1 = 9$

$2x = 10$ — Add 1 to both sides.

$x = 5$ — Divide both sides by 2.

Check $\sqrt{2x - 1} + 4 = 7$

$\sqrt{2(5) - 1} + 4$	7
$\sqrt{10 - 1} + 4$	7
$\sqrt{9} + 4$	7
$3 + 4$	7
7	7 ✓

Solve each equation. Check your answer.

2a. $\sqrt{x} - 2 = 1$ **2b.** $\sqrt{x + 7} = 5$ **2c.** $\sqrt{3x + 7} - 1 = 3$

EXAMPLE 3 **Solving Radical Equations by Multiplying or Dividing**

Solve each equation. Check your answer.

A $3\sqrt{x} = 21$

Method 1

$3\sqrt{x} = 21$

$\sqrt{x} = 7$ — Divide both sides by 3.

$(\sqrt{x})^2 = (7)^2$ — Square both sides.

$x = 49$

Method 2

$3\sqrt{x} = 21$

$(3\sqrt{x})^2 = 21^2$ — Square both sides.

$9x = 441$

$x = 49$ — Divide both sides by 9.

Check $3\sqrt{x} = 21$

$3\sqrt{49}$	21	Substitute 49 for x in the original equation.
$3(7)$	21	Simplify.
21	21 ✓	

Solve each equation. Check your answer.

B $\dfrac{\sqrt{x}}{3} = 5$

Method 1

$\sqrt{x} = 15$ *Multiply both sides by 3.*

$(\sqrt{x})^2 = (15)^2$ *Square both sides.*

$x = 225$

Method 2

$\left(\dfrac{\sqrt{x}}{3}\right)^2 = (5)^2$ *Square both sides.*

$\dfrac{x}{9} = 25$

$x = 225$ *Multiply both sides by 9.*

Check $\dfrac{\sqrt{x}}{3} = 5$

$\dfrac{\sqrt{225}}{3}$	5
$\dfrac{15}{3}$	5
5	5 ✓

Substitute 225 for x in the original equation.

Simplify.

 **CHECK IT OUT!**   Solve each equation. Check your answer.

3a. $2\sqrt{x} = 22$ **3b.** $2 = \dfrac{\sqrt{x}}{4}$ **3c.** $\dfrac{2\sqrt{x}}{5} = 4$

EXAMPLE **4**   **Solving Radical Equations with Square Roots on Both Sides**

Solve each equation. Check your answer.

A $\sqrt{x + 1} = \sqrt{3}$

$\left(\sqrt{x + 1}\right)^2 = \left(\sqrt{3}\right)^2$ *Square both sides.*

$x + 1 = 3$

$x = 2$ *Subtract 1 from both sides.*

Check $\sqrt{x + 1} = \sqrt{3}$

$\sqrt{2 + 1}$	$\sqrt{3}$
$\sqrt{3}$	$\sqrt{3}$ ✓

B $\sqrt{x + 8} - \sqrt{3x} = 0$

$\sqrt{x + 8} = \sqrt{3x}$ *Add $\sqrt{3x}$ to both sides.*

$\left(\sqrt{x + 8}\right)^2 = \left(\sqrt{3x}\right)^2$ *Square both sides.*

$x + 8 = 3x$

$8 = 2x$ *Subtract x from both sides.*

$4 = x$ *Divide both sides by 2.*

Check $\sqrt{x + 8} - \sqrt{3x} = 0$

$\sqrt{4 + 8} - \sqrt{3(4)}$	0
$\sqrt{12} - \sqrt{12}$	0
0	0 ✓

 **CHECK IT OUT!**   Solve each equation. Check your answer.

4a. $\sqrt{3x + 2} = \sqrt{x + 6}$ **4b.** $\sqrt{2x - 5} - \sqrt{6} = 0$

Remember!

Recall from Chapter 10 that an extraneous solution is a number that is not a solution of the original equation. See Lesson 10-7.

Squaring both sides of an equation may result in an extraneous solution.

Suppose your original equation is $x = 3$. $x = 3$

Square both sides. Now you have a new equation. $x^2 = 9$

Solve this new equation for x by taking the square root of both sides.

$\sqrt{x^2} = \sqrt{9}$

$x = 3 \text{ or } x = -3$

Now there are two solutions of the new equation. One $(x = 3)$ is a solution of the original equation. The other $(x = -3)$ is extraneous—it is not a solution of the original equation. Because of extraneous solutions, it is especially important to check your answers to radical equations.

EXAMPLE 5 **Extraneous Solutions**

Solve $\sqrt{6-x}=x$. Check your answer.

$$\left(\sqrt{6-x}\right)^2=(x)^2 \qquad \textit{Square both sides.}$$
$$6-x=x^2$$
$$x^2+x-6=0 \qquad \textit{Write in standard form.}$$
$$(x-2)(x+3)=0 \qquad \textit{Factor.}$$
$$x-2=0 \ \text{or} \ x+3=0 \qquad \textit{Zero-Product Property}$$
$$x=2 \ \text{or} \qquad x=-3 \qquad \textit{Solve for x.}$$

Helpful Hint

The equation in Example 5 has one solution. If all of the solutions of an equation are extraneous, then the original equation has no solutions.

Check

$$\begin{array}{c|c} \sqrt{6-x}=x & \\ \hline \sqrt{6-2} & 2 \\ \sqrt{4} & 2 \\ 2 & 2 \ \checkmark \end{array}$$ *Substitute 2 for x in the equation.*

$$\begin{array}{c|c} \sqrt{6-x}=x & \\ \hline \sqrt{6-(-3)} & -3 \\ \sqrt{9} & -3 \\ 3 & -3 \ \textsf{X} \end{array}$$ *Substitute −3 for x in the equation.*

−3 does not check; it is extraneous. The only solution is 2.

 Solve each equation. Check your answer.

   5a. $11+\sqrt{5x}=6$ **5b.** $x=\sqrt{-3x-2}$ **5c.** $x-2=\sqrt{x}$

EXAMPLE 6 *Geometry Application*

Geometry

A rectangle has an area of 52 square feet. Its length is 13 feet, and its width is $\sqrt{x}$ feet. What is the value of x? What is the width of the rectangle?

| $A = 52$ ft^2 | $\sqrt{x}$ ft |

13 ft

$$A=\ell w \qquad \textit{Use the formula for area of a rectangle.}$$
$$52=13\sqrt{x} \qquad \textit{Substitute 52 for A, 13 for }\ell\textit{, and }\sqrt{x}\textit{ for w.}$$
$$\frac{52}{13}=\frac{13\sqrt{x}}{13} \qquad \textit{Divide both sides by 13.}$$
$$4=\sqrt{x}$$
$$4^2=\left(\sqrt{x}\right)^2 \qquad \textit{Square both sides.}$$
$$16=x$$

Check
$$\begin{array}{c|c} A=\ell w & \\ 52=13\sqrt{x} & \\ \hline 52 & 13\sqrt{16} \\ 52 & 13(4) \\ 52 & 52 \ \checkmark \end{array}$$ *Substitute 16 for x in the equation.*

The value of x is 16. The width of the rectangle is $\sqrt{16}=4$ feet.

 **6.** A rectangle has an area of 15 cm^2. Its width is 5 cm, and its length is $\left(\sqrt{x+1}\right)$ cm. What is the value of x? What is the length of the rectangle?

THINK AND DISCUSS

1. Compare the two methods used in Example 3A. Which method do you prefer? Why?

2. What is the first step to solve $\sqrt{x-2} + 3 = 8$? Why?

3. **GET ORGANIZED** Copy and complete the graphic organizer. Write and solve a radical equation, using the boxes to show each step.

Solving Radical Equations

| 1. | → | 2. | → | 3. | → | 4. |

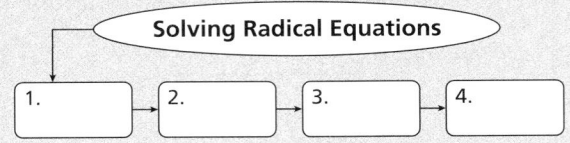

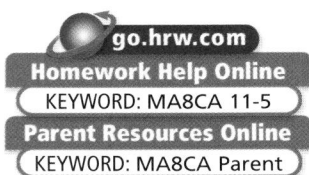

Extension of 🔑 2.0; 25.2

GUIDED PRACTICE

1. Vocabulary Is $x = \sqrt{3}$ a *radical equation*? Why or why not?

SEE EXAMPLE **1**
p. 722

Solve each equation. Check your answer.

2. $\sqrt{x} = 7$ **3.** $4 = \sqrt{-2y}$ **4.** $\sqrt{20a} = 10$ **5.** $12 = \sqrt{-x}$

SEE EXAMPLE **2**
p. 723

6. $\sqrt{x} + 6 = 11$ **7.** $\sqrt{2x-5} = 7$ **8.** $\sqrt{2-a} = 3$ **9.** $\sqrt{2x} - 3 = 7$

10. $\sqrt{x-2} = 3$ **11.** $\sqrt{x+3} = 1$ **12.** $\sqrt{x-1} = 2$ **13.** $\sqrt{4y+13} - 1 = 6$

SEE EXAMPLE **3**
p. 723

14. $-2\sqrt{x} = -10$ **15.** $\dfrac{\sqrt{a}}{2} = 4$ **16.** $5\sqrt{-x} = 20$ **17.** $\dfrac{3\sqrt{x}}{4} = 3$

18. $\dfrac{5\sqrt{x}}{6} = 10$ **19.** $2\sqrt{x} = 8$ **20.** $\dfrac{\sqrt{x}}{3} = 3$ **21.** $\dfrac{3\sqrt{x}}{2} = 1$

22. $13\sqrt{2x} = 26$ **23.** $\dfrac{\sqrt{x}}{5} = 2$ **24.** $\dfrac{\sqrt{x-7}}{3} = 1$ **25.** $4\sqrt{2x-1} = 12$

SEE EXAMPLE **4**
p. 724

Solve each equation. Check your answer.

26. $\sqrt{5-x} = \sqrt{6x-2}$ **27.** $\sqrt{x+7} = \sqrt{3x-19}$ **28.** $0 = \sqrt{2x} - \sqrt{x+3}$

29. $\sqrt{x-5} = \sqrt{7-x}$ **30.** $\sqrt{-x} = \sqrt{2x+1}$ **31.** $\sqrt{3x+1} - \sqrt{2x+3} = 0$

SEE EXAMPLE **5**
p. 725

Solve each equation. Check your answer.

32. $\sqrt{x-5} + 5 = 0$ **33.** $\sqrt{3x} + 5 = 3$ **34.** $\sqrt{2-7x} = 2x$ **35.** $x = \sqrt{12+x}$

36. $6 + \sqrt{x-1} = 4$ **37.** $\sqrt{6-3x} + 2 = x$ **38.** $\sqrt{x-2} = 2 - x$ **39.** $10 + \sqrt{x} = 5$

SEE EXAMPLE **6**
p. 725

40. Geometry A trapezoid has an area of 14 cm². The length of one base is 4 cm and the length of the other base is 10 cm. The height is $\left(\sqrt{2x+3}\right)$ cm. What is the value of x? What is the height of the trapezoid? (*Hint:* The formula for the area of a trapezoid is $A = \frac{1}{2}(b_1 + b_2)h$.)

PRACTICE AND PROBLEM SOLVING

Independent Practice

For Exercises	See Example
41–44	1
45–48	2
49–52	3
53–58	4
59–66	5
67	6

Extra Practice

Skills Practice p. EP22

Application Practice p. EP34

Solve each equation. Check your answer.

41. $\sqrt{3x} = 12$ **42.** $2 = \sqrt{-2x}$ **43.** $\sqrt{-a} = 5$ **44.** $11 = \sqrt{c}$

45. $\sqrt{x-7} = 8$ **46.** $\sqrt{x} - 4 = 0$ **47.** $\sqrt{1-3x} = 5$ **48.** $\sqrt{5x+1} + 2 = 6$

49. $5\sqrt{x} = 30$ **50.** $\frac{\sqrt{2x}}{2} = 4$ **51.** $5\sqrt{-x} = 20$ **52.** $3\sqrt{3p} = 9$

Solve each equation. Check your answer.

53. $\sqrt{3x-13} = \sqrt{x+3}$ **54.** $\sqrt{x} - \sqrt{6-x} = 0$ **55.** $\sqrt{x+5} = \sqrt{2x-4}$

56. $\sqrt{4x-2} = \sqrt{3x+4}$ **57.** $\sqrt{5x-6} = \sqrt{16-6x}$ **58.** $\sqrt{12x-3} = \sqrt{4x+93}$

Solve each equation. Check your answer.

59. $\sqrt{x+6} = 1$ **60.** $-2\sqrt{x} = 6$ **61.** $x = \sqrt{2x+15}$ **62.** $\sqrt{6x} + 9 = 2$

63. $\sqrt{4-3x} = x$ **64.** $\sqrt{5x+4} = x - 4$ **65.** $\sqrt{2x+2} = 2x$ **66.** $\sqrt{x+3} + 10 = 7$

67. Geometry A triangle has an area of 60 in². Its base is 10 inches and its height is $\sqrt{x}$ inches. What is the value of x? What is the height of the triangle? (*Hint:* The formula for the area of a triangle is $A = \frac{1}{2}bh$.)

Translate each sentence into an equation. Then solve the equation and check your answer.

68. The square root of three times a number is nine.

69. The difference of the square root of a number and three is four.

70. The square root of the difference of a number and three is four.

71. A number is equal to the square root of the sum of that number and six.

Geometry **Find the dimensions of each rectangle given its perimeter.**

72. 5 m, $(\sqrt{x+7})$ m, $P = 18$ m

73. $(\sqrt{x+3})$ in., 1 in., $P = 8$ in.

74. $3\sqrt{x}$ cm, $2\sqrt{x}$ cm, $P = 30$ cm

Transportation

State Highway 1 (sometimes called the Pacific Coast Highway) closely follows the terrain and contours of the California coastline. It was the first designated scenic highway in the state.

75. Physical Science The formula $v = \frac{\sqrt{2Em}}{m}$ describes the relationship between an object's mass m in kilograms, the object's velocity v in meters per second, and the object's kinetic energy E in joules.

  a. A baseball with a mass of 0.14 kg is thrown with a velocity of 28 m/s. How much kinetic energy does the baseball have?

  b. What is the kinetic energy of an object at rest ($v = 0$)?

76. Meteorology The formula $t = \sqrt{\frac{d^2}{216}}$ gives the time t in hours that a storm with diameter d miles will last. What is the diameter of a storm that lasts 1 hour? Round your answer to the nearest hundredth.

77. Transportation A sharp curve may require a driver to slow down to avoid going off the road. The equation $v = \sqrt{2.5r}$ describes the relationship between the radius r in feet of an unbanked curve and the maximum velocity v in miles per hour that a car can safely go around the curve. An engineer is designing a highway with a maximum speed limit of 65 mi/h. What is the radius of an unbanked curve for which this is the maximum safe speed?

78. **Write About It** Explain why it is important to check solutions when solving radical equations.

79. **Multi-Step** Solve for x and y in the equations $\sqrt{x} + \sqrt{y} = \sqrt{81}$ and $6\sqrt{y} = 24$. (*Hint:* Solve for y first, and then use substitution to solve for x.)

Reasoning Tell whether the following statements are *always*, *sometimes*, or *never* true. If the answer is *sometimes*, give one example that is true and one that is false.

80. If $a = b$, then $a^2 = b^2$.

81. If $a^2 = b^2$, then $a = b$.

82. When solving radical equations, the value of the variable is nonnegative.

83. **/// ERROR ANALYSIS ///** Two students solved $\sqrt{5 - x} = \sqrt{x + 9}$. Which is incorrect? Explain the error.

A

$$\sqrt{5 - x} = \sqrt{x + 9}$$
$$\left(\sqrt{5 - x}\right)^2 = \left(\sqrt{x + 9}\right)^2$$
$$5 - x = x + 9$$
$$-2x = 4$$
$$x = -2$$

Check $\sqrt{5 - (-2)}$? $\sqrt{(-2) + 9}$
$$\sqrt{7} = \sqrt{7} \checkmark$$

B

$$\sqrt{5 - x} = \sqrt{x + 9}$$
$$\left(\sqrt{5 - x}\right)^2 = \left(\sqrt{x + 9}\right)^2$$
$$5 - x = x + 9$$
$$4 = 2x$$
$$2 = x$$

Check $\sqrt{5 - 2}$? $\sqrt{2 + 9}$
$$\sqrt{3} \neq \sqrt{11} \; \mathbf{X}$$
no solution

84. **Estimation** The relationship between a circle's radius and its area can be modeled by $r = \sqrt{\dfrac{A}{\pi}}$, where r is the radius and A is the area. Solutions to this equation are graphed at right. Use the graph to estimate the radius of a circle with an area of 29 m^2.

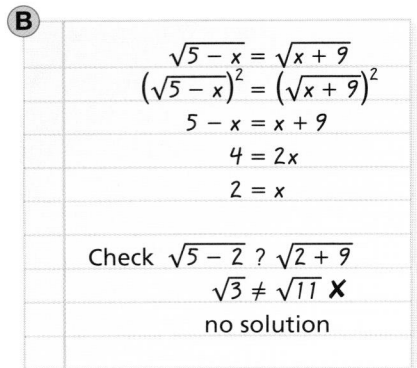

Area and Radius of a Circle

85. **Critical Thinking** Suppose that the equation $\sqrt{-x} = k$ has a solution. What does that tell you about the value of x? the value of k? Explain.

CONCEPT CONNECTION

86. This problem will prepare you for the Concept Connection on page 730.

  a. The Demon Drop is a free-fall ride at Ohio's Cedar Point amusement park. The maximum speed on the Demon Drop is 42 miles per hour. Convert this speed to feet per second. (*Hint:* There are 5280 feet in a mile.)

  b. The Demon Drop is 131 feet tall. Most of the drop is a vertical free fall, but near the bottom, the track curves so that the cars slow down gradually. The velocity of any object in free fall is $v = 8\sqrt{d}$, where v is the velocity in feet per second and d is the distance the object has fallen in feet. Use this equation and your answer to part **a** to estimate the free-fall distance.

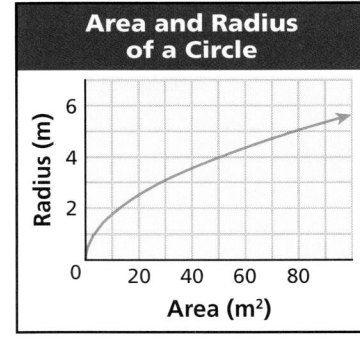

131 ft

87. Which of the following is the solution of $\sqrt{8 - 2x} - 2 = 2$?

    Ⓐ −4   Ⓑ −2   Ⓒ 2   Ⓓ 4

88. For which of the following values of k does the equation $\sqrt{x + 1} + k = 0$ have no real solution?

    Ⓐ −2   Ⓑ −1   Ⓒ 0   Ⓓ 1

89. Which of the following is the solution of $x = \sqrt{12 - x}$?

    Ⓐ −4   Ⓑ −3   Ⓒ 3   Ⓓ 4

90. Which of the following is the solution of $\sqrt{x + 13} = 5\sqrt{x - 11}$?

    Ⓐ 9   Ⓑ 12   Ⓒ 16   Ⓓ 17

91. Which of the following is an extraneous solution of $\sqrt{3x - 2} = x - 2$?

    Ⓐ 1   Ⓑ 2   Ⓒ 3   Ⓓ 6

CHALLENGE AND EXTEND

Solve each equation. Check your answer.

92. $\sqrt{x + 3} = x + 1$ **93.** $\sqrt{x - 1} = x - 1$ **94.** $x - 1 = \sqrt{2x + 6}$

95. $\sqrt{x^2 + 5x + 11} = x + 3$ **96.** $\sqrt{x^2 + 9x + 14} = x + 4$ **97.** $x + 2 = \sqrt{x^2 + 5x + 4}$

98. Graphing Calculator Solve $\sqrt{2x - 2} = -\sqrt{x}$ and check your answer. Then use your graphing calculator for the following:

    a. Graph $y = \sqrt{2x - 2}$ and $y = -\sqrt{x}$ on the same screen. Make a sketch of the graphs.

    b. Use the graphs in part **a** to explain your solution to $\sqrt{2x - 2} = -\sqrt{x}$.

99. Graphing Calculator Solve $x = \sqrt{x + 6}$ and check your answer. Then use your graphing calculator for the following:

    a. Graph $y = x$ and $y = \sqrt{x + 6}$ on the same screen. Make a sketch of the graphs.

    b. Use the graphs in part **a** to explain your solution to $x = \sqrt{x + 6}$.

100. Find the domain for the function $y = \dfrac{4}{\sqrt{x - 2}}$. Is the domain for this function different from the domain for the function $y = \sqrt{x - 2}$? Why or why not?

SPIRAL STANDARDS REVIEW
🔑 9.0, 17.0

Give the domain and range of each relation. *(Lesson 4-2)*

101. $\{(1, 3), (-6, 2), (3, 2), (5, 4)\}$ **102.** $\{(-2, 1), (12, 3), (-2, 3), (4, 8)\}$

103.

x	3	4	6	7	9
y	2	1	0	−5	−8

104.

x	5	2	−3	4	5
y	7	2	6	2	5

Solve each system by substitution. *(Lesson 6-2)*

105. $\begin{cases} y = 2x + 5 \\ y = 5x - 4 \end{cases}$ **106.** $\begin{cases} y = 6x - 17 \\ y = -x + 11 \end{cases}$ **107.** $\begin{cases} y = -3x + 12 \\ y = x - 8 \end{cases}$

Graph each square-root function. *(Lesson 11-1)*

108. $f(x) = \sqrt{x + 3}$ **109.** $f(x) = \sqrt{3x - 6}$ **110.** $f(x) = 2\sqrt{x} + 1$

CONCEPT CONNECTION

ADMIT ONE
221948
221948

Radical Functions and Equations

Eye in the Sky The London Eye is a giant observation wheel in London, England. It carries people in enclosed capsules around its circumference. Opened on December 31, 1999, to welcome the new millennium, its diameter is 135 meters. On the London Eye, riders can see a distance of 40 kilometers.

1. What is the circumference of the London Eye? Use 3.14 for π.

2. The London Eye's velocity in meters per second can be found using the equation $v = \sqrt{0.001r}$, where r is the radius of the wheel in meters. Find the velocity in meters per second. Round to the nearest hundredth.

3. Another way to find the velocity is to divide the distance around the wheel by the time for the ride. A ride on the London Eye lasts 30 minutes.

a. Use this method to find the velocity of the wheel in meters per second to the nearest hundredth.

b. Is your answer to part **a** the same as your answer to problem 2? If not, explain any differences.

4. When a rider is at the highest point on the London Eye, how far is he from the bottom of the ride? Explain.

5. When a rider is at half the maximum height, her distance from the bottom of the ride can be found using the equation $d = \sqrt{2r^2}$. Explain where this equation comes from. Then find this distance. Round to the nearest hundredth.

READY TO GO ON?

Quiz for Lessons 11-1 Through 11-5

☑ 11-1 Square-Root Functions

1. The distance in kilometers that a person can see to the horizon can be approximated by the formula $D = 113\sqrt{h}$, where h is the person's height in kilometers above sea level. What is the distance to the horizon observed by a mountain climber who is 0.3 km above sea level? Round your answer to the nearest tenth.

Find the domain of each square-root function.

2. $y = \sqrt{3x} - 7$

3. $y = \sqrt{x - 5}$

4. $y = \sqrt{2x - 6}$

Graph each square-root function.

5. $y = \sqrt{x - 6}$

6. $y = \sqrt{x} + 5$

7. $y = \sqrt{8 - 4x}$

☑ 11-2 Radical Expressions

Simplify. All variables represent nonnegative numbers.

8. $\sqrt{75}$

9. $\sqrt{\dfrac{300}{3}}$

10. $\sqrt{a^2 b^3}$

11. $\sqrt{98xy^2}$

12. $\sqrt{\dfrac{32}{25}}$

13. $\sqrt{\dfrac{128}{121}}$

14. $\sqrt{\dfrac{4b^2}{81}}$

15. $\sqrt{\dfrac{75a^9}{49a^3}}$

16. How long is the diagonal of a rectangular television screen that is 19.2 inches long and 14.4 inches high?

☑ 11-3 Adding and Subtracting Radical Expressions

Simplify each expression. All variables represent nonnegative numbers.

17. $12\sqrt{7} - 5\sqrt{7}$

18. $3\sqrt{x} + 3\sqrt{x}$

19. $\sqrt{12} + \sqrt{75}$

20. $5\sqrt{50} + \sqrt{98}$

21. $4\sqrt{3} - 3\sqrt{4}$

22. $\sqrt{98x} + \sqrt{18x} - \sqrt{200x}$

☑ 11-4 Multiplying and Dividing Radical Expressions

Multiply. Write each product in simplest form. All variables represent nonnegative numbers.

23. $\sqrt{6}\,\sqrt{11}$

24. $\sqrt{3}\,\sqrt{8}$

25. $4\sqrt{12x}\,\sqrt{3x}$

26. $\left(3 - \sqrt{3}\right)\left(5 + \sqrt{3}\right)$

Simplify each quotient. All variables represent nonnegative numbers.

27. $\dfrac{\sqrt{19}}{\sqrt{3}}$

28. $\dfrac{\sqrt{14}}{\sqrt{8}}$

29. $\dfrac{\sqrt{6b}}{\sqrt{8}}$

30. $\dfrac{\sqrt{27}}{\sqrt{3t}}$

☑ 11-5 Solving Radical Equations

Solve each equation. Check your answer.

31. $\sqrt{x} - 4 = 21$

32. $-3\sqrt{x} = -12$

33. $\dfrac{5\sqrt{x}}{2} = 40$

34. $\sqrt{4x - 2} - \sqrt{43 - x} = 0$

35. $\sqrt{20 + x} = x$

36. $\sqrt{4x} + 12 = 10$

11-6 Geometric Sequences

California Standards

Preview of Algebra II
Preparation for 22.0 Students **find the general term** and the sums of arithmetic series and **of both finite and infinite geometric series.**

Vocabulary
geometric sequence
common ratio

Who uses this?
Bungee jumpers can use geometric sequences to calculate how high they will bounce.

The table shows the heights of a bungee jumper's bounces.

Bounce	1	2	3
Height (ft)	200	80	32

The height of the bounces shown in the table above form a *geometric sequence*. In a **geometric sequence**, the ratio of successive terms is the same number r, called the **common ratio**.

EXAMPLE **1** | **Extending Geometric Sequences**

Find the next three terms in each geometric sequence.

A 1, 3, 9, 27, …

Step 1 Find the value of r by dividing each term by the one before it.

1   3   9   27

$\frac{3}{1} = 3$ $\frac{9}{3} = 3$ $\frac{27}{9} = 3$ ← The value of r is 3.

Step 2 Multiply each term by 3 to find the next three terms.

27   81   243   729

$\times 3$ $\times 3$ $\times 3$

The next three terms are 81, 243, and 729.

Helpful Hint

When the terms in a geometric sequence alternate between positive and negative, the value of r is negative.

B $-16, 4, -1, \frac{1}{4}, …$

Step 1 Find the value of r by dividing each term by the one before it.

-16 4 -1 $\frac{1}{4}$

$\frac{4}{-16} = -\frac{1}{4}$ $\frac{-1}{4} = -\frac{1}{4}$ $\frac{\frac{1}{4}}{-1} = -\frac{1}{4}$ ← The value of r is $-\frac{1}{4}$.

Step 2 Multiply each term by $-\frac{1}{4}$ to find the next three terms.

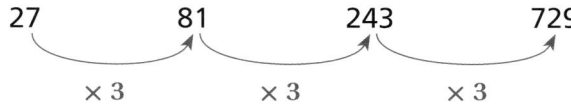

$\frac{1}{4}$ $-\frac{1}{16}$ $\frac{1}{64}$ $-\frac{1}{256}$

$\times \left(-\frac{1}{4}\right)$ $\times \left(-\frac{1}{4}\right)$ $\times \left(-\frac{1}{4}\right)$

The next three terms are $-\frac{1}{16}, \frac{1}{64}$, and $-\frac{1}{256}$.

 **Find the next three terms in each geometric sequence.**

1a. 5, −10, 20, −40, … **1b.** 512, 384, 288, …

Recall that the variable a is often used to represent terms in a sequence. The variable a_4 (read "a sub 4") is the fourth term in a sequence. To designate any term, or the nth term, you write a_n, where n can be any natural number.

1	2	3	4…	n	← Position
↓	↓	↓	↓		
3	6	12	24…		← Term
a_1	a_2	a_3	a_4	a_n	

The sequence above starts with the first term, 3. The common ratio r is 2. You can use the first term, 3, and the common ratio, 2, to write a rule for finding a_n.

Words	Numbers	Algebra
1st term	3	a_1
2nd term = 1st term times common ratio	$3 \cdot 2^1 = 6$	$a_1 \cdot r^1$
3rd term = 1st term times common ratio squared	$3 \cdot 2 \cdot 2 = 3 \cdot 2^2 = 12$	$a_1 \cdot r^2$
4th term = 1st term times common ratio cubed	$3 \cdot 2 \cdot 2 \cdot 2 = 3 \cdot 2^3 = 24$	$a_1 \cdot r^3$
nth term = 1st term times common ratio to the power $(n-1)$	$3 \cdot 2^{n-1}$	$a_1 \cdot r^{n-1}$

The pattern in the table shows that to get the nth term, multiply the **first term** by the **common ratio** raised to the power $(n-1)$.

 **Finding the nth Term of a Geometric Sequence**

The nth term of a geometric sequence with **common ratio** r and **first term** a, is

$$a_n = a_1 r^{n-1}$$

EXAMPLE 2 **Finding the nth Term of a Geometric Sequence**

A The first term of a geometric sequence is 128, and the common ratio is 0.5. What is the 10th term of the sequence?

$a_n = a_1 r^{n-1}$ *Write the formula.*

$a_{10} = 128(0.5)^{10-1}$ *Substitute 128 for a_1, 10 for n, and 0.5 for r.*

$= 128(0.5)^9$ *Simplify the exponent.*

$= 0.25$ *Use a calculator.*

The 10th term of the sequence is 0.25.

B For a geometric sequence, $a_1 = 8$ and $r = 3$. Find the 5th term of this sequence.

$a_n = a_1 r^{n-1}$ *Write the formula.*

$a_5 = 8(3)^{5-1}$ *Substitute 8 for a_1, 5 for n, and 3 for r.*

$= 8(3)^4$ *Simplify the exponent.*

$= 648$ *Use a calculator.*

The 5th term of the sequence is 648.

C What is the 13th term of the geometric sequence $8, -16, 32, -64, \ldots$?

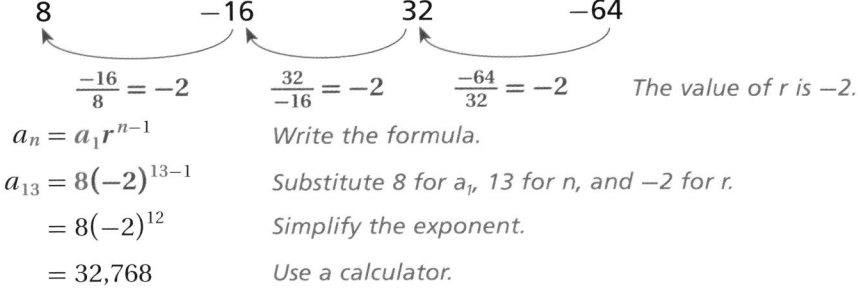

$\dfrac{-16}{8} = -2 \qquad \dfrac{32}{-16} = -2 \qquad \dfrac{-64}{32} = -2 \qquad$ *The value of r is −2.*

$a_n = a_1 r^{n-1}$ *Write the formula.*

$a_{13} = 8(-2)^{13-1}$ *Substitute 8 for a_1, 13 for n, and −2 for r.*

$= 8(-2)^{12}$ *Simplify the exponent.*

$= 32{,}768$ *Use a calculator.*

The 13th term of the sequence is 32,768.

 **2.** What is the 8th term of the geometric sequence 1000, 500, 250, 125, … ?

EXAMPLE 3   *Sports Application*

A bungee jumper jumps from a bridge. The diagram shows the jumper's height above the ground at the top of each bounce. The heights form a geometric sequence. What is the jumper's height at the top of the 5th bounce?

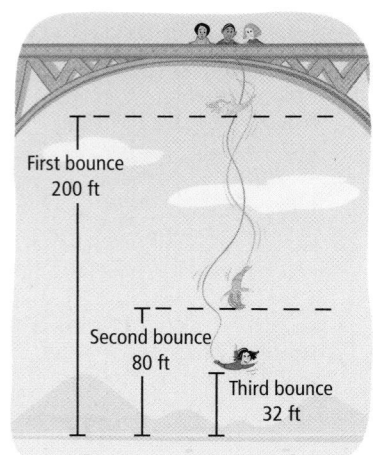

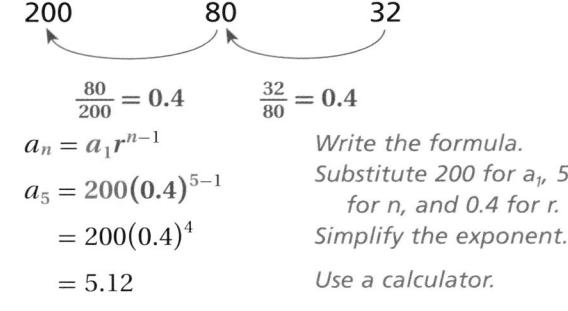

$\dfrac{80}{200} = 0.4 \qquad \dfrac{32}{80} = 0.4$

$a_n = a_1 r^{n-1}$ *Write the formula.*

$a_5 = 200(0.4)^{5-1}$ *Substitute 200 for a_1, 5 for n, and 0.4 for r.*

$= 200(0.4)^4$ *Simplify the exponent.*

$= 5.12$ *Use a calculator.*

The height of the 5th bounce is 5.12 feet.

 **3.** The table shows a car's value for 3 years after it is purchased. The values form a geometric sequence. How much will the car be worth in the 10th year?

Year	Value ($)
1	10,000
2	8,000
3	6,400

THINK AND DISCUSS

1. How do you determine whether a sequence is geometric?

2. GET ORGANIZED Copy and complete the graphic organizer. In each box, write a way to represent the geometric sequence.

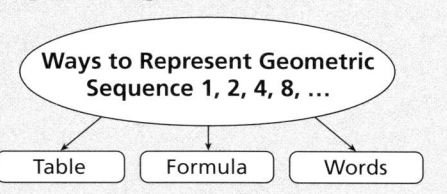

California Standards Practice

Preparation for Algebra II 22.0;
1A24.1, 1A25.1

go.hrw.com
Homework Help Online
KEYWORD: MA8CA 11-6
Parent Resources Online
KEYWORD: MA8CA Parent

GUIDED PRACTICE

1. **Vocabulary** What is the *common ratio* of a geometric sequence?

SEE EXAMPLE **1**
p. 732

Find the next three terms in each geometric sequence.

2. 2, 4, 8, 16, …   3. 400, 200, 100, 50, …   4. 4, −12, 36, −108, …

SEE EXAMPLE **2**
p. 733

5. The first term of a geometric sequence is 1, and the common ratio is 10. What is the 10th term of the sequence?

6. What is the 11th term of the geometric sequence 3, 6, 12, 24, … ?

SEE EXAMPLE **3**
p. 734

7. **Sports** In the NCAA men's basketball tournament, 64 teams compete in round 1. Fewer teams remain in each following round, as shown in the graph, until all but one team have been eliminated. The numbers of teams in each round form a geometric sequence. How many teams compete in round 5?

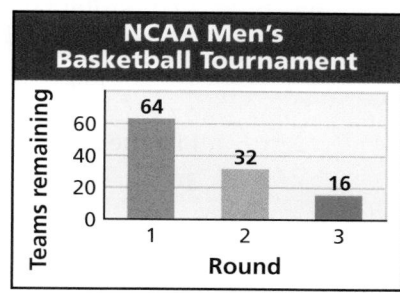

PRACTICE AND PROBLEM SOLVING

Independent Practice

For Exercises	See Example
8–13	1
14–15	2
16	3

Extra Practice

Skills Practice p. EP23
Application Practice p. EP34

Find the next three terms in each geometric sequence.

8. −2, 10, −50, 250, …   9. 32, 48, 72, 108, …   10. 625, 500, 400, 320, …

11. 6, 42, 294, …   12. 6, −12, 24, −48, …   13. $40, 10, \frac{5}{2}, \frac{5}{8}, …$

14. The first term of a geometric sequence is 18 and the common ratio is 3.5. What is the 5th term of the sequence?

15. What is the 14th term of the geometric sequence 1000, 100, 10, 1, … ?

16. **Physical Science** A ball is dropped from a height of 500 meters. The table shows the height of each bounce, and the heights form a geometric sequence. How high does the ball bounce on the 8th bounce? Round your answer to the nearest tenth of a meter.

Bounce	Height (m)
1	400
2	320
3	256

Find the missing term(s) in each geometric sequence.

17. 20, 40, ▢, ▢, …   18. ▢, 6, 18, ▢, …   19. 9, 3, 1, ▢, …

20. 3, 12, ▢, 192, ▢, …   21. $7, 1, ▢, ▢, \frac{1}{343}, …$ 22. $▢, 100, 25, ▢, \frac{25}{16}, …$

23. −3, ▢, −12, 24, ▢, …   24. ▢, ▢, 1, −3, 9, …   25. 1, 17, 289, ▢, …

Determine whether each sequence could be geometric. If so, give the common ratio.

26. 2, 10, 50, 250, …   27. $15, 5, \frac{5}{3}, \frac{5}{9}, …$ 28. 6, 18, 24, 38, …

29. 9, 3, −1, −5, …   30. 7, 21, 63, 189, …   31. 4, 1, −2, −4, …

32. Multi-Step Billy earns money by mowing lawns for the summer. He offers two payment plans, as shown at right.

   a. Do the payments for plan 2 form a geometric sequence? Explain.

   b. If you were one of Billy's customers, which plan would you choose? (Assume that the summer is 10 weeks long.) Explain your choice.

33. Measurement When you fold a piece of paper in half, the thickness of the folded piece is twice the thickness of the original piece. A piece of copy paper is about 0.1 mm thick.

   a. How thick is a piece of copy paper that has been folded in half 7 times?

   b. Suppose that you could fold a piece of copy paper in half 12 times. How thick would it be? Write your answer in centimeters.

List the first four terms of each geometric sequence.

34. $a_1 = 3$, $a_n = 3(2)^{n-1}$
   35. $a_1 = -2$, $a_n = -2(4)^{n-1}$
   36. $a_1 = 5$, $a_n = 5(-2)^{n-1}$

37. $a_1 = 2$, $a_n = 2(2)^{n-1}$
   38. $a_1 = 2$, $a_n = 2(5)^{n-1}$
   39. $a_1 = 12$, $a_n = 12\left(\dfrac{1}{4}\right)^{n-1}$

40. Reasoning Use deductive reasoning to show that if the value of r is doubled in a geometric sequence, then each term is multiplied by 2^{n-1}, where n represents the term number.

For help with deductive reasoning, see p. 99, p. 169, and p. 311.

41. Geometry The steps below describe how to make a geometric figure by repeating the same process over and over on a smaller and smaller scale.

   Step 1 (stage 0) Draw a large square.

   Step 2 (stage 1) Divide the square into four equal squares.

   Step 3 (stage 2) Divide each small square into four equal squares.

   Step 4 Repeat Step 3 indefinitely.

   a. Draw stages 0, 1, 2, and 3.

   b. How many small squares are in each stage? Organize your data relating stage and number of small squares in a table.

   c. Does the data in part **b** form a geometric sequence? Explain.

   d. Write a rule to find the number of small squares in stage n.

42. Write About It Write a series of steps for finding the nth term of a geometric sequence when you are given the first several terms.

CONCEPT CONNECTION

43. This problem will prepare you for the Concept Connection on page 762.

   a. Three years ago, the annual tuition at a university was $3000. The following year, the tuition was $3300, and last year, the tuition was $3630. If the tuition has continued to grow in the same manner, what is the tuition this year? What do you expect it to be next year?

   b. What is the common ratio?

   c. What would you predict the tuition was 4 years ago? How did you find that value?

736 *Chapter 11 Radical and Exponential Functions*

44. Which of the following could be a geometric sequence?

    Ⓐ $\dfrac{1}{2}, 1, \dfrac{3}{2}, 2, \ldots$ Ⓒ 3, 8, 13, 18, …

    Ⓑ −2, −6, −10, −14, …   Ⓓ 5, 10, 20, 40, …

45. Which equation represents the nth term in the geometric sequence 2, −8, 32, −128, …?

    Ⓐ $a_n = (-4)^n$ Ⓑ $a_n = (-4)^{n-1}$ Ⓒ $a_n = 2(-4)^n$ Ⓓ $a_n = 2(-4)^{n-1}$

46. The frequency of a musical note, measured in hertz (Hz), is called its pitch. The pitches of the A keys on a piano form a geometric sequence, as shown.

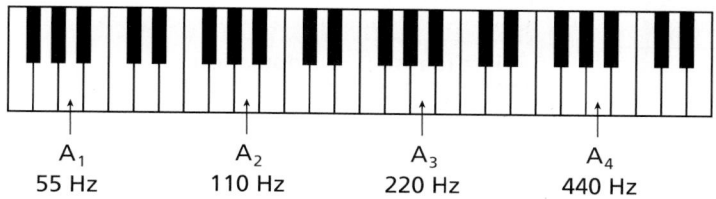

A₁   A₂   A₃   A₄
55 Hz   110 Hz   220 Hz   440 Hz

What is the frequency of A_7?

    Ⓐ 880 Hz   Ⓑ 1760 Hz   Ⓒ 3520 Hz   Ⓓ 7040 Hz

CHALLENGE AND EXTEND

Find the next three terms in each geometric sequence.

47. $x, x^2, x^3, \ldots$ **48.** $2x^2, 6x^3, 18x^4, \ldots$ **49.** $\dfrac{1}{y^3}, \dfrac{1}{y^2}, \dfrac{1}{y}, \ldots$ **50.** $\dfrac{1}{(x+1)^2}, \dfrac{1}{x+1}, 1, \ldots$

51. The 10th term of a geometric sequence is 0.78125. The common ratio is −0.5. Find the first term of the sequence.

52. The first term of a geometric sequence is 12 and the common ratio is $\dfrac{1}{2}$. Is 0 a term in this sequence? Explain.

53. A geometric sequence starts with 14 and has a common ration of 0.4. Colin finds that another number in the sequence is 0.057344. Which term in the sequence did Colin find?

54. The first three terms of a sequence are 1, 2, and 4. Susanna said the 8th term of this sequence is 128. Paul said the 8th term is 29. Explain how the students found their answers. Why could these both be considered correct answers?

SPIRAL STANDARDS REVIEW   🔑 4.0, 🔑 6.0, 🔑 20.0

Solve each inequality and graph the solutions. *(Lesson 3-4)*

55. $3(b - 4) > 18$ **56.** $-12 + x \le -8$ **57.** $c + \dfrac{2}{3} < \dfrac{1}{3}$

Graph the solutions of each linear inequality. *(Lesson 6-5)*

58. $y < 2x - 4$ **59.** $3x + y > 6$ **60.** $-y \le 2x + 1$

Solve by using the Quadratic Formula. Check your answer. *(Lesson 9-8)*

61. $3x^2 - 4x = -1$ **62.** $5x^2 + 1 = 6x$ **63.** $\dfrac{1}{2}x^2 + \dfrac{3}{2}x = 14$

64. $2x^2 - 5 = 5x$ **65.** $2x^2 = -8x + 3$ **66.** $-8x^2 + 2x + 3 = 0$

Exponential Functions

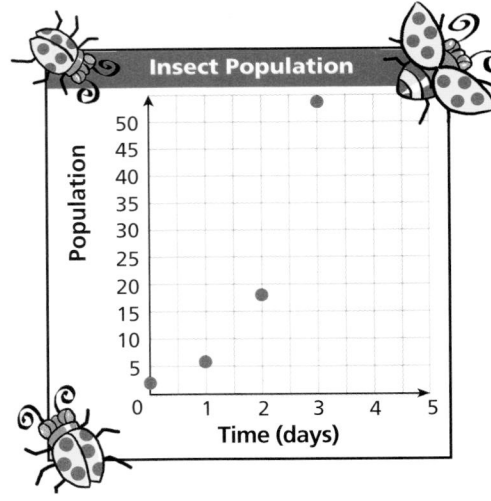

Insect Population

California Standards

Preview of Algebra II

12.0 Students know the laws of fractional exponents, **understand exponential functions,** and use these functions in problems involving exponential growth and decay.

Vocabulary
exponential function

Who uses this?
Scientists model populations with exponential functions.

The table and the graph show an insect population that increases over time.

Time (days)	Population
0	2
1	6
2	18
3	54

) × 3
) × 3
) × 3

A function rule that describes the pattern above is $f(x) = 2(3)^x$. This type of function, in which the independent variable appears in an exponent, is an **exponential function**. Notice that **2** is the starting population and **3** is the amount by which the population is multiplied each day.

Know it!
Note

> ### Exponential Functions
> An exponential function has the form $f(x) = ab^x$, where $a \neq 0$, $b \neq 1$, and $b > 0$.

EXAMPLE 1 **Evaluating an Exponential Function**

A The function $f(x) = 2(3)^x$ models an insect population after x days. What will the population be on the 5th day?

$f(x) = 2(3)^x$ *Write the function.*

$f(5) = 2(3)^5$ *Substitute 5 for x.*

$\quad\;\; = 2(243)$ *Evaluate 3^5.*

$\quad\;\; = 486$ *Multiply.*

There will be 486 insects on the 5th day.

Helpful Hint

In Example 1B, round your answer to the nearest whole number because there can only be a whole number of prairie dogs.

B The function $f(x) = 1500(0.995)^x$, where x is the time in years, models a prairie dog population. How many prairie dogs will there be in 8 years?

$f(x) = 1500(0.995)^x$

$f(8) = 1500(0.995)^8$ *Substitute 8 for x.*

$\quad\;\; \approx 1441$ *Use a calculator. Round to the nearest whole number.*

There will be about 1441 prairie dogs in 8 years.

CHECK IT OUT!

1. The function $f(x) = 8(0.75)^x$ models the width of a photograph in inches after it has been reduced by 25% x times. What is the width of the photograph after it has been reduced 3 times?

Exponential functions have *constant ratios*. As the *x*-values increase by a constant amount, the *y*-values are multiplied by a constant amount. This amount is the constant ratio and is the value of *b* in $f(x) = ab^x$.

x	y = 2(3)^x
1	6
2	18
3	54
4	162

+1 between x-values; ×3 between y-values.

EXAMPLE 2   Identifying an Exponential Function

Tell whether each set of ordered pairs satisfies an exponential function. Explain your answer.

A $\{(-1, 1.5), (0, 3), (1, 6), (2, 12)\}$

x	y
−1	1.5
0	3
1	6
2	12

+1 between x-values; ×2 between y-values.

This is an exponential function. As the *x*-values increase by a constant amount, the *y*-values are multiplied by a constant amount.

B $\{(-1, -9), (1, 9), (3, 27), (5, 45)\}$

x	y
−1	−9
1	9
3	27
5	45

+2 between x-values; y-values multiplied by ×(−1), ×3, ×$\frac{5}{3}$.

This is *not* an exponential function. As the *x*-values increase by a constant amount, the *y*-values are *not* multiplied by a constant amount.

 **CHECK IT OUT!** Tell whether each set of ordered pairs satisfies an exponential function. Explain your answer.

2a. $\{(-1, 1), (0, 0), (1, 1), (2, 4)\}$

2b. $\{(-2, 4), (-1, 2), (0, 1), (1, 0.5)\}$

To graph an exponential function, choose several values of *x* (positive, negative, and 0) and generate ordered pairs. Plot the points and connect them with a smooth curve.

EXAMPLE 3   Graphing y = ab^x with a > 0 and b > 1

Graph $y = 3(4)^x$.

Choose several values of x and generate ordered pairs.

x	y = 3(4)^x
−1	0.75
0	3
1	12
2	48

Graph the ordered pairs and connect with a smooth curve.

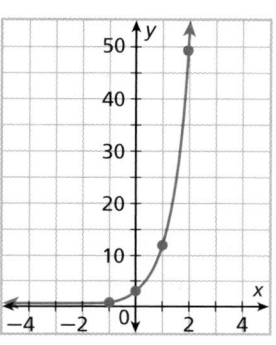

 **CHECK IT OUT!** Graph each exponential function.

3a. $y = 2^x$

3b. $y = 0.2(5)^x$

EXAMPLE 4 Graphing $y = ab^x$ with $a < 0$ and $b > 1$

Graph $y = -5(2)^x$.

Choose several values of x and generate ordered pairs.

x	$y = -5(2)^x$
-1	-2.5
0	-5
1	-10
2	-20

Graph the ordered pairs and connect with a smooth curve.

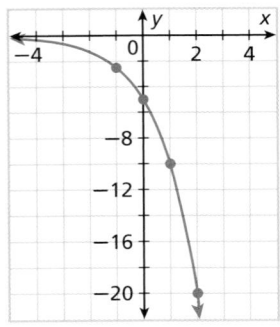

CHECK IT OUT! **4a.** Graph $y = -6^x$.   **4b.** Graph $y = -3(3)^x$.

EXAMPLE 5 Graphing $y = ab^x$ with $0 < b < 1$

Graph each exponential function.

A $y = 3\left(\dfrac{1}{2}\right)^x$

Choose several values of x and generate ordered pairs.

x	$y = 3\left(\dfrac{1}{2}\right)^x$
-1	6
0	3
1	1.5
2	0.75

Graph the ordered pairs and connect with a smooth curve.

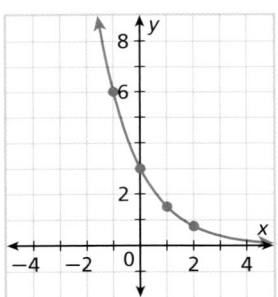

B $y = -2(0.4)^x$

Choose several values of x and generate ordered pairs.

x	$y = -2(0.4)^x$
-2	-12.5
-1	-5
0	-2
1	-0.8

Graph the ordered pairs and connect with a smooth curve.

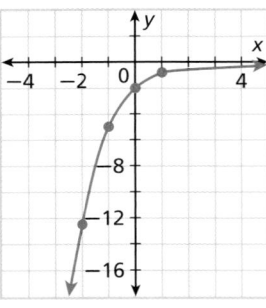

CHECK IT OUT! **Graph each exponential function.**

5a. $y = 4\left(\dfrac{1}{4}\right)^x$ **5b.** $y = -2(0.1)^x$

The box summarizes the general shapes of exponential function graphs.

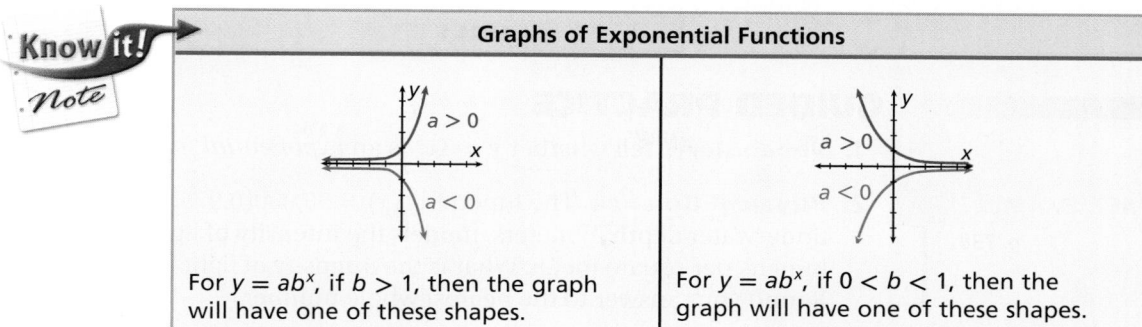

Graphs of Exponential Functions

For $y = ab^x$, if $b > 1$, then the graph will have one of these shapes.

For $y = ab^x$, if $0 < b < 1$, then the graph will have one of these shapes.

EXAMPLE 6 *Statistics Application*

In the year 2000, the world population was about 6 billion, and it was growing by 1.21% each year. At this growth rate, the function $f(x) = 6(1.0121)^x$ gives the population, in billions, x years after 2000. Using this model, in about what year will the population reach 7 billion?

Enter the function into the Y= editor of a graphing calculator.

Caution!

The function values give the population *in billions*, so a *y*-value of 7 means 7 billion.

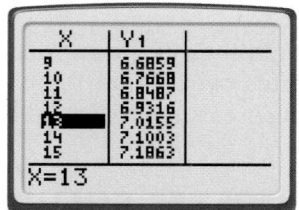

TABLE
Press **2nd** **GRAPH**. *Use the arrow keys to find a y-value as close to 7 as possible. The corresponding x-value is 13.*

The world population will reach 7 billion in about 2013.

6. An accountant uses $f(x) = 12{,}330(0.869)^x$, where x is the time in years since the purchase, to model the value of a car. When will the car be worth $2000?

THINK AND DISCUSS

1. How can you find the constant ratio of a set of exponential data?

2. GET ORGANIZED Copy and complete the graphic organizer. In each box, give an example of an appropriate exponential function and sketch its graph.

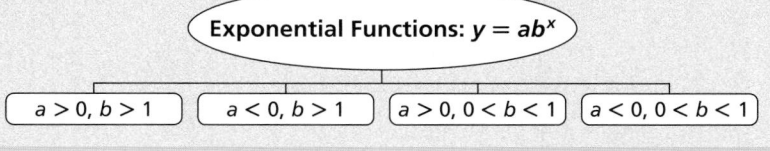

Exponential Functions: $y = ab^x$

| $a > 0, b > 1$ | $a < 0, b > 1$ | $a > 0, 0 < b < 1$ | $a < 0, 0 < b < 1$ |

California
Standards Practice
Preview of Algebra II ✪ 12.0;
1A24.1

go.hrw.com
Homework Help Online
KEYWORD: MA8CA 11-7
Parent Resources Online
KEYWORD: MA8CA Parent

GUIDED PRACTICE

1. **Vocabulary** Tell whether $y = 3x^4$ is an *exponential function*. Explain your answer.

SEE EXAMPLE **1**
p. 738

2. **Physical Science** The function $f(x) = 50{,}000(0.975)^x$, where x represents the underwater depth in meters, models the intensity of light below the water's surface in lumens per square meter. What is the intensity of light 200 meters below the surface? Round your answer to the nearest whole number.

SEE EXAMPLE **2**
p. 739

Tell whether each set of ordered pairs satisfies an exponential function. Explain your answer.

3. $\{(-1, -1), (0, 0), (1, -1), (2, -4)\}$

4. $\{(0, 1), (1, 4), (2, 16), (3, 64)\}$

SEE EXAMPLE **3**
p. 739

Graph each exponential function.

5. $y = 3^x$

6. $y = 5^x$

7. $y = 10(3)^x$

8. $y = 5(2)^x$

SEE EXAMPLE **4**
p. 740

9. $y = -2(3)^x$

10. $y = -4(2)^x$

11. $y = -3(2)^x$

12. $y = 2(3)^x$

SEE EXAMPLE **5**
p. 740

13. $y = -\left(\frac{1}{4}\right)^x$

14. $y = \left(\frac{1}{3}\right)^x$

15. $y = 2\left(\frac{1}{4}\right)^x$

16. $y = -2(0.25)^x$

SEE EXAMPLE **6**
p. 741

17. The function $f(x) = 57.8(1.02)^x$ gives the approximate number of passenger cars, in millions, in the United States x years after 1960. Using this model, in about what year will the number of passenger cars reach 200 million?

PRACTICE AND PROBLEM SOLVING

Independent Practice

For Exercises	See Example
18–20	1
21–24	2
25–27	3
28–30	4
31–33	5
34	6

Extra Practice

Skills Practice p. EP23
Application Practice p. EP34

18. **Sports** If a golf ball is dropped from a height of 27 feet, the function $f(x) = 27\left(\frac{2}{3}\right)^x$ gives the height in feet of each bounce, where x is the bounce number. What will be the height of the 4th bounce?

19. Suppose the depth of a lake can be described by the function $y = 334(0.976)^x$, where x represents the number of weeks from today. Today, the depth of the lake is 334 ft. What will the depth be in 6 weeks? Round your answer to the nearest whole number.

20. **Physical Science** A ball rolling down a slope travels continuously faster. Suppose the function $y = 1.3(1.41)^x$ describes the speed of the ball in inches per minute. How fast will the ball be rolling in 15 minutes? Round your answer to the nearest hundredth.

Tell whether each set of ordered pairs satisfies an exponential function. Explain your answer.

21. $\left\{(-2, 9), (-1, 3), (0, 1), \left(1, \frac{1}{3}\right)\right\}$

22. $\{(-1, 0), (0, 1), (1, 4), (2, 9)\}$

23. $\{(-1, -5), (0, -3), (1, -1), (2, 1)\}$

24. $\{(-3, 6.25), (-2, 12.5), (-1, 25), (0, 50)\}$

Graph each exponential function.

25. $y = 1.5^x$

26. $y = \frac{1}{3}(3)^x$

27. $y = 100(0.7)^x$

28. $y = -2(4)^x$

29. $y = -1(5)^x$

30. $y = -\frac{1}{2}(4)^x$

31. $y = 4\left(\frac{1}{2}\right)^x$

32. $y = -2\left(\frac{1}{3}\right)^x$

33. $y = 0.5(0.25)^x$

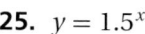

34. Technology Moore's law states that the maximum number of transistors that can fit on a silicon chip doubles every two years. The function $f(x) = 42(1.41)^x$ models the number of transistors, in millions, that can fit on a chip, where x is the number of years since 2000. Predict what year it will be when a chip can hold 1 billion transistors.

35. Multi-Step A computer randomly creates three different functions. The functions are $y = (3.1x + 7)^2$, $y = 4.8(2)^x$, and $y = \frac{1}{5}(6)^x$.

　a. Identify which function or functions are exponential.

　b. Josie input an x-value into one of the exponential functions, and the computer returned a y-value of 38.4. Which function did Josie use?

　c. Evaluate $y = 4.8(2)^x$ for $x = 0$ and $x = 4$

　d. Evaluate $y = \frac{1}{5}(6)^x$ for $x = 0$ and $x = 4$

　e. What can Josie tell about the difference between the graphs of the two exponential functions from the answers to part **c** and **d**?

36. Contests As a promotion, a clothing store draws the name of one of its customers each week. The prize is a coupon for the store. If the winner is not present at the drawing, he or she cannot claim the prize, and the amount of the coupon increases for the following week's drawing. The function $f(x) = 20(1.2)^x$ gives the amount of the coupon in dollars after x weeks of the prize going unclaimed.

　a. What is the amount of the coupon after 2 weeks of the prize going unclaimed?

　b. After how many weeks of the prize going unclaimed will the amount of the coupon be greater than $100?

　c. What is the original amount of the coupon?

　d. Find the percent increase each week.

37. Critical Thinking In the definition of exponential function, the value of b cannot be 1, and the value of a cannot be 0. Why?

 Graphing Calculator Graph each group of functions on the same screen. How are their graphs alike? How are they different?

38. $y = 2^x, y = 3^x, y = 4^x$

39. $y = \left(\frac{1}{2}\right)^x, y = \left(\frac{1}{3}\right)^x, y = \left(\frac{1}{4}\right)^x$

Evaluate each of the following for the given value of x.

40. $f(x) = 4^x; x = 3$

41. $f(x) = -(0.25)^x; x = 1.5$

42. $f(x) = 0.4(10)^x; x = -3$

43. This problem will prepare you for the Concept Connection on page 762.

CONCEPT CONNECTION

　a. The annual tuition at a community college since 2001 is modeled by the equation $C = 2000(1.08)^n$, where C is the tuition cost and n is the number of years since 2001. What was the tuition cost in 2001?

　b. What is the annual percentage of tuition increase?

　c. Find the tuition cost in 2006.

44. Write About It Your employer offers two salary plans. With plan A, your salary is given by $y = 10{,}000(2x)$, where x is the number of years you have worked for the company. With plan B, your salary is given by $y = 10{,}000(2)^x$. Which plan would you choose? Why?

Multiple Choice For Exercises 45–47, choose the best answer.

45. Which graph shows an exponential function?

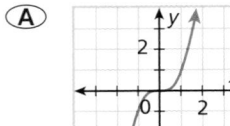

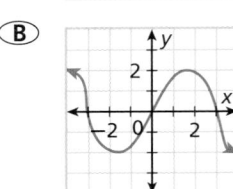
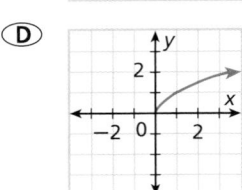

46. The function $f(x) = 15(1.4)^x$ represents the area in square inches of a photograph after it has been enlarged x times by a factor of 140%. What is the area of the photograph after it has been enlarged 4 times?

(A) 5.6 square inches   (C) 41.16 square inches

(B) 57.624 square inches   (D) 560 square inches

47. If n represents the stage number, which expression could represent the number of squares in the nth stage?

 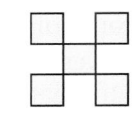 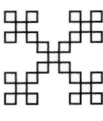

Stage 0   Stage 1   Stage 2

(A) $5n$ (B) $2.5 \cdot 2^n$ (C) 25^{n-1} (D) 5^n

CHALLENGE AND EXTEND

Solve each equation. Check your answer.

48. $4^x = 64$ **49.** $\left(\frac{1}{3}\right)^x = \frac{1}{27}$ **50.** $2^x = \frac{1}{16}$

 51. Reasoning Graph the following functions: $y = 2(2)^x$, $y = 3(2)^x$, $y = -2(2)^x$. Then use inductive reasoning to make a conjecture about the relationship between the value of a and the y-intercept of $y = ab^x$.

 SPIRAL STANDARDS REVIEW    4.0, 11.0, 14.0

52. The average of Roger's three test scores must be at least 90 to earn an A in his science class. Roger has scored 88 and 89 on his first two tests. Write and solve an inequality to find what he must score on the third test to earn an A. *(Lesson 3-4)*

Find the missing term in each perfect-square trinomial. *(Lesson 8-5)*

53. $x^2 + 10x + \blacksquare$ **54.** $4x^2 + \blacksquare + 64$ **55.** $\blacksquare + 42x + 49$

56. Solve $x^2 + 4x = 5$ by completing the square. Check your answer. *(Lesson 9-7)*

Changing Dimensions

What happens to the volume of a three-dimensional figure when you repeatedly double the dimensions?

California Standards

Reinforcement of 7MG2.3 Compute the length of the perimeter, the surface area of the faces and **the volume of a three-dimensional object** built from rectangular solids. **Understand that when the lengths of all dimensions are multiplied by a scale factor,** the surface area is multiplied by the square of the scale factor and **the volume is multiplied by the cube of the scale factor.**

Recall these formulas for the volumes of common three-dimensional figures.

Cube $V = s^3$

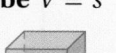

Rectangular Prism $V = \ell w h$

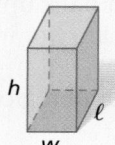

Pyramid $V = \frac{1}{3}(\text{area of base}) \cdot h$

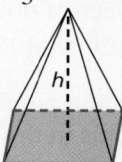

Base

Changing the dimensions of three-dimensional figures results in geometric sequences.

Example

Find the volume of a cube with a side length of 3 cm. Double the side length and find the new volume. Repeat two more times. Show the patterns for the side lengths and volumes as geometric sequences. Identify the common ratios.

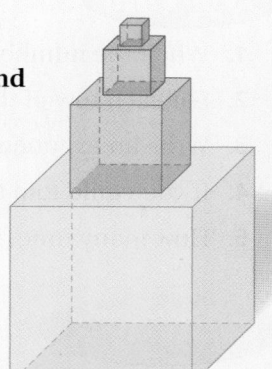

Cube	Side Length (cm)	Volume (cm³)
1	3	27
2	6	216
3	12	1,728
4	24	13,824

(×2 between side lengths; ×8 between volumes)

The side lengths and the volumes form geometric sequences. The sequence of the side lengths has a common ratio of 2. The sequence of the volumes has a common ratio of 2^3, or 8.

The patterns in the example above are a specific instance of a general rule.

> When the dimensions of a solid figure are multiplied by k, the volume of the figure is multiplied by k^3.

Try This

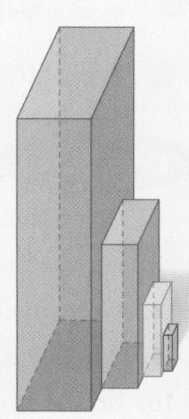

1. The large rectangular prism at right is 8 in. wide, 16 in. long, and 32 in. tall. The dimensions are multiplied by $\frac{1}{2}$ to create each next smaller prism. Show the patterns for the dimensions and the volumes as geometric sequences. Identify the common ratios.

2. A pyramid has a height of 8 cm and a square base of 3 cm on each edge. Triple the dimensions two times. Show the patterns for the dimensions and the volumes as geometric sequences. Identify the common ratios.

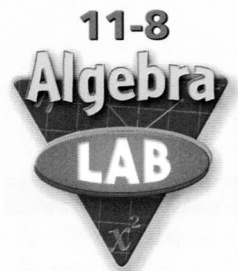

11-8
Algebra LAB

Model Growth and Decay

You can fold and cut paper to
model quantities that increase
or decrease exponentially.

Use with Lesson 11-8

California Standards

2.0 Students understand and use such operations as taking the opposite, finding the reciprocal, taking a root, and raising to a fractional power. **They understand and use the rules of exponents.**

Activity 1

1 Copy the table at right.

2 Fold a piece of notebook paper in half. Then open it back up. Count the number of regions created by the fold. Record your answer in the table.

3 Now fold the paper in half twice. Record the number of regions created by the folds in the table.

4 Repeat this process for 3, 4, and 5 folds.

Folds	Regions
0	1
1	
2	
3	
4	
5	

Try This

1. When the number of folds increases by 1, the number of regions ____?____ .

2. For each row of the table, write the number of regions as a power of 2.

3. Write an exponential expression for the number of regions formed by n folds.

4. If you could fold the paper 8 times, how many regions would be formed?

5. How many times would you have to fold the paper to make 512 regions?

Activity 2

1 Copy the table at right.

2 Begin with a square piece of paper. The area of the paper is 1 square unit. Cut the paper in half. Each piece has an area of $\frac{1}{2}$ square unit. Record the result in the table.

3 Cut one of those pieces in half again, and record the area of one of the new, smaller pieces in the table.

4 Repeat this process for 3, 4, and 5 cuts.

Cuts	Area
0	1
1	
2	
3	
4	
5	

Try This

6. When the number of cuts increases by 1, the area ____?____ .

7. For each row of the table, write the area as a power of 2.

8. Write an exponential expression for the area after n cuts.

9. What would be the area after 7 cuts?

10. How many cuts would you have to make to get an area of $\frac{1}{256}$ square unit?

11-8 Exponential Growth and Decay

Vocabulary
exponential growth
compound interest
exponential decay
half-life

Why learn this?

Exponential growth and decay describe many real-world situations, such as the value of an investment. (See Example 1.)

Exponential growth occurs when a quantity increases by the same rate *r* in each time period *t*. When this happens, the value of the quantity at any given time can be calculated as a function of the rate and the original amount.

Exponential Growth

An exponential growth function has the form $y = a(1 + r)^t$, where $a > 0$.

   y represents the final amount.

   a represents the original amount.

   r represents the rate of growth expressed as a decimal.

   t represents time.

EXAMPLE 1 **Exponential Growth**

Helpful Hint

In Example 1, round to the nearest hundredth because the problem deals with money. This means you are rounding to the nearest cent.

The original value of an investment is $1400, and the value increases by 9% each year. Write an exponential growth function to model this situation. Then find the value of the investment in 25 years.

Step 1 Write the exponential growth function for this situation.

$y = a(1 + r)^t$ *Write the formula.*

$= 1400(1 + 0.09)^t$ *Substitute 1400 for a and 0.09 for r.*

$= 1400(1.09)^t$ *Simplify.*

Step 2 Find the value in 25 years.

$y = 1400(1.09)^t$

$= 1400(1.09)^{25}$ *Substitute 25 for t.*

$\approx 12{,}072.31$ *Use a calculator and round to the nearest hundredth.*

The value of the investment in 25 years is $12,072.31.

 **1.** An investment is increasing in value at a rate of 8% per year, and its value in 2000 was $1200. Write an exponential growth function to model this situation. Then find the investment's value in 2006.

A common application of exponential growth is *compound interest*. Recall that simple interest is earned or paid only on the principal. **Compound interest** is interest earned or paid on *both* the principal and previously earned interest.

Compound Interest

$$A = P\left(1 + \frac{r}{n}\right)^{nt}$$

A represents the balance after *t* years.

P represents the principal, or original amount.

r represents the annual interest rate expressed as a decimal.

n represents the number of times interest is compounded per year.

t represents time in years.

EXAMPLE 2 *Finance Application*

Write a compound interest function to model each situation. Then find the balance after the given number of years.

A   **$1000 invested at a rate of 3% compounded quarterly; 5 years**

Step 1   Write the compound interest function for this situation.

$A = P\left(1 + \frac{r}{n}\right)^{nt}$ *Write the formula.*

$= 1000\left(1 + \frac{0.03}{4}\right)^{4t}$ *Substitute 1000 for P, 0.03 for r, and 4 for n.*

$= 1000(1.0075)^{4t}$ *Simplify.*

Step 2   Find the balance after 5 years.

$A = 1000(1.0075)^{4(5)}$ *Substitute 5 for t.*

$= 1000(1.0075)^{20}$

≈ 1161.18 *Use a calculator and round to the nearest hundredth.*

The balance after 5 years is $1161.18.

Reading Math

For compound interest,
- *annually* means "once per year" ($n = 1$).
- *quarterly* means "4 times per year" ($n = 4$).
- *monthly* means "12 times per year" ($n = 12$).

B   **$18,000 invested at a rate of 4.5% compounded annually; 6 years**

Step 1   Write the compound interest function for this situation.

$A = P\left(1 + \frac{r}{n}\right)^{nt}$ *Write the formula.*

$= 18{,}000\left(1 + \frac{0.045}{1}\right)^{t}$ *Substitute 18,000 for P, 0.045 for r, and 1 for n.*

$= 18{,}000(1.045)^{t}$ *Simplify.*

Step 2   Find the balance after 6 years.

$A = 18{,}000(1.045)^{6}$ *Substitute 6 for t.*

$\approx 23{,}440.68$ *Use a calculator and round to the nearest hundredth.*

The balance after 6 years is $23,440.68.

 **Write a compound interest function to model each situation. Then find the balance after the given number of years.**

2a. $1200 invested at a rate of 3.5% compounded quarterly; 4 years

2b. $4000 invested at a rate of 3% compounded monthly; 8 years

Exponential decay occurs when a quantity decreases by the same rate r in each time period t. Just like exponential growth, the value of the quantity at any given time can be calculated by using the rate and the original amount.

> ## Exponential Decay
>
> An exponential decay function has the form $y = a(1 - r)^t$, where $a > 0$.
>
> y represents the final amount.
>
> a represents the original amount.
>
> r represents the rate of decay as a decimal.
>
> t represents time.

Notice an important difference between exponential growth functions and exponential decay functions. For exponential growth, the value inside the parentheses will be greater than 1 because r is added to 1. For exponential decay, the value inside the parentheses will be less than 1 because r is subtracted from 1.

EXAMPLE 3 Exponential Decay

The population of a town is decreasing at a rate of 1% per year. In 2000 there were 1300 people. Write an exponential decay function to model this situation. Then find the population in 2008.

Step 1 Write the exponential decay function for this situation.

$y = a(1 - r)^t$ *Write the formula.*

$\quad = 1300(1 - 0.01)^t$ *Substitute 1300 for a and 0.01 for r.*

$\quad = 1300(0.99)^t$ *Simplify.*

Step 2 Find the population in 2008.

$y = 1300(0.99)^8$ *Substitute 8 for t.*

$\quad \approx 1200$ *Use a calculator and round to the nearest whole number.*

The population in 2008 will be approximately 1200 people.

3. The fish population in a local stream is decreasing at a rate of 3% per year. The original population was 48,000. Write an exponential decay function to model this situation. Then find the population after 7 years.

> **Helpful Hint**
>
> In Example 3, round your answer to the nearest whole number because there can only be a whole number of people.

A common application of exponential decay is *half-life*. The **half-life** of a substance is the time it takes for one-half of the substance to decay into another substance.

> ## Half-life
>
> $A = P(0.5)^t$
>
> A represents the final amount.
>
> P represents the original amount.
>
> t represents the number of half-lives in a given time period.

EXAMPLE 4 *Science Application*

Fluorine-20 has a half-life of 11 seconds.

A **Find the amount of fluorine-20 left from a 40-gram sample after 44 seconds.**

> **Step 1** Find t, the number of half-lives in the given time period.
>
> $$\frac{44 \text{ s}}{11 \text{ s}} = 4$$ *Divide the time period by the half-life. The value of t is 4.*
>
> **Step 2** $A = P(0.5)^t$ *Write the formula.*
>
> $\quad\quad = 40(0.5)^4$ *Substitute 40 for P and 4 for t.*
>
> $\quad\quad = 2.5$ *Use a calculator.*
>
> There are 2.5 grams of fluorine-20 remaining after 44 seconds.

B **Find the amount of fluorine-20 left from a 40-gram sample after 2.2 minutes. Round your answer to the nearest hundredth.**

> **Step 1** Find t, the number of half-lives in the given time period.
>
> $2.2(60) = 132$ *Find the number of seconds in 2.2 minutes.*
>
> $\frac{132 \text{ s}}{11 \text{ s}} = 12$ *Divide the time period by the half-life. The value of t is $\frac{132}{11} = 12$.*
>
> **Step 2** $A = P(0.5)^t$ *Write the formula.*
>
> $\quad\quad = 40(0.5)^{12}$ *Substitute 40 for P and 12 for t.*
>
> $\quad\quad \approx 0.01$ *Use a calculator. Round to the nearest hundredth.*
>
> There is about 0.01 gram of fluorine-20 remaining after 2.2 minutes.

 **CHECK IT OUT!**

4a. Cesium-137 has a half-life of 30 years. Find the amount of cesium-137 left from a 100-milligram sample after 180 years.

4b. Bismuth-210 has a half-life of 5 days. Find the amount of bismuth-210 left from a 100-gram sample after 5 weeks. (*Hint:* Change 5 weeks to days.)

THINK AND DISCUSS

1. Describe three real-world situations that can be described by exponential growth or exponential decay functions.

2. The population of a town after t years can be modeled by $P = 1000(1.02)^t$. Is the population increasing or decreasing? By what percentage rate?

3. An exponential function is a function of the form $y = ab^x$. Explain why both exponential growth functions and exponential decay functions are exponential functions.

Know it!
Note

4. GET ORGANIZED Copy and complete the graphic organizer.

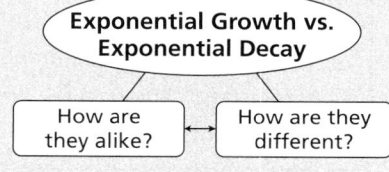

Exercises

California
Standards Practice
Preview of Algebra II ⟶ 12.0;
1A25.2

GUIDED PRACTICE

1. **Vocabulary** The function $y = 0.68(2)^x$ is an example of _____?_____.
   (*exponential growth* or *exponential decay*)

SEE EXAMPLE **1**
p. 747

Write an exponential growth function to model each situation. Then find the value of the function after the given amount of time.

2. The cost of tuition at a college is $12,000 and is increasing at a rate of 6% per year; 4 years.

3. The number of student-athletes at a local high school is 300 and is increasing at a rate of 8% per year; 5 years.

SEE EXAMPLE **2**
p. 748

Write a compound interest function to model each situation. Then find the balance after the given number of years.

4. $1500 invested at a rate of 3.5% compounded annually; 4 years

5. $4200 invested at a rate of 2.8% compounded quarterly; 6 years

SEE EXAMPLE **3**
p. 749

Write an exponential decay function to model each situation. Then find the value of the function after the given amount of time.

6. The value of a car is $18,000 and is depreciating at a rate of 12% per year; 10 years.

7. The amount (to the nearest hundredth) of a 10-mg dose of a certain antibiotic decreases in your bloodstream at a rate of 16% per hour; 4 hours.

SEE EXAMPLE **4**
p. 750

8. Bismuth-214 has a half-life of approximately 20 minutes. Find the amount of bismuth-214 left from a 30-gram sample after 1 hour.

9. Mendelevium-258 has a half-life of approximately 52 days. Find the amount of mendelevium-258 left from a 44-gram sample after 156 days.

PRACTICE AND PROBLEM SOLVING

Independent Practice

For Exercises	See Example
10–13	1
14–17	2
18–19	3
20	4

Extra Practice

Skills Practice p. EP23

Application Practice p. EP34

Write an exponential growth function to model each situation. Then find the value of the function after the given amount of time.

10. Annual sales for a company are $149,000 and are increasing at a rate of 6% per year; 7 years.

11. The population of a small town is 1600 and is increasing at a rate of 3% per year; 10 years.

12. A new savings account starts at $700 and increases at 1.2% yearly; 8 years.

13. Membership of a local club grows at a rate of 7.8% yearly and currently has 30 members; 6 years.

Write a compound interest function to model each situation. Then find the balance after the given number of years.

14. $28,000 invested at a rate of 4% compounded annually; 5 years

15. $7000 invested at a rate of 3% compounded quarterly; 10 years

16. $3500 invested at a rate of 1.8% compounded monthly; 4 years

17. $12,000 invested at a rate of 2.6% compounded annually; 15 years

Write an exponential decay function to model each situation. Then find the value of the function after the given amount of time.

18. The population of a town is 18,000 and is decreasing at a rate of 2% per year; 6 years.

19. The value of a book is $58 and decreases at a rate of 10% per year; 8 years.

20. The half-life of bromine-82 is approximately 36 hours. Find the amount of bromine-82 left from an 80-gram sample after 6 days.

Identify each of the following functions as exponential growth or decay. Then give the rate of growth or decay as a percent.

21. $y = 3(1.61)^t$ 22. $y = 39(0.098)^t$ 23. $y = a\left(\dfrac{2}{3}\right)^t$ 24. $y = a\left(\dfrac{3}{2}\right)^t$

25. $y = a(1.1)^t$ 26. $y = a(0.8)^t$ 27. $y = a\left(\dfrac{5}{4}\right)^t$ 28. $y = a\left(\dfrac{1}{2}\right)^t$

Write an exponential growth or decay function to model each situation. Then find the value of the function after the given amount of time.

29. The population of a country is 58,000,000 and grows by 0.1% per year; 3 years.

30. An antique car is worth $32,000, and its value grows by 7% per year; 5 years.

31. An investment of $8200 loses value at a rate of 2% per year; 7 years.

32. A new car is worth $25,000, and its value decreases by 15% each year; 6 years.

33. The student enrollment in a local high school is 970 students and increases by 1.2% per year; 5 years.

34. **Archaeology** Carbon-14 dating is a way to determine the age of very old organic objects. Carbon-14 has a half-life of about 5700 years. An organic object with $\frac{1}{2}$ as much carbon-14 as its living counterpart died 5700 years ago. In 1999, archaeologists discovered the oldest bridge in England near Testwood, Hampshire. Carbon dating of the wood revealed that the bridge was 3500 years old. Suppose that when the bridge was built, the wood contained 15 grams of carbon-14. How much carbon-14 would it have contained when it was found by the archaeologists? Round to the nearest hundredth.

A computer-generated image of what the bridge at Testwood might have looked like

35. **///ERROR ANALYSIS///** Two students were asked to find the value of a $1000-item after 3 years. The item was depreciating (losing value) at a rate of 40% per year. Which is incorrect? Explain the error.

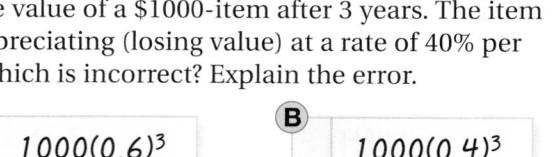

A
| $1000(0.6)^3$ |
| $216 |

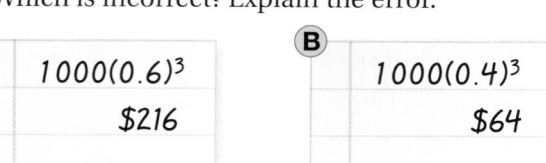

B
| $1000(0.4)^3$ |
| $64 |

36. **Critical Thinking** The value of a certain car can be modeled by the function $y = 20,000(0.84)^t$, where t is time in years. Will the value ever be zero? Explain.

37. The value of a rare baseball card increases every year at a rate of 4%. Today, the card is worth $300. The owner expects to sell the card as soon as the value is over $600. How many years will the owner wait before selling the card? Round your answer to the nearest whole number.

Atlantic Ocean
North Sea
England
Testwood

38. This problem will prepare you for the Concept Connection on page 762.

   a. The annual tuition at a prestigious university was $20,000 in 2002. It generally increases at a rate of 9% each year. Write a function to describe the cost as a function of the number of years since 2002. Use 2002 as year zero when writing the function rule.

   b. What do you predict the cost of tuition will be in 2008?

   c. Use a table of values to find the first year that the cost of the tuition will be more than twice the cost in 2002.

39. Multi-Step At bank A, $600 is invested with an interest rate of 5% compounded annually. At bank B, $500 is invested with an interest rate of 6% compounded quarterly. Which account will have a larger balance after 10 years? 20 years?

40. Estimation The graph shows the decay of 100 grams of sodium-24. Use the graph to estimate the number of hours it will take the sample to decay to 10 grams. Then estimate the half-life of sodium-24.

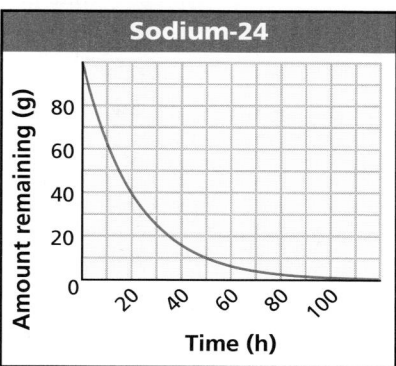

41. Graphing Calculator Use a graphing calculator to graph $y = 10(1 + r)^x$ for $r = 10\%$ and $r = 20\%$. Compare the two graphs. How does the value of r affect the graphs?

42. Write About It Write a real-world situation that could be modeled by $y = 400(1.08)^t$.

43. Write About It Write a real-world situation that could be modeled by $y = 800(0.96)^t$.

44. Critical Thinking The amount of water in a container doubles every minute. After 6 minutes, the container is full. Your friend says it was half full after 3 minutes. Do you agree? Why or why not?

Multiple Choice For Exercises 45–47, choose the best answer.

45. A population of 500 is decreasing by 1% per year. Which function models this situation?

   Ⓐ $y = 500(0.01)^t$ Ⓑ $y = 500(0.1)^t$ Ⓒ $y = 500(0.9)^t$ Ⓓ $y = 500(0.99)^t$

46. Which function is NOT an exponential decay model?

   Ⓐ $y = 5\left(\dfrac{1}{3}\right)^x$ Ⓑ $y = -5\left(\dfrac{1}{3}\right)^x$ Ⓒ $y = 5(3)^{-x}$ Ⓓ $y = 5\left(3^{-1}\right)^x$

47. Stephanie wants to save $1000 for a down payment on a car that she wants to buy in 3 years. She opens a savings account that pays 5% interest compounded annually. About how much should Stephanie deposit now to have enough money for the down payment in 3 years?

   Ⓐ $295   Ⓑ $333   Ⓒ $500   Ⓓ $865

48. Short Response In 2000, the population of a town was 1000 and was growing at a rate of 5% per year.

   a. Write an exponential growth function to model this situation.

   b. In what year will the population be 1300? Show how you found your answer.

CHALLENGE AND EXTEND

49. You invest $700 at a rate of 6% compounded quarterly. Use a graph to estimate the number of years it will take for your investment to increase to $2300.

50. Omar invested $500 at a rate of 4% compounded annually. How long will it take for Omar's money to double? How long would it take if the interest were 8% compounded annually?

51. An 80-gram sample of a radioactive substance decayed to 10 grams after 300 minutes. Find the half-life of the substance.

52. Praseodymium-143 has a half-life of 2 weeks. The original measurement for the mass of a sample was lost. After 6 weeks, 15 grams of praseodymium-143 remain. How many grams was the original sample?

53. Phillip invested some money in a business 8 years ago. Since then, his investment has grown at an average rate of 1.3% compounded quarterly. Phillip's investment is now worth $250,000. How much was his original investment? Round your answer to the nearest dollar.

54. Personal Finance Anna has a balance of $200 that she owes on her credit card. She plans to make a $30 payment each month. There is also a 1.5% finance charge (interest) on the remaining balance each month. Copy and complete the table to answer the questions below. You may add more rows to the table as necessary.

Month	Balance ($)	Monthly Payment ($)	Remaining Balance ($)	1.5% Finance Charge ($)	New Balance ($)
1	200	30	170	2.55	172.55
2	172.55	30			
3		30			
4		30			

a. How many months will it take Anna to pay the entire balance?

b. By the time Anna pays the entire balance, how much total interest will she have paid?

 SPIRAL STANDARDS REVIEW 🔑 2.0

Write and solve a proportion for each situation. *(Lesson 2-5)*

55. A daffodil that is 1.2 feet tall casts a shadow that is 1.5 feet long. At the same time, a nearby lamppost casts a shadow that is 20 feet long. The daffodil's height and its shadow are in the same proportion as the lamppost and its shadow. What is the height of the the lamppost?

56. A green rectangular throw pillow measures 20 inches long by 10 inches wide. A proportionally similar yellow throw pillow is 12 inches long. What is the width of the yellow pillow?

Simplify. *(Lesson 7-3)*

57. $\left(x^5\right)^4$

58. $\left(c^6\right)^3 \cdot \left(c^2\right)^{-3}$

59. $pq^7 \cdot p^3q \cdot p^2q^8$

60. The function $f(x) = 0.10(2)^x$ gives the total fine in dollars for a library book that is x days overdue. What is the fine if a book is 4 days overdue? How many days overdue is a book if the fine is $12.80? *(Lesson 11-7)*

Linear, Quadratic, and Exponential Models

California Standards

Preview of Algebra II

🔑 **12.0 Students** know the laws of fractional exponents, **understand exponential functions,** and use these functions in problems involving exponential growth and decay.

Extension of 🔑 1A7.0 Students verify that a point lies on a line, given an equation of the line. **Students are able to derive linear equations by using the point-slope formula.**

Why learn this?

Different situations in sports can be described by linear, quadratic, or exponential models.

The sports data below show three kinds of variable relationships—linear, quadratic, and exponential.

Linear	Quadratic	Exponential

Training Heart Rate

Age (yr)	Beats/min
20	170
30	161.5
40	153
50	144.5

Volleyball Height

Time (s)	Height (ft)
0.4	10.44
0.8	12.76
1	12
1.2	9.96

Volleyball Tournament

Round	Teams Left
1	16
2	8
3	4
4	2

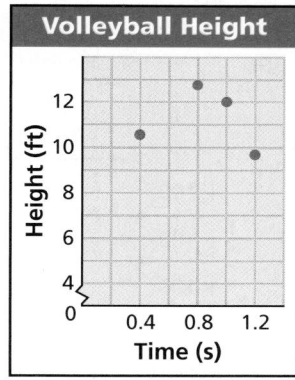

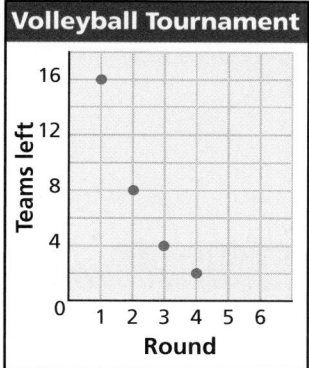

In the real world, people often gather data and then must decide what kind of relationship (if any) they think best describes their data.

EXAMPLE 1 Graphing Data to Choose a Model

Graph the data set. Which kind of model best describes the data?

°C	0	5	10	15	20
°F	32	41	50	59	68

Plot the data points and connect them.
The data appear to be linear.

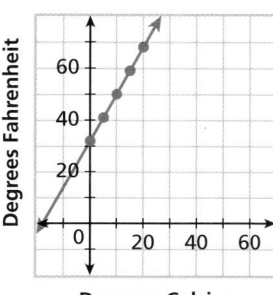

Celsius to Fahrenheit

Graph each data set. Which kind of model best describes the data?

1a. $\{(-3, 0.30), (-2, 0.44), (0, 1), (1, 1.5), (2, 2.25), (3, 3.38)\}$

1b. $\{(-3, -14), (-2, -9), (-1, -6), (0, -5), (1, -6), (2, -9), (3, -14)\}$

Another way to decide which kind of relationship (if any) best describes a data set is to use patterns. Look at a table or list of ordered pairs in which there is a constant change in *x*-values.

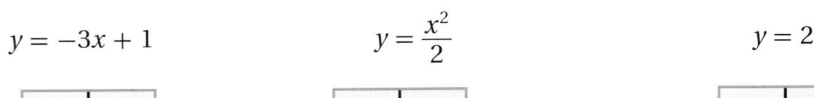

$$y = -3x + 1$$

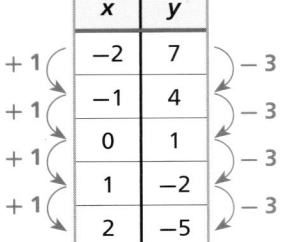

$$y = \frac{x^2}{2}$$

$$y = 2^x$$

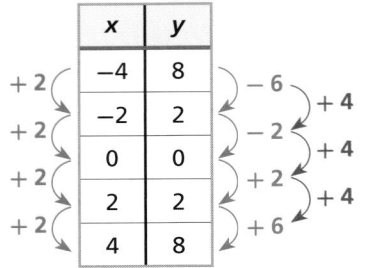

Linear functions have constant **first** differences.

Quadratic functions have constant **second** differences.

Exponential functions have a constant ratio.

EXAMPLE 2 Using Patterns to Choose a Model

Look for a pattern to determine which kind of model best describes the data.

 A

Height of Bridge Suspension Cables	
Cable's Distance from Tower (ft)	Cable's Height (ft)
0	400
100	256
200	144
300	64

+ 100, + 100, + 100 (distance)
− 144, − 112, − 80 (first differences)
+ 32, + 32 (second differences)

For every constant change in distance of +100 feet, there is a constant second difference of +32.

The data appear to be quadratic.

Caution!

When solving problems like those in Example 2, be sure there is a constant change in the *x*-values.

B

Value of a Car	
Car's Age (yr)	Value ($)
0	20,000
1	17,000
2	14,450
3	12,282.50

+ 1, + 1, + 1 (age)
× 0.85, × 0.85, × 0.85

For every constant change in age of +1 year, there is a constant ratio of 0.85.

The data appear to be exponential.

2. Look for a pattern in the data set $\{(-2, 10), (-1, 1), (0, -2), (1, 1), (2, 10)\}$ to determine which kind of model best describes the data.

After deciding which model best fits the data, you can write a function. Recall the general forms of linear, quadratic, and exponential functions.

General Forms of Functions

LINEAR	QUADRATIC	EXPONENTIAL
$y = mx + b$	$y = ax^2 + bx + c$	$y = ab^x$

EXAMPLE 3

PROBLEM SOLVING

Problem-Solving Application

Use the data in the table to describe how the ladybug population is changing. Then write a function that models the data. Use your function to predict the ladybug population after one year.

Ladybug Population	
Time (mo)	Ladybugs
0	10
1	30
2	90
3	270

1 Understand the Problem

The **answer** will have three parts—a description, a function, and a prediction.

2 Make a Plan

Determine whether the data is linear, quadratic, or exponential. Use the general form to write a function. Then use the function to find the population after one year.

3 Solve

Step 1 Describe the situation in words.

Ladybug Population	
Time (mo)	Ladybugs
0	10
1	30
2	90
3	270

$+1$ $+1$ $+1$ $\times 3$ $\times 3$ $\times 3$

Each month, the ladybug population is multiplied by 3. In other words, the population triples each month.

Step 2 Write the function.

There is a constant ratio of 3. The data appear to be exponential.

$y = ab^x$ *Write the general form of an exponential function.*

$y = a(3)^x$ *Substitute the constant ratio, 3, for b.*

$10 = a(3)^0$ *Choose an ordered pair from the table, such as (0, 10). Substitute for x and y.*

$10 = a(1)$ *Simplify. $3^0 = 1$*

$10 = a$ *The value of a is 10.*

$y = 10(3)^x$ *Substitute 10 for a in $y = a(3)^x$.*

Helpful Hint

You can choose any given ordered pair to substitute for *x* and *y*. However, choosing an ordered pair that contains 0 will often result in easier calculations.

Step 3 Predict the ladybug population after one year.

$$y = 10(3)^x$$ *Write the function.*

$$= 10(3)^{12}$$ *Substitute 12 for x (1 year = 12 mo).*

$$= 5,314,410$$ *Use a calculator.*

There will be 5,314,410 ladybugs after one year.

 Look Back

You chose the ordered pair $(0, 10)$ to write the function. Check that every other ordered pair in the table satisfies your function.

$y = 10(3)^x$	
30	$10(3)^1$
30	$10(3)$
30	30 ✓

$y = 10(3)^x$	
90	$10(3)^2$
90	$10(9)$
90	90 ✓

$y = 10(3)^x$	
270	$10(3)^3$
270	$10(27)$
270	270 ✓

 **3.** Use the data in the table to describe how the oven temperature is changing. Then write a function that models the data. Use your function to predict the temperature after 1 hour.

Oven Temperature				
Time (min)	0	10	20	30
Temperature (°F)	375	325	275	225

Student to Student

Checking Units

I used to get a lot of answers wrong because of the units. If a question asked for the value of something after 1 year, I would always just substitute 1 into the function.

I finally figured out that you have to check what x is. If x represents months and you're trying to find the value after 1 year, then you have to substitute 12, not 1, because there are 12 months in a year.

Michael Gambhir
Warren High School

THINK AND DISCUSS

1. Do you think that every data set will be able to be modeled by a linear, quadratic, or exponential function? Why or why not?

2. In Example 3, is it certain that there will be 5,314,410 ladybugs after one year? Explain.

 **3. GET ORGANIZED** Copy and complete the graphic organizer. In each box, list some characteristics and sketch a graph of each type of model.

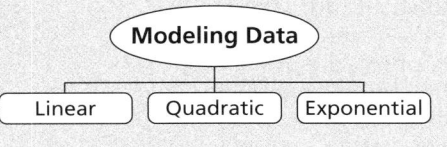

11-9

Exercises

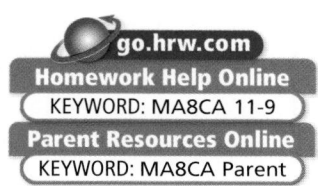

California
Standards Practice
Preview of Algebra II ← 22.0;
Extension of ← 1A7.0; 25.2

go.hrw.com
Homework Help Online
KEYWORD: MA8CA 11-9
Parent Resources Online
KEYWORD: MA8CA Parent

GUIDED PRACTICE

SEE EXAMPLE 1
p. 755

Graph each data set. Which kind of model best describes the data?

1. $\{(-1, 4), (-2, 0.8), (0, 20), (1, 100), (-3, 0.16)\}$

2. $\{(0, 3), (1, 9), (2, 11), (3, 9), (4, 3)\}$

3. $\{(2, -7), (-2, -9), (0, -8), (4, -6), (6, -5)\}$

SEE EXAMPLE 2
p. 756

Look for a pattern in each data set to determine which kind of model best describes the data.

4. $\{(-2, 1), (-1, 2.5), (0, 3), (1, 2.5), (2, 1)\}$

5. $\{(-2, 0.75), (-1, 1.5), (0, 3), (1, 6), (2, 12)\}$

6. $\{(-2, 2), (-1, 4), (0, 6), (1, 8), (2, 10)\}$

SEE EXAMPLE 3
p. 757

7. Consumer Economics Use the data in the table to describe the cost of grapes. Then write a function that models the data. Use your function to predict the cost of 6 pounds of grapes.

Total Cost of Grapes				
Amount (lb)	1	2	3	4
Cost ($)	1.79	3.58	5.37	7.16

PRACTICE AND PROBLEM SOLVING

Independent Practice

For Exercises	See Example
8–10	1
11–13	2
14	3

Graph each data set. Which kind of model best describes the data?

8. $\{(-3, -5), (-2, -8), (-1, -9), (0, -8), (1, -5), (2, 0), (3, 7)\}$

9. $\{(-3, -1), (-2, 0), (-1, 1), (0, 2), (1, 3), (2, 4), (3, 5)\}$

10. $\{(0, 0.1), (2, 0.9), (3, 2.7), (4, 8.1)\}$

Extra Practice
Skills Practice p. EP23
Application Practice p. EP34

Look for a pattern in each data set to determine which kind of model best describes the data.

11. $\{(-2, 5), (-1, 4), (0, 3), (1, 2), (2, 1)\}$

12. $\{(-2, 12), (-1, 15), (0, 16), (1, 15), (2, 12)\}$

13. $\{(-2, 8), (-1, 4), (0, 2), (1, 1), (2, 0.5)\}$

14. Business Use the data in the table to describe how the company's sales are changing. Then write a function that models the data. Use your function to predict the amount of sales after 10 years.

Company Sales				
Year	0	1	2	3
Sales ($)	25,000	30,000	36,000	43,200

15. Multi-Step Jay's hair grows about 6 inches each year. Write a function that describes the length ℓ in inches that Jay's hair will grow for each year k. Which kind of model best describes the function?

Tell which kind of model best describes each situation.

16. The height of a plant at weekly intervals over the last 6 weeks was 1 inches, 1.5 inches, 2 inches, 2.5 inches, 3 inches., and 3.5 inches.

17. The number of games a baseball player played in the last four years was 162, 162, 162, and 162.

18. The height of a ball in a certain time interval was recorded as 30.64 feet, 30.96 feet, 31 feet, 30.96 feet, and 30.64 feet.

Write a function to model each set of data.

19.
x	−1	0	1	2	4
y	0.05	0.2	0.8	3.2	51.2

20.
x	−2	0	2	4	8
y	5	4	3	2	0

Tell which kind of model best describes each graph.

21.
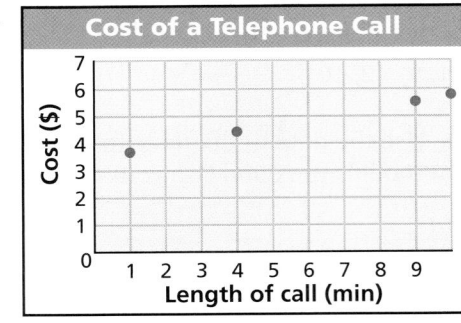

22.
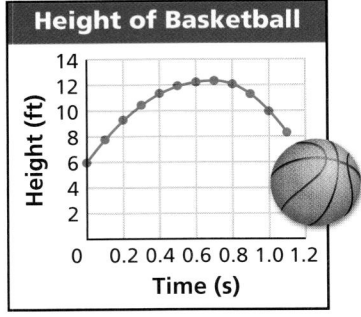

23. **Write About It** Write a set of data that you could model with an exponential function. Explain why the exponential model would work.

24. /// **ERROR ANALYSIS** /// A student concluded that the data set would best be modeled by a quadratic function. Explain the student's error.

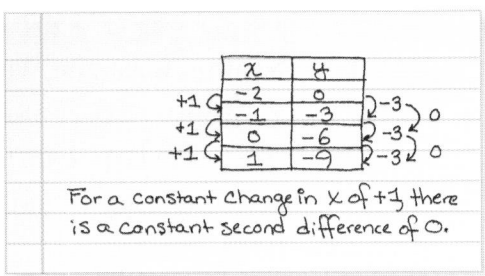

25. **Critical Thinking** Sometimes the graphs of quadratic data and exponential data can look very similar. Describe how you can tell them apart.

CONCEPT CONNECTION

26. This problem will prepare you for the Concept Connection on page 762.
   a. Examine the two models that represent annual tuition for two colleges. Describe each model as linear, quadratic, or exponential.
   b. Write a function rule for each model.
   c. Both models have the same values for 2004. What does this mean?
   d. Why do both models have the same value for year 1?

Years After 2004	Tuition at College 1 ($)	Tuition at College 2 ($)
0	2000.00	2000.00
1	2200.00	2200.00
2	2400.00	2420.00
3	2600.00	2662.00
4	2800.00	2928.20

Multiple Choice For Exercises 27–29, choose the best answer.

27. Which function best models the data: $\{(-4, -2), (-2, -1), (0, 0), (2, 1), (4, 2)\}$?

　Ⓐ $y = \left(\dfrac{1}{2}\right)^x$　　　　Ⓑ $y = \dfrac{1}{2}x^2$　　　　Ⓒ $y = \dfrac{1}{2}x$　　　　Ⓓ $y = \left(\dfrac{1}{2}x\right)^2$

28. A city's population is increasing at a rate of 2% per year. Which type of model describes this situation?

　Ⓐ Exponential　　Ⓑ Quadratic　　Ⓒ Linear　　Ⓓ None of these

29. Which data set is best modeled by a linear function?

　Ⓐ $\{(-2, 0), (-1, 2), (0, -4), (1, -1), (2, 2)\}$

　Ⓑ $\{(-2, 2), (-1, 4), (0, 6), (1, 16), (2, 32)\}$

　Ⓒ $\{(-2, 2), (-1, 4), (0, 6), (1, 8), (2, 10)\}$

　Ⓓ $\{(-2, 0), (-1, 5), (0, 7), (1, 5), (2, 0)\}$

CHALLENGE AND EXTEND

30. **Finance** An accountant estimates that a certain new automobile worth $18,000 will lose value at a rate of 16% per year.

　a. Make a table that shows the worth of the car for years 0, 1, 2, 3, and 4. What is the real-world meaning of year 0?

　b. Which type of model best represents the data in your table? Explain.

　c. Write a function for your data.

　d. What is the value of the car after $5\frac{1}{2}$ years?

　e. What is the value of the car after 8 years?

31. **Pet Care** The table shows general guidelines for the weight of a Great Dane at various ages.

　a. None of the three models in this lesson—linear, quadratic, or exponential—fits this data exactly. Which of these is the *best* model for the data? Explain your choice.

　b. What would you predict for the weight of a Great Dane who is 1 year old?

　c. Do you think you could use your model to find the weight of a Great Dane at any age? Why or why not?

Great Dane	
Age (mo)	Weight (kg)
2	12
4	23
6	33
8	40
10	45

SPIRAL STANDARDS REVIEW

🔑 2.0

Find each root. *(Lesson 11-5)*

32. $\sqrt{169}$　　　　33. $\sqrt[3]{216}$　　　　34. $\sqrt{400}$　　　　35. $\sqrt[4]{81}$

36. $\sqrt[5]{32}$　　　　37. $\sqrt{121}$　　　　38. $\sqrt{49}$　　　　39. $\sqrt{625}$

Solve by using square roots. Check your answer. *(Lesson 9-6)*

40. $4x^2 = 100$　　　　41. $10 - x^2 = 10$　　　　42. $16x^2 + 5 = 86$

Simplify. All variables represent nonnegative numbers. *(Lesson 11-2)*

43. $\sqrt{24}$　　　　44. $\sqrt{108}$　　　　45. $\sqrt{\dfrac{4}{12}}$　　　　46. $\sqrt{\dfrac{21}{50}}$

47. $\sqrt{\dfrac{x^7}{x^3}}$　　　　48. $\sqrt{\dfrac{25r^9}{16r}}$　　　　49. $\sqrt{242}$　　　　50. $\sqrt{112}$

CONCEPT CONNECTION

Exponential Functions

Dollars for Scholars In 1980, the average annual tuition at two-year colleges was $350. Since then, the cost of tuition has increased by an average of 9% each year.

1. Write a function rule that models the annual growth in tuition at two-year colleges since 1980. Let 1980 be year zero in your function. Identify the variables, and tell which is independent and which is dependent.

2. Use your function to determine the average annual tuition in 2006. Use a table and a graph to support your answer.

3. Use your function to predict the average annual tuition at two-year colleges for the year you plan to graduate from high school.

4. In what year is the average annual tuition twice as much as in 1980? Use a table and a graph to support your answer.

5. In what year does the average annual tuition reach $1000? Use a table and a graph to support your answer.

Quiz for Lessons 11-6 Through 11-9

11-6 Geometric Sequences

Find the next three terms in each geometric sequence.

1. 3, 6, 12, 24, …

2. −1, 2, −4, 8, …

3. −2400, −1200, −600, −300, …

4. The first term of a geometric sequence is 2 and the common ratio is 3. What is the 8th term of the sequence?

5. The table shows the distance swung by a pendulum during its first three swings. The values form a geometric sequence. What will be the length of the 7th swing?

Swing	Length (cm)
1	1000
2	800
3	640

11-7 Exponential Functions

6. The function $f(x) = 3(1.1)^x$ gives the length (in inches) of an image after being enlarged by 10% x times. What is the length of the image after it has been enlarged 4 times? Round your answer to the nearest hundredth.

Graph each exponential function.

7. $y = 3^x$

8. $y = 2(2)^x$

9. $y = -2(4)^x$

10. $y = -(0.5)^x$

11. The function $f(x) = 40(0.8)^x$ gives the amount of a medication in milligrams present in a patient's system x hours after taking a 40-mg dose. In how many hours will there be less than 2 mg of the drug in a patient's system?

11-8 Exponential Growth and Decay

Write a function to model each situation. Then find the value of the function after the given amount of time.

12. Fiona's salary is $30,000, and she expects to receive a 3% raise each year; 10 years.

13. $2000 is invested at a rate of 4.5% compounded monthly; 3 years.

14. A $1200 computer is losing value at a rate of 20% per year; 4 years.

15. Strontium-90 has a half-life of 29 years. About how much strontium-90 will be left from a 100-mg sample after 290 years? Round your answer to the nearest thousandth.

11-9 Linear, Quadratic, and Exponential Models

Graph each data set. Which kind of model best describes the data?

16. $\{(-2, 5), (3, 10), (0, 1), (1, 2), (0.5, 1.25)\}$

17. $\{(0, 3), (2, 12), (-1, 1.5), (-3, 0.375), (4, 48)\}$

Look for a pattern in each data set to determine which kind of model best describes the data.

18. $\{(-2, -6), (-1, -5), (0, -4), (1, -3), (2, -2)\}$

19. $\{(-2, -24), (-1, -12), (0, -6), (1, -3)\}$

20. Use the data in the table to describe how the value of the stamp is changing. Then write a function that models the data. Use your function to predict the value of the stamp in 11 years.

Value of Collectible Stamp				
Year	0	1	2	3
Value ($)	5.00	6.00	7.20	8.64

Vocabulary

Complete the sentences below with vocabulary words from the list above.

1. $y = \sqrt{2x}$ is an example of a(n) ___?___.

2. A(n) ___?___ function has the form $y = a(1 - r)^t$, where $a > 0$.

3. In the formula $a_n = a_1 r^{n-1}$, the variable r represents the ___?___.

4. $f(x) = 2^x$ is an example of a(n) ___?___.

11-1 Square-Root Functions (pp. 700–704)

 Ext. of ☞ **1A2.0**

EXAMPLE

■ **Graph** $y = 3\sqrt{x - 2}$.

Step 1 Find the domain of the function.

$x - 2 \geq 0$ *The radicand must be greater*

   $x \geq 2$ *than or equal to 0.*

Step 2 Generate ordered pairs.

x	$y = 3\sqrt{x-2}$
2	0
3	3
6	6
11	9
18	12

Choose x-values greater than or equal to 2 that form a perfect square under the radical sign.

Step 3 Plot and connect the points.

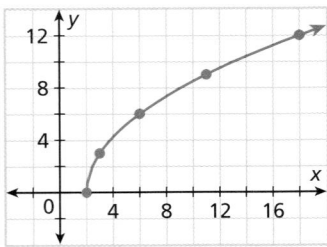

EXERCISES

5. If you know the surface area S of a cube, you can use the formula $\ell = \sqrt{\frac{S}{6}}$ to find the length ℓ of a side. What is the side length of a cube whose surface area is 135 cm²? Round your answer to the nearest hundredth of a centimeter.

Find the domain of each square-root function.

6. $y = \sqrt{x} + 5$ 7. $y = \sqrt{x + 4}$

8. $y = 8 - \sqrt{3x}$ 9. $y = 2\sqrt{x + 2}$

10. $y = 1 + \sqrt{3x - 4}$ 11. $y = \sqrt{2x + 6}$

12. $y = \sqrt{2x - 7}$ 13. $y = \sqrt{5x + 18}$

14. $y = \sqrt{4x - 3}$ 15. $y = 3\sqrt{x - 1}$

Graph each square-root function.

16. $y = \sqrt{x} + 8$ 17. $y = \sqrt{x - 3}$

18. $y = -\sqrt{2x}$ 19. $y = \sqrt{x} - 1$

20. $y = 2\sqrt{x + 3}$ 21. $y = \sqrt{5 - x}$

22. $y = \sqrt{7 - 4x}$ 23. $y = 3\sqrt{x - 1}$

24. $y = 1 + \sqrt{x + 1}$ 25. $y = \frac{1}{2}\sqrt{x - 2}$

11-2 Radical Expressions (pp. 705–710)

EXAMPLE

Simplify. All variables represent nonnegative numbers.

■ $\sqrt{50x^4}$

$\sqrt{(25)(2)x^4}$ *Factor the radicand.*

$\sqrt{25}\,\sqrt{2}\,\sqrt{x^4}$ *Use the Product Property.*

$5x^2\sqrt{2}$ *Simplify.*

■ $\sqrt{\dfrac{m^3}{4}}$

$\dfrac{\sqrt{m^3}}{\sqrt{4}}$ *Use the Quotient Property.*

$\dfrac{\sqrt{m^2}\,\sqrt{m}}{\sqrt{4}}$ *Use the Product Property.*

$\dfrac{m\sqrt{m}}{2}$ *Simplify.*

EXERCISES

Simplify. All variables represent nonnegative numbers.

26. $\sqrt{121}$

27. $\sqrt{n^4}$

28. $\sqrt{(x+3)^2}$

29. $\sqrt{\dfrac{75}{3}}$

30. $\sqrt{36d^2}$

31. $\sqrt{y^6 x}$

32. $\sqrt{12}$

33. $\sqrt{32ab^5}$

34. $\sqrt{\dfrac{5}{4}}$

35. $\sqrt{\dfrac{t^3}{100t}}$

36. $\sqrt{\dfrac{8}{18}}$

37. $\sqrt{\dfrac{32p^4}{49}}$

38. $\sqrt{\dfrac{s^2 t^9}{s^4}}$

39. $\sqrt{\dfrac{72b^6}{225}}$

11-3 Adding and Subtracting Radical Expressions (pp. 711–715)

EXAMPLE

■ Simplify $\sqrt{50x} - \sqrt{2x} + \sqrt{12x}$.

$\sqrt{50x} - 1\sqrt{2x} + \sqrt{12x}$

$\sqrt{(25)(2)x} - 1\sqrt{2x} + \sqrt{(4)(3)x}$

$\sqrt{25}\,\sqrt{2x} - 1\sqrt{2x} + \sqrt{4}\,\sqrt{3x}$

$5\sqrt{2x} - 1\sqrt{2x} + 2\sqrt{3x}$

$4\sqrt{2x} + 2\sqrt{3x}$

EXERCISES

Simplify each expression. All variables represent nonnegative numbers.

40. $6\sqrt{7} + 3\sqrt{7}$

41. $4\sqrt{3} - \sqrt{3}$

42. $3\sqrt{2} + 2\sqrt{3}$

43. $9\sqrt{5t} - 8\sqrt{5t}$

44. $\sqrt{50} - \sqrt{18}$

45. $\sqrt{12} + \sqrt{20}$

46. $\sqrt{20x} - \sqrt{80x}$

47. $4\sqrt{54} - \sqrt{24}$

11-4 Multiplying and Dividing Radical Expressions (pp. 716–721)

EXAMPLES

■ Multiply $\left(\sqrt{3} + 6\right)^2$. Write the product in simplest form.

$\left(\sqrt{3} + 6\right)^2$

$\left(\sqrt{3} + 6\right)\left(\sqrt{3} + 6\right)$ *Expand the expression.*

$3 + 6\sqrt{3} + 6\sqrt{3} + 36$ *Use the FOIL method.*

$39 + 12\sqrt{3}$ *Simplify.*

■ Simplify the quotient $\dfrac{\sqrt{5}}{\sqrt{3}}$.

$\dfrac{\sqrt{5}}{\sqrt{3}}\left(\dfrac{\sqrt{3}}{\sqrt{3}}\right) = \dfrac{\sqrt{15}}{3}$ *Rationalize the denominator.*

EXERCISES

Multiply. Write each product in simplest form. All variables represent nonnegative numbers.

48. $\sqrt{2}\,\sqrt{7}$

49. $3\sqrt{2x}\,\sqrt{14}$

50. $\sqrt{2}\left(4 - \sqrt{8}\right)$

51. $\left(8 + \sqrt{7}\right)^2$

Simplify each quotient. All variables represent nonnegative numbers.

52. $\dfrac{4}{\sqrt{5}}$

53. $\dfrac{a\sqrt{9}}{\sqrt{2}}$

54. $\dfrac{\sqrt{8}}{2\sqrt{6}}$

55. $\dfrac{\sqrt{5}}{\sqrt{2n}}$

11-5 Solving Radical Equations (pp. 722–729)

Ext. of ➤ 1A2.0

EXAMPLE

■ Solve $\sqrt{4x+1} - 8 = -3$. Check your answer.

$$\sqrt{4x+1} - 8 = -3$$

$$\sqrt{4x+1} = 5 \qquad \text{Add 8 to both sides.}$$

$$\left(\sqrt{4x+1}\right)^2 = (5)^2 \qquad \text{Square both sides.}$$

$$4x + 1 = 25$$

$$4x = 24 \qquad \text{Subtract 1 from both sides.}$$

$$x = 6 \qquad \text{Divide both sides by 4.}$$

Check $\sqrt{4x+1} - 8 = -3$

$\sqrt{4(6)+1} - 8$	-3
$\sqrt{25} - 8$	-3
$5 - 8$	-3
-3	-3 ✓

EXERCISES

Solve each equation. Check your answer.

56. $\sqrt{x} = 8$ **57.** $\sqrt{2x} = 4$

58. $\sqrt{x+6} = 3$ **59.** $-3\sqrt{x} = -15$

60. $3\sqrt{-x} = 27$ **61.** $\dfrac{4\sqrt{x}}{5} = 8$

62. $\sqrt{x+1} = \sqrt{3x-5}$ **63.** $\sqrt{x-2} + 4 = 3$

64. $12 = 4\sqrt{2x+1}$ **65.** $\sqrt{x-5} = \sqrt{7-x}$

66. $\sqrt{x+2} = 3$ **67.** $\sqrt{2x-3} = 4$

68. $4\sqrt{x-3} = 12$ **69.** $\sqrt{x+6} = x$

70. $\sqrt{3x+4} = x$ **71.** $\sqrt{2x+6} = x - 1$

11-6 Geometric Sequences (pp. 732–737)

Prep for 2A22.0

EXAMPLE

■ What is the 10th term of the geometric sequence $-6400, 3200, -1600, 800, \dots$?

Find the common ratio by dividing consecutive terms.

$$\dfrac{3200}{-6400} = -0.5 \qquad \dfrac{-1600}{3200} = -0.5$$

$$a_n = a_1 r^{n-1} \qquad \text{Write the formula.}$$

$$a_{10} = -6400(-0.5)^{10-1} \qquad \text{Substitute.}$$

$$= -6400(-0.5)^9 \qquad \text{Simplify.}$$

$$= 12.5$$

EXERCISES

Find the next three terms in each geometric sequence.

72. $1, 3, 9, 27, \dots$ **73.** $3, -6, 12, -24, \dots$

74. $80, 40, 20, 10, \dots$ **75.** $-1, -4, -16, -64, \dots$

76. The first term of a geometric sequence is 4 and the common ratio is 5. What is the 10th term?

77. What is the 15th term of the geometric sequence $4, 12, 36, 108, \dots$?

11-7 Exponential Functions (pp. 738–744)

Preview of ➤ 2A12.0

EXAMPLE

■ Tell whether the ordered pairs $\{(1, 4), (2, 16), (3, 36), (4, 64)\}$ satisfy an exponential function. Explain.

x	y
1	4
2	16
3	36
4	64

As the x-values increase by a constant amount, the y-values are not multiplied by a constant amount. This function is not exponential.

EXERCISES

Tell whether each set of ordered pairs satisfies an exponential function. Explain.

78. $\{(0, 1), (2, 9), (4, 81), (6, 729)\}$

79. $\{(-2, -8), (-1, -4), (0, 0), (1, 4)\}$

Graph each exponential function.

80. $y = 4^x$ **81.** $y = \left(\dfrac{1}{4}\right)^x$

11-8 Exponential Growth and Decay (pp. 747–754)

Preview of ✿ 2A12.0

EXAMPLE

■ The value of a piece of antique furniture has been increasing at a rate of 2% per year. In 1990, its value was $800. Write an exponential growth function to model the situation. Then find the value of the furniture in the year 2010.

Step 1 $y = a(1 + r)^t$ *Write the formula.*

     $y = 800(1 + 0.02)^t$ *Substitute.*

     $y = 800(1.02)^t$ *Simplify.*

Step 2 $y = 800(1.02)^{20}$ *Substitute 20 for t.*

     ≈ 1188.76 *Simplify and round.*

The furniture's value will be $1188.76.

EXERCISES

82. The number of students in the book club is increasing at a rate of 15% per year. In 2001, there were 9 students in the book club. Write an exponential growth function to model the situation. Then find the number of students in the book club in the year 2008.

83. The population of a small town is decreasing at a rate of 4% per year. In 1970, the population was 24,500. Write an exponential decay function to model the situation. Then find the population in the year 2020.

11-9 Linear, Quadratic, and Exponential Models (pp. 755–761)

Preview of ✿ 2A12.0; Ext. of ✿ 1A7.0

EXAMPLE

■ Use the data in the table to describe how Jasmin's debt is changing. Then write a function that models the data. Use your function to predict Jasmin's debt after 8 years.

Jasmin's Debt

Years	Debt ($)
1	130
2	260
3	520
4	1040

+1 ... ×2

Jasmin's debt doubles every year.

For a constant change in time (+1), there is a constant ratio of 2, so the data is exponential.

   $y = ab^x$ *Write the general form.*

   $y = a(2)^x$ *Substitute 2 for b.*

   $130 = a(2)^1$ *Substitute (1, 130) for x and y.*

   $a = 65$ *Solve for a.*

   $y = 65(2)^x$ *Replace a and b in $y = ab^x$.*

   $y = 65(2)^8$ *Substitute 8 for x.*

   $y = 16,640$ *Simplify with a calculator.*

Jasmin's debt in 8 years will be $16,640.

EXERCISES

Graph each data set. Which kind of model best describes the data?

84. $\{(-2, -12), (-1, -3), (0, 0), (1, -3), (2, -12)\}$

85. $\{(-2, -2), (-1, 2), (0, 6), (1, 10), (2, 14)\}$

86. $\{(-2, -\frac{1}{4}), (-1, -\frac{1}{2}), (0, -1), (1, -2), (2, -4)\}$

Look for a pattern in each data set to determine which kind of model best describes the data.

87. $\{(0, 2), (1, 6), (2, 18), (3, 54), (4, 162)\}$

88. $\{(0, 0), (2, -20), (4, -80), (6, -180), (8, -320)\}$

89. $\{(-8, 5), (-4, 3), (0, 1), (4, -1), (8, -3)\}$

90. Write a function that models the data. Then use your function to predict how long the humidifier will produce steam with 10 quarts of water.

Input and Output of a Humidifier

Water Volume (qt)	Steam Time (h)
3	4.5
4	6
5	7.5
6	9

CHAPTER 11

Find the domain of each square-root function.

1. $y = 6 + \sqrt{x}$

2. $y = -2\sqrt{x + 9}$

3. $y = x + \sqrt{3x - 3}$

Graph each square-root function.

4. $y = \sqrt{x} + 2$

5. $y = \sqrt{x - 1}$

6. $y = -3\sqrt{2x}$

Simplify. All variables represent nonnegative numbers.

7. $\sqrt{27}$

8. $\sqrt{75m^4}$

9. $\sqrt{\dfrac{x^6}{y^2}}$

10. $\sqrt{\dfrac{p^9}{144p}}$

11. $4\sqrt{10} - 2\sqrt{10}$

12. $5\sqrt{3y} + \sqrt{3y}$

13. $\sqrt{8} - \sqrt{50}$

14. $2\sqrt{75} - \sqrt{32} + \sqrt{48}$

15. $\sqrt{2}\sqrt{3m}$

16. $\dfrac{\sqrt{128d}}{\sqrt{5}}$

17. $\sqrt{3}(\sqrt{21} - 2)$

18. $(\sqrt{3} - 2)(\sqrt{3} + 4)$

Solve each equation. Check your answer.

19. $\sqrt{2x} = 6$

20. $\sqrt{3x + 4} - 2 = 5$

21. $\dfrac{2\sqrt{x}}{3} = 8$

22. $\sqrt{5x + 1} = \sqrt{2x - 2}$

Find the next three terms in each geometric sequence.

23. 2, 6, 18, 54, …

24. 4800, 2400, 1200, 600, …

25. $-4, 20, -100, 500, …$

26. **Communication** If school is cancelled, the school secretary calls 2 families. Each of those families calls 2 other families. In the third round of calls, each of the 4 families calls 2 more families. If this pattern continues, how many families are called in the seventh round of calls?

Graph each exponential function.

27. $y = -2(4)^x$

28. $y = 3(2)^x$

29. $y = 4\left(\dfrac{1}{2}\right)^x$

30. $-\left(\dfrac{1}{3}\right)^x$

31. A teacher is repeatedly enlarging a diagram on a photocopier. The function $f(x) = 3(1.25)^x$ represents the length of the diagram, in centimeters, after x enlargements. What is the length after 5 enlargements? Round to the nearest centimeter.

32. Chelsea invested $5600 at a rate of 3.6% compounded quarterly. Write a compound interest function to model the situation. Then find the balance after 6 years.

33. The number of trees in a forest is decreasing at a rate of 5% per year. The forest had 24,000 trees 15 years ago. Write an exponential decay function to model the situation. Then find the number of trees now.

Look for a pattern in each data set to determine which kind of model best describes the data.

34. $\{(-10, -17), (-5, -7), (0, 3), (5, 13), (10, 23)\}$

35. $\{(1, 3), (2, 9), (3, 27), (4, 81), (5, 243)\}$

36. Use the data in the table to describe how the bacteria population is changing. Then write a function that models the data. Use your function to predict the bacteria population after 10 hours.

Bacteria Population				
Time (h)	0	1	2	3
Bacteria	6	18	54	162

COLLEGE ENTRANCE EXAM PRACTICE

FOCUS ON SAT MATHEMATICS SUBJECT TESTS

Colleges use standardized test scores to confirm what your academic record indicates. Because courses and instruction differ from school to school, standardized tests are one way in which colleges try to compare students fairly when making admissions decisions.

You will need to use a calculator on the SAT Mathematics Subject Tests. If you do not already have a graphing calculator, consider getting one because it may give you an advantage when solving some problems. Spend time getting used to your calculator before the test.

You may want to time yourself as you take this practice test. It should take you about 6 minutes to complete.

---

1. What is the domain of $y = \sqrt{x - 4}$?

   (A) $x \geq -2$

   (B) $x \geq 2$

   (C) $x \geq -4$

   (D) $x \geq 4$

   (E) $x > 4$

2. $\dfrac{\sqrt{8}\sqrt{3}}{\sqrt{5}} =$

   (A) $2\sqrt{3}$

   (B) $\dfrac{2\sqrt{3}}{5}$

   (C) $\sqrt{12}$

   (D) $\dfrac{4\sqrt{30}}{5}$

   (E) $\dfrac{2\sqrt{30}}{5}$

3. If $\dfrac{\sqrt{6 - 3x}}{5} = 3$, what is the value of x?

   (A) -3

   (B) -13

   (C) -73

   (D) -77

   (E) -89

4. The third term of a geometric sequence is 32 and the fifth term is 512. What is the eighth term of the sequence?

   (A) 544

   (B) 1232

   (C) 8192

   (D) 32,768

   (E) 2,097,152

5. A band releases a new CD and tracks its sales. The table shows the number of copies sold each week (in thousands). Which type of function best models this data?

CD Sales	
Week	Copies Sold (thousands)
1	129.5
2	155
3	179.5
4	203
5	225.5
6	247

   (A) Linear function

   (B) Quadratic function

   (C) Exponential function

   (D) Square-root function

   (E) Absolute-value function

STRATEGIES FOR SUCCESS

Multiple Choice: *None of the Above* or *All of the Above*

In some multiple-choice test items, one of the options is *None of the above* or *All of the above*. To answer these types of items, first determine whether each of the other options is true or false. If you find that more than one option is true, then the correct choice is likely to be *All of the above*. If none of the options are true, the correct choice is *None of the above*.

If you do not know how to solve the problem and have to guess, *All of the above* is most often correct, and *None of the above* is usually incorrect.

EXAMPLE 1

Which of the following quadratic polynomials has two roots?

   Ⓐ $x^2 - 5x - 14$ Ⓒ $14x^2 + 3 - 23x$

   Ⓑ $3x^2 + 14x + 13$ Ⓓ All of the above

Notice that choice D is All of the above. This means that you must look at each option. As you consider each option, mark it true or false in your test booklet.

A You could solve each related quadratic equation to answer this question. But you don't need to find the actual roots, just the number of them. Using the discriminant will save time. For a quadratic equation $ax^2 + bx + c = 0$, the discriminant is $b^2 - 4ac$.

Write the related quadratic equation in choice A in standard form: $x^2 - 5x - 14 = 0$.

   $a = 1$ $b = -5$ $c = -14$ $b^2 - 4ac = 81$

When the discriminant is positive, the equation has two solutions. Therefore, the polynomial has two roots. Choice A is true.

B Write the related equation in standard form: $3x^2 + 14x + 13 = 0$

   $a = 3$ $b = 14$ $c = 13$ $b^2 - 4ac = 40$

The discriminant is positive, so the equation has two solutions and the polynomial has two roots. Choice B is also true. The answer is likely to be Choice D, *All of the above*, but you should also check whether Choice C is true.

C Write the related equation in standard form: $14x^2 - 23x + 3 = 0$

   $a = 14$ $b = -23$ $c = 3$ $b^2 - 4ac = 361$

The discriminant is positive. Choice C is true as well.

Because A, B, and C are all true, the correct response is D, *All of the above*.

Be careful of problems that contain more than one negative word, such as *no*, *not*, or *never*. Read the problem and each option twice before selecting an answer.

Read each test item and answer the questions that follow.

Item A
The mean score on a test is 68. Which CANNOT be true?

(A) Every score is 68.

(B) Half of the scores are 68, and half of the scores are 0.

(C) Half of the scores are 94, and half of the scores are 42.

(D) None of the above

---

1. What is the definition of *mean*?

2. If you find that an option is true, is that the correct response? Explain.

3. Willie determined that A and C could both be true, so he chose D as his response. Do you agree? Why or why not?

Item B
What is the probability of rolling a 2 on a number cube?

(A) $16.\overline{6}\%$

(B) $1 - P\left(\text{rolling } 1, 3, 4, 5, \text{ or } 6\right)$

(C) $\dfrac{1}{6}$

(D) All of the above

---

4. What is the complement of rolling a 2? Is choice B correct? Explain.

5. If you roll a number cube, how many possible outcomes are there? How does this information help you solve this problem?

6. Is the value given in choice C equivalent to any other choice? If so, which one(s)?

7. How many choices are true? What is the correct response to the test item?

Item C
Which expression is equivalent to $(8x - 4z) - (5z + x)$?

(A) $8x - 4z - 5z + x$

(B) $9x - 9z$

(C) $8x - 4z - 5z - x$

(D) None of the above

---

8. Kyle finds that choices A and B are both false. To save time, he selects choice D as his answer because he figures it is likely that choice C will also be false. Do you think Kyle made a wise decision? Why or why not?

9. Determine whether choices A, B, and C are true, and then give the correct response to this test item.

Item D
Which point is on the line that passes through $(1, 5)$ and $(2, 0)$?

(A) $(-3, 5)$

(B) $(-1, -15)$

(C) $(0, 10)$

(D) All of the above

---

10. What information do you need in order to determine whether a point lies on a line? How can you use the information given in the problem to find this?

11. How can you determine whether choice D is the correct response to the test item?

CHAPTER 11

MASTERING THE STANDARDS

go.hrw.com
Standards Practice Online
KEYWORD: MA8CA Practice

CUMULATIVE ASSESSMENT, CHAPTERS 1–11

Multiple Choice

1. Which of the following is the simplified form of the expression $\frac{x^2 - 3x + 2}{x^2 - 4}$?

   (A) $\frac{x-1}{x-2}$
   (B) $\frac{x-1}{x+2}$
   (C) $\frac{x+1}{x+2}$
   (D) $\frac{x+1}{x-2}$

2. Which of these is the graph of $y = x^2 - 2x - 3$?

   (A)

   (B)

   (C)

   (D)

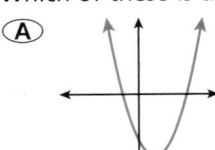

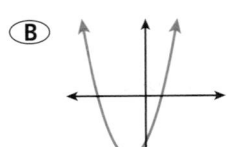

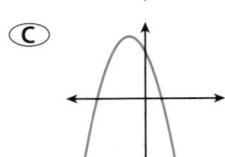

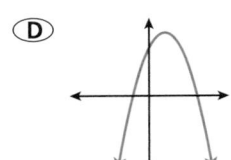

3. Which property is illustrated by the equation $3(w + 4) = 3w + 12$?

   (A) Associative Property of Addition
   (B) Associative Property of Multiplication
   (C) Commutative Property of Multiplication
   (D) Distributive Property

4. Which expression is equivalent to $\left(m^2 m^{\frac{1}{2}}\right)^6$?

   (A) $m^{\frac{5}{2}}$
   (B) m^6
   (C) $m^{\frac{15}{2}}$
   (D) m^{15}

5. Which line passes through the point $(-4, -3)$ and is perpendicular to the line $3x + y = -5$?

   (A) $3x + y = -15$
   (B) $3x - y = -15$
   (C) $x - 3y = 5$
   (D) $x + 3y = 5$

6. Leah graphed a quadratic function that intersected the x-axis at two points. Which function could she have graphed?

   (A) $y = x^2 - 6x + 9$
   (B) $y = x^2 + 2x - 24$
   (C) $y = x^2 + 10x + 25$
   (D) $y = x^2 + x + 4$

7. What is the solution to the system of equations below?

   $$\begin{cases} 2x - y = 2 \\ y = 3x - 5 \end{cases}$$

   (A) $(4, 6)$
   (B) $(3, 4)$
   (C) $(2, 1)$
   (D) $(0, 2)$

8. What is the complete factorization of $2x^3 + 18x$?

   (A) $2x(x^2 + 9)$
   (B) $2x(x + 3)^2$
   (C) $2x(x + 3)(x - 3)$
   (D) $2(x^3 + 18)$

9. What is the product of $2x - 5$ and $3x + 2$?

   (A) $6x^2 - 4x - 10$
   (B) $6x^2 - 11x - 10$
   (C) $6x^2 - 15x - 10$
   (D) $6x^2 - 19x - 10$

When a test item gives an equation to be solved, it may be quicker to work backward from the answer choices by substituting them into the equation. If time remains, check your answer by solving the equation.

10. Which shows the product of 5.1×10^4 and 3×10^9 written in scientific notation?

Ⓐ 1.53×10^{12}

Ⓑ 1.53×10^{14}

Ⓒ 15.3×10^{12}

Ⓓ 15.3×10^{13}

11. Which functions have all real numbers as their domain?

  I $y = \dfrac{1}{x + 1}$

  II $y = (x + 1)^2$

  III $y = |x + 1|$

Ⓐ I only

Ⓑ I and II

Ⓒ II and III

Ⓓ I, II, and III

Gridded Response

12. Use the Quadratic Formula to find the positive solution of $3x^2 - 8x - 2 = 0$. Round your answer to the nearest tenth.

13. The graph of $f(x)$ is shown below. How many zeros does $f(x)$ have?

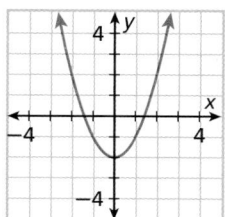

14. Scott is finding the equation of the line that has an x-intercept of -4 and a y-intercept of 3. He writes the equation in the form $Ax + By = 12$. What value should he use for B?

15. Tonya graphs the lines described by $x + 2y = -2$ and $-x + 3y = -8$. What is the x-coordinate of the point of intersection of the lines?

Short Response

16. A chemist has 400 milliliters of a solution that is 50% alcohol. She wants to add alcohol to the solution to make a solution that is 75% alcohol.

  a. Write an equation that you can use to find out how many milliliters of alcohol the chemist should add to the solution. Be sure to explain what any variables represent.

  b. Solve the equation to determine the number of milliliters of alcohol the chemist should add. Show your work.

17. Ella and Mia went on a camping trip. The total cost for their trip was $124, which the girls divided evenly. Ella paid for 4 nights at the campsite and $30 for supplies. Mia paid for 2 nights at the campsite and $46 for supplies.

  a. Write an equation that could be used to find the cost of one night's stay at the campsite. Explain what each variable in your equation represents.

  b. Solve your equation from part **a** to find the cost of one night's stay at the campsite. Show your work.

Extended Response

18. The figure gives the dimensions of a rectangular flower bed.

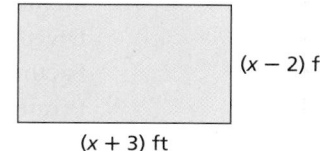

  a. The area of the flower bed is 24 ft². Use the formula for the area of a rectangle to write an equation based on the figure.

  b. Multiply the binomials in your equation and simplify to write a new equation in the form $ax^2 + bx + c = 0$.

  c. Solve the equation. Show your work. Do all of the solutions make sense in this situation? Explain.

  d. What are the length and width of the flower bed?

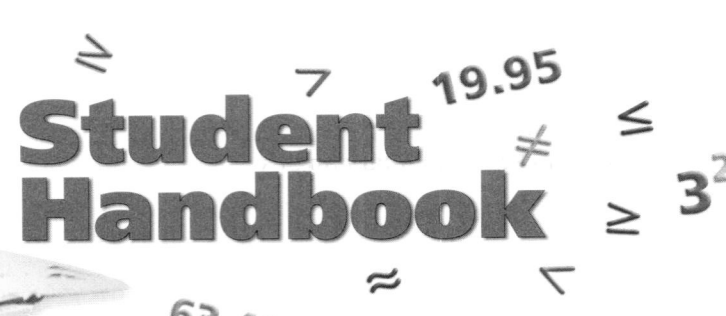

Student Handbook

Measurement and Geometry

Statistics, Data Analysis, and Probability

Extra Practice

Chapter 1 ▪ Skills Practice

Lesson 1-1

Give two ways to write each algebraic expression in words.

1. $x + 8$ **2.** $6(y)$ **3.** $g - 4$ **4.** $\frac{12}{h}$

Evaluate each expression for the replacement set {2, 4, 5.5}.

5. $8 + a$ **6.** $\frac{a}{8}$ **7.** $8 - a$ **8.** $8a$

Write an algebraic expression for each verbal expression. Then evaluate the algebraic expression for the given values of *y*.

	Verbal	Algebraic	$y = 9$	$y = 6$
9.	*y* reduced by 4			
10.	the quotient of *y* and 3			
11.	5 more than *y*			
12.	the sum of *y* and 2			

Lesson 1-2

Add or subtract using a number line.

13. $-7 - 9$ **14.** $-2.2 + 4.3$ **15.** $-5\frac{1}{2} - 2\frac{1}{2}$ **16.** $3.4 - 6.5$

Subtract.

17. $12 - 47$ **18.** $1.3 - 9.2$ **19.** $1\frac{1}{3} - 4\frac{2}{3}$

Compare. Write <, >, or =.

20. $-5 - (-8)$ ▒ $-4 - 9$ **21.** $|-6 - (-2)|$ ▒ $7 - 4$ **22.** $-2 - 5$ ▒ $7 - 14$

Evaluate the expression $g - (-7)$ for each value of *g*.

23. $g = 121$ **24.** $g = 1.25$ **25.** $g = -\frac{2}{5}$ **26.** $g = -8\frac{1}{3}$

Lesson 1-3

Find the value of each expression.

27. $-24 \div (-8)$ **28.** $5(-9)$ **29.** $-5.2 \div -1.3$

30. $\frac{2}{7} \div \left(-\frac{6}{7}\right)$ **31.** $0 \div \left(-\frac{4}{5}\right)$ **32.** $\frac{9}{10} \div 0$

Evaluate each expression for $x = -8$, $y = 6$, and $z = -4$.

33. xy **34.** yz **35.** $\frac{y}{z}$ **36.** $\frac{z}{x}$

Let *a* represent a positive number, *b* represent a negative number, and *z* represent zero. Tell whether each expression is positive, negative, zero, or undefined.

37. ab **38.** $-bz$ **39.** $-\frac{a}{b}$ **40.** $\frac{ab}{z}$

Lesson 1-4

Write each expression as repeated multiplication. Then simplify the expression.

41. 3^3 **42.** -2^4 **43.** $(-5)^3$ **44.** $(-1)^5$

Write each expression using a base and an exponent.

45. $5 \cdot 5 \cdot 5 \cdot 5 \cdot 5$ **46.** $4 \cdot 4 \cdot 4$ **47.** $2 \cdot 2 \cdot 2 \cdot 2$

Write the exponent that makes each equation true.

48. $2^{▒} = 16$ **49.** $4^{▒} = 256$ **50.** $(-3)^{▒} = 81$ **51.** $-5^{▒} = -125$

Chapter 1 ▪ Skills Practice

Lesson 1-5

Find each root.

52. $-\sqrt[3]{64}$ **53.** $\sqrt{144}$ **54.** $\sqrt{25}$

55. $\sqrt{169}$ **56.** $\sqrt{225}$ **57.** $\sqrt[3]{343}$

Compare. Write $<$, $>$, or $=$.

58. $\sqrt{118}$ ▮ 11   **59.** 6 ▮ $\sqrt{35}$ **60.** 14 ▮ $\sqrt{196}$ **61.** $\sqrt{50}$ ▮ 7

62. $\sqrt{142}$ ▮ 12   **63.** 8 ▮ $\sqrt{65}$ **64.** $\sqrt{102}$ ▮ 10   **65.** $\sqrt{81}$ ▮ 9

Write all classifications that apply to each real number.

66. -44 **67.** $\sqrt{49}$ **68.** 15.982 **69.** $\frac{1}{9}$

Lesson 1-6

Name the property that is illustrated in each equation.

70. $56 + x = x + 56$ **71.** $10 \cdot (3 \cdot 11) = (10 \cdot 3) \cdot 11$

72. $(6 + x)5 = 6(5) + x(5)$ **73.** $(4 + x) + 15 = 4 + (x + 15)$

Write each product using the Distributive Property. Then simplify.

74. $12(108)$ **75.** $7(89)$ **76.** $11(33)$

77. $16(1003)$ **78.** $8(207)$ **79.** $18(999)$

For the set $\{-2, -1, 0, 1, 2\}$, find a counterexample to show that each statement is false.

80. The set is closed under addition.

81. The set is closed under subtraction.

82. The set is closed under multiplication.

83. The set is closed under division.

Lesson 1-7

Evaluate each expression for the given value of the variable.

84. $22 - 3g + 5$ for $g = 4$ **85.** $12 - 30 \div h$ for $h = 6$ **86.** $\sqrt{(11j + j)} + 6$ for $j = 3$

Simplify each expression.

87. $4 + 12 \div |3 - 9|$ **88.** $-36 - \sqrt{4 + 15 \div 3}$ **89.** $\dfrac{5 - \sqrt{12(3)}}{-4 + \sqrt{2(8)}}$

90. $-5 + 38 + 5 + 62$ **91.** $2\frac{1}{3} - 42 + 7\frac{2}{3}$ **92.** $\frac{1}{5} \cdot 4 \cdot 25$

93. $\dfrac{\sqrt[3]{27} \div 3}{4(6 - 5) - 3}$ **94.** $5(9 - 7)^2 + 8$ **95.** $|10 - 13|^2 - 6$

Simplify each expression by combining like terms.

96. $7a - 3a$ **97.** $-2b - 12b$ **98.** $4c + 5c^2 - c$

99. $4x^2 - x + 3x$ **100.** $5y - 3y + 5$ **101.** $-z + 8z^2 - 3z^2$

102. $2m - 4m^2 + 4m$ **103.** $6j + 3j + 10j^2$ **104.** $4f^2 - 3f + 1$

Use properties and operations to show that the first expression simplifies to the second expression.

105. $6(p - 2) + 3p$; $9p - 12$

106. $-4 + 3r - 7(2s - r)$; $10r - 14s - 4$

Chapter 2 ■ Skills Practice

Lesson 2-1

Solve each equation. Check your answer.

1. $x - 9 = 5$

2. $4 = y - 12$

3. $a + \dfrac{3}{5} = 7$

4. $7.3 = b + 3.4$

5. $-6 + j = 5$

6. $-1.7 = -6.1 + k$

7. $\dfrac{n}{5} = 15$

8. $-6 = \dfrac{k}{4}$

9. $\dfrac{r}{2.6} = 5$

10. $3b = 27$

11. $56 = -7d$

12. $-3.6 = -2f$

13. $\dfrac{1}{4}z = 3$

14. $12 = \dfrac{4}{5}g$

15. $\dfrac{1}{3}a = -5$

Write an equation to represent each relationship. Then solve the equation.

16. A number decreased by 7 is equal to 10.

17. The sum of 6 and a number is -3.

18. A number multiplied by 4 is -20.

19. The quotient of a number and 5 is 7.

Lesson 2-2

Solve each equation. Check your answer.

20. $2k + 7 = 15$

21. $11 - 5m = -4$

22. $23 = 9 - 2d$

23. $\dfrac{2}{5}b + 6 = 10$

24. $\dfrac{f}{3} - 4 = 2$

25. $6n + 4 = 22$

26. $3d - 4 = 11$

27. $3t + t = 28$

28. $\dfrac{m}{4} + \dfrac{1}{2} = \dfrac{3}{4}$

29. $11 = 4c + 3$

30. $6 = 4 + \dfrac{a}{5}$

31. $7 = -2p + 13$

32. $5q + 4 = 24$

33. $15 - \dfrac{z}{3} = 21$

34. $8 = 2y - 6$

Write an equation to represent each relationship. Solve each equation.

35. The difference of 11 and 4 times a number equals 3.

36. Thirteen less than 5 times a number is equal to 7.

37. A number times 4 increased by 2 equals 22.

38. Three multiplied by a number all divided by 2 equals 12.

Lesson 2-3

Solve each equation. Check your answer.

39. $\dfrac{t - 5}{2} = 4$

40. $\dfrac{11y + 2}{3} = 8$

41. $\dfrac{2t + 4}{5} = 2$

42. $a + 4a - 6 = 54$

43. $12 + 5f - 2f = 9$

44. $-n - 8 - 3n = -16$

45. $p(3 + 5) - 4 = 76$

46. $7(h - 2) = 21$

47. $4\left(k - \dfrac{1}{2}\right) = 42$

48. $6 = \dfrac{r + 8}{2}$

49. $w - 3w + 8 = 16$

50. $14 = x(13 - 11)$

51. $3(s + 4) = 15$

52. $10 + m - 4m = 4$

53. $\dfrac{v - 5}{5} = 9$

Write an equation to represent each relationship. Then solve.

54. A number decreased by 2 multiplied by 5 equals 30.

55. Six plus a number all divided by 4 equals 5.

56. A number times 6 minus 12 added to 4 times the number equals 30.

57. Ten minus a number times 4 is the same as five minus 7.

Extra Practice

Chapter 2 ▪ Skills Practice

Lesson 2-4

Solve each equation. Check your answer.

58. $5b - 3 = 4b + 1$

59. $3g + 7 = 11g - 17$

60. $-8 + 4y = y - 6 + 3y - 2$

61. $7 + 3d - 5 = -1 + 2d - 12 + d$

62. $2s + 6 = 3s - 7$

63. $-3h + 12 - 4h = -7h - 9 - 16$

64. $6k - 15 - k = 5k - 9 - 6$

65. $c + 22 - \dfrac{3}{4}c = 5 - \dfrac{1}{2}c + 17$

Write an equation to represent each relationship. Then solve the equation.

66. Three more than one-half a number is the same as 17 minus three times the number.

67. Two times the difference of a number and 4 is the same as 5 less than the number.

68. A number plus 5 is the same as 3 times the number minus 13.

69. Two times a number minus 9 is equal to 3 minus 4 times the number.

Lesson 2-5

Find each unit rate.

70. A long-distance runner ran 9000 meters in 30 minutes.

71. A hummingbird flapped its wings 770 times in 14 seconds.

72. A car traveled 210 miles in 3 hours.

73. A printer printed 60 pages in 5 minutes.

Solve each proportion.

74. $\dfrac{h}{4} = \dfrac{5}{6}$

75. $\dfrac{5}{m} = \dfrac{2}{5}$

76. $\dfrac{r}{3} = \dfrac{10}{7}$

77. $\dfrac{2}{3} = \dfrac{2x}{8}$

78. $\dfrac{5}{x-3} = \dfrac{3}{10}$

79. $\dfrac{b-2}{4} = \dfrac{7}{12}$

80. Find 25% of 60.

81. Find 40% of 95.

82. What percent of 75 is 15?

83. What percent of 60 is 33?

84. 91 is what percent of 65?

85. 35% of what number is 24.5?

86. Find 34% of 50.

87. What percent of 95 is 38?

88. 55% of what number is 11?

89. Find 115% of 40.

Lesson 2-6

Solve for the indicated variable.

90. $q - 3r = 2$ for r

91. $\dfrac{5-c}{6} = d - 7$ for c

92. $2x + 3\dfrac{y}{4} = 5$ for y

93. $2fgh - 3g = 10$ for h

94. $2a + a - r = 5$ for r

95. $3g + 4h = 7$ for g

96. $st - k = 3k$ for s

97. $\dfrac{11x + y}{4} = y - 1$ for y

98. $\dfrac{5m}{n} - 3d = 12$ for m

99. $4us + 3c = 8c$ for u.

Lesson 2-7

Solve each equation. Check your answer.

100. $|a| = 13$

101. $|x| - 16 = 3$

102. $|g + 5| = 11$

103. $|7s| - 6 = 8$

104. $\left|\dfrac{f}{2} + 1\right| = 15$

105. $|p - 5| - 12 = -9$

106. $\left|\dfrac{1}{2} + t\right| - 2 = -\dfrac{3}{2}$

107. $|b + 1| - 17 = -20$

108. $|4p| + 5 = 5$

109. $500 = 25|z| + 200$

110. $|7j + 14| - 5 = 16$

111. $\dfrac{|p - 2| - 15}{5} = -1$

Extra Practice

Lesson 3-1

Describe the solutions of each inequality in words.

1. $3 + v < -2$ **2.** $15 \le k + 4$ **3.** $-3 + n > 6$ **4.** $1 - 4x \ge -2$

Graph each inequality.

5. $f \ge 2$ **6.** $m < -1$ **7.** $\sqrt{4^2 + 3^2} > c$ **8.** $(-1 - 1)^2 \le p$

Write the inequality shown by each graph.

9.

10.

11.

12.

13.

14.

Write each inequality with the variable on the left. Graph the solutions.

15. $14 > b$ **16.** $9 \le g$ **17.** $-2 < x$ **18.** $-4 \ge k$

Lesson 3-2

Solve each inequality and graph the solutions.

19. $8 \ge d - 4$ **20.** $-5 < 10 + w$ **21.** $a + 4 \le 7$ **22.** $9 + j > 2$

Write an inequality to represent each statement. Solve the inequality and graph the solutions. Check your answer.

23. Five more than a number v is less than or equal to 9.

24. A number t decreased by 2 is at least 7.

25. Three less than a number r is less than -1.

26. A number k increased by 1 is at most -2.

Use the inequality $4 + z \le 11$ to fill in the missing numbers.

27. $z \le \blacksquare$ **28.** $z - \blacksquare \le 4$ **29.** $z - 3 \le \blacksquare$

Lesson 3-3

Solve each inequality and graph the solutions. Check your answer.

30. $24 > 4b$ **31.** $27g \le 81$ **32.** $\dfrac{x}{5} < 3$ **33.** $10y \ge 2$

34. $4p < -2$ **35.** $\dfrac{3s}{8} > 3$ **36.** $0 \ge \dfrac{3}{7}d$ **37.** $\dfrac{a}{8} \ge \dfrac{3}{4}$

38. $-3k \le -12$ **39.** $\dfrac{-2e}{5} \ge 4$ **40.** $8 < -12y$ **41.** $-3.5 > 14c$

42. $9 > \dfrac{h}{-2}$ **43.** $49 > -7m$ **44.** $60 \le -12c$ **45.** $-\dfrac{1}{3}q < -6$

Write an inequality for each statement. Solve the inequality and graph the solutions. Check your answer.

46. The product of $\dfrac{1}{2}$ and a number is not more than 6.

47. The quotient of r and -5 is greater than 3.

48. The product of -11 and a number is greater than -33.

49. The quotient of w and -4 is less than or equal to -6.

Extra Practice

Lesson 3-4

Solve each inequality and graph the solutions. Check your answer.

50. $3t - 2 < 5$　　　　**51.** $-6 < 5b - 4$　　　　**52.** $4 < \dfrac{2f + 3}{2}$

53. $10 \le 3(4 - r)$　　　**54.** $\dfrac{2}{3} + \dfrac{3}{4}h < \dfrac{4}{3}$　　　**55.** $\dfrac{1}{5}(10k - 2) > 1$

56. $-n - 3 < -2^3$　　　**57.** $37 - 4d \le \sqrt{3^2 + 4^2}$　　　**58.** $-\dfrac{3}{4}(8q - 2^2) < -3$

Use the inequality $-6 - 2w \ge 10$ to fill in the missing numbers.

59. $w \le$ ▭　　　　**60.** $w - 3 \le$ ▭　　　　**61.** ▭ $+ w \le 1$

Write an inequality for each statement. Solve the inequality and graph the solutions.

62. Twelve is less than or equal to the product of 6 and the difference of 5 and a number.

63. The difference of one-third a number and 8 is more than -4.

64. One-fourth of the sum of $2x$ and 4 is more than 5.

Lesson 3-5

Solve each inequality and graph the solutions. Check your answer.

65. $4v - 2 \le 3v$　　　　**66.** $2(7 - s) > 4(s + 2)$　　　　**67.** $\dfrac{1}{3}u - \dfrac{5}{2} \ge \dfrac{1}{6}u$

Solve each inequality.

68. $3 + 3c < 6 + 3c$　　　**69.** $4(k + 2) \ge 4k + 5$　　　**70.** $2(5 - b) \le 3 - 2b$

Write an inequality to represent each relationship. Solve your inequality.

71. The difference of three times a number and 5 is more than the number times 4.

72. One less than a number is greater than the product of 3 and the difference of 5 and the number.

Lesson 3-6

Solve each compound inequality and graph the solutions.

73. $6 < 3 + x < 8$　　　　　　　**74.** $-1 \le b + 4 \le 3$

75. $k + 5 \le -3$ OR $k + 5 \ge 1$　　　**76.** $r - 3 > 2$ OR $r + 1 < 4$

Write the compound inequality shown by each graph.

77.
$$\leftarrow\!\!+\!\!-\!\!+\!\!-\!\!\oplus\!\!-\!\!+\!\!-\!\!\bullet\!\!-\!\!+\!\!-\!\!+\!\!\rightarrow$$
$$-3\ -2\ -1\ \ 0\ \ 1\ \ 2\ \ 3$$

78.
$$\leftarrow\!\!+\!\!-\!\!\bullet\!\!-\!\!+\!\!-\!\!+\!\!-\!\!\oplus\!\!-\!\!+\!\!-\!\!+\!\!\rightarrow$$
$$-6\ -4\ -2\ \ 0\ \ 2\ \ 4\ \ 6$$

Write and graph a compound inequality for the numbers described.

79. all real numbers less than 2 and greater than or equal to -1

80. all real numbers between -3 and 1

Solve each compound inequality and graph the solutions.

81. $2r + 3 \ge 1$ AND $3r - 4 \le 5$　　　**82.** $f - 2 > 6$ OR $f + 2 < 6$

Lesson 3-7

Solve each inequality and graph the solutions.

83. $|n + 5| \le 26$　　　**84.** $|x| + 6 < 13$　　　**85.** $4|k| < 12$

86. $|c - 8| > 18$　　　**87.** $6|p| \ge 48$　　　**88.** $|3 + t| - 1 \ge 5$

Solve each inequality.

89. $|a| - 2 \le -5$　　　**90.** $2|w| + 5 < 3$　　　**91.** $|s| + 12 > 8$

Write and solve an absolute-value inequality for each expression. Graph the solutions on a number line.

92. all numbers whose absolute value is greater than 14

93. all numbers whose absolute value multiplied by 3 is less than 27

Lesson 4-1

Choose the graph that best represents each situation.

1. A person blows up a balloon with a steady airstream.

2. A person blows up a balloon steadily and then lets it deflate.

3. A person blows up a balloon slowly at first and then uses more and more air.

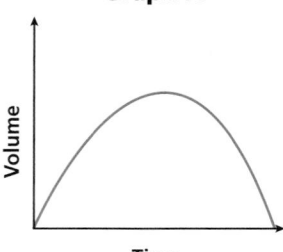

Graph A

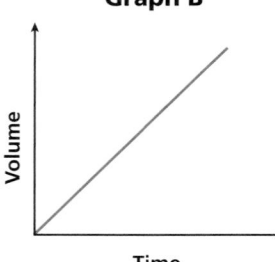

Graph B

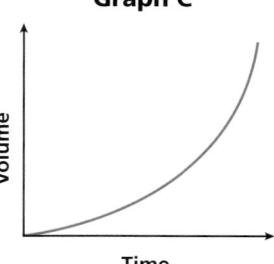

Graph C

Lesson 4-2

Express each relation as a table, as a graph, and as a mapping diagram.

4. $\{(0, 2), (-1, 3), (-2, 5)\}$

5. $\{(2, 8), (4, 6), (6, 4), (8, 2)\}$

Give the domain and range for each relation. Tell whether the relation is a function. Explain.

6. $\{(3, 4), (-1, 2), (2, -3), (5, 0)\}$

7. $\{(5, 4), (0, 2), (5, -3), (0, 1)\}$

8.

x	2	0	1	2	-1
y	1	0	-1	-2	-3

9.

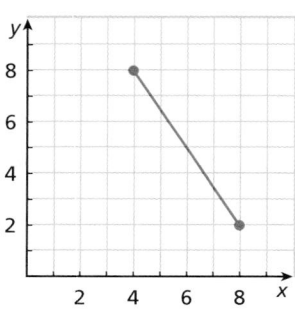

Lesson 4-3

Determine a relationship between the x- and y-variables. Write an equation.

10. $\{(1, 3), (2, 6), (3, 9), (4, 12)\}$

11. $\{(1, 1), (2, 4), (3, 9), (4, 16)\}$

Identify the independent and dependent variables. Write a rule in function notation for each situation.

12. A science tutor charges students $15 per hour.

13. A circus charges a $10 entry fee and $1.50 for each pony ride.

Evaluate each function for the given input values.

14. For $f(a) = 6 - 4a$, find $f(a)$ when $a = 2$ and when $a = -3$.

15. For $g(d) = \frac{2}{5}d + 3$, find $g(d)$ when $d = 10$ and when $d = -5$.

16. For $h(w) = 2 - w^2$, find $h(w)$ when $w = -1$ and when $w = -2$.

Graph each function.

17. $f(x) = 4 - 2x$

18. $y + 3 = 2x$

19. $y = -5 + x^2$

For each function, determine whether the given points are on the graph.

20. $y = \frac{x}{3} + 4$; $(-3, 3)$ and $(3, 5)$

21. $y = x^2 - 1$; $(-2, 3)$ and $(2, 5)$

Extra Practice

Lesson 4-4

Describe the correlation illustrated by each scatter plot.

22. 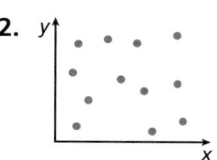 **23.** 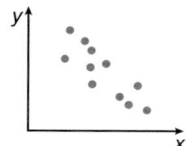 **24.**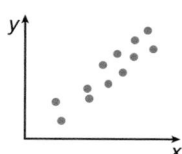

Identify the correlation you would expect to see between each pair of data sets. Explain.

25. the number of chess pieces captured and the number of pieces still on the board

26. a person's height and the color of the person's eyes

27. the number of pages in a book and the number of books in a library

28. the number of shirts purchased and the amount of money spent

29. the number of guests at a hotel and the number of available rooms

Choose the scatter plot that best represents the described situation. Explain.

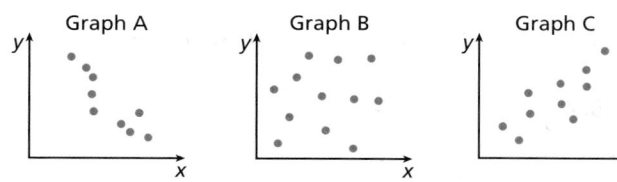

Graph A   Graph B   Graph C

30. the number of students in a class and the grades on a test

31. the number of students in a class and the number of empty desks

32. the number of correct answers on a test and the test grade

Lesson 4-5

Determine whether each sequence appears to be an arithmetic sequence. If so, find the common difference and the next three terms.

33. $-10, -7, -4, -1, \ldots$ **34.** $8, 5, 1, -4, \ldots$

35. $1, -2, 3, -4, \ldots$ **36.** $-19, -9, 1, 11, \ldots$

37. $7, 13, 18, 24, \ldots$ **38.** $13, 19, 25, 31, \ldots$

Find the indicated term of each arithmetic sequence.

39. 15th term: $-5, -1, 3, 7, \ldots$ **40.** 20th term: $a_1 = 2; d = -5$

41. 12th term: $8, 16, 24, 32, \ldots$ **42.** 21st term: $5.2, 5.17, 5.14, 5.11, \ldots$

43. 17th term: $4, 7, 10, 13, \ldots$ **44.** 31st term: $a_1 = 8; d = 9$

45. 16th term: $22, 17, 12, 7, \ldots$ **46.** 26th term: $a_1 = 3.1; d = 4$

Find the common difference for each arithmetic sequence.

47. $0, 7, 14, 21, \ldots$ **48.** $132, 121, 110, 99, \ldots$ **49.** $\frac{1}{4}, 1, \frac{7}{4}, \frac{10}{4}, \ldots$

50. $1.4, 2.2, 3, 3.8, \ldots$ **51.** $-7, -2, 3, 8, \ldots$ **52.** $7.28, 7.21, 7.14, 7.07, \ldots$

Find the next four terms in each arithmetic sequence.

53. $-3, -6, -9, -12, \ldots$ **54.** $2, 9, 16, 23, \ldots$

55. $-\frac{1}{3}, \frac{1}{3}, 1, \frac{5}{3}, \ldots$ **56.** $-4.3, -3.2, -2.1, -1, \ldots$

Extra Practice

Lesson 5-1

Graph each linear equation. Then tell whether it represents a function.

1. $y = -3x - 5$ **2.** $y = x$ **3.** $x = -3$

Without graphing, tell whether each point is on the graph of the given line.

4. $11x - 3y = 5;\ (1, 2)$ **5.** $5x + \frac{1}{2}y = 18;\ (3, -6)$

6. $5x + \frac{1}{2}y = 3;\ (-1, 4)$ **7.** $x - 5y = 17;\ (7, -2)$

8. $4x + 2y = 2;\ (-2, 5)$ **9.** $5x + y = 18;\ (3, -3)$

10. $3.5x + 2.4y = 23.6;\ (4, 4)$ **11.** $\frac{3}{4}x - 3y = 0;\ (8, -2)$

Write each equation in standard form and give the values of *A*, *B*, and *C*. Then describe the graph.

12. $12y = 15 - x$ **13.** $-4x + 13 = y$ **14.** $-\frac{3}{2}y = \frac{7}{5} - \frac{5}{6}x$ **15.** $7x = 5y + 2$

16. $7y = 24$ **17.** $10 + \frac{1}{2}x = -8y$ **18.** $6x = 20 + 4y$ **19.** $16 = 13x$

Lesson 5-2

Find the *x*- and *y*-intercepts.

20. 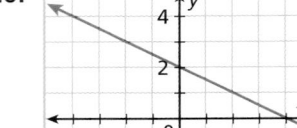 **21.**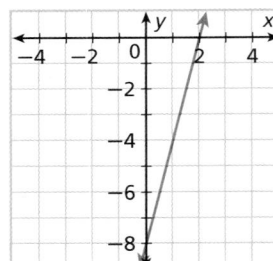

22. $-4x = 2y - 1$ **23.** $x - y = 3$ **24.** $2x - 3y = 12$ **25.** $2.5x + 2.5y = 5$

Use intercepts to graph the line described by each equation.

26. $15 = -3x - 5y$ **27.** $4y = 2x + 8$ **28.** $y = 6 - 3x$ **29.** $-2y = x + 2$

Lesson 5-3

Find the slope of each line.

30. 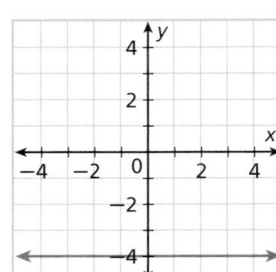 **31.**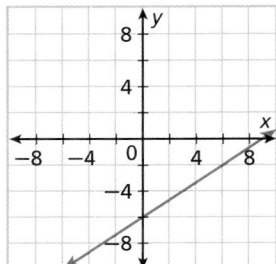

Find the slope of the line that contains each pair of points.

32. $(-1, 2)$ and $(-4, 8)$ **33.** $(2, 6)$ and $(0, 1)$ **34.** $(-2, 3)$ and $(4, 0)$

Find the slope of the line described by each equation.

35. $2y = 42 - 6x$ **36.** $3x + 4y = 12$ **37.** $3x = 15 + 5y$

Extra Practice

Lesson 5-4

Tell whether each equation represents a direct variation. If so, identify the constant of variation.

38. $x - 2y = 0$ **39.** $x - y = 3$ **40.** $3y = 2x$

41. The value of y varies directly with x, and $y = 2$ when $x = -3$. Find y when $x = 6$.

42. The value of y varies directly with x, and $y = -3$ when $x = 9$. Find y when $x = 12$.

43. The value of y varies directly with x, and $y = 3$ when $x = 9$. Find y when $x = 21$.

44. The value of y varies directly with x, and $y = \frac{1}{2}$ when $x = \frac{1}{4}$. Find y when $x = \frac{1}{2}$.

Each ordered pair is a solution of a direct variation. Write the equation of direct variation.

45. $(1, 4)$ **46.** $(-2, 12)$ **47.** $\left(\frac{1}{2}, -3\right)$ **48.** $(5, 2)$

49. $(8, 12)$ **50.** $(7, -2)$ **51.** $(12, -3)$ **52.** $(5, 15)$

Lesson 5-5

Write the equation that describes each line in slope-intercept form.

53. slope $= 2$, y-intercept $= -2$ **54.** slope $= 0.25$, y-intercept $= 4$

55. slope $= -2$, y-intercept $= 3$ **56.** slope $= \frac{1}{3}$, y-intercept $= 2$

57. slope $= 7$, y-intercept $= 5$ **58.** slope $= \frac{3}{4}$, y-intercept $= -12$

59. slope $= -\frac{5}{2}$, y-intercept $= 0$ **60.** slope $= 0.94$, y-intercept $= 3.7$

Write each equation in slope-intercept form. Then graph the line described by the equation.

61. $2y = x - 3$ **62.** $-3x - 2y = 1$ **63.** $2y - \frac{1}{2}x = 2$

Lesson 5-6

Write an equation in point-slope form for the line with the given slope that contains the given point.

64. slope $= 2$; $(0, 3)$ **65.** slope $= -1$; $(1, -1)$ **66.** slope $= \frac{1}{2}$; $(2, 4)$

67. slope $= \frac{1}{3}$; $(1, 2)$ **68.** slope $= -2$; $(3, 1)$ **69.** slope $= 3$; $(-2, -5)$

Write an equation in slope-intercept form for the line through the two points.

70. $(-1, 1)$ and $(1, -2)$ **71.** $(3, 1)$ and $(2, -3)$ **72.** $(4, -5)$ and $(2, -1)$

73. $(5, 6)$, $(2, -3)$ **74.** $(-1, 3)$, $(6, 31)$ **75.** $(0, -1)$, $(3, 35)$

76. $\left(\frac{1}{2}, 7\right)$, $(4, 35)$ **77.** $(3, -15)$, $(-2, 10)$ **78.** $(-6, 1)$, $(1, -13)$

Lesson 5-7

79. Identify which lines are parallel: $y = 3x - 2$; $y = -2$; $y = 3x + 7$; $y = 0$

80. Identify which lines are perpendicular: $y = -2(2x - 1)$; $y = \frac{1}{2}(x + 3)$; $y = \frac{1}{4}(x + 8)$; $y - 4 = 2(3 - 2x)$

Write an equation in slope-intercept form for the line that is parallel to the given line and that passes through the given point.

81. $y = -2x + 3$; $(1, 4)$ **82.** $y = x - 5$; $(2, -4)$ **83.** $y = 3x$; $(-1, 5)$

Write an equation in slope-intercept form for the line that is perpendicular to the given line and that passes through the given point.

84. $y = x + 1$; $(3, -2)$ **85.** $y = -4x - 1$; $(-1, 0)$ **86.** $y = 4x + 5$; $(2, -1)$

Extra Practice

Lesson 6-1

Tell whether the ordered pair is a solution of the given system.

1. $(1, 3);\begin{cases}2x - 3y = -7 \\ -5x + 3y = 4\end{cases}$ **2.** $(-2, 2);\begin{cases}4x + 3y = -2 \\ -2x - 2y = 2\end{cases}$ **3.** $(4, -3);\begin{cases}-2x - 3y = 1 \\ x + 2y = -2\end{cases}$

Solve each system by graphing. Check your answer.

4. $\begin{cases}y = x + 1 \\ y = -2x - 2\end{cases}$ **5.** $\begin{cases}3x + y = -8 \\ 3y = \frac{1}{2}x - 5\end{cases}$ **6.** $\begin{cases}x = 2 - 2y \\ -1 = -2x - 3y\end{cases}$

Lesson 6-2

Solve each system by substitution. Check your answer.

7. $\begin{cases}y = 12 - 3x \\ y = 2x - 3\end{cases}$ **8.** $\begin{cases}2x + y = -6 \\ -5x + y = 1\end{cases}$ **9.** $\begin{cases}y = 11 - 3x \\ -2x + y = 1\end{cases}$

10. $\begin{cases}2x + 3y = 2 \\ -\frac{1}{2}x + 2y = -6\end{cases}$ **11.** $\begin{cases}3x - 2y = -3 \\ y = 7 - 4x\end{cases}$ **12.** $\begin{cases}4y - 2x = -2 \\ x + 3y = -4\end{cases}$

Two angles whose measures have a sum of 90° are called complementary angles. For Exercises 13–15, x and y represent complementary angles. Find the measure of each angle.

13. $\begin{cases}x + y = 90 \\ y = 9x - 10\end{cases}$ **14.** $\begin{cases}x + y = 90 \\ y - 4x = 15\end{cases}$ **15.** $\begin{cases}x + y = 90 \\ y = 2x + 15\end{cases}$

Lesson 6-3

Solve each system by elimination. Check your answer.

16. $\begin{cases}x - 3y = -1 \\ -x + 2y = -2\end{cases}$ **17.** $\begin{cases}-3x - y = 1 \\ 5x + y = -5\end{cases}$ **18.** $\begin{cases}-x - 3y = -1 \\ 3x + 3y = 9\end{cases}$

19. $\begin{cases}3x - 2y = 2 \\ 3x + y = 8\end{cases}$ **20.** $\begin{cases}5x - 2y = -15 \\ 2x - 2y = -12\end{cases}$ **21.** $\begin{cases}-4x - 2y = -4 \\ -4x + 3y = -24\end{cases}$

22. $\begin{cases}-3x - 3y = 3 \\ 2x + y = -4\end{cases}$ **23.** $\begin{cases}4x - 3y = -1 \\ 2x - 2y = -4\end{cases}$ **24.** $\begin{cases}3x + 6y = 0 \\ 7x + 4y = 20\end{cases}$

Lesson 6-4

Solve each system of linear equations.

25. $\begin{cases}y = 2x + 4 \\ -2x + y = 6\end{cases}$ **26.** $\begin{cases}-y = 3 - 5x \\ y - 5x = 6\end{cases}$ **27.** $\begin{cases}y + 2 = 3x \\ 3x - y = -1\end{cases}$

28. $\begin{cases}2y = 6 - 6x \\ 3y + 9x = 9\end{cases}$ **29.** $\begin{cases}y - 1 = -3x \\ 12x + 4y = 4\end{cases}$ **30.** $\begin{cases}4x - 2y = 4 \\ 3y = 6(x - 1)\end{cases}$

Classify each system. Give the number of solutions.

31. $\begin{cases}2y = 2(4x - 3) \\ y - 1 = 4x\end{cases}$ **32.** $\begin{cases}3y + 6x = 9 \\ 2(y - 3) = -4x\end{cases}$ **33.** $\begin{cases}3x - 13 = 2y \\ -3y = 2x\end{cases}$

Lesson 6-5

Solve each system of linear equations.

34. $\begin{cases} x + y = 0 \\ y = 4x + 5 \end{cases}$
35. $\begin{cases} 2x - y = 6 \\ 5x + y = 22 \end{cases}$
36. $\begin{cases} y = 3x + 1 \\ y = -x + 9 \end{cases}$

Lesson 6-6

Tell whether the ordered pair is a solution of the given inequality.

37. $(3, 6); y > 2x + 4$
38. $(-2, -8); y \le 3x - 2$
39. $(-3, 3); y \ge -2x + 5$

40. $\left(\dfrac{1}{2}, -\dfrac{3}{4}\right); y > \dfrac{x}{2} - 1$
41. $(-4, -2); y \ge 3x + 5$
42. $(3, 7); y \le 3x - 2$

43. $(5, 0); y < -x + 4$
44. $\left(\dfrac{3}{2}, 2\right); y > 4x - 6$
45. $(-10, 12); \ y \ge -5x - 32$

Graph the solutions of each linear inequality.

46. $y > 2x$
47. $y \le -3x + 2$
48. $y \ge 2x - 1$
49. $-y < -x + 4$

50. $y \ge -2x + 4$
51. $y > -x - 3$
52. $y < \dfrac{1}{2}x + 1\dfrac{1}{2}$
53. $y \le 4x - (-1)$

Write an inequality to represent each graph.

54.

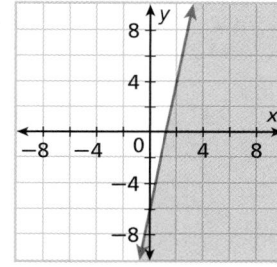

55.

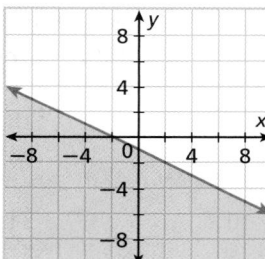

Lesson 6-7

Tell whether the ordered pair is a solution of the given system.

56. $(2, 5); \begin{cases} y > 3x - 3 \\ y \ge x + 1 \end{cases}$
57. $(3, 9); \begin{cases} y > -3x - 2 \\ y < 2x + 3 \end{cases}$
58. $(2, 3); \begin{cases} y > 2x \\ y \le x - 3 \end{cases}$

59. $(4, -9); \begin{cases} y > -3x + 2 \\ y < 2x - 16 \end{cases}$
60. $(-3, 2); \begin{cases} y \le -3x - 6 \\ y \ge x + 4 \end{cases}$
61. $(1, 7); \begin{cases} y \ge 5x + 2 \\ y > 5x + 2 \end{cases}$

Graph each system of linear inequalities. Give two ordered pairs that are solutions and two that are not solutions.

62. $\begin{cases} x + 4y < 2 \\ 2y > 3x + 8 \end{cases}$
63. $\begin{cases} y \le 6 - 2x \\ x - 2y < -2 \end{cases}$
64. $\begin{cases} 2x - 2 > -3y \\ -x + 3y \ge -10 \end{cases}$

Graph each system of linear inequalities.

65. $\begin{cases} y > 2x + 1 \\ y < 2x - 2 \end{cases}$
66. $\begin{cases} y < 3x - 1 \\ y > 3x - 4 \end{cases}$
67. $\begin{cases} y \ge -x + 2 \\ y \ge -x + 5 \end{cases}$

68. $\begin{cases} y \ge 2x - 3 \\ y \ge 2x + 3 \end{cases}$
69. $\begin{cases} y > -4x - 2 \\ y \le -4x - 5 \end{cases}$
70. $\begin{cases} y \ge -2x + 1 \\ y < -2x + 6 \end{cases}$

Extra Practice

Lesson 7-1

Simplify.

1. 3^{-4}
2. 5^{-3}
3. -4^0
4. -2^{-5}
5. 6^{-3}

6. $(-2)^{-4}$
7. 1^{-7}
8. $(-4)^{-3}$
9. $(-5)^0$
10. $(-1)^{-5}$

Evaluate each expression for the given value(s) of the variable(s).

11. x^{-4} for $x = 2$
12. $(c + 3)^{-3}$ for $c = -6$

13. $3j^{-7}k^{-1}$ for $j = -2$ and $k = 3$
14. $(2n - 2)^{-4}$ for $n = 3$

Simplify.

15. b^4g^{-5}
16. $\dfrac{k^{-3}}{r^5}$
17. $5s^{-3}c^0$
18. $\dfrac{z^{-4}}{5t^{-2}}$

19. $\dfrac{f^2}{3a^{-4}}$
20. $\dfrac{-3t^4}{q^{-5}}$
21. $\dfrac{a^0k^{-4}}{p^2}$
22. $3f^{-1}y^{-5}$

Lesson 7-2

Find the value of each power of 10.

23. 10^{-7}
24. 10^9
25. 10^6
26. 10^{-8}

Write each number as a power of 10.

27. $10,000,000$
28. 0.00001
29. $10,000,000,000,000$

Find the value of each expression.

30. 72.19×10^{-2}
31. 0.096×10^{-7}
32. 7384.5×10^6

Write each number in scientific notation.

33. $3,605,000$
34. 0.0063
35. $100,500,000$

Lesson 7-3

Simplify.

36. $3^4 \cdot 3^2$
37. $r^7 \cdot r^0$
38. $(k^4)^4$

39. $(b^4)^3$
40. $(c^3d^2)^3 \cdot (cd^2)^{-2}$
41. $(-3q^3)^{-2}$

Find the missing exponent in each expression.

42. $a^{\blacksquare}a^6 = a^9$
43. $(a^3b^{\blacksquare})^3 = \dfrac{a^9}{b^6}$
44. $(a^4b^{-2})^{\blacksquare} \cdot a^3 = \dfrac{b^4}{a^5}$

Lesson 7-4

Simplify.

45. $\dfrac{3^{11}}{3^8}$
46. $\dfrac{4^4 \cdot 5^3}{3^2 \cdot 4^3 \cdot 5^3}$
47. $\dfrac{6h^4}{12h^3}$
48. $\dfrac{r^6s^5}{r^5s^6}$

Simplify each quotient and write the answer in scientific notation.

49. $(4 \times 10^7) \div (1.6 \times 10^5)$
50. $(10 \times 10^4) \div (2 \times 10^7)$
51. $(2.5 \times 10^8) \div (5 \times 10^3)$

Simplify.

52. $\left(\dfrac{2}{3}\right)^4$
53. $\left(\dfrac{x^2y^2}{y^3}\right)^2$
54. $\left(\dfrac{4}{5}\right)^{-3}$
55. $\left(\dfrac{2xy^2}{3(xy)^2}\right)^{-3}$

Chapter 7 ■ Skills Practice

Lesson 7-5

Simplify each expression.

56. $27^{\frac{1}{3}}$

57. $256^{\frac{1}{4}}$

58. $169^{\frac{1}{2}}$

59. $0^{\frac{1}{5}}$

60. $4^{\frac{3}{2}}$

61. $49^{\frac{3}{2}}$

62. $36^{\frac{3}{2}}$

63. $16^{\frac{5}{4}}$

Simplify. All variables represent nonnegative numbers.

64. $\sqrt{x^2y^6}$

65. $\sqrt[3]{a^9b^{15}}$

66. $\dfrac{(m^8)^{\frac{1}{2}}}{\sqrt{m^4}}$

67. $\left(\sqrt[5]{g^{60}}\right)^{\frac{1}{3}}\sqrt[7]{t^{14}}$

Lesson 7-6

Find the degree of each monomial.

68. 4^7

69. x^3y

70. $\dfrac{r^6st^2}{2}$

71. 9^0

Find the degree of each polynomial.

72. $a^2b + b - 2^2$

73. $5x^4y^2 - y^5z^2$

74. $3g^4h + h^2 + 4j^6$

75. $4nm^7 - m^6p^3 + p$

Write each polynomial in standard form. Then give the leading coefficient.

76. $4r - 5r^3 + 2r^2$

77. $-3b^2 + 7b^6 + 4 - b$

78. $\dfrac{1}{2}t^3 + t - \dfrac{1}{3}t^5 + 4$

Classify each polynomial according to its degree and number of terms.

79. $3x^2 + 4x - 5$

80. $-4x^2 + x^6 - 4 + x^3$

81. $x^3 - 7^2$

Lesson 7-7

Add or subtract.

82. $4y^3 - 2y + 3y^3$

83. $9k^2 + 5 - 10k^2 - 6$

84. $7 - 3n^2 + 4 + 2n^2$

85. $\left(9x^6 - 5x^2 + 3\right) + \left(6x^2 - 5\right)$

86. $\left(2y^5 - 5y^2\right) + \left(3y^5 - y^3 + 2y^2\right)$

87. $\left(r^3 + 2r + 1\right) - \left(2r^3 - 4\right)$

88. $\left(10s^2 + 5\right) - \left(5s^2 + 3s - 2\right)$

89. $\left(2s^7 - 6s^3 + 2\right) - \left(3s^7 + 2\right)$

Lesson 7-8

Multiply.

90. $\left(3a^7\right)\left(2a^4\right)$

91. $\left(-3xy^3\right)\left(2x^2z\right)\left(yz^4\right)$

92. $\left(4k\ell^3m\right)\left(-2k^2m^2\right)$

93. $3jk^2\left(2j^2 + k\right)$

94. $4q^3r^2\left(2qr^2 + 3q\right)$

95. $3xy^2\left(2x^2y - 3y\right)$

96. $(x - 3)(x + 1)$

97. $(x - 2)(x - 3)$

98. $\left(x^2 + 2xy\right)\left(3x^2y - 2\right)$

99. $\left(x^2 - 3x\right)\left(2xy - 3y\right)$

100. $(x - 2)\left(x^2 + 3x - 4\right)$

101. $(2x - 1)\left(-2x^2 - 3x + 4\right)$

102. $(x + 3)\left(2x^4 - 3x^2 - 5\right)$

103. $(3a + b)\left(2a^2 + ab - 2b^2\right)$

104. $\left(a^2 - b\right)\left(3a^2 - 2ab + 3b^2\right)$

Lesson 7-9

Multiply.

105. $(x + 3)^2$

106. $(3 + 2x)^2$

107. $\left(4x + 2y\right)^2$

108. $(3x - 2)^2$

109. $(5 - 2x)^2$

110. $(3x - 5y)^2$

111. $(3 + x)(3 - x)$

112. $(x - 5)(x + 5)$

113. $(2x + 1)(2x - 1)$

114. $\left(x^2 + 4\right)\left(x^2 - 4\right)$

115. $\left(2 + 3x^3\right)\left(2 - 3x^3\right)$

116. $\left(4x^3 - 3y\right)\left(4x^3 + 3y\right)$

Lesson 8-1

Write the prime factorization of each number.

1. 24   **2.** 78   **3.** 88   **4.** 63

5. 128   **6.** 102   **7.** 71   **8.** 125

Find the GCF of each pair of numbers.

9. 18 and 66   **10.** 24 and 104   **11.** 30 and 75

12. 24 and 120   **13.** 36 and 99   **14.** 42 and 72

Find the GCF of each pair of monomials.

15. $4a^3$ and $9a^4$ **16.** $6q^2$ and $15q^5$ **17.** $6x^2$ and $14y^3$

18. $4z^2$ and $10z^5$ **19.** $5g^3$ and $9g$ **20.** $12x^2$ and $21y^2$

Lesson 8-2

Factor each polynomial. Check your answer.

21. $6b^2 - 15b^3$ **22.** $11t^4 - 9t^3$ **23.** $10v^3 - 25v$

24. $12r + 16r^3$ **25.** $17a^4 - 35a^2$ **26.** $9f + 18f^5 + 12f^2$

Factor each expression.

27. $3(a + 3) + 4a(a + 3)$ **28.** $5(k - 4) - 2k(k - 4)$ **29.** $5(c - 3) + 4c^2(c - 3)$

30. $3(t - 4) + t(t - 4)$ **31.** $5(2r - 1) - s(2r - 1)$ **32.** $7(3d + 4) - 2e(3d + 4)$

Factor each polynomial by grouping. Check your answer.

33. $x^3 + 3x^2 - 2x - 6$ **34.** $2m^3 - 3m^2 + 8m - 12$ **35.** $3k^3 - k^2 + 15k - 5$

36. $15r^3 + 25r^2 - 6r - 10$ **37.** $12n^3 - 6n^2 - 10n + 5$ **38.** $4z^3 - 3z^2 + 4z - 3$

39. $2k^2 - 3k + 12 - 8k$ **40.** $3p^2 - 2p + 8 - 12p$ **41.** $10d^2 - 6d + 9 - 15d$

42. $6a^3 - 4a^2 + 10 - 15a$ **43.** $12s^3 - 2s^2 + 3 - 18s$ **44.** $4c^3 - 3c^2 + 15 - 20c$

Lesson 8-3

Factor each trinomial. Check your answer.

45. $x^2 + 15x + 36$ **46.** $x^2 + 13x + 40$ **47.** $x^2 + 10x + 16$

48. $x^2 - 9x + 18$ **49.** $x^2 - 11x + 28$ **50.** $x^2 - 13x + 42$

51. $x^2 + 4x - 21$ **52.** $x^2 - 5x - 36$ **53.** $x^2 - 7x - 30$

54. Factor $c^2 - 2c - 48$. Show that the original polynomial and the factored form describe the same sequence of values for $c = 0$, 1, 2, 3, and 4.

Copy and complete the table.

	$x^2 + bx + c$	Sign of c	Binomial Factors	Sign of Numbers in Binomials
	$x^2 + 9x + 20$	Positive	$(x + 4)(x + 5)$	Both positive
55.	$x^2 - x - 20$	?		?
56.	$x^2 - 2x - 8$	?		?
57.	$x^2 - 6x + 8$	?		?

Lesson 8-4

Factor each trinomial. Check your answer.

58. $2x^2 + 13x + 15$

59. $3x^2 + 14x + 16$

60. $8x^2 - 16x + 6$

61. $6x^2 + 11x + 4$

62. $3x^2 - 11x + 6$

63. $10x^2 - 31x + 15$

64. $6x^2 - 5x - 4$

65. $8x^2 - 14x - 15$

66. $4x^2 - 11x + 6$

67. $12x^2 - 13x + 3$

68. $6x^2 - 7x - 10$

69. $6x^2 + 7x - 3$

70. $2x^2 + 5x - 12$

71. $6x^2 - 5x - 6$

72. $8x^2 + 10x - 3$

73. $10x^2 - 11x - 6$

74. $4x^2 - x - 5$

75. $6x^2 - 7x - 20$

76. $-2x^2 + 11x - 5$

77. $-6x^2 - x + 12$

78. $-8x^2 - 10x - 3$

79. $-4x^2 + 16x - 15$

80. $-10x^2 + 21x + 10$

81. $-3x^2 + 13x - 14$

Lesson 8-5

Determine whether each trinomial is a perfect square. If so, factor. If not, explain.

82. $x^2 - 8x + 16$

83. $4x^2 - 4x + 1$

84. $x^2 - 8x + 9$

85. $9x^2 - 14x + 4$

86. $4x^2 + 12x + 9$

87. $x^2 + 8x - 16$

88. $9x^2 - 42x + 49$

89. $4x^2 + 18x + 25$

90. $16x^2 - 24x + 9$

Determine whether each binomial is the difference of two squares. If so, factor. If not, explain.

91. $4 - 16x^4$

92. $-t^2 - 35$

93. $c^2 - 25$

94. $g^5 - 9$

95. $v^4 - 64$

96. $x^2 - 120$

97. $x^2 - 36$

98. $9m^2 - 15$

99. $25c^2 - 16$

Find the missing term in each perfect-square trinomial.

100. $4x^2 - 20x + $ ▧

101. $9x^2 + $ ▧ $ + 1$

102. ▧ $ - 56x + 49$

103. $9b^2 - $ ▧ $ + 25$

104. ▧ $ + 28a + 49$

105. $4a^2 + 4a + $ ▧

Lesson 8-6

Tell whether each polynomial is completely factored. If not, factor it.

106. $5(16x^2 + 4)$

107. $3r(2x - 3)(2x + 3)$

108. $(9d - 6)(2d - 7)$

109. $(5 - h)(6 - 5h)$

110. $12y^2 - 2y - 24$

111. $3f(2f^2 + 5fg + 2g^2)$

Factor each polynomial completely. Check your answer.

112. $12b^3 - 48b$

113. $24w^4 - 20w^3 - 16w^2$

114. $18k^3 - 32k$

115. $4a^3 + 12a^2 - a^2b - 3ab$

116. $3x^3y - 6x^2y^2 + 3xy^3$

117. $36p^2q - 64q^3$

118. $32a^4 - 8a^2$

119. $m^3 + 5m^2n + 6mn^2$

120. $4x^2 - 3x^2 - 16x + 48x$

121. $18d^2 + 3d - 6$

122. $2r^2 - 9r - 18$

123. $8y^2 + 4y - 4$

124. $81 - 36u^2$

125. $8x^4 + 12x^2 - 20$

126. $10j^3 + 15j^2 - 70j$

127. $27z^3 - 18z^2 + 3z$

128. $4b^2 + 2b - 72$

129. $3f^2 - 3g^2$

Extra Practice

Lesson 9-1

Without graphing, tell whether each point is on the graph of the given equation.

1. $y = x^2 - 16$; $(5, 9)$ **2.** $y = \frac{1}{2}x^2 + 2x$; $(4, 14)$

3. $y = -3x^2 + 4x + 16$; $(-2, 20)$ **4.** $y = x^2 - 8x$; $(-3, 33)$

5. $y = \frac{1}{4}x^2 - x$; $(6, 3)$ **6.** $y - 9 = 3x^2$; $(-1, 6)$

Graph each quadratic function.

7. $y = 2x^2$ **8.** $y = -3x^2 + 1$ **9.** $y = -\frac{1}{2}x^2 + 5$ **10.** $y = x^2 - 3$

Tell whether the graph of each quadratic function opens upward or downward.

11. $y = -3x^2$ **12.** $y = \frac{2}{3}x^2$ **13.** $y = x^2 + 2$ **14.** $y = -4x^2 + 2x$

Identify the vertex of each parabola. Then find the domain and range.

15. 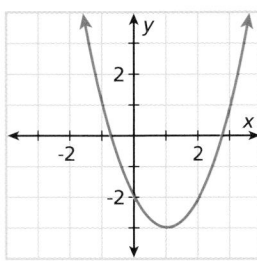   **16.** 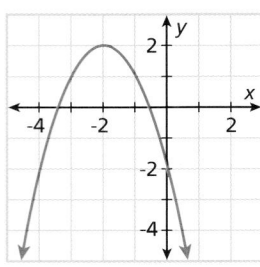   **17.**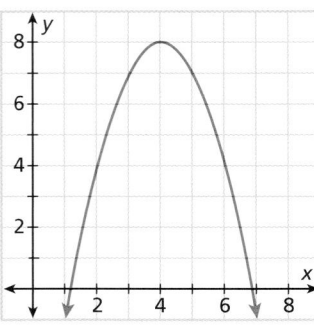

Lesson 9-2

Find the zeros of each quadratic function and the axis of symmetry of each parabola from the graph.

18. 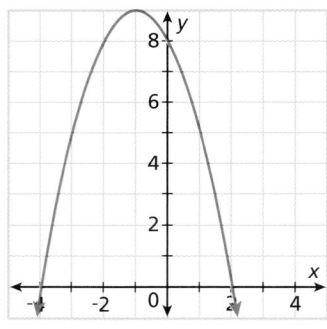   **19.** 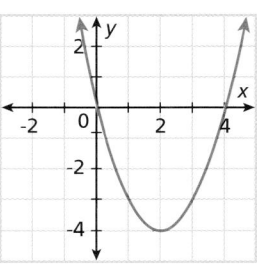   **20.**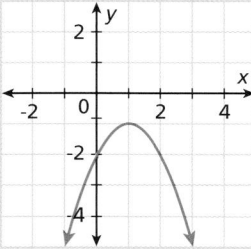

Find the vertex.

21. $y = 3x^2 - 6x + 2$ **22.** $y = -2x^2 + 8x - 3$ **23.** $y = x^2 + 2x - 4$

Lesson 9-3

Graph each quadratic function.

24. $y = x^2 - 4x + 1$ **25.** $y = -x^2 - x + 4$ **26.** $y = 3x^2 - 3x + 1$

27. $y - 2 = 2x^2$ **28.** $y + 3x^2 = 3x - 1$ **29.** $y - 4 = x^2 + 2x$

Lesson 9-4

Solve each quadratic equation by graphing the related function.

30. $x^2 - x - 2 = 0$ **31.** $x^2 - 2x + 8 = 0$ **32.** $2x^2 + 4x - 6 = 0$

33. $2x^2 + 9x = -4$ **34.** $2x^2 + 3 = 0$ **35.** $2x^2 - 2x - 12 = 0$

36. $3x^2 = -3x + 6$ **37.** $x^2 = 4$ **38.** $2x^2 + 6x - 20 = 0$

39. $-3x^2 - 2 = 0$ **40.** $x^2 = -2x + 8$ **41.** $x^2 - 2x = 15$

Chapter 9 ▪ Skills Practice

Lesson 9-5

Use the Zero Product Property to solve each equation. Check your answer.

42. $(x + 3)(x - 2) = 0$
43. $(x - 4)(x + 2) = 0$
44. $(x)(x - 4) = 0$

45. $(2x + 6)(x - 2) = 0$
46. $(3x - 1)(x + 3) = 0$
47. $(x)(2x - 4) = 0$

Solve each quadratic equation by factoring. Check your answer.

48. $x^2 + 5x + 6 = 0$
49. $x^2 - 3x - 4 = 0$
50. $x^2 + x - 12 = 0$

51. $x^2 + x - 6 = 0$
52. $x^2 - 6x + 5 = 0$
53. $x^2 + 4x - 12 = 0$

54. $x^2 = 6x - 9$
55. $2x^2 + 4x = 6$
56. $x^2 + 2x = -1$

57. $3x^2 = 3x + 6$
58. $x^2 = x + 12$
59. $4x^2 + 8x + 4 = 0$

Lesson 9-6

Solve using square roots. Check your answer.

60. $x^2 = 169$
61. $x^2 = 121$
62. $x^2 = 289$

63. $x^2 = -64$
64. $x^2 = 81$
65. $x^2 = -441$

66. $4x^2 - 196 = 0$
67. $0 = 3x^2 - 48$
68. $24x^2 + 96 = 0$

69. $10x^2 - 75 = 15$
70. $0 = 4x^2 + 144$
71. $5x^2 - 105 = 20$

Solve. Round to the nearest hundredth.

72. $4x^2 = 160$
73. $0 = 3x^2 - 66$
74. $250 - 5x^2 = 0$

75. $0 = 9x^2 - 72$
76. $48 - 2x^2 = 42$
77. $6x^2 = 78$

Lesson 9-7

Complete the square to form a perfect-square trinomial.

78. $x^2 - 8x + \blacksquare$
79. $x^2 + x + \blacksquare$
80. $x^2 + 10x + \blacksquare$

81. $x^2 - 5x + \blacksquare$
82. $x^2 + 6x + \blacksquare$
83. $x^2 - 7x + \blacksquare$

Solve by completing the square.

84. $x^2 + 6x = 91$
85. $x^2 + 10x = -16$
86. $x^2 - 4x = 12$

87. $x^2 - 8x = -12$
88. $x^2 - 12x = -35$
89. $-x^2 - 6x = 5$

90. $-x^2 - 4x + 77 = 0$
91. $-x^2 = 10x + 9$
92. $-x^2 + 63 = -2x$

Lesson 9-8

Solve using the Quadratic Formula. Round to the nearest hundredth if necessary. Check your answer.

93. $x^2 + 3x - 4 = 0$
94. $x^2 - 2x - 8 = 0$
95. $x^2 + 2x - 3 = 0$

96. $x^2 - x - 10 = 0$
97. $2x^2 - x - 4 = 0$
98. $2x^2 + 3x - 3 = 0$

Solve using at least two different methods. Check your answer.

99. $3x^2 - 8x - 16 = 0$
100. $x^2 - 49 = 0$
101. $x^2 - 2x + 1 = 0$

102. $x^2 - 3x - 10 = 0$
103. $x^2 + \frac{7}{2}x = 2$
104. $12 = x^2 - 4x$

Lesson 9-9

Find the number of solutions of each equation.

105. $x^2 + 4x + 1 = 0$
106. $2x^2 - 3x + 2 = 0$
107. $x^2 - 5x + 2 = 0$

108. $2x^2 - 4x + 2 = 0$
109. $x^2 + 2x - 5 = 0$
110. $2x^2 - 2x - 3 = 0$

Find the number of x-intercepts of each function by using the discriminant.

111. $y = 5x^2 + 10x - 6$
112. $y = 3x^2 + 12x + 4$
113. $y = x^2 + 5 - 4x$

114. $y = 3x^2 + 6x + 3$
115. $y = x + 5x^2 + 9$
116. $y = 18 + 6x + \frac{1}{2}x^2$

Extra Practice

Lesson 10-1

Tell whether each relationship is an inverse variation. Explain.

1.

x	y
4	8
8	16
16	32
32	64

2.

x	y
2	6
3	4
6	2
12	1

3.

x	y
−1	24
2	−12
4	−6
8	−3

4. $3xy = 10$

5. $y - x = 6$

6. $6xy = -1$

7. Write and graph the inverse variation in which $y = 4$ when $x = 3$.

8. Write and graph the inverse variation in which $y = \frac{1}{2}$ when $x = 6$.

9. Let $x_1 = 6$, $y_1 = 8$, and $x_2 = 12$. Let y vary inversely as x. Find y_2.

10. Let $x_1 = -4$, $y_1 = -2$, and $y_2 = 16$. Let y vary inversely as x. Find x_2.

Lesson 10-2

Identify the excluded values for each rational function.

11. $y = \frac{16}{x}$

12. $y = \frac{1}{x - 1}$

13. $y = -\frac{3}{x + 5}$

14. $y = \frac{20}{x + 20}$

Identify the asymptotes.

15. $y = \frac{2}{x - 4}$

16. $y = \frac{8}{x + 5}$

17. $y = \frac{7}{3x - 2} - 6$

18. $y = \frac{3}{2x - 2} + 4$

Graph each function.

19. $y = \frac{1}{x + 3}$

20. $y = \frac{1}{x - 2}$

21. $y = \frac{1}{x} + 4$

22. $y = \frac{3}{x - 2}$

23. $y = \frac{1}{x - 3} + 2$

24. $y = \frac{1}{x - 5} - 6$

25. $y = \frac{1}{x + 2} + 5$

26. $y = \frac{1}{x + 5} + 1$

Lesson 10-3

Find any excluded values of each rational expression.

27. $\frac{3}{7x}$

28. $\frac{-2}{x^2 - x}$

29. $\frac{6}{x^2 + x - 12}$

30. $\frac{p + 1}{p^2 + 4p - 5}$

Simplify each rational expression, if possible. Identify any excluded values.

31. $\frac{4m^2}{12m}$

32. $\frac{7x^5}{28x}$

33. $\frac{4x^2 - 8x}{x - 2}$

34. $\frac{2y}{y - 1}$

35. $\frac{5x^3 + 20x^2}{x + 4}$

36. $\frac{a + 1}{a - 2}$

37. $\frac{3y^3 + 3y}{y^2 + 1}$

38. $\frac{x^3 + 4x}{x^2 + 4}$

Simply each rational expression, if possible.

39. $\frac{b + 2}{b^2 + 5b + 6}$

40. $\frac{x - 3}{x^2 - 6x + 9}$

41. $\frac{y^2 - 4y - 5}{y^2 - 2y - 3}$

42. $\frac{(m + 2)^2}{m^2 - 6m - 16}$

43. $\frac{x^2 - 9}{x^2 + x - 12}$

44. $\frac{2 - m}{3m^2 - 6m}$

45. $\frac{x - 4}{12x^2 - 3x^3}$

46. $\frac{6 - 3x}{x^2 - 6x + 8}$

Lesson 10-4

Multiply. Simplify your answer.

47. $\dfrac{4a^3}{b^3} \cdot \dfrac{ab}{6a^2}$

48. $\dfrac{x-3}{2} \cdot \dfrac{8}{4x-12}$

49. $\dfrac{x-2}{x-5} \cdot \dfrac{2x-10}{3}$

50. $\dfrac{a^2b^3}{6a^3c} \cdot \dfrac{9b^2}{12b^5c^2}$

51. $\dfrac{3x}{2x+4} \cdot \dfrac{3x+6}{9}$

52. $\dfrac{1}{2x+4}(x^2-2x-8)$

53. $\dfrac{3x}{4x-20}(x^2+x-30)$

54. $\dfrac{4r^3+8r}{r^3} \cdot \dfrac{r}{3r^2+6}$

55. $\dfrac{a^2-3a-10}{a^2-a-6} \cdot \dfrac{a^2-2a-3}{a-5}$

56. $\dfrac{4b^2+4}{b-1} \cdot \dfrac{b^2-1}{8b^2+8}$

57. $\dfrac{pq+2q}{pq+1} \cdot \dfrac{3pq+3}{pq^2+2q^2}$

58. $\dfrac{r^2+3r+2}{4r+4} \cdot \dfrac{2r+6}{r^2-2r-8}$

Divide. Simplify your answer.

59. $\dfrac{3x^2y^3}{x^3z^2} \div \dfrac{6y^4}{x^2z^5}$

60. $\dfrac{x^2+4x+3}{3x^3+9x^2} \div (x^2-1)$

61. $\dfrac{p-1}{p^2+4p-5} \div \dfrac{p^2-2p}{p^2+3p-10}$

Lesson 10-5

Add. Simplify your answer.

62. $\dfrac{3x}{4x^3} + \dfrac{5x}{4x^3}$

63. $\dfrac{x^2+1}{x-1} + \dfrac{1-3x}{x-1}$

64. $\dfrac{2x^2}{x^2-2x-3} + \dfrac{2x}{x^2-2x-3}$

Subtract. Simplify your answer.

65. $\dfrac{5}{6y^4} - \dfrac{2}{6y^4}$

66. $\dfrac{5a^2+1}{a^2-a-6} - \dfrac{15a+1}{a^2-a-6}$

67. $\dfrac{m^2+2m}{m^2-9} - \dfrac{m+12}{m^2-9}$

Find the LCM of the given expressions.

68. $8x^5y^8,\ 6x^4y^9$

69. $x^2-4,\ x^2+7x+10$

70. $d^2-2d-3,\ d^2+d-12$

Add or subtract. Simplify your answer.

71. $\dfrac{5}{y^2} - \dfrac{3}{4y^2}$

72. $\dfrac{5}{x^2-x-6} + \dfrac{1}{x+2}$

73. $\dfrac{3x}{x-2} - \dfrac{x}{2-x}$

Lesson 10-6

Divide.

74. $(12y^5-16y^2+4y) \div 4y^2$

75. $(6m^4-18m+3) \div 6m^2$

76. $(16x^4+20x^3-4x) \div -4x^3$

77. $\dfrac{b^2-4b-5}{b+1}$

78. $\dfrac{2x^2+9x+4}{x+4}$

79. $\dfrac{6a^2-13a-5}{3a+1}$

Divide using long division.

80. $(a^2-5a-6) \div (a+1)$

81. $(2x^2+10x+8) \div (x+4)$

82. $(3y^2-11y+10) \div (y-2)$

83. $(3x^2-2x-7) \div (x-2)$

84. $(2x^2+2x-9) \div (x+3)$

85. $(5x^3+2x^2-4) \div (x-2)$

Lesson 10-7

Solve. Check your answer.

86. $\dfrac{5}{x+1} = \dfrac{4}{x-1}$

87. $\dfrac{4}{t} = \dfrac{10}{t+9}$

88. $\dfrac{8}{m} = \dfrac{6}{m+1}$

89. $\dfrac{4}{a-2} = \dfrac{8}{a+1}$

90. $\dfrac{3}{2y+4} = \dfrac{1}{y}$

91. $\dfrac{5}{4w-2} = \dfrac{6}{5w-2}$

92. $\dfrac{1}{2} + \dfrac{3}{2m} = -\dfrac{1}{m^2}$

93. $\dfrac{x}{2} + \dfrac{3}{2} = \dfrac{2}{x}$

94. $1 - \dfrac{3}{a} = \dfrac{10}{a^2}$

95. $\dfrac{3}{x+4} = \dfrac{x-5}{x+4}$

96. $\dfrac{2}{x} = \dfrac{x+2}{x^2-4}$

97. $\dfrac{4x}{x-4} - 7 = \dfrac{16}{x-4}$

Lesson 10-8

Solve. Check your answer.

98. $\dfrac{4}{3}m - \dfrac{5}{2}m = 1$

99. $\dfrac{400+k}{660+k} = 0.75$

100. $\dfrac{100}{h-5} = \dfrac{100}{h} + 10$

Chapter 11 ▪ Skills Practice

Extra Practice

Lesson 11-1

Find the domain of each square-root function.

1. $y = \sqrt{x+1}$ **2.** $y = \sqrt{x-2} + 4$ **3.** $y = \sqrt{4+x}$

4. $y = \sqrt{3x-6}$ **5.** $y = 1 + \sqrt{\dfrac{x}{3}}$ **6.** $y = \sqrt{4x-1}$

Graph each square-root function.

7. $y = \sqrt{x+2}$ **8.** $y = \sqrt{x} - 3$ **9.** $y = \sqrt{3x} + 1$

10. $y = -\sqrt{x}$ **11.** $y = 2\sqrt{x+1}$ **12.** $y = 3\sqrt{x} - 2$

Lesson 11-2

Simplify each expression.

13. $\sqrt{\dfrac{128}{2}}$ **14.** $\sqrt{7^2 + 24^2}$ **15.** $\sqrt{(4-x)^2}$

16. $\sqrt{\dfrac{3}{48}}$ **17.** $\sqrt{y^2 + 4y + 4}$ **18.** $\sqrt{5^2 - 4^2}$

Simplify. All variables represent nonnegative numbers.

19. $\sqrt{72}$ **20.** $\sqrt{75x^4y^3}$ **21.** $\sqrt{\dfrac{11}{81}}$

22. $\sqrt{\dfrac{64}{x^6}}$ **23.** $\sqrt{\dfrac{16a^4}{25b^2}}$ **24.** $\sqrt{\dfrac{18x^4}{49x^3}}$

Lesson 11-3

Add or subtract.

25. $5\sqrt{7} + 3\sqrt{7}$ **26.** $6\sqrt{2} + \sqrt{2}$ **27.** $5\sqrt{3} - 2\sqrt{3}$

28. $\sqrt{5} + 7\sqrt{5} - 9\sqrt{5}$ **29.** $2\sqrt{y} + 4\sqrt{y} - 3\sqrt{y}$ **30.** $5\sqrt{3} + 4\sqrt{2} - 3\sqrt{3}$

Simplify each expression. All variables represent nonnegative numbers.

31. $\sqrt{75} + \sqrt{27}$ **32.** $\sqrt{45} - \sqrt{20}$ **33.** $2\sqrt{12} + \sqrt{18}$

34. $3\sqrt{27x} + \sqrt{48x}$ **35.** $5\sqrt{20y} - 2\sqrt{80y}$ **36.** $\sqrt{28a} + 2\sqrt{63a} - \sqrt{175a}$

37. $\sqrt{50y} - 2\sqrt{18y} + 3\sqrt{8y}$ **38.** $\sqrt{12x} - \sqrt{27x} - \sqrt{5x}$ **39.** $5\sqrt{180s} - 6\sqrt{80s}$

Lesson 11-4

Multiply. Write each product in simplest form. All variables represent nonnegative numbers.

40. $\sqrt{5}\sqrt{10}$ **41.** $\sqrt{6}\sqrt{12}$ **42.** $\left(3\sqrt{3}\right)^2$

43. $\left(2\sqrt{7}\right)^2$ **44.** $\sqrt{6x}\sqrt{15x}$ **45.** $\sqrt{3}\left(2 + \sqrt{27}\right)$

46. $2\sqrt{5}\left(\sqrt{20} + 3\right)$ **47.** $\sqrt{2x}\left(3 + \sqrt{8x}\right)$ **48.** $\left(4 + \sqrt{3}\right)\left(1 - \sqrt{3}\right)$

49. $\left(3 + \sqrt{5}\right)\left(8 - \sqrt{5}\right)$ **50.** $\left(4 + \sqrt{2}\right)^2$ **51.** $\left(5 - \sqrt{3}\right)^2$

Simplify each quotient. All variables represent nonnegative numbers.

52. $\dfrac{\sqrt{5}}{\sqrt{3}}$ **53.** $\dfrac{2\sqrt{7}}{\sqrt{5}}$ **54.** $\dfrac{\sqrt{3}}{\sqrt{20}}$

55. $\dfrac{5\sqrt{7}}{\sqrt{50}}$ **56.** $\dfrac{\sqrt{12a}}{\sqrt{32}}$ **57.** $\dfrac{\sqrt{200x}}{\sqrt{28}}$

Lesson 11-5

Solve each equation. Check your answer.

58. $\sqrt{x} = 11$ **59.** $\sqrt{3x} = 9$ **60.** $\sqrt{-2x} = 10$

61. $5 = \sqrt{-4x}$ **62.** $\sqrt{x} + 5 = 12$ **63.** $\sqrt{x} - 4 = 1$

64. $\sqrt{3x+1} = 4$ **65.** $\sqrt{2x+5} = 3$ **66.** $\sqrt{x-4} + 1 = 7$

67. $\sqrt{6-3x} - 2 = 4$ **68.** $\sqrt{6-x} - 5 = -3$ **69.** $4\sqrt{x} = 20$

Chapter 11 ▪ Skills Practice

Lesson 11-6

Find the next three terms in each geometric sequence.

70. $1, 5, 25, 125 \ldots$

71. $736, 368, 184, 92, \ldots$

72. $-2, 6, -18, 54, \ldots$

73. $8, 2, \dfrac{1}{2}, \dfrac{1}{8}, \ldots$

74. $7, -14, 28, -56, \ldots$

75. $\dfrac{1}{9}, \dfrac{1}{3}, 1, 3, \ldots$

76. The first term of a geometric sequence is 2, and the common ratio is 3. What is the 8th term of the sequence?

77. What is the 8th term of the sequence $600, 300, 150, 75, \ldots$?

Lesson 11-7

Tell whether each set of ordered pairs satisfies an exponential function. Explain your answer.

78. $\left\{\left(-1, \dfrac{1}{2}\right), (0, 2), (1, 8), (2, 32)\right\}$

79. $\left\{\left(-1, -\dfrac{1}{2}\right), (0, 0), \left(1, \dfrac{1}{2}\right), (2, 4)\right\}$

80. $\left\{(-1, 4), (0, 1), \left(1, \dfrac{1}{4}\right), \left(2, \dfrac{1}{16}\right)\right\}$

81. $\left\{(0, 0), (1, 3), (2, 12), (3, 27)\right\}$

Graph each exponential function.

82. $y = 3(2)^x$

83. $y = \dfrac{1}{2}(4)^x$

84. $y = -3^x$

85. $y = -\dfrac{1}{2}(2)^x$

86. $y = 5\left(\dfrac{1}{2}\right)^x$

87. $y = -2(0.25)^x$

Lesson 11-8

Write an exponential growth function to model each situation. Then find the value of the function after the given amount of time.

88. The rent for an apartment is $6600 per year and increasing at a rate of 4% per year; 5 years.

89. A museum has 1200 members and the number of members is increasing at a rate of 2% per year; 8 years.

Write a compound interest function to model each situation. Then find the balance after the given number of years.

90. $4000 invested at a rate of 4% compounded quarterly; 3 years

91. $5200 invested at a rate of 2.5% compounded annually; 6 years

Write an exponential decay function to model each situation. Then find the value of the function after the given amount of time.

92. The cost of a stereo system is $800 and is decreasing at a rate of 6% per year; 5 years.

93. The population of a town is 14,000 and is decreasing at a rate of 2% per year; 10 years.

Lesson 11-9

Graph each data set. Which kind of model best describes the data?

94. $\left\{(0, 3), (1, 0), (2, -1), (3, 0), (4, 3)\right\}$

95. $\left\{(-4, -4), (-3, -3.5), (-2, -3), (-1, -2.5), (0, -2), (1, -1.5)\right\}$

96. $\left\{(0, 4), (1, 2), (2, 1), (3, 0.5), (4, 0.25)\right\}$

Look for a pattern in each data set to determine which kind of model best describes the data.

97. $\left\{(-1, -5), (0, -5), (1, -3), (2, 1), (3, 7)\right\}$

98. $\left\{(0, 0.25), (1, 0.5), (2, 1), (3, 2), (4, 4)\right\}$

99. $\left\{(-2, 11), (-1, 8), (0, 5), (1, 2), (2, -1)\right\}$

Extra Practice

Extra Practice

Chapter 1 ■ Applications Practice

Biology Use the following information for Exercises 1 and 2. *(Lesson 1-1)*

In general, every cell in the human body contains 46 chromosomes.

1. Write an expression for the number of chromosomes in *c* cells.

2. Find the number of chromosomes in 8, 15, and 50 cells.

3. On a winter day in Fairbanks, Alaska, the temperature dropped from 12°F to −16°F. How many degrees did the temperature drop? *(Lesson 1-2)*

4. Geography The elevation of the Dead Sea in Jordan is −411 meters. The greatest elevation on Earth is Mt. Everest, at 8850 meters. What is the difference in elevation between these two locations? *(Lesson 1-2)*

5. Jeremy is raising money for his school by selling magazine subscriptions. Each subscription costs $16.75. During the first week, he sells 12 subscriptions. How much money does he raise? *(Lesson 1-3)*

6. As a service charge, Nadine's checking account is adjusted by −$3 each month. What is the total amount of the adjustment over the course of one year? *(Lesson 1-3)*

7. To go from one figure to the next in the sequence of figures, each square is split into four smaller squares. How many squares will be in Figure 5? *(Lesson 1-4)*

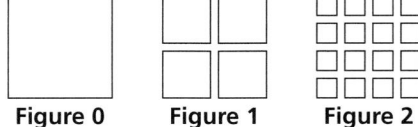

Figure 0   Figure 1   Figure 2

8. When you fold a sheet of paper in half and then open it, the crease creates 2 regions. Folding the paper in half 2 times creates 4 regions. How many regions do you create when you fold a sheet of paper in half 5 times? *(Lesson 1-4)*

9. Dan began his stamp collection with just 5 stamps in the first year. Every year thereafter, his collection grew 5 times as large as the year before. How many stamps were in Dan's collection after 4 years? *(Lesson 1-4)*

10. An art museum exhibits a square painting that has an area of 75 square feet. Find its side length to the nearest tenth. *(Lesson 1-5)*

11. Travel The base of the Washington Monument in Washington, D.C., is a square with an area of 336 yards. Find the length of one side of the monument's base to the nearest tenth. *(Lesson 1-5)*

Use the following information for Exercises 12 and 13. *(Lesson 1-6)*

The display case in a shoe store has a row of men's boots and a row of women's boots. There are 8 pairs of boots per row.

12. Write an expression that can be used to find the total number of pairs of boots.

13. Write an equivalent expression using the Distributive Property.

14. The toll to cross a bridge is $2 for cars, $5 for trucks, and $10 for buses. The total amount of money collected can be found using the expression $2C + 5T + 10B$. Use the table to find the total amount of money collected between 10 A.M. and 11 A.M. *(Lesson 1-7)*

Bridge Tolls, 10 A.M. to 11 A.M.	
Type of Vehicle	**Number**
Car *C*	104
Truck *T*	20
Bus *B*	3

15. The expression $\frac{5}{9}(F - 32)$ converts a temperature *F* in degrees Fahrenheit to a temperature in degrees Celsius. Convert 77°F to degrees Celsius. *(Lesson 1-7)*

Use the following information for Exercises 16 and 17. *(Lesson 1-7)*

An airplane has 12 rows of seats in first class and 35 rows of seats in coach. Each row has the same number of seats.

16. The total number of seats in the plane is $12x + 35x$, where *x* is the number of seats in a row. Simplify the expression.

17. Find the total number of seats in a plane that has 6 seats per row.

Chapter 2 ■ Applications Practice

1. **Economics** In 2004, the average price of an ounce of gold was $47 more than the average price in 2003. The 2004 price was $410. Write and solve an equation to find the average price of an ounce of gold in 2003. *(Lesson 2-1)*

2. During a renovation, 36 seats were removed from a theater. The theater now seats 580 people. Write and solve an equation to find the number of seats in the theater before the renovation. *(Lesson 2-1)*

3. A case of juice drinks contains 12 bottles and costs $18. Write and solve an equation to find the cost of each drink. *(Lesson 2-1)*

4. **Astronomy** Objects weigh about 3 times as much on Earth as they do on Mars. A rock weighs 42 kg on Mars. Write and solve an equation to find the rock's weight on Earth. *(Lesson 2-1)*

5. The county fair's admission fee is $8 and each ride costs $2.50. Sonia spent a total of $25.50. How many rides did she go on? *(Lesson 2-2)*

6. At the beginning of a block party, the temperature was 84°. During the party, the temperature dropped 3° every hour. At the end of the party, the temperature was 66°. How long was the party? *(Lesson 2-2)*

7. The students at a dance school are divided evenly among six teachers. This semester, there are 15 new students at the school, giving each teacher 20 students. How many students were at the school last semester? *(Lesson 2-3)*

8. Olga always orders the same meal at her favorite restaurant. She leaves a $2 tip after each meal. After 4 meals, Olga has paid a total of $44. How much does each meal cost? *(Lesson 2-3)*

9. **Consumer Economics** A health insurance policy costs $700 per year, plus a $15 payment for each visit to the doctor's office. A different plan costs $560 per year, but each office visit is $50. Find the number of office visits for which the two plans have the same total cost. *(Lesson 2-4)*

10. The ratio of students to adults on a school camping trip is $9:2$. There are 6 adults on the trip. How many students are there? *(Lesson 2-5)*

11. Paul has 8 jazz CDs. The jazz CDs are 5% of his collection. How many CDs does Paul have? *(Lesson 2-5)*

12. **Sports** Last season, a baseball team had 32 players on their active roster, 3 of whom were catchers. To the nearest percent, what percent of the players were catchers? *(Lesson 2-5)*

13. **Geometry** The formula $A = \frac{1}{2}bh$ gives the area A of a triangle with base b and height h. *(Lesson 2-6)*

    a. Solve $A = \frac{1}{2}bh$ for h.

    b. Find the height of a triangle with an area of 30 square feet and a base of 6 feet.

14. The volume of a rectangular prism can be found by using the formula $V = Ah$, where V represents the volume in units cubed, A represents the area of the base in units squared, and h represents the height of the prism. Solve the equation for A. What is the area of the base of a prism with volume 54 in. and height 4.5 in.? *(Lesson 2-6)*

15. Charles is hanging a poster on his wall. He wants the top of the poster to be 84 inches from the floor but would be happy for it to be 3 inches higher or lower. Write and solve an absolute-value equation to find the maximum and minimum acceptable heights. *(Lesson 2-7)*

16. Write and solve an absolute-value equation that represents two numbers x that are 4.5 units from 12 on the number line. *(Lesson 2-7)*

17. Lily has entered a contest where she must guess within 2% of the actual cost of the prize. The actual cost of the prize is $135. Write and solve an absolute-value equation to find the maximum and minimum prices that Lily can guess to win the prize. *(Lesson 2-7)*

1. At a food-processing factory, each box of cereal must weigh at least 15 ounces. Define a variable and write an inequality for the acceptable weights of the cereal boxes. Graph the solutions. *(Lesson 3-1)*

2. In order to qualify for a discounted entry fee at a museum, a visitor must be less than 13 years old. Define a variable and write an inequality for the ages that qualify for the discounted entry fee. Graph the solutions. *(Lesson 3-1)*

3. A restaurant can seat no more than 102 customers at one time. There are already 96 customers in the restaurant. Write and solve an inequality to find out how many additional customers could be seated in the restaurant. *(Lesson 3-2)*

4. **Meteorology** A hurricane is a tropical storm with a wind speed of at least 74 mi/h. A meteorologist is tracking a storm whose current wind speed is 63 mi/h. Write and solve an inequality to find out how much greater the wind speed must be in order for this storm to be considered a hurricane. *(Lesson 3-2)*

Hobbies Use the following information for Exercises 5–7. *(Lesson 3-3)*

When setting up an aquarium, it is recommended that you have no more than one inch of fish per gallon of water. For example, in a 30-gallon tank, the total length of the fish should be at most 30 inches.

Freshwater Fish	
Name	Length (in.)
Red tail catfish	3.5
Blue gourami	1.5

5. Write an inequality to show the possible numbers of blue gourami you can put in a 10-gallon aquarium.

6. Find the possible numbers of blue gourami you can put in a 10-gallon aquarium.

7. Find the possible numbers of red tail catfish you can put in a 20-gallon aquarium.

8. The admission fee at an amusement park is $12, and each ride costs $3.50. The park also offers an all-day pass with unlimited rides for $33. For what numbers of rides is it cheaper to buy the all-day pass? *(Lesson 3-4)*

9. The table shows the cost of Internet access at two different cafes. For how many hours of access is the cost at Cyber Station less than the cost at Web World? *(Lesson 3-5)*

Internet Access	
Cafe	Cost
Cyber Station	$12 one-time membership fee $1.50 per hour
Web World	No membership fee $2.25 per hour

10. Larissa is considering two summer jobs. A job at the mall pays $400 per week plus $15 for every hour of overtime. A job at the movie theater pays $360 per week plus $20 for every hour of overtime. How many hours of overtime would Larissa have to work in order for the job at the movie theater to pay a higher salary than the job at the mall? *(Lesson 3-5)*

11. **Health** For maximum safety, it is recommended that food be stored at a temperature between 34°F and 40°F inclusive. Write a compound inequality to show the temperatures that are within the recommended range. Graph the solutions. *(Lesson 3-6)*

12. **Physical Science** Color is determined by the wavelength of light. Wavelengths are measured in nanometers (nm). Our eyes see the color green when light has a wavelength between 492 nm and 577 nm inclusive. Write a compound inequality to show the wavelengths that produce green light. Graph the solutions. *(Lesson 3-6)*

13. Alison is running two miles. She ran the first mile in 8 min and wants to run a second mile within 0.75 min of the first mile time. Write and solve an absolute-value inequality to find the range of times for which Alison is aiming. *(Lesson 3-7)*

1. Donnell drove on the highway at a constant speed and then slowed down as she approached her exit. Sketch a graph to show the speed of Donnell's car. Tell whether the graph is continuous or discrete. *(Lesson 4-1)*

2. Lori is buying mineral water for a party. The bottles are available in six-packs. Sketch a graph showing the number of bottles Lori will have if she buys 1, 2, 3, 4, or 5 six-packs. Tell whether the graph is continuous or discrete. *(Lesson 4-1)*

3. **Health** To exercise effectively, it is important to know your maximum heart rate. You can calculate your maximum heart rate in beats per minute by subtracting your age from 220. *(Lesson 4-2)*

   a. Express the age x and the maximum heart rate y as a relation in table form by showing the maximum heart rate for people who are 20, 30, 35, and 40 years old.

   b. Is this relation a function? Why or why not?

4. **Sports** The table shows the number of games won by four baseball teams and the number of home runs each team hit. Is this relation a function? Explain. *(Lesson 4-2)*

Season Statistics	
Wins	**Home Runs**
95	185
93	133
80	140
93	167

5. Michael uses 5.5 cups of flour for each loaf of bread that he bakes. He plans to bake a maximum of 4 loaves. Write a function rule to describe the number of cups of flour used. Find a reasonable domain and range for the function. *(Lesson 4-3)*

6. A gym offers the following special rate. New members pay a $425 initiation fee and then pay $90 per year for 1, 2, or 3 years. Write a function rule to describe the situation. Find a reasonable domain and range for the function. *(Lesson 4-3)*

7. The function $y = 3.5x$ describes the number of miles y that the average turtle can walk in x hours. Graph the function. Use the graph to estimate how many miles a turtle can walk in 4.5 hours. *(Lesson 4-3)*

8. **Earth Science** The Kangerdlugssuaq glacier in Greenland is flowing into the sea at the rate of 1.6 meters per hour. The function $y = 1.6x$ describes the number of meters y that flow into the sea in x hours. Graph the function. Use the graph to estimate the number of meters that flow into the sea in 8 hours. *(Lesson 4-3)*

9. The scatter plot shows a relationship between the number of lemonades sold in a day and the day's high temperature. Based on this relationship, predict the number of lemonades that will be sold on a day when the high temperature is 96°F. *(Lesson 4-4)*

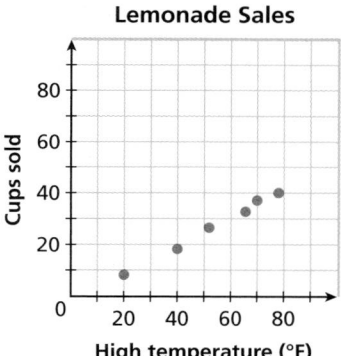

Lemonade Sales

10. The Elmwood Public Library has 85 Spanish books in its collection. Each month, the librarian plans to order 8 new Spanish books. How many Spanish books will the library have after 15 months? *(Lesson 4-5)*

11. Nikki purchases a card that she can use to ride the bus in her town. The card costs $45, and each time she rides the bus $1.50 is deducted from the value of the card. How much money will be left on the card after Nikki has taken 12 bus rides? *(Lesson 4-5)*

Extra Practice

1. Jennifer is having prints made of her photographs. Each print costs $1.50. The function $f(x) = 1.50x$ gives the total cost of the x prints. Graph this function and give its domain and range. *(Lesson 5-1)*

2. Rolando is serving on jury duty. He is paid $40, plus $15 for each day that he serves. The function $f(x) = 15x + 40$ gives Rolando's total pay for x days. Graph this function and give its domain and range. *(Lesson 5-1)*

3. The Chang family lives 400 miles from Denver. They drive to Denver at a constant speed of 50 mi/h. The function $f(x) = 400 - 50x$ gives their distance in miles from Denver after x hours. *(Lesson 5-2)*

   a. Graph this function and find the intercepts.

   b. What does each intercept represent?

4. Judith and Marie are helping their friends change the light bulbs on a wall fixture. They placed the base of the ladder 3 feet from the wall. The top of the ladder meets the wall 8 ft above the ground. What is the slope of the ladder? *(Lesson 5-3)*

5. Danny's kite is 45 ft in the air. The slope of the string is $\frac{9}{2}$. How far away is Danny from the spot on the ground directly below the kite? *(Lesson 5-3)*

6. The graph shows the temperature of an oven at different times. Find the slope of the line. Then tell what the slope represents. *(Lesson 5-3)*

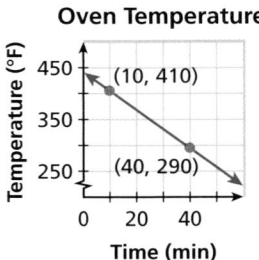

Oven Temperature

7. **Sports** Competitive race-walkers move at a speed of about 9 miles per hour. Write a direct variation equation for the distance y that a race-walker will cover in x hours. Then graph. *(Lesson 5-4)*

8. A bicycle rental costs $10 plus $1.50 per hour. The cost as a function of the number of hours is shown in the graph. *(Lesson 5-5)*

   a. Write an equation that represents the cost of a bicycle rental as a function of the number of hours.

   b. Identify the slope and y-intercept and describe their meanings in this situation.

   c. Find the cost of renting a bike for 6 hours.

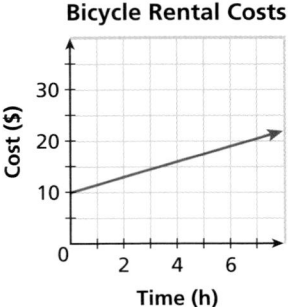

Bicycle Rental Costs

9. A hot-air balloon is moving at a constant rate. Its altitude is a linear function of time, as shown in the table. Write an equation in slope-intercept form that represents this function. Then find the balloon's altitude after 25 minutes. *(Lesson 5-6)*

Balloon's Altitude	
Time (min)	Altitude (m)
0	250
7	215
12	190

10. **Geometry** Show that the points $A(2, 3)$, $B(3, 1)$, $C(-1, -1)$, and $D(-2, 1)$ are the vertices of a rectangle. *(Lesson 5-7)*

11. Write an equation describing the line that is parallel to the y-axis and 8 units to the left of the y-axis. *(Lesson 5-7)*

12. Write an equation describing the line that is parallel to the x-axis and 5 units above the x-axis. *(Lesson 5-7)*

1. Net Sounds, an online music store, charges $12 per CD plus $3 for shipping and handling. Web Discs charges $10 per CD plus $9 for shipping and handling. For how many CDs will the cost be the same? What will that cost be? *(Lesson 6-1)*

2. At Rocco's Restaurant, a large pizza costs $12 plus $1.25 for each additional topping. At Pizza Palace, a large pizza costs $15 plus $0.75 for each additional topping. For how many toppings will the cost be the same? What will that cost be? *(Lesson 6-1)*

Use the following information for Exercises 3 and 4. *(Lesson 6-2)*

The coach of a baseball team is deciding between two companies that manufacture team jerseys. One company charges a $60 setup fee and $25 per jersey. The other company charges a $200 setup fee and $15 per jersey.

3. For how many jerseys will the cost at the two companies be the same? What will that cost be?

4. The coach is planning to purchase 20 jerseys. Which company is the better option? Why?

5. **Geometry** The length of a rectangle is 5 inches greater than the width. The sum of the length and width is 41 inches. Find the length and width of the rectangle. *(Lesson 6-2)*

6. At a movie theater, tickets cost $9.50 for adults and $6.50 for children. A group of 7 moviegoers pays a total of $54.50. How many adults and how many children are in the group? *(Lesson 6-3)*

7. **Sports** The table shows the time it took two runners to complete the Boston Marathon in several different years. If the patterns continue, will Shanna ever complete the marathon in the same number of minutes as Maria? Explain. *(Lesson 6-4)*

Marathon Times (min)				
	2003	2004	2005	2006
Shanna	190	182	174	166
Maria	175	167	159	151

8. Jordan leaves his house and rides his bike at 10 mi/h. After he goes 4 miles, his brother Tim leaves the house and rides in the same direction at 12 mi/h. If their rates stay the same, will Tim ever catch up to Jordan? Explain. *(Lesson 6-4)*

9. A 25% saltwater solution is mixed with a 45% saltwater solution to make 25 liters of a 37% solution. How many liters of each solution were mixed? *(Lesson 6-5)*

10. The sum of the digits of a two-digit number is 4. When the digits are reversed, the new number is 18 less than the original number. What is the original number? *(Lesson 6-5)*

11. Charmaine is buying almonds and cashews for a reception. She wants to spend no more than $18. Almonds cost $4 per pound, and cashews cost $5 per pound. Write a linear inequality to describe the situation. Graph the solutions. Then give two combinations of nuts that Charmaine could buy. *(Lesson 6-6)*

12. Luis is buying T-shirts to give out at a school fund-raiser. He must spend less than $100 for the shirts. Child shirts cost $5 each, and adult shirts cost $8 each. Write a linear inequality to describe the situation. Graph the solutions. Then give two combinations of shirts that Luis could buy. *(Lesson 6-6)*

13. Nicholas is buying treats for his dog. Beef cubes cost $3 per pound, and liver cubes cost $2 per pound. He wants to buy at least 2 pounds of each type of treat, and he wants to spend no more than $14. Graph all possible combinations of the treats that Nicholas could buy. List two possible combinations. *(Lesson 6-7)*

14. **Geometry** The perimeter of a rectangle is at most 20 inches. The length and the width are each at least 3 inches. Graph all possible combinations of lengths and widths that result in such a rectangle. List two possible combinations. *(Lesson 6-7)*

1. The eye of a bee is about 10^{-3} m in diameter. Simplify this expression. *(Lesson 7-1)*

2. A typical stroboscopic camera has a shutter speed of 10^{-6} seconds. Simplify this expression. *(Lesson 7-1)*

3. **Space Exploration** During a mission that took place in August, 2005, the Space Shuttle *Discovery* traveled a total distance of 9.3×10^6 km. The Space Shuttle's velocity was 28,000 km/h. *(Lesson 7-2)*

   a. Write the total distance that the Space Shuttle traveled in standard form.

   b. Write the Space Shuttle's velocity in scientific notation.

4. There are approximately 10,000,000 grains in a pound of salt. Write this number in scientific notation. *(Lesson 7-2)*

5. A high-speed centrifuge spins at a speed of 2×10^4 rotations per minute. How many rotations does it make in one hour? Write your answer in scientific notation. *(Lesson 7-3)*

6. **Astronomy** Earth travels approximately 5.8×10^8 miles as it makes one orbit of the Sun. How far does Earth travel in 50 years? (*Note:* One year is one orbit of the Sun.) Write your answer in scientific notation. *(Lesson 7-3)*

7. **Geography** In 2005, the population of Indonesia was 2.4×10^8. This was 8 times the population of Afghanistan. What was the population of Afghanistan in 2005? Write your answer in standard form. *(Lesson 7-4)*

8. The Golden Gate Bridge weighs about 8×10^8 kg. The Eiffel Tower weighs about 1×10^7 kg. How many times heavier is the Golden Gate Bridge than the Eiffel Tower? Write your answer in standard form. *(Lesson 7-4)*

9. Carl has 4 identical cubes lined up in a row and wants to find the total length of the cubes. He knows that the volume of one cube is 343 in³. Use the formula $s = V^{\frac{1}{3}}$ to find the length of one cube. What is the length of the row of cubes? *(Lesson 7-5)*

10. A rock is thrown off a 220-foot cliff with an initial velocity of 50 feet per second. The height of the rock above the ground is given by the polynomial $-16t^2 - 50t + 220$, where t is the time in seconds after the rock has been thrown. What is the height of the rock above the ground after 2 seconds? *(Lesson 7-6)*

11. The sum of the first n natural numbers is given by the polynomial $\frac{1}{2}n^2 + \frac{1}{2}n$. Use this polynomial to find the sum of the first 9 natural numbers. *(Lesson 7-6)*

12. **Biology** The population of insects in a meadow depends on the temperature. A biologist models the population of insect A with the polynomial $0.02x^2 + 0.5x + 8$ and the population of insect B with the polynomial $0.04x^2 - 0.2x + 12$, where x represents the temperature in degrees Fahrenheit. *(Lesson 7-7)*

    a. Write a polynomial that represents the total population of both insects.

    b. Write a polynomial that represents the difference of the populations of insect B and insect A.

13. **Geometry** The length of the rectangle shown is 1 inch longer than 3 times the width.

    a. Write a polynomial that represents the area of the rectangle.

    b. Find the area of the rectangle when the width is 4 inches. *(Lesson 7-8)*

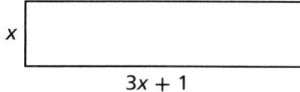

14. A cabinet maker starts with a square piece of wood and then cuts a square hole from its center as shown. Write a polynomial that represents the area of the remaining piece of wood. *(Lesson 7-9)*

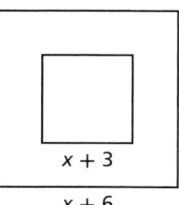

1. Ms. Andrews's class has 12 boys and 18 girls. For a class picture, the students will stand in rows on a set of steps. Each row must have the same number of students, and each row will contain only boys or girls. How many rows will there be if Ms. Andrews puts the maximum number of students in each row? *(Lesson 8-1)*

2. A museum director is planning an exhibit of Native American baskets. There are 40 baskets from North America and 32 baskets from South America. The baskets will be displayed on shelves so that each shelf has the same number of baskets. Baskets from North and South America will not be placed together on the same shelf. How many shelves will be needed if each shelf holds the maximum number of baskets? *(Lesson 8-1)*

3. The area of a rectangular painting is $\left(3x^2 + 5x\right)$ ft². Factor this polynomial to find expressions for the dimensions of the painting. *(Lesson 8-2)*

4. **Geometry** The surface area of a cylinder with radius r and height h is given by the expression $2\pi r^2 + 2\pi rh$. Factor this expression. *(Lesson 8-2)*

5. The area of a rectangular classroom in square feet is given by $x^2 + 9x + 18$. The width of the classroom is $(x + 3)$ ft. What is the length of the classroom? *(Lesson 8-3)*

Gardening Use the following information for Exercises 6 and 7.

A rectangular flower bed has a width of $(x + 4)$ ft. The bed will be enlarged by increasing the length, as shown. *(Lesson 8-3)*

6. The original flower bed has an area of $\left(x^2 + 9x + 20\right)$ ft². What is its length?

7. The enlarged flower bed will have an area of $\left(x^2 + 12x + 32\right)$ ft². What will be the new length of the flower bed?

8. A rectangular poster has an area of $\left(6x^2 + 19x + 15\right)$ in². The width of the poster is $(2x + 3)$ in. What is the length of the poster? *(Lesson 8-4)*

9. **Physical Science** The height of an object thrown upward with a velocity of 38 feet per second from an initial height of 5 feet can be modeled by the polynomial $-16t^2 + 38t + 5$, where t is the time in seconds. Factor this expression. Then use the factored expression to find the object's height after $\frac{1}{2}$ second. *(Lesson 8-4)*

10. A rectangular pool has an area of $\left(9x^2 + 30x + 25\right)$ ft². The dimensions of the pool are of the form $ax + b$, where a and b are whole numbers. Find an expression for the perimeter of the pool. Then find the perimeter when $x = 5$. *(Lesson 8-5)*

11. **Geometry** The area of a square is $9x^2 - 24x + 16$. Find the length of each side of the square. Is it possible for x to equal 1 in this situation? Why or why not? *(Lesson 8-5)*

Architecture Use the following information for Exercises 12–14. *(Lesson 8-6)*

An architect is designing a rectangular hotel room. A balcony that is 5 feet wide runs along the length of the room, as shown in the figure.

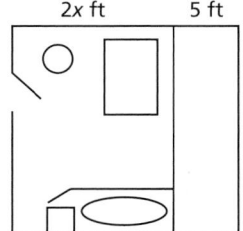

12. The area of the room, including the balcony, is $\left(4x^2 + 12x + 5\right)$ ft². Tell whether the polynomial is fully factored. Explain.

13. Find the length and width of the room (including the balcony).

14. How long is the balcony when $x = 9$?

1. The height in feet of a football x seconds after it is kicked into the air is modeled by the function $y = -16x^2 + 36x$. *(Lesson 9–1)*

   a. In this situation, what is a reasonable domain?

   b. How long is the football in the air?

2. The height of the curved roof of a camping tent can be modeled by $f(x) = -0.5x^2 + 3x$, where x is the width in feet. Find the height of the tent at its tallest point. *(Lesson 9-2)*

3. **Engineering** A small bridge passes over a stream. The height in feet of the bridge's curved arch support can be modeled by $f(x) = -0.25x^2 + 2x + 1.5$, where the x-axis represents the level of the water. Find the height of the arch support. *(Lesson 9-2)*

4. **Sports** The height in meters of a football that is kicked from the ground is approximated by $f(x) = -5x^2 + 20x$, where x is the time in seconds after the ball is kicked. Find the ball's maximum height and the time it takes the ball to reach this height. Then find how long the ball is in the air. *(Lesson 9-3)*

5. A model rocket is launched into the air with an initial velocity of 144 feet per second. The quadratic function $y = -16x^2 + 144x$ models the height of the rocket after x seconds. How long is the rocket in the air? *(Lesson 9-4)*

6. A gymnast jumps on a trampoline. The quadratic function $y = -16x^2 + 24x$ models her height in feet above the trampoline after x seconds. How long is the gymnast in the air? *(Lesson 9-4)*

7. A child standing on a rock tosses a ball into the air. The height of the ball above the ground is modeled by $h = -16t^2 + 28t + 8$, where h is the height in feet and t is the time in seconds. Find the time it takes the ball to reach the ground. *(Lesson 9-5)*

8. A fireworks rocket is shot directly up from the edge of a rooftop. The height of the rocket above the ground is modeled by $h = -16t^2 + 40t + 24$, where h is the height in feet and t is the time in seconds. Find the time it takes the rocket to hit the ground. *(Lesson 9-5)*

9. **Geometry** The base of the triangle in the figure is five times the height. The area of the triangle is 400 in². Find the height of the triangle to the nearest tenth. *(Lesson 9-6)*

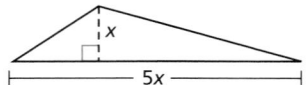

10. The length of a rectangular swimming pool is 8 feet greater than the width. The pool has an area of 240 ft². Find the length and width of the pool. *(Lesson 9-7)*

11. **Geometry** One base of a trapezoid is 4 ft longer than the other base. The height of the trapezoid is equal to the shorter base. The trapezoid's area is 80 ft². Find the height. $\left(\text{Hint: } A = \frac{1}{2}h\left(b_1 + b_2\right)\right)$ *(Lesson 9-7)*

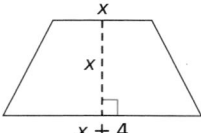

12. A referee tosses a coin into the air at the start of a football game to decide which team will get the ball. The height of the coin above the ground is modeled by $h = -16t^2 + 12t + 4$, where h is the height in feet and t is the time in seconds after the coin is tossed. Will the coin reach a height of 8 feet? Use the discriminant to explain your answer. *(Lesson 9-9)*

13. When Marshall came home from school, he kicked his shoe off of his foot into the air. The height of the shoe in feet can be modeled by the quadratic function $h = -0.8s^2 + 2s$, where s is the number of seconds after the shoe is kicked. *(Lesson 9-8)*

    a. Find the height of the shoe after 1 second.

    b. For how long is the shoe in the air?

    c. Find the maximum height of the shoe.

1. The inverse variation $xy = 200$ relates the number of words per minute x at which a person types to the number of minutes y that it takes to type a 200-word paragraph. Determine a reasonable domain and range and then graph this inverse variation. Use the graph to estimate how many minutes it would take to type the paragraph at a rate of 60 words per minute. *(Lesson 10-1)*

2. **Business** The owner of a deli finds that the number of sandwiches sold in one day varies inversely as the price of the sandwiches. When the price is \$4.50, the deli sells 60 sandwiches. How many sandwiches can the owner expect to sell when the price is \$3.60? *(Lesson 10-1)*

3. A gardener has \$30 in his budget to buy packets of seeds. He receives 3 free packets of seeds with his order. The number of packets y he can buy is $y = \frac{30}{x} + 3$, where x is the price per packet. Describe the reasonable domain and range values. Then graph the function. *(Lesson 10-2)*

4. Ashley wants to save \$1000 for a trip to Europe. She puts aside x dollars per month, and her grandmother contributes \$10 per month. The number of months y it will take to save \$1000 is $y = \frac{1000}{x + 10}$. Describe the reasonable domain and range values. Then graph the function. *(Lesson 10-2)*

5. **Geometry** Find the ratio of the area of a circle to the circumference of the circle. (*Hint:* For a circle, $A = \pi r^2$ and $C = 2\pi r$). For what radius is this ratio equal to 1? *(Lesson 10-3)*

6. **Geometry** For a cylinder with radius r and height h, the volume is $V = \pi r^2 h$, and the surface area is $S = 2\pi r^2 + 2\pi rh$. What is the ratio of the volume to the surface area for a cylinder? What is this ratio when $r = h = 1$? *(Lesson 10-3)*

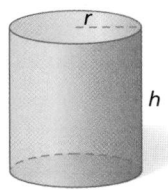

7. A committee consists of five more women than men. The chairperson randomly chooses one person to serve as secretary and a different person to serve as treasurer. Write and simplify an expression that represents the probability that both people who are chosen are men. What is the probability of choosing two men if there are 6 men on the committee? *(Lesson 10-4)*

8. **Transportation** A delivery truck makes a delivery to a town 150 miles away traveling r miles per hour. On the return trip, the delivery truck travels 20% faster. Write and simplify an expression for the truck's round-trip delivery time in terms of r. Then find the round-trip delivery time if the truck travels 55 mi/h on its way to the delivery. *(Lesson 10-5)*

9. **Recreation** Jordan is hiking 2 miles to a vista point at the top of a hill and then back to his campsite at the base of the hill. His downhill rate is 3 times his uphill rate, r. Write and simplify an expression in terms of r for the time that the round-trip hike will take. Then find how long the hike will take if Jordan's uphill rate is 2 mi/h. *(Lesson 10-5)*

10. **Geometry** The volume of a rectangular prism is the area of the base times the height. A rectangular prism has a volume given by $(2x^2 + 7x + 5)$ cm^3 and a height given by $(x + 1)$ cm. What is the area of the base of the rectangular prism? *(Lesson 10-6)*

11. Tanya can deliver newspapers to all of the houses on her route in 1 hour. Her brother, Nick, can deliver newspapers along the same route in 2 hours. How long will it take to deliver the newspapers if they work together? *(Lesson 10-7)*

12. **Agriculture** Grains are harvested using a combine. A farm has two combines—one that can harvest the wheat field in 9 hours and another that can harvest the wheat field in 11 hours. How long will it take to harvest the wheat field using both combines? *(Lesson 10-8)*

1. The function $f(x) = \sqrt{1.44x}$ gives the approximate distance in miles to the horizon as observed by a person whose eye level is x feet above the ground. Jamal stands on a tower so that his eyes are 180 ft above the ground. What is the distance to the horizon? Round your answer to the nearest tenth. (*Lesson 11-1*)

2. **Geometry** Given the surface area, S, of a sphere, the formula $r = \sqrt{\frac{S}{4\pi}}$ can be used to find the sphere's radius. What is the radius of a sphere with a surface area of 100 m²? Use 3.14 for π. Round your answer to the nearest hundredth of a meter. (*Lesson 11-1*)

3. **Cooking** A chef has a square baking pan with sides 8 inches long. She wants to know if an 11-inch fish can fit in the pan. Find the length of the diagonal of the pan. Give the answer as a radical expression in simplest form. Then estimate the length to the nearest tenth of an inch. Tell whether the fish will fit in the pan. (*Lesson 11-2*)

4. Alicia wants to put a fence around the irregular garden plot shown. Find the perimeter of the plot. Give your answer as a radical in simplest form. (*Lesson 11-3*)

5. **Physical Science** The velocity of an object in meters per second is given by $\frac{\sqrt{2}\sqrt{E}}{\sqrt{m}}$, where E is kinetic energy in Joules and m is mass in kilograms. What is the velocity of an object that has 40 Joules of kinetic energy and a mass of 10 kilograms? Give the answer as a radical expression in simplest form. Then estimate the velocity to the nearest tenth. (*Lesson 11-4*)

6. A rectangular window has an area of 40 ft². The window is 8 feet long and its height is $\sqrt{x+2}$ ft. What is the value of x? What is the height of the window? (*Lesson 11-5*)

7. Scientists who are developing a vaccine track the number of new infections of a disease each year. The values in the table form a geometric sequence. To the nearest whole number, how many new infections will there be in the 6th year? (*Lesson 11-6*)

Year	Number of New Infections
1	12,000
2	9000
3	6750

8. **Finance** For a savings account that earns 5% interest each year, the function $f(x) = 2000(1.05)^x$ gives the value of a $2000 investment after x years. (*Lesson 11-7*)

   a. Find the investment's value after 5 years.

   b. Approximately how many years will it take for the investment to be worth $3100?

9. **Chemistry** Cesium-137 has a half-life of 30 years. Find the amount left from a 200-gram sample after 150 years. (*Lesson 11-8*)

10. The cost of tuition at a dance school is $300 a year and is increasing at a rate of 3% a year. Write an exponential growth function to model the situation and find the cost of tuition after 4 years. (*Lesson 11-8*)

11. Use the data in the table to describe how the price of the company's stock is changing. Then write a function that models the data. Use your function to predict the price of the company's stock after 7 years. (*Lesson 11-9*)

Stock Prices				
Year	0	1	2	3
Price ($)	10.00	11.00	12.20	13.31

12. Use the data in the table to describe the rate at which Susan reads. Then write a function that models the data. Use your function to predict the number of pages Susan will read in 6 hours. (*Lesson 11-9*)

Total Number of Pages Read				
Time (h)	1	2	3	4
Pages	48	96	144	192

Skills Bank

Place Value

The number 5,304,293,087,201.286 is shown in the place-value chart below.

Trillions	Billions	Millions	Thousands	Ones	.	Tenths	Hundredths	Thousandths
5,	304,	293,	087,	201	.	2	8	6

EXAMPLE 1 Use the place-value chart to find the place value of the underlined digit.

A 5,30<u>4</u>,293,087,201.286
billions

B 5,304,2<u>9</u>3,087,201.286
ten millions

C 5,304,293,087,201.28<u>6</u>
thousandths

Expanded form shows a number as the sum of the values of each digit.

EXAMPLE 2 Write 16,752,045.12 in expanded form.

$10,000,000 + 6,000,000 + 700,000 + 50,000 + 2,000 + 40 + 5 + 0.1 + 0.02$

PRACTICE

Use the place-value chart to find the place value of the underlined digit.

1. 22.3<u>8</u>

2. 1,2<u>3</u>8,400

3. <u>2</u>,809,354.003

Write each number in expanded form.

4. 899,456

5. 1645.445

6. 3,009,844,002,359

Times Tables

You can use a multiplication table to multiply and to write *number families*. A **number family** is a group of related number sentences that use the same numbers.

EXAMPLE 1

Find 8 · 9.
Find where the 8's row and the 9's column intersect.
$8 \cdot 9 = 72$

EXAMPLE 2

Write a multiplication and division number family for 8, 9, and 72.

$8 \cdot 9 = 72$
$9 \cdot 8 = 72$
$72 \div 9 = 8$
$72 \div 8 = 9$

×	1	2	3	4	5	6	7	8	9	10	11	12
1	1	2	3	4	5	6	7	8	9	10	11	12
2	2	4	6	8	10	12	14	16	18	20	22	24
3	3	6	9	12	15	18	21	24	27	30	33	36
4	4	8	12	16	20	24	28	32	36	40	44	48
5	5	10	15	20	25	30	35	40	45	50	55	60
6	6	12	18	24	30	36	42	48	54	60	66	72
7	7	14	21	28	35	42	49	56	63	70	77	84
8	8	16	24	32	40	48	56	64	72	80	88	96
9	9	18	27	36	45	54	63	72	81	90	99	108
10	10	20	30	40	50	60	70	80	90	100	110	120
11	11	22	33	44	55	66	77	88	99	110	121	132
12	12	24	36	48	60	72	84	96	108	120	132	144

PRACTICE

Multiply. Write a multiplication and division number family for each set of numbers.

1. 4 · 8
2. 5 · 12
3. 3 · 11
4. 8 · 7
5. 9 · 6
6. 12 · 12

Compare and Order Rational Numbers

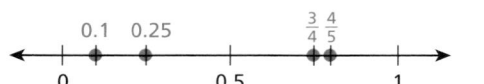 **7NS1.1**

You can compare and order rational numbers by graphing them on the number line.

EXAMPLE Order 0.25, $\frac{3}{4}$, 0.1, and $\frac{4}{5}$ from least to greatest.

$$\frac{3}{4} = 0.75$$

$$\frac{4}{5} = 0.8$$

On the number line, the values increase from left to right: 0.1, 0.25, $\frac{3}{4}$, $\frac{4}{5}$.

PRACTICE

Order each set of numbers from least to greatest.

1. 2.6, $2\frac{2}{5}$, $2\frac{1}{2}$

2. 0.45, $\frac{3}{8}$, $\frac{4}{9}$

3. 0.55, $\frac{2}{3}$, 0.6

4. 5.25, $5\frac{1}{3}$, 5.05, 5.5

5. 0.4, $\frac{3}{5}$, $\frac{1}{4}$, 0.42

6. $\frac{5}{8}$, $\frac{4}{9}$, 0.6, $\frac{6}{7}$

Inverse Operations

Inverse operations "undo" each other. Addition and subtraction are inverse operations. Multiplication and division are inverse operations.

EXAMPLE Use inverse operations to check each answer.

A $567 - 180 \overset{?}{=} 487$

$487 + 180$ — *Use addition to check subtraction.*

667

$667 \neq 567$

incorrect

B $110 \div 11 \overset{?}{=} 10$

$10 \cdot 11$ — *Use multiplication to check division.*

110

$110 = 110$

correct

PRACTICE

Use inverse operations to check each answer.

1. $51 + 25 = 86$

2. $14 \cdot 4 = 48$

3. $144 \div 4 = 36$

4. $345 - 72 = 273$

5. $134 + 653 = 787$

6. $364 \div 7 = 52$

7. $500 - 428 = 82$

8. $6 \cdot 25 = 150$

Mental Math

Mental math strategies include using the Distributive Property, using the Commutative Property, and using facts about powers of 10.

EXAMPLE   Use mental math to solve each problem.

A 6 • 17

Break 17 into 10 + 7. Then use the Distributive Property.

$$6 \cdot 17 = 6(10 + 7)$$
$$= 6(10) + 6(7)$$
$$= 60 + 42$$
$$= 102$$

B 225 + 78 + 75

Use the Commutative Property to add or multiply numbers in a different order.

$$225 + 78 + 75 = 225 + 75 + 78$$
$$= 300 + 78$$
$$= 378$$

C 132 • 100,000

Count the number of zeros in 100,000. Move the decimal point that many places right.

$$132 \cdot 100{,}000 = 13{,}200{,}000$$
$$= 13{,}200{,}000$$

PRACTICE

Use mental math to solve each problem.

1. 3987 • 10,000

2. 5 • 29

3. 950 + 273 + 50

4. 12 • 41

5. 25 • 42 • 4

6. 4.5 • 100 • 2

Divisibility

A number is divisible by another number if their quotient is a whole number with no remainder.

You can use the divisibility rules below to determine whether one number is divisible by another without having to perform any division. These rules are particularly useful when you are working with large numbers.

A number is divisible by...	Divisible	Not divisible
2 if the last digit is an even number.	72	131
3 if the sum of the digits is divisible by 3.	123	916
4 if the last two digits form a number divisible by 4.	1024	823
5 if the last digit is 0 or 5.	100	52
6 if the number is divisible by 2 and 3.	120	592
9 if the sum of the digits is divisible by 9.	1692	9059
10 if the last digit is 0.	460	205

PRACTICE

Determine whether each number is divisible by 2, 3, 4, 5, 6, 9, or 10.

1. 266

2. 654

3. 894

4. 10,020

5. 4688

6. 2269

7. 363

8. 76,708

9. 481

10. 1552

Factoring Numbers

Whole numbers that are multiplied to find a product are called **factors** of that product. A number is divisible by its factors.

$3 \cdot 5 = 15$

$15 \div 3 = 5$ ← 15 is divisible by 3 and 5.

$15 \div 5 = 3$

Factors   Product

EXAMPLE   **List all of the factors of each number.**

A 24

Begin listing factors in pairs.

$24 = 1 \cdot 24$	*1 and 24 are factors.*
$24 = 2 \cdot 12$	*2 and 12 are factors.*
$24 = 3 \cdot 8$	*3 and 8 are factors.*
$24 = 4 \cdot 6$	*4 and 6 are factors.*
	5 is not a factor.
$24 = 6 \cdot 4$	*6 and 4 have already been listed, so stop here.*

The factors of 24 are 1, 2, 3, 4, 6, 8, 12, and 24.

B 15

Begin listing factors in pairs.

$15 = 1 \cdot 15$	*1 and 15 are factors.*
	2 is not a factor.
$15 = 3 \cdot 5$	*3 and 5 are factors.*
	4 is not a factor.
$15 = 5 \cdot 3$	*5 and 3 have already been listed, so stop here.*

The factors of 15 are 1, 3, 5, and 15.

C 17

Begin listing factors in pairs.

$17 = 1 \cdot 17$	*1 and 17 are factors.*
	17 is not divisible by any other whole numbers.

The factors of 17 are 1 and 17.

PRACTICE

List all of the factors of each number.

1. 12

2. 21

3. 52

4. 81

5. 34

6. 82

7. 67

8. 87

9. 75

Prime and Composite Numbers

A **prime number** is a whole number greater than 1 that has exactly 2 factors, 1 and itself. For example, 11 is a prime number because it is divisible by only 1 and 11.

A **composite number** is a whole number greater than 1 with more than 2 factors. For example, 25 is a composite number because it is divisible by 1, 5, and 25.

The numbers 0 and 1 are neither prime nor composite.

EXAMPLE Determine whether each number is prime or composite.

 19
Factors: 1, 19
19 is prime.

 20
Factors: 1, 2, 4, 5, 10, 20
20 is composite.

PRACTICE

Determine whether each number is prime or composite.

1. 7   **2.** 15   **3.** 18   **4.** 8

5. 113   **6.** 31   **7.** 12   **8.** 49

9. 77   **10.** 67   **11.** 9   **12.** 79

Prime Factorization

A composite number can be expressed as a product of its factors in many different ways. But there is only one way to write a composite number as a product of prime numbers (except for changes in order). This product is the **prime factorization** of the number. To find the prime factorization of a number, you can use a **factor tree.**

EXAMPLE Find the prime factorization of 42 by using a factor tree.

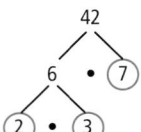

Write the number to be factored.

Choose any two factors of 42.

Continue until each branch ends in a prime factor.

The prime factorization of 42 is $2 \cdot 3 \cdot 7$.

PRACTICE

Find the prime factorization of each number.

1. 20   **2.** 81   **3.** 28   **4.** 115   **5.** 300

6. 90   **7.** 27   **8.** 125   **9.** 450   **10.** 51

Decimals, Fractions, and Percents

A **percent** is a ratio of a number to 100. Numbers can be represented by decimals, percents, or fractions. You should be able to change a number from one form to another.

EXAMPLE

A Write 0.43 as a percent.

Method 1 Multiply by 100.

$0.43 \cdot 100$ *Multiply by 100.*

43%   *Add the percent symbol.*

Method 2 Use place value.

$0.43 = \dfrac{43}{100}$ *Write the decimal as a fraction.*

43%   *Write the numerator with a percent symbol.*

B Write $\dfrac{4}{5}$ as a percent.

Method 1 Write an equivalent fraction with a denominator of 100.

$\dfrac{4 \cdot 20}{5 \cdot 20} = \dfrac{80}{100}$ *Multiply the denominator by a number so that the product is 100. Then multiply the numerator by the same number.*

$\dfrac{80}{100} = 80\%$ *Write the numerator with a percent symbol.*

Method 2 Use division to write the fraction as a decimal.

$5\overline{)4.0}^{\,0.8}$ *Divide the numerator by the denominator.*

$0.8 = 80\%$ *Write the quotient as a percent.*

C Write 38% as a fraction.

$38\% = \dfrac{38}{100}$ *Write the percent as a fraction with a denominator of 100.*

$= \dfrac{19}{50}$ *Simplify.*

PRACTICE

Write each decimal as a percent.

1. 0.39   **2.** 0.125   **3.** 0.8   **4.** 0.112   **5.** 0.6

Write each fraction as a percent.

6. $\dfrac{11}{25}$ **7.** $\dfrac{7}{8}$ **8.** $\dfrac{7}{10}$ **9.** $\dfrac{1}{2}$ **10.** $\dfrac{9}{20}$

Write each percent as a fraction.

11. 74%   **12.** 40%   **13.** 59%   **14.** 4%   **15.** 28%

Greatest Common Factor (GCF)

 6NS2.4

The **greatest common factor (GCF)** of two or more whole numbers is the greatest factor that the numbers share.

EXAMPLE   Find the GCF of 18 and 30.

Method 1 List all the factors of both numbers.

Find all the common factors.

18: 1, 2, 3, 6, 9, 18

30: 1, 2, 3, 5, 6, 10, 15, 30

The common factors are 1, 2, 3, and 6.

The GCF is 6.

Method 2 Find the prime factorization.

Then find the common prime factors.

18: $2 \cdot 3 \cdot 3$

30: $2 \cdot 3 \cdot 5$

The common prime factors are 2 and 3.

The product of these is the GCF.

So the GCF is $2 \cdot 3 = 6$.

PRACTICE

Find the GCF of each pair of numbers.

1. 27, 36   **2.** 28, 40   **3.** 24, 64   **4.** 14, 28   **5.** 54, 72

Least Common Multiple (LCM)

6NS2.4

The **least common multiple (LCM)** of two or more whole numbers is the smallest multiple that the numbers share.

EXAMPLE   Find the LCM of 10 and 15.

Method 1 List multiples of both numbers.

Look for common multiples.

10: 10, 20, 30, 40, 50, 60

30: 30, 60, 90, 120, 150

The LCM is 30.

Method 2 Find the prime factorization.

Align common factors.

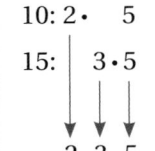

10: $2 \cdot \quad 5$

15: $\quad 3 \cdot 5$

To find the LCM, multiply one number from each column.

$2 \cdot 3 \cdot 5$

So the LCM is $2 \cdot 3 \cdot 5 = 30$.

PRACTICE

Find the LCM of each pair of numbers.

1. 12, 18   **2.** 5, 12   **3.** 8, 10   **4.** 15, 25   **5.** 7, 9

Finding a Common Denominator

You must often rewrite two or more fractions so that they have the same denominator, or a **common denominator.** One way to find a common denominator is to multiply the denominators. Or you can use the **least common denominator (LCD),** which is the LCM of the denominators.

EXAMPLE   Rewrite $\frac{1}{6}$ and $\frac{4}{9}$ so that they have a common denominator.

Method 1 Multiply the denominators: $6 \cdot 9 = 54$

$\frac{1}{6} = \frac{5 \cdot 9}{6 \cdot 9} = \frac{45}{54}$ $\frac{4}{9} = \frac{4 \cdot 6}{9 \cdot 6} = \frac{24}{54}$ *Rewrite each fraction using the common denominator.*

Method 2 Find the LCD. The LCM of the denominators, 6 and 9, is 18. So the LCD is **18**.

$\frac{1}{6} = \frac{5 \cdot 3}{6 \cdot 3} = \frac{15}{18}$ $\frac{4}{9} = \frac{4 \cdot 2}{9 \cdot 2} = \frac{8}{18}$ *Rewrite each fraction using the LCD.*

Two ways to write $\frac{1}{6}$ and $\frac{4}{9}$ with a common denominator are $\frac{45}{54}$ and $\frac{24}{54}$ or $\frac{15}{18}$ and $\frac{8}{18}$.

PRACTICE

Rewrite each pair of fractions so that they have a common denominator.

1. $\frac{1}{3}, \frac{3}{4}$ 2. $\frac{1}{2}, \frac{5}{8}$ 3. $\frac{3}{4}, \frac{1}{6}$ 4. $\frac{1}{4}, \frac{3}{14}$ 5. $\frac{5}{6}, \frac{3}{5}$

Adding and Subtracting Fractions

To add or subtract fractions, first make sure they have a common denominator. Then add or subtract the numerators and keep the common denominator.

EXAMPLE   Add or subtract. Write your answer in simplest form.

A $\frac{7}{10} - \frac{3}{10}$

$\frac{7}{10} - \frac{3}{10} = \frac{7-3}{10} = \frac{4}{10} = \frac{2}{5}$ *Subtract the numerators. Keep the denominator.*

B $\frac{5}{6} + \frac{3}{8}$

Step 1 Find the LCD. The LCD is 24.

Step 2 Rewrite the factions using the LCD: $\frac{5}{6} = \frac{5 \cdot 4}{6 \cdot 4} = \frac{20}{24}$ $\frac{3}{8} = \frac{3 \cdot 3}{8 \cdot 3} = \frac{9}{24}$

Step 3 Add: $\frac{20}{24} + \frac{9}{24} = \frac{29}{24}$ *Add the numerators. Keep the denominator.*

PRACTICE

Add or subtract. Write your answer in simplest form.

1. $\frac{3}{5} + \frac{1}{5}$ 2. $\frac{8}{9} - \frac{5}{9}$ 3. $\frac{3}{8} + \frac{1}{4}$ 4. $\frac{8}{9} - \frac{4}{5}$ 5. $\frac{7}{10} - \frac{3}{8}$

Skills Bank

Multiplying and Dividing Fractions

When multiplying or dividing fractions, you do *not* need to find a common denominator.

To multiply fractions, multiply the numerators and then multiply the denominators. Write your answer in simplest form.

EXAMPLE 1   **Multiply $\frac{3}{4} \cdot \frac{2}{5}$. Write your answer in simplest form.**

$$\frac{3}{4} \cdot \frac{2}{5}$$

$$= \frac{3 \cdot 2}{4 \cdot 5} \qquad \text{\textit{Multiply numerators and denominators.}}$$

$$= \frac{6}{20}$$

$$= \frac{3}{10} \qquad \text{\textit{Write in simplest form.}}$$

Two numbers are **reciprocals** if their product is 1. To find the reciprocal of a fraction, switch the numerator and denominator. Remember that whole numbers can be written with a denominator of 1. For example, $8 = \frac{8}{1}$. Switch the numerator and the denominator to find the reciprocal: $\frac{1}{8}$.

Dividing by a fraction is the same as multiplying by its reciprocal. So, to divide fractions, multiply the first fraction by the reciprocal of the second fraction.

EXAMPLE 2   **Divide $\frac{2}{3} \div \frac{1}{5}$. Write your answer in simplest form.**

$$\frac{2}{3} \div \frac{1}{5}$$

$$= \frac{2}{3} \cdot \frac{5}{1} \qquad \text{\textit{Rewrite division as multiplication by the reciprocal.}}$$

$$= \frac{2 \cdot 5}{3 \cdot 1} \qquad \text{\textit{Multiply numerators and denominators.}}$$

$$= \frac{10}{3} \qquad \text{\textit{Write in simplest form.}}$$

PRACTICE

Multiply or divide. Write your answer in simplest form.

1. $\frac{1}{5} \cdot \frac{3}{5}$ 2. $\frac{7}{8} \cdot \frac{4}{5}$ 3. $\frac{7}{12} \div \frac{1}{2}$ 4. $\frac{2}{9} \div \frac{6}{7}$ 5. $\frac{1}{2} \cdot \frac{4}{7}$

6. $\frac{3}{5} \div \frac{4}{5}$ 7. $\frac{6}{15} \cdot \frac{5}{12}$ 8. $\frac{5}{8} \div \frac{3}{4}$ 9. $\frac{2}{5} \div \frac{6}{7}$ 10. $\frac{1}{3} \cdot \frac{3}{8}$

Skills Bank

Discounts and Markups

A **discount** is an amount by which an original price is reduced. A **markup** is an amount by which a wholesale price is increased.

EXAMPLE

A Admission to the museum is $8. Students receive a 15% discount. How much is the discount? How much do students pay?

$100\% - 15\% = 85\%$	*Subtract the percent discount from 100%.*
$0.85(\$8.00) = \$6.80$	*Find 85% of $8.00. The result is the student price.*
$\$8.00 - \$6.80 = \$1.20$	*Subtract $6.80 from $8.00. The result is the amount of the discount.*

The amount of the discount is $1.20. Students pay $6.80.

B The wholesale cost of a DVD is $7. The markup is 75%. What is the amount of the markup? What is the selling price?

$100\% + 75\% = 175\%$	*Add the percent markup to 100%.*
$1.75(\$7.00) = \$12.25$	*Find 175% of $7.00. The result is the selling price.*
$\$12.25 - \$7.00 = \$5.25$	*Subtract $7.00 from $12.25. The result is the amount of the markup.*

The amount of the markup is $5.25. The selling price is $12.25.

PRACTICE

1. What is the final price on a $185 leather jacket that is on sale for 40% off?

2. A video game has a 70% markup. The wholesale cost is $9. What is the selling price?

Commission

A **commission** is money paid to a person or a company for making a sale. Usually the commission is a percent of the sale amount.

EXAMPLE

Ms. Barnes earns a base salary of $42,000 plus a 1.5% commission on sales. Her total sales one year were $700,000. Find her total pay for that year.

$42,000 + 1.5\%$ of $700,000$	*total pay = base salary + commission*
$= 42,000 + (0.015)(700,000)$	*Write the percent as a decimal.*
$= 42,000 + 10,500$	*Multiply.*
$= 52,500$	*Add.*

Ms. Barnes's total pay was $52,500.

PRACTICE

1. A telemarketer earns $350 per week plus a 12% commission on sales. Find his total pay for a week in which his sales are $940.

Simple Interest

Interest is the amount of money charged for borrowing money, or the amount of money earned when saving or investing money. **Principal** is the amount borrowed or invested. **Simple interest** is interest paid only on the principal.

Simple interest paid annually: $I = Prt$ where   *I* is the amount of interest.

           P **is the principal.**

           r **is the interest rate per year as a decimal.**

           t **is the time in years.**

EXAMPLE   **Find the simple interest paid annually for 2 years on a $900 loan at 16% per year.**

$I = Prt$ *Write the formula for simple interest.*

$I = (900)(0.16)(2)$ *Substitute. Write the percent as a decimal.*

$I = 288$ *Multiply.*

The amount of interest is $288.

PRACTICE

1. Find the simple interest earned after 2 years on an investment of $3000 at 4.5% earned annually.

Percent Change

Percent change is an increase or decrease given as a percent of the original amount. **Percent increase** describes an amount that has grown. **Percent decrease** describes an amount that has been reduced.

EXAMPLE

A   **Find the percent increase or decrease from 25 to 49.**

$$\frac{\text{amount of change}}{\text{original amount}} = \frac{49 - 25}{25} = \frac{24}{25} = 0.96 = 96\%$$

From 25 to 49 is a 96% increase.

B   **Find the percent increase or decrease from 50 to 45.**

$$\frac{\text{amount of change}}{\text{original amount}} = \frac{50 - 45}{50} = \frac{5}{50} = \frac{1}{10} = 10\%$$

From 50 to 45 is a 10% decrease.

PRACTICE

Find each percent increase or decrease.

1. from 200 to 110   **2.** from 25 to 30   **3.** from 80 to 115   **4.** from 10 to 8

Translate from Words to Math

Some words indicate certain math operations. Common math words and phrases are shown below. Some are listed in more than one column, so always read the problem carefully.

Addition	Subtraction	Multiplication	Division
add, plus, total, sum, more, more than, increased by, in all, combined	subtract, minus, difference, less, less than, more, more than, decreased by	multiply, times, of, product, per, for each, total	divide, divided by, quotient, divide equally, per, percent

EXAMPLE

A Caroline saved \$42 in September, \$25 in October, and \$$d$ in November. How much money did she save in all?

The words "in all" indicate addition.

$42 + 25 + d = 67 + d$

Caroline saved $(67 + d)$ dollars in all.

B Jamal bought g gallons of gas for \$1.98 per gallon. What is the total amount he paid?

The word "per" could mean multiplication or division. But "total" indicates multiplication.

$g \cdot 1.98 = 1.98g$

Jamal paid a total of \$$1.98g$.

PRACTICE

1. Sarah worked h hours this week and earned a total of \$112.50. How much does she earn per hour? What words tell you which operation to use?

2. Lance biked m miles on Monday. On Thursday he biked 5.75 miles less than he did on Monday. How far did he bike on Thursday? What words tell you which operation to use?

Cubic Functions

In a **cubic function**, the greatest power of any variable term is 3. The simplest cubic function is $y = x^3$. Its graph is shown at right. Cubic equations can be solved by graphing the related function and finding the x-value when $y = 0$.

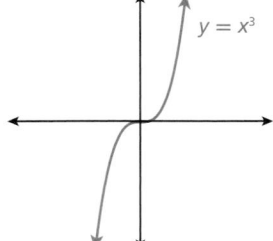

$y = x^3$

EXAMPLE

Graph $y = 2x^3$. Use the graph to solve $2x^3 = 0$.

Create a table of ordered pairs. Then plot each point and connect them with a smooth curve.

To solve $2x^3 = 0$, find the value of x when $y = 0$. The solution is $x = 0$.

x	$y = 2x^3$	(x, y)
-2	$2(-2)^3 = 2(-8) = -16$	$(-2, -16)$
-1	$2(-1)^3 = 2(-1) = -2$	$(-1, -2)$
0	$2(0)^3 = 2(0) = 0$	$(0, 0)$
1	$2(1)^3 = 2(1) = 2$	$(1, 2)$
2	$2(2)^3 = 2(8) = 16$	$(2, 16)$

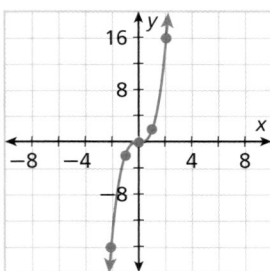

PRACTICE

Graph each cubic function.

1. $y = x^3 - 2$
2. $y = \frac{1}{2}x^3$
3. $y = x^3 + 1$
4. $y = -x^3$

Measurement

| The measurements for time are the same worldwide. | 1 min = 60 s
1 h = 60 min
1 day = 24 h | 1 wk = 7 days
1 yr = 12 mo
1 yr = 365 days | 1 yr = 52 wk
1 leap yr = 366 days |

The **customary system** of measurement is used in the United States.

Length
12 in. = 1 ft
3 ft = 1 yd
5280 ft = 1 mi

Capacity
8 oz = 1 c
2 c = 1 pt
2 pt = 1 qt
1 gal = 4 qt

Weight
16 oz = 1 lb
2000 lb = 1 ton

The **metric system** is used elsewhere and in science worldwide.

Length
1 mm = 0.001 m
1 cm = 10 mm
1 m = 100 cm
1 km = 1000 m

Capacity
1 mL = 0.001 L
1 kL = 1000 L

Mass
1 g = 1000 mg
1 kg = 1000 g

Use the table below to convert from metric to customary measurements.

Length	Capacity	Mass/Weight	Temperature
1 cm ≈ 0.394 in.	1 L ≈ 1.057 qt	1 g ≈ 0.0353 oz	
1 m ≈ 3.281 ft	1 L ≈ 0.264 gal	1 kg ≈ 2.205 lb	$F = \left(\frac{9}{5} \cdot C\right) + 32$
1 m ≈ 1.094 yd	1 L ≈ 4.227 c	1 kg ≈ 0.001 ton	
1 km ≈ 0.621 mi	1 mL ≈ 0.338 fl oz	1 metric T ≈ 1.102 ton	

Use the table below to convert from customary to metric measurements.

Length	Capacity	Weight/Mass	Temperature
1 in. ≈ 2.540 cm	1 qt ≈ 0.946 L	1 oz ≈ 28.350 g	
1 ft ≈ 0.305 m	1 gal ≈ 3.785 L	1 lb ≈ 0.454 kg	$C = \frac{5}{9} \cdot (F - 32)$
1 yd ≈ 0.914 m	1 c ≈ 0.237 L	1 ton ≈ 907.185 kg	
1 mi ≈ 1.609 km	1 fl oz ≈ 29.574 mL	1 ton ≈ 0.907 metric ton	

EXAMPLE

A Write <, =, or >.

35 in. ▓ **1 yd**

35 in. ▓ 3 ft   *1 yd = 3 ft*
35 in. < 36 in.   *3 ft = 36 in.*
35 in. < 1 yd

B Convert 32 km/h to mi/h.

1 km/h ≈ 0.621 mi/h

32 km/h ≈ 32 · 0.621 mi/h
32 km/h ≈ 19.872 mi/h

C Convert 25°C to °F.

$F = \left(\frac{9}{5} \cdot 25\right) + 32$

$F = 45 + 32$
$F = 77°F$

PRACTICE

Write <, >, or =.

1. 3 lb ▓ 40 oz

2. 200 cm ▓ 2 m

3. 6 c ▓ 2 qt

Convert.

4. 15 mi/h to km/h

5. 2 weeks to hours

6. 32 fl oz to mL

7. 95°F to °C

8. 14 tons to kg

Complementary and Supplementary Angles

6MG2.1

Complementary angles are angles whose measures add to 90°. ∠1 and ∠2 are complementary.

Supplementary angles are angles whose measures add to 180°. ∠3 and ∠4 are supplementary.

Complementary and supplementary angles may or may not be *adjacent* (have a ray in common).

EXAMPLE

A The angles shown are complementary. Find the unknown angle measure.

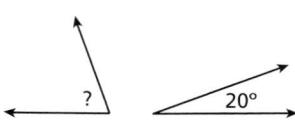

$90 - 20 = 70°$

B The two angles that form a draw bridge are supplementary. One angle measures 30°. What is the measure of the other angle?

$180 - 30 = 150$

The other angle measures 150°.

PRACTICE

1. Find the complement and supplement of a 48° angle.

Tell whether each pair of angles is complementary, supplementary, or neither.

2. ∠1 and ∠4

3. ∠2 and ∠3

4. ∠1 and ∠2

5. ∠4 and ∠5

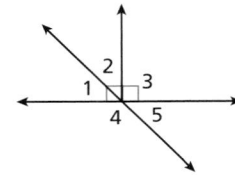

Vertical Angles

6MG2.1

When two lines intersect, each pair of nonadjacent angles forms a pair of **vertical angles**. Vertical angles always have the same measure. In the section of fencing shown, there are two pairs of vertical angles: ∠1 and ∠3, ∠4 and ∠2.

EXAMPLE

Find the measures of ∠BEC, ∠AEB, and ∠DEC.

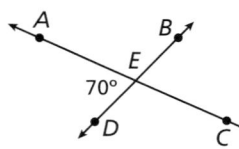

m∠BEC = 70°   *∠AED and ∠BEC are vertical.*

m∠AEB = 110°   *∠AED and ∠AEB are supplementary.*

m∠DEC = 110°   *∠AEB and ∠DEC are vertical.*

PRACTICE

1. Name two pairs of vertical angles.

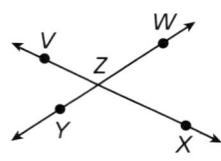

2. Find m∠PTS, m∠PTQ, and m∠QTR.

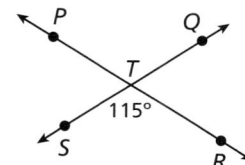

Perimeter

The **perimeter** of a polygon is the sum of the lengths of its sides. The following formulas can be used to find the perimeters of rectangles and squares.

Rectangle	$2\ell + 2w$
Square	$4s$

EXAMPLE 1 Find the perimeter of each figure.

A
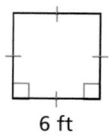

6 ft

$P = 4s$
$\quad = 4(6)$
$\quad = 24 \text{ ft}$

B
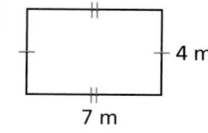

4 m

7 m

$P = 2\ell + 2w$
$\quad = 2(7) + 2(4)$
$\quad = 14 + 8$
$\quad = 22 \text{ m}$

C
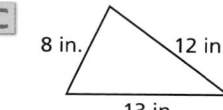

8 in.   12 in.

13 in.

$P = 8 + 12 + 13$
$\quad = 33 \text{ in.}$

EXAMPLE 2 Estimate the perimeter of the figure.

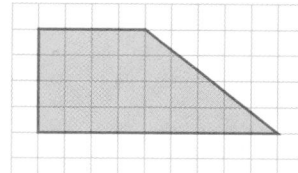

Find the length of the nondiagonal lines.
  top: 4 units
  left: 4 units
  bottom: 9 units

Estimate the length of the diagonal line.
  right: ≈ 6 units

Add the lengths of all four sides:
  $P \approx 4 + 4 + 9 + 6$
  $\quad \approx 23 \text{ units}$

PRACTICE

Find the perimeter of each figure.

1.
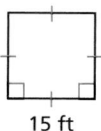

15 ft

2.
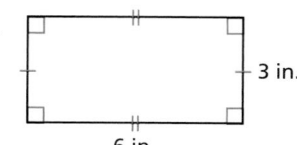

3 in.

6 in.

3.
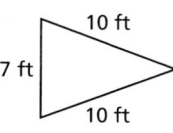

10 ft

7 ft

10 ft

Estimate the perimeter of each figure.

4.
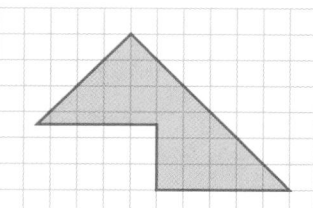

5.
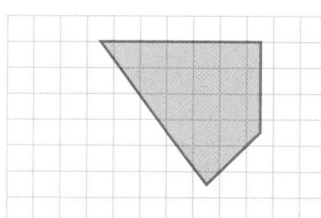

Skills Bank

Area

The **area** of a polygon is the number of nonoverlapping square units that will exactly cover its interior.

Formulas for the areas of some polygons are given at right.

Square	s^2	s: length of one side
Rectangle	ℓw	ℓ: length, w: width
Parallelogram	bh	b: base, h: height
Triangle	$\frac{1}{2}bh$	b: base, h: height
Trapezoid	$\frac{1}{2}h(b_1 + b_2)$	b_1: top base, b_2: bottom base, h: height

EXAMPLE 1 Find the area of each polygon.

A

5 ft

$A = s^2$
$\quad = 5^2$
$\quad = 25 \text{ ft}^2$

B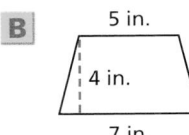

5 in.
4 in.
7 in.

$A = \frac{1}{2}h(b_1 + b_2)$
$\quad = \frac{1}{2}(4)(5 + 7)$
$\quad = 2 \cdot 12$
$\quad = 24 \text{ in}^2$

EXAMPLE 2 Estimate the area of the figure.

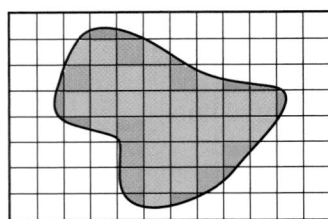

Count full squares: 21 red squares
Count almost full squares: 8 blue squares
Count squares that are about half full: 6 green squares ≈ 3 full squares
Do not count almost empty purple squares.
Add: 21 + 8 + 3 ≈ 32

$A \approx 32$ square units

PRACTICE

Find the area of each polygon.

1.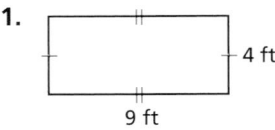

4 ft

9 ft

2.

6m
12 m

3.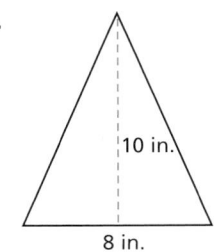

10 in.

8 in.

Estimate the area of each figure.

4.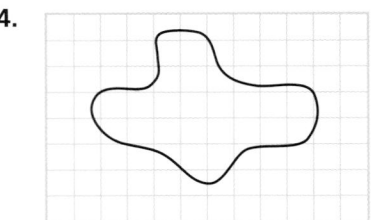

5.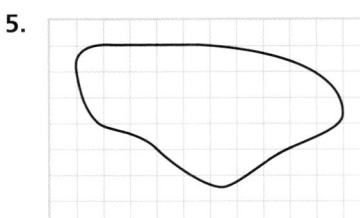

Circles

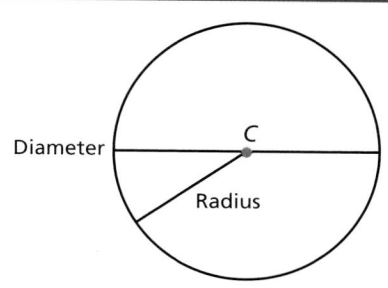

A **circle** is the set of all points in a plane that are a given distance from a given point, known as the **center.** The center names the circle. The circle shown at right is referred to as circle C.

A **diameter** is a line segment that passes through the center and whose endpoints are points on the circle.

A **radius** is a segment whose endpoints are the center of the circle and a point on the circle. Any radius of a circle is half as long as any diameter of that circle.

Circumference is the distance around a circle. The ratio of circumference to diameter is the same for all circles and is denoted by the Greek letter π (*pi*), which is approximately 3.14.

Circle Formulas	
Area: $A = \pi r^2$	Circumference: $C = \pi d$ or $C = 2\pi r$

EXAMPLE 1 Find the circumference of each circle. Use 3.14 for π.

A

15 ft

$C = \pi d$
$\approx 3.14(15)$
≈ 47.1 ft

B
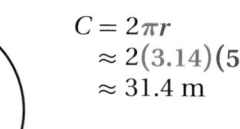
5 m

$C = 2\pi r$
$\approx 2(3.14)(5)$
≈ 31.4 m

EXAMPLE 2 Find the area of each circle. Use 3.14 for π.

A
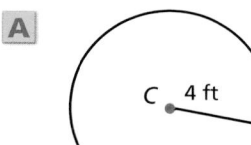
C 4 ft

$A = \pi r^2$
$\approx 3.14(4)^2$
$\approx 3.14(16)$
≈ 50.24 ft^2

B
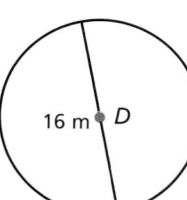
16 m D

$A = \pi r^2$
$\approx 3.14(8)^2$
$\approx 3.14(64)$
≈ 200.96 m^2

PRACTICE

1. The radius of a circle is 13 inches. What is the diameter of the circle? Use 3.14 for π.

2. The diameter of a circle is 22 feet. What is the radius of the circle? Use 3.14 for π.

Find the circumference and area of each circle.

3.
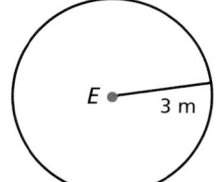
E 3 m

4.
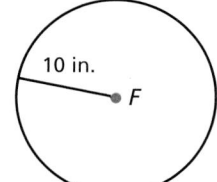
10 in. F

5.
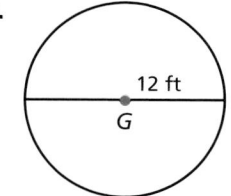
12 ft G

Classify Triangles and Quadrilaterals

A triangle can be classified according to its angle measurements or according to the number of congruent sides it has.

Classifying by Angles		Classifying by Sides	
Acute	Three acute angles	Scalene	No sides congruent
Right	One right angle	Isosceles	At least 2 sides congruent
Obtuse	One obtuse angle	Equilateral	All sides congruent

EXAMPLE 1 Classify each triangle according to its angles and sides.

A

acute isosceles

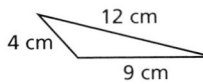

B

obtuse scalene

C

acute equilateral

Quadrilaterals can also be classified according to their sides and angles.

Parallelograms	
Parallelogram 2 pairs of parallel congruent sides	
Rectangle 4 right angles	
Rhombus 4 congruent sides	
Square 4 right angles and 4 congruent sides	

Other Quadrilaterals	
Trapezoid exactly 1 pair of parallel sides	
Isosceles Trapezoid congruent, nonparallel legs	
Kite 2 pairs of adjacent congruent sides	

EXAMPLE 2 Tell whether the following statement is always, sometimes, or never true: A square is a rectangle.

always   *A rectangle must have four right angles, and a square always has four right angles.*

PRACTICE

Classify each triangle according to its angles and sides.

1.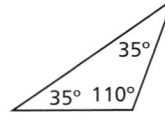

2.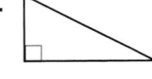

3.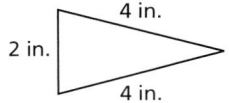

Tell whether each statement is always, sometimes, or never true.

4. A rectangle is a square.

5. A trapezoid is a parallelogram.

Draw a triangle or a quadrilateral that matches the given description.

6. an obtuse scalene triangle

7. a quadrilateral with exactly two right angles

Skills Bank

Congruence

Congruent segments are segments that have the same length.

Congruent angles are angles that have the same measure.

Figures are **congruent** if all pairs of corresponding angles are congruent and all pairs of corresponding sides are congruent.

EXAMPLE Identify the corresponding angles and sides.

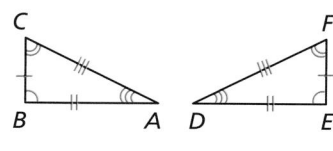

$\angle A \cong \angle D$ $\overline{AB} \cong \overline{DE}$

$\angle B \cong \angle E$ $\overline{BC} \cong \overline{EF}$

$\angle C \cong \angle F$ $\overline{AC} \cong \overline{DF}$

The order of the letters in $\triangle ABC \cong \triangle DEF$ shows which angles and sides are congruent. Congruent sides and angles are also identified by the same mark.

$\triangle ABC \cong \triangle DEF$

PRACTICE

Identify the corresponding angles and sides by using congruence statements.

1.
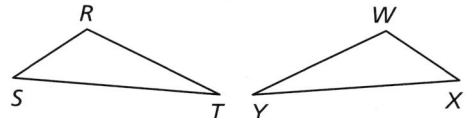

2. $\triangle JKL \cong \triangle OPQ$

Pythagorean Theorem

In the right triangle shown, a and b are the lengths of the legs, and c is the length of the hypotenuse. The **Pythagorean Theorem** states the following: If a triangle is a right triangle, then $a^2 + b^2 = c^2$. The converse of the theorem is also true: For any triangle, if $a^2 + b^2 = c^2$, then the triangle is a right triangle.

 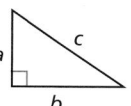

EXAMPLE 1   **Find the missing measure. Round to the nearest tenth if necessary.**

A
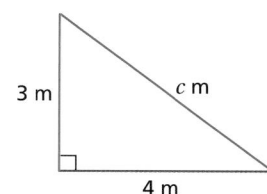

$a^2 + b^2 = c^2$

$3^2 + 4^2 = c^2$

$9 + 16 = c^2$

$25 = c^2$

$\sqrt{25} = \sqrt{c^2}$

$5 \text{ m} = c$

B
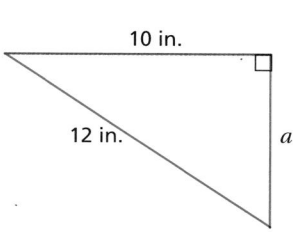

$a^2 + b^2 = c^2$

$a^2 + 10^2 = 12^2$

$a^2 + 100 = 144$

$a^2 = 44$

$\sqrt{a^2} = \sqrt{44}$

$a \approx 6.6 \text{ in.}$

EXAMPLE 2   **Determine whether a triangle with side lengths of 8 cm, 14 cm, and 20 cm is a right triangle.**

$a^2 + b^2 = c^2$	
$8^2 + 14^2$	20^2
$64 + 196$	400
260	400 ✗

c is always the longest side.

The triangle is not a right triangle.

PRACTICE

Find the missing measure. Round to the nearest tenth if necessary.

1.
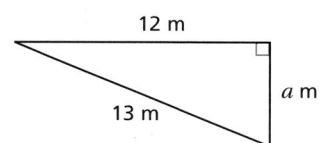

2.
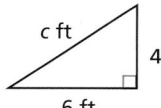

3. A leg is 6 ft long and the hypotenuse is 10 ft long.

4. Both legs are 20 mm long.

5. Determine whether a triangle with side lengths of 16 ft, 30 ft, and 34 ft is a right triangle.

Three-Dimensional Figures

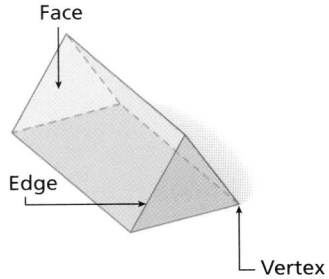

Face

Edge

Vertex

Polyhedrons are three-dimensional figures made up of polygons which are called **faces.** The sides where faces intersect are **edges.** Any point where three or more edges intersect is a **vertex.**

EXAMPLE **1** Tell how many faces, edges, and vertices the figure has.

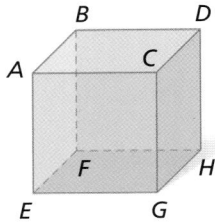

6 faces   *ABCD, ABFE, BFHD, DCGH, ACGE, FHGE*

12 edges $\overline{AB}, \overline{BD}, \overline{DC}, \overline{AC}, \overline{AE}, \overline{BF}, \overline{DH}, \overline{CG}, \overline{EF}, \overline{FH}, \overline{HG}, \overline{EG}$

8 vertices   *A, B, C, D, E, F, G, H*

A **prism** has two faces called **bases.** The bases are congruent, parallel polygons. The faces that are not bases are parallelograms.

Pyramids have only one base, and the faces other than the base are triangles. Both prisms and pyramids are named according to the polygon that forms the base or bases.

EXAMPLE **2** Name each figure.

A

*Two congruent bases
Bases are rectangles.*
rectangular prism

B

*One base
Base is a pentagon.*
pentagonal pyramid

Some three-dimensional figures are not polyhedrons because they are not made up of polygons.
Cones and **cylinders** have circles as bases. A cone has one base, and a cylinder has two congruent parallel bases.

Cone   **Cylinder**

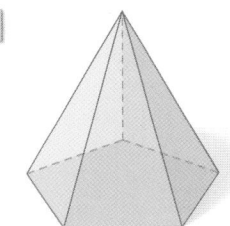

Base

PRACTICE

Name each figure. If the figure is a polyhedron, tell how many faces, edges, and vertices the figure has.

1.
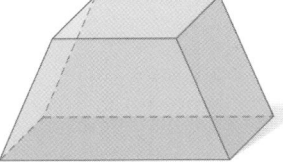

2.
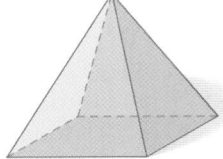

3.
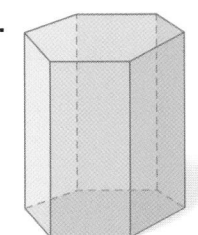

4.
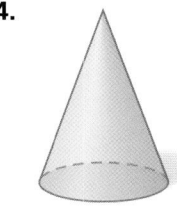

Skills Bank

Volume

The **volume** of a three-dimensional figure is the number of nonoverlapping cubic units that will exactly fill its interior. The formulas for the volumes of some types of three-dimensional figures are given in the table.

Notice that a cube is listed in the table. A cube is a prism, so the formula for a prism can be used; however, since all sides in a cube are congruent, the formula s^3 is more convenient.

Prism	Bh	B: area of base h: height of prism
Cube	s^3	s: length of one side
Pyramid	$\frac{1}{3}Bh$	B: area of base h: height of pyramid
Cylinder	$\pi r^2 h$	r: radius h: height
Cone	$\frac{1}{3}\pi r^2 h$	r: radius h: height

EXAMPLE **1**   Find the volume of each figure. Use 3.14 for π.

A

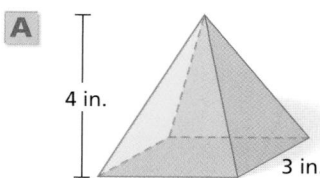

4 in.

3 in.

3 in.

$$V = \frac{1}{3}Bh$$
$$= \frac{1}{3}(9)(4)$$
$$= 3(4)$$
$$= 12 \text{ in}^3$$

B

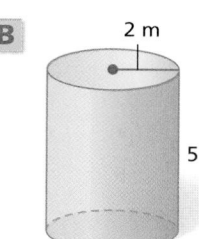

2 m

5 m

$$V = \pi r^2 h$$
$$\approx 3.14(2)^2(5)$$
$$\approx 3.14(4)(5)$$
$$\approx 62.8 \text{ m}^3$$

EXAMPLE **2**   Estimate the volume of the figure.

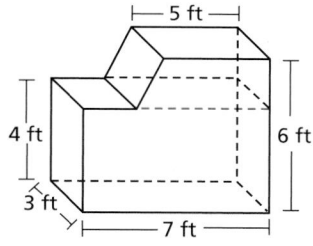

5 ft

4 ft

3 ft

7 ft

6 ft

Find the volume of the rectangular prism (bottom part):
$$Bh = 21(4) = 84$$

Estimate the top part as a rectangular prism with $w = 3$ ft, $\ell = 5$ ft, and $h = 6$ ft $- 4$ ft $= 2$ ft.
$$Bh = 15(2) = 30$$

Add the volumes of the two prisms:
$$84 + 30 = 114$$

The volume is approximately 114 ft^3.

PRACTICE

Find or estimate the volume of each figure. Use 3.14 for π.

1.

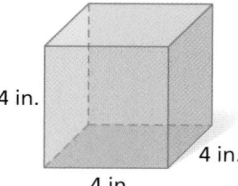

4 in.

4 in.

4 in.

2.

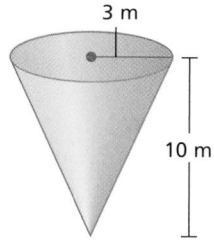

3 m

10 m

4 in.

3.

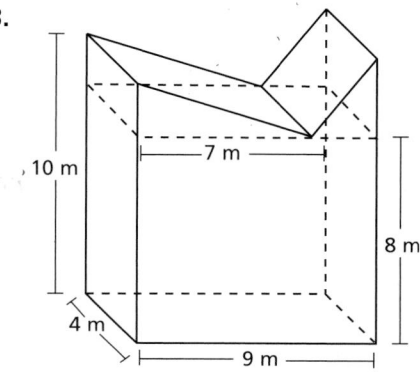

10 m

7 m

4 m

8 m

9 m

Surface Area

The **surface area** of a three-dimensional figure is the sum of the areas of its surfaces.

Formulas for the surface areas of some three-dimensional figures are given in the table.

Prism	$2B + Ph$	B: area of base P: perimeter of base h: height
Pyramid	$B + \frac{1}{2}P\ell$	B: area of base P: perimeter of base ℓ: slant height
Cube	$6s^2$	s: length of one side
Cylinder	$2\pi r^2 + 2\pi rh$	r: radius; h: height
Cone	$\pi r^2 + \pi r\ell$	r: radius; ℓ: slant height

Skills Bank

EXAMPLE **1** Find the surface area of each figure. Use 3.14 for π.

A
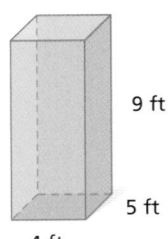
9 ft
5 ft
4 ft

$S = 2B + Ph$
$\quad = 2(20) + 18(9)$
$\quad = 40 + 162$
$\quad = 202 \text{ ft}^2$

B
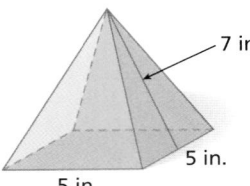
7 in.
5 in.
5 in.

$S = B + \frac{1}{2}P\ell$
$\quad = 25 + \frac{1}{2}(20)(7)$
$\quad = 25 + 70$
$\quad = 95 \text{ in}^2$

C
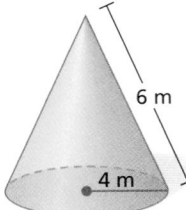
6 m
4 m

$S = \pi r^2 + \pi r\ell$
$\quad \approx 3.14(4)^2 + 3.14(4)(6)$
$\quad \approx 50.24 + 75.36$
$\quad \approx 125.6 \text{ m}^2$

EXAMPLE **2** The net of a prism is shown below. Estimate the surface area of the prism.

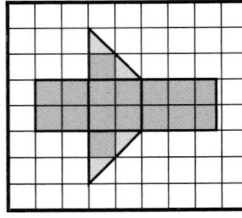

Count full squares: $\approx$ 16 red squares
Count squares that are half full: 4 blue half squares = 2 full squares
Add: 16 + 2 = 18

$S \approx 18$ square units

PRACTICE

Find or estimate the surface area of each figure. Use 3.14 for π.

1.
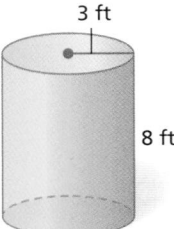
3 ft
8 ft

2.
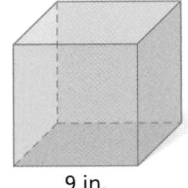
9 in.

3.
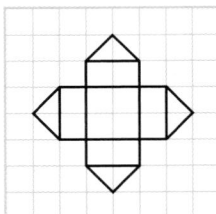

The Coordinate Plane

The **coordinate plane** is formed by the intersection of two perpendicular number lines called **axes.** The point of intersection, called the **origin,** is at 0 on each number line. The horizontal number line is called the **x-axis,** and the vertical number line is called the **y-axis.**

Points on the coordinate plane are described using ordered pairs. An **ordered pair** consists of an **x-coordinate** and a **y-coordinate** and is written (x, y). Points are often named with a capital letter.

The axes divide the coordinate plane into four **quadrants.** Points that lie on an axis are not in any quadrant.

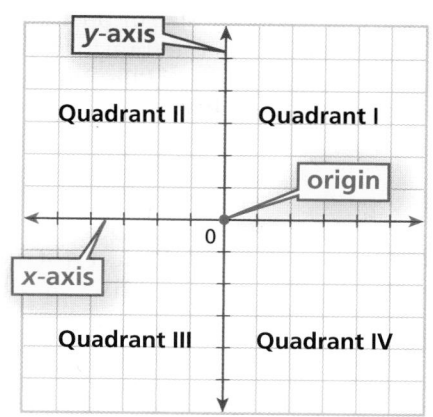

EXAMPLE 1 Graph each point.

A $M(3, 4)$
Start at the origin.
Move 3 units right and 4 units up.

B $N(-2, 0)$
Start at the origin.
Move 2 units left.

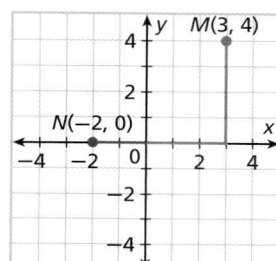

EXAMPLE 2 Name the quadrant in which each point lies.

A P
Quadrant III

B Q
Quadrant II

C R
no quadrant (x-axis)

D S
Quadrant IV

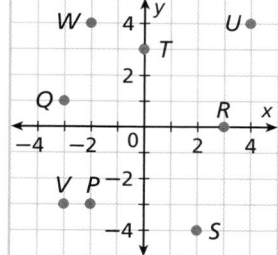

PRACTICE

Graph each point.

1. $R(2, -3)$ **2.** $S(0, 2)$ **3.** $T(-2, 6)$

4. $J(4, 5)$ **5.** $K(-3, 2)$ **6.** $L(6, 0)$

Use the graph in Example 2 to name the quadrant in which each point lies.

7. T **8.** U **9.** V

Transformations in the Coordinate Plane

 7MG3.2

A **transformation** is a change in the size or position of a figure. If the **preimage,** or original figure, is named *ABC*, then the transformed figure, or **image,** is named *A'B'C'*. Transformations include **translations** (slides), **reflections** (flips), and **rotations** (turns), for which preimages and images are congruent.

Skills Bank

EXAMPLE 1

A Translate *ABC* 2 units right and 1 unit up.

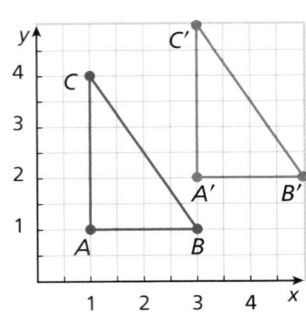

Move each vertex 2 units right and 1 unit up.

B Reflect *ABC* across the y-axis.

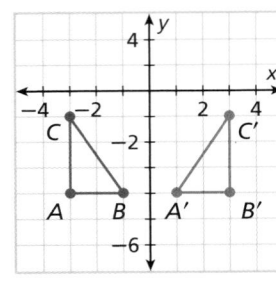

The y-axis is a line of symmetry.

C Rotate *ABC* 90° clockwise about point *A*.

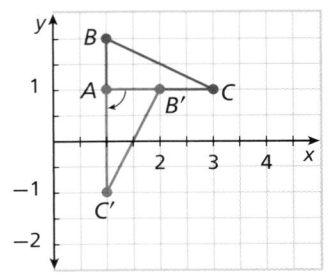

A' is the same as A. Maintain the same side lengths on the image.

EXAMPLE 2   Could *ABCD* be transformed into *A'B'C'D'*? Explain.

The figures are congruent, so a translation, rotation, or reflection is possible. Study the figures. If A' B' C' D' is translated 1 unit right, both figures would be symmetric about the x-axis.

ABCD can be transformed into *A'B'C'D'* by reflecting it across the x-axis and translating it 1 unit left.

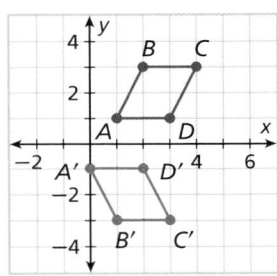

PRACTICE

1. Translate *ABCD* 2 units left and 4 units down.

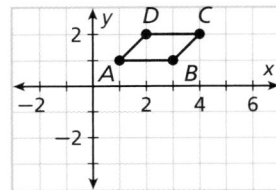

2. Graph *A*(1, −2), *B*(3, −2), and *C*(2, −4). Rotate *ABC* 90° counterclockwise about *A* and reflect it across the x-axis.

Use the graph for Exercises 3 and 4.

3. Could *ABCD* be transformed into *A'B'C'D'*? Explain.

4. Could *FGHJKL* be transformed into *F'G'H'J'K'L'*? Explain.

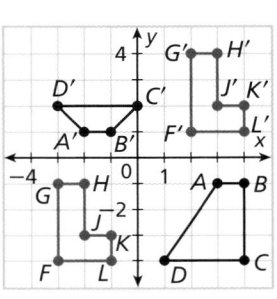

Measures of Central Tendency

Measures of central tendency are values that represent a data set and can be considered typical of the set. These measures are the *mean*, *median*, and *mode*.

	It is...	Find by...
Mean	The average.	Adding the data values and dividing by the number of values.
Median	The "middle value."	First ordering the data values from least to greatest. If there are an *odd* number of values, the median is the middle number. If there are an *even* number of values, the median is the mean of the two middle values.
Mode	The value or values that occur most often. If every value occurs the same number of times, the data set has no mode.	Choosing the value or values that occur more often than any other.

EXAMPLE   Find the mean, median, and mode of each data set.

A   18, 22, 13, 16, 15, 18, 10

mean:

$$\frac{18 + 22 + 13 + 16 + 15 + 18 + 10}{7} = \frac{112}{7} = 16$$

The mean is 16.

median:

Order the data values from least to greatest. There are an odd number of values. Choose the middle number.

10, 13, 15, ⓰, 18, 18, 22

The median is 16.

mode:

Every value occurs once except 18, which occurs twice.

The mode is 18.

B   These are the number of people who attended a seminar each of four days: 102, 96, 88, 109.

mean: $\frac{102 + 96 + 88 + 109}{4} = \frac{395}{4} = 98.75$

The mean is 98.75.

median:

Order the data values from least to greatest. There are an even number of values. Find the mean of the two middle numbers.

88, ⟨96, 102,⟩ 109

$$\frac{96 + 102}{2} = \frac{198}{2} = 99$$

The median is 99.

mode:

Every value occurs once.

There is no mode.

PRACTICE

Find the mean, median, and mode of each data set.

1.

High Temperatures (°F)						
Sun	Mon	Tue	Wed	Thu	Fri	Sat
85	81	83	85	86	82	84

2. These are the ages of the students in an after-school club: 14, 15, 14, 16, 15, 17, 14, 15.

3. Jenny took a survey of her classmates to find out how much they each paid for their notebooks. Here are their responses: 85¢, 55¢, 80¢, 85¢, 75¢, 95¢, 85¢, 75¢, 67¢.

A **population** is a group that someone is gathering information about.

A **sample** is part of a population. For example, if 5 students are chosen to represent a class of 20 students, the 5 chosen students are a sample of the population of 20 students.

The sample is a **random sample** if every member of the population has an equal chance of being chosen for the sample.

EXAMPLE   Explain whether each sample is random.

A Carlos wrote the name of each student in his class on a slip of paper and put the papers into a hat. Then, without looking at the slips, he drew the names of the students who would complete his survey.

Each name is in the hat once, so each has an equal chance of being selected. The sample is random.

B Jamal telephoned people on a list of 100 names in the order in which they appeared. He surveyed the first 20 people who answered their phone.

Names at the beginning of the list have a greater chance of being selected than those at the end of the list, so the sample is not random.

PRACTICE

Explain whether each sample is random.

1. Rebecca surveyed every person in a theater who was sitting in a seat along the aisle.

2. Inez assigned 50 people a number from 1 to 50. Then she used a calculator to generate 10 random numbers from 1 to 50 and surveyed those with matching numbers.

Bias

 6SDAP2.5

Bias is error that favors part of a population and/or does not accurately represent the population. Bias can occur from using sampling methods that are not random or from asking confusing or leading questions.

EXAMPLE   Explain why each survey is biased.

A Jenn went to a movie theater and asked people who exited if they agree that the theater should be torn down to build office space.

People usually only go to movies if they enjoy them, so those exiting a movie theater would not want it torn down. People who do not use the theater did not have a chance to answer.

B A student asked, "A new cafeteria would mean that loud construction would take place for several weeks. Also, the hallways would become even more congested in that area. Do you want a new cafeteria?"

The question only mentions the bad things that could come from a new cafeteria, not the good ones, such as better food or more seats.

PRACTICE

Explain why each survey is biased.

1. A surveyor asked, "Is it not true that you do not oppose the candidate's views?"

2. Brendan asked everyone on his track team how they thought the money from the athletic department fund-raiser should be spent.

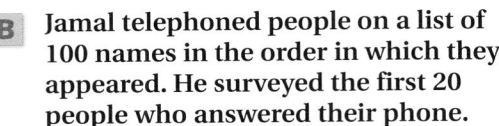

Bar Graphs and Histograms

A **bar graph** displays data using vertical or horizontal bars that do not touch.

A **histogram** is a bar graph used to display the frequency of data divided into equal intervals. The bars must be of equal width and should touch, but not overlap.

E X A M P L E   **Use the data in the table to make a bar graph.**

Livestock Show Entries					
Animal	Chicken	Goat	Horse	Pig	Sheep
Number	38	10	32	12	25

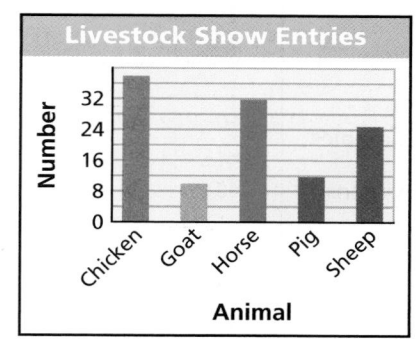

Step 1   Determine an appropriate scale. The scale must include all data values. The scale is separated into equal parts called intervals.

Step 2   Use the data to determine the lengths of the bars. Draw bars of equal width that do not touch.

Step 3   Title the graph. Label the horizontal and vertical scales.

PRACTICE

1. Use the data in the table to make a histogram.

Damien's Math Test Scores					
75	84	68	72	59	88
72	77	81	84	60	70

Box and Whisker Plots

A **box-and-whisker plot** is a graph showing the **lower extreme** (the least value), the **upper extreme** (the greatest value), the median, the **lower quartile** (the median of the lower half of the data), and the **upper quartile** (the median of the upper half of the data).

E X A M P L E   **Use the data to make a box-and-whisker plot.**

3	4	8	12	7	5	4	12	3	9	9
11	4	14	8	2	10	3	10	11	4	

Step 1   Order the data from least to greatest. Find the lower extreme, the upper extreme, the lower quartile, the **upper quartile**, and the median.

2, 3, 3, 3, 4, 4, 4, 4, 5, 7, 8, 8, 9, 9, 10, 10, 11, 11, 12, 12, 14

Step 2   Draw a number line and plot a point above each value from Step 1. Draw a box through the lower and upper quartiles and a vertical line through the median. Draw lines (whiskers) from the box to the upper and lower extremes.

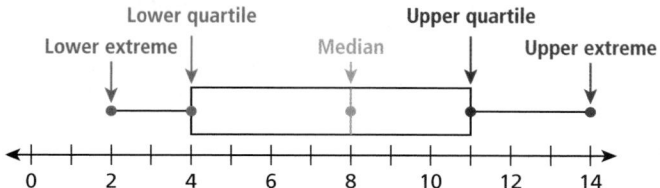

PRACTICE

1. Use the data to make a box-and whisker plot.

13, 14, 18, 13, 12, 17, 15, 12, 13, 19, 11, 14, 14, 18, 22, 23

Circle Graphs

A **circle graph** shows parts of a whole. The entire circle represents 100% of the data, and each sector represents a percent of the total.

EXAMPLE   Use the data to make a circle graph.

Crop	Acres
Corn	70
Fallow	50
Mixed vegetables	10
Soybeans	40
Wheat	30

% of total acres

$\frac{70}{200} = 35\%$

$\frac{50}{200} = 25\%$

$\frac{10}{200} = 5\%$

$\frac{40}{200} = 20\%$

$\frac{30}{200} = 15\%$

Degrees of circle

$0.35(360) = 126°$

$0.25(360) = 90°$

$0.05(360) = 18°$

$0.2(360) = 72°$

$0.15(360) = 54°$

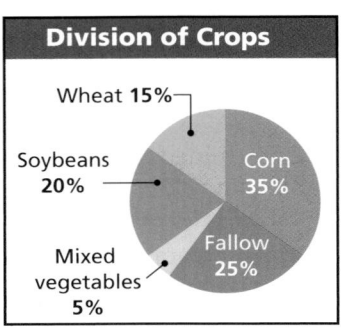

PRACTICE

1. Use the data to make a circle graph.

Degrees Held by Faculty		
PhD	Master's	Bachelor's
7	24	31

Venn Diagrams

Venn diagrams are used to show relationships between two or more sets of numbers or objects. They show which elements are common between sets.

EXAMPLE   In a group of 15 students, 10 play basketball or baseball, 5 play basketball, and 3 play both sports. Draw a Venn diagram. How many students play baseball?

Draw two overlapping ovals, one for each sport. Three students will be in the overlapping region. Since 5 students play basketball, and 3 of them also play baseball, 2 students play only basketball.

There are 10 student players in all, and 5 are already represented in the graph. Therefore, the remaining 5 play only baseball.

Adding the 3 students who also play basketball, a total of 8 students play baseball.

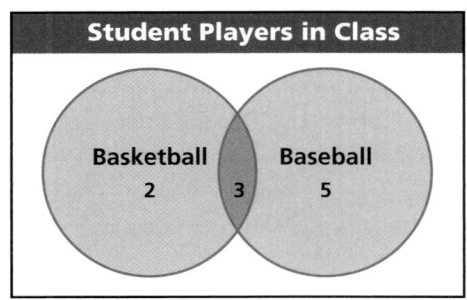

PRACTICE

In a group of 138 people, 55 own a cat, 27 own a cat and a dog, and 42 own neither pet.

1. How many people own only a cat?

2. How many people own a dog?

Theoretical Probability

An **experiment** is an activity involving chance that can have different results. Flipping a coin and rolling a number cube are examples of experiments.

The different results that can occur are called **outcomes** of the experiment. If you are flipping a coin, "heads" is a possible outcome. An **event** is an outcome or set of outcomes in an experiment. **Probability** is a measure of how likely a particular event is to occur. The higher the probability, the more likely the event will occur.

When all possible outcomes have the same chance of occurring, the outcomes are said to be **equally likely**. The **theoretical probability** of an event is the ratio of the number of ways the event can occur to the total number of equally likely outcomes.

$$\text{Theoretical probability} = \frac{\text{number of ways the event can occur}}{\text{total number of equally likely outcomes}}$$

EXAMPLE 1 **Find the theoretical probability of rolling a 3 on a fair number cube.**

$$\text{Theoretical probability} = \frac{\text{number of ways the event can occur}}{\text{total number of equally likely outcomes}}$$

$$= \frac{1}{6} \quad \longleftarrow \text{There is one 3 on a number cube.}$$
$$\quad \longleftarrow \text{There are 6 equally likely outcomes on a number cube.}$$

$$= 0.1\overline{6}$$

$$= 16\frac{2}{3}\%$$

The **complement of an event** is the set of all possible outcomes that are not included in the event. The sum of the probabilities of an event and its complement is 1, or 100%, because every event will either happen or not happen.

EXAMPLE 2 **The weather forecaster predicts a 20% chance of snow. What is the probability that it will not snow?**

P(snow) + P(not snow) =	100%	*Either it will snow or it will not snow.*
20% + P(not snow) =	100%	*P(snow) = 20%*
− 20%	− 20%	*Subtract 20% from both sides.*
P(not snow) =	80%	

PRACTICE

An experiment consists of rolling a fair number cube. Find the theoretical probability of each outcome.

1. rolling a 1 or a 6

2. rolling an even number

3. rolling a multiple of 3

4. rolling a number greater than 5

5. A jar has green, blue, purple, and white marbles. The probability of choosing a green marble is 0.2, the probability of choosing blue is 0.3, and the probability of choosing purple is 0.1. What is the probability of choosing white?

Experimental Probability

Performing an experiment is one way to estimate the probability of an event. If an experiment is repeated many times, the **experimental probability** of an event is the ratio of the number of times the event occurs to the total number of times the experiment is performed. Each time that the experiment is performed is a **trial**. The more trials performed, the more accurate the experimental probability will be.

$$\text{Experimental probability} = \frac{\text{number of times the event occurs}}{\text{total number of trials}}$$

EXAMPLE

Ian tossed a coin 30 times and recorded whether the result was "heads" or "tails." Based on Ian's results, what is the experimental probability that the next toss will be "heads"?

Heads	ＨＴ ＨＴ ＨＴ I
Tails	ＨＴ ＨＴ IIII

$$\text{Experimental probability} = \frac{\text{number of times the event occurs}}{\text{total number of trials}}$$

$$P(\text{heads}) = \frac{16}{30}$$

$$= \frac{8}{15}$$

The experimental probability that Ian's next toss will be "heads" is $\frac{8}{15}$.

PRACTICE

Jennifer has a bag of marbles. She removed one marble, recorded the color, and placed it back in the bag. She repeated this process several times and recorded her results in the table.

Use the table for Exercises 1 and 2.

White	ＨＴ
Red	III
Yellow	ＨＴ
Black	ＨＴ ＨＴ II

1. Based on Jennifer's results, find the experimental probability that a marble selected from the bag will be red.

2. Find the experimental probability that a marble selected from the bag will NOT be black.

3. One game of bowling consists of ten frames. Elise usually rolls 3 strikes in each game. What is the experimental probability that Elise will roll a strike in a particular frame?

4. A manufacturer inspects 800 light bulbs and finds that 796 of them have no defects. What is the experimental probability that a randomly chosen light bulb from this manufacturer will have no defects?

5. Ms. Bleakman checks 32 papers and finds 2 with no name. What is the experimental probability that a paper chosen at random will have no name?

6. A tennis player served the ball 16 times and 2 of those serves were aces (unreturned serves). What is the experimental probability that the player's next serve will be an ace?

Compound Events

A **compound event** consists of two or more single events.

EXAMPLE

Christine rolls a fair number cube and then tosses a fair coin. Find the probability that the number cube will show an even number and that the coin will show "heads."

	1	2	3	4	5	6
H	1,H	2,H	3,H	4,H	5,H	6,H
T	1,T	2,T	3,T	4,T	5,T	6,T

Use a table to list all possible outcomes. Circle or highlight the outcomes with an even number and "heads."

$$P(\text{even, heads}) = \frac{3 \text{ ways outcome can occur}}{12 \text{ equally likely outcomes}}$$

$$= \frac{3}{12}$$

$$= \frac{1}{4}$$

In the Example, a table was used to list the possible outcomes. Another way to list outcomes of a compound event is to use a **tree diagram.**

List all possible outcomes for the number cube.

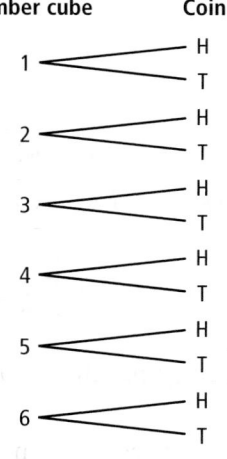

Number cube   Coin

1 — H, T
2 — H, T
3 — H, T
4 — H, T
5 — H, T
6 — H, T

Then, for each outcome of the number cube, list all possible outcomes for the coin.

PRACTICE

Use the spinner for Exercises 1–3.

1. If you spin the spinner twice, what is the probability that it will land on blue on the first spin and on green on the second spin?

2. What is the probability that the spinner will land on either red or yellow on the first spin and on blue on the second spin?

3. What is the probability that the spinner will land on the same color twice in a row?

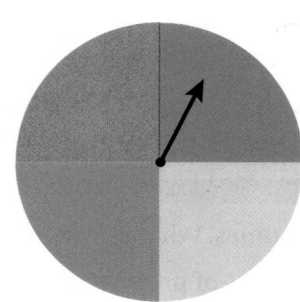

Independent and Dependent Events

For two **independent events,** the occurrence of one event has no effect on the probability that the second event will occur. To find the probability that two independent events will occur, multiply the individual probabilities.

Probability of Two Independent Events

$$P(A \text{ and } B) = P(A) \cdot P(B)$$

EXAMPLE 1 An experiment consists of randomly selecting a marble from a bag, replacing it, and then selecting another marble. The bag contains 7 blue marbles and 3 red marbles. What is the probability of selecting a red marble and then a blue marble?

Because the first marble selected is replaced, the number of possible outcomes for each selection is the same. These events are independent.

$$P(\text{red, blue}) = P(\text{red}) \cdot P(\text{blue})$$

$$= \frac{3}{10} \cdot \frac{7}{10}$$

$$= \frac{21}{100}$$

$$= 21\%$$

For two **dependent events,** the occurrence of one event has an effect on the probability that the second event will occur. To find the probability that two dependent events will occur, multiply probabilities as shown below.

Probability of Two Dependent Events

$$P(A \text{ and } B) = P(A) \cdot P(B \text{ after } A)$$

EXAMPLE 2 There are 7 pink flowers and 5 yellow flowers in a bunch. Jane selects a flower at random, and then Leah selects a flower at random from the remaining flowers. What is the probability that Jane selects a pink flower and Leah selects a yellow flower?

Because the first flower selected is not replaced, the number of possible outcomes for each selection is different. These events are dependent.

$$P(\text{pink, yellow}) = P(\text{pink}) \cdot P(\text{yellow after pink})$$

Jane selects one of 7 pink flowers from 12 total flowers.

$$= \frac{7}{12} \cdot \frac{5}{11}$$

Then Leah selects one of 5 yellow flowers from 11 remaining flowers.

$$= \frac{35}{132}$$

$$\approx 26.5\%$$

PRACTICE

1. A coin is flipped 4 times. What is the probability of flipping 4 heads in a row?

2. A snack cart has 6 bags of pretzels and 10 bags of trail mix. Grant selects a bag at random, and then Iris selects a bag at random. What is the probability that Grant selects pretzels and Iris selects trail mix?

Selected Answers

Chapter 1

1-1

Check It Out! 1a. Possible answers: 4 decreased by n; n less than 4
1b. Possible answers: the quotient of t and 5; t divided by 5
1c. Possible answers: the sum of 9 and q; q added to 9 **1d.** Possible answers: the product of 3 and h; 3 times h **2a.** $65t$ **2b.** $m + 5$ **3a.** $\frac{4}{3}$; 2; 6 **3b.** 13; 12; 6 **3c.** 2.15; 3.15; 9.15
4a. $63s$ **4b.** 756 bottles; 1575 bottles; 3150 bottles

Exercises 1. variable **3.** Possible answers: the quotient of f and 3; f divided by 3 **5.** Possible answers: 9 decreased by y; y less than 9
7. Possible answers: the sum of t and 12; t increased by 12
9. Possible answers: x decreased by 3; the difference of x and 3
11. $w + 4$ **13.** 12, 16, 36 **15.** 6, 8, 18
17. Possible answers: the product of 5 and p; 5 groups of p
19. Possible answers: the sum of 3 and x; 3 increased by x **21.** Possible answers: negative 3 times s; the product of negative 3 and s
23. Possible answers: 14 decreased by t; the difference of 14 and t
25. $t + 20$ **27.** 1, 7, 12 **29.** 1, 4, $\frac{13}{2}$
31a. $h - 40$, **31b.** 0; 4; 8; 12 **33.** $2x$
35. $y + 10$ **37.** $9w$; 9 in^2; 72 in^2; 81 in^2; 99 in^2 **39.** 13; 14; 15; 16
41. 6; 10; 13; 15 **43a.** $47.84 + m$;
43b. $58.53 - s$ **45.** $x + 7$; 19; 21
46. $\frac{x}{2}$; 6; 7 **47.** $x + 3$; 15; 17 **49.** A
51. 36 **53.** 1 **55.** 45° **57.** 90°
59. $\frac{1}{2}$ **61.** 1

1-2

Check It Out! 1a. 4 **1b.** -10
1c. 1.5 **2a.** -12 **2b.** -35.8
2c. -16 **3a.** -8 **3b.** 4 **3c.** -2
4. 13,018 ft

Exercises 1. opposite **3.** -8.5
5. $9\frac{1}{4}$ **7.** 1 **9.** -13 **11.** $-1\frac{3}{5}$
13. 4 **15.** $-11\frac{3}{4}$ **17.** -30 **19.** 14
21. $-\frac{1}{2}$ **23.** 23°F **25.** 0.75
27. $-12\frac{2}{5}$ **29.** -12 **31.** 37 **33.** 0

35. $\frac{1}{10}$ **37.** > **39.** > **41.** <
43. 11,331 ft **45.** always **47.** A
51. A **53.** -9 **55.** 2 **59.** 12,660.5 ft
61. 44 in^2 **63.** 13 cm **65.** 12 **67.** 4

1-3

Check It Out! 1a. -7 **1b.** 44
1c. -42 **2a.** $\frac{1}{12}$ **2b.** $-\frac{1}{4}$ **2c.** $-\frac{1}{2}$
3a. 0 **3b.** 0 **3c.** 0 **4.** 7.875 mi

Exercises 1. Switch the numerator and denominator. The reciprocal of $\frac{1}{2}$ is $\frac{2}{1}$, or 2. **3.** -121 **5.** 7 **7.** 2
9. undefined **11.** 0 **13.** about $210,000,000 **15.** -32 **17.** $\frac{9}{10}$
19. -3 **21.** 0 **23.** 0 **25.** $-15°$F
27. -4 **29.** -62 **31.** 18.75
33. 1 **35.** -12 **37.** $\frac{3}{2}$ **39.** negative
41. negative **43.** positive
45. undefined **47.** 1 **49.** $\frac{1}{2}$
51. $-\frac{1}{5}$ **53.** $\frac{9}{8}$ **55.** 15 h per semester **57.** < **59.** > **61.** =
63a. positive **63b.** negative
63c. The product of two negative numbers is positive. The product of that positive number and a negative number is negative.
63d. no **65.** $75\left(\frac{1}{15}\right)$ **67.** $-121\left(\frac{1}{11}\right)$
69. sometimes **71.** The product of two negative numbers is positive and the product of a negative number and a positive number is negative. You know that the product is positive and one factor is negative, so the second factor must also be negative. **73.** B
75. Clarinets: 1 half note = $\frac{1}{2}$ whole note, 8 half notes = 4 whole notes. Find the number of quarter notes that have the same length as 4 whole notes. $4 \div \frac{1}{4} = 16$; the flutes play 16 quarter notes. **77.** $\frac{25}{49}$ **79.** 5
81. 1 **83.** $-\frac{27}{64}$ **89.** $85 **91.** 12.6
93. 6.3 **95.** -6 **97.** 8

1-4

Check It Out! 1a. 2^2 **1b.** x^3
2a. -125 **2b.** -36 **2c.** $\frac{27}{64}$ **3a.** 8^2
3b. $(-3)^3$ **4.** $2^8 = 256$

Exercises 1. the number of times to use the base as a factor **3.** 2^3
5. 49 **7.** -32 **9.** 9^2 **11.** $(-4)^3$

13. 3^4 **15.** $3^5 = 243$ **17.** 3^3 **19.** 27
21. -16 **23.** 7^2 **25.** $(-2)^3$ **27.** 4^3
29. $2^4 = 16$ **31.** < **33.** = **35.** =
37. > **39.** 8; $2 \cdot 2 \cdot 2 = 8$
41. -64; $(-4)(-4)(-4) = -64$
43. -1; $(-1)(-1)(-1) = -1$
45. $\frac{1}{27}$; $\left(\frac{1}{3}\right)\left(\frac{1}{3}\right)\left(\frac{1}{3}\right) = \frac{1}{27}$ **47a.** 36 in^2
47b. 9 in^2 **47c.** 27 in^2 **49.** 6^2
51. $(-1)^4$ **53.** $\left(\frac{1}{9}\right)^3$ **55.** between 8000 cm^3 and 15,625 cm^3 **57.** 2
59. 4 **61.** 2 **63.** 4 **65a.** 100, 1000, 10,000 **65b.** The exponent is the same as the number of zeros in the number. **67.** C **69.** B **71.** 64
73. 65,536 **75a.** $4 \cdot 4$; $4 \cdot 4 \cdot 4$
75b. $4 \cdot 4 \cdot 4 \cdot 4 \cdot 4 = 4^5$ **77.** 5
79. Possible answers: 5 minus x; x less than 5 **81.** Possible answers: c divided by d; the quotient of c and d
83. $\frac{5}{2}$ **85.** 280

1-5

Check It Out! 1a. 2 **1b.** -5 **1c.** 3
2a. $\frac{2}{3}$ **2b.** $\frac{1}{2}$ **2c.** $-\frac{2}{7}$ **3.** about 5.1 ft
4a. $\mathbb{Q}$, rep. dec. **4b.** $\mathbb{Q}$, term. dec., $\mathbb{Z}$
4c. irr. **4d.** $\mathbb{N}$, $\mathbb{W}$, $\mathbb{Z}$, $\mathbb{Q}$, term. dec.

Exercises 3. -15 **5.** 5 **7.** -3
9. -4 **11.** $\frac{2}{3}$ **13.** $\frac{3}{8}$ **15.** $\frac{1}{4}$ **17.** $-\frac{1}{5}$
19. $\mathbb{Q}$, term. dec., $\mathbb{Z}$ **21.** irr.
23. 11 **25.** -10 **27.** $\frac{1}{5}$ **29.** $-\frac{1}{2}$
31. about 14.9 yd **33.** $\mathbb{Q}$, term. dec., $\mathbb{Z}$, $\mathbb{W}$, $\mathbb{N}$ **35.** irr. **37.** > **39.** < **41.** 45; $\mathbb{Q}$, term. dec., $\mathbb{Z}$, $\mathbb{W}$, $\mathbb{N}$ **43.** 34.625; $\mathbb{Q}$, term. dec. **45.** always **47.** always
51. 18 **53.** A **55.** D **57.** 0.9 **59.** -0.1
61. 4 **63.** 65 **65a.** No **67.** $\frac{1}{2}$ **69.** $-\frac{3}{16}$
71. $-\frac{7}{2}$ **73.** $-\frac{8}{125}$ **75.** 64

1-6

Check It Out! 1a. Comm. Prop. of Add. **1b.** Assoc. Prop. of Add.
1c. Comm. Prop. of Mult.
2. Possible answer: $6 \div 2 \neq 2 \div 6$
3a. $9(50) + 9(2)$; 468
3b. $12(100) - 12(2)$; 1176
3c. $7(30) + 7(4)$; 238
4a. Possible answer: -2 and -1 are negative integers, but $(-2)(-1) = 2$, which is not a negative integer.
4b. Possible answer: 15 is a whole number, but $\sqrt{15}$ is not a whole number.

Exercises 1. Associative **3.** Assoc. Prop. of Add. **5.** Comm. Prop. of Mult. **7.** $14(1000) + 14(2)$; 14,028 **9.** $9(40) - 9(2)$; 342 **11.** $12(100) + 12(12)$; 1344 **15.** Comm. Prop. of Add. **17.** Assoc. Prop. of Mult. **19.** Comm. Prop. of Mult. **23.** $8(30) - 8(1)$; 232 **25.** $6(50) + 6(3)$; 318 **27.** $3(150) - 3(1)$; 447 **31a.** Amy: 98:21; Julie: 81:12; Mardi: 83:39 **31b.** Julie, Mardi, Amy **33.** Dist. Prop. **35.** Dist. Prop. **37a.** 336 ft^2 **37b.** 336 ft^2 **37c.** By the Dist. Prop., $8 \cdot 12 + 8 \cdot 14 + 8 \cdot 16 = 8(12 + 14 + 16)$. **41.** A **43.** yes **45.** no **47.** -5; 61 **49.** yes **51.** 1, -1, -2 **53.** 27, 45, 54 **55.** 4^2 **57.** 3^3 **59.** -9 **61.** $\frac{2}{3}$

1-7

Check It Out! 1a. 48 **1b.** 1 **1c.** 21 **2.** 400 **3a.** $100p$ **3b.** $-28.5t$ **3c.** $2m^2 + m^3$ **4.** $6(x - 4) + 9$

$6(x) - 6(4) + 9$ Dist. Prop.
$6x - 24 + 9$ Multiply.
$6x - 15$ Combine like terms.

Exercises 3. 15 **5.** -3 **7.** -22 **9.** $16x$ **11.** $6a$ **13.** $20x^2 + x$ **19.** -17 **21.** 47 **23.** -10 **25.** -14 **27.** $\frac{1}{4}$ **29.** $12x$ **31.** x **33.** $8x^2 - 2x$ **35.** $13y - 10$ **37.** $4(y + 6) + 9$

$4y + 24 + 9$ Dist. Prop.
$4y + 33$ Combine like terms.

41a. 55 **41b.** 498 **41c.** 250 **41d.** 10 **41e.** 30 **41f.** 70 **43.** 1 **45.** 14 **47.** 92 **49.** $6p + 9$ **51a.** $\frac{57.823}{6}$ **51b.** 9.637 **55a.** equal **55b.** 96π **55c.** $2(16\pi) + 96\pi = 128\pi$ **57.** D **59.** 4 **61.** 1 **63.** $12x + 116$ **65.** $-3b - 7$ **69a.** Dist. Prop. **69b.** Multiply **71.** $-6\frac{1}{3}$ **73.** -2.4 **75.** 324 **77.** $\frac{1}{4}$ **79.** 18 **81.** -11

Study Guide: Review

1. constant **2.** whole numbers **3.** coefficient **4.** term **5.** $1.99g$ **6.** $t + 3$ **7.** -5; 0; 5 **8.** -5; 0; 5

9. -4; 1; 6 **10.** $150 \div m$; 30; 25; 15 **11.** -14 **12.** -4.6 **13.** $4\frac{1}{2}$ **14.** -1 **15.** -24 **16.** 14.3 **17.** 5 **18.** 2231 ft **19.** 90 **20.** 0 **21.** -15.2 **22.** -8 **23.** 0 **24.** undefined **25.** 9 **26.** $-\frac{2}{3}$ **27.** $\frac{15}{7}$ **28.** 3,650,000 steps **29.** $4 \cdot 4 \cdot 4 = 64$ **30.** $(-3)(-3)(-3) = -27$ **31.** $(-3)(-3)(-3)(-3) = 81$ **32.** $-1 \cdot 5 \cdot 5 = -25$ **33.** $\left(\frac{2}{3}\right)\left(\frac{2}{3}\right)\left(\frac{2}{3}\right) = \frac{8}{27}$ **34.** $\left(-\frac{4}{5}\right)\left(-\frac{4}{5}\right) = \frac{16}{25}$ **35.** 2^4 **36.** $(-10)^3$ **37.** $(-8)^2$ **38.** 12^1 **39.** 729 in^3 **40.** 6 **41.** 14 **42.** -13 **43.** -12 **44.** $\frac{5}{6}$ **45.** $\frac{1}{3}$ **46.** 4 **47.** $\frac{9}{11}$ **48.** 3 **49.** rational number, terminating decimal, integer, whole number, natural number **50.** rational number, terminating decimal, integer, whole number **51.** rational number, terminating decimal, integer **52.** rational number, terminating decimal **53.** irrational number **54.** rational number, repeating decimal **55.** rational number, terminating decimal, integer, whole number **56.** rational number, terminating decimal **57.** rational number, terminating decimal **58.** 3.6 ft **59.** 3.9 ft **60.** Associative Property of Addition **61.** Associative Property of Multiplication **62.** Commutative Property of Addition **63.** Commutative Property of Multiplication **64.** Possible answer: $6 \div 3 \neq 3 \div 6$ **65.** $3(20) + 3(7)$; 81 **66.** $6(10) + 6(2)$; 72 **67.** $8(10) + 8(7)$; 136 **68.** $7(20) + 7(2)$; 154 **69.** Possible answer: $\sqrt{2} \cdot \sqrt{2} = 2$ **70.** 40 **71.** 270 **72.** 31 **73.** 3 **74.** 35.5 **75.** 40 **76.** $6 **77.** $4x$ **78.** $7y^2$ **79.** $4x + 24$ **80.** $2x^2 + 2$ **81.** $-4y + 3y^2$ **82.** $8y - a$ **83.** $8.84

84.

	Statements	Reasons
1.	$2(x + 5) - 3$	
2.	$2x + 2(5) - 3$	Distributive Property
3.	$2x + 10 - 3$	Multiply.
4.	$2(x) + 2(5) - 3$	Combine like terms.

85.

	Statements	Reasons
1.	$(5 + y - 3) + 4y$	
2.	$(5 - 3 + y) + 4y$	Commutative Property of Addition
3.	$(2 + y) + 4y$	Combine like terms.
4.	$2 + (y + 4y)$	Associative Property of Addition
5.	$2 + 5y$	Combine like terms.
6.	$5y + 2$	Commutative Property of Addition

Chapter 2

2-1

Check It Out! 1a. 8.8 **1b.** 0 **1c.** 8 **2a.** 50 **2b.** -20 **2c.** 56 **3a.** 9.3 **3b.** 2 **3c.** 612 **4.** $\frac{m}{3} = 10,000$; 30,000 ft

Exercises 3. 21 **5.** -30 **7.** 0.6 **9.** 19 **11.** 7 **13.** 5 **15.** 32 **17.** 14 **19.** -9 **21.** 9 **23.** 17 **25.** 0 **27.** 5 **29.** 24 **31.** -3 **33.** -36 **35.** 2.1 **37.** 15 **39.** $-\frac{7}{12}$ **41.** 30 **43.** -12 **45.** $80 = 10a$; 8 mg **47.** $x - 13 = 7$; $x = 20$ **49.** $x + 8 = 16$; $x = 8$ **51.** $30,246 = a + 17,366$; 12,880 ft **55a.** 2000 acres **55b.** 5000 acres **55c.** Divide 780 by 7. **57.** $42 + x = 90$; $x = 48$ **59.** A **61a.** $6x = 4.80$ **61b.** $0.80 **63.** $\frac{29}{12}$ **65.** $\frac{1}{4}$ **67.** 22 **69.** -78 **71.** $-\frac{3}{4}$ **73.** 15 m **75.** 10 cm **77.** $12(40) + 12(3)$; 516

2-2

Check It Out! 1a. 1 **1b.** 6 **1c.** 0 **2a.** $\frac{55}{4}$ **2b.** $\frac{1}{2}$ **2c.** 15 **3a.** $60 **3b.** 2

Exercises 1. 2 **3.** 66 **5.** 2 **7.** $\frac{1}{2}$ **9.** 52 **11.** $\frac{17}{5}$ **13.** 15 passes **15.** 4 **17.** 5 **19.** -9 **21.** $\frac{1}{4}$ **23.** 1 **25.** 3 **27.** $2x - 7 = 19$; $x = 13$ **29.** $30 + 5x = 80$; $x = 10$ **31.** $64 + 3x = -2$; $x = -22$ **33a.** $1963 - 5s = 1863$; $s = 20$ **33b.** 3 **35.** 8 **37.** 4.5 **39.** -10 **41.** 10 **43.** 4.5 **45.** 3 **47.** $5k - 70 = 60$; 26 in.

49a.

Cost of Fighting Fire	
Acres	Cost ($)
100	22,500
200	45,000
500	112,500
1000	225,000
1500	337,500
n	$225n$

49b. $c = 225n$ **53.** D **55.** -6 **57.** 2
59. 5 **61a.** 1.65 **61b.** 3.3
61c. c doubles **63.** integer, rational,
terminating decimal
65. terminating decimal,
rational **67.** $9(20) + 9(8)$; 252
69. $13(20) + 13(1)$; 273 **71.** $7(10) +$
$7(9)$; 133 **73.** $8(30) + 8(3)$; 264
75. 21 **77.** 0 **79.** 28 **81.** -42

2-3

Check It Out! 1a. $-\frac{11}{5}$ **1b.** 6
2a. $-\frac{5}{6}$ **2b.** -5 **2c.** 8 **3a.** 2 **3b.** 4
3c. 8 **4a.** $50 **4b.** $18.15

Exercises 1. 5 **3.** $\frac{4}{3}$ **5.** 3 **7.** 22
9. 3 **11.** 3 **13.** 16 **15.** -5 **17.** 30
19. 6 **21.** $\frac{27}{2}$ **23.** 7 **25.** 100 **27.** -13
29. $\frac{8}{3}$ **31.** $-\frac{2}{5}$ **33.** 16 **35.** Amanda:
$20; Casey: $10 **37.** -1 **39.** 10
41. -3 **43.** $x = 2$ **45.** $d = -\frac{17}{3}$
47. $16 + 7 - 4x = 3$; $x = 5$
49. $\frac{1}{2}x + 2(x - 5) = 0$; $x = 4$
51. $2x + 115 = 180$; $x = 32.5$
53. -2 **55.** -10 **57.** 1 **59.** $\frac{25}{6}$ **61.** 2, 3
63. 102 and 104 **67.** Dist. Prop.,
Comm. Prop. of Add., Comm. Prop.
of Mult., Assoc. Prop. of Add.
69. D **71.** $10 **73.** 8 **75.** $\frac{29}{2}$ **77.** 2
79. Comm. Prop. of Add. **81.** $8m$
83. $118v$ **85.** $12c + x$ **87.** 3 **89.** -6

2-4

Check It Out! 1a. -2 **1b.** 2 **2a.** 4
2b. -2 **3a.** $\varnothing$ **3b.** all real numbers
4. 10 years old

Exercises 3. 1 **5.** 40 **7.** $-\frac{2}{3}$ **9.** 3
11. $\varnothing$ **13.** all real numbers **15.** 6
17. 6 **19.** 2.85 **21.** 10 **23.** 6 **25.** 14
27. $\frac{3}{4}$ **29.** -4 **31.** $\varnothing$ **33a.** 15 weeks
33b. 180 lb **35.** always **37.** -4
39. 7 **41.** -3 **43.** 2 **45.** 1 **47.** $-\frac{7}{5}$
49. 4 **51.** $\varnothing$ **53.** 9 **59.** A **61.** C **63.** 2

65. $\varnothing$ **67.** -20 **69.** 6, 7, 8 **71.** $1.68
73. $3y$ cm **75.** -63 **77.** 4 **79.** 2
81. -125 **83.** 15 **85.** 3

2-5

Check It Out! 1. 15 **2a.** $7.50/h
2b. 6 envelopes/min **3a.** -20
3b. 5.75 **4a.** 12 **4b.** 320 **5a.** about
0.2 in. **5b.** 6 in.

Exercises 1. The ratios are equal.
3. $48 **5.** 50 rotations/s **7.** 24
9. 6 **11.** -7.5 **13.** 30 **15.** 65.55
17. 65.5% **19.** $\frac{3}{5} = \frac{h}{4.9}$; 2.94 m
21. 72 **23.** $403.90/oz **25.** 10
27. -1 **29.** 31.5 **31.** 63 **33.** 300%
35. 4 **37.** 2 **39.** 49%; 51% **41a.** 40%
41b. action **41c.** 3% **41d.** 36.9%
45. D **47.** 40°; 50°
49. 17.2%
51.
$$\frac{3}{x} = \frac{5}{x-1}$$
$$(x)\frac{3}{x} = (x)\frac{5}{x-1}$$
$$3 = \frac{5x}{x-1}$$
$$3(x-1) = \frac{5x}{x-1}(x-1)$$
$$3(x-1) = 5x$$
53. -27 **55.** $-\frac{1}{32}$ **57.** 10^2 **59.** -5
65. 8

2-6

Check It Out! 1. about 1.46 h
2. $i = f + gt$ **3a.** $t = \frac{5-b}{2}$ **3b.** $V = \frac{m}{D}$

Exercises 1. A literal equation
contains more than one variable.
A formula shows how to determine
the value of one variable when
you know the value(s) of one or
more other variables. So a formula
always contains more than
one variable, making it a literal
equation. **3.** $w = \frac{V}{\ell h}$ **5.** $m = 4n + 8$
7. $a = \frac{10}{b+c}$ **9.** $I = A - P$
11. $x = \frac{k+5}{y}$ **13.** $\frac{x-2}{z} = y$
15. $x = 5(a + g)$ **17.** $x = \frac{y-b}{m}$
19. $T = \frac{PV}{nR}$ **21.** $T = M + R$
23. $b = \frac{c-2a}{2}$ **25.** $r = 7 - ax$
27. $x = \frac{5-4y}{3}$ **31.** $a = \frac{t-g}{-0.0035}$
35. C **37.** D **39.** $a = \frac{5}{2}\left(c + \frac{3}{4}b\right)$
41. $d = 500\left(t - \frac{1}{2}\right)$ **43.** $s = \frac{v^2 - u^2}{2a}$
45. 120 s **47.** 12 **49.** -6 **51.** 20
53. 12

2-7

Check It Out! 1a. -7, 7 **1b.** -5.5,
10.5 **2a.** $\varnothing$ **2b.** 4 **3.** $|x - 134| =$
0.18; min. height: 133.82 m; max.
height: 134.18 m

Exercises 1. -6, 6 **3.** -2, 2 **5.** $-\frac{3}{2}, \frac{1}{2}$
7. $\varnothing$ **9.** $\varnothing$ **11.** 2.8 **13.** $|x - 207| = 2$;
mile markers 205 and 209 **15.** -9,
13 ft **17.** -2, 2 **19.** 18.8, 65.28
21. $-\frac{14}{3}$, 4 **23.** 0 **25.** 0 **27.** $\frac{2}{3}$
29. $|x - 5| = 0.001$; 4.999 mm;
5.001 mm **31.** $|x - 7| = 2$; 5, 9
33. $|x - 1500| = 75$; 1575 bricks;
1425 bricks **35.** $|x| = 3$
37. $|x - 2| = 3$ **39.** sometimes
41. always **43a.** $|t - 24| = 5$
43b. 19; 29 **43c.** yes **43d.** The
measurements are correct to within
5 mi/h. **47.** C **49.** B **51.** Div. Prop.
of Eq.; Subtr. Prop. of Eq.; Div. Prop.
of Eq. **53.** 9.5 **55.** 15 **57.** 6 **59.** 9
61. $m = 7 - 5n$ **63.** $y = \frac{1-3x}{2}$
65. $e = \frac{5}{c+d}$

Study Guide: Review

1. literal equation **2.** ratio **3.** 36
4. -2 **5.** -21 **6.** 18 **7.** $\frac{9}{8}$ **8.** $\frac{7}{3}$
9. $t = 5.1$ **10.** $x = 25.5$ **11.** 7
12. $s = -7$ **13.** $f = 120$ **14.** $m = 15$
15. $j = 72$ **16.** $n = 36$ **17.** $k = 0.875$
18. $c = 12.5$ **19.** $27 + s = 108$; 81
20. $213 **21.** 17.5 **22.** -5 **23.** $z = 6$
24. $h = 4$ **25.** $k = 40$ **26.** $f = -\frac{3}{2}$
27. $h = \frac{16}{3}$ **28.** $k = 3$ **29.** $t = 13$
30. $a = -4$ **31.** $x = 2$ **32.** $x = 1$
33. 92 **34.** $a = 13$ **35.** $y = -6$ **36.** 15
37. $x = 6$ **38.** $h = 3$ **39.** $z = 2$
40. $w = -0.4$ **41.** $x = -2$ **42.** 18
43. 1 **44.** 41; 123°; 57° **45.** $5; $2
46. $x = -2$ **47.** $r = -2$ **48.** 1 **49.** $-\frac{2}{3}$
50. $\varnothing$ **51.** all real numbers
52. $x = 3.5$ **53.** $c = \frac{18}{7}$ **54.** $x = 7$
55. $x = 6$ **56.** $n = -2$ **57.** $x = 3$
58. 9 **59.** $\frac{16}{1}$ **60.** $n = 1.6$ **61.** $x = 54$
62. 1.37 ft **63.** 5.29 **64.** 3105
65. 66.7% **66.** 400% **67.** 133.3
68. 240 **69.** 80% **70.** $n = \frac{360}{c}$
71. $a = \frac{2S}{n} - \ell$ **72.** $x = \frac{225 - y}{0.25}$
73. 3.7 gal **74.** $x = 15, -27$
75. $y = 7, -3$ **76.** $y = 9, -9$
77. $x = 17.4, -6.6$ **78.** $g = -4, -8$
79. $x = \frac{5}{7}, -\frac{5}{7}$ **80.** $|x - 5| = 55$; min.
speed: 50 mi/h; max. speed: 60 mi/h

Chapter 3

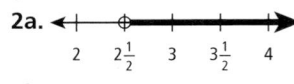

3-1

Check It Out! 1. all real numbers greater than 4

2a.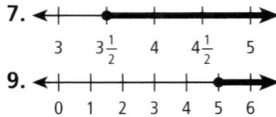
(number line: open circle at $2\frac{1}{2}$, arrow right; labels 2, $2\frac{1}{2}$, 3, $3\frac{1}{2}$, 4)

2b. (number line: closed circle at -1, arrow right; labels -3, -2, -1, 0, 1, 2, 3)

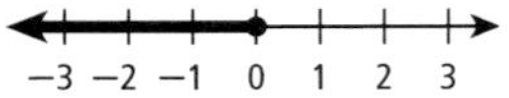

2c. (number line: closed circle at -3, arrow left; labels -6, -5, -4, -3, -2, -1, 0)

3. $x < 2.5$ **4.** $d =$ amount employee can earn per hour; $d \geq 8.25$

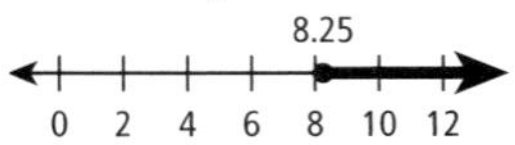

(number line: closed circle at 8.25, arrow right; labels 0, 2, 4, 6, 8, 10, 12)

Exercises 1. A solution of an inequality makes the inequality true when substituted for the variable. **3.** all real numbers greater than -3 **5.** all real numbers greater than or equal to 3

7. (number line: closed circle at 4, arrow right; labels 3, $3\frac{1}{2}$, 4, $4\frac{1}{2}$, 5)

9. (number line: closed circle at 5, arrow right; labels 0, 1, 2, 3, 4, 5, 6)

11. $b > -8\frac{1}{2}$ **13.** $d < -7$ **15.** $f \leq 14$ **17.** $r < 140$ **19.** all real numbers less than 2 **21.** all real numbers less than or equal to 12

23. (number line: closed circle at $-\frac{1}{2}$, arrow right; labels -2, $-1\frac{1}{2}$, -1, $-\frac{1}{2}$, 0)

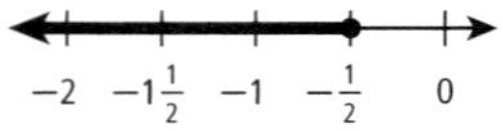

25. (number line: closed circle at 1, arrow right; labels 0, 1, 2, 3, 4, 5, 6)

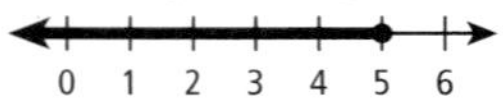

27. $v < -11$ **29.** $x > -3.3$ **31.** $z \geq 9$ **33.** $y =$ years of experience; $y \geq 5$ **35.** h is less than -5. **37.** r is greater than or equal to -2. **39.** $p \leq 17$ **41.** $f > 0$ **43.** $p =$ profits; $p < 10,000$ **45.** $e =$ elevation; $e \leq 5000$ **47.** x represents the age in years of a child at a childcare center when x is positive. **49.** x represents the number of millions of albums sold by a popular band. **51.** D **53.** C **55a.** $125 - s \geq 90$; $s \leq 35$

55b. (number line: closed circle at 35, arrow left; labels 0, 35)

55c. $s + 15 \leq 35$; $s \leq 20$ where s is nonnegative **59.** D **61.** C **63.** any numbers such that $|x| < |y|$ **65.** < **67.** any number between 0.35 and 1.27 **69.** Draw an empty circle at 5. Then draw arrows going left and right from 5. **71.** 10 **73.** 7

75. $3x + 3$ **77.** $b = 9$ **79.** $\emptyset$

3-2

Check It Out! 1a. $s \leq 9$
(number line: closed circle at 9, arrow left; labels 0, 3, 6, 9, 12)

1b. $t < 5\frac{1}{2}$
(number line: open circle at $5\frac{1}{2}$, arrow left; labels 4, $4\frac{1}{2}$, 5, $5\frac{1}{2}$, 6)

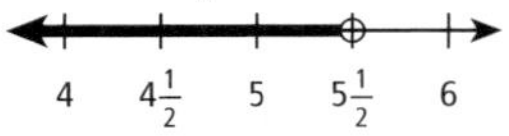

1c. $q < 11$
(number line: open circle at 11, arrow left; labels 9, 10, 11, 12, 13)

2. $11 + m \leq 15$; $m \leq 4$; Sarah can consume 4 mg or less without exceeding the RDA. **3.** $250 + p > 282$; $p > 32$; Josh needs to bench press more than 32 additional pounds to break the school record.

Exercises 1. $p > 6$ **3.** $x \leq -15$ **5.** $102 + t \leq 104$; $t \leq 2$ where t is nonnegative **7.** $a \geq 5$ **9.** $x < 15$ **11.** $1400 + 243 + w \leq 2000$; $w \leq 357$ where w is nonnegative **13.** $x - 10 > 32$; $x > 42$ **15.** $r - 13 \leq 15$; $r \leq 28$ **17.** $q > 51$ **19.** $p \leq 0.8$ **21.** $c > -202$ **23.** $x \geq 0$ **25.** $21 + d \leq 30$; $d \leq 9$ where d is nonnegative **27.** $x < 3$; B **29.** $x \leq 3$; D **31.** $936 + 4254 + p \leq 45,611$; $5190 + p \leq 45,611$; $p \leq 40,421$ where p is nonnegative **33.** When you isolate the variable in each inequality, you get $x \geq 2$ and $x \geq 2$. **35a.** $411 + 411 = 882$ miles **35b.** $822 + m \leq 1000$

(number line: open circle at 0, closed circle at 178; label 178)

35c. $m \leq 178$, but m cannot be negative. **37.** A **39.** D **41.** $r \leq 5\frac{1}{10}$ **43.** sometimes **45.** always **47.** $y = 3 - \frac{2}{3}x$ **49.** $a = \frac{c}{2+b}$ **51.** $k = 2s - 11$ **53.** 4, -4 **55.** 5, -5 **57.** 4, $-\frac{14}{3}$ **55.** $x \geq -1$

3-3

Check It Out! 1a. $k > 6$ 
(number line: open circle at 6, arrow right; labels 0, 2, 4, 6, 8, 10, 12)

1b. $q \leq -10$
(number line: closed circle at -10, arrow left; labels 0, 10)

1c. $g > 36$
(number line: open circle at 36, arrow right; labels 34, 35, 36, 37, 38)

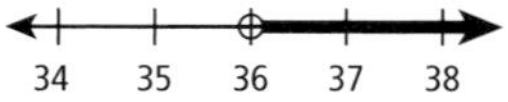

2a. $x \geq -10$
(number line: closed circle at -10, arrow right; labels -10, -8, -6, -4, -2)

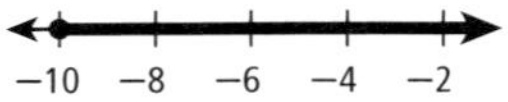

2b. $h > -17$
(number line: open circle at -17, arrow right; labels -19, -18, -17, -16, -15)

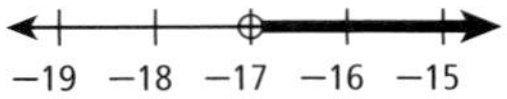

3. $10g \leq 128$; $g \leq 12.8$; 0, 1, 2, 3, 4, 5, 6, 7, 8, 9, 10, 11, or 12 servings

Exercises 1. $b > 9$ **3.** $d > 18$ **5.** $m \leq 1.1$ **7.** $s > -2$ **9.** $x > 5$ **11.** $n > -0.4$ **13.** $d > -3$ **15.** $t > -72$ **17.** $80n \leq 550$; $n \leq 6.875$; 0, 1, 2, 3, 4, 5, or 6 nights **19.** $j \leq 12$ **21.** $d < 7$ **23.** $h \leq \frac{8}{7}$ **25.** $c \leq -12$ **27.** $b \geq \frac{1}{10}$ **29.** $b \leq -16$ **31.** $r < -\frac{3}{2}$ **33.** $y < 2$ **35.** $t > 4$ **37.** $z < -11$ **39.** $k \leq -7$ **41.** $p \geq -12$ **43.** $x > -3$ **45.** $x < 20$ **47.** $p \leq -6$ **49.** $b < 2$ **51.** $7x \geq 21$; $x \geq 3$ **53.** $-\frac{4}{5}b \leq -16$; $b \geq 20$ **57.** $t \leq -3$; C **59.** $t \leq 3$; A **61.** 26 bags **63.** Multiplying both sides of an inequality by zero makes both sides equal zero, so there is no longer an inequality to solve. **65.** $12.5g \leq 800$; $g \leq 64$ where g is nonnegative **67.** B **69.** B **71.** $g \leq \frac{-14}{5}$ **73.** $m > \frac{4}{15}$ **75.** $x = 5$ **77.** no; $0 < 1$ but $1 \not< 0$ **79.** 2^3 **81.** \$1.89/gal **83.** 35 words/min **85.** $t < 1$ **87.** $b < 14$

3-4

Check It Out! 1a. $x \leq -6$
(number line: closed circle at -6, arrow left; labels -8, -6, -4, -2, 0)

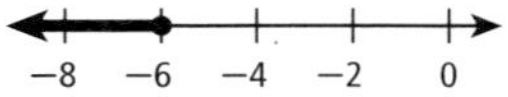

1b. $x < -11$
(number line: open circle at -11, arrow left; labels -13, -12, -11, -10, -9)

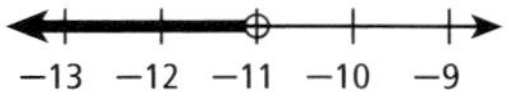

1c. $n \leq -10$
(number line: closed circle at -10, arrow left; labels -12, -11, -10, -9, -8)

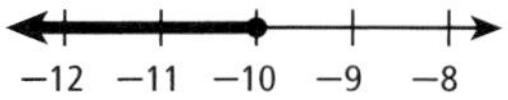

2a. $m > 10$
(number line: open circle at 10, arrow right; labels 8, 9, 10, 11, 12)

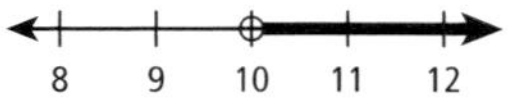

2b. $x > -4$
(number line: open circle at -4, arrow right; labels -6, -5, -4, -3, -2, -1, 0)

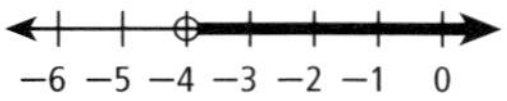

2c. $x > 2\frac{1}{3}$
(number line: open circle at $2\frac{1}{3}$, arrow right; labels 0, 1, 2, 3, 4)

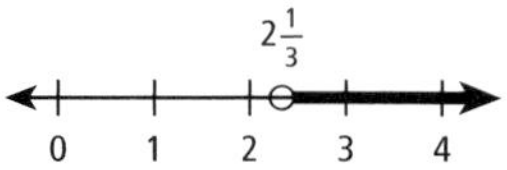

3. $\frac{95 + x}{2} \geq 90$; $95 + x \geq 180$; $x \geq 85$; Jim's score must be at least 85.

Exercises 1. $m > 6$ **3.** $x \leq -2$ **5.** $x > -16$ **7.** $x \geq -9$ **9.** $x > -\frac{1}{2}$ **11.** $x \leq 19$ **13.** $x > 1$

15. $300 + 0.1x > 1200$; sales of more than \$9000 **17.** $x \leq 1$ **19.** $w < -2$
21. $x < -6$ **23.** $f < -4.5$ **25.** $w > 0$
27. $v > \frac{2}{3}$ **29.** $x > -5$ **31.** $x < -2$
33. $a \geq 11$ **35.** $x > 3$ **37.** $29.99 < 19.99 + 0.35x$; $x > 28.57$; starting at 29 min **39.** $x \leq 2$ **41.** $x < 4$
43. $x < -6$ **45.** $r < 8$ **47.** $x < 7$
49. $p \geq 18$ **51.** $\frac{1}{2}x + 9 < 33$; $x < 48$
53. $4(x + 12) \leq 16$; $x \leq -8$
55. $x \geq 4$; B **57.** $x \leq -2$; A
59. $225 + 400 < 275 + 15m$; $23\frac{1}{3} < m$; 24 months or more
61a.

Number	Process	Cost
1	$350 + 3$	353
2	$350 + 3(2)$	356
3	$350 + 3(3)$	359
10	$350 + 3(10)$	380
n	$350 + 3n$	$350 + 3n$

61b. $c = 350 + 3n$ **61c.** $350 + 3n \leq 500$; $n \leq 50$; 50 CDs or fewer **65.** B
67. 59 **69.** $x > 5$ **71.** $x > 0$ **73.** $x \geq 0$
75. $-3x > 0$; $x < 0$ **77.** 7 **79.** $\frac{2}{3}$
81. -1 **83.** $25 + 2m = 10 + 2.5m$; $m = 30$ **85.** $a \geq 6$

3-5

Check It Out! **1a.** $x \leq -2$
1b. $t < -1$
2. more than 160 flyers
3a. $r \leq 2$
3b. $x < 3$
4a. no solutions **4b.** all real numbers

Exercises **1.** $x < 3$ **3.** $x < 2$
5. $c < -2$ **7.** $100 + 4p < 7p$;
$p > 33.33$; they'll have to sell at least 34 pizzas. **9.** $p < -17$
11. $x > 3$ **13.** $t < 6.8$ **15.** $\varnothing$ **17.** all real numbers **19.** $\varnothing$ **21.** $y > -2$
23. $b \geq -7$ **25.** $m > 5$ **27.** $x \geq 2$
29. $w \geq 6$ **31.** $r \geq -4$ **33.** $\varnothing$ **35.** all real numbers **37.** all real numbers
39. $t < -7$ **41.** $x > 3$ **43.** $x < 2$
45. $x > -2$ **47.** $x \leq -6$
49. $s > 26.67$; 27 s **51a.** $400 + 4.50n$

51b. $12n$ **51c.** $400 + 4.50n < 12n$;
$n > 53\frac{1}{3}$; 54 CDs or more
53. $5x - 10 < 6x - 8$; $x > -2$
55. $\frac{3}{4}x \geq x - 5$; $x \leq 20$ **57.** no
59. x can never be greater than itself plus 1. **61.** D **63.** A
67. $x < -3$ **69.** $w \geq -1\frac{6}{7}$ **73.** $\frac{2}{5} = \frac{w}{65}$;
$w = 26$ in. **75.** $y = $ years; $y \geq 14$

3-6

Check It Out! **1.** $1.0 \leq c \leq 3.0$
2a. $1 < x < 5$
2b. $-3 \leq n < 2$
3a. $r < 10$ OR $r > 14$
3b. $x \geq 3$ OR $x < -1$
4a. $-9 < y < -2$
4b. $x \leq -3$ OR $x \geq 2$

Exercises **1.** intersection
3. $-5 < x < 5$ **5.** $0 < x < 3$
7. $x < -8$ OR $x > 4$ **9.** $n < 1$ OR $n > 4$
11. $-5 \leq a \leq -3$ **13.** $c < 1$ OR $c \geq 9$
15. $16 \leq k \leq 50$ **17.** $3 \leq n \leq 6$
19. $2 < x < 6$ **21.** $x < 0$ OR $x > 3$
23. $x < -3$ OR $x > 2$ **25.** $q < 0$ OR $q \geq 2$ **27.** $-2 < s < 1$ **29a.** $225 + 80n$ gives the cost of the studio and technicians. They will spend between \$200 and \$550.
29b. $-0.3125 \leq n \leq 4.0625$;
n cannot be negative.
29c. They need to raise an additional \$155. **31.** $1 \leq x \leq 2$ **33.** $-10 \leq x \leq 10$ **35.** $t < 0$ OR $t > 100$
37. $-2 < x < 5$ **39.** $a < 0$ OR $a > 1$
41. $n < 2$ OR $n > 5$ **43.** $7 \leq m \leq 60$
47. D **49.** B **51.** $0.5 < c < 3$ **53.** $s \leq 6$ OR $s \geq 9$ **55.** $-1 \leq x \leq 3$
57. $4x - 5$

$4(x - 3) + 7$	
$4x - 12 + 7$	Distribute 4.
$4x - 5$	Combine like terms.

59. $3a + 3$

$6a - 3(a - 1)$	
$6a - 3a + 3$	Distribute 3.
$3a + 3$	Combine like terms.

61. 3 **63.** $d = rt$; 126.8 mi
65. $x > -1$

3-7

Check It Out! **1a.** $-3 \leq x \leq 3$
1b. $-15 \leq x \leq 9$
2a. $x \leq -2$ OR $x \geq 2$
2b. $x \leq -6$ OR $x \geq 1$
3. $|p - 125| \leq 75$; $50 \leq p \leq 200$
4a. all real numbers **4b.** $\varnothing$

Exercises **1.** $-3 \leq x \leq 3$
3. $-2 < x < 2$ **5.** $4 < x < 6$
7. $x < -22$ OR $x > 22$ **9.** $x \leq -4$ OR $x \geq 4$ **11.** $x \leq 1$ OR $x \geq 5$
13. $|x - 55| \leq 25$; $30 \leq x \leq 80$
15. $\varnothing$ **17.** all real numbers **19.** $\varnothing$
21. $2 < x < 4$ **23.** $-3 < x < 3$
25. $-6 < x < 0$ **27.** $x \leq -10$ OR $x \geq 10$ **29.** $x \leq -10$ OR $x \geq 6$
31. $x < -1$ OR $x > 2$ **33.** $\varnothing$ **35.** all real numbers **37.** $\varnothing$ **39.** always
41. sometimes **43.** $|x - 2| \leq 3$;
$-1 \leq x \leq 5$ **45.** $|a| \leq 2$ **47.** $|c| \geq 6\frac{1}{2}$
49a. 10,010 Hz **49b.** $|x - 10,010| \leq 9990$ **51.** $|n - 23| > 12$ **53.** $k \leq 1$; the inequality is equivalent to $|x| < k - 1$, and this has no solutions when the expression on the right side is less than or equal to 0 (i.e., when $k - 1 \leq 0$ or $k \leq 1$). **55.** B **57.** B
61. $1\frac{1}{2}$ **63.** $2\frac{1}{2}$ **65.** all real numbers less than 2 **67.** all real numbers greater than or equal to -6 **69.** $0 < x < 4$
71. $x < 1$ OR $x > 4$

Study Guide: Review

1. inequality **2.** union **3.** compound inequality **4.** intersection
5. solution of an inequality
6.
7.
8.

9.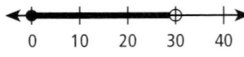
(number line: 9, 9.5, 10, 10.5, 11; closed dot at 9.5)

10.
(number line: −6 −5 −4 −3 −2 −1 0; open dot at −4, arrow right)

11.
(number line: 0 1 2 3 4 5 6; open dot at 3, arrow left)

12. $a < 2$ **13.** $k \geq -3.5$

14. $q < -10$ **15.** $t = $ temperature;
$t \geq 72$
(number line: 0, 72; closed dot at 72, arrow right)

16. $s = $ students; $s \leq 12$ where s is a natural number
(number line: 0, 12; open dot at 0, closed dot at 12)

17. $m = $ minutes; $m < 30$ where m is nonnegative
(number line: 0 10 20 30 40; closed dot at 0, open dot at 30)

18. $t < 7$
(number line: 0, 7; open dot at 7, arrow left)

19. $k \leq 2$
(number line: 0, 2; closed dot at 2, arrow left)

20. $m > -5$
(number line: −5, 0; open dot at −5, arrow right)

21. $x \geq 4.5$
(number line: 0, 4.5; closed dot at 4.5, arrow right)

22. $w < 9.5$
(number line: 0, 9.5; open dot at 9.5, arrow left)

23. $a < 5$
(number line: 0, 5; open dot at 5, arrow left)

24. $h < 1$
(number line: 0, 1; open dot at 1, arrow left)

25. $v < -2$
(number line: −2, 0; open dot at −2, arrow left)

26. $4.5 + m \geq 10$; $m \geq 5.5$; Tammy must run 5.5 mi or more. **27.** $32 + d \leq 50$; $d \leq 18$; Rob can spend $18 or less.

28. $a \leq 5$
(number line: 0, 5; closed dot at 5, arrow left)

29. $t > -3$
(number line: −3, 0; open dot at −3, arrow right)

30. $p > 8$
(number line: 0, 8; open dot at 8, arrow right)

31. $x \leq -25$
(number line: −25, 0; closed dot at −25, arrow left)

32. $n > 6$
(number line: 0, 6; open dot at 6, arrow right)

33. $g < -12$
(number line: −12, 0; open dot at −12, arrow left)

34. $k > -7$
(number line: −7, 0; open dot at −7, arrow right)

35. $r < -9$
(number line: −9, 0; open dot at −9, arrow left)

36. $h < -3$
(number line: −3, 0; open dot at −3, arrow left)

37. $g < -2.5$
(number line: 0, 2.5; open dot at 2.5, arrow left)

38. 0, 1, 2, 3, 4, 5, 6, 7 **39.** $0.75n \geq 250$; $n \geq 333\frac{1}{3}$; they must sell at least 334 lanyards.

40. $x < 5$
(number line: 0, 5; open dot at 5, arrow left)

41. $t \geq 6$
(number line: 0, 6; closed dot at 6, arrow right)

42. $m > -11$
(number line: −11, 0; open dot at −11, arrow right)

43. $x < -1$
(number line: −1, 0; open dot at −1, arrow left)

44. $h > -3$
(number line: −3, 0; open dot at −3, arrow right)

45. $x > 1\frac{1}{2}$
(number line: 0, $1\frac{1}{2}$; open dot at $1\frac{1}{2}$, arrow right)

46. $b \leq 10$
(number line: 0, 10; closed dot at 10, arrow left)

47. $y > 3\frac{1}{2}$
(number line: 0, $3\frac{1}{2}$; open dot at $3\frac{1}{2}$, arrow right)

48. $n > -15$
(number line: −15, 0; open dot at −15, arrow right)

49. 0, 1, 2, 3, 4, 5, 6, 7, 8, 9, 10, 11, 12, or 13

50. $m < -1$
(number line: −1, 0; open dot at −1, arrow left)

51. $y \geq -2$
(number line: −2, 0; closed dot at −2, arrow right)

52. $c < -3$
(number line: −3, 0; open dot at −3, arrow left)

53. $q \leq -4$
(number line: −4, 0; closed dot at −4, arrow left)

54. $x > 2$
(number line: 0, 2; open dot at 2, arrow right)

55. $t < 3$
(number line: 0, 3; open dot at 3, arrow left)

56. no solutions **57.** all real numbers

58. $p > -\frac{1}{2}$
(number line: $-\frac{1}{2}$, 0; open dot at $-\frac{1}{2}$, arrow right)

59. all real numbers

60. $k > 2$
(number line: 0, 2; open dot at 2, arrow right)

61. no solutions **62.** $210 + 16m > 175 + 20m$; $8.75 > m$

63. $-10 < t < 4$
(number line: −10, 4; open dots at −10 and 4)

64. $-6 < k \leq 7$
(number line: −6, 7; open dot at −6, closed dot at 7)

65. $r > 7$ OR $r < -2$
(number line: −2, 7; open dots at −2 and 7, arrows out)

66. $\varnothing$

67. $-2 < p \leq 5$
(number line: −2, 5; open dot at −2, closed dot at 5)

68. all real numbers
(number line: arrows both directions)

69. $68 \leq t \leq 84$ **70.** $102 \leq n \leq 183.6$

71. $-22 \leq x \leq 22$
(number line: −22 −11 0 11 22; closed dots at −22 and 22)

72. $x < -12$ OR $x > 4$
(number line: −12 −8 −4 0 4 8; open dots at −12 and 4, arrows out)

73. $-4 \leq x \leq 4$
(number line: −4 −2 0 2 4 6; closed dots at −4 and 4)

74. $-18 < x < 0$
(number line: −18 −15 −12 −9 −6 −3 0; open dots at −18 and 0)

75. $x \le -3$ OR $x \ge 3$

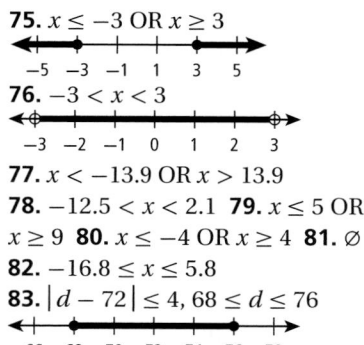

76. $-3 < x < 3$

77. $x < -13.9$ OR $x > 13.9$

78. $-12.5 < x < 2.1$ **79.** $x \le 5$ OR $x \ge 9$ **80.** $x \le -4$ OR $x \ge 4$ **81.** $\varnothing$

82. $-16.8 \le x \le 5.8$

83. $|d - 72| \le 4$, $68 \le d \le 76$

Chapter 4

4-1

Check It Out! 1. graph C

2a. discrete;

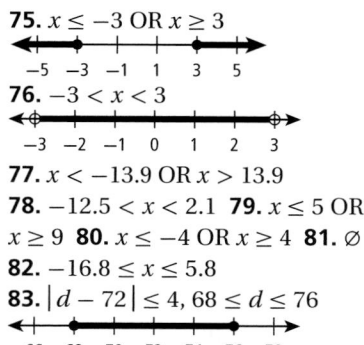

Keyboarding

2b. continuous;

Water Tank

3. Possible answer: When the number of students reaches a certain point, the number of pizzas bought increases.

Exercises 1. continuous
3. graph B **5.** graph C **11.** graph A
13. continuous;

Puppy's Weight

19. The point of intersection represents the time of day when you will be the same distance from the base of the mountain on both the hike up and the hike down.

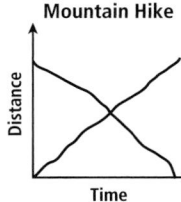

Mountain Hike

23. C **27.** Container C **29.** −8
31. $\frac{1}{9}$ **33.** $n - 5 = -2$; 3 **35.** −23, 15

4-2

Check It Out! 1.

x	y
1	3
2	4
3	5

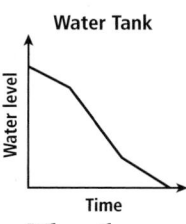

2a. D: {6, 5, 2, 1}; R: {−4, −1, 0}
2b. D: {1, 4, 8}; R: {1, 4}
3a. D: {−6, −4, 1, 8}; R: {1, 2, 9}; function; each domain value is paired with exactly one range value. **3b.** D: {2, 3, 4}; R: {−5, −4, −3}; not a function; the domain value 2 is paired with both −5 and −4.

Exercises

3.

x	y
1	1
1	2

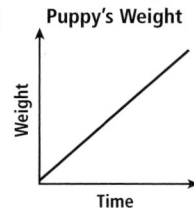

5.

x	y
−7	7
−3	3
−1	1
5	−5

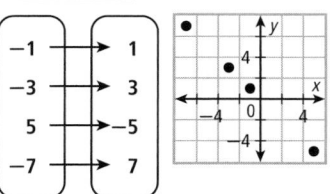

7. D: {−5, 0, 2, 5}; R: {−20, −8, 0, 7} **9.** D: {2, 3, 5, 6, 8}; R: {4, 9, 25, 36, 81} **11.** D: {1}; R: {−2, 0, 3, 8}; not a function; the domain value 1 is paired with several different range values.

13. D: {−2, −1, 0, 1, 2}; R: {1}; function; each element in the domain is paired with exactly one element in the range.

15.

x	y
−2	−4
−1	−1
0	0
1	−1
2	−4

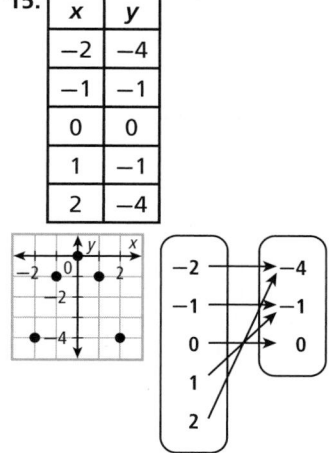

17. D: {3}; R: $1 \le y \le 5$ **19.** D: $-2 \le x \le 2$; R: $0 \le y \le 2$; function; each domain value is paired with exactly one range value.
21. yes

x	y
1	125
2	175
3	225
4	275

23. yes

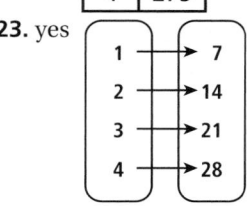

25. yes

Hours x	Cost y
1	9
2	11
3	13
4	15
5	15

27. no **29a.** D: $0 \le t \le 5$; R: $0 \le v \le 750$ **29b.** yes **29c.** $(2, 300)$; $(3.5, 525)$ **33.** B **35a.** $\{(-3, 5), (-1, 7), (0, 9), (1, 11), (3, 13)\}$
35b. D: {−3, −1, 0, 1, 3}; R: {5, 7, 9, 11, 13} **35c.** yes **37.** all real numbers **39.** $\frac{3}{4} = \frac{x}{36}$; 27 cm
41. $x + 45 \ge 64$; $x \ge 19$

Check It Out! 1. $y = 3x$

2a. yes

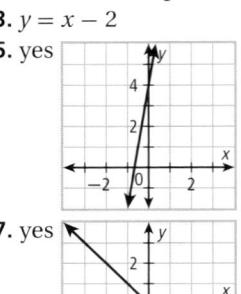

2b. yes

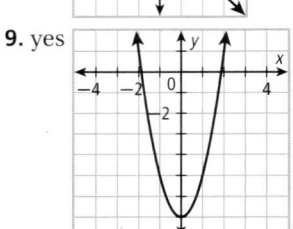

3a. ind. var.: hours; dep. var.: cost; $f(x) = 28x$ **3b.** ind. var.: pounds; dep. var.: cost; $f(x) = 1.69x$ **3c.** ind. var.: people; dep. var.: cost; $f(x) = 6 + 29.99x$ **4.** $h(1) = 1$; $h(-3) = -7$

Exercises 1. dependent
3. $y = x - 2$
5. yes

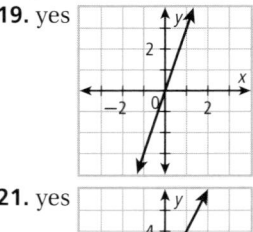

7. yes

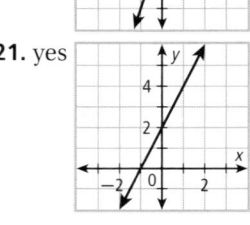

9. yes

11. ind. var.: hours; dep. var.: cost; $f(h) = 75h$ **13.** $f(0) = 2$; $f(1) = 9$ **15.** $h(27) = -1$; $h(-15) = -15$ **17.** $y = -x$
19. yes

21. yes

23. yes

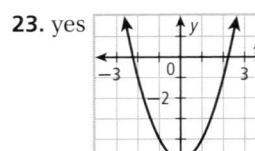

25. yes

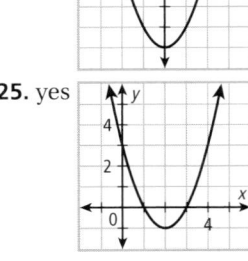

27. ind. var.: days late; dep. var.: total cost; $f(x) = 3.99 + 0.99x$
29. ind. var.: gallons of gas; dep, var.: miles; $f(x) = 28x$ **31.** $g(1) = 7$; $g(2) = 10$ **33.** yes; no **35.** yes; no **37a.** yes; ind. var.: hours; dep. var.: distance; $f(h) = 630h$
37b. 7560 mi

39.

x	0	1	2	3
h(x)	0	2	6	12

41. D: all real numbers; R: all real numbers **43.** D: all real numbers; R: all real numbers **45.** D: all real numbers; R: $y \geq -5$ **47.** -10
49. Rashid must multiply $150 by the number of months he saves for, not add the number of months to 150. **51a.** $v = 1250t$ **51b.** ind. var.: time; dep. var.: volume **51c.** 8 h **53.** B **55.** the same; x-value; x-value; y-values; x-value; more than one **61.** 6 **63.** 1 **65.** ∅ **67.** all real numbers **69.** all real numbers **71.** D: $\{-3, -1, 0, 1, 3\}$; R: $\{4, 2, 0, -4\}$; function; each domain value is paired with exactly one range value.

Check It Out!
1. Football Team Scores

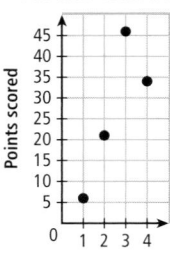

2. positive correlation **3a.** No correlation; the temperature in Houston has nothing to do with the number of cars sold in Boston.

3b. Positive correlation; as the number of family members increases, more food is needed, so the grocery bill increases too.
3c. Negative correlation; as the number of times you sharpen your pencil increases, the length of the pencil decreases. **4.** Graph A; it cannot be graph B because graph B shows negative minutes; it cannot be graph C because graph C shows the temperature of the pie increasing, a positive correlation. **5.** about 75 rolls

Exercises 3. no **5.** positive correlation **7.** negative correlation **9.** positive correlation **11.** Graph A **15.** positive correlation **17.** positive correlation **19.** Graph A **23.** positive correlation **25.** B

27a. Juan's Trip

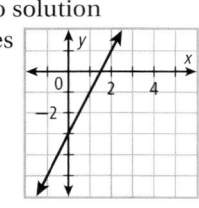

27b. Positive correlation; as time increases, the number of miles also increases. **29.** C
35. $5(n + 2) = 2n - 8$, $n = -6$
37. no solution
39. yes

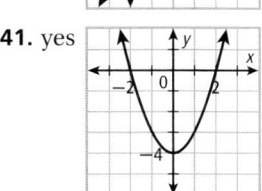

41. yes

Check It Out! 1a. yes; $d = \frac{1}{2}$; $\frac{5}{4}, \frac{7}{4}, \frac{9}{4}$ **1b.** no **1c.** yes; $d = -3$; $-8, -11, -14$ **2a.** -343 **2b.** 19.6 **3.** 750 lb

Exercises 1. common difference **3.** yes; $d = -0.7$; $-0.7, -1.4, -2.1$ **5.** no **7.** -53 **9.** no **11.** yes; $d = -9$; $-58, -67, -76$ **13.** 5.9 **15.** 9500 mi

17. $\frac{1}{4}$ **19.** -2.2 **21.** 0.07 **23.** $-\frac{3}{8}$,
$-\frac{1}{2}, -\frac{5}{8}, -\frac{3}{4}$ **25.** $-0.2, -0.7, -1.2$,
-1.7 **27.** $-0.3, -0.1, 0.1, 0.3$ **29.** 22
31. 122 **33a.** It could be arithmetic
because you pay \$2 per lap, so the
common difference could be 2.
33b. \$11, \$13, \$15; $a_n = 2n + 7$
33c. \$37 **33d.** no **35.** -104.5 **37.** $\frac{20}{3}$
39a. $a_n = 6 + 3(n - 1)$ **39b.** 48
39c. \$7800 **39d.** $a_n = 7 + 3(n - 1)$;
\$8200 **41a.**

Time Interval	Mile Marker
1	520
2	509
3	498
4	487
5	476
6	465

41b. $a_n = 520 + (n - 1)(-11)$
41c. number of miles per interval
41d. 421 **43.** A **45.** 20th and 21st
terms **47a.** session 16; yes; she
increases the amount she runs by
1.5 miles each time **47b.** Thursday
49. 16 **51.** $t < -2$ OR $t > 2$
53. negative correlation

Study Guide: Review

1. domain **2.** negative correlation
3. term
4. continuous

5. continuous

6. continuous

7. Possible answer: A family buys
a fish tank and some fish. After
two weeks, they buy some more
fish. After two more weeks, they
buy even more fish. **8.** Possible
answer: A monkey swings from a
high branch to a lower branch.
He climbs along the branch. Then
he jumps to a higher branch and
takes a nap.

9.

x	−1	0	2
y	0	1	1

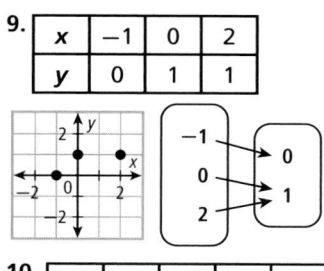

10.

x	−2	−1	2	3
y	−1	1	3	4

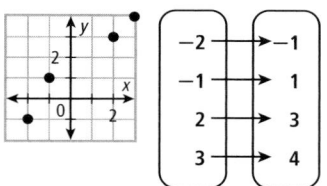

11. D: $\{-4, -2, 0, 2\}$; R: $\{-1, 1, 3, 5\}$
12. D: $\{-2, -1, 0, 1, 2\}$; R: $\{-1, 0\}$
13. D: $\{0, 1, 4\}$; R: $\{-2, -1, 0, 1, 2\}$
14. D: $-4 \leq x \leq 3$; R: $-3 \leq y \leq 5$
15. D: $\{-5, -3, -1, 1\}$; R: $\{-3, -2, -1, 0\}$; function; every element of
the domain is assigned to exactly
one element in the range.
16. D: $\{-4, -2, 0, 2\}$; R: $\{-2, 1\}$;
function; each element of the domain
is assigned to exactly one element
in the range. **17.** D: $\{1, 2, 3, 4\}$;
R: $\{-1, 0, 1, 2, 3\}$; not a function; the
x-value 1 is assigned to the y-value 3
and the y-value -1. **18.** $\{(1, 5.00),$
$(2, 6.50), (3, 8.00), (4, 9.50),$
$(5, 11.00)\}$; yes; each x-value has
exactly one y-value. **19.** yes; each
element in the domain is assigned
to exactly one element in the range.

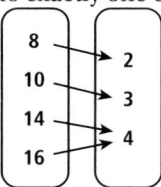

20. The value of y is 7 less than x;
$y = x - 7$ **21.** The value of y is $\frac{1}{2}$
times x; $y = \frac{1}{2}x$ **22.** The value of y is
9 times x; $y = 9x$ **23.** independent
variable: number of cakes;
dependent variable: cost;
$f(c) = 6c$ **24.** independent variable:
number of CDs Raul will buy;
dependent variable: number of
CDs Tim will buy; $g(n) = 2n$ **25.** 14
26. -11 **27.** 6, -1 **28.** $k(4) = 15$;
$k(-6) = 25$ **29.** $w(16) = -1.5$;
$w(12.25) = -2$

30. yes

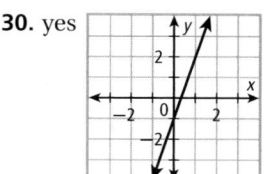

31. yes

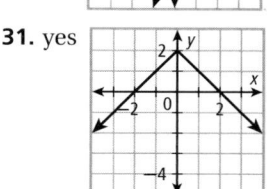

32. yes

33. yes

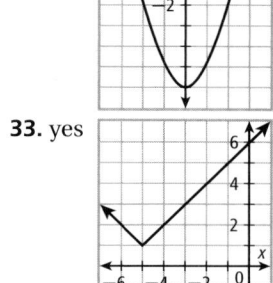

34. D: all real numbers; R: all real
numbers **35.** D: all real numbers;
R: all real numbers **36.** D: all real
numbers; R: $y \geq -6$ **37.** D: all real
numbers; R: $y \geq 5$
38.

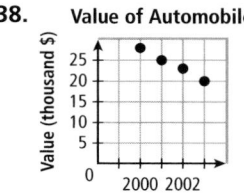

Value of Automobile

Negative correlation; as the time
increases, the value of the automobile
decreases. **39.** Possible answer: 33
40. yes; -6; $-4, -10, -16$ **41.** no
42. no **43.** yes; 2.5; 2, 4.5, 7 **44.** 105
45. -62 **46.** 20 **47.** \$420 **48.** $-15.5°C$

Chapter 5

5-1

Check It Out! 1a. yes **1b.** yes
1c. no **2a.** no **2b.** yes **2c.** yes
3a. $5x - y = 9$; $A = 5, B = -1, C = 9$;
nonhoriz., nonvert. line **3b.** $0x +$
$y = 12$; $A = 0, B = 1, C = 12$; horiz.
line **3c.** $x + 0y = 2$; $A = 1, B = 0$,
$C = 2$; vert. line **4.** D: $\{0, 1, 2, 3, \dots\}$
R: $\{\$10, \$13, \$16, \$19, \dots\}$

Exercises 1. no **3.** no **5.** yes
7. no **9.** yes **11.** $2x + 3y = 5$; $A = 2$,
$B = 3$, $C = 5$; nonhoriz., nonvert.
line **13.** $x - 5y = -3$; $A = 1$, $B = -5$,
$C = -3$; nonhoriz., nonvert. line
15. D: $x \geq 0$; R: $y \geq 0$ **17.** yes
19. yes **21.** yes **23.** no **25.** no
27. no **29.** $-2x + 4y = 0$; $A = -2$,
$B = 4$, $C = 0$; nonhoriz., nonvert.
line **31.** $3x + 0y = 3$; $A = 3$, $B = 0$,
$C = 3$; vert. line **33.** The equation
will be either $Ax = 1$ or $Bx = 1$; the
graph will be either a vertical or
horizontal line. **35.** yes **37.** yes
39. yes; $-4x + y = 2$; $A = -4$;
$B = 1$; $C = 2$ **41.** no **43.** yes; $x = 7$;
$A = 1$; $B = 0$; $C = 7$; **45.** yes;
$3x - y = 1$; $A = 3$; $B = -1$; $C = 1$
47. yes; $5x - 2y = -3$; $A = 5$,
$B = -2$, $C = -3$ **49.** no

51.
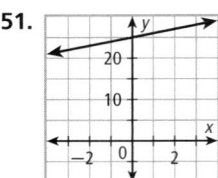

53.
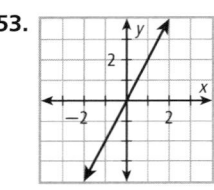

55.
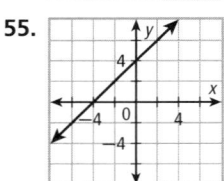

57.
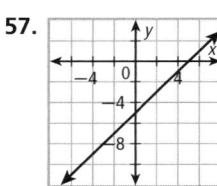

59a. $f(x) = 8x$

59b.

Molly's Earnings

59c. yes **61a.**
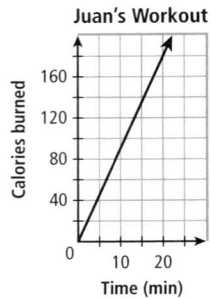
Juan's Workout

61b. The graph forms a line.
63. no **65.** C **69.** linear **71.** not
linear **73.** -1 **75.** $\frac{1}{9}$ **77.** 2
79. $\varnothing$ **81.** $-22 \leq x \leq 24$ **83.** $\varnothing$

5-2

Check It Out! 1a. x-int.: -2;
y-int.: 3 **1b.** x-int.: -10; y-int.: 6
1c. x-int.: 4; y-int.: 8 **2a.** x-int.: 30;
y-int.: 20;
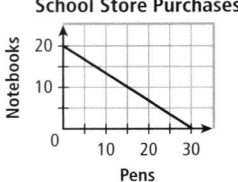
School Store Purchases

2b. x-int.: pens that can be purchased
if no notebooks are purchased; y-int.:
notebooks that can be purchased if
no pens are purchased.

3a.
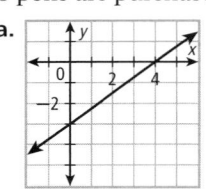

3b.
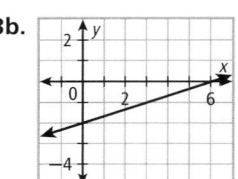

Exercises 1. y-intercept **3.** x-int.:
2; y-int.: -4 **5.** x-int.: 2; y-int.: -1
7. x-int.: 2; y-int.: 8
9.
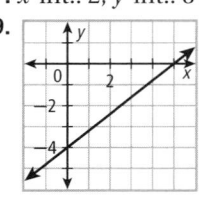

11.
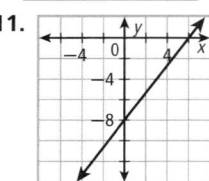

13. x-int.: -1; y-int.: 3 **15.** x-int.:
-4; y-int.: 2 **17.** x-int.: -4; y-int.: 2
19. x-int.: 2; y-int.: 8 **21.** x-int.: $\frac{1}{8}$;
y-int.: -1

23a.
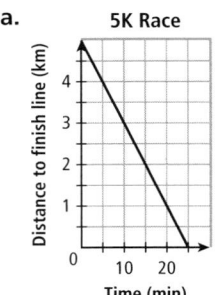
5K Race

x-int.: 25; y-int.: 5
23b. x-int.: total time to run race
(when distance to finish line is 0);
y-int.: total length of race
(when time is 0)

25.
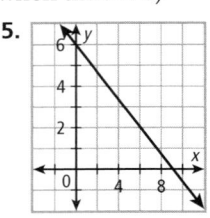

27.
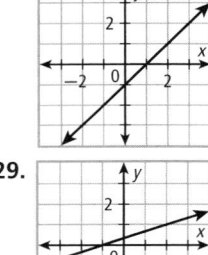

29.
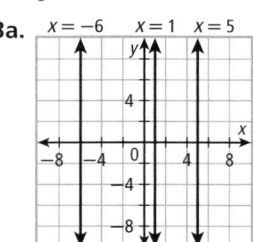

31a. x-int.: 600; y-int.: 7.5
31b. x-int.: number of years after
1800 when there will be no acres of
tropical forest; y-int.: million acres
of tropical forest in 1800

33a.
$x = -6$ $x = 1$ $x = 5$

$x = -6$: x-int.: -6, no y-int.; $x = 1$:
x-int.: 1, no y-int.; $x = 5$: x-int.: 5,
no y-int. **33b.** $y = -3$: no x-int.,
y-int.: -3; $y = 2$: no x-int., y-int.: 2;
$y = 7$: no x-int., y-int.: 7

33c. Horiz.: For $y = c$, the y-int. is c, and there is no x-int. Vert.: For $x = k$, the x-int. is k, and there is no y-int. **35.** A **37.** B **41.** A

43.
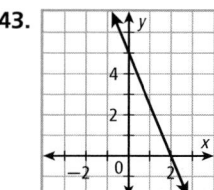

45.
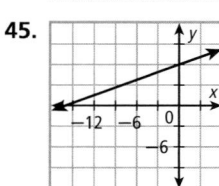

47. 600 in^3 **49.** $m \geq -6$ **51.** yes

5-3

Check It Out! **1.** $-\frac{1}{2}$ **2a.** undefined **2b.** 0 **3a.** $m = 0$ **3b.** $m = 3$ **4a.** undefined **4b.** positive **5.** $m = \frac{1}{2}$; the height of the plant is increasing at a rate of 1 cm every 2 days. **6.** $m = -\frac{2}{3}$

Exercises **1.** rise **3.** $\frac{1}{2}$ **5.** 0 **7.** 1 **9.** $-\frac{1}{2}$ **11.** 2 **13.** negative **15.** 10; the money earned is increasing at a rate of \$10/h. **17.** -4 **19.** $\frac{9}{5}$ **21.** undefined **23.** 0 **25.** positive **27.** zero **29.** $-\frac{9}{5000}$; the boiling point is decreasing at a rate of 9 °F for each 5000 ft above sea level. **31.** $-\frac{13}{5}$ **33.** $\frac{17}{18}$ **35a.** In 165 s, about 425 files were scanned. **37.** 10 **41a.** -1 **44b.** For each year that a person ages, the maximum heart rate decreases by 1 beat/min. **43.** D **45.** $-\frac{b}{a}$ **47.** $\frac{3-2y}{2}$ **49.** $x = \frac{1}{2}$ **51.** $k = 4.85$ **53.** $f = 41$ **55.** yes **57.** x-int.: -3; y-int.: -9

5-4

Check It Out! **1a.** no **1b.** yes; $-\frac{3}{4}$ **c.** yes; -3 **2a.** no; possible answer: the value of $\frac{y}{x}$ is not the same for each ordered pair. **2b.** yes; possible answer: the value of $\frac{y}{x}$ is the same for each ordered pair. **2c.** no; possible answer: the value of $\frac{y}{x}$ is not the same for each ordered pair. **3.** 90

4. $y = 4x$

Perimeter of a Square
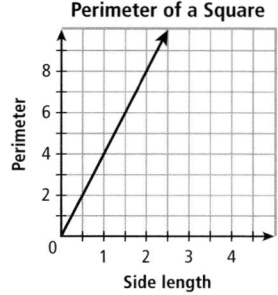
Side length

Exercises **1.** direct variation **3.** yes **5.** no **7.** 18 **9.** $y = 5x$ **11.** yes **13.** yes **15.** -16 **17.** $y = 2.50x$ **19.** no **21.** $y = -3x$ **23.** $y = 4x$ **25.** $y = 2x$ **27.** $y = 7x$ **29.** $k = -\frac{2}{9}x$ **31.** $k = \frac{4}{3}x$ **33.** $y = -6x$ **35.** $y = \frac{2}{7}x$ **37a.** $y = 15x$

36b.
Washing Machine Efficiency
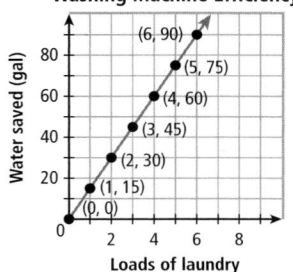
Loads of laundry

36c. 1560 gal **41.** C **43.** B **45a.** 4 gal **45b.** no **45c.** 750 gal; 250 gal **47.** 6 **49.** D: {1, 2, 3, 4}; R: {-5, -4, -3, -2}; yes **51.** D: {-3, -2, -1, -2}; R: {9, 6, 3, 0}; no **53.** 2

5-5

Check It Out!

1a.
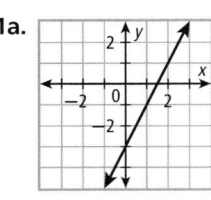

1b.
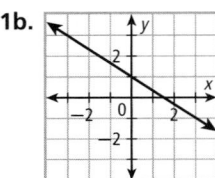

2. $y = 8x - 25$ **3a.** $y = \frac{2}{3}x$
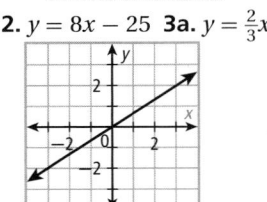

3b. $y = -3x + 5$
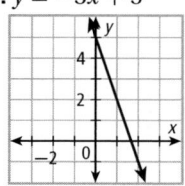

3c. $y = -4$
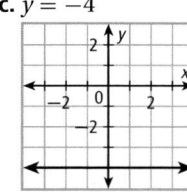

4a. $y = 18x + 200$ **4b.** slope: 18; cost per person; y-int.: 200; fee **4c.** \$3800

Exercises **1.**
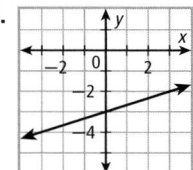

3.
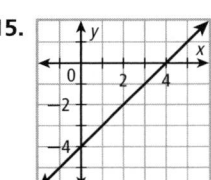

5. $y = 8x + 2$ **7.** $y = -3$ **9.** $y = \frac{2}{5}x - 6$ **11.** $y = -2x + 4$

13.

15.

17. $y = 5x - 9$ **19.** $y = -\frac{1}{2}x + 7$ **21.** $y = -\frac{1}{2}x + 3$ **23.** $y = x + 6$ **25.** $y = \frac{7}{2}$ **27.** $y = \frac{1}{2}x + 4$ **29.** $y = -2x + 8$ **31.** student A **35.** impossible **37.** A **41.** B **43.** B **45.** $y = \frac{1}{3}x - 3$ **47.** -6 **49.** $3x + 4 \leq 10$ **51.** $n \leq 8$ **53.** $t < -3$ **55.** x-int.: 3; y-int.: 6

5-6

Check It Out! 1.

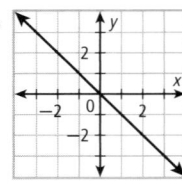

2a. $y - 1 = 2\left(x - \frac{1}{2}\right)$ **2b.** $y + 4 = 0(x - 3)$ **3.** $y = \frac{1}{3}x + 2$
4a. $y = 6x - 8$ **3b.** $y = \frac{2}{3}x - 1$
5. $y = 2.25x + 6$; $53.25

Exercises 1.

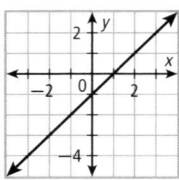

3.

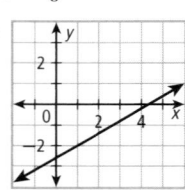

5. $y - 5 = -4(x - 1)$
7. $y = -\frac{1}{3}x + 7$ **9.** $y = \frac{1}{3}x$
11. $y = 3x - 13$ **13.** $y = -x$
15. $y = -\frac{1}{3}x + \frac{4}{3}$ **17.** $y = -x + 15$
19. $y = \frac{1}{5}x + 3$; 9 ft

21.

23. $y - 5 = \frac{2}{9}(x + 1)$ **25.** $y - 8 = 8(x - 1)$ **27.** $y - 7 = 3(x - 4)$
29. $y = -\frac{2}{7}x + 1$ **31.** $y = -\frac{1}{4}x$
33. $y = -5x + 13$ **35.** $y = \frac{1}{7}x + 7$
37. $y = -5x - 3$ **39.** $y = 2x + 11$
41. $y = -\frac{1}{500}x + 212$; 200°F
43. $y = 6$; $x = 6$ **49.** D **51.** slope: $\frac{5}{2}$;
y-int.: 2 **53.** $y = \frac{2}{3}x$ **55.** $m > -2$
AND $m < 1$

57.

59. $y = 3x - 5$

5-7

Check It Out! 1a. $y = 2x + 2$ and $y = 2x + 1$ **1b.** $y = 3x$ and $y - 1 = 3(x + 2)$ **2.** slope of $\overline{AB} = 0$; slope of $\overline{BC} = \frac{5}{3}$; slope of $\overline{CD} = 0$; slope of $\overline{AD} = \frac{5}{3}$; $\overline{AB}$ is parallel to $\overline{CD}$ because they have the same slope. $\overline{AD}$ is parallel to $\overline{BC}$ because they have the same slope. Since opposite sides are parallel, $ABCD$ is a parallelogram. **3.** $y = -4$ and $x = 3$; $y - 6 = 5(x + 4)$ and $y = -\frac{1}{5}x + 2$ **4.** slope of $\overline{PQ} = 2$; slope of $\overline{QR} = -1$; slope of $\overline{PR} = -\frac{1}{2}$; $\overline{PQ}$ is perpendicular to $\overline{PR}$ because the product of their slopes is -1. Since PQR contains a right angle, PQR is a right triangle. **5a.** $y = \frac{4}{5} + 3$
5b. $y = -\frac{1}{5}x + 2$

Exercises 1. parallel **3.** $y = \frac{3}{4}x - 1$ and $y - 3 = \frac{3}{4}(x - 5)$ **5.** $y = \frac{2}{3}x - 4$ and $y = -\frac{3}{2}x + 2$; $y = -1$ and $x = 3$ **7.** slope of $\overline{PQ} = 2$; slope of $\overline{QR} = -\frac{1}{2}$; slope of $\overline{RS} = 2$; slope of $\overline{PS} = -\frac{1}{2}$ **9.** $x = 7$ and $x = -9$; $y = -\frac{5}{6}x + 8$ and $y = -\frac{5}{6}x - 4$
11. $y = -3x + 2$ and $3x + y = 27$; $y = \frac{1}{2}x - 1$ and $-x + 2y = 17$
13. $y = 6x$ and $y = -\frac{1}{6}x$; $y = \frac{1}{6}x$ and $y = -6x$ **15.** $x - 6y = 15$ and $y = -6x - 8$; $y = 3x - 2$ and $3y = -x - 11$ **17.** $y = -\frac{6}{7}x$
19. neither **21.** parallel
23. $y = \frac{1}{2}x - 5$ **25.** $y = 2x + 5$
27. $y = 3x + 13$ **29.** $y = -x + 5$
31. $y = 4x - 23$ **33.** $y = -\frac{3}{4}x$
35. $y = -x + 1$ **37.** $y = \frac{2}{5}x - \frac{31}{5}$
39. $y = -\frac{1}{5}x - \frac{11}{5}$ **41.** $y = -\frac{1}{2}x - \frac{1}{2}$
43. $y = \frac{1}{2}x + 6$ **45.** $y = x - 3$
47. $y = -4$ **51a.** $y = 50x$
51b. $y = 50x + 30$ **51c.** no **53.** C
55. They cannot be parallel because they both contain point B. Therefore they must be the same line. **57.** $-\frac{1}{5}$ **59.** $94 + 2t > 112 + t$; $t > 18$ **61.**

63. $y = \frac{2}{3}x - 5$ **65.** $y = -\frac{1}{2}x - \frac{1}{2}$
67. $y = 3$

Study Guide: Review

1. direct variation **2.** y-intercept
3. slope; y-intercept **4.** yes **5.** yes
6. yes **7.** yes **8.** no **9.** yes **10.** yes
11. no **12.** $5x + y = 1$; $A = 5$; $B = 1$;
$C = 1$; nonhoriz., nonvert. line
13. $x + 6y = -2$; $A = 1$; $B = 6$;
$C = -2$; nonhoriz., nonvert. line
14. $7x - 4y = 0$; $A = 7$; $B = -4$;
$C = 0$; nonhoriz., nonvert. line
15. $y = 9$; $A = 0$; $B = 1$; $C = 9$; horiz.
line **16.** x-int.: 2; y-int.: -4
17. x-int.: 5; y-int.: 6 **18.** x-int.: 3;
y-int.: -9 **19.** x-int.: $-\frac{1}{2}$; y-int.: 1
20. x-int.: -18; y-int.: 3 **21.** x-int.: $\frac{1}{3}$;
y-int.: $-\frac{1}{4}$ **22.** 5 **23.** $-\frac{4}{3}$ **24.** -3
25. $-\frac{1}{2}$ **26.** 3 **27.** 7 **28.** 4 **29.** -5
30. -1 **31.** 1 **32.** 2 **33.** undefined
34. 0 **35.** yes; -6 **36.** yes; 1 **37.** no
38. yes; $-\frac{1}{2}$ **39.** -12

40.

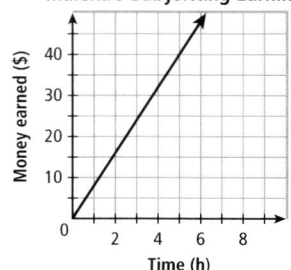

Maleka's Babysitting Earnings

41.

42.

43. $y = \frac{1}{3}x + 5$ **44.** $y = 4x - 9$

45.

46.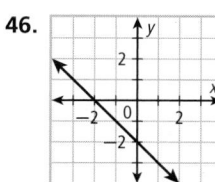

47. $y - 3 = 2(x - 1)$ **48.** $y - 4 = -5(x + 6)$ **49.** $y = 2x + 2$
50. $y = -x + 3$ **51.** $y = 2x + 8$
52. $y = 2$ **53.** $y = -\frac{1}{3}x + 48$; 8 in.
54. $y = -\frac{1}{3}x$ and $y = -\frac{1}{3}x - 6$
55. $y - 2 = -4(x - 1)$ and $y = -4x - 2$ **56.** $y - 1 = -5(x - 6)$ and $y = \frac{1}{5}x + 2$ **57.** $y - 2 = 3(x + 1)$ and $y = -\frac{1}{3}x$ **58.** slope of $\overline{AB} = \frac{3}{8}$; slope of $\overline{AC} = -\frac{8}{3}$; $\overline{AB}$ is perpendicular to $\overline{AC}$ because the product of their slopes is -1. Therefore ABC is a right triangle.
59. $y = 2x - 3$

Chapter 6

6-1

Check It Out! 1a. yes **1b.** no
2a. $(-2, 3)$ **2b.** $(3, -2)$ **3.** 5 movies; $25

Exercises 1. an ordered pair that satisfies both equations **3.** yes
5. $(2, 1)$ **7.** $(-4, 7)$ **9.** no **11.** yes
13. $(3, 3)$ **15.** $(3, -1)$
17a. $\begin{cases} y = 2x \\ y = 16 + 0.50x \end{cases}$

17b. It represents how many carnations need to be sold to break even. **17c.** no **19.** $(-2.4, -9.3)$
21. $(0.3, -0.3)$ **23.** 45 white; 120 pink **25.** 8 yr **27.** Every point on a line satisfies the related linear equation. A point that is on both lines (the intersection point) satisfies both equations. **29.** C
31. month 11; 400 **33.** 42 **35.** 2.2
37. 1 **39.** 2 **41.** $c \leq -9$

6-2

Check It Out! 1a. $(-2, 1)$
1b. $(0, 2)$ **1c.** $(3, -10)$ **2.** $(-1, 6)$
3a. 10 months **3b.** $860; the first option; the first option is cheaper for the first 9 months; the second option is cheaper after 10 months.

Exercises 1. $(9, 35)$ **3.** $(3, 8)$
5. $\left(-\frac{15}{2}, -12\right)$ **7a.** 3 months; $136
7b. Green Lawn **9.** $(-4, 2)$
11. $\left(\frac{1}{2}, \frac{1}{2}\right)$ **13.** $(1, 5)$ **15.** $(3, -2)$
17a. 6 months; $360 **17b.** the second option **19.** $(2, -2)$
21. $(8, 6)$ **23.** $(-9, -14.8)$ **25.** 4; 66
27. $\begin{cases} x + y = 1000 \\ 0.05x + 0.06y = 58 \end{cases}$; $200 at 5%; $800 at 6% **29.** $m\angle x = 60°$; $m\angle y = 30°$ **31.** $m\angle x = 29°$; $m\angle y = 61°$ **35a.** $\begin{cases} 2x + y = 26 \\ x = y - 8 \end{cases}$

35b. book: $6; backpack: $14 **37.** D
39. $\begin{cases} n + u = 378 \\ 4n = 5u \end{cases}$; 210 new cars; 168 used cars **41.** $x = 2$; $y = 1$; $z = 4$
43. yes **45.** yes **47.** x-int.: 15; y-int.: -5 **49.** no **51.** no

6-3

Check It Out! 1. $(-2, 4)$ **2.** $(4, 1)$
3a. $(2, 0)$ **3b.** $(3, 4)$ **4.** 9 lilies; 4 tulips

Exercises 1. $(-4, 1)$ **3.** $(-2, -4)$
5. $(-6, 30)$ **7.** $(3, 2)$ **9.** $(4, -3)$
11. $(-1, -2)$ **13.** $(1, 5)$ **15.** $\left(6, -\frac{1}{2}\right)$
17. $(-1, 2)$ **19.** $(-1, 2)$
21. $\begin{cases} \ell - w = 2 \\ 2\ell + 2w = 40 \end{cases}$; length: 11 units; width: 9 units
23a.

Classes	+	Fee	=	Total Price
2x	+	y	=	18
6x	−	y	=	38

23b. $\begin{cases} 2x + y = 18 \\ 6x - y = 38 \end{cases}$ **23c.** 7; 4
25. $(3, 3)$ **27.** $\frac{46}{7}, \frac{8}{7}$ **29.** $\frac{15}{7}, \frac{9}{7}$
31a. $\begin{cases} 3A + 2B = 16 \\ 2A + 3B = 14 \end{cases}$
31b. $A = 4$; $B = 2$ **31c.** Buying the first package will save $8; buying the second package will save $7.
33. A **35a.** $\begin{cases} s + n = 358 \\ 1.50s + 3.25n = 752.25 \end{cases}$
35b. $s = 235$; $n = 123$ **37.** $x = 4$; $y = -1$; $z = 10$ **39.** pen = $2; notebook = $6; bag = $9 **41.** $y = 3x$
43. $y = 2x - 9$ **45.** $y = \frac{1}{2}x + 10$
47. $(4, 9)$

6-4

Check It Out! 1. no solution
2. infinitely many solutions
3a. consistent, dependent; infinitely many solutions **3b.** consistent, independent; one solution
3c. inconsistent; no solution
4. Yes; the graphs of the two equations have different slopes so they intersect.

Exercises 1. consistent **3.** no sol.
5. inf. many solutions **7.** inf. many solutions **9.** inconsis.; no sol.
11. yes **13.** no solution **15.** no solution **17.** inf. many solutions
19. inf. many solutions **21.** consis., indep.; one sol. **23.** yes **25.** There are infinitely many answers for the cost of each video game and DVD. The system is consistent and dependent. **27.** They will always have the same amount; both started with 2 and add 4 every year.
29. The graph will be 2 parallel lines. **31.** student A **33.** D
35. $p = q$; $p \neq q$ **37.** 11 km
39. $-3.5, 8.5$ **41.** $-\frac{13}{3}, 1$
43. $(-2, -4)$

6-5

Check It Out! 1. 1.5 mi/h; 9 mi
2. 25 g of the 9% solution; 5 g of the 15% solution **3.** 89

Exercises 1. 1 mi/h; 5 mi/h **3.** 59
5. 300 mL of each
7a.

	Quarters	+	Dimes	=	Total
Number of Coins	q	+	d	=	250
Value in Dollars	0.25q	+	0.1d	=	39.25

7b. $\begin{cases} q + d = 250 \\ 0.25q + 0.1d = 39.25 \end{cases}$
7c. 95 quarters; 155 dimes
9a. $f + 4$; $d + 4$
9b. $\begin{cases} f = d + 32 \\ f + 4 = 5(d + 4) \end{cases}$
9c. father: 36; daughter: 4 **11.** 49
13a. $\begin{cases} a + c = 100 \\ 13a + 8c = 1100 \end{cases}$
13b. 60 adults'; 40 children's
13c. 80 adults'; 20 children's **17.** D
19. Maya: 25; David: 20

23. $7a - 2(a) - 2(1)$ (Dist. Prop.); $7a - 2a - 2$ (Multiply.); $5a - 2$ (Combine like terms.) **25.** $-3, 3$ **27.** $-4, 3$ **29.** $\varnothing$ **31.** inf. many solutions

6-6

Check It Out! **1a.** no **b.** yes

2a.
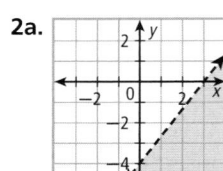

2b.
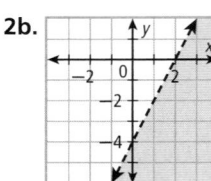

2c.
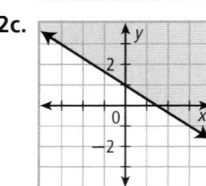

3a. $2.5b + 2g \le 6$

3b.
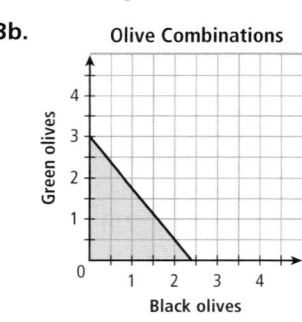
Olive Combinations

3c. Possible answer: $(1 \text{ lb black}, 1 \text{ lb green})$, $(0.5 \text{ lb black}, 2 \text{ lb green})$
4a. $y < -x$ **4b.** $y \ge -2x - 3$

Exercises **1.** no **3.** yes

5.
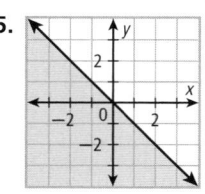

7.
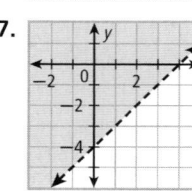

9a. $r + p \le 16$
9b.
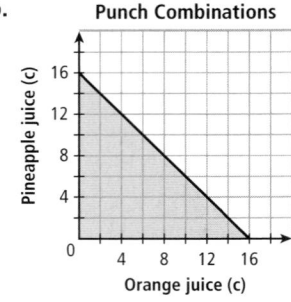
Punch Combinations

11. $y \ge x + 5$ **13.** yes

15.
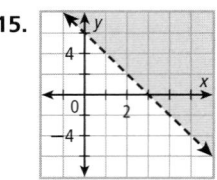

17.
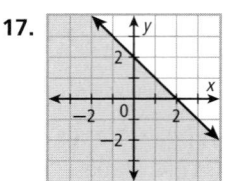

19a. $3b + 2d \le 30$
19b. Food Combinations
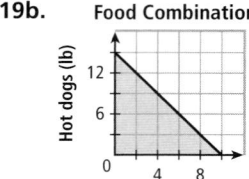

21. $y \le -\frac{1}{5}x + 3$
23.
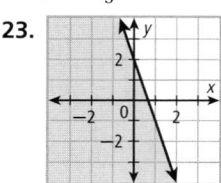

25.
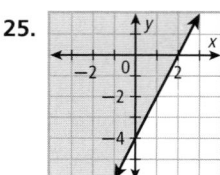

27a. $2x + 2y \le 18$
27b. Rectangular Garden
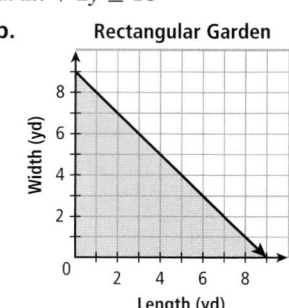

27c. 4 yd × 4 yd
29.
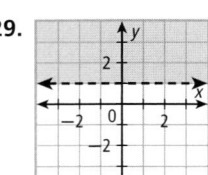

31.
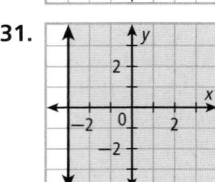

33.
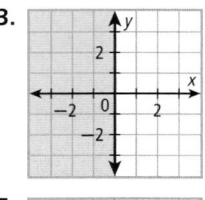

35.
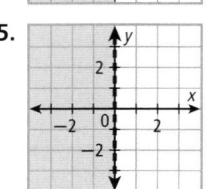

37. $7a + 4s \ge 280$ **41.** student A
43. B **45.** C **47.**
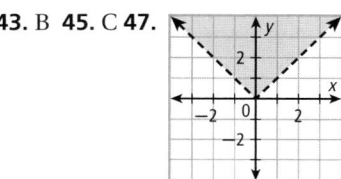

49. $y \ge \frac{1}{2}x + 3$ **51.** yes **53.** yes
55. $y = \frac{3}{4}x + \frac{7}{4}$ **57.** $y = 3x + 1$
59. $y = -\frac{1}{2}x + \frac{1}{2}$ **61.** $(-2, 15)$
63. $(2, 5)$ **65.** $(12, 3)$

6-7

Check It Out! **1a.** yes **1b.** no

2.
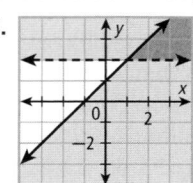

Possible answer: solutions: $(3, 3)$, $(4, 4)$; not solutions: $(-3, 1)$, $(-1, -4)$
2b.
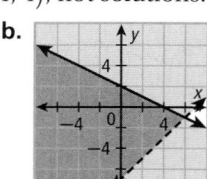

Possible answer: solutions: $(0, 0)$, $(3, -2)$; not solutions: $(4, 4)$, $(1, -6)$

3a.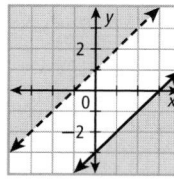

3b.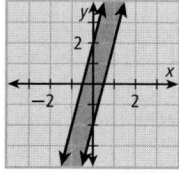

3c.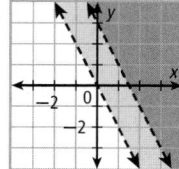

4.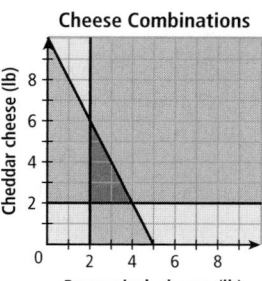

Cheese Combinations

Possible answer:
$(3\text{ lb pepper jack, }2\text{ lb cheddar})$,
$(2.5\text{ lb pepper jack, }4\text{ lb cheddar})$

Exercises 1. all **3.** yes

9.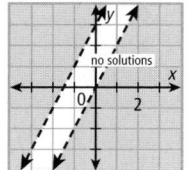

11.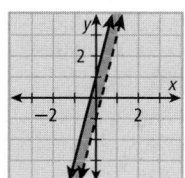

13.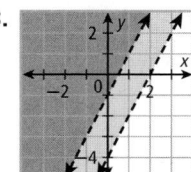

17. yes

23.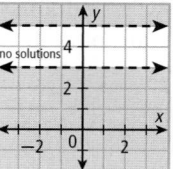

25.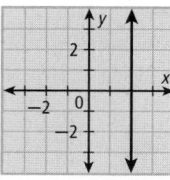

27.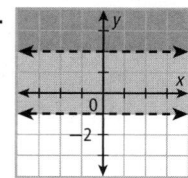

31.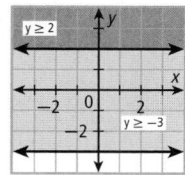

33.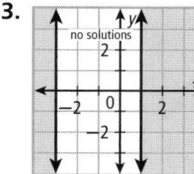

35. $\begin{cases} y > x + 1 \\ y < x + 3 \end{cases}$ **37.** $\begin{cases} y < 2 \\ x \ge -2 \end{cases}$

39. student B **41.** Yes; the solutions of the system $\begin{cases} y \ge x + 4 \\ y \le x + 4 \end{cases}$ are represented by all the ordered pairs on the line $y = x + 4$ **45.** B
47. about 12 sq. units

49.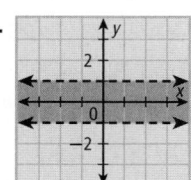

51. 25 cm^2 **53.** 12.5 cm^2 **55.** no
57. yes

59.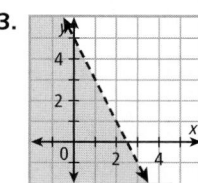

1. independent system **2.** system of linear equations **3.** solution of a system of linear inequalities
4. inconsistent system
5. independent system **6.** no **7.** yes
8. yes **9.** no **10.** $(-1, -1)$ **11.** $(3, 4)$
12. 8 h; $10 **13.** $(-9, -6)$
14. $\left(\frac{1}{2}, -2\right)$ **15.** $(-1, 6)$ **16.** $(4, -5)$
17. $(-5, 2)$ **18.** $(6, 6)$ **19.** 10 h; $1350; Motor Works; 8 hours will cost $30 less at Motor Works.
20. $(-1, 3)$ **21.** $(5, -3)$ **22.** $(11, 1)$
23. $(0, 3)$ **24.** $(-2, 8)$; possible answer: substitution; the second equation is already solved for y, and y has a coefficient of 1 in the first equation. **25.** $(3, -5)$; possible answer: graphing; both equations are already in slope-intercept form.
26. $(4, -6)$; possible answer: substitution; the second equation is already solved for y. **27.** $(2, 2)$; possible answer: elimination; the coefficients of the y-terms are opposites. **28.** consistent, independent; one solution
29. inconsistent; no solution
30. consistent, dependent; infinitely many solutions
31. inconsistent; no solution
32. consistent, independent; one solution **33.** consistent, dependent; infinitely many solutions **34.** inconsistent; no solution **35.** Gena: 3 ft/s; walkway: 1 ft/s **36.** Blake: 8 yd/min; current: 2 yd/min **37.** 30 mL of the 20% solution and 10 mL of the 60% solution **38.** 29 **39.** no **40.** yes
41. yes **42.** no

43.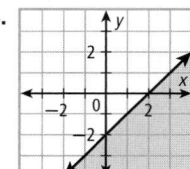

44.

45.

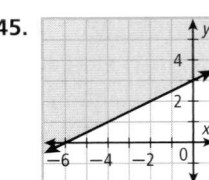

46.

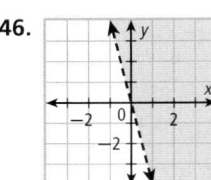

47.

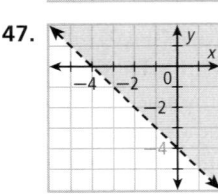

48.

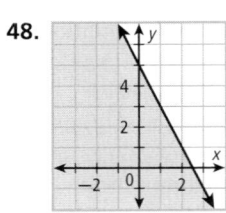

49. Let x = slices of pizza and y = bottles of soda; $2x + 1y \geq 450$

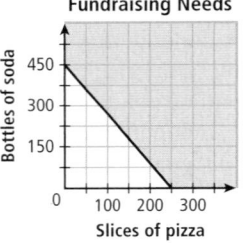

Possible answer: $(200, 50)$, $(150, 150)$ **50.** no **51.** yes
52. Possible answer: solutions: $(-6, 6)$, $(-10, 0)$; not solutions: $(0, 0)$, $(4, -4)$

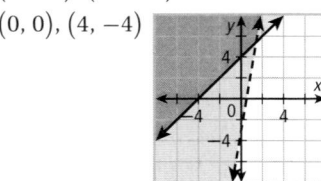

53. Possible answer: solutions: $(0, 0)$, $(-5, 0)$; not solutions: $(8, 0)$ $(3, -3)$

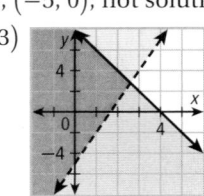

54. Possible answer: solutions: $(-6, 2)$, $(-8, 1)$; not solutions: $(0, 0)$, $(4, 1)$

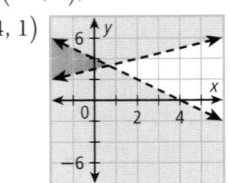

55.

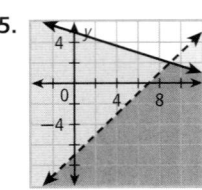

Possible answer: solutions: $(8, -8)$, $(9, 0)$; not solutions: $(0, 0)$, $(0, -4)$

56.

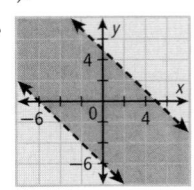

57.

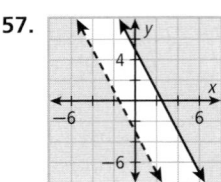

Chapter 7

7-1

Check It Out! **1.** $\frac{1}{125}$ m **2a.** $\frac{1}{10,000}$
2b. $\frac{1}{16}$ **2c.** $-\frac{1}{32}$ **2d.** $-\frac{1}{32}$ **3a.** $\frac{1}{64}$ **3b.** 2
4a. $\frac{2}{m^3}$ **4b.** $\frac{1}{7r^3}$ **4c.** $g^4 h^6$

Exercises **1.** $\frac{1}{10,000,000}$ m **3.** 1 **5.** $\frac{1}{27}$
7. $-\frac{1}{512}$ **9.** 1 **11.** $\frac{1}{16}$ **13.** $\frac{1}{256}$ **15.** $-\frac{1}{32}$
17. $\frac{3}{k^4}$ **19.** $x^{10}d^3$ **21.** $\frac{g^6}{f^4}$ **23.** $\frac{p^7}{q}$ **25.** 1
27. $\frac{1}{81}$ **29.** $-\frac{1}{36}$ **31.** 1 **33.** $-\frac{1}{3}$ **35.** 4
37. $\frac{1}{256}$ **39.** 1 **41.** $\frac{1}{144}$ **43.** $\frac{1}{k^4}$ **45.** $\frac{b^3}{2}$
47. $-\frac{5}{x^3}$ **49.** $\frac{2g^{10}}{7}$ **51.** $s^5 t^{12}$ **53.** 1
55. $\frac{1}{q^2}$ **57.** $\frac{h^3}{6m^2k}$ **59.** $\frac{1}{16}$ **61.** $-\frac{1}{6}$ **63.** 3
65. $\frac{1}{81}$ **67.** $\frac{a^3}{b^2}$ **69.** $\frac{w^2}{y}$ **71.** $-\frac{5}{y^6}$
73. $2a^3 b$ **75.** $\frac{1}{3x^8 y^{12}}$ **77.** red blood
cell: $\frac{1}{125,000}$ m; white blood
cell: $\frac{3}{250,000}$ m; platelet: $\frac{3}{1,000,000}$ m
79. never **81.** sometimes
83. sometimes **87.** 81 **89.** 1 **91.** −3
93. −1 **95.** D **97.** A **99.** $\frac{1}{a^n}$; a^{-n} is
the same as $\frac{1}{a^n}$ and b^0 is 1. So you
have $\frac{1}{a^n} \cdot 1$, or simply $\frac{1}{a^n}$.

101.

n	1^n	$(-1)^n$
−1	1	−1
−2	1	1
−3	1	−1
−4	1	1
−5	1	−1

$(1)^n = 1$; $(-1)^n = -1$ if n is odd,
and $(-1)^n = 1$ if n is even. **103.** −2
105. 4 **107.** 28 **109.** ind.: number of
days; dep.: total cost; $f(x) = 10x + 30$
111. $y = \frac{1}{3}x + 5$

7-2

Check It Out! **1a.** 0.01 **1b.** 100,000
1c. 10,000,000,000 **2a.** 10^8 **2b.** 10^{-4}
2c. 10^{-1} **3a.** 85,340,000 **3b.** 0.00163
4a. 1.43×10^5 km **4b.** 13,000 m/s
5. 2×10^{-12}, 4×10^{-3}, 5.2×10^{-3},
3×10^{14}, 4.5×10^{14}, 4.5×10^{30}

Exercises **1.** A number written in
scientific notation is a product with
2 parts: a decimal greater than
or equal to 1 and less than 10
and a power of 10. **3.** 0.00001
5. 100,000,000 **7.** 10^{-6}
9. 650,300,000 **11.** 0.092
13. 5.85×10^{-3}, 2.5×10^{-1},
8.5×10^{-1}, 3.6×10^8, 8.5×10^8
15. 0.000000001
17. 100,000,000,000,000 **19.** 10^6
21. 92,000 **23.** 0.00042
25. 10,000,000,000,000
27. 1.23×10^{-3}, 1.32×10^{-3},
3.12×10^{-3}, 2.13×10^{-1},
2.13×10^1, 3.12×10^2
29. 2.7×10^7 **31.** 2.35×10^5
33. 6×10^{-7} **35.** 4.12×10^{-2}
37. yes **39.** no **41.** yes **43.** yes
45a. 490,000,000; 740,000,000;
1,329,000,000 **45b.** Zorah's
observation is correct. **47.** 10^{-3}
49a. 300,000,000 **49c.** 6.8×10^{-7}
51. A **53.** about 7 times
55. $m \geq 45$ **57.** $n > 50$ **59.** $(-2, 1)$
61. $(-4, 2)$ **63.** $(7, 1)$ **65.** 1

7-3

Check It Out! **1a.** 7^{12} **1b.** 3×5^{10}
1c. $\frac{m^5}{n^4}$ **1d.** $\frac{1}{x^7}$ **2.** 6.696×10^8 mi
3a. 3^{20} **3b.** 1 **3c.** a^{18} **4a.** $64p^3$
4b. $25t^4$ **4c.** $\frac{1}{y^4}$

Exercises **1.** 2^5 **3.** n^8
5. 7.5×10^8 mi **7.** y^{32} **9.** $\frac{1}{3^4}$, or $\frac{1}{81}$

11. x^7y^{13} **13.** $36k^2$ **15.** $-8x^{15}$
17. b^{10} **19.** 6^8 **21.** $\frac{x}{y^3}$ **23.** 2^9, or
512 **25.** $\frac{1}{x^2}$ **27.** $\frac{a^{12}}{b^5}$ **29.** $27x^3$
31. $p^{28}q^{14}$ **33.** $-256x^{12}$ **35.** 6 **37.** 3
39. 8 **41.** $2x^3$ **43.** $2m^{10}n^6$ **45.** $108x^{13}$
47. $125x^6$ **49.** $3a^6$ **51.** 10^3, or
1000 **53.** Earth: 9.3×10^7 mi; Mars:
1.4136×10^8 mi; Jupiter: 4.836×10^8 mi; Saturn: 8.928×10^8 mi
55a. Exponents are multiplied but
should be added; x^6.
55b. Exponents are added but
should be multiplied; x^{20}
55c. Exponent is written as a power
but should be multiplied; x^6 **57.** $\frac{a^7}{b^5}$
59. $15m^{12}n^9$ **61.** $9s^2t^7$ **63.** t^7
65a. 9^3, or 729. Round -3.031
to -3. **65b.** 0.0245 **69.** $17k^2$ **71.** $6x^4$
73. $15a^2b^3$ **75a.** 6×10^{-7} m
75b. 3×10^8 m/s **75c.** Assoc. and
Comm. Properties of Mult.
77. $(6ab)^2$ **79.** $\left(\frac{1}{2kmn}\right)^2$ **81.** C **83.** A
85. 3^{2x} **87.** $x+1$ **89.** x^{3y+3z} **91.** x^{x^2}
93. $x=4$ **95.** $x=4$ **97.** 1.728 cm^3
99. $8+6x=71+3$; 11
101. $|x-120|=12$; 108°F; 132°F
103. 0.000495 **105.** 6,000,000

7-4

Check It Out! 1a. 4 **1b.** $\frac{1}{y^3}$
1c. $\frac{n^3}{m^5}$ **1d.** $\frac{3}{16}$ **2.** 1.1×10^{-2}
3. $12,800 **4a.** $\frac{2^6}{3^4}$, or $\frac{64}{81}$ **4b.** $\frac{a^5b^{20}}{c^{10}d^{15}}$
4c. $\frac{a^3}{b^3}$ **5a.** $\frac{9^3}{4^3}$, or $\frac{729}{64}$ **5b.** $\frac{b^8c^{12}}{16a^4}$ **5c.** $\frac{t}{s^4}$

Exercises 1. 25 **3.** 3 **5.** 7×10^2 **7.** 1
9. $\frac{4}{25}$ **11.** $\frac{1}{a^6b^4}$ **13.** $\frac{16}{9}$ **15.** $\frac{2b^2}{3a^2}$ **17.** 27
19. x^5 **21.** 5×10^{-7} **23.** 7×10^{-3}
25. 2×10^{27} kg **27.** $\frac{a^{12}}{b^6}$ **29.** $\frac{y^3}{x^6}$
31. $\frac{y^{25}}{x^{10}}$ **33.** $\frac{196}{9x^2}$ **35.** $2d^2$ **37.** $\frac{3x^5}{4}$ **39.** $\frac{c^4}{a^4}$
41. $\frac{25}{p^2}$ **43.** $\frac{1}{100}$ **45.** -1 **47.** 2000: 3×10^1; 1995: 2.84×10^1; 1990: 2.65×10^1
51. 3 **53.** 3;4 **55.** B **57.** A **59.** 3 **63.** 1
65. 12 **67.** $x=-\frac{1}{2}$ **69.** 1 **71.** $-125x^{12}$

7-5

Check It Out! 1a. 3 **1b.** 15
2a. 8 **2b.** 1 **2c.** 81 **3.** 1944
4a. xy^3 **4b.** xy

Exercises 1. 5 **3.** 4 **5.** 3 **7.** 6 **9.** 5
11. 10 **13.** 4 **15.** 32 **17.** 125 **19.** 256
21. 0 **23.** x^2y **25.** x^3y^3 **27.** a^2 **29.** 1
31. 10 **33.** 8 **35.** 2 **37.** 2 **39.** 14

41. 8 **43.** 8 **45.** 64 **47.** 1000
49. 243 **51.** $2g$ **53.** $2m$ **55.** $3x^2$
57. ab^4 **59.** a^8b **61.** 1 **63.** 0 **65.** 625
67. 3 **69.** $\frac{2}{3}$ **71.** $\frac{1}{4}$ **73.** $\frac{4}{9}$ **75.** $\frac{8}{343}$
77. $\frac{1}{27}$ **79.** $\frac{16}{625}$ **81.** 1.86 in. **83.** $n^{\frac{2}{3}}$
will be less than n because $\frac{2}{3} < 1$.
$n^{\frac{3}{2}}$ will be greater than n because
$\frac{3}{2} > 1$. **85a.** 10 in. **85b.** The distance
doubles (20 in.). **87.** B **89.** C **91.** a
93. x^3 **95.** 3 **97.** 36π cm^2; both
volume and surface area are
described by 36π (although the units
are different). **99.** -1 **101.** $n < 3$
103. $y \le -2$ **105.** D: {$-2, -1, -0, 1$};
R: {0, 1, 2, 3}; function; each domain
value is paired with exactly one
range value. **107.** D: $1 \le x \le 4$;
R: $2 \le y \le 4$; function; each domain
value is paired with exactly one
range value.

7-6

Check It Out! 1a. 3 **1b.** 1 **1c.** 3
2a. $x^5 + 9x^3 - 4x^2 + 16$; 1
2b. $-3y^8 + 18y^5 + 14y$; -3
3a. constant monomial
3b. cubic polynomial
3c. 8th degree trinomial
4. 1606 ft **5.** yes

Exercises 1. d **3.** a **5.** 3 **7.** 0
9. $-8a^9 + 9a^8$; -8 **11.** $3x^2 + 2x - 1$;
3 **13.** $5c^4 + 5c^3 + 3c^2 - 4$; 5
15. linear binomial **17.** quartic
polynomial **19.** quartic
trinomial **21.** no **23.** yes **25.** yes
27. 4 **29.** 6 **31.** 7 **33.** 1
35. $4.9t^3 - 4t^2 + t + 2.5$; 4.9
37. $x^{10} + x^7 - x^5 + x^3 - x$; 1
39. $5x^3 + 3x^2 + 5x - 4$; 5
41. $-d^3 + 3d^2 + 4d + 5$; -1
43. $-x^5 - x^3 + 4x^2 + 1$; -1
45. linear monomial
47. quadratic trinomial
49. quartic trinomial **51.** quadratic
monomial **53.** yes **55.** yes **57.** no
59. always **61.** never **63a.** 58.05 in^3
63b. 66 in^3 **63c.** 0 **63d.** yes
65. -48; 0; 3270 **75.** A **77.** C
79a. 58 cm; 65 cm **79b.** 50.310 cm
79c. The first three terms of the
polynomial will equal 0, so just
look at the constant.
81. $90 - m - 2m = 45$; 15 min
83. inconsistent; no solutions
85. consistent and independent;
one solution **87.** $\frac{x^2}{y^5}$ **89.** $\frac{p^8}{16}$

7-7

Check It Out! 1a. $5s^2 + 6$
1b. $20z^4 - 6$ **1c.** $x^8 + 6y^8$
1d. b^3c^2 **2.** $12a^3 + 15a^2 - 16a$
3. $-2x^2 - x$ **4.** $-0.05x^2 + 46x - 3200$

Exercises 1. $-3a^2 + 9a$ **3.** $0.26r^4 + 0.32r^3$ **5.** $3b^3c^2$ **7.** $23n^3 + 3n + 15$
9. $9x^2 - x - 6$ **11.** $4c^4 + 8c + 6$
13. $-3r + 11$ **15.** $8a^2 + 5a + 9$
17. $12n^2 + 6n - 3m$ **19.** $d^5 + 1$
21. $5x$ **23.** $2x^3 - 5$ **25.** $10t^2 + t$
27. $x^5 + x^4$ **29.** $-2t^3 + 8t^2$
31. $-6m^3 + 2m^2 + 5m + 3$
33. $4w^2 + 6w + 4$ **35.** $t - 5$
37. $2n - 2$ **39.** $6x^2 - x - 1$
41. $-u^3 + 3u^2 + 3u + 6$ **43.** $x = \frac{3}{2}$,
or 1.5 **45.** B **47.** $3x + 6$ **49.** $6x + 14$
51. $2x^2 + x - 5$
53a.

rectangle labeled $x + 4$ along the top and $x - 3$ along the right side

53b. $4x + 2$ **53c.** 62 ft **55.** B
57. $3x^2 - 2$ **63.** $d \ge -7$ **65.** $t < 0$
67. $y = \frac{1}{4}x + 3$ **69.** b^{11} **71.** $9z^{12}$

7-8

Check It Out! 1a. $18x^5$ **1b.** $10r^2t^4$
1c. $4x^5y^5z^7$ **2a.** $8x^2 + 2x + 6$
2b. $15a^3b + 3ab^2$ **2c.** $5r^3s^2 - 15r^2s^3$
3a. $a^2 - a - 12$ **3b.** $x^2 - 6x + 9$
3c. $2a^2 + 7ab^2 - 4b^4$ **4a.** $x^3 - x^2 - 6x + 18$ **4b.** $3x^3 - 4x^2 + 11x + 10$
5a. $x^2 - 4x$ **5b.** 12 m^2

Exercises 1. $14x^6$ **3.** $3r^5s^5t^5$
5. $21x^7y^3$ **7.** $4x^2 + 8x + 4$
9. $6a^5b^2 + 2a^4b^3$ **11.** $10x^3y^4 - 5x^2y^2$
13. $x^2 - x - 2$ **15.** $x^2 - 4x + 4$
17. $4a^4 - 2ab - 12a^3b^2 + 6b^3$
19. $x^3 + 3x^2 - 7x + 15$ **21.** $-6x^4 + 12x^3 + 4x^2 - 18x + 20$ **23.** $x^3 - 4x^2 - 4x - 5$ **25a.** $2x^2 - 3x$
25b. 20 in^2 **27.** $-12r^5s^5$ **29.** $10a^4$
31. $-6a^5b^6$ **33.** $-12a^7b^7c^8$
35. $9s^2 + 54s$ **37.** $27x^3 - 12x^2$
39. $10s^3t^3 - 15s^2t^5$ **41.** $-10x^3 + 15x^2 + 5x$ **43.** $-14x^6y^3 + 7x^5y^4$
45. $x^2 + 8x + 16$ **47.** $5x^2 + 13x - 6$
49. $10x^2 - x - 2$ **51.** $7x^2 - 52x - 32$
53. $x^3 - x^2 - x + 10$ **55.** $-10x^4 + 2x^3 + 20x^2 - 19x + 3$ **57.** $8x^5 - 2x^4 - 12x^3 + 17x^2 - 21$ **59.** $x^3 - 3x - 2$ **61.** $-x^3 + 3x^2 - 3x + 1$
63. $16x^2 - 48x + 36$

65a. 3; 2; $10x^5 + 5x^3$; 5 **65b.** 2; 2; $x^4 - x^3 + 2x^2 - 2x$; 4 **65c.** 1; 3; $x^4 - 5x^3 + 6x^2 + x - 3$; 4 **65d.** $m + n$
67. $12x^2 + 12x + 3$ **69a.** $2x^2$
69b. 800 m^2 **71.** $2x^2 - 7x - 30$
73. $8x^2 - 16xy + 6y^2$ **75.** $6x^2 - 9x - 6$
77. $x^3 + 3x^2$ **79.** $2x^3 - 7x^2 - 10x + 24$ **81.** $8p^3 - 36p^2q + 54pq^2 - 27q^3$
85. $x = 0$ **87.** C **89.** D **91.** $-x^2 - 6$
93a. $x^2 - 1$ **93b.** $8x + 16$ **95.** $x^3 + 3x^2 + 2x$ **97.** $a = 2$

99.

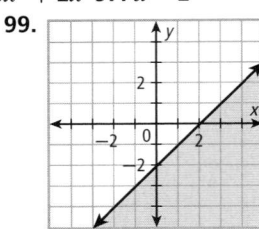

101.

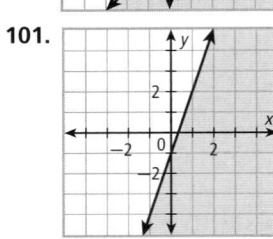

103. x^4y^3 **105.** a^4b^6

7-9

Check It Out! **1a.** $x^2 + 12x + 36$
1b. $25a^2 + 10ab + b^2$ **1c.** $1 + 2c^3 + c^6$
2a. $x^2 - 14x + 49$ **2b.** $9b^2 - 12bc + 4c^2$ **2c.** $a^4 - 8a^2 + 16$ **3a.** $x^2 - 64$
3b. $9 - 4y^4$ **3c.** $81 - r^2$ **4.** 25

Exercises **3.** $4 + 4x + x^2$ **5.** $4x^2 + 24x + 36$ **7.** $4a^2 + 28ab + 49b^2$
9. $x^2 - 4x + 4$ **11.** $64 - 16x + x^2$
13. $49a^2 - 28ab + 4b^2$ **15.** $x^2 - 36$
17. $4x^4 - 9$ **19.** $4x^2 - 25y^2$ **21.** $x^2 + 6x + 9$ **23.** $x^4 + 2x^2y^2 + y^4$ **25.** $4 + 12x + 9x^2$ **27.** $s^4 - 14s^2 + 49$ **29.** $a^2 - 16a + 64$ **31.** $9x^2 - 24x + 16$ **33.** $a^2 - 100$ **35.** $49x^2 - 9$ **37.** $25a^4 - 81$
39. $\pi x^2 + 8\pi x + 16\pi$ **41.** $x^2 + 2xy + y^2$
43. $x^4 - 16$ **45.** $x^4 - 8x^2 + 16$ **47.** $1 + 2x + x^2$ **49.** $x^6 - 2a^3x^3 + a^6$
51. $36a^2 - 25b^2$ **53.** 4; 4 **55.** 25; 25
57. 9; 9 **59.** -5; -5 **61.** 840 **65.** 1, 4, 9, 16, 25, 36, 49, 64, 81, 100 **67.** B
69. D **71.** $x^3 + 4x^2 - 16x - 64$
73. Since $x^2 + bx + c$, then $x^2 + bx + c = (x + y)(x + y)$, where y is an integer. After using FOIL, $(x + y)(x + y) = x^2 + (2y)x + y^2$ and $x^2 + (2y)x + y^2 = x^2 + (b)x + c$. You can see that $c = y^2$, or $\sqrt{c} = \pm y$, and $b = 2y$, or $b = \pm 2\sqrt{c}$.

75. 13 cm
77.

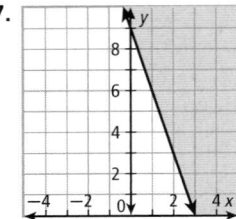

79. $12x^2 + 6x$ **81.** $-3p^3 - 8p$

Study Guide: Review

1. cubic **2.** standard form of a polynomial **3.** monomial
4. trinomial **5.** scientific notation
6. $\frac{1}{32}$ in. **7.** 1 **8.** 1 **9.** $\frac{1}{125}$ **10.** $\frac{1}{10,000}$, or 0.0001 **11.** $\frac{1}{16}$ **12.** $\frac{1}{256}$ **13.** $\frac{27}{4}$
14. $\frac{1}{m^2}$ **15.** b **16.** $-\frac{1}{2x^2y^4}$ **17.** $2b^6c^4$
18. $\frac{3a^2}{4c^2}$ **19.** $\frac{s^3}{qr^2}$ **20.** 10,000,000
21. 0.00001 **22.** 10^2 **23.** 10^{-11}
24. 325,000 **25.** 1800 **26.** 0.17
27. 0.000299 **28.** 5.8×10^{-7}, 6.3×10^{-3}, 2.2×10^2, 1.2×10^4
29. \$38,500,000,000 **30.** 5^9
31. $2^3 \cdot 3^4$ **32.** b^{10} **33.** r^5 **34.** x^{12}
35. 1 **36.** $\frac{1}{2^3}$, or $\frac{1}{8}$ **37.** $\frac{1}{5^4}$, or $\frac{1}{625}$
38. $\frac{1}{16b^6}$ **39.** $g^{12}h^8$ **40.** x^4y^2
41. $-x^4y^2$ **42.** x^6y^{15} **43.** j^6k^9 **44.** $\frac{1}{5}$
45. m^8n^{30} **46.** 8×10^{11} **47.** 9×10^7
48. 1×10^{10} **49.** 2.8×10^{15}
50. 6×10^1 **51.** 1.8×10^{-8}
52. 3.55×10^7 **53.** 64 **54.** m^5 **55.** $\frac{7}{32}$
56. $6b$ **57.** t^3v^4 **58.** 16 **59.** 5×10^1
60. 2.5×10^7 **61.** 9 **62.** 7 **63.** 16
64. 8 **65.** z^2 **66.** $5x^2$ **67.** x^4y^3
68. m^2n^4 **69.** 0 **70.** 3 **71.** 6 **72.** 1
73. $3n^2 + 2n - 4$; 3 **74.** $-a^6 - a^4 + 3a^3 + 2a$; -1 **75.** linear binomial
76. quintic monomial **77.** quartic trinomial **78.** constant monomial
79. $-4t + 3$ **80.** $-6x^6 - x^5$ **81.** $3h^3 - 3h^2 + 5$ **82.** $2m^2 - 5m - 1$ **83.** $p^2 + 5p + 8$ **84.** $-7z^2 - z + 10$ **85.** $3g^2 + 2g + 4$ **86.** $-x^2 + 4x + 8$ **87.** $8r^2$
88. $6a^6b$ **89.** $18x^3y^2$ **90.** $3s^6t^{14}$
91. $2x^2 - 8x + 12$ **92.** $-3a^2b^2 + 6a^3b^2 - 15a^2b$ **93.** $a^2 - 3a - 18$
94. $b^2 - 6b - 27$ **95.** $x^2 - 12x + 20$
96. $t^2 - 1$ **97.** $8q^2 + 34q + 30$
98. $20g^2 - 37g + 8$ **99.** $p^2 - 8p + 16$
100. $x^2 + 24x + 144$ **101.** $m^2 + 12m + 36$ **102.** $9c^2 + 42c + 49$
103. $4r^2 - 4r + 1$ **104.** $9a^2 - 6ab + b^2$ **105.** $4n^2 - 20n + 25$ **106.** $h^2 - 26h + 169$ **107.** $x^2 - 1$ **108.** $z^2 - 225$
109. $c^4 - d^2$ **110.** $9k^4 - 49$

Chapter 8

8-1

Check It Out! **1a.** $2^3 \cdot 5$ **1b.** $3 \cdot 11$
1c. 7^2 **1d.** 19 **2a.** 4 **2b.** 5 **3a.** $9g^2$
3b. 1 **3c.** 1 **4.** 7

Exercises **3.** $3^2 \cdot 2^2$ **5.** $3^3 \cdot 2$
7. 7 (prime) **9.** $3 \cdot 5^2$ **11.** 7 **13.** 7
15. 18 **17.** x^2 **19.** 2 **21.** 1 **23.** $2 \cdot 3^2$
25. $2^2 \cdot 3$ **27.** 17 **29.** 7^2 **31.** 9 **33.** 10
35. 2 **37.** $9s$ **39.** $3w^2$ **41.** $3x$ **43.** 5
45. $4x^2$ **47.** $2n$ **51.** 15 rows
53. 8 and 20; 4 **55.** 63 and 105; 21 **57.** 54 and 72; 18 **59.** 36; 2; 9; 3; $2^3 \cdot 3^2$ **61.** 105; 5; 7; $2 \cdot 3 \cdot 5 \cdot 7$ **63.** 2; 2; 27; 3; $2^2 \cdot 3^3$ **65.** 24; 2; 6; 3; $2^4 \cdot 3$
67. 2; 2; 10; 5; $2^3 \cdot 5$ **69a.** $2t + t^2$
69b. t **71.** A **73.** $4n$ **75.** 25 **77.** xy
79. $1 \cdot 20$; $2 \cdot 10$; $4 \cdot 5$; $20 \cdot 1$; $10 \cdot 2$; $5 \cdot 4$ **83.** $y = 9$ and $y = 8$
85. $3x^2 + 14x - 3$

8-2

Check It Out! **1a.** $b(5 + 9b^2)$
1b. cannot be factored
1c. $-y^2(18y + 7)$
1d. $2x^2(4x^2 + 2x - 1)$
2. $2x$ cm; $(x + 2)$ cm
3a. $(4s - 5)(s + 6)$
3b. $(7x + 1)(2x + 3)$ **3c.** cannot be factored **3d.** $(5x - 2)^2$
4a. $(2b^2 + 3)(3b + 4)$
4b. $(4r + 1)(r^2 + 6)$
5a. $(5x^2 - 4)(3 - 2x)$
5b. $(8 - x)(y - 1)$

Exercises **1.** $5a(3 - a)$
3. $7(-5x + 6)$ **5.** $2h(6h^3 + 4h - 3)$
7. $m(9m + 1)$ **9.** $3(12f + 6f^2 + 1)$
11. $(2b + 5)(b + 3)$ **13.** cannot be factored **15.** $(x^2 + 2)(x + 4)$
17. $(7r^2 + 6)(r - 5)$
19. $(2b^2 + 5)(2b - 3)$
21. $2(r - 2)(r - 3)$
23. $(2m^2 - 3)(m - 3)$
25. $(7q - 2)(2q - 3)$ **27.** $9y(y + 5)$
29. $-d^2(4d^2 - d + 3)$
31. $x^2(-14x^2 + 5)$ **33.** $7c(3c + 2)$
35. $P(1 + rt)$ **37.** cannot be factored **39.** $(-3 + 4b)(b + 2)$
41. $(6y + 1)(y - 7)$
43. $(2a^2 + 3)(a - 4)$
45. $(n^2 + 5)(n - 2)$
47. $(6x^2 + 1)(x + 3)$
49. $(2m^2 - 3)(m - 1)$

51. $(b^2 - 2)(b + 4)$
53. $(2f^2 - 5)(3f - 4)$ **55.** $3v$ **57.** $2k$
59. 2; binomial; $x(x + 5)$
61. 3; trinomial; $a^2(a^2 + a + 1)$
63a. $100x^3$; $200x^2$; $400x$
63b. $100x^3 + 200x^2 + 400x + 800$
63c. $100(x^2 + 4)(x + 2)$; $1603.12
69a. Comm. Prop. of Add. **b.** Assoc.
Prop. of Add. **c.** Distrib. Prop.
d. Distrib. Prop. **71.** D **73.** C
75. $-9ab(8ab + 5)$
77. $(a + c)(b + d)$
79. $(x^2 + 3)(x - 4)$
81. $\overline{AB}$ and $\overline{CD}$ are both horiz., so
they have the same slope and are
parallel. The slope of both $\overline{AD}$ and
$\overline{BC}$ is 4, so they are parallel. Two
pairs of parallel sides define
a parallelogram. **83.** $(-1, 6)$
85. 5^2 **87.** $\frac{x^5}{z^3}$

8-3

Check It Out! **1a.** $(x + 4)(x + 6)$
1b. $(x + 4)(x + 3)$
2a. $(x + 6)(x + 2)$
2b. $(x - 2)(x - 3)$
2c. $(x + 6)(x + 7)$
2d. $(x - 8)(x - 5)$
3a. $(x + 5)(x - 3)$
3b. $(x - 4)(x - 2)$
3c. $(x - 10)(x + 2)$
4.

n	$n^2 - 7n + 10$
0	$0^2 - 7(0) + 10 = 10$
1	$1^2 - 7(1) + 10 = 4$
2	$2^2 - 7(2) + 10 = 0$
3	$3^2 - 7(3) + 10 = -2$
4	$4^2 - 7(4) + 10 = -2$

n	$(n - 5)(n - 2)$
0	$(0 - 5)(0 - 2) = 10$
1	$(1 - 5)(1 - 2) = 4$
2	$(2 - 5)(2 - 2) = 0$
3	$(3 - 5)(3 - 2) = -2$
4	$(4 - 5)(4 - 2) = -2$

Exercises
1. $(x + 4)(x + 9)$ **3.** $(x + 4)(x + 10)$
5. $(x + 3)(x + 2)$ **7.** $(x + 2)(x + 8)$
9. $(x - 3)(x - 8)$ **11.** $(x - 1)(x - 6)$
13. $(x + 9)(x - 3)$
15. $(x - 9)(x + 5)$
17. $(x - 2)(x + 1)$

19.

n	$n^2 + 6n - 7$
0	$0^2 + 6(0) - 7 = -7$
1	$1^2 + 6(1) - 7 = 0$
2	$2^2 + 6(2) - 7 = 9$
3	$3^2 + 6(3) - 7 = 20$
4	$4^2 + 6(4) - 7 = 33$

n	$(n + 7)(n - 1)$
0	$(0 + 7)(0 - 1) = -7$
1	$(1 + 7)(1 - 1) = 0$
2	$(2 + 7)(2 - 1) = 9$
3	$(3 + 7)(3 - 1) = 20$
4	$(4 + 7)(4 - 1) = 33$

21. $(x + 3)(x + 10)$
23. $(x + 5)(x + 8)$
25. $(x + 4)(x + 12)$
27. $(x + 2)(x + 14)$
29. $(x - 1)(x - 5)$
31. $(x - 4)(x - 8)$
33. $(x + 7)(x - 3)$
35. $(x - 13)(x + 1)$
37. $(x - 7)(x + 5)$ **39.** C **41.** D
45. $(x - 2)(x - 9)$
47. $(x + 1)(x + 9)$
49. $(x + 6)(x + 7)$
51. $(x + 2)(x + 9)$
53. $(x - 3)(x + 8)$
55. $(x - 5)(x + 9)$
57. approximately 1.5 **59a.** length:
$(x + 2)$ ft; width: $(x + 1)$ ft
59b. length: $(x + 3)$ ft; width:
$(x + 5)$ ft **59c.** The length will
increase by 1 ft. The width will
increase by 4 ft.
61. $x^2 + 6x + 8$; $(x + 4)(x + 2)$
67a. $d = t^2$ **67b.** $d = 4t$ **67c.** $t(t - 4)$
69. true **71.** false **73.** 4 **75.** 4
77a. $(x + 10)$ ft **b.** $\ell = (x + 14)$ ft;
$w = (x + 6)$ ft
c. $A = (x^2 + 20x + 84)$ ft^2 **79.** D
81. C **83.** $(x^2 + 9)(x^2 + 9)$
85. $(d^2 + 21)(d^2 + 1)$
87. $(de - 5)(de + 4)$ **89.** 16; 11; 29
91a. $(x + 7)$ ft **91b.** $(4x + 26)$ ft
91c. $92.00 **91d.** $36.96
91e. $128.96 **93.** $(7, 5)$ **95.** x^5
97. t^{12} **99.** $(x + 2)(x^2 + 5)$
101. $(p - 2)(2p^3 + 7)$

8-4

Check It Out! **1a.** $(3x + 1)(2x + 3)$
1b. $(3x + 4)(x - 2)$
2a. $(2x + 5)(3x + 1)$
2b. $(3x - 4)(3x - 1)$
2c. $(3x + 4)(x + 3)$
3a. $(3x - 1)(2x + 3)$
3b. $(4n + 3)(n - 1)$
4a. $-1(2x + 3)(3x + 4)$
4b. $-1(3x + 2)(x + 5)$

Exercises **1.** $(2x + 5)(x + 2)$
3. $(5x - 3)(x + 2)$
5. $(3x + 4)(x - 6)$ **7.** $(x + 2)(5x + 1)$
9. $(4x - 5)(x - 1)$
11. $(5x + 4)(x + 1)$
13. $(2a - 1)(2a + 5)$
15. $(2x - 3)(x + 2)$
17. $(10x + 1)(x - 1)$
19. $(2x + 3)(4 - x)$
21. $-1(5x + 3)(x - 2)$
23. $-1(2x - 1)(2x + 5)$
25. $(3x + 2)(3x + 1)$
27. $(n + 2)(3n + 2)$
29. $(4c - 5)(c - 3)$
31. $(2x + 5)(4x + 1)$
33. $(5x - 6)(x + 3)$
35. $(10n - 7)(n - 1)$
37. $(7x + 1)(x + 2)$
39. $(3x - 4)(x - 5)$
41. $(x - 7)(4x - 3)$
43. $(4y - 1)(3y + 5)$
45. $(2x - 1)(2x + 3)$
47. $(3x + 5)(x - 3)$
49. $-1(2x - 3)(2x + 5)$
51. $-1(3x - 2)(x + 1)$
53. $2x^2 - 5x + 2$; $(x - 2)(2x - 1)$
55. $(9n + 8)(n + 1)$
57. $(2x - 1)(2x - 5)$
59. $(3x + 8)(x + 2)$
61. $(3x + 4)(2x - 3)$
63. $(2x - 3)(2x - 3)$
65. $(6x - 1)(2x - 1)$
67. $(15x + 8)(x + 1)$
69. not factorable
73. $4x(x + 2) + 1(x + 2)$
$(4x + 1)(x + 2)$
75a. $-16t^2 + 20t + 6$
75b. $-2(4t + 1)(2t - 3)$ **75c.** 10 ft
77a. $2t^2 - 10t + 8 = 0$
77b. $2(t - 1)(t - 4)$ **77c.** When
$t = 1$ or $t = 4$, one of the factors
in part **b** is equal to 0, making the
product equal to 0. **79.** B **81.** C
83. B **85.** A **87.** $(2x + 1)(2x + 1)$
89. $(9x + 1)(9x + 1)$
91. $(5x + 2)(5x + 2)$
93. -7; -5; 5; 7 **95.** -6; 6
101. $(x + 1)(x - 9)$

Check It Out! 1a. $(x + 2)^2$
1b. $(x - 7)^2$ **1c.** no; $-6x \neq 2(3x)(2)$
2. $4(3x + 1)$ m; 40 m
3a. $(1 - 2x)(1 + 2x)$
3b. $(p^4 + 7q^3)(p^4 - 7q^3)$
3c. No; $4y^5$ is not a perfect square.

Exercises 1. yes; $(x - 2)^2$
3. yes; $(3x - 2)^2$ **5.** yes; $(x - 3)^2$
7. $4(x + 12)$; 88 yd
9. yes; $(s + 4)(s - 4)$
11. yes; $(2x^2 + 3y)(2x^2 - 3y)$
13. yes; $(x^3 + 3)(x^3 - 3)$
15. no **17.** no; $10x \neq 2(5x)(2)$
19. yes; $(4x - 5)^2$ **21.** yes;
$(1 + 2x)(1 - 2x)$ **23.** no **25.** yes;
$(9 - 10x^2)(9 + 10x^2)$ **27.** 49 **29.** $4y^2$
31. $(10x + 9y)(10x - 9y)$; difference
of 2 squares
33. $(2r^3 + 5s^3)(2r^3 - 5s^3)$; difference
of 2 squares **35.** $(x^7 + 12)(x^7 - 12)$;
difference of 2 squares **37.** Multiply
a binomial by itself. Choose 2
perfect squares, find 2 times the
product of their square roots, and
then write these 3 expressions as a
sum. **39.** $c = 32$ **41a.** $5z - 4$
41b. $20z - 16$ **41c.** 11; 44; 121
43a. 0; 0; 100; 100; 0 **43b.** 16; 16;
36; 36; −24 **43c.** 25; 25; 25; 25; −25
43d. 36; 36; 16; 16; −24 **43e.** 100;
100; 0; 0; 0 **45.** $a - b$; $a + b$ **47.** C
49. 1 **51a.** $a = 2$; $b = (v + 2)$
51b. $[2 + (v + 2)][2 - (v + 2)] =$
$(v + 4)(-v) = -v^2 - 4v$ **53.** $a = 3y$;
$b = 4$; $(3y - 4)(9y^2 + 12y + 16)$
54. $a = n^2$; $b = 2$;
$(n^2 - 2)(n^4 + 2n + 4)$
55. D: {5, 4, 3, 2}; R: {2, 1, 0, −1};
yes **57.** D: {2}; R: {−8, −2, 4, 10};
no **59.** $6a^3 + 14a^2 - 10a$
61. $t^2 - 8t + 16$ **63.** $(x + 3)(x - 4)$

Check It Out! 1a. yes **1b.** no;
$4(x + 1)^2$ **2a.** $4x(x + 2)^2$
2b. $2y(x - y)(x + y)$
3a. $(3x + 4)(x + 1)$
3b. $2p^3(p + 6)(p - 1)$
3c. $3q^4(3q + 4)(q + 2)$ **3d.** $2(x^4 + 9)$

Exercises 1. yes **3.** yes **5.** no;
$4(2p^2 + 1)(2p^2 - 1)$
7. $3x^3(x + 2)(x - 2)$ **9.** $2p(2q + 1)^2$
11. $mn(n^2 + m)(n^2 - m)$
13. $3x^2(2x - 3)(x + 1)$

15. $(p^3 + 1)(p^2 + 3)$
17. unfactorable **19.** no;
$2xy(y^2 - 4y + 5)$ **22.** yes **23.** yes
25. $-4x(x - 3)^2$ **27.** $5(d - 3)(d - 9)$
29. $2x(7x + 5y)(7x - 5y)$
31. unfactorable
33. $(p^2 + 4)(p + 2)(p - 2)$
34. $2m^4(m - 6)(2m - 3)$
37. $x^2 + 12x + 36 = (x + 6)^2$
39. $s^2 - 16s + 28 = (s - 2)(s - 14)$
41. $b^2 - 49 = (b + 7)(b - 7)$
45. $(3x - 1)(x + 7)$
47. $(3x + y - 3)(3x - y - 7)$
49a. $4x^2 - 100 = 4(x^2 - 25) =$
$4(x - 5)(x + 5)$
49b. $4x^2 - 100 =$
$(2x + 10)(2x - 10) =$
$2(x + 5)(2)(x - 5) =$
$4(x + 5)(x - 5)$ **53.** 8 **55.** C **57.** C
59a. $V = 8p\left[\pi(3p + 1)^2\right]$
59b. $r = (3p + 1)$ cm
59c. $h = 8$ cm; $V = 128\pi$ cm^3
61. $h^2(h^4 + 1)(h^2 + 1)$
63. $x^{n+3}(x^2 + x + 1)$
65. D: {−1, 0, 1, 2}; R: {−2, 1, 4, 7};
function; each element in the
domain is assigned to exactly 1
element in the range.
67. $y = -5x + 4$ and $y = \frac{1}{5}x + 2$
70. $(2x - 1)(2x + 3)$
71. $(3x + 2)(2x - 5)$

Study Guide: Review

1. prime factorization **2.** greatest
common factor **3.** $2^2 \cdot 3$ **4.** $2^2 \cdot 5$
5. 2^5 **6.** prime **7.** $2^3 \cdot 5$ **8.** 2^6
9. $2 \cdot 3 \cdot 11$ **10.** $2 \cdot 3 \cdot 19$ **11.** 5
12. 12 **13.** 1 **14.** 27 **15.** 4 **16.** 3
17. $2x$ **18.** $9b^2$ **19.** $25r$ **20.** 6 boxes;
13 rows **21.** $5x(1 - 3x^2)$
22. $16(-b + 2)$ **23.** $-7(2v + 3)$
24. $4(a^2 - 3a - 2)$
25. $5g(g^2 - 3)(g^2 + 1)$
26. $10(4p^2 - p + 3)$
27. $(6x + 5)$ ft by x ft
28. $(2x + 9)(x - 4)$
29. $(t - 6)(3t + 5)$
30. $(5 - 3n)(6 - n)$
31. $(b + 2)(b + 4)$
32. $(x^2 + 7)(x - 3)$
33. $(n^2 + 1)(n - 4)$
34. $(2b + 5)(3b - 4)$
35. $(2h^2 - 7)(h + 7)$
36. $(3t + 1)(t + 6)$
37. $(5m^2 - 1)(2m + 3)$
38. $(4p - 3)(2p^2 + 1)$

39. $-1(r - 5)(r - 2)$
40. $(b^2 - 5)(b - 3)$
41. $(t + 4)(-t^2 + 6)$
42. $-1(3h - 1)(h - 4)$
43. $-1(d - 1)^2$ **44.** $(2 - b)(5b - 6)$
45. $(t + 1)(5 - t)$
46. $(2b^2 + 5)(4 - b)$
47. $-1(3r - 1)(r - 1)$
48. left rectangle: $2x^2 + 3x$; right
rectangle: $8x + 12$; combined:
$2x^2 + 8x + 3x + 12$; $(2x + 3)(x + 4)$
49. $(x + 1)(x + 5)$ **50.** $(x + 2)(x + 4)$
51. $(x + 3)(x + 5)$ **52.** $(x - 6)(x - 2)$
53. $(x + 5)^2$ **54.** $(x - 2)(x - 11)$
55. $(x + 4)(x + 20)$ **56.** $(x - 6)(x - 20)$
57. $(x + 12)(x - 7)$ **58.** $(x + 3)(x - 8)$
59. $(x + 4)(x - 7)$ **60.** $(x - 1)(x + 5)$
61. $(x + 3)(x - 2)$ **62.** $(x + 5)(x - 4)$
63. $(x - 8)(x + 6)$ **64.** $(x - 9)(x + 4)$
65. $(x - 12)(x + 6)$
66. $(x - 10)(x + 7)$
67. $(x + 20)(x - 6)$
68. $(x + 7)(x - 1)$ **69.** $(y + 3)$ m
70. $(2x + 1)(x + 5)$
71. $(3x + 7)(x + 1)$
72. $(2x - 1)(x - 1)$
73. $(3x + 2)(x + 2)$
74. $(5x + 3)(x + 5)$
75. $(2x - 3)(3x - 5)$
76. $(4x + 5)(x + 2)$
77. $(3x + 4)(x + 2)$
78. $(7x - 2)(x - 5)$
79. $(3x + 2)(3x + 4)$
80. $(2x + 1)(x - 1)$
81. $(3x + 1)(x - 4)$
82. $(2x - 1)(x - 5)$
83. $(7x + 2)(x - 3)$
84. $(5x + 1)(x - 2)$
85. $-1(2x - 1)(3x + 2)$
86. $(6x + 5)(x - 1)$
87. $(3x - 2)(2x + 7)$
88. $-1(2x + 1)(2x - 5)$
89. $-1(2x - 3)(5x + 2)$
90. $12x^2 - 11x - 5$; $(4x - 5)(3x + 1)$
91. yes; $(x + 6)^2$ **92.** no; $5x \neq 2(x)(5)$
93. no; $-2x \neq 2(2x)(1)$
94. yes; $(3x + 2)^2$ **95.** no; $8x \neq$
$2(4x)(2)$ **96.** yes; $(x + 7)^2$ **97.** yes;
$(10x - 9)(10x + 9)$ **98.** No; 2 is
not a perfect square. **99.** No; 5
and 10 are not perfect squares.
100. yes; $-(12 + x^3)(-12 - x^3)$
101. no; terms must be subtracted
102. yes; $25(2p - q)(2p + q)$
103. $(x - 5)(x + 5)$; difference of 2
squares **104.** $(x + 10)^2$; perfect-
square trinomial

Selected Answers

105. $(j - k^2)(j + k^2)$; difference of 2 squares **106.** $(3x - 7)^2$; perfect-square trinomial **107.** $(9x + 8)^2$; perfect-square trinomial
108. $(4b^2 - 11c^3)(4b^2 + 11c^3)$; difference of 2 squares
109. no; $2(2x + 3)(x + 1)$ **110.** yes
111. no; $(b^2 + 9)(b - 3)(b + 3)$
112. yes **113.** $4(x - 4)(x + 4)$
114. $3b^3(b - 4)(b + 2)$
115. $a^2b^3(a - b)(a + b)$
116. $t^4(t^8 + 1)(t^4 + 1)(t^2 + 1)$ $(t + 1)(t - 1)$ **117.** $5(x + 3)(x + 1)$
118. $2x^2(x - 5)(x + 5)$
119. $2(s + 4)(t + 4)$
120. $5m(5m + 2)(m - 4)$
121. $4x(4x^2 + 1)(2x - 3)$
122. $6s^2t(s + t)^2$
123. $2(m + 3)(m - 3)(5m + 2)$

Chapter 9

9-1

Check It Out! 1a. yes **1b.** yes
1c. no
2a.

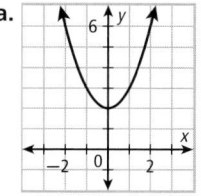

2b.

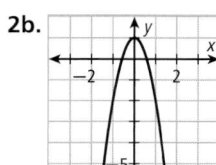

3a. Because $a < 0$, the parabola opens downward. **3b.** Because $a > 0$, the parabola opens upward.
4a. vertex: $(-2, 5)$; maximum: 5
4b. vertex: $(3, -1)$; minimum: -1
5a. D: all real numbers; R: $y \geq -4$
5b. D: all real numbers; R: $y \leq 3$

Exercises 1. minimum **3.** no
5. yes **7.** yes
9.

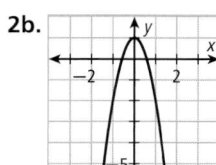

11.

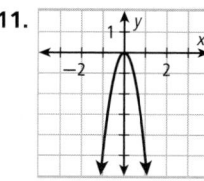

13.

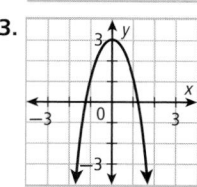

15.

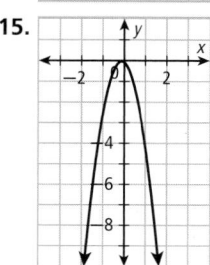

17. upward; $a > 0$ **19.** upward; $a > 0$ **21.** downward; $a < 0$
23. $(-3, -4)$; minimum: -4
25. D: all real numbers; R: $y \leq 4$
27. D: all real numbers; R: $y \geq -4$
29. yes **31.** no **33.** no
35.

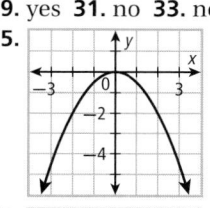

37.

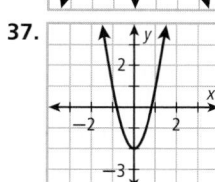

39. upward; $a > 0$
41. vertex: $(0, -5)$; minimum: -5
43. D: all real numbers; R: $y \leq 0$
45. D: all real numbers; R: $y \geq -2$
47. never **49.** always
51. sometimes **53.** no **55.** yes
57. yes **59a.** about 0.375 s
59b. about 2.25 m **59c.** The independent variable x represents the time since the volleyball is served, so this only makes sense for nonnegative numbers.
61. quadratic **63.** quadratic
65. neither **67.** linear

69a.

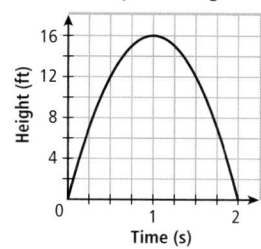

69b. $t \geq 0$ **69c.** 16 ft **69d.** 2 s
71a.

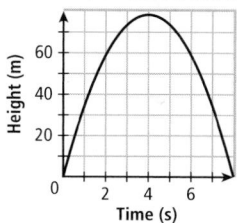

71b. maximum; the greatest height reached by the rocket **73.** C
75. yes

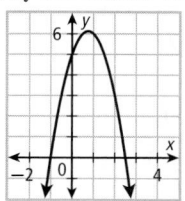

77. $f(x) = x^2 - 4 \rightarrow$ D: all real numbers; R: $y \geq -4$;
$f(x) = -(x + 2)^2 \rightarrow$ D: all real numbers; R: $y \leq 0$ **79.** $(-2)^4$
81. $42\frac{3}{4}$ mi **83.** ind. var.: hours; dep. var.: pay; $f(x) = 9x$

9-2

Check It Out! 1a. no zeros
1b. 3 **2a.** $x = -3$ **2b.** $x = 1$
3. $x = -\frac{1}{4}$ **4.** $(2, -14)$ **5.** 7 ft

Exercises 1. An x-intercept is a value of x where $f(x) = 0$. **3.** -1
5. no zeros **7.** $x = 2$ **9.** $x = -2$
11. $x = -\frac{3}{4}$ **13.** $(1, 8)$ **15.** $(-2, -11)$
17. $(3, 10)$ **19.** no zeros **21.** $-8, -2$
23. $x = 6$ **25.** $x = -\frac{1}{2}$ **27.** $x = 5$
29. $(-3.5, -12.25)$ **31.** $(4, 32)$
33. $\left(\frac{1}{4}, 2\frac{1}{16}\right)$ **35.** The equation for the axis of symmetry is $x = -\frac{b}{2a}$. If $b = 0$, then the axis of symmetry is $x = 0$, or the y-axis. **37.** 0 **39.** 2
41. B **43.** 2 **45.** 25 ft; 100 ft **47.** yes
49. $x^2 + 6x$ **51.** yes

Check It Out!

1a.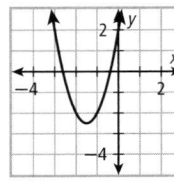

1b.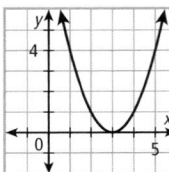

2. maximum height: 9 ft at 0.75 s; time it takes to reach the pool: 1.5 s

Exercises

1.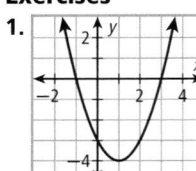

3.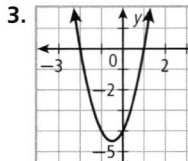

5.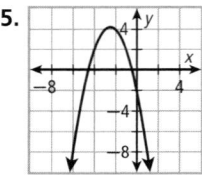

7. maximum height: 144 ft at 3 s; time in the air: 6 s

9.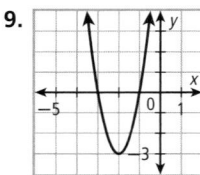

11.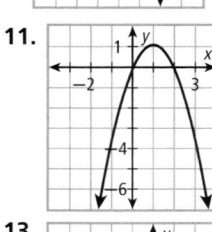

13.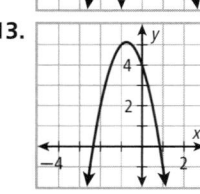

15. $x = 4$; $(4, -16)$ **17.** $x = 0$; $(0, 4)$

19. $x = -\frac{1}{2}$; $\left(-\frac{1}{2}, -\frac{15}{4}\right)$

21.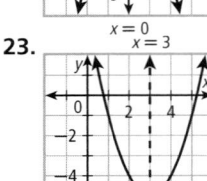

23.

25.

27a.

Falling Sunglasses
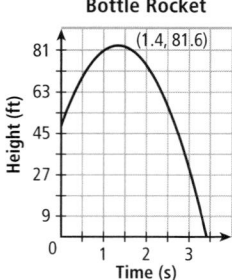

27b. D: $\{x : 0 \le x \le 3.16\}$;
R: $\{y : 0 \le x \le 50\}$ **27c.** 3.16 s
29. $(-1, 4)$; reflect the given point across the axis of symmetry.
31. 12 cm/s **33.** $(-1, 6)$; the axis of symmetry is a vertical line through the vertex. So its equation is $x = 0$. Reflect the point $(1, 6)$ across the axis of symmetry.
35a. $h(t) = -16t^2 + 45t + 50$
35b. $(1.4, 81.6)$
35c.

Bottle Rocket

35d. The vertex represents the time, 1.4 s, that the water bottle has spent in the air when it reaches its highest point, 81.6 ft. **37.** A **39.** D

41. -1; the axis of symmetry is $x = 1$. The given zero is 2 units from the axis of symmetry. The other zero is the same number of units from the axis of symmetry but on the opposite side. **43.** 3; 6
45. none; 3 **47.** $(3, -1)$ **49.** no

Check It Out! **1a.** $x = -4$ **1b.** no zeros **1c.** $x = -2$ or $x = 2$ **2a.** 1, -2 **2b.** $\frac{1}{3}$ **2c.** no real roots **3.** 2 s

Exercises **1.** -2, 2 **3.** no real solutions **5.** -3, 3 **7.** 3 **9.** -4, -1
11. -1, -7 **13.** 5 s **15.** no real solutions **17.** $x = -5$ **19.** 1
21. -3, 3 **23.** about 9.5 s
25. sometimes **27.** sometimes
29.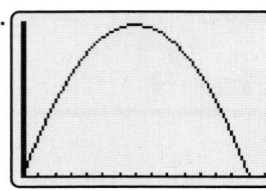

784 ft; 14 s
31. -3, 4 **33.** -1 **35.** no real solutions **39a.** 5 s **39b.** 100 ft
39c. 2.5 s **39d.** 84 ft; yes **41.** B
43. $x \approx 2.3$ or $x \approx 1$ **45.** $x \approx -1$ or $x \approx 0.75$ **47.** $y = \frac{1}{2}x + 2$ **49.** $y = 1$
51. 20 **53.** $\frac{y^6}{x^9}$ **55.** $\frac{9t^2}{16s^2}$ **57.** $-125k^3$

Check It Out! **1a.** 0, -4 **1b.** -4, 3 **2a.** 3 **2b.** 1, -5 **2c.** $-\frac{5}{3}$ **2d.** $\frac{1}{3}$, 1 **3.** 1.5 s

Exercises **1.** -2, 8 **3.** -7, -9
5. -11, 0 **7.** -6, 2 **9.** 2, 3
11. -8, -2 **13.** 4 **15.** 6 **17.** 8
19. 1 s **21.** -4, -7 **23.** 0, 9
25. $-\frac{1}{2}$, $\frac{1}{3}$ **27.** -2, 4 **29.** -5
31. -2 **33.** 1 **35.** 1 **37.** 1 **39.** B
41. 6 m **43.** 6 s **45.** no
47a. 3 s **47b.** 64 ft **47c.** yes **49.** A
51. $3x$ **53.** $(m, 0)$ and $(n, 0)$ **55.** -8
57. 15 **59.** $5m = 65$; 13 **61.** 4, -3

Check It Out! **1a.** ± 11 **1b.** 0 **1c.** $\varnothing$
2a. $\varnothing$ **2b.** $\pm \frac{1}{6}$ **3a.** ± 9.49 **3b.** ± 5.66
3c. $\varnothing$ **4.** 45 ft

Exercises **1.** ± 15 **3.** $\varnothing$ **5.** $\varnothing$ **7.** ± 5
9. $\varnothing$ **11.** ± 2 **13.** ± 5.20 **15.** ± 4.47
17. ± 13 **19.** $\varnothing$ **21.** $\varnothing$ **23.** $\pm \frac{2}{9}$

25. $\pm\frac{5}{8}$ **27.** $\pm\frac{13}{7}$ **29.** ±4.69
31. ±10.20 **33.** ±7.07 **35.** 6.1 s
37. $a=-6$ and $b=-3$ or $a=6$ and
$b=3$ **39.** about 2.5 s **41.** always
43. 3.75 s **45a.** a must be greater
than 0. **45b.** a must be equal to 0.
45c. a must be less than 0. **47.** no;
$x=\pm\frac{\sqrt{2}}{2}$, irrational **49.** yes; $x=\pm\frac{1}{2}$,
rational **53.** C **55.** $\pm\frac{1}{4}$ **57.** $\pm\frac{8}{11}$
59. 13 **61.** $y=4x-7$ and
$-y=4(2-x)$ **63.** $-6, 1$ **65.** $-4, 3$
67. $-9, 1$

9-7

Check It Out! **1a.** 36 **1b.** $\frac{25}{4}$ **1c.** 16
2a. $-9, -1$ **2b.** $4\pm\sqrt{21}$ **3a.** $-\frac{1}{3}, 2$
3b. no real solutions **4.** 16.4 ft by
24.4 ft

Exercises **3.** 4 **5.** $-5, -1$ **7.** $-6, 5$
9. 1, 9 **11.** $\frac{-5\pm3\sqrt{5}}{2}$ **13.** no real
solutions **15.** $4\pm\sqrt{10}$ **17.** 7.2 m;
11.2 m **19.** 1 **21.** $-2, 12$ **23.** $-13, -2$
25. $-6, 8$ **27.** $-2, 3$ **29.** $\frac{-1\pm\sqrt{5}}{2}$
31. $\frac{-15\pm\sqrt{105}}{2}$ **33.** 4 in. **35.** $1\pm\sqrt{7}$
37. $-3, \frac{1}{2}$ **39.** $-10, 2$ **41.** 81 **43.** $\frac{49}{4}$
45. 9 **47a.** $(10+2x)(34+2x)=640$
47b. 3 ft **49.** If $(x+2)^2=81$, then
$x+2=9$ or $x+2=-9$. The correct
answer is $x=7$ or $x=-11$.
51. $-6\pm3\sqrt{3}$ **53.** -6 **55.** no real
roots **57.** no real roots **61a.** $-16t^2+$
$64t+32=0$ **61b.** 4 **61c.** ≈4.4 s
63. B **65.** B **67.** $-\frac{3}{2}, \frac{2}{3}$
69. $-\frac{2}{3}-\frac{\sqrt{7}}{3}, -\frac{2}{3}+\frac{\sqrt{7}}{3}$ **71.** $0, -\frac{b}{a}$
73.

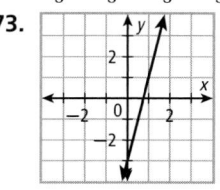

75.

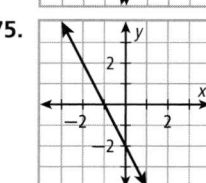

77. $x^2-8x+16$ **79.** $t^2-8t+16$
81. $64b^4-4$ **83.** ±1 **85.** ±4 **87.** ±15
89. ±1.55 **91.** ±5.10 **93.** ±1.48

9-8

Check It Out! **1a.** $2, -\frac{1}{3}$ **1b.** $2, -\frac{1}{5}$
2. $\approx0.13, \approx3.87$ **3a.** $-2, -5$
3b. $-2, 7$ **3c.** $\approx-4.39, \approx2.39$

Exercises **1.** 1, 4 **3.** $-1, 7$ **5.** $-\frac{4}{3}, 2$
7. $\approx\pm1.73$ **9.** $\approx0.30, \approx6.70$
11. $\approx5.32, \approx-1.32$ **13.** $\approx3, -4$
15. $-\frac{1}{2}, 1$ **17.** $1, -\frac{7}{2}$ **19.** $4, \frac{1}{3}$
21. $\frac{1}{3}, -1$ **23.** $\approx\pm1.29$ **25.** $-1, -3$
27. $3, -4$ **29.** $-3, -4$ **31.** $-\frac{3}{2}, -2$
33. $-3, -4$ **35.** $9x^2-12x+4=0; \frac{2}{3}$
37. $2x^2-2x-4=0; 2, -1$
39. $4x^2+7x-2=0; \frac{1}{4}, -2$
41. $7.2x^2+3.6x=0; 0, -\frac{1}{2}$
43. $\frac{7}{2}, -3$ **45.** 5 **47.** $-\frac{3}{2}, 6$ **51a.** no
51b. no **51c.** $\approx-0.36, 5$ **53.** $a=1$,
$b=1, c=7$ **55.** $a=10, b=-17$,
$c=2$ **57.** $a=0.5, b=1.5, c=3.7$
59. $a=\frac{1}{2}, b=\frac{3}{4}, c=1$ **61.** $a=24$,
$b=29, c=-13$ **65.** $1, -\frac{3}{2}$ **67.** $-\frac{1}{3}, 1$
69. $\pm\sqrt{3}$ **71.** $-\$56.25$ **73.** C **75.** A
77. yes **79.** $x\le8$
81. $(r^3+t)(s^2+5)$
83. $(n^4-2)(n-6)$ **85.** $-10, 4$
87. $-6, 1$ **89.** $5, -1$

9-9

Check It Out! **1a.** 0 **1b.** 1 **2a.** 0
2b. 2 **3.** No; for the equation
$45=-16t^2+20t+0$, the
discriminant is negative, so the
weight will not ring the bell.

Exercises **1.** no **3.** 1 **5.** 0 **7.** 2 **9.** 0
11. 0 **13.** 0 **15.** 0 **17.** 2 **19.** 1 **21.** 0
23. 1 **25.** 2 **27.** 1 **29.** 0 **31.** 2 **33.** no
35. $-5, 3$ **37.** $0, -10$ **39.** $6, -5$
41. 2 solutions; $8, -1$
43. 2 x-intercepts; $9\ -4$
45. 1 x-intercept; $-\frac{2}{3}$ **47a.** ≈1.76 s
47b. 2 **47c.** no **49a.** no **49b.** yes
49c. 5.24 s **51.** A
55. $8x^2-19x-34=0$; 2 solutions;
$\approx-1.19, \approx3.57$
57. $8x^2-6x+39=0; \varnothing$
59. $2x^2+4x+4=0; \varnothing$
61. $a=\frac{31.5+28.7+19.2+21.3+36.5}{5}$;
27.44 **63.** $y=\frac{1}{2}x+8$
65. $y=3x+2$ **67.** $y=\frac{3}{4}x-5$
69. $(b^2+2)(b-4)$ **71.** ≈-1.92,
≈3.92 **73.** 5, 8

Study Guide: Review

1. vertex **2.** minimum; maximum
3. zero of a function **4.** discriminant
of a quadratic equation
5. completing the square **6.** yes
7. no **8.** yes **9.** no

10.

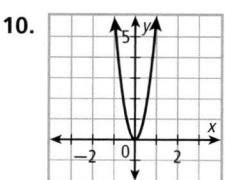

11.

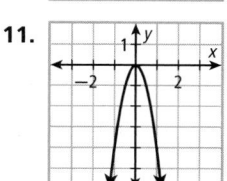

12.

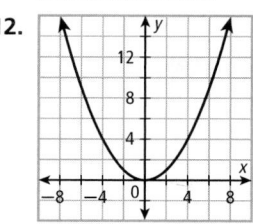

13.

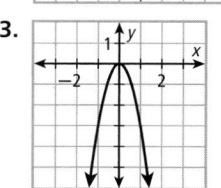

14. Upward; the value of a is
positive. **15.** Downward; the value
of a is negative. **16.** $(-2, -4)$;
minimum: -4 **17.** -5 and 2 **18.** -1
and 2 **19.** $x=6$; $(6, 4)$ **20.** $x=-1$;
$(-1, -18)$

21.

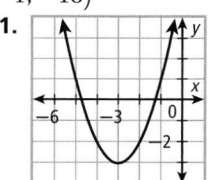

22.

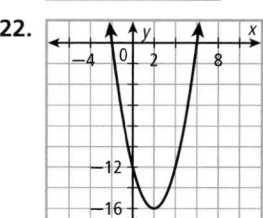

23.

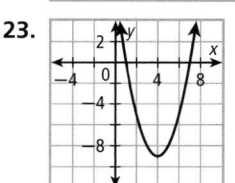

24.

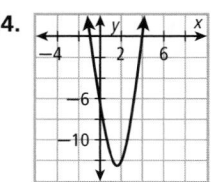

25.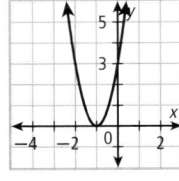

26.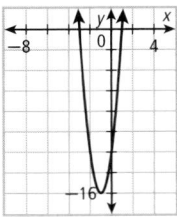

27.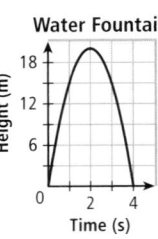
Water Fountain

In 2 s, the water reaches its maximum height of 20 m. It takes a total of 4 s for the water to reach the ground.

28.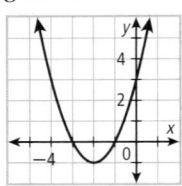
$x = -3$ or $x = -1$

29.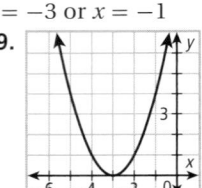
$x = -3$

30.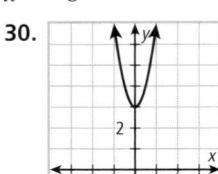
no real solutions (∅)

31.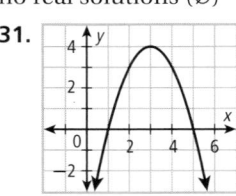
$x = 1$ or $x = 5$

32.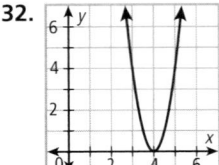
$x = 4$

33.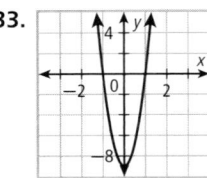
$x = 1$ or $x = -1$

34.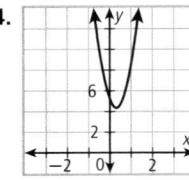
no real solutions (∅)

35. $x = -5$ or -1 **36.** $x = -7$ or -2
37. $x = -3$ or 5 **38.** $x = -1$ or 2
39. $x = -5$ **40.** $x = 4.5$
41. $x^2 + 2x = 48$; 6 ft **42.** $x = \pm 8$
43. $x = \pm 12$ **44.** ∅ **45.** $x = 0$
46. $x = \pm 5$ **47.** $x = \pm \frac{5}{2}$ **48.** 4 ft
49. $x = -8$ or 6 **50.** $x = -7$ or 3
51. $x = 1$ or 5 **52.** $x = 5 \pm \sqrt{5}$,
or $\approx 2.76, \approx 7.24$ **53.** 16 ft by 12 ft
54. $x = -1$ or 6 **55.** $x = -\frac{1}{2}$ or 5
56. $x = 1$ **57.** $x = \frac{6 \pm \sqrt{8}}{2}$,
or $\approx 1.59, \approx 4.41$ **58.** $-3.1, -4.2$
59. $1, -3$ **60.** no x-intercepts
61. $-\frac{1}{3}, -2$ **62.** 1 **63.** 0 **64.** 2 **65.** 2
66. 2 **67.** 0 **68.** 1 **69.** 0

Chapter 10

10-1

Check It Out! **1a.** No; the product xy is not constant. **1b.** Yes; the product xy is constant. **1c.** No; the equation cannot be written in the form $y = \frac{k}{x}$.

2. $y = \frac{5}{x}$

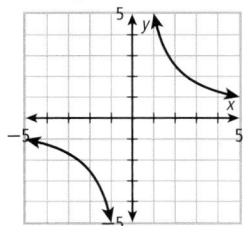

3. D: $x > 0$; R: $y > 0$

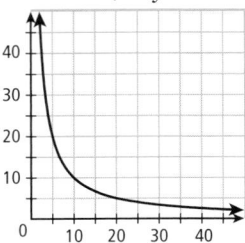

4. 3 **5.** 80.625 lb

Exercises **1.** The graph of an inverse variation consists of 2 disconnected branches. **3.** no
5. yes **7.** $y = \frac{-6}{x}$ **9.** 4 **11.** 16 teeth
13. yes **15.** no **17.** $y = \frac{2}{x}$ **19.** 2
21. 12 yd **23.** direct; 8 **25.** neither
27. inverse; 12 **29.** inverse; 15
31. $d = \frac{10}{n}$; inverse **33.** neither
35. $y = \frac{2000}{x}$;
D: natural numbers; R: $y > 0$

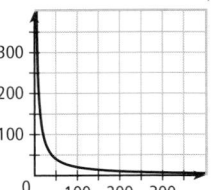

37. In an inverse variation function, $xy = k$ and $k \neq 0$. So neither x nor y can be 0. **41.** C **43.** C **45.** the linear function $y = 0$ **47.** ≈ 888.9 watts
49. D: $\{-4, -2, 0, 2, 4\}$; R: $\{1, 3, 5\}$; yes **51.** $-1, 7$ **53.** 2

10-2

Check It Out! **1a.** 0 **1b.** 1 **1c.** -4
2a. $x = 5$; $y = 0$ **2b.** $x = -4$; $y = 5$
2c. $x = -77$; $y = -15$

3a.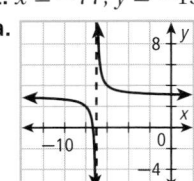

3b.

4a. D: $x > 0$; R: natural numbers > 10

4b.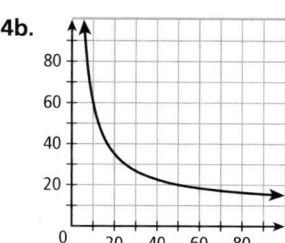

Exercises **1.** excluded value
3. none **5.** 4 **7.** $x = -5$; $y = 0$
9. $x = -9$; $y = -10$

11.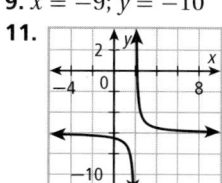

13.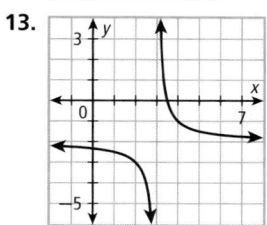

15. 0 **17.** 0 **19.** $x = 4$; $y = 0$
21. $x = 3$; $y = 4$

23.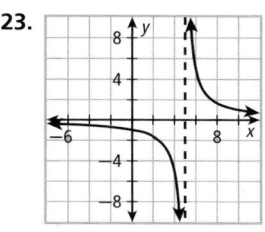

25.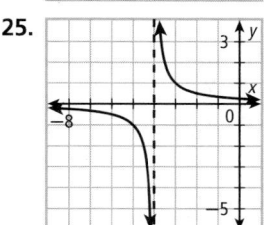

27a. D: $x > 0$; R: natural numbers > 5

27b.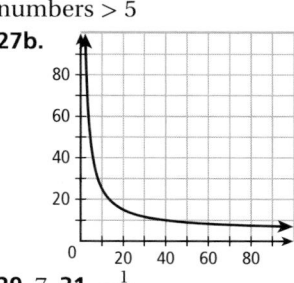

29. 7 **31.** $-\frac{1}{2}$

33.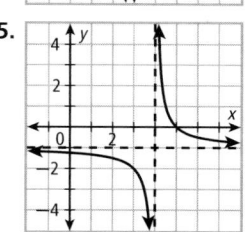

35.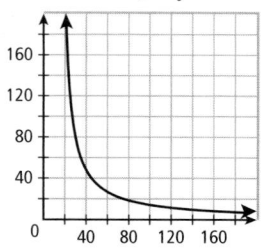

37. $x = -1$; $y = 0$ **39.** $x = 2$;
$y = 5$ **41.** B **43.** C
45. D: $x > 15$; R: $y > 0$

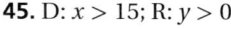

47. shifted 6 units right

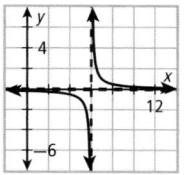

49. shifted 4 units up

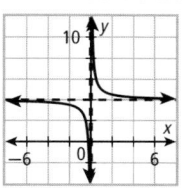

51. $x > 2$ **53.** $x > -\frac{1}{5}$ **55.** I and III; II
and IV **59.** D

61.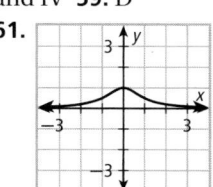

61a. yes **61b.** D: all real numbers
61c. R: $0 < y \leq 1$ **61d.** no **65.** $r \geq -8$
67. $g \leq -5$ **69.** $m < 3$ **71.** $-2, 3$
73. 26 in. by 30 in.

10-3

Check It Out! **1a.** none **1b.** $0, -5$
1c. $-3, -4$ **2a.** $\frac{m}{3}$; $m \neq 0$ **2b.** $6p$
2c. $\frac{3n}{n-2}$; $n \neq 2$ **3a.** $\frac{1}{r+5}$ **3b.** $\frac{b-5}{b+5}$
4a. $-\frac{3}{4+x}$ **4b.** $-\frac{1}{x+1}$ **4c.** $\frac{3}{x+11}$
5. The barrel cactus with a radius of
3 inches has less chance of survival
because its surface-area-to-volume
ratio is greater.

Exercises **1.** Both the numerator and
denominator are polynomials.
3. 0, 8 **5.** $\frac{a}{2}$; $a \neq 0$ **7.** $\frac{2}{y+3}$; $y \neq -3$
9. $\frac{h}{h+2}$; $h \neq -2$ **11.** $\frac{1}{b+1}$ **13.** $\frac{c+2}{c-4}$
15. $\frac{j-5}{j-3}$ **17.** $-\frac{2}{8+n}$ **19.** $\frac{-5}{r+6}$
21. $-\frac{5}{10+q}$ **23a.** $\frac{b_2}{b_1+b_2}$ **23b.** They
will be the same: $\frac{b_2}{b_1+b_2}$. **25.** 0
27. $-\frac{1}{2}$, 4 **29.** already simplified;
$m \neq 4$ **31.** $\frac{t}{8}$; $t \neq 0$ **33.** $\frac{z-1}{z+1}$ **35.** $\frac{p-7}{p-5}$
37. $\frac{2}{x-4}$ **39.** $-\frac{1}{b+7}$ **41a.** $\frac{2(\ell w + \ell h + wh)}{\ell wh}$
41b. box A **43.** $\frac{p+6}{12}$ **45.** $\frac{1}{3}$ **47.** $\frac{3w+7}{3}$
49. 1 **51.** $-\frac{5+x}{x+2}$ **53a.** $\frac{6}{s}$ **53b.** 3
53c. 1 **57.** A **59.** sometimes
61. sometimes **63.** $\frac{a-3}{a+5}$ **65.** ± 14
67. $-2, 0$ **69.** D: {4, 5, 25, 29};
R: {−7, 2, 22}

71.

73. $\frac{5}{h^3}$ **75.** already simplified

10-4

Check It Out! **1a.** $-\frac{9}{4}$ **1b.** $\frac{5x^2y^4}{6}$
2. $\frac{3m-15}{m-6}$ **3a.** $\frac{n+4}{n^2+2n}$ **3b.** $\frac{p^2-p-20}{p^3+16p}$
4a. $\frac{3x-15}{x^5}$ **4b.** $\frac{2w^6}{v^2x^3}$ **4c.** $\frac{x}{x^2+5x+6}$
5. ≈ 0.23

Exercises **1.** $\frac{6h}{5jk^2}$ **3.** $\frac{2x-4}{3}$ **5.** $\frac{a}{6}$
7. $3y - 6$ **9.** $\frac{m^2-10m}{2}$
11. $a^3 + 10a^2 + 25a$ **13.** $\frac{a+6b}{b^2}$
15. $\frac{1}{2}$ **17.** $\frac{2r+28}{r-4}$ **19.** b **21.** $\frac{1}{3x-15}$
23. $-\frac{3p^8q^2}{7r^4}$ **25.** $\frac{10y+20}{3y+15}$
27. $4m^2 - 4m$ **29.** $\frac{3n^2-3n}{n+8}$ **31.** 1
33. $-\frac{1}{2a^3}$ **35a.** $\frac{x^2}{4(4x^2+8x-1)}$ **35b.** $\frac{9}{236}$
37. B **39.** $\frac{1}{2m}$ **41.** $\frac{1}{16x}$ **43.** 1 **45a.** 64 cm

45b. 80 cm **45c.** 4 **47.** C **49.** $\frac{1}{3x^2 + 9x}$
51. $\frac{1}{3}$ **53.** $\frac{x}{z^2}$ **55.** $\frac{1}{2a+2}$
57. $12 + 9 + m \le 30$; $0 \le m \le 9$
59. $y = 5x - 7$ and $y = 5x + 5$;
$y = -x + 5$ and $y = -x - 7$
61. $\frac{1}{x-2}$; $x \ne 2$ **63.** $\frac{2x-5}{x^2-4}$; $x \ne 2, -2$

10-5

Check It Out! 1a. 2 **1b.** $3y$
2a. $\frac{3}{a-2}$ **2b.** $\frac{4b+12}{b^2+3b-4}$ **3a.** $15f^2h^2$
3b. $(x-6)(x+2)(x+5)$ **4a.** $\frac{4d-3}{3d^2}$
4b. $\frac{a+8}{a-2}$ **5.** $\frac{5}{24}$ h, or 12.5 min
Exercises 1. $\frac{2}{y}$ **3.** $\frac{1}{x-4}$ **5.** $\frac{2}{a+1}$
7. $6x^3y^2z$ **9.** $(y+4)(y-4)(y+9)$
11. $\frac{x+3}{x+2}$ **13a.** $\frac{260}{r}$ **13b.** $6\frac{1}{2}$ h
15. $a - 1$ **17.** m **19.** $3a + 1$
21. $36a(3a+1)$ **23.** $10xy^3z$
25. $(y+5)(y+2)(y+4)$ **27.** $\frac{y+2}{3(y-3)}$
29. $\frac{19}{21z}$ **31.** $\frac{-m^2-6m}{4(m-2)^2}$ **33a.** $\frac{700}{r}$
33b. 14 h **33c.** Divide the total
distance (500 mi) by the total
time. **35.** $\frac{1}{7+c}$ **37.** $\frac{3}{2b^2}$ **39.** $\frac{x-5}{3}$
41. $\frac{8x+20}{(x+4)(x+2)}$ **43.** student A
47. $4x^2$; $8x^2$; $8x^3$ **49.** D **51.** D
53. $\frac{x-4y}{(x+y)(x-y)}$; $x \ne y$ and $x \ne -y$
55. $\frac{az+by+cx}{xyz}$; $x \ne 0, y \ne 0$, and
$z \ne 0$ **57.** $(2x-5)(3x+1)$
59. $5(h+3)(h-4)$
61. $14t(4t+3)(t-1)$ **63.** $-2, 6$
65. $-\frac{1}{3}$ **67.** $\frac{n}{n-2}$; $-5, 2$

10-6

Check It Out! 1a. $-2p + 1 - \frac{3}{p}$
1b. $x^2 + \frac{1}{3} - \frac{5}{2x}$ **2a.** $k + 5$ **2b.** $b - 7$
2c. $s + 6$ **3a.** $2y + 1$ **3b.** $a - 2$
4a. $3m - 5 + \frac{13}{m+3}$ **4b.** $y + 6 + \frac{20}{y-3}$
5a. $x^2 - 2x - 4 + \frac{-7}{x-2}$
5b. $2p^2 - 2p + 6 + \frac{-7}{p+1}$
Exercises 1. $2x - \frac{1}{2}$ **3.** $7b - \frac{14}{3} + \frac{8}{b}$
5. $2x + 4 + \frac{3}{x}$ **7.** $2x - 3$ **9.** $2y + 5$
11. $x + 1$ **13.** $c + 3$ **15.** $x - 2$
17. $a + 2 + \frac{-1}{a+2}$ **19.** $n + 4 + \frac{-1}{n+4}$
21. $4n - 5 + \frac{-2}{2n+1}$ **23.** $-2x^2 +$
$6x - 15 + \frac{35}{x+3}$ **25.** $m + 1 + \frac{3}{m-1}$
27. $4k^2 - 4k + 2 + \frac{-10}{k+1}$ **29.** $3t +$
$4 - \frac{2}{t}$ **31.** $-4p + 1 + \frac{2}{p^3}$ **33.** $4t + 3$
35. $x - 3$ **37.** $3a - 1$ **39.** $3x +$
$4 + \frac{14}{x-2}$ **41.** $3x + 1 + \frac{-2}{2x-1}$
43. $2t^2 - 6t + 25 + \frac{-216}{3t+9}$ **45.** -20

47. $2x - 5 + \frac{3}{x+1}$ **49a.** The values
of y are negative and decreasing.
49b. The values of y are positive
and decreasing. **49c.** The function
is not defined at $x = 5$.
51. $0.5m + 1$ **53a.** $y = \frac{12x}{x-12}$
53b. The function is undefined at
$x = 12$. **57.** C **59.** B **61.** $3x - \frac{1}{2y} + \frac{2y}{x}$
63. $x + 2$ **65.** 3 m **67.** 3 weeks
69. $4(x+1)$ **71.** $2k^2 + 5k + 2$

10-7

Check It Out! 1a. 2 **1b.** 1 **1c.** $-\frac{7}{6}$
2a. -4 **2b.** -4 **2c.** 1, 3 **3.** $22\frac{2}{9}$ min,
or $\approx$ 22 min 13 s **4a.** 5 **4b.** 1, 5 **4c.** 4
Exercises 1. rational equation **3.** 8
5. -20 **7.** 5 **9.** 3 **11.** $-\frac{5}{2}$ **13.** 18
15. 1, 6 **17.** $-7, 1$ **19.** $-1, 5$ **21.** ∅
23. -6 **25.** -1 **27.** 4 **29.** ∅ **31.** ∅
33. 3, 6 **35.** 2, 4 **37.** -1 **39.** 2 **41.** ∅
43. 2 **45.**

	Karla	Andrew
Books	12	18
Stacks	x	$x - 2$
Books per Stack	$\frac{12}{x}$	$\frac{18}{x-2}$

47. no **49.** B **51.** D **53.** 3
55. $y = 3x + 1$ and $y = 3x - 1$ are
parallel. **57.** $y = x - 2$ and
$y = x + 3$ are parallel; $y = -x - 3$
is perpendicular to both $y = x - 2$
and $y = x + 3$. **59.** (4, 7) **61.** $(-5, -6)$

10-8

Check It Out! 1. $22\frac{2}{9}$ min, or about
22 min 13 s **2.** 750 mL **3.** 5 h
Exercises 1. $1\frac{7}{8}$ h **3.** 4 h **5.** 4 h
7. 60 mi/h
9a.

	Area (m²)	Length (m)	Width (m)
Rectangle A	96	ℓ	$\frac{96}{\ell}$
Rectangle B	96	2ℓ	$\frac{96}{2\ell}$

9b. $\frac{96}{\ell} = \frac{96}{2\ell} + 4$ **9c.** length: 12 m;
width: 8 m **11.** -2 or 2 **13a.** $\frac{1}{12} =$
$\frac{1}{x} + \frac{1}{x-10}$ **13b.** 30 cm **13c.** 20 cm
17. B **19.** Eddie: 6 h; Luke: 3 h;
Ryan: 4 h **21.** yes **23.** yes **25.** yes
27. yes; $(2x+3)^2$ **29.** no **31.** no
33. $x + 1$ **35.** $x + 4$ **37.** $x - 6$

Study Guide: Review

1. rational expression **2.** rational
function **3.** rational equation
4. inverse variation
5. discontinuous function
6. Yes; the product xy is
constant. **7.** No; the product xy is
not constant.
8. $y = -\frac{4}{x}$

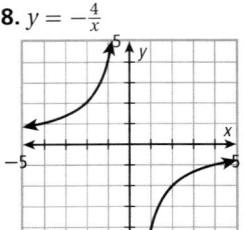

9. $y = \frac{1}{x}$

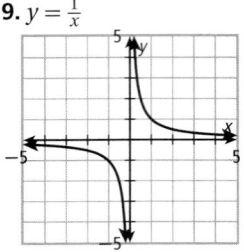

10. -15 **11.** $13,200 **12.** -4; $x = -4$;
$y = 0$ **13.** -1; $x = -1$; $y = 3$ **14.** -3;
$x = -3$; $y = -4$ **15.** $\frac{7}{4}$; $x = \frac{7}{4}$; $y = 5$
16.

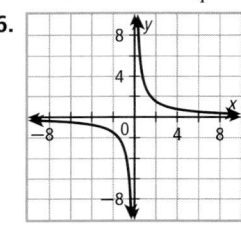

17.

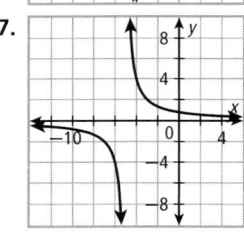

18.

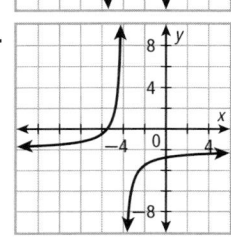

19.

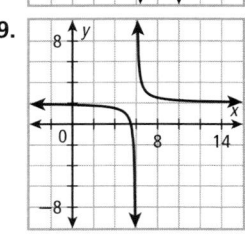

20. D: $x > 0$; R: $y > 0$

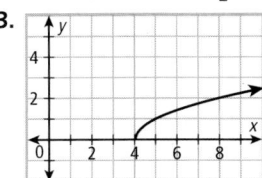

21. 0 **22.** 7 **23.** 0, 1 **24.** $-1, 5$
25. $5, -5$ **26.** $4, 7$ **27.** $\frac{1}{3r}$; $r \neq 0$
28. $\frac{1}{2k-3}$; $k \neq 0$ and $k \neq \frac{3}{2}$ **29.** $\frac{1}{x-2}$;
$x \neq -6$ and $x \neq 2$ **30.** $\frac{-2}{x+3}$; $x \neq \pm 3$
31. $\frac{3}{x-1}$; $x \neq -5$ and $x \neq 1$ **32.** $\frac{x+3}{x-5}$;
$x \neq -6$ and $x \neq 5$ **33.** $\frac{4}{\pi}$ **34.** $\frac{2b^2+2b}{3}$
35. $\frac{4x^2-12x}{3}$ **36.** $\frac{15b^2}{2}$ **37.** $\frac{-3c^3}{4d^2}$
38. $\frac{b+2}{2b^2+8b}$ **39.** $\frac{n^2+3n+2}{n^2-n-42}$ **40.** $\frac{1}{b-3}$
41. $\frac{y^2}{3}$ **42.** $\frac{12n^3}{m}$ **43.** $\frac{x^2+2x-3}{4x^2-16}$
44. $10a^2b^2$ **45.** $10x(x-3)$ **46.** $\frac{b^2+8}{2b}$
47. $\frac{3x^2+2x-4}{x^2-2}$ **48.** $\frac{8p-2}{p^2-4p+2}$
49. $\frac{5b-1}{7-b}$ **50.** $\frac{-10}{n^2-1}$ **51.** $\frac{7m+2}{10m^2}$
52. $\frac{h^2+5h-1}{h-5}$ **53.** $\frac{40}{3r}$ **54.** $x - \frac{2}{x} + \frac{5}{x^2}$
55. $x + 2$ **56.** $3n + 1$ **57.** $x + 2$
58. $x + 6$ **59.** $3b^2 + 6b + 8 + \frac{18}{b-2}$
60. $-4x^2 + 10x - 17 + \frac{34}{x+2}$ **61.** $-\frac{3}{4}$
62. $\frac{12}{7}$ **63.** $-\frac{18}{11}$ **64.** $-\frac{7}{6}$ **65.** $-\frac{2}{3}$
66. $-\frac{1}{3}, 1$ **67.** -3 **68.** ± 1 **69.** $-\frac{1}{12}$
70. -2 **71.** $4, 5$ **72.** $-12, 1$ **73.** -19
74. 0 **75.** $7\frac{1}{5}$ h, or 7 h 12 min
76. 80 mL

Chapter 11

11-1

Check It Out! **1a.** 40 ft/s
1b. 30.98 ft/s **2.** $x \geq \frac{1}{2}$
3.

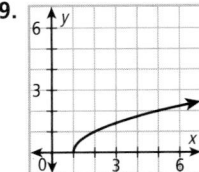

Exercises **1.** There is no variable
under the square-root sign.
3. $x \geq -6$ **5.** $x \geq 0$ **7.** $x \geq -3$
9.

11.

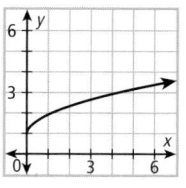

13.

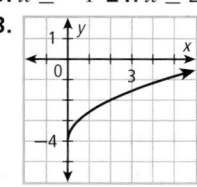

15. 49.96 mi/h **17.** $x \geq -1$
19. $x \geq -4$ **21.** $x \geq 2$
23.

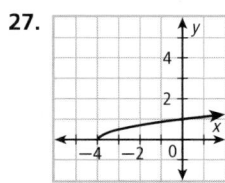

25.

27.

29a.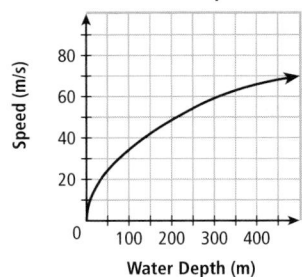

29b. $x \geq 0$ **29c.** $y \geq 0$
31.

Tsunami Speed

70 m/s

35. no **37.** A **39.** C **41.** $x \leq -5$ OR
$x \geq 5$ **43.** $x \leq -4$ OR $x \geq \frac{3}{2}$
45. D: $x \leq 3$; R: $y \leq 4$ **49a.** When
$x = 2$ or $x = 4$, the expression under
the square-root sign is negative.
49b. 3, 1 **51.** $y = -\frac{1}{2}x + 2$

53. $9x^2 - 6x + 1$ **55.** $a^2 - 2ab^2c + b^4c^2$ **57.** $9r^2 - 4s^2$ **59.** $x - 14$
61. $2r + 1$ **63.** $3s + 4$

11-2

Check It Out! **1a.** 8 **1b.** 7
1c. 13 **1d.** $|3 - x|$ **2a.** $8\sqrt{2}$
2b. $xy\sqrt{x}$ **2c.** $4a\sqrt{3b}$ **3a.** $\frac{2}{3}$ **3b.** $\frac{6}{x^2}$
3c. $\frac{y^3}{2}$ **4a.** $\frac{2\sqrt{5}}{7}$ **4b.** $\frac{z^2\sqrt{z}}{5y}$ **4c.** $\frac{p^3}{q^5}$
5. $60\sqrt{2}$ ft; 84.9 ft

Exercises **1.** $3x - 6$ **3.** 7 **5.** $6\sqrt{5}$
7. $18\sqrt{2}$ **9.** $4x^2y\sqrt{2y}$ **10.** $10a\sqrt{2b}$
12. $\frac{\sqrt{7}}{4}$ **13.** $\frac{\sqrt{6}}{7}$ **15.** $\frac{\sqrt{x}}{3}$ **17.** $\frac{6\sqrt{3}}{7}$
19. $\frac{16\sqrt{2}}{9}$ **21.** $\frac{5x\sqrt{2}}{13}$ **23.** $5\sqrt{41}$ mi;
32 mi **25.** 20 **27.** 9 **29.** $|x + 1|$
31. $|x - 3|$ **33.** $20\sqrt{10}$ **35.** $8rs\sqrt{5}$
37. $\frac{3\sqrt{5}}{2}$ **39.** $\frac{\sqrt{14}}{3}$ **41.** $\frac{x\sqrt{x}}{y^3}$ **43.** $\frac{8s\sqrt{3}}{7}$
45. $-20\sqrt{3}$ **47.** $15x\sqrt{7}$ **49.** x
51. $\frac{x^3\sqrt{x}}{3}$ **53.** $\sqrt{36}$; 6 **55.** $\sqrt{50}$; $5\sqrt{2}$
57. $\sqrt{3}$ **59.** $\sqrt{20}$; $2\sqrt{5}$ **61.** 42 ft;
length of missing side $\approx$ 17.2 ft,
which will need to be rounded up
to 18. $10 + 14 + 18 = 42$ ft
63a. $v = 8\sqrt{h}$; 93.6 ft/s
63b. Pythagorean Theorem
63c. 171.4 ft
65. Sears: $\frac{10\sqrt{87}}{3}$ mi; 31.1 mi
Empire: $\frac{50\sqrt{3}}{3}$ mi; 28.9 mi
Aon: $\frac{4\sqrt{426}}{3}$ mi; 27.5 mi
67. C **69.** C **71.** $x\sqrt{x+1}$ **73a.** $|x|$
73b. x^2 **73c.** $|x^3|$ **73d.** x^4 **73e.** $|x^5|$
73f. x^n; $|x^n|$ **75.** yes **77.** no
79. $x \geq 2$ **81.** $x \geq 1$ **83.** $x \leq 6$

11-3

Check It Out! **1a.** $-\sqrt{7}$ **1b.** $3\sqrt{3}$
1c. $8\sqrt{n}$ **1d.** $\sqrt{2s} + 8\sqrt{5s}$ **2a.** $5\sqrt{6}$
2b. $12\sqrt{3} - 3\sqrt{2}$ **2c.** $5\sqrt{3y}$
3. $10\sqrt{b}$ in.

Exercises **3.** $10\sqrt{5}$ **5.** $3\sqrt{7} + 5\sqrt{2}$
7. $5\sqrt{6a} + 6\sqrt{5a}$ **9.** $13\sqrt{3}$
11. $-\sqrt{5x}$ **13.** $8\sqrt{2t} - 4\sqrt{3t}$
15. $6\sqrt{3}$ **17.** $-3\sqrt{11}$ **19.** $-4\sqrt{n}$
21. $7\sqrt{7}$ **23.** $12\sqrt{2}$ **25.** $3\sqrt{7x} -$
$12\sqrt{3x}$ **27.** $3\sqrt{5j}$ **29.** $2\sqrt{3m}$
31. $12\sqrt{7}$ **33.** 0 **35.** $7\sqrt{3}$ **37.** $7\sqrt{2}$
39a. $3\sqrt{11}$; $2\sqrt{11}$; $5\sqrt{11}$ **39b.** $10\sqrt{11}$
39c. Because the areas found in
parts **a** and **b** must be equal, the
model shows that $3\sqrt{11} + 2\sqrt{11} +$
$5\sqrt{11} = (3 + 2 + 5)\sqrt{11} = 10\sqrt{11}$.
41. $2\sqrt{3} + 5\sqrt{5} + 5$ **43.** $8\sqrt{7x} -$
$\sqrt{70x}$ **45.** $35\sqrt{5k}$ **47.** $5\sqrt{3} + 5\sqrt{5}$

51. 9 **53.** 18 **55.** $36x^2$ **57.** $16\sqrt{3}$ in.; $8\sqrt{3}$ in.; $24\sqrt{3}$ in. **59.** B **61.** A
63. $\sqrt{x}(x + 2)$ **65.** 0
67. $(x + 2)\sqrt{x - 1}$ **69.** $3\sqrt{x + 1} - x\sqrt{x + 2}$ **71.** $m_{AB} = 1$, $m_{BC} = \frac{1}{6}$, $m_{CD} = 1$, $m_{AD} = \frac{1}{6}$. Since $m_{AB} = m_{CD}$, $\overline{AB} \parallel \overline{CD}$. Since $m_{BC} = m_{AD}$, $\overline{BC} \parallel \overline{AD}$. Because both pairs of opposite sides are parallel, $ABCD$ is a parallelogram.
73. $-3, 1$ **75.** $9, -2$ **77.** $x \geq -3$

11-4

Check It Out! 1a. $5\sqrt{2}$ **1b.** 63
1c. $2m\sqrt{7}$ **2a.** $4\sqrt{3} - 3\sqrt{6}$
2b. $5\sqrt{2} + 4\sqrt{15}$ **3a.** $83 + 18\sqrt{2}$
3b. $17 - \sqrt{3}$ **4a.** $\frac{\sqrt{65}}{5}$ **4b.** $\frac{\sqrt{21a}}{6}$
4c. $\frac{8\sqrt{35}}{7}$

Exercises 1. $\sqrt{6}$ **3.** 125 **5.** $3\sqrt{30a}$
7. $2\sqrt{6} + \sqrt{42}$ **9.** $\sqrt{35} - \sqrt{21}$
11. $5\sqrt{3} + 4\sqrt{5}$ **13.** $12 + 7\sqrt{2}$
15. $-5 - 2\sqrt{3}$ **17.** $81 - 30\sqrt{2}$
19. $\frac{\sqrt{26}}{2}$ **21.** $\frac{\sqrt{33}}{18}$ **23.** $\frac{2\sqrt{7}}{7}$ **25.** $\frac{\sqrt{5x}}{5x}$
27. $3\sqrt{10}$ **29.** 8 **31.** $6d\sqrt{7}$
33. $4\sqrt{5} - 5\sqrt{2}$ **35.** $2\sqrt{3} - 2\sqrt{5}$
37. $3 + 12\sqrt{3}$ **39.** $75 + 19\sqrt{15}$
41. $10 - \sqrt{2}$ **43.** $67 + 16\sqrt{3}$ **45.** $\frac{5\sqrt{6}}{2}$
47. $\frac{\sqrt{3x}}{x}$ **49.** $\frac{7\sqrt{2x}}{2}$ **51.** $2\sqrt{y}$
53. 180 in^2 **55.** $(6\sqrt{10} - 2\sqrt{5})$ cm^2
57. $\sqrt{30}$ **59.** $-5 - 2\sqrt{3}$ **61.** $3\sqrt{2}$
63. $134\sqrt{3} + 96$ **65.** $x - 2\sqrt{xy} + y$
67. $3 + 2\sqrt{3x} + x$ **69.** $\frac{\pi\sqrt{6}}{4}$ s ≈ 1.9 s
71. 269.5 ft^2 **75.** B **77.** D
79. $-4\sqrt{3} + 4\sqrt{5}$ **81.** $-5 - 2\sqrt{6}$
83. $2 - \sqrt{3}$ **85.** $2\sqrt{6} + 2\sqrt{5}$
87. $x < 8$ **89.** $x \geq 2$
91. $(3x + 1)(2x + 3)$ **93.** $3(x + 5)^2$
95. $4x(2x + 1)(x - 3)$ **97.** $\frac{3\sqrt{2}}{2}$
99. $\frac{5a^2\sqrt{2}}{3}$

11-5

Check It Out! 1a. 36 **1b.** 3 **1c.** $\frac{1}{3}$
2a. 9 **2b.** 18 **2c.** 3 **3a.** 121 **3b.** 64
3c. 100 **4a.** 2 **4b.** $\frac{11}{2}$ **5a.** $\varnothing$ **5b.** $\varnothing$
5c. 4 **6.** 8; 3 cm

Exercises 1. no **3.** -8 **5.** -144
7. 27 **9.** 50 **11.** -2 **13.** 9 **15.** 64
17. 16 **19.** 16 **21.** $\frac{4}{9}$ **23.** 100 **25.** 5
27. 13 **29.** 6 **31.** 2 **33.** $\varnothing$ **35.** 4
37. 2 **39.** $\varnothing$ **41.** 48 **43.** -25 **45.** 71
47. -8 **49.** 36 **51.** -16 **53.** 8 **55.** 9
57. 2 **59.** -5 **61.** 5 **63.** 1 **65.** 1
67. $x = 144$; 12 in. **69.** $\sqrt{x} - 3 = 4$;
49 **71.** $x = \sqrt{x + 6}$; 3 **73.** 3 in. by
1 in. **75a.** 54.88 joules **75b.** 0 joules
77. 1690 ft **79.** $x = 25$; $y = 16$

81. sometimes **83.** student B
85. $x \leq 0$ since the square root is only defined for nonnegative values. $k \geq 0$ since the value of the square root must be nonnegative.
87. A **89.** C **91.** A **93.** 1, 2 **95.** 2
97. 0

99a.

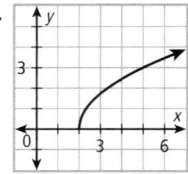

99b. The solution is $x = 3$, which is the x-value of the point where the graphs intersect.
101. D: $\{-6, 1, 3, 5\}$; R: $\{2, 3, 4\}$
103. D: $\{3, 4, 6, 7, 9\}$; R: $\{-8, -5, 0, 1, 2\}$ **105.** $(3, 11)$ **107.** $(5, -3)$

109.

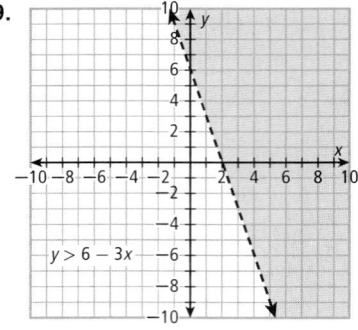

11-6

Check It Out! 1a. $80, -160, 320$
1b. $216, 162, 121.5$ **2.** 7.8125
3. $\$1342.18$

Exercises 1. the value that each term is multiplied by to get the next term **3.** $25, 12.5, 6.25$
5. $1,000,000,000$ **7.** 4 **9.** $162, 243, 364.5$ **11.** $2058; 14,406; 100,842$
13. $\frac{5}{32}, \frac{5}{128}, \frac{5}{512}$ **15.** 0.0000000001, or 1×10^{-10} **17.** $80; 160$ **19.** $\frac{1}{3}$
21. $\frac{1}{7}; \frac{1}{49}$ **23.** $6; -48$ **25.** 4913
27. yes; $\frac{1}{3}$ **29.** no **31.** no
33a. 1.28 cm **33b.** 40.96 cm
35. $-2, -8, -32, -128$ **37.** $2, 4, 8, 16$ **39.** $12, 3, \frac{3}{4}, \frac{3}{16}$
41a. Stage 0:

Stage 1:

Stage 2:

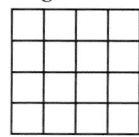

Stage 3:

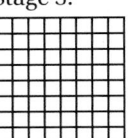

41b.

Stage	Squares
0	1
1	4
2	16
3	64

41c. yes; $r = 4$ **41d.** $a_n = 4(4)^{n-1}$, or 4^n **43a.** $\$3993$; $\$4392.30$ **43b.** 1.1
43c. $\$2727.27$; divide tuition 3 years ago ($\$3000$) by 1.1 (the common ratio) **45.** D **47.** x^4, x^5, x^6
49. $1, y, y^2$ **51.** -400 **53.** the 7th term **55.** $b > 10$ **57.** $c < -\frac{1}{3}$
59.

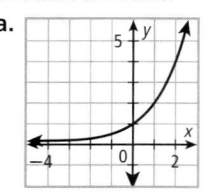

$y > 6 - 3x$

61. $1, \frac{1}{3}$ **63.** $4, -7$
65. $\approx 0.35, \approx -4.35$

11-7

Check It Out! 1. 3.375 in. **2a.** No; as the x-values change by a constant amount, the y-values are not multiplied by a constant amount. **2b.** Yes; as the x-values change by a constant amount, the y-values are multiplied by a constant amount.
3a.

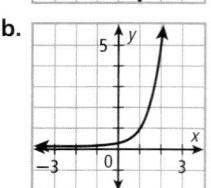

3b.

4a.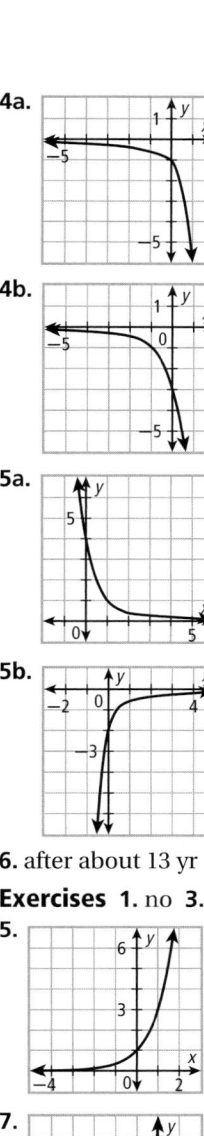

4b.

5a.

5b.

6. after about 13 yr

Exercises 1. no **3.** no

5.

7.

9.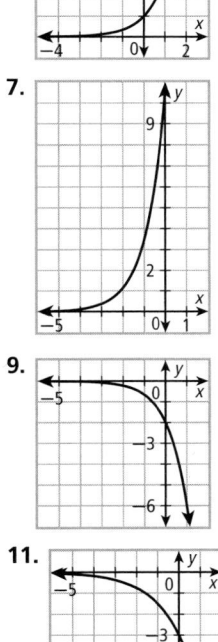

11.

13.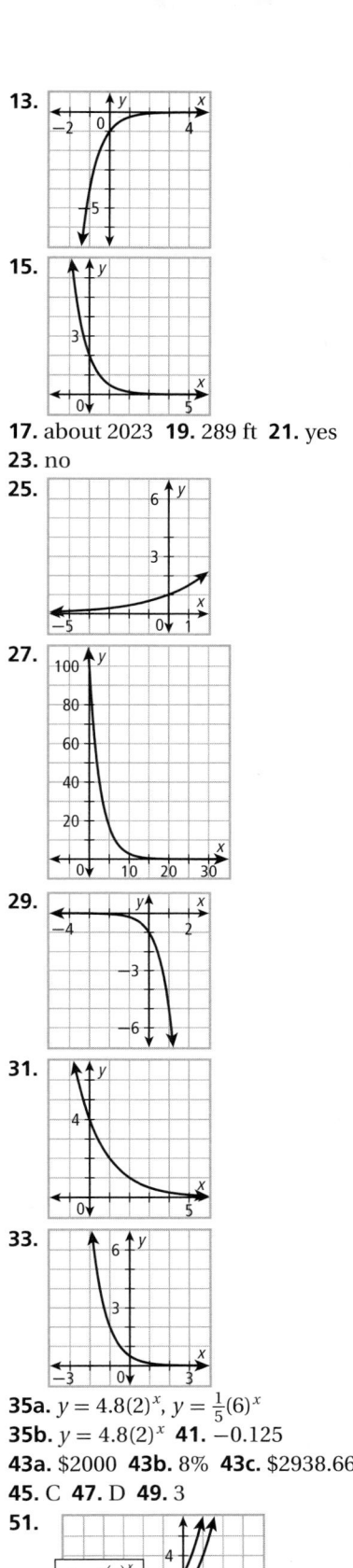

15.

17. about 2023 **19.** 289 ft **21.** yes
23. no

25.

27.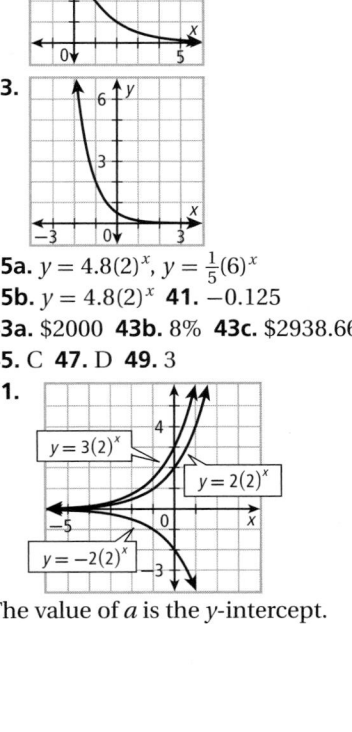

29.

31.

33.

35a. $y = 4.8(2)^x$, $y = \frac{1}{5}(6)^x$
35b. $y = 4.8(2)^x$ **41.** -0.125
43a. $2000 **43b.** 8% **43c.** $2938.66
45. C **47.** D **49.** 3
51.

The value of a is the y-intercept.

53. 25 **55.** $9x^2$

11-8

Check It Out! 1. $y = 1200(1.08)^t$;
$1904.25 **2a.** $A = 1200(1.00875)^{4t}$;
$1379.49 **2b.** $A = 4000(1.0025)^{12t}$;
$5083.47 **3.** $y = 48,000(0.97)^t$;
38,783 **4a.** 1.5625 mg **4b.** 0.78125 g

Exercises 1. exponential growth
3. $y = 300(1.08)^t$; 441 **5.** $A = 4200$
$(1.007)^{4t}$; $4965.43 **7.** $y = 10(0.84)^t$;
4.98 mg **9.** 5.5 g **11.** $y = 1600$
$(1.03)^t$; 2150 **13.** $A = 30(1.078)^t$;
47 members **15.** $A = 7000$
$(1.0075)^{4t}$; $9438.44 **17.** $A = 12,000$
$(1.026)^t$; $17,635.66 **19.** $y = 58(0.9)^t$;
$24.97 **21.** growth; 61% **23.** decay;
$33\frac{1}{3}$% **25.** growth; 10% **27.** growth;
25% **29.** $y = 58,000,000(1.001)^t$;
58,174,174 **31.** $y = 8200(0.98)^t$;
$7118.63 **33.** $y = 970(1.012)^t$;
1030 **35.** B **37.** 18 yr **39.** A; B

41.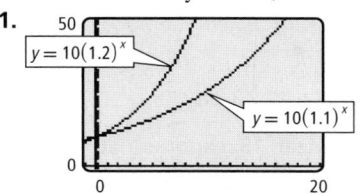

The graph when r is 20% rises faster
than when r is 10%. The greater the
value of r, the faster the graph will
rise. **45.** D **47.** D **49.** about 20 yr
51. 100 min, or 1 h 40 min
53. $225,344 **55.** 16 ft **57.** x^{20}
59. $p^6 q^{16}$

11-9

Check It Out!
1a.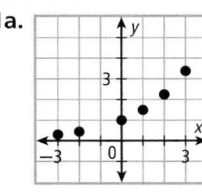

exponential

1b.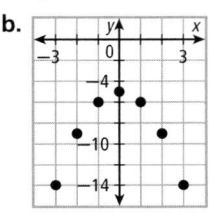

quadratic

2. quadratic **3.** The oven
temperature decreases by 50°F
every 10 min; $y = -5x + 375$; 75°F

Exercises

1.

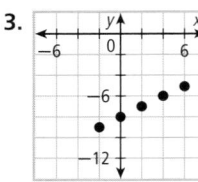

exponential

3.

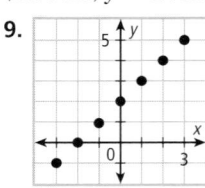

linear

5. exponential **7.** Grapes cost $1.79/lb; $y = 1.79x$; $10.74

9.

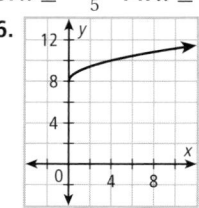

linear

11. linear **13.** exponential **15.** $\ell = 6k$; linear **17.** linear **19.** $y = 0.2(4)^x$
21. linear **27.** C **29.** C **33.** 6 **35.** 3
37. 11 **39.** 25 **41.** 0 **43.** $2\sqrt{6}$ **45.** $\frac{\sqrt{3}}{3}$
47. x^2 **49.** $11\sqrt{2}$

Study Guide: Review

1. square-root function **2.** exponential decay **3.** common ratio
4. exponential function **5.** 4.74 cm
6. $x \geq 0$ **7.** $x \geq -4$ **8.** $x \geq 0$ **9.** $x \geq -2$
10. $x \geq \frac{4}{3}$ **11.** $x \geq -3$ **12.** $x \geq \frac{7}{2}$
13. $x \geq -\frac{18}{5}$ **14.** $x \geq \frac{3}{4}$ **15.** $x \geq 1$

16.

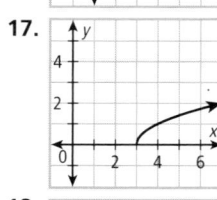

17.

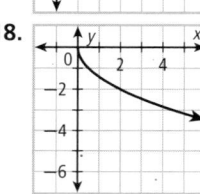

18.

19.

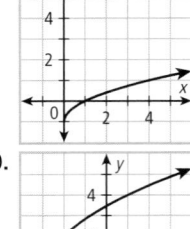

20.

21.

22.

23.

24.

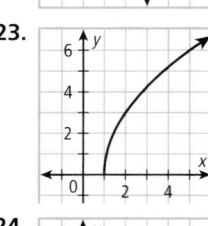

25.

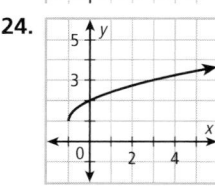

26. 11 **27.** n^2 **28.** $x + 3$ **29.** 5
30. $6d$ **31.** $y^3\sqrt{x}$ **32.** $2\sqrt{3}$
33. $4b^2\sqrt{2ab}$ **34.** $\frac{\sqrt{5}}{2}$ **35.** $\frac{t}{10}$ **36.** $\frac{2}{3}$
37. $\frac{4p^2\sqrt{2}}{7}$ **38.** $\frac{t^4\sqrt{t}}{s}$ **39.** $\frac{2b^3\sqrt{2}}{5}$
40. $9\sqrt{7}$ **41.** $3\sqrt{3}$ **42.** $3\sqrt{2} + 2\sqrt{3}$
43. $\sqrt{5t}$ **44.** $2\sqrt{2}$ **45.** $2\sqrt{3} + 2\sqrt{5}$
46. $-2\sqrt{5x}$ **47.** $10\sqrt{6}$ **48.** $\sqrt{14}$
49. $6\sqrt{7x}$ **50.** $4\sqrt{2} - 4$
51. $71 + 16\sqrt{7}$ **52.** $\frac{4\sqrt{5}}{5}$ **53.** $\frac{3a\sqrt{2}}{2}$
54. $\frac{\sqrt{3}}{3}$ **55.** $\frac{\sqrt{10n}}{2n}$ **56.** $x = 64$ **57.** $x = 8$
58. $x = 3$ **59.** $x = 25$ **60.** $x = -81$
61. $x = 100$ **62.** $x = 3$ **63.** $\varnothing$

64. $x = 4$ **65.** $x = 6$ **66.** $x = 7$
67. $x = \frac{19}{2}$ **68.** $x = 12$ **69.** $x = 3$
70. $x = 4$ **71.** $x = 5$ **72.** 81, 243, 729
73. 48, −96, 192 **74.** 5, 2.5, 1.25
75. −256, −1024, −4096
76. 7,812,500 **77.** 19,131,876
78. Yes; as the x-values change by a constant amount, the y-values are multiplied by a constant amount. **79.** No; as the x-values change by a constant amount, the y-values are not multiplied by a constant amount.

80.

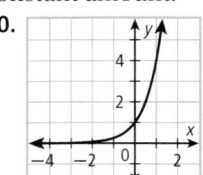

81.

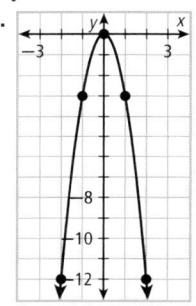

82. $y = 9(1.15)^t$; 24
83. $y = 24,500(0.96)^t$; 3182

84.

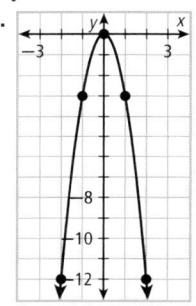

quadratic

85.

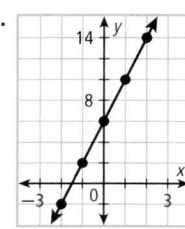

linear

86.

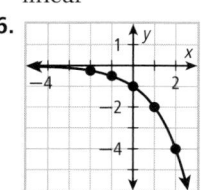

exponential
87. exponential **88.** quadratic
89. linear **90.** $y = 1.5x$; 15 h

Glossary/Glosario

A

ENGLISH	SPANISH	EXAMPLES
absolute value (p. 14) The absolute value of x is the distance from zero to x on the number line, denoted $\lvert x \rvert$. $\lvert x \rvert = \begin{cases} x & \text{if } x \geq 0 \\ -x & \text{if } x < 0 \end{cases}$	**valor absoluto** El valor absoluto de x es la distancia de cero a x en la recta numérica, y se expresa $\lvert x \rvert$. $\lvert x \rvert = \begin{cases} x & \text{si } x \geq 0 \\ -x & \text{si } x < 0 \end{cases}$	$\lvert 3 \rvert = 3$ $\lvert -3 \rvert = 3$
absolute-value equation (p. 114) An equation that contains a variable within an absolute value.	**ecuación de valor absoluto** Ecuación que contiene una variable dentro de un valor absoluto.	$\lvert x + 4 \rvert = 7$
absolute-value inequality (p. 178) An inequality that contains a variable within an absolute value.	**desigualdad de valor absoluto** Desigualdad que contiene una variable dentro de un valor absoluto.	$\lvert x + 4 \rvert > 7$
acute angle (p. SB63) An angle that measures greater than 0° and less than 90°.	**ángulo agudo** Ángulo que mide más de 0° y menos de 90°.	
acute triangle (p. SB18) A triangle with three acute angles.	**triángulo acutángulo** Triángulo con tres ángulos agudos.	
Addition Property of Equality (p. 72) For real numbers a, b, and c, if $a = b$, then $a + c = b + c$.	**Propiedad de igualdad de la suma** Dados los números reales a, b y c, si $a = b$, entonces $a + c = b + c$.	$\begin{aligned} x - 6 &= 8 \\ \underline{+6} \quad &\underline{+6} \\ x \quad &= 14 \end{aligned}$
Addition Property of Inequality (p. 142) For real numbers a, b, and c, if $a < b$, then $a + c < b + c$. Also holds true for $>$, $\leq$, $\geq$, and $\neq$.	**Propiedad de desigualdad de la suma** Dados los números reales a, b y c, si $a < b$, entonces $a + c < b + c$. Es válido también para $>$, $\leq$, $\geq$ y $\neq$.	$\begin{aligned} x - 6 &< 8 \\ \underline{+6} \quad &\underline{+6} \\ x \quad &< 14 \end{aligned}$
additive inverse (p. 15) The opposite of a number. Two numbers are additive inverses if their sum is zero. *See also* opposite.	**inverso aditivo** El opuesto de un número. Dos números son inversos aditivos si su suma es cero. *Ver tambien* opuesto.	The additive inverse of 5 is −5. The additive inverse of −5 is 5.
algebraic expression (p. 6) An expression that contains at least one variable.	**expresión algebraica** Expresión que contiene por lo menos una variable.	$2x + 3y$ $4x$
algebraic order of operations *See* order of operations.	**orden algebraico de las operaciones** *Ver* orden de las operaciones.	
AND (p. 170) A logical operator representing the intersection of two sets.	**Y** Operador lógico que representa la intersección de dos conjuntos.	$A = \{2, 3, 4, 5\}$ $B = \{1, 3, 5, 7\}$ The set of values that are in A AND B is $A \cap B = \{3, 5\}$.

ENGLISH	SPANISH	EXAMPLES
angle (p. SB14) A figure formed by two rays with a common endpoint.	**ángulo** Figura formada por dos rayos con un extremo común.	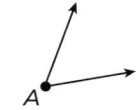
area (p. SB16) The number of nonoverlapping unit squares of a given size that will exactly cover the interior of a plane figure.	**área** Cantidad de cuadrados unitarios de un determinado tamaño no superpuestos que cubren exactamente el interior de una figura plana.	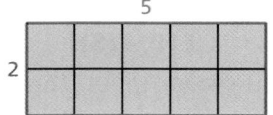 The area is 10 square units.
arithmetic sequence (p. 234) A sequence whose successive terms differ by the same nonzero constant d, called the *common difference*.	**sucesión aritmética** Sucesión cuyos términos sucesivos difieren en la misma constante distinto de cero d, denominado *diferencia común*.	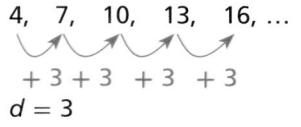
Associative Property of Addition (p. 42) For all real numbers a, b, and c, $(a + b) + c = a + (b + c)$.	**Propiedad asociativa de la suma** Dados tres números reales cualesquiera a, b y c, $(a + b) + c = a + (b + c)$.	$(5 + 3) + 7 = 5 + (3 + 7)$
Associative Property of Multiplication (p. 42) For all real numbers a, b, and c, $(a \cdot b) \cdot c = a \cdot (b \cdot c)$.	**Propiedad asociativa de la multiplicación** Dados tres números reales cualesquiera a, b y c, $(a \cdot b) \cdot c = a \cdot (b \cdot c)$.	$(5 \cdot 3) \cdot 7 = 5 \cdot (3 \cdot 7)$
asymptote (p. 634) A line that a graph gets closer to as the value of a variable becomes extremely large or small.	**asíntota** Línea recta a la cual se aproxima una gráfica a medida que el valor de una variable se hace sumamente grande o pequeño.	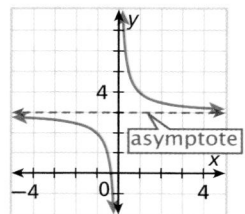
average *See* mean.	**promedio** *Ver* media.	
axis of the coordinate plane (p. SB23) One of two perpendicular number lines, called the x-axis and the y-axis, used to define the location of a point in the coordinate plane.	**eje del plano cartesiano** Una de las dos rectas numéricas perpendiculares, denominadas eje x y eje y, utilizadas para definir la ubicación de un punto en el plano cartesiano.	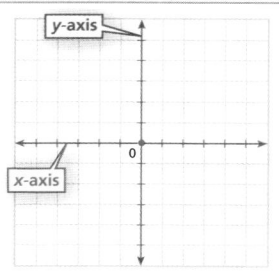
axis of symmetry (p. 554) A line that divides a plane figure or a graph into two congruent reflected halves.	**eje de simetría** Línea que divide una figura plana o una gráfica en dos mitades reflejadas congruentes.	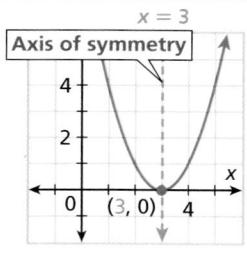

ENGLISH	SPANISH	EXAMPLES
bar graph (p. SB27) A graph that uses vertical or horizontal bars to display data.	**gráfica de barras** Gráfica con barras horizontales o verticales para mostrar datos.	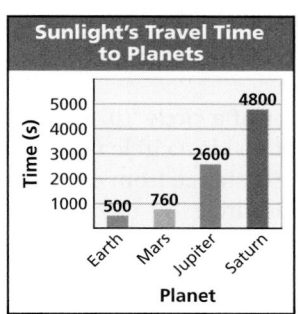
base of an exponential function (p. 738) The value of b in a function of the form $f(x) = ab^x$, where a and b are real numbers with $a \neq 0$, $b > 0$, and $b \neq 1$.	**base de una función exponencial** Valor de b en una función del tipo $f(x) = ab^x$, donde a y b son números reales con $a \neq 0$, $b > 0$ y $b \neq 1$.	In the function $f(x) = 5(2)^x$, the base is 2.
base of a power (p. 26) The number in a power that is used as a factor.	**base de una potencia** Número de una potencia que se utiliza como factor.	$3^4 = 3 \cdot 3 \cdot 3 \cdot 3 = 81$ 3 is the base.
bias (p. SB26) An error that favors part of a population and/or does not accurately represent the population.	**muestra no representativa** Error que favorece a una parte de una población y/o no representa con exactitud a la población.	To find out about the exercise habits of average Americans, a fitness magazine surveyed its readers about how often they exercise. The population is all Americans and the sample is readers of the fitness magazine. This sample will likely be biased because readers of fitness magazines may exercise more often than other people do.
binomial (p. 431) A polynomial with two terms.	**binomio** Polinomio con dos términos.	$x + y$ $2a^2 + 3$ $4m^3n^2 + 6mn^4$
boundary line (p. 364) A line that divides the coordinate plane into two half-planes.	**línea de límite** Línea que divide el plano cartesiano en dos semiplanos.	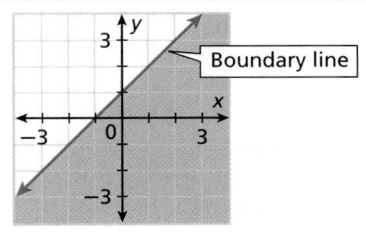
box-and-whisker plot (p. SB27) A method of showing how data is distributed by using the median, quartiles, and extreme values; also called a *box plot*.	**gráfica de mediana y rango** Método para mostrar la distribución de datos utilizando la mediana, los cuartiles y los valores extremos; también llamado *gráfica de caja*.	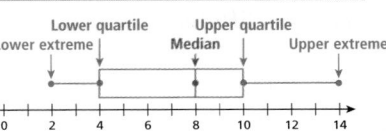

ENGLISH	SPANISH	EXAMPLES
Cartesian coordinate system *See* coordinate plane.	**sistema de coordenadas cartesianas** *Ver* plano cartesiano.	
center of a circle (p. SB17) The point inside a circle that is the same distance from every point on the circle.	**centro de un círculo** Punto dentro de un círculo que se encuentra a la misma distancia de todos los puntos del círculo.	*A*
circle (p. SB17) The set of points in a plane that are a fixed distance from a given point called the center of the circle.	**círculo** Conjunto de puntos en un plano que se encuentran a una distancia fija de un punto determinado denominado centro del círculo.	
circle graph (p. SB28) A way to display data by using a circle divided into non-overlapping sectors.	**gráfica circular** Forma de mostrar datos mediante un círculo dividido en sectores no superpuestos.	**Residents of Mesa, AZ** 65+ 13%, 45–64 19%, Under 18 27%, 18–24 11%, 25–44 30%
circumference (p. SB17) The distance around a circle.	**circunferencia** Distancia alrededor de un círculo.	Circumference
closure (p. 44) A set of numbers is said to be closed, or to have closure, under a given operation if the result of the operation on any two numbers in the set is also in the set.	**cerradura** Se dice que un conjunto de números es cerrado, o tiene cerradura, respecto de una operación determinada, si el resultado de la operación entre dos números cualesquiera del conjunto también está en el conjunto.	The set of integers is closed under addition because the sum of any two integers is also an integer. The set of whole numbers is not closed under subtraction because the difference of any two whole numbers may not be another whole number; for example, $2 - 4 = -2$.
coefficient (p. 49) A number multiplied by a variable.	**coeficiente** Número multiplicado por una variable.	In the expression $2x + 3y$, 2 is the coefficient of x and 3 is the coefficient of y.
commission (p. SB10) Money paid to a person or company for making a sale, usually a percent of the sale amount.	**comisión** Dinero que se paga a una persona o empresa por realizar una venta; generalmente se trata de un porcentaje del total de la venta.	
common difference (p. 234) In an arithmetic sequence, the nonzero constant difference of any term and the previous term.	**diferencia común** En una sucesión aritmética, diferencia constante distinta de cero entre cualquier término y el término anterior.	In the arithmetic sequence 3, 5, 7, 9, 11, …, the common difference is 2.
common factor (p. 479) A factor that is common to all terms of an expression or to two or more expressions.	**factor común** Factor que es común a todos los términos de una expresión o a dos o más expresiones.	Expression: $4x^2 + 16x^3 - 8x$ Common factor: $4x$ Expressions: 12 and 18 Common factors: 2, 3, and 6

Glossary/Glosario

ENGLISH	SPANISH	EXAMPLES
common ratio (p. 732) In a geometric sequence, the constant ratio of any term and the previous term.	**razón común** En una sucesión geométrica, la razón constante entre cualquier término y el término anterior.	In the geometric sequence 32, 16, 8, 4, 2, . . ., the common ratio is $\frac{1}{2}$.
Commutative Property of Addition (p. 46) For any two real numbers a and b, $a + b = b + a$.	**Propiedad conmutativa de la suma** Dados dos números reales cualesquiera a y b, $a + b = b + a$.	$3 + 4 = 4 + 3 = 7$
Commutative Property of Multiplication (p. 46) For any two real numbers a and b, $a \cdot b = b \cdot a$.	**Propiedad conmutativa de la multiplicación** Dados dos números reales cualesquiera a y b, $a \cdot b = b \cdot a$.	$3 \cdot 4 = 4 \cdot 3 = 12$
complementary angles (p. SB14) Two angles whose measures have a sum of 90°.	**ángulos complementarios** Dos ángulos cuyas medidas suman 90°.	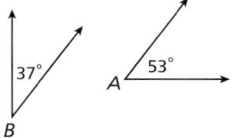
complement of an event (p. SB29) The set of all outcomes that are not the event.	**complemento de un suceso** El conjunto de todos los resultados que no están en el suceso.	In the experiment of rolling a number cube, the complement of rolling a 3 is rolling a 1, 2, 4, 5, or 6.
completing the square (p. 591) A process used to form a perfect-square trinomial. To complete the square of $x^2 + bx$, add $\left(\frac{b}{2}\right)^2$.	**completar el cuadrado** Proceso utilizado para formar un trinomio cuadrado perfecto. Para completar el cuadrado de $x^2 + bx$, hay que sumar $\left(\frac{b}{2}\right)^2$.	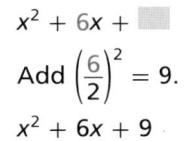 $x^2 + 6x + $ ▨ Add $\left(\frac{6}{2}\right)^2 = 9$. $x^2 + 6x + 9$
composite figure (p. 78) A plane figure made up of triangles, rectangles, trapezoids, circles, and other simple shapes, or a three-dimensional figure made up of prisms, cones, pyramids, cylinders, and other simple three-dimensional figures.	**figura compuesta** Figura plana compuesta por triángulos, rectángulos, trapecios, círculos y otras figuras simples, o figura tridimensional compuesta por prismas, conos, pirámides, cilindros y otras figuras tridimensionales simples.	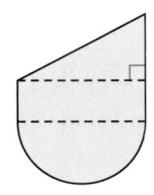
composite number (p. SB5) A whole number greater than 1 with more than two positive factors.	**número compuesto** Número cabal mayor que 1 que tiene más de dos factores positivos.	4, 6, 8, and 9 are composite numbers.
compound event (p. SB32) An event made up of two or more simple events.	**suceso compuesto** Suceso formado por dos o más sucesos simples.	In the experiment of tossing a coin and rolling a number cube, the event of the coin showing heads and the number cube showing 3 is a compound event.
compound inequality (p. 170) Two inequalities that are combined into one statement by the word *and* or *or*.	**desigualdad compuesta** Dos desigualdades unidas en un enunciado por la palabra *y* u *o*.	$x \geq 2$ AND $x < 7$ (also written $2 \leq x < 7$) $x < 2$ OR $x > 6$

ENGLISH	SPANISH	EXAMPLES
compound interest (p. 748) Interest earned or paid on both the principal and previously earned interest. The formula for compound interest is $A = P\left(1 + \frac{r}{n}\right)^{nt}$, where A is the final amount, P is the principal, r is the interest rate expressed as a decimal, n is the number of times interest is compounded, and t is the time.	**interés compuesto** Intereses ganados o pagados sobre el capital y los intereses ya devengados. La fórmula de interés compuesto es $A = P\left(1 + \frac{r}{n}\right)^{nt}$, donde A es la cantidad final, P es el capital, r es la tasa de interés expresada como un decimal, n es la cantidad de veces que se capitaliza el interés y t es el tiempo.	If \$100 is put into an account with an interest rate of 5% compounded monthly, then after 2 years, the account will have $100\left(1 + \frac{0.05}{12}\right)^{12 \cdot 2} = \$110.49$.
compound statement (p. 170) Two statements that are connected by the word *and* or *or*.	**enunciado compuesto** Dos enunciados unidos por la palabra *y* u *o*.	The sky is blue and the grass is green. I will drive to school or I will take the bus.
conclusion (p. 38) The part of a conditional statement following the word *then*.	**conclusión** Parte de un enunciado condicional que sigue a la palabra *entonces*.	If $x + 1 = 5$, then $\underline{x = 4}$. Conclusion
conditional statement (p. 38) A statement that can be written in "if-then" form.	**enunciado condicional** Enunciado que se puede expresar como "si p, entonces q."	If $x + 1 = 5$, then $x = 4$.
cone (p. SB20) A three-dimensional figure with a circular base lying in one plane plus a vertex not lying in that plane. The remaining surface of the cone is formed by joining the vertex to points on the circle by line segments.	**cono** Figura tridimensional con una base circular que está en un plano, más un vértice que no está en ese plano. El resto de la superficie del cono se forma uniendo el vértice con los puntos del círculo por medio de segmentos de recta.	
congruent (p. SB19) Having the same size and shape, denoted by $\cong$.	**congruente** Que tiene el mismo tamaño y la misma forma, expresado por $\cong$.	$\overline{PQ} \cong \overline{RS}$
congruent angles (p. SB19) Angles that have the same measure.	**ángulos congruentes** Ángulos que tienen la misma medida.	$\angle ABC \cong \angle DEF$
congruent segments (p. SB19) Segments that have the same length.	**segmentos congruentes** Segmentos que tienen la misma longitud.	$\overline{PQ} \cong \overline{SR}$
conjecture (p. 233) A statement that is believed to be true.	**conjetura** Enunciado que se supone verdadero.	A sequence begins with the terms 2, 4, 6, 8, 10. A reasonable conjecture is that the next term in the sequence is 12.
conjugate of an irrational number (p. 721) The conjugate of a number in the form $a + \sqrt{b}$ is $a - \sqrt{b}$.	**conjugado de un número irracional** El conjugado de un número en la forma $a + \sqrt{b}$ es $a - \sqrt{b}$.	The conjugate of $1 + \sqrt{2}$ is $1 - \sqrt{2}$.

ENGLISH	SPANISH	EXAMPLES
consistent system (p. 350) A system of equations or inequalities that has at least one solution.	**sistema consistente** Sistema de ecuaciones o desigualdades que tiene por lo menos una solución.	$\begin{cases} x + y = 6 \\ x - y = 4 \end{cases}$ solution: $(5, 1)$
constant (p. 6) A value that does not change.	**constante** Valor que no cambia.	$3, 0, \pi$
constant of variation (p. 282) The constant k in direct and inverse variation equations.	**constante de variación** La constante k en ecuaciones de variación directa e inversa.	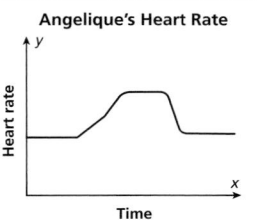
continuous graph (p. 201) A graph made up of connected lines or curves.	**gráfica continua** Gráfica compuesta por líneas rectas o curvas conectadas.	**Angelique's Heart Rate**
contradiction (p. 484) Two statements that cannot both be true at the same time.	**contradicción** Dos enunciados que no pueden ser verdaderos al mismo tiempo.	$x + 1 = 2$ $x + 1 = 0$
converse of a conditional statement (p. 39) The statement formed by exchanging the hypothesis and conclusion of a conditional statement.	**recíproco de enunciado condicional** Enunciado que se forma intercambiando la hipótesis y la conclusión de un enunciado condicional.	Statement: If $n + 1 = 3$, then $n = 2$. Converse: If $n = 2$, then $n + 1 = 3$.
coordinate (p. SB23) A number used to identify the location of a point. On a number line, one coordinate is used. In the coordinate plane, two coordinates — called the x-coordinate and the y-coordinate — are used.	**coordenada** Número utilizado para identificar la ubicación de un punto. En una recta numérica se utiliza una coordenada. En el plano cartesiano se utilizan dos coordenadas, denominadas coordenada x y coordenada y.	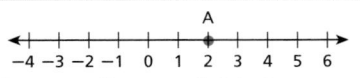 The coordinate of A is 2. 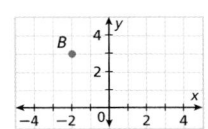 The coordinates of B are $(-2, 3)$.
coordinate plane (p. SB23) A plane that is divided into four regions by a horizontal line called the x-axis and a vertical line called the y-axis.	**plano cartesiano** Plano dividido en cuatro regiones por una línea horizontal denominada eje x y una línea vertical denominada eje y.	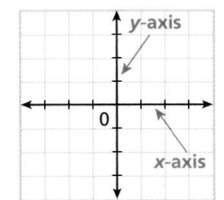
correlation (p. 224) A measure of the strength and direction of the relationship between two variables or data sets.	**correlación** Medida de la fuerza y dirección de la relación entre dos variables o conjuntos de datos.	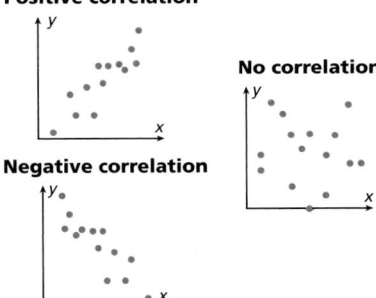

ENGLISH	SPANISH	EXAMPLES
corresponding angles of polygons (p. SB19) Angles in the same position in two different polygons that have the same number of angles.	**ángulos correspondientes de los polígonos** Ángulos que tienen la misma posición relativa en dos polígonos diferentes que tienen el mismo número de ángulos.	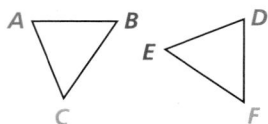 ∠A and ∠D are corresponding angles.
corresponding sides of polygons (p. SB19) Sides in the same position in two different polygons that have the same number of sides.	**lados correspondientes de los polígonos** Lados que tienen la misma posición en dos polígonos diferentes que tienen el mismo número de lados.	$\overline{AB}$ and $\overline{DE}$ are corresponding sides.
counterexample (p. 43) An example that proves that a conjecture or statement is false.	**contraejemplo** Ejemplo que demuestra que una conjetura o enunciado es falso.	15 is a counterexample to the statement that all odd numbers are prime, because 15 is odd but not prime.
Cross Product Property (p. 103) For any real numbers a, b, c, and d, where $b \neq 0$ and $d \neq 0$, if $\frac{a}{b} = \frac{c}{d}$, then $ad = bc$.	**Propiedad de productos cruzados** Dados los números reales a, b, c y d, donde $b \neq 0$ y $d \neq 0$, si $\frac{a}{b} = \frac{c}{d}$, entonces $ad = bc$.	If $\frac{4}{6} = \frac{10}{x}$, then $4x = 60$, so $x = 15$.
cross products (p. 103) In the statement $\frac{a}{b} = \frac{c}{d}$, bc and ad are the cross products.	**productos cruzados** En el enunciado $\frac{a}{b} = \frac{c}{d}$, bc y ad son productos cruzados.	$\frac{1}{2} = \frac{3}{6}$ Cross products: $2 \cdot 3 = 6$ and $1 \cdot 6 = 6$
cube (p. SB20) A prism with six square faces.	**cubo** Prisma con seis caras cuadradas.	
cube in numeration (p. 26) The third power of a number.	**cubo en numeración** Tercera potencia de un número.	8 is the cube of 2 because $2^3 = 8$
cube root (p. 32) A number, written as $\sqrt[3]{x}$, whose cube is x.	**raíz cúbica** Número, expresado como $\sqrt[3]{x}$, cuyo cubo es x.	$\sqrt[3]{64} = 4$, because $4^3 = 64$; 4 is the cube root of 64.
cubic function (p. SB12) A function in which the greatest power of any variable term is 3.	**función cúbica** Función en la que la mayor potencia de cualquier variable es 3.	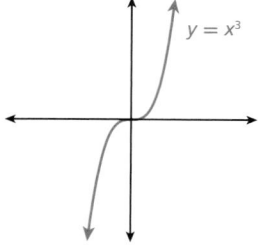 $y = x^3$
cubic polynomial (p. 431) A polynomial of degree 3.	**polinomio cúbico** Polinomio de grado 3.	$x^3 + 4x^2 - 6x + 2$
customary system of measurement (p. SB13) The system of measurement often used in the United States.	**sistema usual de medidas** El system de medidas que se usa comúnmente en Estados Unidos.	inches, feet, miles, ounces, pounds, tons, cups, quarts, gallons
cylinder (p. SB20) A three-dimensional figure with two parallel congruent circular bases. The third surface of the cylinder consists of all parallel circles of the same radius whose centers lie on the segment joining the centers of the bases.	**cilindro** Figura tridimensional con dos bases circulares paralelas y congruentes. La tercera superficie del cilindro consiste en todos los círculos paralelos del mismo radio cuyo centro está en el segmento que une los centros de la bases.	

ENGLISH	SPANISH	EXAMPLES
data (p. SB26) Information gathered from a survey or experiment.	**datos** Información reunida en una encuesta o experimento.	
deductive reasoning (p. 99) The process of using logic to draw conclusions.	**razonamiento deductivo** Proceso en el que se utiliza la lógica parar sacar conclusions.	
degree of a monomial (p. 430) The sum of the exponents of the variables in the monomial.	**grado de un monomio** Suma de los exponentes de las variables del monomio.	$4x^2y^5z^3$ Degree: $2 + 5 + 3 = 10$ $5 = 5x^0$ Degree: 0
degree of a polynomial (p. 430) The degree of the term of the polynomial with the greatest degree.	**grado de un polinomio** Grado del término del polinomio con el grado máximo.	$3x^2y^2 + 4xy^5 - 12x^3y^2$ ↑ ↑ ↑ Degree 4 Degree 6 Degree 5 Degree 6
dependent events (p. SB31) Events for which the occurrence or nonoccurrence of one event affects the probability of the other event.	**sucesos dependientes** Dos sucesos son dependientes si el hecho de que uno de ellos ocurra o no afecta la probabilidad del otro suceso.	From a bag containing 3 red marbles and 2 blue marbles, drawing a red marble, and then drawing a blue marble without replacing the first marble are dependent events.
dependent system (p. 351) A system of equations that has infinitely many solutions.	**sistema dependiente** Sistema de ecuaciones que tiene infinitamente muchas soluciones.	$\begin{cases} x + y = 2 \\ 2x + 2y = 4 \end{cases}$
dependent variable (p. 216) A variable whose value depends on the value of a variable called the independent variable.	**variable dependiente** Variable cuyo valor depende del valor de una variable llamada variable independiente.	A math tutor charges \$35 per hour. In this situation, the total fee is the dependent variable. It depends on the number of tutoring hours.
diameter (p. SB17) A segment that has endpoints on a circle and that passes through the center of the circle; also the length of that segment.	**diámetro** Segmento que atraviesa el centro de un círculo y cuyos extremos están sobre la circunferencia; longitud de dicho segmento.	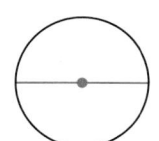
difference of two cubes (p. 520) A polynomial of the form $a^3 - b^3$, which may be written as the product $(a - b)(a^2 + ab + b^2)$.	**diferencia de dos cubos** Polinomio del tipo $a^3 - b^3$, que se puede expresar como el producto $(a - b)(a^2 + ab + b^2)$.	$x^3 - 8 = (x - 2)(x^2 + 2x + 4)$
difference of two squares (p. 457) A polynomial of the form $a^2 - b^2$, which may be written as the product $(a + b)(a - b)$.	**diferencia de dos cuadrados** Polinomio del tipo $a^2 - b^2$, que se puede expresar como el producto $(a + b)(a - b)$.	$x^2 - 4 = (x + 2)(x - 2)$

Glossary/Glosario

ENGLISH	SPANISH	EXAMPLES
direct variation (p. 282) A linear relationship between two variables, x and y, that can be written in the form $y = kx$, where k is a nonzero constant.	**variación directa** Relación lineal entre dos variables, x e y, que puede expresarse en la forma $y = kx$, donde k es una constante distinta de cero.	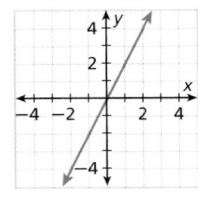 $y = 2x$
discontinuous function (p. 634) A function whose graph has one or more jumps, breaks, or holes.	**función discontinua** Función cuya gráfica tiene uno o más saltos, interrupciones u hoyos.	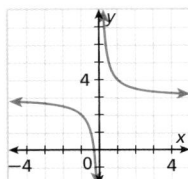
discount (p. SB10) An amount by which an original price is reduced.	**descuento** Cantidad por la que se reduce un precio original.	
discrete graph (p. 201) A graph made up of unconnected points.	**gráfica discreta** Gráfica compuesta de puntos no conectados.	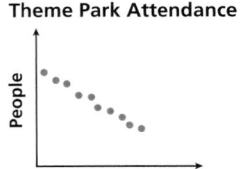
discriminant (p. 605) The discriminant of the quadratic equation $ax^2 + bx + c = 0$ is $b^2 - 4ac$.	**discriminante** El discriminante de la ecuación cuadrática $ax^2 + bx + c = 0$ es $b^2 - 4ac$.	The discriminant of $2x^2 - 5x - 3$ is $(-5)^2 - 4(2)(-3)$ or 49.
Distance Formula (p. 588) In the coordinate plane, the distance from (x_1, y_1) to (x_2, y_2) is $d = \sqrt{(x_2 - x_1)^2 + (y_2 - y_1)^2}$.	**Fórmula de distancia** En el plano cartesiano, la distancia desde (x_1, y_1) hasta (x_2, y_2) es $d = \sqrt{(x_2 - x_1)^2 + (y_2 - y_1)^2}$.	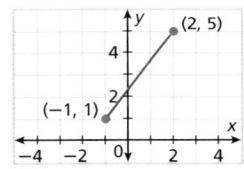 The distance from $(2, 5)$ to $(-1, 1)$ is $d = \sqrt{(-1-2)^2 + (1-5)^2}$ $= \sqrt{(-3)^2 + (-4)^2}$ $= \sqrt{9 + 16} = \sqrt{25} = 5$.
Distributive Property (p. 47) For all real numbers a, b, and c, $a(b + c) = ab + ac$, and $(b + c)a = ba + ca$.	**Propiedad distributiva** Dados los números reales a, b y c, $a(b + c) = ab + ac$, y : $(b + c)a = ba + ca$.	$3(4 + 5) = 3 \cdot 4 + 3 \cdot 5$ $(4 + 5)3 = 4 \cdot 3 + 5 \cdot 3$
Division Property of Equality (p. 73) For real numbers a, b, and c, where $c \neq 0$, if $a = b$, then $\frac{a}{c} = \frac{b}{c}$.	**Propiedad de igualdad de la división** Dados los números reales a, b y c, donde $c \neq 0$, si $a = b$, entonces $\frac{a}{c} = \frac{b}{c}$.	$4x = 12$ $\frac{4x}{4} = \frac{12}{4}$ $x = 3$

Glossary/Glosario

ENGLISH	SPANISH	EXAMPLES
Division Property of Inequality (p. 148) For real numbers a, b, and c, where $c > 0$, if $a < b$, then $\frac{a}{c} < \frac{b}{c}$. For real numbers a, b, and c, where $c < 0$, if $a < b$, then $\frac{a}{c} > \frac{b}{c}$. Also holds true for $>$, $\leq$, $\geq$, and $\neq$.	**Propiedad de desigualdad de la división** Dados los números reales a, b, y c, donde $c > 0$, si $a < b$, entonces $\frac{a}{c} < \frac{b}{c}$. Dados los números reales a, b, y c, donde $c < 0$, si $a < b$, entonces $\frac{a}{c} > \frac{b}{c}$. Es válido también para $>$, $\leq$, $\geq$, y $\neq$.	$4x \geq 12$ $\frac{4x}{4} \geq \frac{12}{4}$ $x \geq 3$ $-4x \geq 12$ $\frac{4x}{-4} \leq \frac{12}{-4}$ $x \leq -3$
domain (p. 206) The set of all first coordinates (or x-values) of a relation or function.	**dominio** Conjunto de todos los valores de la primera coordenada (o valores de x) de una función o relación.	The domain of the function $f(x) = \sqrt{x}$ is $x \geq 0$.

 E

ENGLISH	SPANISH	EXAMPLES
edge (p. SB20) A segment that is the intersection of two faces of a polyhedron.	**artista** Segmento que constituye la intersección de dos caras de un poliedro.	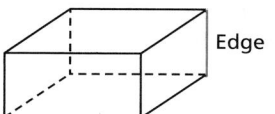 Edge
element (p. 76) Each member in a set.	**elemento** Cada miembro en un conjunto.	For the set {1, 3, 6, 9}, the elements are 1, 3, 6, and 9.
elimination method (p. 343) A method used to solve systems of equations in which one variable is eliminated by adding or subtracting two equations of the system.	**eliminación** Método utilizado para resolver sistemas de ecuaciones por el quale se elimina una variable sumando o restando dos ecuaciones del sistema.	
empty set (p. 93) The set with no elements denoted $\varnothing$ or { }.	**conjunto vacío** Conjunto sin elementos expresado $\varnothing$ o { }.	The solution set of $|x| < 0$ is the empty set.
equally likely outcomes (p. SB29) Outcomes are equally likely if they have the same probability of occurring. If an experiment has n equally likely outcomes, then the probability of each outcome is $\frac{1}{n}$.	**resultados igualmente probables** Los resultados son igualmente probables si tienen la misma probabilidad de ocurrir. Si un experimento tiene n resultados igualmente probables, entonces la probabilidad de cada resultado es $\frac{1}{n}$.	If a fair coin is tossed, then $P(\text{heads}) = P(\text{tails}) = \frac{1}{2}$. So the outcome "heads" and the outcome "tails" are equally likely.
equation (p. 72) A mathematical statement that two expressions are equal.	**ecuación** Enunciado matemático que indica que dos expresiones son iguales.	$x + 4 = 7$ $2 + 3 = 6 - 1$ $(x - 1)^2 + (y + 2)^2 = 4$
equilateral triangle (p. SB18) A triangle with three congruent sides.	**triángulo equilátero** Triángulo con tres lados congruentes.	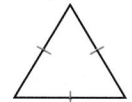
equivalent equations (p. 79) Equations that have the same solution set.	**ecuaciones equivalentes** Ecuaciones con la misma solución.	$x = 5$ and $x + 2 = 7$ are equivalent equations.
equivalent inequalities (p. 142) Inequalities that have the same solution set.	**desigualdades equivalentes** Desigualdades con la misma solución.	$x > 5$ and $x + 2 > 7$ are equivalent inequalities.

ENGLISH	SPANISH	EXAMPLES
evaluate (p. 7) To find the value of an algebraic expression by substituting a number for each variable and simplifying by using the order of operations.	**evaluar** Calcular el valor de una expresión algebraica sustituyendo cada variable por un número y simplificando mediante el orden de las operaciones.	Evaluate $2x + 7$ for $x = 3$. $2x + 7$ $2(3) + 7$ $6 + 7$ 13
event (p. SB29) An outcome or set of outcomes in a probability experiment.	**suceso** Resultado o conjunto de resultados en un experimento de probabilidad.	In the experiment of rolling a number cube, the event "an odd number" consists of the outcomes 1, 3, and 5.
excluded values (p. 634) Values of x for which a function or expression is not defined.	**valores excluidos** Valores de x para los cuales no está definida una función o expresión.	The excluded values of $$f(x) = \frac{(x + 2)}{(x - 1)(x + 4)}$$ are $x = 1$ and $x = -4$, which would make the denominator equal to 0.
experiment (p. SB29) An activity involving chance that can have different results.	**experimento** Actividad que implica probabilidad y puede tener diferentes resultados.	Tossing a coin 10 times and noting the number of heads.
experimental probability (p. SB30) The ratio of the number of times an event occurs to the number of trials, or times, that an activity is performed.	**probabilidad experimental** Razón entre la cantidad de veces que ocurre un suceso y la cantidad de pruebas, o veces, que se realiza una actividad.	Kendra attempted 27 free throws and made 16 of them. The experimental probability that she will make her next free throw is P(free throw) $=$ $$\frac{\text{number made}}{\text{number attempted}} = \frac{16}{27} \approx 0.59.$$
exponent (p. 26) The number that indicates how many times the base in a power is used as a factor.	**exponente** Número que indica la cantidad de veces que la base de una potencia se utiliza como factor.	$3^4 = 3 \cdot 3 \cdot 3 \cdot 3 = 81$ 4 is the exponent.
exponential decay (p. 749) An exponential function of the form $f(x) = ab^x$ in which $0 < b < 1$. If r is the rate of decay in decimal form, then the function can be written $y = a(1 - r)^t$, where a is the initial amount and t is the time.	**decremento exponencial** Función exponencial del tipo $f(x) = ab^x$ en la cual $0 < b < 1$. Si r es la tasa decremental en forma decimal, entonces la función se puede expresar como $y = a(1 - r)^t$, donde a es la cantidad inicial y t es el tiempo.	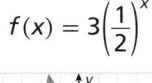 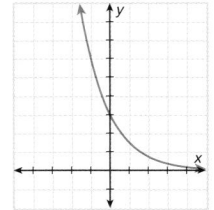
exponential expression (p. 757) An algebraic expression in which the variable is in an exponent with a fixed number as the base.	**expresión exponencial** Expresión algebraica en la que la variable está en un exponente y que tiene un número fijo como base.	2^{x+1}
exponential function (p. 738) A function of the form $f(x) = ab^x$, where a and b are real numbers with $a \neq 0$, $b > 0$, and $b \neq 1$.	**función exponencial** Función del tipo $f(x) = ab^x$, donde a y b son números reales con a $\neq$ 0, $b > 0$ y $b \neq 1$.	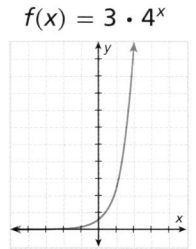

ENGLISH	SPANISH	EXAMPLES
exponential growth (p. 747) An exponential function of the form $f(x) = ab^x$ in which $b > 1$. If r is the rate of growth in decimal form, then the function can be written $y = a(1 + r)^t$, where a is the initial amount and t is the time.	**crecimiento exponencial** Función exponencial del tipo $f(x) = ab^x$ en la que $b > 1$. Si r es la tasa de crecimiento en forma decimal, entonces la función se puede expresar como $y = a(1 + r)^t$, donde a es la cantidad inicial y t es el tiempo.	$f(x) = 2^x$ 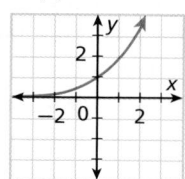
expression (p. 6) A mathematical phrase that contains operations, numbers, and/or variables.	**expresión** Frase matemática que contiene operaciones, números y/o variables.	$6x + 1$
extraneous solution (p. 675) A solution of a derived equation that is not a solution of the original equation.	**solución extraña** Solución de una ecuación derivada que no es una solución de la ecuación original.	To solve $\sqrt{x} = -2$, square both sides; $x = 4$. **Check** $\sqrt{4} = -2$ is false, so 4 is an extraneous solution.

ENGLISH	SPANISH	EXAMPLES
face of a polyhedron (p. SB20) A flat surface of the polyhedron.	**cara de un poliedro** Superficie plana de un poliedro.	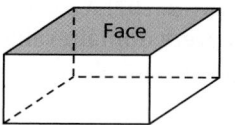
factor (p. 478) A number or expression that is multiplied by another number or expression to get a product. *See also* factoring.	**factor** Número o expresión que se multiplica por otro número o expresión para obtener un producto. *Ver también* factoreo.	$12 = 3 \cdot 4$ 3 and 4 are factors of 12. $x^2 - 1 = (x - 1)(x + 1)$ $(x - 1)$ and $(x + 1)$ are factors of $x^2 - 1$.
factoring (p. 478) The process of writing a number or algebraic expression as a product.	**factorización** Proceso por el que se expresa un número o expresión algebraica como un producto.	$x^2 - 4x - 21 = (x - 7)(x + 3)$
factor tree (p. SB5) A diagram showing how a whole number breaks down into its prime factors.	**árbol de factores** Diagrama que muestra cómo se descompone un número cabal en sus factores primo.	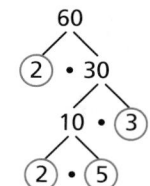
first differences (p. 756) The differences between y-values of a function for evenly spaced x-values.	**primeras diferencias** Diferencias entre los valores de y de una función para valores de x espaciados uniformemente.	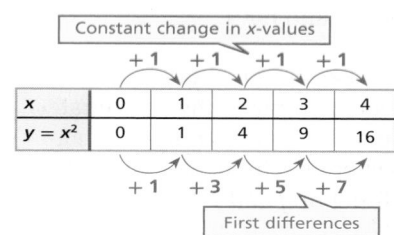
first quartile *See* lower quartile.	**primer cuartil** *Ver* cuartil inferior.	

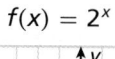

ENGLISH	SPANISH	EXAMPLES

FOIL (p. 447) A mnemonic (memory) device for a method of multiplying two binomials:
Multiply the **First** terms.
Multiply the **Outer** terms.
Multiply the **Inner** terms.
Multiply the **Last** terms.

FOIL Regla mnemotécnica para recordar el método de multiplicación de dos binomios:
Multiplicar los términos **Primeros** (*First*).
Multiplicar los términos **Externos** (*Outer*).
Multiplicar los términos **Internos** (*Inner*).
Multiplicar los términos **Últimos** (*Last*).

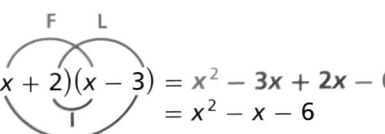
$$(x + 2)(x - 3) = x^2 - 3x + 2x - 6$$
$$= x^2 - x - 6$$

---

formula (p. 109) A literal equation that states a rule for a relationship among quantities.

fórmula Ecuación literal que establece una regla para una relación entre cantidades.

$$A = \pi r^2$$

---

fractional exponent (p. 423) An exponent that can be expressed as $\frac{m}{n}$ such that if m and n are integers, then $b^{\frac{m}{n}} = \sqrt[n]{b^m} = \left(\sqrt[n]{b}\right)^m$.

exponente fraccionario Exponente que se puede expresar como $\frac{m}{n}$ tal que si m y n son números enteros, entonces $b^{\frac{m}{n}} = \sqrt[n]{b^m} = \left(\sqrt[n]{b}\right)^m$.

$$64^{\frac{1}{6}} = \sqrt[6]{64}$$

---

function (p. 207) A relation in which every domain value is paired with exactly one range value.

función Relación en la que a cada valor de dominio corresponde exactamente un valor de rango.

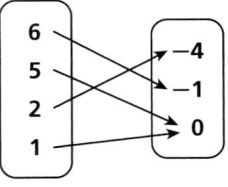

---

function notation (p. 216) If x is the independent variable and y is the dependent variable, then the function notation for y is $f(x)$, read "f of x," where f names the function.

notación de función Si x es la variable independiente e y es la variable dependiente, entonces la notación de función para y es $f(x)$, que se lee "f de x," donde f nombra la función.

equation: $y = 2x$
function notation: $f(x) = 2x$

---

geometric sequence (p. 732) A sequence in which the ratio of successive terms is a constant r, called the common ratio, where $r \neq 0$ and $r \neq 1$.

sucesión geométrica Sucesión en la que la razón de los términos sucesivos es una constante r, denominada razón común, donde $r \neq 0$ y $r \neq 1$.

1, 2, 4, 8, 16, ...
$\cdot 2 \cdot 2 \cdot 2 \cdot 2$ $r = 2$

---

graph of a function (p. 214) The set of points in the coordinate plane with coordinates (x, y), where x is in the domain of the function f and $y = f(x)$.

gráfica de una función Conjunto de los puntos de el plano cartesiano con coordenadas (x, y), donde x está en el dominio de la función f e $y = f(x)$.

---

graph of an inequality in one variable (p. 137) The set of points on the number line that are solutions of the inequality.

gráfica de una desigualdad en una variable Conjunto de los puntos de la recta numérica que representan soluciones de la desigualdad.

$x \geq 2$
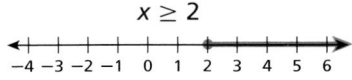

ENGLISH	SPANISH	EXAMPLES

graph of an inequality in two variables (p. 364) The set of points in the coordinate plane whose coordinates (x, y) are solutions of the inequality.

gráfica de una desigualdad en dos variables Conjunto de los puntos de el plano cartesiano cuyas coordenadas (x, y) son soluciones de la desigualdad.

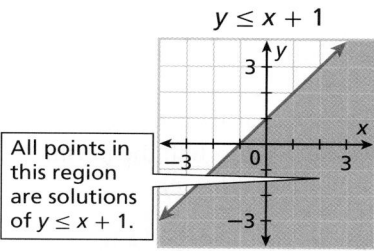

$y \leq x + 1$

All points in this region are solutions of $y \leq x + 1$.

---

graph of an ordered pair (p. SB23) For the ordered pair (x, y), the point in the coordinate plane that is a horizontal distance of x units from the origin and a vertical distance of y units from the origin.

gráfica de un par ordenado Dado el par ordenado (x, y), punto en el plano cartesiano que está a una distancia horizontal de x unidades desde el origen y a una distancia vertical de y unidades desde el origen.

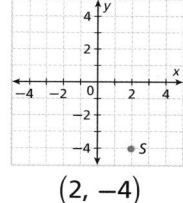

$(2, -4)$

---

graph of a system of linear inequalities (p. 371) The region in the coordinate plane consisting of points whose coordinates are solutions to all of the inequalities in the system.

gráfica de un sistema de desigualdades lineales Región de el plano cartesiano que consta de puntos cuyas coordenadas son soluciones de todas las desigualdades del sistema.

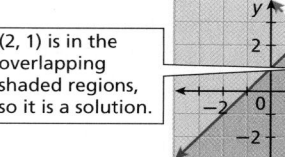

$(2, 1)$ is in the overlapping shaded regions, so it is a solution.

---

greatest common factor (GCF) (p. 479, p. SB7) For two or more numbers, the largest whole number that divides evenly into each number. For two or more monomials that contain variables, the product of the largest integer and the largest power of each variable that divide evenly into each term.

máximo común divisor (MCD) Dados dos o más números, el número cabal mayor que divide exactamente cada número. Dados dos o más monomios que contienen variables, el producto del entero mayor y la potencia mayor de cada variable que divide exactamente cada término.

The GCF of 27 and 45 is 9.

The GCF of $4x^3y$ and $6x^2y$ is $2x^2y$.

---

grouping symbols (p. 48) Symbols such as parentheses ( ), brackets [ ], and braces { } that separate part of an expression. A fraction bar, absolute-value symbols, and radical symbols may also be used as grouping symbols.

símbolos de agrupación Símbolos tales como paréntesis ( ), corchetes [ ] y llaves { } que separan parte de una expresión. La barra de fracciones, los símbolos de valor absoluto y los símbolos de radical también se pueden utilizar como símbolos de agrupación.

$6 + \{3 - [(4 - 3) + 2] + 1\} - 5$
$6 + \{3 - [1 + 2] + 1\} - 5$
$6 + \{3 - 3 + 1\} - 5$
$6 + 1 - 5$
2

 H

---

half-life (p. 749) The half-life of a substance is the time it takes for one-half of the substance to decay into another substance.

vida media La vida media de una sustancia es el tiempo que tarda la mitad de la sustancia en desintegrarse y transformarse en otra sustancia.

Carbon-14 has a half-life of 5730 years, so 5 g of an initial amount of 10 g will remain after 5730 years.

---

half-plane (p. 364) The part of the coordinate plane on one side of a line, which may include the line.

semiplano La parte del plano cartesiano de un lado de una línea, que puede incluir la línea.

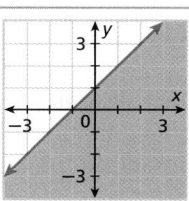

Glossary/Glosario (sidebar)

ENGLISH	SPANISH	EXAMPLES

Heron's Formula (p. 710) A triangle with side lengths a, b, and c has area
$A = \sqrt{s(s-a)(s-b)(s-c)}$,
where s is one-half the perimeter, or $s = \frac{1}{2}(a+b+c)$.

fórmula de Herón Un triángulo con longitudes de lado a, b y c tiene un área $A = \sqrt{s(s-a)(s-b)(s-c)}$, donde s es la mitad del perímetro ó $s = \frac{1}{2}(a+b+c)$.

---

histogram (p. SB27) A bar graph used to display data grouped in class intervals. The width of each bar is proportional to the class interval, and the area of each bar is proportional to the frequency.

histograma Gráfica de barras utilizada para mostrar datos agrupados en intervalos de clases. El ancho de cada barra es proporcional al intervalo de clase y el área de cada barra es proporcional a la frecuencia.

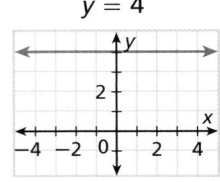

Starting Salaries
Frequency: 40, 30, 20, 10, 0
Salary range (thousand $): 20–29, 30–39, 40–49, 50–59

---

horizontal line (p. 273) A line described by the equation $y = b$, where b is the y-intercept.

línea horizontal Línea descrita por la ecuación $y = b$, donde b es la intersección con el eje y.

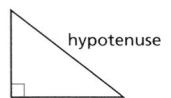

$y = 4$

---

hypotenuse (p. SB19) The side opposite the right angle in a right triangle.

hipotenusa Lado opuesto al ángulo recto de un triángulo rectángulo.

hypotenuse

---

hypothesis (p. 38) The part of a conditional statement following the word *if*.

hipótesis La parte de un enunciado condicional que sigue a la palabra *si*.

If $\underline{x + 1 = 5}$, then $x = 4$.
Hypothesis

---

identity (p. 93) An equation that is true for all values of the variables.

identidad Ecuación verdadera para todos los valores de las variables.

$3 = 3$
$2(x - 1) = 2x - 2$

---

image (p. SB24) A shape that results from a transformation of a figure known as the preimage.

imagen Forma resultante de la transformación de una figura conocido como imagen original.

Preimage, Image
$\triangle ABC \rightarrow \triangle A'B'C'$

---

inconsistent system (p. 350) A system of equations or inequalities that has no solution.

sistema inconsistente Sistema de ecuaciones o desigualdades que no tiene solución.

$\begin{cases} x + y = 0 \\ x + y = 1 \end{cases}$

---

independent events (p. SB31) Events for which the occurrence or nonoccurrence of one event does not affect the probability of the other event.

sucesos independientes Dos sucesos son independientes si el hecho de que se produzca o no uno de ellos no afecta la probabilidad del otro suceso.

From a bag containing 3 red marbles and 2 blue marbles, drawing a red marble, replacing it, and then drawing a blue marble are independent events.

---

independent system (p. 351) A system of equations that has exactly one solution.

sistema independiente Sistema de ecuaciones que tiene sólo una solución.

$\begin{cases} x + y = 7 \\ x - y = 1 \end{cases}$
Solution: (4, 3)

Glossary/Glosario

ENGLISH	SPANISH	EXAMPLES
independent variable (p. 216) A variable whose value determines the value of a variable called the dependent variable.	**variable independiente** Variable cuyo valor determina el valor de una variable llamada variable dependiente.	A math tutor charges $35 per hour. In this situation, the number of tutoring hours is the independent variable. It determines the total fee.
index (p. 422) In the radical $\sqrt[n]{x}$, which represents the nth root of x, n is the index. In the radical $\sqrt{x}$, the index is understood to be 2.	**índice** En el radical $\sqrt[n]{x}$, que representa la enésima raíz de x, n es el índice. En el radical $\sqrt{x}$, se da por sentado que el índice es 2.	The radical $\sqrt[3]{8}$ has an index of 3.
indirect proof (p. 484) A proof in which the statement to be proved is assumed to be false and then deductive reasoning is used to find a contradiction.	**demostración indirecta** Prueba en la que se supone que el enunciado a demonstrar es falso y se muestra una contradicción.	
inductive reasoning (p. 233) The process of conjecturing that a general rule or statement is true because specific cases are true.	**razonamiento inductivo** Proceso de razonamiento por el que se determina que una regal o enunciado son verdaderos porque ciertos casos especificos son verdaderos.	A sequence begins with the terms 2, 4, 6, 8, 10. You notice that each term is two more than the previous term. You use inductive reasoning to predict that the next term is 12.
inequality (p. 136) A mathematical statement that compares two expressions by using one of the following signs: $<$, $>$, $\leq$, $\geq$, or $\neq$.	**desigualdad** Enunciado matemático que compara dos expresiones utilizando uno de los siguientes signos: $<$, $>$, $\leq$, $\geq$, o $\neq$.	$x \geq 2$ (number line from −4 to 6 with closed circle at 2 and arrow to right)
input (p. 217) A value that is substituted for the independent variable in a function.	**entrada** Valor que sustituye a la variable independiente en una función.	For the function $f(x) = x + 5$, the input 3 produces an output of 8.
input-output table (p. 213) A table that displays input values of a function or relation together with the corresponding outputs.	**tabla de entrada y salida** Tabla que muestra los valores de entrada de una función o relación junto con las correspondientes salidas.	Input / Output table: x: 1, 2, 3, 4 y: 4, 7, 10, 13
integers (p. 33) The set of whole numbers and their opposites.	**enteros** El conjunto de números cabales y sus opuestos.	$\{..., -3, -2, -1, 0, 1, 2, 3, ...\}$
intercept *See* x-intercept and y-intercept.	**intersección** *Ver* intersección con el eje x e intersección con el eje y.	
interest (p. SB11) The amount of money charged for borrowing money or the amount of money earned when saving or investing money. *See also* compound interest, simple interest.	**interés** Cantidad de dinero que se cobra por prestar dinero o cantidad de dinero que se gana cuando se ahorra o invierte dinero. *Ver también* interés compuesto, interés simple.	
intersection (p. 171) The intersection of two sets is the set of all elements that are common to both sets, denoted by $\cap$.	**intersección** La intersección de dos conjuntos es el conjunto de todos los elementos que son comunes a ambos conjuntos, expresado por $\cap$.	$A = \{1, 2, 3, 4\}$ $B = \{1, 3, 5, 7, 9\}$ $A \cap B = \{1, 3\}$

ENGLISH	SPANISH	EXAMPLES
inverse operations (p. 72) Operations that undo each other.	**operaciones inversas** Operaciones que se anulan entre sí.	Addition and subtraction of the same quantity are inverse operations: $5 + 3 = 8$, $8 - 3 = 5$ Multiplication and division by the same quantity are inverse operations: $2 \cdot 3 = 6$, $6 \div 3 = 2$
Inverse Property of Addition (p. 15) For any real number a, $a + (-a) = (-a) + a = 0$.	**propiedad inversa de la suma** Dado cualquier número real a, $a + (-a) = (-a) + a = 0$.	$4 + (-4) = (-4) + 4 = 0$
Inverse Property of Multiplication (p. 21) For any real number $a\,(a \neq 0)$, $a \cdot \frac{1}{a} = \frac{1}{a} \cdot a = 1$.	**propiedad inversa de la multiplicación** Dado cualquier número real $a\,(a \neq 0)$, $a \cdot \frac{1}{a} = \frac{1}{a} \cdot a = 1$.	$2 \cdot \frac{1}{2} = \frac{1}{2} \cdot 2 = 1$
inverse variation (p. 627) A relationship between two variables, x and y, that can be written in the form $y = \frac{k}{x}$, where k is a nonzero constant and $x \neq 0$.	**variación inversa** Relación entre dos variables, x e y, que puede expresarse en la forma $y = \frac{k}{x}$, donde k es una constante distinta de cero y $x \neq 0$.	$y = \frac{8}{x}$ 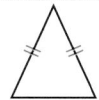
irrational number (p. 33) A real number that cannot be expressed as a ratio of two integers.	**número irracional** Número real que no se puede expresar como una razón de enteros.	$\sqrt{2}$, π
isolate the variable (p. 72) A variable is isolated when it appears by itself on one side of an equation and does not appear on the other side.	**despejar la variable** Una variable está despejada cuando aparece sola en uno de los lados de una ecuación y no aparece en el otro lado.	$\begin{aligned} 10 &= 6 - 2x \\ \underline{-6} & \quad \underline{-6} \\ 4 &= -2x \\ \frac{4}{-2} &= \frac{-2x}{-2} \\ -2 &= x \end{aligned}$
isosceles trapezoid (p. SB18) A trapezoid whose nonparallel sides are congruent.	**trapecio isósceles** Trapecio cuyos lados no paralelos son congruentes.	
isosceles triangle (p. SB15) A triangle with at least two congruent sides.	**triángulo isósceles** Triángulo que tiene al menos dos lados congruentes.	

K

kite (p. SB18) A quadrilateral with two pairs of adjacent congruent sides.	**cometa o papalote** Cuadrilátero con dos pares de lados adyacentes congruentes.	

L

leading coefficient (p. 431) The coefficient of the first term of a polynomial in standard form.	**coeficiente principal** Coeficiente del primer término de un polinomio en forma estándar.	$3x^2 + 7x - 2$ Leading coefficient: 3
least common denominator (LCD) (p. 661) The least common multiple of the denominators of two or more rational expressions.	**mínimo común denominador (MCD)** Mínimo común múltiplo de los denominadores de dos o más expresiones racionales.	The LCD of $\frac{3}{4}$ and $\frac{5}{6}$ is 12. The LCD of $\frac{1}{6x^2}$ and $\frac{5}{8x}$ is $24x^2$.

ENGLISH	SPANISH	EXAMPLES
least common multiple (LCM) (p. 660, SB7) For two or more whole numbers, the smallest multiple that the numbers share. For two or more monomials that contain variables, the product of the smallest positive integer and the lowest power of each variable that divide evenly into each term.	**mínimo común múltiplo (MCM)** Dados dos o más números cabales, el múltiplo menor que los números comparten. Dados dos o más monomios que contienen variables, el producto del menor entero positive y la potencia menor de cada variable que divide exactamente cada término.	The LCM of 10 and 18 is 90. The LCM of $6x^2$ and $8x$ is $24x^2$.
leg of a right triangle (p. SB19) One of the two sides of a right triangle that form the right angle.	**cateto de un triángulo rectángulo** Uno de los dos lados de un triángulo rectángulo que forman el ángulo recto.	
like radicals (p. 711) Radical terms having the same radicand and index.	**radicales semejantes** Términos radicales que tienen el mismo radicando e índice.	$3\sqrt{2x}$ and $\sqrt{2x}$
like terms (p. 49) Terms with the same variables raised to the same exponents.	**términos semejantes** Términos con las mismas variables elevadas a los mismos exponentes.	$3a^3b^2$ and $7a^3b^2$
linear equation in one variable (p. 256) An equation that can be written in the form $ax = b$ where a and b are constants and $a \neq 0$.	**ecuación lineal en una variable** Ecuación que puede expresarse en la forma $ax = b$ donde a y b son constantes y $a \neq 0$.	$x + 1 = 7$
linear equation in two variables (p. 256) An equation that can be written in the form $Ax + By = C$ where A, B, and C are constants and A and B are not both 0.	**ecuación lineal en dos variables** Ecuación que puede expresarse en la forma $Ax + By = C$ donde A, B y C son constantes y A y B no son ambas 0.	$2x + 3y = 6$
linear function (p. 256) A function that can be written in the form $y = mx + b$, where x is the independent variable and m and b are real numbers. Its graph is a line.	**función lineal** Función que puede expresarse en la forma $y = mx + b$, donde x es la variable independiente y m y b son números reales. Su gráfica es una línea.	$y = x - 1$
linear inequality in one variable (p. 364) An inequality that can be written in one of the following forms: $ax < b$, $ax > b$, $ax \leq b$, $ax \geq b$, or $ax \neq b$, where a and b are constants and $a \neq 0$.	**desigualdad lineal en una variable** Desigualdad que puede expresarse de una de las siguientes formas: $ax < b$, $ax > b$, $ax \leq b$, $ax \geq b$ o $ax \neq b$, donde a y b son constantes y $a \neq 0$.	$3x - 5 \leq 2(x + 4)$
linear inequality in two variables (p. 364) An inequality that can be written in one of the following forms: $Ax + By < C$, $Ax + By > C$, $Ax + By \leq C$, $Ax + By \geq C$, or $Ax + By \neq C$, where A, B, and C are constants and A and B are not both 0.	**desigualdad lineal en dos variables** Desigualdad que puede expresarse de una de las siguientes formas: $Ax + By < C$, $Ax + By > C$, $Ax + By \leq C$, $Ax + By \geq C$ o $Ax + By \neq C$, donde A, B y C son constantes y A y B no son ambas 0.	$2x + 3y > 6$

Glossary/Glosario

literal equation (p. 110) An equation that contains two or more variables.

ecuación literal Ecuación que contiene dos o más variables.

$d = rt$

$A = \frac{1}{2}h(b_1 + b_2)$

---

lower extreme (p. SB27) The least value in a data set.

extremo inferior El valor meno de un conjunto de datos.

For the data set {3, 3, 5, 7, 8, 10, 11, 11, 12}, the lower extreme is 3.

---

lower quartile (p. SB27) The median of the lower half of a data set. Also called *first quartile*.

cuartil inferior Mediana de la mitad inferior de un conjunto de datos. También se llama *primer cuartil*.

Lower half   Upper half
18, ㉓, 28,   49, 36, 42
Lower quartile

---

mapping diagram (p. 206) A diagram that shows the relationship of elements in the domain to elements in the range of a relation or function.

diagrama de correspondencia Diagrama que muestra la relación entre los elementos del dominio y los elementos del rango de una función.

Mapping Diagram

Domain   Range

2 → A, B, C

---

markup (p. SB10) The amount by which a wholesale cost is increased.

margen de ganancia Cantidad que se agrega a un costo mayorista.

---

maximum of a function (p. 546) The *y*-value of the highest point on the graph of the function.

máximo de una función Valor de *y* del punto más alto en la gráfica de la función.

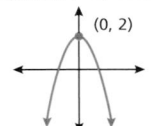
(0, 2)

The maximum of the function is 2.

---

mean (p. SB25) The sum of all the values in a data set divided by the number of data values. Also called the *average*.

media Suma de todos los valores de un conjunto de datos dividida entre el número de valores de datos. También llamada *promedio*.

Data set: 4, 6, 7, 8, 10

Mean: $\frac{4 + 6 + 7 + 8 + 10}{5}$

$= \frac{35}{5} = 7$

---

measure of central tendency (p. SB25) A measure that describes a data set.

medida de tendencia dominante Medida que describe un conjunto de datos.

mean, median, or mode

---

median (p. SB25) For an ordered data set with an odd number of values, the median is the middle value. For an ordered data set with an even number of values, the median is the average of the two middle values.

mediana Dado un conjunto de datos ordenado con un número impar de valores, la mediana es el valor medio. Dado un conjunto de datos con un número par de valores, la mediana es el promedio de los dos valores medios.

8, 9, ⑨, 12, 15   Median: 9

4, 6, ⑦, ⑩, 10, 12

Median: $\frac{7 + 10}{2} = 8.5$

---

metric system (p. SB13) A decimal system of weights and measures that is used universally in science and commonly throughout the world.

sistema métrico Sistema decimal de pesos y medidas empleado universalmente en las ciencias y por lo general en todo el mundo.

centimeters, meters, kilograms, milliliters, liters

---

minimum of a function (p. 546) The *y*-value of the lowest point on the graph of the function.

mínimo de una función Valor de *y* del punto más bajo en la gráfica de la función.

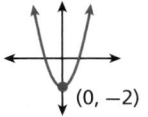
(0, −2)

The minimum of the function is −2.

Glossary/Glosario

ENGLISH	SPANISH	EXAMPLES

mode (p. SB25) The value or values that occur most frequently in a data set; if all values occur with the same frequency, the data set is said to have no mode.

moda El valor o los valores que se presentan con mayor frecuencia en un conjunto de datos. Si todos los valores se presentan con la misma frecuencia, se dice que el conjunto de datos no tiene moda.

Data: 3, 6, 8, 8, 10 Mode: 8

Data: 2, 5, 5, 7, 7 Modes: 5, 7

Data: 2, 3, 6, 9, 11 No mode

monomial (p. 430) A number, a variable, or a product of numbers and variables with whole-number exponents.

monomio Número, variable, o producto de números y variables con exponentes de números cabales, o polinomio con un término.

$3x^2y^4$

Multiplication Property of Equality (p. 73) If a, b, and c are real numbers and $a = b$, then $ac = bc$.

Propiedad de igualdad de la multiplicación Si a, b y c son números reales y $a = b$, entonces $ac = bc$.

$\frac{1}{3}x = 7$

$(3)\left(\frac{1}{3}x\right) = (3)(7)$

$x = 21$

Multiplication Property of Inequality (p. 148) For real numbers a, b, and c, where $c > 0$, if $a < b$, then $ac < bc$.

For real numbers a, b, and c, where $c < 0$, if $a < b$, then $ac > bc$. Also holds true for $>$, $\leq$, $\geq$, and $\neq$.

Propiedad de desigualdad de la multiplicación Dados los números reales a, b, y c, donde $c > 0$, si $a < b$, entonces $ac < bc$.

Dados los números reales a, b, y c, donde $c < 0$, si $a < b$, entonces $ac > bc$. Es válido también para $>$, $\leq$, $\geq$, y $\neq$.

$\frac{1}{3}x > 7$

$(3)\left(\frac{1}{3}x\right) > (3)(7)$

$x > 21$

$-x \leq 2$

$(-1)(-x) \geq (-1)(2)$

$x \geq -2$

multiplicative inverse (p. 21) The reciprocal of a number. Two numbers are multiplicative inverses if their product is 1.

inverso multiplicativo Recíproco de un número. Dos números son inversos multiplicativos si su producto es 1.

The multiplicative inverse of 5 is $\frac{1}{5}$.

N

natural numbers (p. 33) The set of counting numbers.

números naturales El conjunto de números que se utilizan para contar.

{1, 2, 3, 4, 5, 6, ...}

negative correlation (p. 225) Two data sets have a negative correlation if one set of data values increases as the other set decreases.

correlación negativa Dos conjuntos de datos tienen una correlación negativa si un conjunto de valores de datos aumenta a medida que el otro conjunto disminuye.

negative exponent (p. 394) For any nonzero real number x and any integer n, $x^{-n} = \frac{1}{x^n}$.

exponente negativo Para cualquier número real distinto de cero x y cualquier entero n, $x^{-n} = \frac{1}{x^n}$.

$x^{-2} = \frac{1}{x^2}$; $3^{-2} = \frac{1}{3^2}$

negative number (p. 36) A number that is less than zero. Negative numbers lie to the left of 0 on a number line.

número negativo Número menor que cero. Los números negativos se ubican a la izquierda del 0 en una recta numérica.

-2 is a negative number.

negative square root (p. 32) The opposite of the principal square root of a number a, written as $-\sqrt{a}$.

raíz cuadrada negativa Opuesto de la raíz cuadrada principal de un número a, que se expresa como $-\sqrt{a}$.

The negative square root of 9 is $-\sqrt{9} = -3$.

ENGLISH	SPANISH	EXAMPLES

net (p. SB22) A diagram of the faces of a three-dimensional figure arranged in such a way that the diagram can be folded to form the three-dimensional figure.

plantilla Diagrama de las caras de una figura tridimensional que se puede plegar para formar la figura tridimensional.

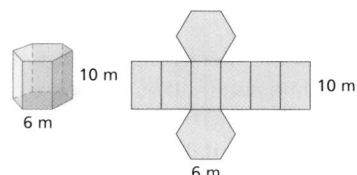

no correlation (p. 225) Two data sets have no correlation if there is no relationship between the sets of values.

sin correlación Dos conjuntos de datos no tienen correlación si no existe una relación entre los conjuntos de valores.

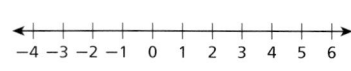

nth root (p. 422) The *n*th root of a number *a*, written as $\sqrt[n]{a}$ or $a^{\frac{1}{n}}$, is a number that is equal to *a* when it is raised to the *n*th power.

enésima raíz La enésima raíz de un número *a*, que se escribe $\sqrt[n]{a}$ o $a^{\frac{1}{n}}$, es un número igual a *a* cuando se eleva a la enésima potencia.

$\sqrt[5]{32} = 2$, because $2^5 = 32$.

number line (p. 14) A line used to represent the real numbers. Every point on the number line represents a real number.

recta numérica Línea utilizada para representar los números reales. Cada punto de la recta numérica representa un número real.

numerical expression (p. 6) An expression that contains only numbers and operations.

expresión numérica Expresión que contiene únicamente números y operaciones.

$2 \cdot 3 + (4 - 6)$

obtuse angle (p. SB18) An angle that measures greater than 90° and less than 180°.

ángulo obtuso Ángulo que mide más de 90° y menos de 180°.

obtuse triangle (p. SB18) A triangle with one obtuse angle.

triángulo obtusángulo Triángulo con un ángulo obtuso.

opposite (p. 15) The opposite of a number *a*, denoted −*a*, is the number that is the same distance from 0 as *a*, on the opposite side of the number line. The sum of opposites is 0.

opuesto El opuesto de un número *a*, expresado −*a*, es el número que se encuentra a la misma distancia de 0 que *a*, del lado opuesto de la recta numérica. La suma de los opuestos es 0.

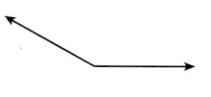

5 and −5 are opposites.

opposite reciprocal (p. 307) The opposite of the reciprocal of a number. The opposite reciprocal of any nonzero number *a* is $-\frac{1}{a}$.

recíproco opuesto Opuesto del recíproco de un número. El recíproco opuesto de *a* es $-\frac{1}{a}$.

The opposite reciprocal of $\frac{2}{3}$ is $-\frac{3}{2}$.

OR (p. 170) A logical operator representing the union of two sets.

O Operador lógico que representa la unión de dos conjuntos.

$A = \{2, 3, 4, 5\}$ $B = \{1, 3, 5, 7\}$
The set of values that are in
A OR *B* is $A \cup B = \{1, 2, 3, 4, 5, 7\}$.

ordered pair (p. SB23) A pair of numbers (*x*, *y*) that can be used to locate a point on the coordinate plane. The first number *x* indicates the distance to the left or right of the origin, and the second number *y* indicates the distance above or below the origin.

par ordenado Par de números (*x*, *y*) que se pueden utilizar para ubicar un punto en el plano cartesiano. El primer número, *x*, indica la distancia a la izquierda o derecha del origen y el segundo número, *y*, indica la distancia hacia arriba o hacia abajo del origen.

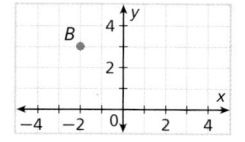

The coordinates of *B* are (−2, 3).

Glossary/Glosario

ENGLISH	SPANISH	EXAMPLES

order of operations (p. 48) A process for evaluating expressions:
First, perform operations in parentheses or other grouping symbols.
Second, evaluate powers and roots.
Third, perform all multiplication and division from left to right.
Fourth, perform all addition and subtraction from left to right.

orden de las operaciones Regla para evaluar las expresiones:
Primero, realizar las operaciones entre paréntesis u otros símbolos de agrupación.
Segundo, evaluar las potencias y las raíces.
Tercero, realizar todas las multiplicaciones y divisiones de izquierda a derecha.
Cuarto, realizar todas las sumas y restas de izquierda a derecha.

$2 + 3^2 - (7 + 5) \div 4 \cdot 3$
$2 + 3^2 - 12 \div 4 \cdot 3$ Add inside parentheses.
$2 + 9 - 12 \div 4 \cdot 3$ Evaluate the power.
$2 + 9 - 3 \cdot 3$ Divide.
$2 + 9 - 9$ Multiply.
$11 - 9$ Add.
2 Subtract.

---

origin (p. SB23) The intersection of the x- and y-axes in the coordinate plane. The coordinates of the origin are $(0, 0)$.

origen Intersección de los ejes x e y en el plano cartesiano. Las coordenadas de origen son $(0, 0)$.

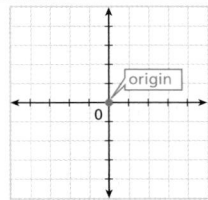

---

outcome (p. SB29) A possible result of a probability experiment.

resultado Resultado posible de un experimento de probabilidad.

In the experiment of rolling a number cube, the possible outcomes are 1, 2, 3, 4, 5, and 6.

---

output (p. 217) The result of substituting a value for the independent variable in a function.

salida Resultado de la sustitución de la variable independiente por un valor en una función.

For the function $f(x) = x^2 + 1$, the input 3 produces an output of 10.

---

parabola (p. 545) The shape of the graph of a quadratic function.

parábola Forma de la gráfica de una función cuadrática.

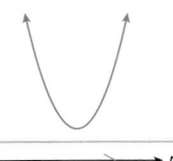

---

parallel lines (p. 304) Lines in the same plane that do not intersect.

líneas paralelas Líneas en el mismo plano que no se cruzan.

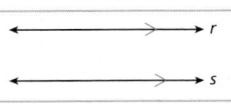

---

parallelogram (p. 305) A quadrilateral with two pairs of parallel sides.

paralelogramo Cuadrilátero con dos pares de lados paralelos.

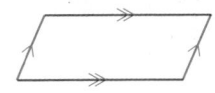

Pascal's triangle (p. 526) A triangular arrangement of numbers in which every row starts and ends with 1 and each other number is the sum of the two numbers above it.

triángulo de Pascal Arreglo triangular de números en el cual cada fila comienza y termina con 1 y los demás números son la suma de los dos valores que están arriba de cada uno.

```
      1
     1 1
    1 2 1
   1 3 3 1
  1 4 6 4 1
```

---

percent (p. 103, p. SB6) A ratio that compares a number to 100.

porcentaje Razón que compara un número con 100.

$\dfrac{17}{100} = 17\%$

---

percent change (p. SB11) An increase or decrease given as a percent of the original amount. *See also* percent decrease, percent increase.

porcentaje de cambio Incremento o disminución dada como un porcentaje de la cantidad original. *Ver también* porcentaje de disminución, porcentaje de incremento.

ENGLISH	SPANISH	EXAMPLES
percent decrease (p. SB11) A decrease given as a percent of the original amount.	**porcentaje de disminución** Disminución dada como un porcentaje de la cantidad original.	If an item that costs $8.00 is marked down to $6.00, the amount of the decrease is $2.00, so the percent decrease is $\frac{2.00}{8.00} = 0.25 = 25\%$.
percent increase (p. SB11) An increase given as a percent of the original amount.	**porcentaje de incremento** Incremento dado como un porcentaje de la cantidad original.	If an item's wholesale cost of $8.00 is marked up to $12.00, the amount of the increase is $4.00, so the percent increase is $\frac{4.00}{8.00} = 0.5 = 50\%$.
perfect square (p. 32) A number whose positive square root is a whole number.	**cuadrado perfecto** Número cuya raíz cuadrada positiva es un número cabal.	36 is a perfect square because $\sqrt{36} = 6$.
perfect-square trinomial (p. 455) A trinomial whose factored form is the square of a binomial. A perfect-square trinomial has the form $a^2 - 2ab + b^2$ or $a^2 + 2ab + b^2$.	**trinomio cuadrado perfecto** Trinomio cuya forma factorizada es el cuadrado de un binomio. Un trinomio cuadrado perfecto tiene la forma $a^2 - 2ab + b^2$ o $a^2 + 2ab + b^2$.	$x^2 + 6x + 9$ is a perfect-square trinomial, because $x^2 + 6x + 9 = (x + 3)^2$.
perimeter (p. SB15) The sum of the lengths of the sides of a polygon.	**perímetro** Suma de las longitudes de los lados de un poligano.	18 ft, 6ft Perimeter $= 18 + 6 + 18 + 6 = 48$ ft
perpendicular (p. 306) Intersecting to form 90° angles.	**perpendicular** Que se cruza para formar ángulos de 90°.	n, m
perpendicular lines (p. 306) Lines that intersect at 90° angles.	**líneas perpendiculares** Líneas que se cruzan en ángulos de 90°.	n, m
point-slope form (p. 298) The point-slope form of a linear equation is $y - y_1 = m(x - x_1)$, where m is the slope and (x_1, y_1) is a point on the line.	**forma de punto y pendiente** La forma de punto y pendiente de una ecuación lineal es $y - y_1 = m(x - x_1)$, donde m es la pendiente y (x_1, y_1) es un punto en la línea.	$y - 3 = 2(x - 3)$ The slope is 2. (3, 3) is on the line.
polyhedron (p. SB20) A three-dimensional figure made up of polygons that intersect only at their edges.	**poliedro** Figura tridimensional cerrada formada por polígonos que se cruzan sólo en sus aristas.	
polynomial (p. 430) A monomial or a sum or difference of monomials.	**polinomio** Monomio o suma o diferencia de monomios.	$2x^2 + 3xy - 7y^2$
polynomial long division (p. 667) A method of dividing one polynomial by another.	**división larga polinomial** Método por el que se divide un polinomio entre otro.	$$\begin{array}{r} x + 1 \\ x + 2 \overline{)\ x^2 + 3x + 5} \\ -(x^2 + 2x) \\ \hline x + 5 \\ -(x + 2) \\ \hline 3 \end{array}$$ $$\frac{x^2 + 3x + 5}{x + 2} = x + 1 + \frac{3}{x + 2}$$

ENGLISH	SPANISH	EXAMPLES
population (p. SB26) The whole group being surveyed.	**población** El grupo completo que es objeto de estudio.	In a survey about eating habits of high school students, the population is all high school students.
positive correlation (p. 225) Two data sets have a positive correlation if both sets of data values increase.	**correlación positiva** (p. 264) Dos conjuntos de datos tienen correlación positiva si los valores de ambos conjuntos de datos aumentan.	
positive number (p. 36) A number greater than zero. Positive numbers lie to the right of 0 on a number line.	**número positivo** Número mayor que cero. Los números positivos se ubican a la derecha del 0 en una recta numérica.	2 is a positive number.
positive square root (p. 32) A positive number that is multiplied by itself to form a product is called the positive square root of that product. A positive square root is indicated by the radical sign.	**raíz cuadrada positiva** Un número positivo que se multiplica por sí mismo para obtener un producto se llama raíz cuadrada positiva de ese producto. Una raíz cuadrada positivo se indica con un signo de radical.	The positive square root of 36 is $\sqrt{36} = 6$.
power (p. 26) An expression written with a base and an exponent or the value of such an expression.	**potencia** Expresión escrita con una base y un exponente o el valor de dicha expresión.	$2^3 = 8$, so 8 is the third power of 2.
Power of a Power Property (p. 410) If a is any nonzero real number and m and n are integers, then $(a^m)^n = a^{mn}$.	**Propiedad de la potencia de una potencia** Dado un número real a distinto de cero y los números enteros m y n, entonces $(a^m)^n = a^{mn}$.	$(6^7)^4 = 6^{7\cdot4}$ $= 6^{28}$
Power of a Product Property (p. 411) If a and b are any nonzero real numbers and n is an integer, then $(ab)^n = a^n b^n$.	**Propiedad de la potencia de un producto** Dados los números reales a y b distintos de cero y un número entero n, entonces $(ab)^n = a^n b^n$.	$(2 \cdot 4)^3 = 2^3 \cdot 4^3$ $= 8 \cdot 64$ $= 512$
Power of a Quotient Property (p. 416, p. 417) If a and b are any nonzero real numbers and n is an integer, then $\left(\frac{a}{b}\right)^n = \frac{a^n}{b^n}$.	**Propiedad de la potencia de un cociente** Dados los números reales a y b distintos de cero y un número entero n, entonces $\left(\frac{a}{b}\right)^n = \frac{a^n}{b^n}$.	$\left(\frac{3}{5}\right)^4 = \frac{3}{5} \cdot \frac{3}{5} \cdot \frac{3}{5} \cdot \frac{3}{5}$ $= \frac{3 \cdot 3 \cdot 3 \cdot 3}{5 \cdot 5 \cdot 5 \cdot 5}$ $= \frac{3^4}{5^4}$
preimage (p. SB24) The original figure in a transformation.	**imagen original** Figura original en una transformación.	$\triangle ABC \rightarrow \triangle A'B'C'$
prime factorization (p. 478, p. SB5) A representation of a number or a polynomial as a product of primes.	**factorización prima** Representación de un número o de un polinomio como producto de números primos.	The prime factorization of 60 is $2 \cdot 2 \cdot 3 \cdot 5$.
prime number (p. 478, p. SB5) A whole number greater than 1 that has exactly two positive factors, itself and 1.	**número primo** Número cabal mayor que 1 que es divisible únicamente entre sí mismo y entre 1.	5 is prime because its only factors are 5 and 1.
principal (p. SB11) An amount of money borrowed or invested.	**capital** Cantidad de dinero que se pide prestado o se invierte.	

Glossary/Glosario

principal square root (p. 32) The positive square root of a number, indicated by the radical sign.

raíz principal Raíz cuadrada positivo de un número, expresada por el signo de radical.

The principal square root of 36 is $\sqrt{36} = 6$.

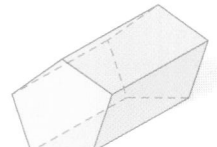

---

prism (p. SB20) A three-dimensional figure with two congruent parallel polygonal bases. The remaining edges join corresponding vertices of the bases so that the remaining faces are rectangles.

prisma Figura tridimensional con dos bases poligonales congruentes y paralelas. El resto de las aristas se unen a los vértices correspondientes de las bases de manera que las otras sean rectángulos.

---

probability (p. SB29) A number from 0 to 1 (or 0% to 100%) that is the measure of how likely an event is to occur.

probabilidad Número entre 0 y 1 (o entre 0% y 100%) que describe cuán probable es que ocurra un suceso.

A bag contains 3 red marbles and 4 blue marbles. The probability of randomly choosing a red marble is $\frac{3}{7}$.

Product of Powers Property (p. 408) If a is any nonzero real number and m and n are integers, then $a^m \cdot a^n = a^{m+n}$.

Propiedad del producto de potencias Dado un número real a distinto de cero y los números enteros m y n, entonces $a^m \cdot a^n = a^{m+n}$.

$$6^7 \cdot 6^4 = 6^{7+4}$$
$$= 6^{11}$$

Product Property of Square Roots (p. 706) For $a \geq 0$ and $b \geq 0$, $\sqrt{ab} = \sqrt{a} \cdot \sqrt{b}$.

Propiedad del producto de raíces cuadradas Dados $a \geq 0$ y $b \geq 0$, $\sqrt{ab} = \sqrt{a} \cdot \sqrt{b}$.

$$\sqrt{9 \cdot 25} = \sqrt{9} \cdot \sqrt{25}$$
$$= 3 \cdot 5 = 15$$

---

proportion (p. 102) A statement that two ratios are equal; $\frac{a}{b} = \frac{c}{d}$.

proporción Ecuación que establece que dos razones son iguales; $\frac{a}{b} = \frac{c}{d}$.

$$\frac{2}{3} = \frac{4}{6}$$

---

pyramid (p. SB20) A three-dimensional figure with a polygonal base lying in one plane plus one additional vertex not lying on that plane. The remaining edges of the pyramid join the additional vertex to the vertices of the base.

pirámide Figura tridimensional con una base poligonal en un plano, más un vértice adicional que no está en ese plano. El resto de las aristas de la pirámide unen el vértice adicional a los vértices de la base.

Pythagorean Theorem (p. SB20) For any right triangle, if the legs have lengths a and b and the hypotenuse has length c, then $a^2 + b^2 = c^2$.

Teorema de Pitágoras Dado un triángulo rectángulo con catetos de longitudes a y b y una hipotenusa de longitud c, entonces $a^2 + b^2 = c^2$.

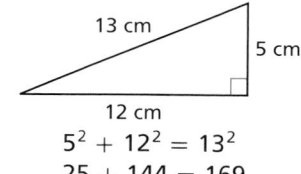

$$5^2 + 12^2 = 13^2$$
$$25 + 144 = 169$$

Pythagorean triple (p. 473) A set of three nonzero whole numbers a, b, and c such that $a^2 + b^2 = c^2$.

Tripleta de Pitágoras Conjunto de tres números cabales distintos de cero a, b y c tal que $a^2 + b^2 = c^2$.

The numbers 3, 4, and 5 form a Pythagorean triple because $3^2 + 4^2 = 5^2$.

---

quadrant (p. SB23) One of the four regions into which the x- and y-axes divide the coordinate plane.

cuadrante Una de las cuatro regiones en las que los ejes x e y dividen el plano cartesiano.

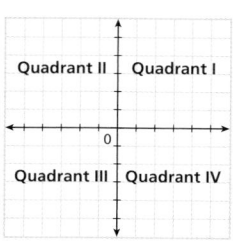

ENGLISH	SPANISH	EXAMPLES
quadratic equation (p. 544) An equation that can be written in the form $ax^2 + bx + c = 0$, where a, b, and c are real numbers and $a \neq 0$.	**ecuación cuadrática** Ecuación que se puede expresar como $ax^2 + bx + c = 0$, donde a, b y c son números reales y $a \neq 0$.	$x^2 + 3x - 4 = 0$ $x^2 - 9 = 0$
Quadratic Formula (p. 598) The formula $x = \frac{-b \pm \sqrt{b^2 - 4ac}}{2a}$, which gives solutions of equations in the form $ax^2 + bx + c = 0$, where $a \neq 0$.	**fórmula cuadrática** La fórmula $x = \frac{-b \pm \sqrt{b^2 - 4ac}}{2a}$, que da soluciones para las ecuaciones del tipo $ax^2 + bx + c = 0$, donde $a \neq 0$.	The solutions of $2x^2 - 5x - 3 = 0$ are given by $$x = \frac{-(-5) \pm \sqrt{(-5)^2 - 4(2)(-3)}}{2(2)}$$ $$= \frac{5 \pm \sqrt{25 + 24}}{4} = \frac{5 \pm 7}{4}.$$ So $x = 3$ or $x = -\frac{1}{2}$.
quadratic function (p. 544) A function that can be written in the form $f(x) = ax^2 + bx + c$, where a, b, and c are real numbers and $a \neq 0$.	**función cuadrática** Función que se puede expresar como $f(x) = ax^2 + bx + c$, donde a, b y c son números reales y $a \neq 0$.	$f(x) = x^2 - 6x + 8$
quadratic polynomial (p. 431) A polynomial of degree 2.	**polinomio cuadrático** Polinomio de grado 2.	$x^2 - 6x + 8$
quartile (p. SB27) The median of the upper or lower half of a data set. *See also* lower quartile, upper quartile.	**cuartil** La mediana de la mitad superior o inferior de un conjunto de datos. *Ver también* cuartil inferior, cuartil superior.	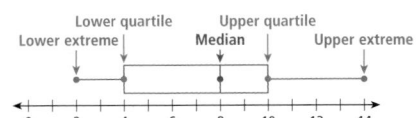
Quotient of Powers Property (p. 415) If a is a nonzero real number and m and n are integers, then $\frac{a^m}{a^n} = a^{m-n}$.	**Propiedad del cociente de potencias** Dado un número real a distinto de cero y los números enteros m y n, entonces $\frac{a^m}{a^n} = a^{m-n}$.	$\frac{6^7}{6^4} = 6^{7-4} = 6^3$
Quotient Property of Square Roots (p. 706) For $a \geq 0$ and $b > 0$, $\sqrt{\frac{a}{b}} = \frac{\sqrt{a}}{\sqrt{b}}$.	**Propiedad del cociente de raíces cuadradas** Dados $a \geq 0$ y $b > 0$, $\sqrt{\frac{a}{b}} = \frac{\sqrt{a}}{\sqrt{b}}$.	$\sqrt{\frac{9}{25}} = \frac{\sqrt{9}}{\sqrt{25}} = \frac{3}{5}$

ENGLISH	SPANISH	EXAMPLES
radical equation (p. 722) An equation that contains a variable within a radical.	**ecuación radical** Ecuación que contiene una variable dentro de un radical.	$\sqrt{x + 3} + 4 = 7$
radical expression (p. 705) An expression that contains a radical sign.	**expresión radical** Expresión que contiene un signo de radical.	$\sqrt{x + 3} + 4$
radical symbol (p. 32) The symbol $\sqrt{}$ used to denote a root. The symbol is used alone to indicate a square root or with an index, $\sqrt[n]{}$, to indicate the nth root.	**símbolo de radical** Símbolo $\sqrt{}$ que se utiliza para expresar una raíz. Puede utilizarse solo para indicar una raíz cuadrada, o con un índice, $\sqrt[n]{}$, para indicar la enésima raíz.	$\sqrt{36} = 6$ $\sqrt[3]{27} = 3$

ENGLISH	SPANISH	EXAMPLES
radicand (p. 705) The expression under a radical sign.	**radicando** Número o expresión debajo del signo de radical.	Expression: $\sqrt{x+3}$ Radicand: $x+3$
radius (p. SB17) A segment whose endpoints are the center of a circle and a point on the circle; the distance from the center of a circle to any point on the circle.	**radio** Segmento cuyos extremos son el centro de un círculo y un punto de la circunferencia; distancia desde el centro de un círculo hasta cualquier punto de la circunferencia.	Radius
random sample (p. SB26) A sample selected from a population so that each member of the population has an equal chance of being selected.	**muestra aleatoria** Muestra seleccionada de una población tal que cada miembro de ésta tenga igual probabilidad de ser seleccionada.	Mr. Hansen chose a random sample of the class by writing each student's name on a slip of paper, mixing up the slips, and drawing five slips without looking.
range of a function or relation (p. 206) The set of all second coordinates (or y-values) of a function or relation.	**rango de una función o relación** Conjunto de todos los valores de la segunda coordenada (o valores de y) de una función o relación.	The range of $y = x^2$ is $y \geq 0$.
rate (p. 102) A ratio that compares two quantities measured in different units.	**tasa** Razón que compara dos cantidades medidas en diferentes unidades.	$\dfrac{55 \text{ miles}}{1 \text{ hour}} = 55 \text{mi/h}$
rate of change (p. 272) A ratio that compares the amount of change in a dependent variable to the amount of change in an independent variable.	**tasa de cambio** Razón que compara la cantidad de cambio de la variable dependiente con la cantidad de cambio de la variable independiente.	The cost of mailing a letter increased from 22 cents in 1985 to 25 cents in 1988. During this period, the rate of change was $\dfrac{\text{change in cost}}{\text{change in year}} = \dfrac{25 - 21}{1988 - 1985} = \dfrac{3}{3}$ $= 1$ cent per year.
ratio (p. 102) A comparison of two numbers or quantities.	**razón** Comparación de dos números o cantidades.	$\dfrac{1}{2}$ or $1:2$
rational equation (p. 674) An equation that contains one or more rational expressions.	**ecuación racional** Ecuación que contiene una o más expresiones racionales.	$\dfrac{x + 2}{x^2 + 3x - 1} = 6$
rational exponent *See* fractional exponent.	**exponente racional** *Ver* exponente fraccionario.	
rational expression (p. 642) A quotient of polynomials.	**expresión racional** Cociente de polinomios.	$\dfrac{x + 2}{x^2 + 3x - 1}$
rational function (p. 634) A function whose rule is a quotient of polynomials.	**función racional** Función cuya regla es un cociente de polinomios.	$f(x) = \dfrac{x + 2}{x^2 + 3x - 1}$
rationalizing the denominator (p. 718) A method of rewriting a fraction by multiplying by another fraction that is equivalent to 1 in order to remove radical terms from the denominator.	**racionalizar el denominador** Método que consiste en escribir nuevamente una fracción multiplicándola por otra fracción equivalente a 1 a fin de eliminar los términos radicales del denominador.	$\dfrac{1}{\sqrt{2}} \cdot \dfrac{\sqrt{2}}{\sqrt{2}} = \dfrac{\sqrt{2}}{2}$

ENGLISH	SPANISH	EXAMPLES
rational number (p. 33) A number that can be written in the form $\frac{a}{b}$, where a and b are integers and $b \neq 0$.	**número racional** Número que se puede expresar como $\frac{a}{b}$, donde a y b son números enteros y $b \neq 0$.	3, 1.75, $0.\overline{3}$, $-\frac{2}{3}$, 0
real numbers (p. 14) The set of all rational or irrational numbers. Every point on the number line represents a real number.	**número real** El conjunto de todos los números racionales o irracionales. Cada punto de la recta numérica representa un número real.	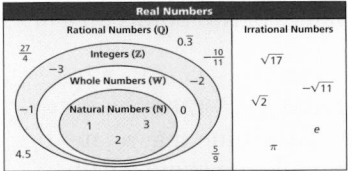

reciprocal (p. 21) For a real number $a \neq 0$, the reciprocal of a is $\frac{1}{a}$. The product of reciprocals is 1.

recíproco Dado el número real $a \neq 0$, el recíproco de a es $\frac{1}{a}$. El producto de los recíprocos es 1.

Number	Reciprocal
2	$\frac{1}{2}$
1	1
-1	-1
0	No reciprocal

ENGLISH	SPANISH	EXAMPLES
rectangle (p. SB18) A quadrilateral with four right angles.	**rectángulo** Cuadrilátero con cuatro ángulos rectos.	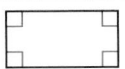
rectangular prism (p. SB20) A three-dimensional figure that has three pairs of opposite parallel congruent faces that are rectangles.	**prisma rectangular** Figura tridimensional con tres pares de caras opuestas, y congruentes que son rectangulós.	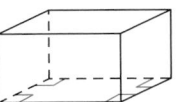
rectangular pyramid (p. SB20) A three-dimensional figure with a rectangular base lying in one plane plus one additional vertex not lying on that plane. The remaining edges of the rectangular pyramid join the additional vertex to the vertices of the base.	**pirámide rectangular** Figura tridimensional con una base rectangular en un plano, más un vértice adicional que no está en ese plano. El resto de las aristas de la pirámide rectangular unen el vértice adicional con los vértices de la base.	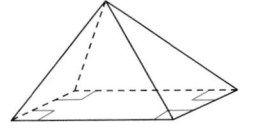
reflection (p. SB24) A transformation that reflects, or "flips," a graph or figure across a line, called the line of reflection.	**reflexión** Transformación en la que una gráfica o figura se refleja o se invierte sobre una línea, denominada la línea de reflexión.	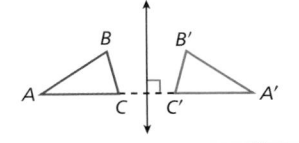
relation (p. 206) A set of ordered pairs.	**relación** Conjunto de pares ordenados.	$\{(0, 5), (0, 4), (2, 3), (4, 0)\}$
repeating decimal (p. 33) A rational number in decimal form that has a block of one or more digits (that are not all zero) after the decimal point that repeat continuously.	**decimal periódico** Número racional en forma decimal que tiene un bloque de uno o más dígitos que se repite continuamente.	$1.\overline{3} = 1.3333...$ $2.\overline{14} = 2.141414...$
replacement set (p. 8) A set of numbers that can be substituted for a variable.	**conjunto de reemplazo** Conjunto de números que pueden sustituir una variable.	
rhombus (p. SB18) A quadrilateral with four congruent sides.	**rombo** Cuadrilátero con cuatro lados congruentes.	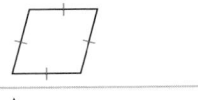
right angle (p. SB63) An angle that measures 90°.	**ángulo recto** Ángulo que mide 90°.	

Glossary/Glosario

ENGLISH	SPANISH	EXAMPLES
right triangle (p. SB18) A triangle with one right angle.	**triángulo rectángulo** Triángulo con un ángulo recto.	
rise (p. 272) The difference in the y-values of two points on a line.	**distancia vertical** Diferencia entre los valores de y de dos puntos de una línea.	For the points $(3, -1)$ and $(6, 5)$, the rise is $5 - (-1) = 6$.
rotation (p. SB24) A transformation that rotates or turns a figure about a point called the center of rotation.	**rotación** Transformación que rota o gira una figura sobre un punto llamado centro de rotación.	
run (p. 272) The difference in the x-values of two points on a line.	**distancia horizontal** Diferencia entre los valores de x de dos puntos de una línea.	For the points $(3, -1)$ and $(6, 5)$, the run is $6 - 3 = 3$.

S

ENGLISH	SPANISH	EXAMPLES
sample (p. SB26) A part of a group being surveyed.	**muestra** Parte de un grupo que es objeto de estudio.	In a survey about eating habits of high school students, a sample is a group of 100 randomly chosen high school students.
scale (p. 104) The ratio between two corresponding measurements.	**escala** Razón entre dos medidas correspondientes.	1 cm : 5 mi
scale drawing (p. 104) A drawing that uses a scale to represent an object as smaller or larger than the actual object.	**dibujo a escala** Dibujo que utiliza una escala para representar un objeto como más pequeño o más grande que el objeto original.	A blueprint is an example of a scale drawing.
scale model (p. 104) A three-dimensional model that uses a scale to represent an object as smaller or larger than the actual object.	**modelo a escala** Modelo tridimensional que utiliza una escala para representar un objeto como más pequeño o más grande que el objeto real.	
scalene triangle (p. SB18) A triangle with no congruent sides.	**triángulo escaleno** Triángulo sin lados congruentes.	
scatter plot (p. 224) A graph with points plotted to show a possible relationship between two sets of data.	**diagrama de dispersión** Gráfica con puntos que se usa para demostrar una relación posible entre dos conjuntos de datos.	
scientific notation (p. 401) A method of writing very large or very small numbers, by using powers of 10, in the form $m \times 10^n$, where $1 \le m < 10$ and n is an integer.	**notación científica** Método que consiste en escribir números muy grandes o muy pequeños utilizando potencias de 10 del tipo $m \times 10^n$, donde $1 \le m < 10$ y n es un número entero.	$12{,}560{,}000{,}000{,}000 = 1.256 \times 10^{13}$ $0.0000075 = 7.5 \times 10^{-6}$

ENGLISH	SPANISH	EXAMPLES

second differences (p. 756) The differences between first differences of a function for evenly spaced x-values.

segundas diferencias Las diferencias entre las primeras diferencias de una función para valores de x espaciados uniformemente.

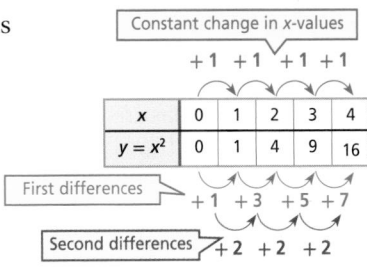

---

sequence (p. 234) A list of numbers that may form a pattern.

sucesión Lista de números que forman un patrón.

$1, 2, 4, 8, 16, \ldots$

---

set-builder notation (p. 142) A notation for a set that uses a rule to describe the properties of the elements of the set.

notación de conjuntos Notación para un conjunto que se vale de una regla para describir las propiedades de los elementos del conjunto.

$\{x : x > 3\}$ is read "The set of all x such that x is greater than 3."

---

simple interest (p. SB11) A fixed percent of the principal. For principal P, interest rate r (expressed as a decimal), and time t in years, the simple interest is $I = Prt$.

interés simple Porcentaje fijo del capital. Dado el capital P, la tasa de interés r (expresada como un decimal) y el tiempo t expresado en años, el interés simple es $I = Prt$.

If $100 is put into an account with a simple interest rate of 5%, then after 2 years, the account will have earned $I = 100 \cdot 0.05 \cdot 2 = \$10$ in interest.

---

simplest form of an exponential expression (p. 408) An exponential expression is in simplest form if it meets the following criteria:
1. There are no negative exponents.
2. The same base does not appear more than once in a product or quotient.
3. No powers, products, or quotients are raised to powers.
4. Numerical coefficients in a quotient do not have any common factor other than 1.

forma simplificada de una expresión exponencial Una expresión exponencial está en forma simplificada si reúne los siguientes requisitos:
1. No hay exponentes negativos.
2. La misma base no aparece más de una vez en un producto o cociente.
3. No se elevan a potencias productos, cocientes ni potencias.
4. Los coeficientes numéricos en un cociente no tienen ningún factor común que no sea 1.

Not Simplest Form	Simplest Form
$7^8 \cdot 7^4$	7^{12}
$(x^2)^{-4} \cdot x^5$	$\dfrac{1}{x^3}$
$\dfrac{a^5 b^9}{(ab)^4}$	ab^5

---

simplest form of a rational expression (p. 643) A rational expression is in simplest form if the numerator and denominator have no common factors.

forma simplificada de una expresión racional Una expresión racional está en forma simplificada cuando el numerador y el denominador no tienen factores comunes.

$$\frac{x^2 - 1}{x^2 + x - 2} = \frac{(x-1)(x+1)}{(x+1)(x+2)}$$
$$= \frac{x-1}{x+2}$$

↑ Simplest form

---

simplest form of a square-root expression (p. 705) A square-root expression is in simplest form if it meets the following criteria:
1. No perfect squares are in the radicand.
2. No fractions are in the radicand.
3. No square roots appear in the denominator of a fraction.

See also rationalizing the denominator.

forma simplificada de una expresión de raíz cuadrada Una expresión de raíz cuadrada está en forma simplificada si reúne los siguientes requisitos:
1. No hay cuadrados perfectos en el radicando.
2. No hay fracciones en el radicando.
3. No aparecen raíces cuadradas en el denominador de una fracción.

Ver también racionalizar el denominador.

Not Simplest Form	Simplest Form
$\sqrt{180}$	$6\sqrt{5}$
$\sqrt{216a^2 b^2}$	$6ab\sqrt{6}$
$\dfrac{\sqrt{7}}{\sqrt{2}}$	$\dfrac{\sqrt{14}}{2}$

ENGLISH	SPANISH	EXAMPLES
simplify (p. 48) To perform all indicated operations.	**simplificar** Realizar todas las operaciones indicadas.	$13 - 20 + 8$ $-7 + 8$ 1
slope (p. 272) A measure of the steepness of a line. If (x_1, y_1) and (x_2, y_2) are any two points on the line, the slope of the line, represented by m, is $m = \frac{y_2 - y_1}{x_2 - x_1}$.	**pendiente** Medida de la inclinación de una línea. Dados dos puntos (x_1, y_1) y (x_2, y_2) en una línea, la pendiente de la línea, denominada m, se representa con la ecuación $m = \frac{y_2 - y_1}{x_2 - x_1}$.	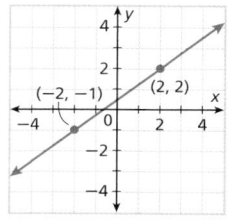 $$m = \frac{y_2 - y_1}{x_2 - x_1} = \frac{-1 - 2}{-2 - 2} = \frac{3}{4}$$
slope-intercept form (p. 291) The slope-intercept form of a linear equation is $y = mx + b$, where m is the slope and b is the y-intercept.	**forma de pendiente-intersección** La forma de pendiente-intersección de una ecuación lineal es $y = mx + b$, donde m es la pendiente y b es la intersección con el eje y.	$y = -2x + 4$ The slope is -2. The y-intercept is 4.
solution of an equation in one variable (p. 72) A value or values that make the equation true.	**solución de una ecuación en una variable** Valor o valores que hacen que la ecuación sea verdadera.	Equation: $x + 2 = 6$ Solution: $x = 4$
solution of an equation in two variables (p. 213) An ordered pair or ordered pairs that make the equation true.	**solución de una ecuación en dos variables** Un par ordenado o pares ordenados que hacen que la ecuación sea verdadera.	Equation: $x + y = 6$ Solution: $(4, 2)$ (one possible solution)
solution of an inequality in one variable (p. 136) A value or values that make the inequality true.	**solución de una desigualdad en una variable** Valor o valores que hacen que la desigualdad sea verdadera.	Inequality: $x + 2 < 6$ Solution: $x < 4$
solution of an inequality in two variables (p. 364) An ordered pair or ordered pairs that make the inequality true.	**solución de una desigualdad en dos variables** Un par ordenado o pares ordenados que hacen que la desigualdad sea verdadera.	Inequality: $3x + 2y \geq 6$ All points in the shaded region represent solutions. 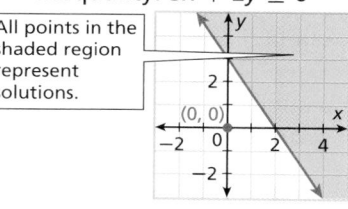
solution of a system of equations in two variables (p. 329) Any ordered pair that satisfies all the equations in the system.	**solución de un sistema de ecuaciones en dos variables** Cualquier par ordenado que resuelva todas las ecuaciones del sistema.	$\begin{cases} x + y = -1 \\ -x + y = -3 \end{cases}$ Solution: $(1, -2)$
solution of a system of inequalities in two variables (p. 371) Any ordered pair that satisfies all the inequalities in the system.	**solución de un sistema de desigualdades en dos variables** Cualquier par ordenado que resuelva todas las desigualdades del sistema.	$\begin{cases} y \leq x + 1 \\ y < -x + 4 \end{cases}$ $(2, 1)$ is in the overlapping shaded regions, so it is a solution. 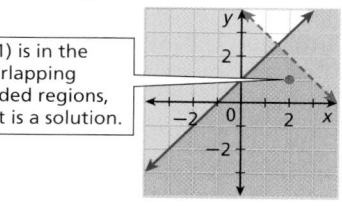
solution set (p. 72) The set of all solutions of a particular problem.	**conjunto solución** Conjunto de todas las soluciones de un problema en particular.	Inequality: $x + 3 \geq 5$ Solution set: $\{x : x \geq 2\}$

ENGLISH	SPANISH	EXAMPLES
square (p. SB18) A quadrilateral with four congruent sides and four right angles.	**cuadrado** Cuadrilátero con cuatro lados congruentes y cuatro ángulos rectos.	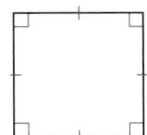
square in numeration (p. 26) The second power of a number.	**cuadrado en numeración** La segunda potencia de un número.	16 is the square of 4 because $4^2 = 16$.
square root (p. 32) A number that is multiplied by itself to form a product is called a square root of that product.	**raíz cuadrada** El número que se multiplica por sí mismo para formar un producto se denomina la raíz cuadrada de ese producto.	The square roots of 16 are 4 and -4 because $4^2 = 4 \cdot 4 = 16$ and $(-4)^2 = -4 \cdot (-4) = 16$.
square-root function (p. 700) A function whose rule contains a variable under a square-root sign.	**función de raíz cuadrada** Función cuya regla contiene una variable bajo un signo de raíz cuadrada.	$y = \sqrt{3x} - 5$
standard form of a linear equation (p. 258) $Ax + By = C$, where A, B, and C are real numbers and A and B are not both 0.	**forma estándar de una ecuación lineal** $Ax + By = C$, donde A, B y C son números reales y A y B no son ambas 0.	$2x + 3y = 6$
standard form of a polynomial (p. 431) A polynomial in one variable is written in standard form when the terms are in order from greatest degree to least degree.	**forma estándar de un polinomio** Un polinomio de una variable se expresa en forma estándar cuando los términos se ordenan de mayor a menor grado.	$4x^5 - 2x^4 + x^2 - x + 1$
standard form of a quadratic equation (p. 577) $ax^2 + bx + c = 0$, where a, b, and c are real numbers and $a \neq 0$.	**forma estándar de una ecuación cuadrática** $ax^2 + bx + c = 0$, donde a, b y c son números reales y $a \neq 0$.	$2x^2 + 3x - 1 = 0$
substitution method (p. 336) A method used to solve systems of equations by solving an equation for one variable and substituting the resulting expression into the other equation(s).	**sustitución** Método utilizado para resolver sistemas de ecuaciones resolviendo una ecuación para una variable y sustituyendo la expresión resultante en las demás ecuaciones.	
Subtraction Property of Equality (p. 72) If a, b, and c are real numbers and $a = b$, then $a - c = b - c$.	**Propiedad de igualdad de la resta** Si a, b y c son números reales y $a = b$, entonces $a - c = b - c$.	$\begin{array}{r} x + 6 = 8 \\ \underline{-6 -6} \\ x = 2 \end{array}$
Subtraction Property of Inequality (p. 142) For real numbers a, b, and c, if $a < b$, then $a - c < b - c$. Also holds true for $>$, $\leq$, $\geq$, and $\neq$.	**Propiedad de desigualdad de la resta** Dados los números reales a, b y c, si $a < b$, entonces $a - c < b - c$. Es válido también para $>$, $\leq$, $\geq$ y $\neq$.	$\begin{array}{r} x + 6 < 8 \\ \underline{-6 \phantom{<} -6} \\ x < 2 \end{array}$
supplementary angles (p. SB14) Two angles whose measures have a sum of 180°.	**ángulos suplementarios** Dos ángulos cuyas medidas suman 180°.	30° 150°

Glossary/Glosario

surface area (p. SB22) The total area of all faces and curved surfaces of a three-dimensional figure.

área total Área total de todas las caras y superficies curvas de una figura tridimensional.

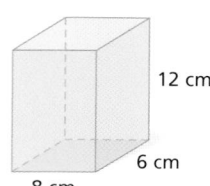

Surface area
$$= 2(8)(12) + 2(8)(6) + 2(12)(6)$$
$$= 432 \text{ cm}^2$$

---

system of linear equations (p. 329) A set of two or more linear equations containing two or more variables.

sistema de ecuaciones lineales Conjunto de dos o más ecuaciones lineales con dos o más variables.

$$\begin{cases} 2x + 3y = -1 \\ x - 3y = 4 \end{cases}$$

---

system of linear inequalities (p. 371) A set of two or more linear inequalities containing two or more variables.

sistema de desigualdades lineales Conjunto de dos o más desigualdades lineales con dos o más variables.

$$\begin{cases} 2x + 3y > -1 \\ x - 3y \leq 4 \end{cases}$$

---

term of an expression (p. 49) The parts of the expression that are added or subtracted.

término de una expresión Parte de una expresión que debe sumarse o restarse.

$$3x^2 + 6x - 8$$

Term Term Term

---

term of a sequence (p. 234) An element or number in the sequence.

término de una sucesión Elemento o número de una sucesión.

5 is the third term in the sequence 1, 3, 5, 7, …

---

terminating decimal (p. 33) A rational number in decimal form that has a finite number of digits after the decimal point.

decimal finito Número racional en forma decimal que tiene un número finito de dígitos después del punto decimal.

1.5, 2.75, 4.0

---

theoretical probability (p. SB29) The ratio of the number of equally likely outcomes in an event to the total number of possible outcomes.

probabilidad teórica Razón entre el número de resultados igualmente probables de un suceso y el número total de resultados posibles.

In the experiment of rolling a number cube, the theoretical probability of rolling an odd number is $\frac{3}{6} = \frac{1}{2}$.

---

third quartile *See* upper quartile.

tercer cuartil *Ver* cuartil superior.

---

transformation (p. SB24) A change in the position, size, or shape of a figure or graph.

transformación Cambio en la posición, tamaño o forma de una figura o gráfica.

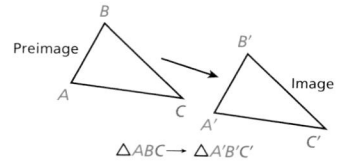

$\triangle ABC \rightarrow \triangle A'B'C'$

---

translation (p. SB24) A transformation that shifts or slides every point of a figure or graph the same distance in the same direction.

traslación Transformación en la que todos los puntos de una figura o gráfica se mueven la misma distancia en la misma dirección.

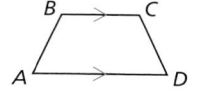

---

trapezoid (p. SB18) A quadrilateral with exactly one pair of parallel sides.

trapecio Cuadrilátero con sólo un par de lados paralelos.

ENGLISH	SPANISH	EXAMPLES
tree diagram (p. SB32) A branching diagram that shows all possible combinations or outcomes of an experiment.	**diagrama de árbol** Diagrama con ramificaciones que muestra todas las combinaciones o resultados posibles de un experimento.	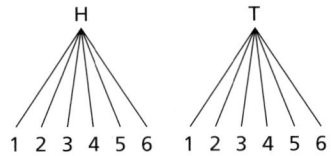 The tree diagram shows the possible outcomes when tossing a coin and rolling a number cube.
trend line (p. 227) A line on a scatter plot that helps show the correlation between data sets more clearly.	**línea de tendencia** Línea en un diagrama de dispersión que sirve para mostrar la correlación entre conjuntos de datos más claramente.	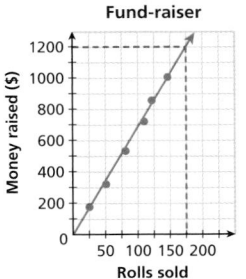
trial (p. SB30) In probability, a single repetition or observation of an experiment.	**prueba** En probabilidad, una sola repetición u observación de un experimento.	In the experiment of rolling a number cube, each roll is one trial.
triangle (p. 177) A three-sided polygon.	**triángulo** Polígono de tres lados.	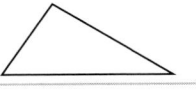
triangular prism (p. SB20) A three-dimensional figure with two congruent parallel triangular bases whose other faces are rectangles.	**prisma triangular** Figura tridimensional con dos bases triangulares paralelas y congruentes cuyas otras caras son rectángulos.	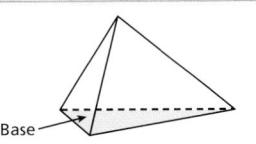
triangular pyramid (p. SB20) A three-dimensional figure with a triangular base lying in one plane plus one additional vertex not lying on that plane. The remaining edges of the triangular pyramid join the additional vertex to the vertices of the base.	**pirámide triangular** Figura tridimensional con una base triangular en un plano, más un vertice adicional que no está en ese plano. El resto de las aristas de la pirámide triangular unen el vértice adicional con los vértices de la base.	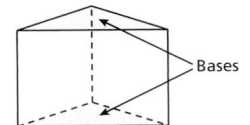
trinomial (p. 431) A polynomial with three terms.	**trinomio** Polinomio con tres términos.	$4x^2 + 3xy - 5y^2$

union (p. 172) The union of two sets is the set of all elements that are in either set, denoted by ∪.	**unión** La unión de dos conjuntos es el conjunto de todos los elementos que se encuentran en ambos conjuntos, expresado por ∪.	$A = \{1, 2, 3, 4\}$ $B = \{1, 3, 5, 7, 9\}$ $A \cup B = \{1, 2, 3, 4, 5, 7, 9\}$
unit rate (p. 102) A rate in which the second quantity in the comparison is one unit.	**tasa unitaria** Tasa en la que la segunda cantidad de la comparación es una unidad.	$\dfrac{30 \text{ mi}}{1 \text{ h}} = 30 \text{ mi/h}$
unlike radicals (p. 711) Radicals with different radicands or indices.	**radicales distintos** Radicales con diferentes radicandos o indices.	$2\sqrt{2}$ and $2\sqrt{3}$ $\sqrt{5}$ and $\sqrt[5]{5}$

ENGLISH	SPANISH	EXAMPLES
unlike terms (p. 49) Terms with different variables or the same variables raised to different powers.	**términos distintos** Términos con variables diferentes o las mismas variables elevadas a potencias diferentes.	$4xy^2$ and $6x^2y$
upper extreme (p. SB27) The greatest value in a data set.	**extremo superior** El valor mayor de un conjunto de datos.	For the data set {3, 3, 5, 7, 8, 11, 11, 12}, the upper extreme is 12.
upper quartile (p. SB27) The median of the upper half of a data set. Also called *third quartile*.	**cuartil superior** La mediana de la mitad superior de un conjunto de datos. También se llama *tercer cuartil*.	Lower half Upper half 18, 23, 28, 49, (36) 42 Upper quartile

ENGLISH	SPANISH	EXAMPLES
value of a function (p. 217) The result of replacing the independent variable with a number and simplifying.	**valor de una función** Resultado de reemplazar la variable independiente por un número y luego simplificar.	The value of the function $f(x) = x + 1$ for $x = 3$ is 4.
value of an expression (p. 7) The result of replacing the variables in an expression with numbers and simplifying.	**valor de una expresión** Resultado de reemplazar las variables de una expresión por un número y luego simplificar.	The value of the expression $x + 1$ for $x = 3$ is 4.
value of a variable (p. 7) A number used to replace a variable.	**valor de una variable** Número utilizado para reemplazar una variable.	When you evaluate the expression $x + 2$ for $x = 3$, the value of the variable is 3.
variable (p. 6) A symbol used to represent a quantity that can change.	**variable** Símbolo utilizado para representar una cantidad que puede cambiar.	In the expression $2x + 3$, x is the variable.
Venn diagram (p. SB28) A diagram used to show relationships between two or more sets.	**diagrama de Venn** Diagrama utilizado para mostrar la relación entre dos o más conjuntos.	Brand A Both Brand B Neither: 15
vertex of a cone (p. SB20) The point opposite the base of the cone.	**vértice de un cono** Punto opuesto a la base del cono.	Vertex
vertex of a parabola (p. 546) The highest or lowest point on the parabola.	**vértice de una parábola** Punto más alto o más bajo de una parábola.	$(0, -2)$ The vertex is $(0, -2)$.
vertex of a polyhedron (p. SB20) Any point on the polyhedron where three or more edges intersect.	**vértice de un poliedro** Punto que representa la intersección de tres o más caras.	Vertex

ENGLISH	SPANISH	EXAMPLES
vertical angles (p. SB14) A pair of nonadjacent angles formed by two intersecting lines.	**ángulos opuestos por el vértice** Par de ángulos no adyacentes formados por dos líneas que se cruzan.	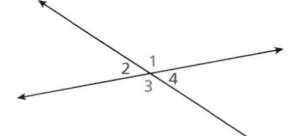 ∠1 and ∠3 are vertical angles. ∠2 and ∠4 are vertical angles.
vertical line (p. 273) A line whose equation is $x = a$, where a is the x-intercept.	**línea vertical** Línea cuya ecuación es $x = a$, donde a es la intersección con el eje x.	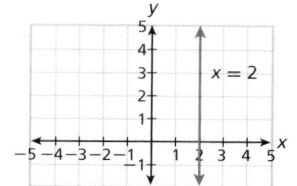
vertical-line test (p. 214) A test used to determine whether a relation is a function. If any vertical line crosses the graph of a relation more than once, the relation is not a function.	**prueba de la línea vertical** Prueba utilizada para determinar si una relación es una función. Si una línea vertical corta la gráfica de una relación más de una vez, la relación no es una función.	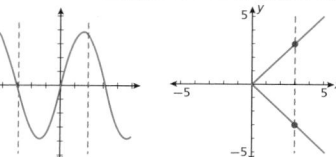 Function Not a function
volume (p. SB21) The number of nonoverlapping unit cubes of a given size that will exactly fill the interior of a three-dimensional figure.	**volumen** Cantidad de cubos unitarios no superpuestos de un determinado tamaño que llenan exactamente el interior de una figura tridimensional.	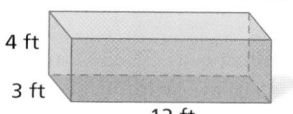 Volume = (3)(4)(12) = 144 ft³

whole numbers (p. 33) The set of natural numbers and zero.	**números cabales** Conjunto de los números naturales y cero.	{0, 1, 2, 3, 4, 5, ...}

X

x-axis (p. SB23) The horizontal axis in the coordinate plane.	**eje x** Eje horizontal en el plano cartesiano.	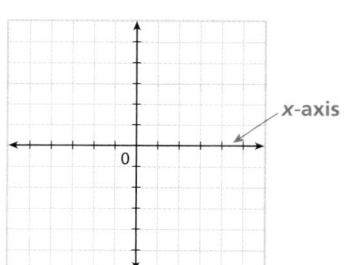
x-coordinate (p. SB23) The first number in an ordered pair, which indicates the horizontal distance of a point from the origin on the coordinate plane.	**coordenada x** Primer número de un par ordenado, que indica la distancia horizontal de un punto desde el origen en un plano cartesiano.	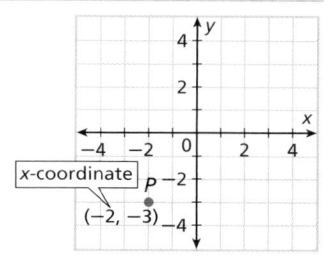

ENGLISH	SPANISH	EXAMPLES
x-intercept (p. 263) The x-coordinate(s) of the point(s) where a graph intersects the x-axis.	**intersección con el eje x** Coordenada(s) x de uno o más puntos donde una gráfica corta el eje x.	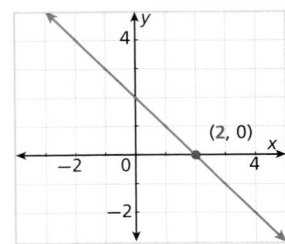 The x-intercept is 2.

ENGLISH	SPANISH	EXAMPLES
y-axis (p. SB23) The vertical axis in the coordinate plane.	**eje y** Eje vertical en el plano cartesiano.	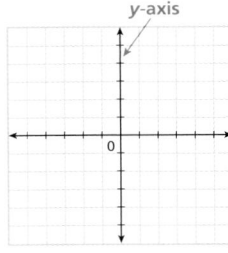
y-coordinate (p. SB23) The second number in an ordered pair, which indicates the vertical distance of a point from the origin on the coordinate plane.	**coordenada y** Segundo número de un par ordenado, que indica la distancia vertical de un punto desde el origen en un plano cartesiano.	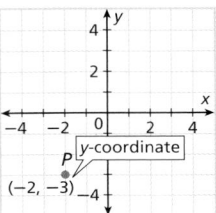
y-intercept (p. 263) The y-coordinate(s) of the point(s) where a graph intersects the y-axis.	**intersección con el eje y** Coordenada(s) y de uno o más puntos donde una gráfica corta el eje y.	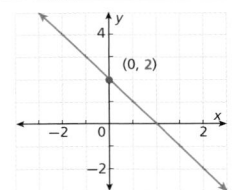 The y-intercept is 2.

Z

ENGLISH	SPANISH	EXAMPLES
zero exponent (p. 394) For any nonzero real number x, $x^0 = 1$.	**exponente cero** Dado un número real distinto de cero x, $x^0 = 1$.	$5^0 = 1$
zero of a function (p. 553) For the function f, any number x such that $f(x) = 0$.	**cero de una función** Dada la función f, todo número x tal que $f(x) = 0$.	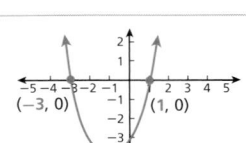 The zeros are −3 and 1.
Zero Product Property (p. 576) For real numbers p and q, if $pq = 0$, then $p = 0$ or $q = 0$.	**Propiedad del producto cero** Dados los números reales p y q, si $pq = 0$, entonces $p = 0$ o $q = 0$.	If $(x - 1)(x + 2) = 0$, then $x - 1 = 0$ or $x + 2 = 0$. So $x = 1$ or $x = -2$.

Glossary/Glosario

Index

Index

Index

Index

Index

Values, excluded, 634
Van Dyk, Ernst, 109
Variable(s), 6
    on both sides
        solving equations with, 92–95
        solving inequalities with, 162–165
    dependent, 216, 218, 219
    expressions and, 6–8
    independent, 216
    solving for, 109–111
Variation
    constant of, 282, 627
    direct, *see* Direct variation
    inverse, *see* Inverse variation
Vertex
    of a cone, SB20
    of a parabola, 546
    of a polyhedron, SB20
        axis of symmetry through, 552
        finding the, 555
Vertical angles, SB14
Vertical line(s), 635
Vertical-line test, 214
Vertical method for multiplication of polynomials, 449
Vocabulary, 9, 17, 23, 29, 95, 111, 139, 174, 203, 209, 218, 228, 237, 260, 266, 285, 308, 332, 353, 368, 374, 403, 433, 459, 481, 548, 557, 595, 631, 639, 646, 676, 702, 708, 713, 726, 735, 742, 751
    learning, 543
Volume, 454, SB21
    estimating, SB21
    of a cone, 454, SB21
    of a cube, 745, SB21
    of a cylinder, 454, SB21
    of a prism, 454, 745, SB21
    of a pyramid, 454, 745, SB21

Walnut, CA, 672
What if...?, 16, 18, 22, 28, 30, 96, 144, 230, 238, 259, 287, 300, 334, 346, 354, 366, 432, 488, 516, 570, 578, 655, 662
Whole numbers, 33
Write About It
    Write About It questions are found in every exercise set. Some examples: 9, 19, 29, 31, 37
Writing Math, 6, 94, 207, 290, 331, 400, 416, 439, 487, 635
Writing Strategies, Write a Convincing Argument/Explanation, 327

x-axis, SB23
x-coordinate, SB23
x-intercept, 263
    exploring, 574–575
x-values, 206

y-axis, SB23
y-coordinate, SB23
y-intercept, 263
y-values, 206
Yosemite National Park, 540, 571

Zero(s)
    divided by a number, 21
    division by, 21
    exploring, 574–575
    finding the axis of symmetry of a parabola by using, 554
    of a function, 553
    properties of, 21
    of quadratic functions, finding, from graphs, 553
Zero exponent, 394
Zero Product Property, 576, 642
Zero slope, 273–274

Credits

Abbreviations used: (t) top, (c) center, (b) bottom, (l) left, (r) right, (bkgd) background

Staff

Bruce Albrecht, Nancy Behrens, Tica Chitrarachis, Lorraine Cooper, Marc Cooper, Jennifer Craycraft, Martize Cross, Nina Degollado, Julie Dervin, Michelle Dike, Lydia Doty, Sam Dudgeon, Kelli R. Flanagan, Stephanie Friedman, Jeff Galvez, Pam Garner, Diannia Green, Tracie Harris, Liz Huckestein, Jevara Jackson, Simon Key, Jane A. Kirschman, Kadonna Knape, Cathy Kuhles, Jill M. Lawson, Liann Lech, Jeff Mapua, Susan Mussey, Kim Nguyen, Manda Reid, Michael Rinella, Annette Saunders, Kay Selke, Robyn Setzen, Patricia Sinnott, Victoria Smith, Dawn Marie Spinozza, Jeannie Taylor, Karen Vigil, April Warn, Kira J. Watkins, Sherri Whitmarsh, David W. Wynn

Photo

All photos Sam Dudgeon/HRW unless otherwise noted.

Title Page: (windsurfer), DY Riess MD/Alamy; (Joshua Tree), Frank Krahmer/zefa/Corbis; (buildings), Toyohiro Yamada/Getty Images; (Big Sur), David Muench/CORBIS; (bridge), George Steinmetz/Corbis.

Front Matter: iii (border), PhotoDisc; iv (bl), Courtesy of Lee Haines; iv (br), Courtesy of Robin Scarcella; v (bl), Courtesy of Charlie Bialowas; v (br), Courtesy of Wendy Taub-Hoglund; vii (border), Charles O'Rear/CORBIS; viii (border), Jan Butchofsky-Houser/CORBIS; ix (border), Randy Faris/CORBIS; x (border), Tom and Pat Leeson; xi (border), Ron Stroud/Masterfile; xii (border), Noah Graham/NBAE via Getty Images; xiii (starry border), ©Royalty-Free/Corbis; xiii (observatory), Bill Ross/CORBIS OUTLINE; xv (border), ©Royalty Free/CORBIS; xvi (border), Tom Paiva/Getty Images; xvii (border), QT Luong/Terra Galleria Photography; xiv (border), ©Mark Gibson Photography.

Chapter One: 2–3 (all), Charles O'Rear/CORBIS; 6 (tr), ©Ray Roberts/Alamy Photos; 6 (sky), PhotoDisc/Getty Images; 8 (tc), Sam Dudgeon/HRW; 8 (c), Sam Dudgeon/HRW; 10 (bl), AP Photo/NASA Haughton-Mars Project 2001, Pascal Lee; 10 (tl), ©Royalty Free/CORBIS; 14 (tr), ©Paul A. Souders/CORBIS; 18 (c), John Sullivan/Ribbit Photography; 18 (bl), ©Royalty Free/CORBIS; 20 (c), ©Craig Aurness/CORBIS; 20 (tc), Derek & Garry Walker/Adams/PictureQuest/Jupiter Images; 22 (cr), ©Dave G. Houser/CORBIS; 24 (cl), Wes Skiles/Karst Productions, Inc.; 24 (bl), ©Royalty Free/CORBIS; 26 (tr), ©Ted Horowitz/CORBIS; 29 (br), Michael Abbey/Photo Researchers, Inc.; 30 (cl), ©2007 The Josef and Anni Albers Foundation/Artist Rights Society (ARS), New York/The Newark Museum/Art Resource, NY; 30 (bl), ©Royalty Free/CORBIS; 30 (cr), PhotoDisc/Getty Images; 36 (bl), ©Royalty Free/CORBIS; 37 (tr), Stephanie Friedman/HRW; 40 (tl), ©Royalty Free/CORBIS; 40 (cr), ©Federico Cabello/SuperStock; 43 (tl), ©BananaStock Ltd.; 46 (bl), PhotoDisc/gettyimages; 49 (tr), AP/Wide World Photos; 52 (tl), Clive Brunskill/Getty Images; 52 (bl), PhotoDisc/gettyimages; 56 (tl), PhotoDisc/gettyimages; 56 (cr), Sam Dudgeon/HRW.

Chapter Two: 68–69 (bkgd), Jan Butchofsky-Houser/CORBIS; 74 (bl), RubberBall/Alamy; 76 (l), ©2001 MBARI; 76 (bl), ©Image Ideas, Inc.; 83 (tl), ©Robert W. Kelley/Time Life Pictures/Getty Images; 83 (cr), ©Corel; 83 (bl), ©Image Ideas, Inc.; 89 (bl), ©Image Ideas, Inc.; 92 (tc), ©Ingram Publishing; 96 (bl), ©Image Ideas, Inc.; 97 (tl), ©Royalty-Free/CORBIS; 98 (bl), Rob Melnychuk/gettyimages; 100 (tl), ©Image Ideas, Inc.; 100 (cr), John Coletti/Index Stock Imagery/Jupiterimages; 100 (b), Brand X Pictures/Jupiterimages; 109 (tr), ©Ezra Shaw/Getty Images; 112 (cr), Aflo Foto Agency/Alamy; 113 (cr), Pixar Animation Studios/ZUMA Press; 116 (tr), Dallas and John Heaton/Stock Connection/Jupiterimages; 118 (cr), David Guttenfelder/AP/Wide World Photos; 120 (cr), Sylvia Pitcher Photolibrary/Alamy; 120 (bl), waring abbott /Alamy.

Chapter Three: 132–133 (bkgd), Randy Faris/CORBIS; 136 (tr), ©Charles Crust; 137 (bl), Digital Vision/gettyimages; 140 (bl), ©Creatas; 146 (tl), Buzz Orr/The Gazette/AP/Wide World Photos; 146 (cr), PhotoDisc/gettyimages; 146 (bl), ©Creatas; 148 (tr), on-page credit; 152 (bl), ©Creatas; 152 (cl), David Brooks/San Diego Union Tribune/Zuma Press/Newscom; 154 (tl), ©Creatas; 156 (tr), ©Peter Beck/CORBIS; 158 (tr), Paul Sakuma/AP/Wide World Photos; 160 (bl), ©Brand X Pictures; 162 (tr), ©Ariel Skelley/CORBIS; 166 (cl), Brad Mitchell/Alamy; 166 (bl), ©Brand X Pictures; 168 (bl), ©Jose Luis Pelaez, Inc./CORBIS; 170 (tr), ©Michele Westmorland/CORBIS; 170 (br), Sam Dudgeon/HRW; 175 (tl), ©Brand X Pictures; 175 (cl), Richard Megna/Fundamental Photographs; 182 (bl), ©Brand X Pictures; 184 (tl), ©Brand X Pictures; 184 (br), Peter Beavis/Taxi/Getty Images; 184 (cr), (bl), PhotoDisc/Getty Images; 186 (b), Jill Stephenson/Alamy.

Chapter Four: 196–197 (bkgd), Tom and Pat Leeson; 200 (tr), ©Royalty-Free/CORBIS; 204 (cl), ©Bettmann/CORBIS; 204 (bl), Sam Dudgeon/HRW; 205 (all), Sam Dudgeon/HRW; 206 (tr), Aflo Sport; 208 (cl), ©Comstock Images/Alamy Photos; 211 (tl), Sam Dudgeon/HRW; 213 (tr), RubberBall/Alamy; 219 (tl), ©Bettmann/CORBIS; 219 (bl), Sam Dudgeon/HRW; 222 (br), Big Cheese Photo/Alamy Photos; 222 (tl), Sam Dudgeon/HRW; 224 (tr), David Welling/Animals Animals; 229 (bl), Roy Toft; 230 (bl), comstock.com; 234 (tr), ©COMSTOCK, Inc.; 238 (cl), Cal Poly College of Engineering/Design by Jeffrey Gordon Smith Landscape Architecture, Los Osos, California; 238 (bl), comstock.com; 240 (tl), comstock.com; 240 (bl), AP Photo/Daniel Hulshizer.

Chapter Five: 252–253 (bkgd), Ron Stroud/Masterfile; 261 (bl), Victoria Smith/HRW; 264 (tl), ©LWA-Dann Tardif/CORBIS; 264 (cr), ©Buddy Mays/CORBIS; 267 (tl), ©John and Lisa Merrill/CORBIS; 268 (tl), Victoria Smith/HRW; 272 (tr), ©Patrick Eden/Alamy Photos; 278 (cl), Garry Black/Masterfile; 279 (tl), Victoria Smith/HRW; 282 (tr), ©Royalty-Free/Corbis; 284 (bl), Genevieve Vallee/Alamy; 286 (cl), Courtesy NASA/JPL-Caltech; 286 (bl), Victoria Smith/HRW; 288 (tl), Victoria Smith/HRW; 288 (br), ©Rick Gomez/CORBIS; 288 (tr), ©age fotostock/SuperStock; 295 (bl), ©Brand X Pictures; 297 (tr), ©Pixtal/SuperStock; 302 (tl), Jake Norton; 302 (bl), ©Brand X Pictures; 303 (bl), image100/Alamy; 309 (bl), ©Brand X Pictures; 312 (tl), ©Brand X Pictures; 312 (b), ©Tim Pannell/CORBIS; 312 (tr), Andy Christiansen/HRW.

Chapter Six: 324–325 (bkgd), Noah Graham/NBAE via Getty Images; 332 (bl), Victoria Smith/HRW; 333 (tl), ©Lee Snider/Photo Images/CORBIS; 334 (bl), ©R. Holz/CORBIS; 336 (tr), ON-PAGE CREDIT; 338 (bl), ©Michael Pole/SuperStock; 341 (bl), Victoria Smith/HRW; 343 (tr), Photofusion Picture Library/Alamy; 346 (tl), Victoria Smith/HRW; 348 (cl), ©UNICOVER CORPORATION 1986; 348 (bl), Victoria Smith/HRW; 354 (bl), Victoria Smith/HRW; 354 (cl), Brad Tanas/Del Air Rockhounds; 356 (tr), Reimar Gaertner/Alamy; 357 (tl), Peter Van Steen/HRW; 357 (cl), Stephanie Friedman/HRW; 360 (bl), Victoria Smith/HRW; 362 (tl), Victoria Smith/HRW; 362 (cr), David Madison ©2005; 362 (b), ©Les Stone/CORBIS; 369 (tl), Max Gibbs/photolibrary.com; 369 (bl), Nathan Kaey/HRW; 369 (cl), PhotoDisc Blue/Getty Images; 371 (tr), ©Justin Pumfrey/Taxi/Getty Images; 375 (cl), ©Reuters/CORBIS; 375 (bl), Nathan Kaey/HRW; 378 (all), Nathan Kaey/HRW.

Chapter Seven: 390–391 (starry bkgd), ©Royalty-Free/Corbis; 390-391 (observatory), Bill Ross/CORBIS OUTLINE; 394 (tr), Advertising Archive; 397 (cr), B. G. Thomson/Photo Researchers, Inc.; 398 (cl), ©PHOTOTAKE Inc./Alamy; 400 (tr), Arscimed/Photo Researchers, Inc.; 402 (tr), Courtesy NASA/JPL-Caltech; 403 (br), ©Visuals Unlimited/Getty Images; 404 (tl), Cern/Photo Researchers, Inc.; 408 (tr), D. Parker/Photo Researchers, Inc.; 410 (bl), ©BananaStock Ltd.; 428 (br), Robert Flusic/PhotoDisc/Getty Images; 430 (tr), ©Jeff Hunter/Getty Images; 434 (tl), ©Don Johnston/Stone/Getty Images; 434 (bl), ©Comstock, Inc.; 441 (frame), ©1998 Image Farm Inc.; 441 (teens), Artville/Getty Images; 442 (bl), ©Comstock,

Credits

Symbols

Relation Symbols

$<$	is less than
$>$	is greater than
$\leq$	is less than or equal to
$\geq$	is greater than or equal to
$\neq$	is not equal to
$\approx$	is approximately equal to
$\cong$	is congruent to

Real Numbers

$\mathbb{R}$	the set of real numbers
$\mathbb{Q}$	the set of rational numbers
$\mathbb{Z}$	the set of integers
$\mathbb{W}$	the set of whole numbers
$\mathbb{N}$	the set of natural numbers

Geometry

$\angle ABC$	angle ABC
$m\angle ABC$	the measure of angle ABC
$\triangle ABC$	triangle ABC
$\overline{AB}$	segment AB

Other

$\pm$	plus or minus
$\lvert -4 \rvert$	the absolute value of -4
$\{$	system
π	pi; $\pi \approx 3.14$ or $\pi \approx \frac{22}{7}$
$\varnothing$	empty set
$f(x)$	function notation; f of x
a_n	the nth term of a sequence
$P(\text{event})$	the probability of an event

Table of Measures

METRIC

Length

1 kilometer (km) = 1000 meters (m)
1 meter = 100 centimeters (cm)
1 centimeter = 10 millimeters (mm)

Capacity and Volume

1 liter (L) = 1000 milliliters (mL)

Mass and Weight

1 kilogram (kg) = 1000 grams (g)
1 gram = 1000 milligrams (mg)

CUSTOMARY

Length

1 mile (mi) = 5280 feet (ft)
1 yard = 3 feet (ft)
1 foot = 12 inches (in.)

Capacity and Volume

1 gallon (gal) = 4 quarts (qt)
1 quart = 2 pints (pt)
1 pint = 2 cups (c)
1 cup = 8 fluid ounces (fl oz)

Mass and Weight

1 ton = 2000 pounds (lb)
1 pound = 16 ounces (oz)

TIME

1 year (yr) = 365 days (d)	1 day = 24 hours (h)
1 year = 12 months (mo)	1 hour = 60 minutes (min)
1 year = 52 weeks (wk)	1 minute = 60 seconds (s)
1 week = 7 days	

Centimeters